DISEASES
OF FOREST AND
SHADE TREES OF
THE UNITED STATES
U. S. DEPARTMENT OF AGRICULTURE
FOREST SERVICE · AGRICULTURE
HANDBOOK NUMBER
386

By
GEORGE H. HEPTING
Chief Plant Pathologist
Forest Disease Research Branch
Division of Forest Insect
and Disease Research

July 1971

Library of Congress Catalog Card Number: 74-607274

For sale by the Superintendent of Documents, U.S. Government Printing Office
Washington, D.C. 20402—Price $4

CONTENTS

iv

DISEASES OF FOREST AND SHADE TREES OF THE UNITED STATES

By George H. Hepting, chief plant pathologist, Forest Disease Research
Branch, Division of Forest Insect and Disease Research,
USDA Forest Service

INTRODUCTION

The purpose of this volume is to bring together the information available on the pathology of the more important forest and shade trees of the United States. While it deals largely with the multitude of tree species indigenous to this country, it also annotates the diseases of many introduced species grown widely for shade and ornament. It includes diseases occurring in continental United States, exclusive of Alaska, and in adjacent parts of Canada. Many small native trees of little importance for timber or shade, and also shrubs, and some of the small exotic trees considered largely horticultural have been omitted. Some trees used mainly for orchard crops have been included but they are treated from the point of view of shade or ornament, rather than fruit production.

As a major effort devoted to describing the pathology of our tree species and to provide aids in diagnosis, this book should not only serve an immediate need but also form a base for the development of succeeding works devoted to improving disease diagnosis in trees in all parts of the world.

Accessibility of subject matter, completeness of coverage, and adequate documentation were the dominating guidelines followed in assembling this work. It is restricted to a consideration of diseases, with insects or other agents discussed only where necessary to the understanding of a disease. The material is arranged first by the tree host species or genus, and within species according to part of the tree mainly attacked, for example, foliage, stem, root, or trunk.

There are, in the English language, several textbooks on forest pathology and a considerable literature on the results of research useful in diagnosis. Most of this literature is organized by the causes of disease rather than by the species of tree attacked.

Many have long felt the need to have the pathology of each of the forest tree or shade tree species important to continental United States and Canada discussed under the tree species, with each presentation preceded by an account of those characteristics of each tree that might help the pathologist better understand its normal and abnormal behavior. Anyone with a problem in diagnosis is usually presented first with a host plant and then with an abnormality of that host, in that order. It helps to have together the diseases and related impacts to which a given species is subject.

1

This attempt to organize information and to document the sources of the information on the pathogens, heart rots, and abiotic disease influences by the tree species is only a beginning. In the future, as knowledge of the pathology of each species is expanded, improved, and better tied to the silvical and normal physiological characteristics of each species, by specialists who know their host plants well, we will ultimately have both a good understanding of the pathology of each species and genus—of how and why this pathology differs from that of another species or genus—and a constantly improving set of tools for the diagnostician.

An entire book could be written on the pathology of certain major species such as Douglas-fir or eastern white pine. Therefore, decisions have had to be made from a wide choice of material, on what to include and what to cite. Two principal guides were used: (1) what are the main characteristics of a tree and its pathogens that will give a picture of its pathology, and (2) what material and references will be of greatest help to the person faced with diagnosing ills of a species?

The following points concerning style represent departures from formal scientific writing:

1. Following the name of a disease, the causal organism often appears after it, in parentheses, without the words "caused by."

2. Authorities for tree and pathogen epithets will be given only in the index, except where needed in the text to avoid confusion.

3. How much is written about an organism depends upon how much need be said to place the disease it causes in perspective, and partly on how much is known about it. The full documentation permits pursuit of additional information on virtually every topic mentioned.

Many coworkers have contributed information used in this work, aside from their publications. The manuscript, in mimeographed form, was distributed to more than 300 pathologists, foresters, and others, and the improvements and additions suggested have been incorporated in the final version. The literature reviewed consists mainly of publications released through 1968 and in some cases beyond that date.

Pacific silver fir
Abies amabilis

One of the West's most beautiful trees, Pacific silver fir has a tall, narrow, pyramidal, spire-like form, and lustrous foliage, silver-gray on the underside (279). It extends from southeastern Alaska along the coast to northwestern Oregon, and along the west slopes of the Cascade Range to southern Oregon. It occupies mainly the lower slopes of canyons, benches, and flats, but also thrives on ridgetops and upper slopes. It is not demanding with respect to soil type, but grows best in soils with good internal drainage and an abundant supply of moisture (382). In the Olympic and Cascade Ranges in Washington and Oregon it grows from about 1,000 to 5,000 ft. in elevation and occasionally higher. The climate of the range of silver fir is classified as humid to superhumid (40 to 140 in.

of rain per year), and with moderate temperatures not varying greatly from season to season. Temperature extremes over the range are from about zero to 90° F (*1367*).

Trees of this species grow slowly, usually reaching only 24 in. in diameter at 200 years. Only occasionally do they live beyond 350 years in the United States (*382*). In British Columbia trees over 500 years old were not uncommon (*458*). Being shallow-rooted, silver fir is subject to windthrow, and its thin bark and flammable foliage make it easily damaged by fire. Temperature extremes also cause some damage. It is moderately resistant to frost damage, although not as resistant as noble fir (*382*), and is not hardy in eastern Canada. The firs as a genus are all sensitive to urban air conditions and to air polluted with sulfur dioxide.

Seedling Diseases.—Pacific silver fir has been cultivated in parts of the East and West yet little is known of its seedling diseases beyond those listed below under Foliage Diseases. In the field, germination on snow, adverse climatic effects, and competing vegetation are considered to contribute more to seedling mortality than diseases (*382*). In the tests reported in the Woody Plant Seed Manual (*1*), Pacific silver fir seed had the lowest germinative capacity (22 percent) of the six western firs listed.

Foliage Diseases.—The following needle cast fungi, all affecting noncurrent year's needles, occur on Pacific silver fir and other firs and are discussed under white fir: *Virgella* (*Hypoderma*) *robusta* (also *H. robustum* var. *latispora*), *Lirula* (*Hypodermella*) *abietisconcoloris*, *L. punctata*, *Lophodermium consociatum*, *Lophomerum* (*Lophodermium*) *autumnale*. In addition to those needle cast fungi on white fir, *Lophodermium uncinatum*, a weak parasite, occurs on needles on heavily shaded branches, and is confined to Pacific silver fir (*323*, *328*). *Lophodermium piceae*, largely a spruce fungus, is also a weak parasite on this species.

The following rusts, the first two of which produce aecia on current year's foliage, occur on silver fir and are discussed under white fir: the yellow-aeciospored *Pucciniastrum epilobii* and *P. goeppertianum;* the white-spored *Uredinopsis pteridis;* and the yellow witches' broom rust, *Melampsorella caryophyllacearum*. *Peridermium rugosum*, a needle rust for which no alternate host is known (*149*), occurs only on Pacific silver fir and grand fir, and another silver fir *Peridermium* has its alternate stages on *Vaccinium* and may be *Pucciniastrum vaccinii*. Ziller (*1664, 1665, 1666*) has added much to our knowledge of the rusts of western firs and hemlock and anyone working with this group should refer to his works.

Dimerosporium (*Meliola*) *abietis* produces a black, sooty surface mold that develops on the sweet secretion of sucking insects, and *Adelopus nudus*, which many consider synonymous with *D. abietis*, also causes a black smudge on needles and forms tiny, black perithecia on the underside of needles (*571*). Another sooty mold, *Phaeosaccardinula dematia*, is epiphyllous on silver fir foliage in moist situations in northern California. Miller and Bonar (*991*) give a good treatment of the sooty molds of California.

Herpotrichia nigra produces a brown felt mold on foliage that had remained long under snow.

Stem Diseases.—Western hemlock dwarfmistletoe (*Arceuthobium campylopodum* f. *abietinum*) attacks Pacific silver fir in

3

stands in which this species is associated with western hemlock. It causes stunting, distortion, loss in vigor, brooming, and other effects, but the more northerly firs are not attacked as severely as *Abies concolor* and *A. magnifica,* which occur further south *(505).* The disease is not important on *A. amabilis* west of the Cascade Range.

Occasional cankers on suppressed trees are caused by *Aleurodiscus amorphus,* which forms flattened, irregular fruiting bodies *(587, 858). Limacinia alaskensis* causes a minor sooty mold mostly on stems in Washington *(1277).*

Scleroderris abieticola is associated with a stem and branch canker of grand fir and Pacific silver fir in which necrosis begins in the autumn and stops when growth starts in the spring. If the stem is not girdled by spring the lesion will heal over. Black apothecia appear on the dead bark during the following summer *(1656).*

The common saprophyte *Dasyscypha agassizii* produces its yellow-orange apothecia on dead bark.

Caliciopsis pseudotsugae can cause branch cankers but is not an economic parasite (see *Pseudotsuga*) *(485).*

Root Diseases.—*Armillaria mellea, Fomes annosus,* and *Polyporus tomentosus* have been reported to cause root and butt rots in the United States; and in British Columbia *(1277)* many other fungi, including *Odontia bicolor, Polyporus abietinus, P. schweinitzii, Poria subacida,* and *P. weirii,* are known in this role. Bier, et al. *(125),* found *P. subacida* the most common root and butt rotter in the Upper Fraser River region of British Columbia, and it rates as a major root rot in the United States. A yellow stringy rot of the roots, caused by *Flammula alnicola,* occurs occasionally in Canada *(374).*

Trunk Rots.—The most intensive studies on the decays of Pacific silver fir have been carried out in British Columbia, where the species makes up an important part of many forests. Foster, et al. *(458),* reported on cull and the fungi causing it in the Kitimat Region; Bier, et al. *(125),* similarly for the Upper Fraser River; and Buckland, et al. *(189),* for the Franklin River area of British Columbia.

The following tabulation gives the percentage of total decayed wood attributed to each fungus (cubic foot basis) at these three locations:

Fungus:	Up. Fraser River *A. amabilis* and *A. lasiocarpa*	Kitimat *A.amabilis*	Franklin River *Abies* spp., mainly *A. amabilis*
	Percent	*Percent*	*Percent*
Brown cubical rots—			
Stereum abietinum	------	4.8	6.2
Fomes pinicola	0.6	2.2	40.5
Polyporus sulphureus	------	1.8	5.7
White rots—			
Echinodontium tinctorium	46.5	64.9	------
Fomes pini	trace	13.0	1.3
Hericium sp.	------	4.8	------
Stereum sanguinolentum	40.8	2.9	------
Fomes annosus	0.1	2.0	trace
Polyporus abietinus	2.2	------	------
Poria subacida	4.0	1.8	11.5
Others, mixed, and unknown	5.8	1.8	34.8

Foster, et al. (458), describe the problems in decay diagnosis in the firs, mentioning the similarity of appearance of the decays caused by *Echinodontium tinctorium* (see *Abies grandis*) and *Stereum sanguinolentum*, and the similarity of *Hericium* sp. decay to *Fomes pini* in some stages. They also describe the external indicators of the decays. Their relationships of decay volume to tree age showed a rapid rise in the percentage of trees with 30 percent of the gross cubic volume rotten, from 8 percent of the trees at 250 years to 23 percent at 300 years, and to 37 percent at 350 years. Bier, et al. (125), found cull to reach 31 percent in the 201–240-year age class.

Silver fir approaching maturity is so subject to decay that short rotations are advisable in certain areas. Bier, et al. (125), working in the Upper Fraser River valley of British Columbia intensively studied decay in *Abies amabilis* and *A. lasiocarpa*, and suggest a rotation age of 121 to 140 years. They report on the relation of decay to many tree and stand factors and discuss the fungi responsible. Twenty-one species are listed, with *Stereum sanguinolentum* responsible for 47 percent, and *Echinodontium tinctorium* 41 percent, of the total decay, by cubic volume.

Buckland, et al. (189), referring to the Fraser River area of Vancouver Island, British Columbia, state that the period of maximum periodic increment for *Abies amabilis* was reached at ages between 275 and 325 years.

The rate of decay of beetle-killed silver fir has been studied in western Washington (1621), and the volume decayed was 9 percent at 2 years after death, 16 percent at 3 years, and 19 percent at 4 years. The principal fungi decaying this killed material were *Fomes pinicola, Stereum chailletii,* and *Polyporus abietinus. Armillaria mellea* appeared at the base of almost all trees but had caused little butt cull. *Polyporus oregonensis* causes a white spongy rot of down silver fir timber (8, 1067).

Boyce (144) studied deterioration following the great Olympic Peninsula blowdown of 1921. Six years later the volume loss, on a board-foot basis, was for western hemlock, 92 percent; Pacific silver fir, 74 percent; Sitka spruce, 46 percent; Douglas-fir, 35 percent; and western redcedar, 27 percent. The main fungi identified as rotting fallen silver fir were *Fomes applanatus, F. pinicola, Polyporus abietinus,* and *F. annosus.*

Mycorrhizal Relations.—The following fungi have been reported (1442) to make mycorrhizal association with Pacific silver fir: *Boletus edulis, B. (Xerocomus) pulverulentus, Cenococcum graniforme, Lactarius deliciosus, L. sanguifluus, Russula delica,* and *R. emetica.* None have been confirmed by pure culture technique.

Balsam fir

Abies balsamea

A tree of cold climates, balsam fir extends from the Northeast and the Lake States into Canada and southward along the crests of the Appalachian Mountains to south-central Virginia. It inhabits cold, moist, but well-drained situations from sea level to high elevations in the North, and from 3,500 to 5,600 ft. (595) in Virginia, where it begins to give way to Fraser fir. It also occurs in and around swamps, flats, and lower hardwood slopes in the North and appears again on the mountaintops all through the Appalachian chain (245). It is shallow-rooted and therefore easily windthrown. It is also particularly sensitive to fire because of the flammable foliage and resin blisters in the bark. Highly resistant to damage by cold, this tree cannot stand hot, dry summers and will seldom survive when brought to elevations much below its natural habitat in the eastern mountains. It is very tolerant to shade when young, ranking in tolerance with the often-associated red spruce (54). Later it needs sunlight. It occurs frequently on rocky, exposed sites on thin but moist soil, pioneering for spruce on cutover upper mountain slopes. It seldom thrives as an ornamental because of its susceptibility to city air pollution and its constant need for quite moist soil and air (245, 279). It has been injured by sulfur dioxide near oil refineries (869). Horticulturists repeatedly warn of the failure of balsam fir when cultivated (52).

According to Sparrow and Sparrow (1332) the sensitivity of balsam fir to gamma radiation from a cobalt-60 source was high among a group of 12 coniferous and hardwood species tested over a period of several years.

Balsam fir is a short-lived species, often becoming decadent by 70 or 80 years, and trees over 150 years old are rare (771, 1342). Its pathology is distinguished by a large number of needle rusts and hypodermataceous fungi, a conspicuous brooming rust, and many damaging root and trunk rots.

Seedling Diseases.—Balsam fir is not a widely-planted species, although the demand for Christmas trees has resulted in some nursery cultivation. Seed germination, averaging only 22 percent, may be so low due to dewinging injury, although slow seed germination is a characteristic of the species. Almost any seedbed is satisfactory except sod. In the field and in the open, heavy mortality the first year may result from high surface soil temperatures, drought, or frost heaving. Ordinarily there is little mortality after the first year. Hardwood leaves can be very damaging to fir seedlings in mixed stands (245). There is virtually no published information on the specific causes of seedling diseases in nurseries, but there may well be some parallels to the nursery diseases of the very similar species *Abies fraseri*.

Foliage Diseases.—Balsam fir is subject to many foliage diseases, but none have an economic impact on wood production. Several fungi of the needle cast group (151, 323) fruit on, and cause loss of, foliage 2 or more years old, and typically on the shaded or lower parts of the crown. These include *Lirula* (*Hypodermella*) *mirabilis,* identified by its pycnidia forming two lines, one along each wing of the needle; *L. nervisequia,* a European species (625); *L. nervata,* with its pycnidia becoming black after spore discharge; *L. abietis-concoloris,* with its pycnidia concolorous with the needle after spore discharge; *L. punctata* (1314), with its pycnidia resembling waxy blisters; *Lophomerum* (*Lophodermium*) *autumnale,* with pycnidia inconspicuous or lacking, and usually following attack by other hypodermataceous fungi; and *Lophodermium lacerum* and *L. piceae* (1314), harmless species not associated with other fungi and often abundant on shaded lower foliage. *Isthmiella* (*Bifusella*) *faullii* has been described as the commonest and most

6

destructive of balsam fir's needle cast fungi in the East, attacking seedlings as well as older trees in closed stands, and yet inoculation results throw some doubt on its pathogenicity (*323*). It is characterized by its sinuous, labyrinthine, effused pycnidia. Darker's revised nomenclature (*328*) is followed in the Hypodermataceae.

Many rusts attack the foliage. *Hyalopsora aspidiotus* forms aecia on needles of the third year, and its alternate host is *Gymnocarpium* (*Phegopteris*) *dryopteris*. *Melampsora abieti-capraearum*, with its flat aecia lacking a peridium, occurs on current needles and goes to *Salix* spp. It is morphologically indistinguishable from *M. epitea* f. sp. *tsugae*, that attacks *Tsuga heterophylla* (*1666*). Three species of *Milesia*, all with hypophyllous, colorless aecia and colorless spores that occur on needles 3 to 9 years old, are separated on uredospore characteristics. They are *M. fructuosa* (= *M. intermedia*), *M. marginalis*, and *M. pycnograndis* (*46*) and have their II and III stages, respectively, on the ferns *Dryopteris* spp., *D. marginalis*, and *Polypodium virginianum*. Faull is followed in the classification of species in *Milesia* (*430*) and *Uredinopsis* (*431, 432*).

Seven other fern rusts are in the genus *Uredinopsis*, and have white, cylindric aecia with colorless spores that occur on current needles. All go to ferns, and are separated on uredospore characters. They are *U. mirabilis*, that goes to *Onoclea; U. osmundae*, that goes to *Osmunda* spp.; *U. phegopteris*, that goes to *Gymnocarpium dryopteris;* and *U. struthiopteridis*, that goes to *Matteuccia struthiopteris; U. atkinsonii*, that goes to *Dryopteris thelypteris; U. ceratophora*, that goes to *Cysopteris;* and *U. longimucronata*.

Two species of *Pucciniastrum* occur on current needles. They both have hypophyllous, cylindric aecia with delicate peridia and yellow aeciospores. *P. epilobii* goes to the common fire-weeds (*Epilobium* spp.) and related species, and *P. goeppertianum* goes to blueberries and huckleberries (*Vaccinium* spp.) (*46*).

Boyce (*149*) discusses in some detail the host relationships of the conifer rusts. For most species his nomenclature differs from Arthur's as supplemented and updated by Cummins (*46*). The latter is followed here with some documented exceptions. The problems in synonymy among names for the fir rusts are not particularly confusing.

A tip blight of balsam fir in the Northeast, caused by *Rehmiellopsis balsameae,* involves yellowing of current needles and a dying back of young twigs. Repeated attacks can kill small trees (*1514*).

A smudgy, surface, black mildew covering green needle tissue, is caused by *Phaeocryptopus nudus* and is very common (*63*). While harmless, it caused some early concern because of similarities with *Phaeocryptopus gäumanni*, a Douglas-fir pathogen. *Dimerosporium* (*Meliola*) *balsamicola* causes a much less common sooty mold on green needles, and can be confused with *P. nudus*. Hahn (*571*) considers these two fungi distinct, and is supported by Barr (*63*).

The foliage of seedlings and small saplings is sometimes blighted by species of *Phacidium* and related genera, which are known to attack only needles covered by snow. Apothecia form on the underside of needles and those of *P. balsameae* may be clearly seen while still covered by the epidermis (151). The perfect stage of this fungus has been given the names *Stegopezizella balsameae* and, more recently, *Sarcotrichila balsameae* (807). The imperfect stage has been called *Gloeosporium balsameae* (136). The other two species on balsam fir are *P.* (*Nothophacidium*) *abietinellum* (1155) and *P. abietis*, the former confined to this species, and the latter widespread on conifers (151). *P. abietis* was the only fungus identified with a notable severe defoliation of trees of all crown classes in 6- to 15-year old stands in Laurentide Park, Quebec, Canada (1314). Reid and Cain (1157) have clarified the relationships among 4 genera of fungi involved in "snowblights" in Canada. *Herpotrichia nigra*, a common, brown, snow-blight fungus of the West, occurs on balsam fir in mountainous parts of Quebec.

A foliage blight in Canada, caused by *Trichosphaeria parasitica*, has been considered beneficial by Smerlis since it hastened the death of intermediate and suppressed trees (1314). This is probably identical to *Acanthostigma parasitica*, a fungus that has been occasionally reported as a cause of needle and twig blight in the Northeast and Canada.

Darker (326) describes *Leptosphaeria faullii* as an agent in the biological control of certain Hypodermataceae. This and other fungi he describes, although themselves saprobes, prevent the maturation of the needle cast fungi by competing for the food supply. Darker's papers on the fungus flora of fir needles are classics in providing an insight into the enormous complex of interactions among the successions of fungi that inhabit needles of *A. balsamea*. Darker (326) describes the saprobe *Rhizothyrium abietis* on dead attached needles of *Abies balsamea* and *Tsuga canadensis*. This curious fungus has a columella emerging from a substomatal cavity from which conidiophores radiate, forming a circular, flat, black pycnidium. The conidia are hyaline, elliptic, and multiseptate.

Stem Diseases.—Balsam fir has many canker diseases, but none are economically important, and the pathogenicity of some of the indicated fungi is in some doubt. Several species of *Dasyscypha* are saprophytes on this species. *D. agassizii* is very common on dead bark, *D. arida* is common from the Lake States west, and *D. calycina* (574) has been reported. *D. resinaria* has caused swollen cankers locally in Minnesota (24). All species produce yellow- to orange-colored apothecia.

Cenangium ferruginosum (542), *Tympanis abietina* and *T. truncatula* (552), and *Ophionectria scolecospora* are also considered saprophytic on balsam fir.

In determining the cause of a dieback of balsam fir in Canada three fungi were implicated and each was proved able, independently, to cause some dieback. Raymond and Reid (1147) provide good descriptions of the fungi which, in order of importance, were *Thyronectria balsamea, Dermea balsamea*, and *Valsa kunzei*.

Valsa (*Cytospora*) *kunzei* causes both a dieback and a canker. Conspicuous branch and twig cankers form, often near nodes, and heavy resin flow is a prominent symptom (1519). In the Lake States, *Cephalosporium album* causes irregularly elliptical, very discrete cankers usually with a branch stub in the center. Resin from broken bark blisters runs down the stem in streaks (253, 257). Ouellette and Bard (1065) also isolated a species of *Cephalo-*

8

sporium from balsam fir cankers in Canada. They considered this fungus different from Christensen's (*253*). Their cankers yielded also a *Cylindrocarpon,* and this was pathogenic, whereas their *Cephalosporium* sp. was not. They consider their *Cylindrocarpon* to closely resemble the conidial stage of *Nectria cucurbitula* var. *macrospora.*

Aleurodiscus amorphus causes cankers on the main stems only, and often kills suppressed saplings (*587*). This fungus is also a common saprophyte. *A. abietis* and *A. laurentianus* fruit on the underside of dead branches on living trees, and *A. lividocoeruleus* fruits on dry, decorticated wood. *A. canadensis* grows on dead stem substrates (*858*).

Occasional cankers on twigs and branches, bearing perithecia of *Valsa friesii* (*Cytospora pinastri*), have been reported in Virginia, New England, and the Lake States. Another uncommon canker is reported due to *Cryptosporium macrospermum* (*8*). In Canada the apothecia- and pycnidia-forming ascomycete *Potebniamyces balsamicola* is associated with a twig and branch blight (*1314*). This fungus is closely related to the cause of the so-called *Phomopsis* disease of conifers, including balsam fir, which Smerlis (*1315*) calls *Potebniamyces coniferarum* and Hahn (*573*) calls *Phacidiella coniferarum.* The relationship of the taxa surrounding these fungi and involving, in addition to the above genera, also *Phacidium, Phacidiella,* and *Phacidiopycnis,* is discussed by Hahn (*573*) and by Smerlis (*1315*).

The most conspicuous disease of balsam fir is the common, yellow witches' broom caused by the rust fungus *Melampsorella caryophyllacearum* (*1106*). Broomed shoots are upright and dwarfed, with short, yellow needles that drop before they are a year old, denuding the shoots. The rust is perennial in the broomed shoots, and also produces trunk and branch swellings. It has its II and III stages on chickweed (species of *Cerastium* and *Stellaria*).

Root Diseases.—The shoe-string root and butt rot caused by *Armillaria mellea* is considered by many as the only important killing disease of balsam fir in the United States. The black rhizomorphs, root collar resinosis, and mycelial fans under the root collar bark characterize this disease (*848*). Root and butt rots are economically important in this short-lived species. The principal ones are two brown cubical rots (*Polyporus balsameus* (*723*) and *Coniophora puteana*) and three white stringy rots (*Poria subacida, Odontia bicolor,* and *Corticium galactinum*). *Armillaria mellea* and *Merulius himantioides* proved to be important butt rot fungi (*73*), and *Polyporus schweinitzii, P. tomentosus,* and some other fungi cause a small percentage of the root and butt rot in balsam fir (*332, 1314*).

The principal fungi involved in the important balsam fir butt rots vary with the region studied, whether Lake States (*771*), New York and New England (*1342*), or Canada (*72*). Davidson's studies in the Canadian Atlantic Provinces show how the proportion of butt decay associated with each of 11 species of fungi varied among seven stands in this region (*332*), and in another Canadian study, by Smerlis (*1314*), *Corticium galactinum* was by far the most frequently isolated fungus of the 11 named species obtained in culture.

A yellow stringy rot, largely of the roots and sometimes butts,

9

caused by *Flammula alnicola* occurs occasionally on balsam fir in Canada (*374*). *Merulius himantioides* causes a brown cubical rot in Quebec and Ontario.

Extensive root mortality of balsam fir follows defoliation by the spruce budworm (*1151*), apparently as a result of root starvation. Stillwell (*1356*) found that the after-effects of budworm attack are evident 40 or more years later, as trunk deformations, buried leaders, and decay that entered killed leaders.

Stillwell and Kelly (*1359*) determined the succession of fungi in balsam fir killed by the spruce budworm in northwestern New Brunswick; *Stereum chailletii*, introduced by woodwasps, was an important and early invader, followed in importance by *Stereum sanguinolentum* and *Polyporus abietinus*. Altogether, 19 species of Hymenomycetes were involved in sapwood decay.

Ruehle (*1222*) lists the root- or root-zone-inhabiting nematodes of *Abies balsamea* as: *Criconemoides lobatum; Rotylenchus robustus; Tylenchorhynchus maximus; Xiphinema americanum;* and unnamed species of *Paratylenchus, Pratylenchus,* and *Rotylenchus.*

Trunk Rots.—The main trunk rot of balsam fir is the non-pocket red heart caused by *Stereum sanguinolentum.* While the butt decay fungi enter mainly from root wounds (*1150*), the red heart fungus enters almost entirely through injuries to the trunk (*333*). *Fomes pini,* a pocket rot fungus, will also cause some heart rot in this species, but occurs in older trees and is rare compared to *S. sanguinolentum. Trametes heteromorpha* and *Hymenochaete tabacina* have also caused rot in living trees in New England. Most of the butt fungi can extend several feet into the trunk, and they play a major role in the high cull in balsam fir as it approaches 70 or 80 years old.

Artificial wounding of balsam fir by Etheridge and Morin (*423*) indicated that *Stereum sanguinolentum* is the main heart rot fungus of living trees that enters major wounds, and that *S. purpureum* mainly rots the heartwood of dead parts of trees, with *S. chailletii* showing a preference for sapwood, and a species of *Corticium* preferring heartwood in living or dead trees. Etheridge (*421*) found that *S. sanguinolentum* becomes established in the heartwood solely through injuries to living stems and branches. In every case studied he could trace infection to such a wound, and never to dead branch stubs resulting from branch death through suppression.

Hubbes and Etheridge (*720*) discovered that there is a chemical basis for balsam fir's susceptibility to certain heartwood fungi. Thus *Stereum sanguinolentum* showed an outstanding capacity to colonize a substrate impregnated with heartwood extractives from this fir. The active principle was destroyed by heat.

Basham and Morawski (*73*), in Ontario, found the rot cull percentage in balsam fir to reach 6 percent at age class 41–60, 9 percent at 81–100, 15 per cent at 101–120, and 22 percent at age class 141 and older. Fourteen Hymenomycetes were isolated more than once, and most of the rot was caused by *Stereum sanguinolentum, Corticium galactinum,* and *Odontia bicolor.*

Trunk injuries by bears on the Gaspé Peninsula led to decay by two fungi exclusively: *S. sanguinolentum* and *S. chailletii.*

The literature on balsam decays and other diseases is one of the most extensive and best for any North American species. The Canadians have made a large proportion of the outstanding research

10

contributions on balsam fir pathology.

Mycorrhizal Relations.—Although the literature on balsam fir pathology is extensive, only two fungi, *Boletus granulatus* and *Cenococcum graniforme*, have been reported to form mycorrhizae with roots of this tree. While neither fungus has been proved through pure culture technique (*1442*), this is not necessary for proof of association in *Cenococcum*.

Miscellaneous Pathology.—The deterioration of windthrown balsam fir timber in Newfoundland was attributed largely to incipient decay by *Stereum chailletii* and advanced deterioration by *Lenzites saepiaria* (*334*). Windthrown timber in New Brunswick, Canada, was attacked by *S. chailletii* and *S. sanguinolentum* that were introduced into the wood largely by siricid woodwasps (*1357*). Studies on the relationship of insects to deterioration and decay in balsam wounded by the spruce budworm have indicated that insect transmission of rot fungi is important in dead and dying trees (*71*). The significance and succession of five fungi consistently associated with the deterioration of balsam fir trees killed by the spruce budworm was worked out by Basham in Canada (*67*). The species involved were decay fungi *S. chailletii* and *Polyporus abietinus*, a yeast, an unidentified "fungus F," and the ascomycete *Ophiostoma bicolor*.

Etheridge and Morin (*424*) found the pith to be a major center of bacterial activity in balsam fir, with low activity in normal heartwood, and virtually none in sapwood. Forty percent of the firs and 90 percent of the black spruces had sterile heart and sapwood. *Retinocyclus abietis* was the only fungus isolated from the wood of the two species.

A blue-stain fungus occurs very frequently in the heartwood of American and Canadian balsam fir. First called *Amphisphaeria thujina*, the fungus has more recently been named *Kirschsteiniella thujina* (*1126*). This fungus is the most common organism in dead branches, through which it enters the trunk of living balsams. When this stain fungus preempts these dead branches, its antagonism to *Stereum sanguinolentum* may prevent such branches from serving as infection courts for the *Stereum*, leaving the latter only injuries on living stems as pathways of entry (*1126*).

Zones of wetwood are commonly associated with areas around dead branches. The condition is related to the capacity of such branches to trap and conduct water to the inner bole (*422*).

Abnormal staminate cone production is caused by *Sclerotinia kerneri*. The flower buds in the leaf axils of young twigs are greatly increased in number. These numerous buds and the cone scales on the thickened twigs, which remain attached in the form of cups, give affected branches a distinctive appearance. Terminal buds are commonly destroyed by the fungus (*235*).

White fir
Abies concolor

White fir is widely distributed in the Rocky Mountain and Pacific Coast regions extending from New Mexico and Wyoming westward to Oregon and California, reaching its best development on northern and eastern slopes in California and southwest Oregon.

It thrives in cool, moist situations and in the higher mountain areas where winters are long and snow deposits are moderate to heavy. White fir sites have a precipitation range of 35 to 75 in. Their temperature extremes range from —38° in Colorado to 98° F. in southern California. The species is very tolerant. Although it grows best on deep, moist loams it often occurs on dry, coarse, disintegrated rock. It does not grow well in the heavier clay soils (938). Growth is rapid up to 50 to 100 years, then slows, with longevity of 200 years common, and a maximum longevity not much over 300 years (1367). White fir is considered by some horticulturists as the most desirable ornamental species for eastern Canada (52).

White fir is easily killed by fire when young. Exposed to salt spray in a New England hurricane, it was one of the most severely damaged species (1632). In the high Sierras the heavy fall of snow often severely damages trees. Young trees are susceptible to sunscald, especially when suddenly exposed. Old-growth stands often have a high incidence of wind shake and rift crack, the latter arising from internal growth stresses (938). In one area in the Sierras late spring freezes frequently damaged the new growth of young trees, and temperatures below 20° F. completely destroyed new growth. Frost cracks are common, and white fir is also subject to windthrow and wind breakage, particularly in stands that received heavy selective cuts. Although the species is considered among the most defective in the West, disease will not be the most critical element in determining rotations in most of the Pacific Coast region (938).

Although white fir did not occur in certain areas studied with respect to sulfur dioxide smelter injury in Montana and Washington, other true firs did occur, and they led all coniferous species in sensitivity to sulfur dioxide injury (1249).

In addition to its defectiveness, white fir is subject to damage from several needle rusts, a brooming rust, needle casts, and highly injurious attack by dwarfmistletoe.

Seedling Damage.—The germination of white fir seed is typically low, usually under 50 percent, and the vitality of seedlings is highly variable (938, 1367). Injury during dewinging accounts for part of this low germinability. Summer drought and winter cold, depending upon the area, accounts for much seedling loss in the field.

Smith and Bega (1323) describe severe damage to coniferous nursery stock, including white fir, in California nurseries (see *Pinus lambertiana*) as a result of mid- to late-season attack of roots by *Sclerotium bataticola* (*Macrophomina phaseoli*).

Foliage Diseases.—White fir is subject to some striking needle diseases. While not often a factor in timber production, they can ruin trees for use as Christmas trees. *Lirula* (*Hypodermella*) *abietis-concoloris* causes a copious shedding of non-current-year's needles, and bears dark-brown pycnidia in the groove on the upper surface of the needle. *Virgella* (*Hypoderma*) *robusta* has concolorous pycnidia that turn black after discharge, and which are aligned in two rows, one on each wing of the needle. *Lirula punctata* is rarely found fruiting and is distinguished by having small, elliptical, waxy pycnidia in one or two scattered rows (323, 328).

12

Lophomerum (*Lophodermium*) *autumnale* has the interesting habit of following *Virgella robusta* in a secondary capacity. *Lophodermium consociatum* also follows *V. robusta* but differs from *Lophomerum autumnale* in having intraepidermal hysterothecia while the latter has subcuticular hysterothecia (*323*). *Lophodermium piceae* occurs only on old needles about to drop from natural causes, or on densely shaded needles. Its large flat pycnidia separate it easily from all other species on *Abies*. *Lophodermium decorum* attacks white fir needles, mainly on shaded, lower branches, in Colorado.

Sarcotrichila (*Stegopezizella, Phacidium*) *balsameae* (*135, 807*) and *Phacidium abietis* (*1157*) cause needle blights of foliage long covered by snow. These fungi form apothecia on the underside of needles (*151*). Snow-covered foliage at high altitudes also is subject to attack by the brown felt blight caused by *Herpotrichia nigra* (*151*). This fungus, and its counterpart *Neopeckia coulteri* on the pines, have often been regarded as attacking only after foliage has been smothered by lack of oxygen. However, John M. Staley[1] has demonstrated attack of inoculated needles of the current growing season that could not be considered senescent.

Several needle rusts attack and fruit on current year's needles. Two species of *Pucciniastrum* have hypophyllous, cylindric aecia, with delicate peridia and yellow aeciospores. *P. epilobii* goes to the common fire-weeds (*Epilobium* spp.) and related species, and *P. goeppertianum* goes to blueberries and huckleberries (*Vaccinium* spp.). Arthur (*46*) relates *Peridermium ornamentale*, another fir needle rust, to *P. goeppertianum*, but others doubt this connection (*149*).

Melampsora abieti-capraearum (*M. epitea*), with its flat aecia lacking a peridium, occurs on curent needles and goes to leaves of willow (*Salix* spp.). It is considered by Ziller (*1666*) to be indistinguishable morphologically from *M. epitea* f. sp. *tsugae* (*Caeoma dubium*) on western hemlock.

Melampsorella caryophyllacearum causes a conspicuous brooming, giving an upright habit to the dwarfed shoots and causing a yellowing of needles that often drop before they are a year old, thus denuding the shoots. The rust is perennial in the shoots and sometimes produces trunk and branch swellings. It has its uredo and telial stages on species of *Cerastium* and *Stellaria* (*46*), and is not as common on white fir as on some of the other firs (*1069*), but Peterson (*1105*) in an account of the spruce and fir broom rusts mentions serious outbreaks of the latter on white fir in New Mexico. He gives a good illustrated account of the fir broom rust, its symptoms, damage, biology, and control (*1106*).

Uredinopsis pteridis is a leaf rust having white, cylindric aecia with colorless spores. Occurring generally on several fir species (*432, 1665*), it has been reported on white fir only in California. Its alternate host is the fern *Pteridium aquilinum*.

Macrophoma parca causes a needle blight chiefly of firs other than white fir, but can team up with *Lirula abietis-concoloris* on

---

[1] Personal communication from John M. Staley, pathologist, USDA Forest Service, Rocky Mountain Forest and Range Experiment Station, Ft. Collins, Colo.

white fir to cause severe defoliation in Arizona[2]. It usually fruits on dead hanging needles.

A needle disease of *Abies concolor* in northern California, and of *Pinus monophylla* further south is caused by *Furcaspora pinicola*. Bonar (*138*) describes and illustrates this curious fungus, that has conidia acrogenous, at first cylindric and 1-celled, but changing to 3-celled by the growing of two divergent cells from the apex of the original cell, forming a bifurcate, 3-celled, hyaline conidium. These spores emerge from acervuli, in a creamy, slimy mass.

The tip blight fungus *Rehmiellopsis balsameae* has caused a shoot and foliage blight on white firs used as ornamentals in the Northeast (*1514*). Needles of the current season's growth are attacked, and cankers may be formed at the base of infected needles.

Stem Diseases.—A tip blight and a brooming rust have already been mentioned. The principal stem disease of white fir, excluding the heart rots, is the fir dwarfmistletoe (*Arceuthobium campylopodum* f. *abietinum*). It causes brooms, branch and trunk swellings, distortion, growth reduction, and mortality (*505*), Scharpf (*1241*) provides a detailed, illustrated account of this fir form of *A. campylopodum*, with emphasis on its attack of *Abies concolor* and *A. magnifica*. Although the forma name is the same for the dwarfmistletoe on these two firs, the white fir form will not attack red fir and vice versa. Parmeter and Scharpf (*1086*) report extensive damage to red and white fir over much of the fir belt of California. Field evidence supported cross-inoculations in showing that the races of *Arceuthobium campylopodum* f. *abietinum* attacking red fir and white fir are different.

On white fir large, rotting, cankered areas on the trunk cause considerable loss (*151*), and the damage to this species from dwarfmistletoe may be extensive and severe (*938*). The Douglas-fir dwarfmistletoe (*A. douglasii*) will damage white fir but the latter is not a common host for it (*526*).

A true mistletoe, *Phoradendron bolleanum* subsp. *pauciflorum*, commonly kills the upper portions of the crowns of white fir in Arizona and the Sierras. Temperature limits its range to south of the Mokelumne drainage in the Sierras (*1491*). The dwarfmistletoe hyperparasite *Septogloeum gillii* attacks *A. campylopodum* f. *abietinum* (*409, 410*).

Aleurodiscus amorphus can cause cankering of suppressed trees, and was particularly aggressive to white fir in an Oregon area (*587*). Its flat, irregular fruiting-bodies are characteristic (*151, 858*).

White fir has been successfully inoculated with the crown gall bacterium, *Agrobacterium tumefaciens*, and gall formation followed (*1319*).

Valsa (*Cytospora*) *abietis* can cause a cankering and death of branches of white fir that have been weakened by other factors (*1616*). It is often the agent that does the killing, following dwarfmistletoe infection. Typical symptoms are early resin infiltration of bark, followed by development of a canker and production of yellow spore horns.

---

[2] Personal communication from Paul D. Keener, deceased, formerly plant pathologist, University of Arizona, Tuscon, Ariz.

14

Root Diseases.—White fir is not subject to any important killing diseases of the roots. Two fungi that kill and rot roots of many conifers, *Armillaria mellea* and *Fomes annosus,* frequently attack the roots and butts of white fir, but their damage is mainly the cull they cause and their subsidiary effect in increasing losses from windthrow and wind breakage (*938*).

Long (*885*) describes many white firs in a stand in New Mexico killed or dying from destruction of the roots by *Polyporus dryadeus,* a common root parasite of oak in the East. Many of the trees bore sporophores at the base.

Nematode species of *Aphelenchoides* and *Hoplolaimus* have been reported from white fir (*1222*).

Trunk Rots.—Many root rot fungi such as *Armillaria mellea, Fomes annosus,* and *Pholiota adiposa* will extend several feet up into the trunks, and the more strictly trunk rot fungi such as *Enchinodontium tinctorium* can extend damage down into roots. Kimmey and Bynum (*799*) describe the rots of red and white firs. They list, in order of importance, the following white rot fungi, which together cause about four-fifths of the decay loss in red and white firs: *P. adiposa, F. annosus, E. tinctorium,* and *A. mellea.* Brown cubical rots make up the other one-fifth of the decay loss, and they are caused by *F. pinicola, Polyporus sulphureus,* and *P. schweinitzii.*

While frost cracks and miscellaneous injuries lead to some decay, most butt rot fungi infect through fire scars or other basal wounds. *Echinodontium tinctorium* (see also *Abies grandis*), however, enters almost exclusively through branch stubs and open knots, and its conks, in great numbers, may appear at these points. The cull percentage in white fir in maturing stands in northwestern California may run as high as 30 to 50 percent (*793*). Kimmey gives cull tables and pertinent descriptive data on the main rots and their indicators for northwestern California (*793*). He has also developed a method of applying cull indicator factors to white and red fir in the Sierras that provided cull estimates that were within 0.5 percent of the cull actually measured on cut trees.

The genus *Echinodontium,* monographed by Gross (*547*), includes only 6 species, 4 of which occur in the United States. Sporulation and sporophore survival in *E. tinctorium* are described by Maloy (*921*).

The ring scale fungus, *Fomes pini,* rarely occurs on the true firs but is the heart rot fungus that most commonly fruits on Douglas-fir (*793*).

White fir was one of the first western species intensively studied in the earliest days of forest pathology research in the United States, and was used by Meinecke in formulating concepts of how disease factors can influence silviculture (*943*).

Tracheomycosis following bark beetle attack was given detailed study for white fir (*1615*). Three species of Scolytid beetles commonly infest white fir, namely, *Scolytus ventralis, S. praeceps,* and *S. subscaber.* Brown discolorations form around the galleries. The principal fungus associated with the first insect was *Trichosporium symbioticum,* and the main fungus associated with the latter two insect species was *Spicaria anomala.* Both fungi were demonstrated to be pathogenic to the cambium of white fir.

A fungus capable of causing either rot of charred logs of *Abies* and *Cupressus* spp. in the West is *Polyporus carbonarius* (*1067*).

Mycorrhizal Relations.—Only one fungus, *Cenococcum graniforme*, has been reported to form mycorrhizae with white fir (*1442*).

Miscellaneous Pathology.—In northeastern California, "wetwood," resulting from sap fermentation, is common in the butt heartwood of white fir. Freezing of this wetwood results in multiple checking of the affected wood, often rendering the butt unmerchantable (*938*).

Rift cracks, mentioned earlier, will often collect water which runs out when trees are felled. The freezing of water in these cracks can be an added cause of frost-cracking.

Young white firs, up to 6 ft. high, that are bent during logging often die a year or two later even though injury may appear superficial. Pines are much less subject to such mortality.

Fraser fir
Abies fraseri

This species is very similar in general appearance to balsam fir but differs in some morphologic aspects (*279*) and attains smaller size. A southern tree, it begins to appear where balsam fir leaves off in western Virginia, and extends southward along the crest of the Appalachian Mountains in West Virginia, Tennessee, North Carolina, and as far south as north Georgia. When young it can tolerate shade, but later requires full light for good growth. It is confined to elevations above 4,000 ft. and requires high soil moisture and air moisture and cool summers. While it requires little soil, being very shallow-rooted, it does not establish itself readily unless there is abundant moist humus. Attempts to grow this tree at elevations under 3,000 ft. have been generally unsuccessful, because it will not withstand the summer heat and drier environment typical of the lower elevations. The species will pioneer the logged-over upper slopes where fires have not destroyed the humus, but it usually ultimately gives way to the very tolerant, but more slow-growing, red spruce.

Fraser fir can withstand sustained temperatures well below zero and is seldom damaged by ice or snow. It will not tolerate drought, high summer or fall temperatures, or fire. The resin blisters in the bark add to the heat of fires, and the crowns are highly flammable. Windthrow is a common cause of loss because of the shallow roots and shallow soil in which the tree typically grows. There are no important fungus enemies of Fraser fir other than those attacking young seedlings in the nursery.

Seedling Diseases.—Heavy losses to Fraser fir have occurred in a North Carolina nursery from two aggressive fungi, *Cylindrocladium scoparium* and *Phytophthora cinnamomi*. The *C. scoparium* disease (see also *Liriodendron*) appears as a reddening needle blight by late summer, followed by needle shedding. Cankers may appear at any point on the stem, and this is the most damaging phase of the disease, since girdling usually results. Affected nursery beds appear as though scorched by fire (*696*).

Phytophthora cinnamomi causes strictly a root and root collar necrosis, particularly on the heavier soils and in the lower spots of the nursery, and killed 50 percent of an acre of Fraser fir nursery seedlings in one year in North Carolina (*819*). The disease was characterized by a red-brown discoloration of the cambial region, which extended from below the root collar to 3 or 4 in. above the ground.

Foliage Diseases.—The needle cast fungus *Lirula* (*Hypodermella*) *abietis-concoloris* can cause a copious shedding of older foliage and is distinguished by its pycnidia becoming concolorous with the leaf surface after discharge (*323*). The rust *Uredinopsis mirabilis*, with hypophyllous aecia on needles of the current season, and with colorless spores, is common on individual needles, and has its II and III stages on the fern *Onoclea sensibilis* (*46, 432*).

A shoot tip and needle blight is caused by *Rehmiellopsis balsameae,* and appears first as a yellowing of current needles and then a dying back of young twigs. Repeated attacks can kill small trees (*1514*). Three other needle fungi have been reported on this tree: *Rhabdogloeum abietinum* (*625*), which is associated with a needle blight and fruits on living needles; *Rhizosphaera pini,* probably a saprophyte on needles; and *Cryptospora pinastri,* which may be parasitic (*8*).

Hahn (*573*) produced lesions on Fraser fir with *Phacidiella coniferarum* (*572*). The imperfect stage, now placed in *Phacidiopycnis*, has long been referred to *Phomopsis* and the disease caused is the common, so-called *Phomopsis* canker of conifers. The perfect stage (*Phacidiella*) has recently been placed in *Potebniamyces* by Smerlis (*1315*).

Adelopus nudus produces a dark, sooty smudge and forms perithecia along the stomatal lines on the underside of the needles (*571*).

Stem Diseases.—Fraser fir has no noteworthy stem diseases except the *Rehmiellopsis* tip blight already mentioned. The bark of dead trunks and branches is frequently covered with the yellow-orange apothecia of *Dasyscypha agassizii,* a harmless saprophyte; and areas of hardened gum commonly bear the much smaller orange apothecia of *Biatorella* (*Zythia*) *resinae.*

One of the few records of parasitism by the apothecial bark fungus *Aleurodiscus amorphus* was on *Abies fraseri* out of its range (*587, 858*).

Root and Stem Rots.—Few decay fungi have been reported as of consequence on Fraser fir. *Armillaria mellea* can kill small trees, especially if near hardwood stumps, and it also causes a root and butt rot (*848*). *Fomes annosus* is known to rot roots of this species in North Carolina. The heart rot called red heart in balsam fir, caused by *Stereum sanguinolentum* (*333*), also occurs on Fraser fir as far south as Tennessee (*1342*). *Polyporus balsameus,* an important, brown, cubical butt rot fungus of the North on balsam fir; and *Poria subacida,* which causes a yellow stringy rot, have been collected on Fraser fir in North Carolina and Tennessee (*892*). The most common saprot of dead wood is caused by *Polyporus abietinus.*

Miscellaneous.—Ruehle (*1224*) lists 6 species of nematodes in 5 genera, associated with Fraser fir in North Carolina.

17

Grand fir

Abies grandis

Grand fir grows in the stream bottoms, valleys, and mountain slopes of western Washington, Oregon, and northwestern California, and also in Idaho and western Montana. It extends well into British Columbia from both the northwestern and Inland Empire parts of its range. Precipitation varies from 20 to 100 in. over the range with only 15 to 25 percent of this falling during the growing season. Snowfall ranges from a few to over 500 in. per year (*452*). Mean annual temperature over the range is from 42° to 50° F. with a minimum of —30° F. in Montana (*1367*). While Parker (*1079*), in one study, found that grand fir foliage could withstand —55° F. without damage, Peace (*1091*) considered this species very susceptible to damage from spring frosts in England. In its native range, sudden extreme cold in the autumn will damage foliage.

Grand fir thrives on deep, well-drained alluvial soils, and does well also on the thinner exposed soils of ridges, and on pure pumice in central and eastern Oregon. However, it.has not done well on heavy clay loam on the Olympic Peninsula. Its altitudinal range along the Pacific Coast is from near sea level to about 1,500 ft. in Washington and 5,000 ft. in California. It is predominantly a lowland species along the coast, but reaches 6,000 ft. in elevation in the Inland Empire (*1367*). Grand fir is moderately tolerant, but is less tolerant than many associated species. It is not a long-lived species for the West, maturing between 90 and 120 years and attaining maximum ages of 250 to 280 years (*279, 452*). This tree has not succeeded when planted in the Northeast.

Fire resistance varies greatly with habitat, and in general grand fir is classed as moderately resistant. Frost cracks and lightning scars occur more commonly on grand fir than on its associated species. Snow causes much damage, and in some study areas accounted for 48 percent of the total mortality. The species is intermediate in susceptibility to windthrow and is subject to much wind breakage because of a high incidence of butt and trunk rot (*581*). It is very sensitive to drought.

Of 12 conifers listed in order of damage from sulfur dioxide in connection with emissions from a smelter in British Columbia (*1249*), grand fir was the most susceptible.

The main pathology problem with grand fir is its defectiveness and rotting readily from bole wounds at an early age. While it is host to many parasites, decay caused by *Echinodontium tinctorium* is the biggest source of loss.

Seedling Diseases.—Grand fir seed has, typically, a low germination percentage, having the lowest (12 percent) of six associated species in one study (*581*), and listed as average for six western firs (28 percent) in the Woody Plant Seed Manual (*1*). The seeds germinate better in the dark than in full light. About 30 percent of the seedlings in the field die the first year and 10 percent die the second. Damping-off accounts for much early mortality, while insolation and drought account for losses late in the season. Seedlings are fairly heat- and drought-resistant when grown in the open where their roots go deepest (*581*). *Rhizina undulata* has killed seedlings

18

in patches a few feet across in Idaho on burned areas. Seedlings have also been killed by the gray mold Botrytis blight (*B. cinerea*) and by the brown felt snow mold, *Herpotrichia nigra*. *Thelephora terrestris* grows around seedlings and is usually harmless but can have a smothering effect (*1540*).

Foliage Diseases.—Grand fir is subject to four of the needle cast fungi discussed under *Abies concolor* and *A. magnifica,* namely, *Virgella robusta, Lirula abietis-concoloris, L. punctata,* and *Lophodermium decorum. L. decorum* occurs on the needles of heavily shaded branches, producing hypophyllous hysterothecia in two rows along the stomatal surfaces. It is confined to grand fir and is likely a very weak parasite (*323*).

Several needle rusts occur on grand fir and they produce aecia only on previous year's needles. Many of these are discussed under *Abies concolor.* These are *Pucciniastrum epilobii, P. goeppertianum, Melampsora abieti-capraearum* (*M. epitea*), *Melampsorella caryophyllacearum,* and *Uredinopsis pteridis.* In addition, the rusts on grand fir include *Peridermium rugosum,* a species confined to grand fir and Pacific silver fir and lacking a known alternate host, and *Uredinopsis hashiokai,* a fern rust (*432, 1665*). Still another fern rust, *Milesia laeviuscula,* produces a *Peridermium* stage on grand fir, with its known distribution so far only near Victoria, British Columbia (*1664*). Ziller's papers on the rusts of western firs and hemlock should be consulted when one is working in this field.

Peterson (*1105, 1106*) gives good accounts of the spruce and fir broom rusts. The latter, *Melampsorella caryophyllacearum,* while not a major pathogen of grand fir, can be conspicuous and locally damaging (see *Abies concolor*). It produces yellow-needled brooms, spike-tops, stem lesions, and growth reduction.

Macrophoma parca, which fruits on dead, hanging needles (*625*), causes a needle blight, and when attacking needles along with *Lirula abietis-concoloris* can result in much disfiguring of trees.

Three species of *Dimerosporium* have been reported on grand fir, *D.* (*Meliola*) *abietis* (*991*), *D. balsamicola,* and *D. tsugae* (*1277*). They form a dense, sooty-black surface coating on needles, living on the sweet secretions of sucking insects. Another surface sooty mold caused by *Adelopus nudus* (= *D. balsamicola?*), with its small perithecia along the stomatal ·lines on the under side of needles, occurs on grand fir (*571, 1277*).

Herpotrichia nigra causes a brown felt blight of foliage that has remained long under snow. *Phacidium abietis,* another snow-mold fungus, also occurs on grand fir but is not economically important (*1157*).

Stem Diseases.—The fir dwarfmistletoe (*Arceuthobium campylopodum* f. *abietinum*) which stunts, deforms, causes brooms, reduces vigor, and results in cankering, breakage, and killing, attacks grand fir occasionally but is not nearly as damaging to this species as it is to *Abies concolor* and *A. magnifica* (*505*).

Valsa (*Cytospora*)*abietis,* a fungus mainly causing cankers on trees injured from other causes, is primarily a pathogen of *A. concolor* and *A. magnifica,* but it also occurs on grand fir (*1616*). *Valsa pini,* a lesser-known fungus, is also reported to form cankers on branches and twigs of grand fir (*1278*).

19

Grand fir in northern Idaho is subject to a branch canker of saplings caused by *Phomopsis boycei*, that is characterized by flagging (shoots bearing conspicuous dead foliage) and stem constriction at the canker with a sometimes knuckle-like swelling of the living tissue at the base of the canker (*565*). Hubert (*725*) noted the similarity of this canker to one caused by *Phoma abietina*. Hahn (*565*) considers the latter not to occur in the United States.

Five species of *Aleurodiscus* (*A. abietis, A. amorphus, A. lividocoeruleus, A. penicillatus,* and *A. weirii*), and the closely related *Aleurocystidiellum subcruenatum*, have been reported on grand fir (*858*). The commonest is *A. amorphus*, which causes cankers on branches of suppressed trees. Its flat, irregular fruiting bodies are characteristic of the genus (*151, 587*).

Funk (*483*) reports *Caliciopsis pseudotsugae* causing small cankers on branches and stems of *Abies amabilis* and *A. grandis*, as well as on Douglas-fir (see *Pseudotsuga*).

Three species of *Dasyscypha* (*D. agassizii, D. arida,* and *D. caliciformis*) are common on dead bark (*1277*). They are all saprophytes and have yellow-orange apothecia.

Scleroderris abieticola is associated with a stem and branch canker of grand fir, subalpine fir, and Pacific silver fir, in which necrosis begins in the autumn and stops when growth starts in the spring. If the stem is not girdled by spring the lesion will heal over. Black apothecia appear on the dead bark during the following summer (*1656*).

Root Diseases.—*Armillaria mellea, Fomes annosus,* and *Poria weirii* are capable of killing trees, although mortality directly traceable to root necrosis by a single fungus is not common with grand fir. *F. annosus* is one of the commonest root rot fungi on this species, but its courts of entry are as likely to be aboveground trunk wounds as on roots (*1623*).

Of the root rot fungi attacking grand fir, Hubert (*731*) considers *Poria weirii* and *Armillaria mellea* the most important, with *Fomes annosus* and *P. subacida* responsible for much windthrow and wind breakage. Maloy and Gross (*923*) found *A. mellea* causing butt rot in many vigorous trees with thrifty crowns. Hubert (*729*) gives special attention to means of identifying the root rots of species in the western white pine type.

The following distinguishing characteristics of four root rots of western white pine are adapted from Hubert (*729*).

Armillaria mellea—Honey-colored mushrooms at tree base. Brown to black rhizomorphs under bark on or near roots or in duff. Resin flow around tree base. Thick radiating mycelial mats, white to purplish, under bark of roots or trunk base. Advanced rot soft, yellowish white, no pockets, narrow black zone lines; in sapwood.

Poria subacida—Conk a tough, poroid, white to yellowish layer, on undersides of roots, in root crotches, and under windfalls. Mycelial mats as thin sheets and irregular patches under root and butt bark, not radial, grayish, becoming yellowish. Hollows often lined with white to yellow, often spongy, mycelial mats. Advanced rot white, stringy to spongy with black spots and white streaks.

Fomes annosus—Conks hard, poroid brackets to irregular masses, zonate above, poroid and whitish below, on undersides of roots, in root crotches, and at soil line of trunk. Sometimes very thin mycelial sheets under or in bark. Advanced decay with small, white, blunt-end pockets with black flecks and ring-scaled, white spongy mass; in sapwood.

Poria weirii—Conks thick, poroid, flat, in several layers, yellowish to dark brown, on undersides of roots, root crotches, windfalls, etc. Hollows and large cracks with linings of dark brown, wooly mycelium. Advanced decay soft, flaky, laminated, brownish, many small pockets; reddish brown tufts of bristle-like hyphae in spaces between layers; in heartwood.

Trunk Rots.—In the past grand fir has been considered a secondary species mainly because of its high percentage of cull from rots (731). Heart rot extending from the roots to the top log has been common. *Echinodontium tinctorium* is the main trunk rot in older stands, and its characteristic toothed conks may appear along the length of the bole, protruding from knots and branch stubs. Hubert (731) points out that in grand fir, in the past, some *Poria weirii* cases have not been recognized as such, and were included as decay by *E. tinctorium*. *P. weirii* has been described from grand fir in British Columbia as well as the Pacific Northwest (190).

The red ring rot caused by *Fomes pini* also occurs in mature grand fir. In this species *F. pini* does not cause the concentric ring pattern that it produces in Douglas-fir.

In a study of decay following logging injury to several western conifers, Wright and Isaac (1623) found that *Fomes annosus* was primarily responsible for such injuries, accounting for 32 percent of the rot, and *Stereum* sp. was second, accounting for 13 percent. They give a good account of the subject of decay associated with trunk wounds, with lists of fungi, their incidence, descriptions of their penetration of the tree, and the rots they cause.

Maloy and Gross (923), working in Idaho, found that decay, largely caused by *Echinodontium tinctorium*, can become serious in grand fir ranging from 40 to 80 years old, if injured. Dead branches, regarded by many as important entry points, were associated with only 6 percent of the decay columns. Scars were associated with 46 percent, dead tops 26 percent, and frost cracks 7 percent of the rot columns. Incipient decay could be confused with compression wood, pitch-soaking, and "water-core" or "wetwood." Kimmey (798) gives a detailed account of *E. tinctorium* and the rot it causes. It is most prevalent in *Abies grandis, A. concolor,* and *Tsuga heterophylla,* but is common on all western firs and is known from other softwoods. The conk is hard, hoof-shaped, and perennial, with upper surface black, dull, rough and cracked, with the under surface thickly set with hard, coarse spines. Inside, the context is a brick- or rust-red. It causes a white rot, with the incipient stage appearing as water-soaked spots. Rust-red streaks appear, and finally the wood becomes soft, stringy, tan to reddish, and with a tendency to separate along the annual rings.

The section on *Abies lasiocarpa* mentions American and Canadian studies that point out the great significance of root and trunk wounds, as compared with branch stubs, in decay of that species.

Hubert (731) discusses rotation ages for grand fir, which might range from 80 to 110 years, depending upon success in reducing the incidence of butt and trunk rots. He discusses the many factors influencing decay in this defective species.

The decay fungi found in young grand fir in Washington by Maloy (922) were *Stereum sanguinolentum, Pholiota adiposa, Hericium abietis,* and *Odontia bicolor*.

Mycorrhizal Relations.—The following fungi are reported to form mycorrhizae with grand fir (1442): *Boletus edulis, Cenococcum* *graniforme, Lactarius deliciosus,* and *Russula delica.*

Miscellaneous Pathology.—A very complete list of the fungi reported to occur on grand fir, together with references to their descriptions, is provided by Shaw (*1277, 1278*).

Subalpine fir

Abies lasiocarpa

Subalpine fir is the smallest of the eight species of true firs indigenous to the western United States (*20*). It is characterized by a slender crown, a narrow, conical, spike-like top, and flat whorls of blue-green foliage (*279*). It is widely distributed from southern Alaska, through British Columbia, along both slopes of the Cascades to southern Oregon. In the Rocky Mountain region it extends, often together with Engelmann spruce, from British Columbia and Alberta south through the Inland Empire, and along the high elevations of the Rockies to Arizona and New Mexico. Two varieties are recognized: the type (*Abies lasiocarpa* var. *lasiocarpa*), and corkbark fir (*A. lasiocarpa* var. *arizonica*), the latter having white, corky bark, and being restricted to the southern Rockies (*20*).

The species thrives in a cold and humid climate with temperature extremes from below —50° to over 90° F., and with average annual temperatures of 25° to 40° F. Precipitation ranges from 20 to 100 in. annually and much of it is snow. The tree is not demanding as to soil type, growing well on alluvial plains and sandy to silt-loam slopes, but poorly on soils very wet much of the year or on rocky or gravelly soils. The elevation range is from near sea level in Alaska to 12,000 ft. in the Southwest. In Washington and Oregon it generally grows at 5,000 to 7,000 ft. The species is very tolerant, being more tolerant than any of its associates (*20*). Longevity is commonly in excess of 200 years, and although individuals grow to over 400 years old, many stands begin breaking up after 150 years (*125, 684*).

The species, like all true firs, is sensitive to air pollution by sulfur dioxide. In the case of studies made near two ore smelters subalpine fir was first out of eight conifers in damage sustained near one smelter, and second only to grand fir, out of 12 conifers observed, in the other area (*1249*). While first in injury by sulfur dioxide in the Washoe, Montana, smelter area, subalpine fir was sixth out of eight in damage from red belt, a form of winter injury (*1249*).

Subalpine fir is sensitive to fire because of its thin bark, its balsam blisters, and its typically low-hanging, flammable foliage. In spite of its cold natural habitat the species has not proved hardy when planted in the Northeast, where it is subject to winter injury (*279*). Planted in eastern Canada, some trees have stood the cold well (*52*). While usually windfirm, strong gusty winds can severely damage, break, and uproot trees (*414*).

The main elements of the pathology of subalpine fir are conspicuous damage by a broom rust, moderate injury from many needle rusts, attack by dwarfmistletoe, and high defect in many areas, due largely to the trunk rot fungus *Stereum sanguinolentum.*

Seedling Diseases.—Seed viability is fair (an average of 38 percent sound), being high for a fir, but low compared to most other western conifers (20). Vitality is described as transient. Seedlings are often killed by drought, heat, cutworms, frost-heaving, damping-off, and rodents (20). Seedlings are subject to occasional damage from the gray-mold Botrytis blight (*B. cinerea*) and from two snow molds: the brown felt blight (*Herpotrichia nigra*) and *Phacidium abietis* (1157), both of which conspicuously grow over needles remaining long under snow. Since subalpine fir is seldom planted in quantity, little is known of its potential nursery diseases (151). *Thelephora terrestris* grows conspicuously around seedlings but does little if any damage.

The yellow witches' broom rust, *Melampsorella caryophyllacearum*, can be an important seedling disease in the field (964).

The ring nematode *Criconemoides annulatum* has been found feeding externally on the roots of subalpine fir in Canada (1222).

Foliage Diseases.—Five needle cast fungi have been reported: *Phaeocryptopus nudus* and *Lophomerum* (*Lophodermium*) *autumnale*, which appear to be secondary; *Lophodermium piceae*, a weak parasite of old, heavily shaded needles (323, 1277); and *Isthmiella* (*Bifusella*) *abietis*, which is confined to *Abies lasiocarpa* and its variety *arizonica*. *I. abietis* is characterized by two lines of pycnidia, one along each side of the sinus on the upper surface of the needles (323). *Lirula abietis-concoloris* is actively pathogenic (1347), as described for *Abies concolor*.

Some rusts fruit on the current year's needles; these include the yellow-aeciospored *Vaccinium* rust *Pucciniastrum goeppertianum* and the fire-weed rust *P. pustulatum*. Others form aecia on older needles, including the white-spored fern rusts *Uredinopsis pteridis* and *U. struthiopteridis;* the caeoma-forming *Melampsora abieti-capraearum* (*M. epitea*) which goes to *Salix;* and the common yellow witches' broom rust, *Melampsorella caryophyllacearum*, which goes to chickweed (*Stellaria* spp. and *Cerastium* spp.). Mielke (964) describes the heavy infection and destructive effect of *M. caryophyllacearum* in some stands of subalpine fir in the Intermountain region. The brooms are upright and compact. Attacks are particularly severe on seedlings and saplings. Some trees may have 30 to 50 brooms each, and in some stands the percentage of trees attacked was as high as 90 percent. Peterson (1105), in his account of the spruce and fir broom rusts, mentions that the fir broom rust reaches its maximum abundance on subalpine fir. He cites the many harmful effects of this rust (see also *Abies concolor*).

Two of the snow molds of foliage have already been mentioned under Seedling Diseases. A third is *Stegopezizella* (*Phacidium*) *balsameae* (136), more recently named *Sarcotrichila balsameae* (1157), which like *Phacidium abietis*, forms apothecia on the underside of needles.

Macrophoma parca is an "imperfect" fungus capable of causing a needle blight of several species of *Abies,* including subalpine fir (625). It commonly fruits on dead hanging needles.

Stem Diseases.—Dwarfmistletoes are not common on subalpine fir, but it is occasionally attacked by the Douglas-fir species, *Arceuthobium douglasii,* in the Southwest; the larch form, *A. campylopodum* f. *laricis,* in the Northwest; and the hemlock form, *A. campylopodum* f. *tsugensis,* in Oregon. All three species cause brooming, trunk and branch swellings, distortion, growth reduction, and mortality (505). Two hyperparasites, *Septogloeum gillii* (410) and a species of *Pestalotia,* have been reported attacking the fir form in Washington (1578).

Staley (1349) reports a girdling canker on branches and on small stems of subalpine fir in Colorado, that bore erumpent apothecia with a black, excipular rind, a gray hymenium, and asci with broadly filiform multi-septate ascospores, similar to those described by Zeller and Gooding (1656) for *Scleroderris abieticola* on *Abies grandis* and *A. amabilis.*

Aleurodiscus amorphus causes a canker on suppressed trees and has flat irregular fruiting bodies (151, 587). *A. cerussatus* grows effused on dead wood (858).

Rehmiellopsis bohemica, a common canker fungus on *Abies* spp. in Europe and a close relative of *R. balsameae* on *A. balsamea* in North America, causes a twig blight of subalpine fir in British Columbia (1514).

In the Inland Empire a twig and branch canker caused by *Phomopsis montanensis* results in constriction at the lesions, with marked swelling at the base (565). Hubert (725) early noted that the canker later ascribed to *P. montanensis* was very similar to the canker caused by *Phoma abietina* in Europe.

Thyronectria balsamea, a myriospored fungus often called *Chilonectria cucurbitula* (1271), is reported causing a canker on subalpine fir in Colorado.

Tympanis abietina, a saprophyte common on *Abies balsamea* in eastern North America, fruits on bark of *A. lasiocarpa* in British Columbia (552, 1277).

Three species of *Dasyscypha* (*D. agassizii, D. arida,* and *D. turbinulata*) are saprobes. They all produce yellow-orange apothecia on dead bark.

Root Diseases.—Major mortality from root disease has not been reported for subalpine fir (684). However, a large number of fungi are known to have the capacity to decay roots of this tree, as listed by Shaw (1277), including such well-known species as *Corticium galactinum, Fomes annosus, Odontia bicolor, Polyporus schweinitzii, P. sulphureus, Poria subacida,* and *P. weirii.*

In a study of decay following wounding of subalpine fir in the Prince George region of British Columbia, root and butt wounds in contact with the ground were invaded mainly by *Stereum sanguinolentum, Armillaria mellea,* and *S. chailletii,* in that order of frequency (1077).

Another study in the Upper Fraser River region of British Columbia (125) disclosed 12 named fungi (and some unidentified forms) as responsible for root and butt rot, with greatest loss in volume attributed to *Poria subacida, Polyporus abietinus, Merulius* sp., *Polyporus hirtus, A. mellea, Coniophora puteana, Polyporus balsameus,* and *Fomes pinicola.*

Both the order of importance and the species of fungi mostly responsible for root and butt rot in subalpine fir in Colorado were quite different from the two Canadian situations. Hinds, Hawksworth, and Davidson (684) mention that little is known of the parasitism of such root and butt fungi, and they list them (12 species) simply as butt rot fungi. In order of volume of wood decayed their most important were *Corticium radiosum, Coniophora* spp. (probably mostly *C. puteana*), *Armillaria mellea, Pholiota squarrosa, Coniophora olivacea, Polyporus tomentosus,* and *Pholiota alnicola.*

A yellow stringy rot—largely of the roots and sometimes butts—caused by *Flammula alnicola,* occurs widely in Canada (*374*).

The nematode *Criconemoides annulatum* has been reported associated with subalpine fir in Canada (*1222*) (see also Seedling Diseases).

Trunk Rots.—All of the fungi mentioned above as root and butt rotters will cause some decay of the bole, with *Armillaria mellea* making the least invasion of the trunk itself. As in the case of the root and butt fungi there have been many differences in amount of damage caused, also, among the more strictly trunk rot fungi, depending upon the locality. However, in each area studied—Colorado (*684*), the Prince George region (*1077*), and the Upper Fraser River region (*125*) of British Columbia—*Stereum sanguinolentum* led, by far, the trunk decay fungi, in cull volume caused. In Colorado the other fungi involved were *Fomes pini, Stereum chailletii, S. abietinum, F. robustus* var. *tsugina,* and *Peniophora luna.* In the Prince George region the others were *Peniophora septentrionalis, Coniophora puteana, Fomes pinicola,* and *Corticium galactinum.* In the Upper Fraser River region *Echinodontium tinctorium* caused almost as much trunk rot as *S. sanguinolentum,* followed, far behind, by seven fungi, each causing only one or two infections out of the 863 infections studied. See *Abies grandis* for an account of *E. tinctorium.* The manner in which the incidence of infection to *Abies* spp., by an important heart rot fungus (e.g., *E. tinctorium*) can vary, depending upon climate and elevation, is brought out by Thomas (*1393*).

The Colorado report of Hinds, et al. (*684*) reviews the literature pertaining to decay in subalpine fir, both Canadian and United States, and draws a distinction between the rots that can be determined with reasonable certainty without cultures and those that definitely require cultures for identification of the cause. The Colorado study revealed cull, on a board-foot basis, to range from 2 percent at age 70 years to 24 percent between about age 70 and age 140, with indications of a break-up of highly defective trees beyond age 175. All rot studies of this tree stress the importance of root and stem wounds as entry points for decay fungi, as contrasted with branch stubs.

Hornibrook (*708*) discusses estimating defect in mature and overmature stands of subalpine fir, Engelmann spruce, and lodgepole pine in the Rocky Mountains, and indicates that for the three species together, 87 percent of the defect was decay. He describes many decay indicators and suggests appropriate deductions for defect.

Bier (*118*) found that the microflora in decay-free heartwood of subalpine fir had an inhibitory effect on *Stereum sanguinolentum,* and postulated that such microfloras may have a role in resistance of heartwood to decay.

Mycorrhizal Relations.—Only two fungi, *Cenococcum graniforme* and *Russula delica,* have been reported to form mycorrhizae with *Abies lasiocarpa* (*1442*).

Miscellaneous Pathology.—Abnormal staminate cone production in *Abies balsamea* is caused by *Sclerotinia kerneri*. Flower buds in the leaf axils of young twigs are greatly increased in number. These numerous buds and the basal cone scales on the thickened twigs, which remain attached in the form of cups, give affected branches a unique appearance. Similar symptoms have been observed on *A. lasiocarpa* in Colorado by R. W. Davidson, but no sclerotia were reported (*235*).

A study of decay in windthrown subalpine fir in British Columbia (*414*) indicated that 84 percent of the rot in this fallen timber was caused by three fungi: *Stereum sanguinolentum, Polyporus abietinus,* and *Fomes pinicola.* By the tenth year after the blow-down, from 66 to 92 percent of the logs were from 51 to 100 percent defective, depending on the height above ground of the trunk sections studied. The authors mention the role of all 12 fungi isolated from fallen and broken subalpine fir and white spruce, and give the percentage of ultimate decay attributable to each.

Kendrick and Molnar (*782*) describe *Ceratocystis dryocoetidis* and its imperfect stage *Verticicladiella dryocoetidis.* This fungus has been frequently isolated from necrotic, spreading lesions associated with attacks by the bark beetle *Dryocoetes confusus* on *Abies lasiocarpa.* The fungus may be responsible for the death of trees that suffered only light bark beetle attacks.

Molnar (*996*) later showed that three other staining fungi were associated with insect attack, and while all four probably played a part in the killing of trees, *C. dryocoetidis* is the most important.

Davidson (*340*) described 5 new species of *Ceratocystis* staining the wood of western conifers (*C. abiocarpa, C. minuta-bicolor, C. nigrocarpa, C. leucocarpa,* and *C. seticollis*). *C. abiocarpa* is common in recently killed trees or logs of subalpine fir and *Ips*-infested *Picea engelmannii.*

California red fir
Abies magnifica

The species (*Abies magnifica*) and its one variety (*A. magnifica* var. *shastensis*) differ only in cone structure and are considered together here because their silvical and pathological characteristics are almost identical. They will be referred to together as red fir. Their range extends from the Cascades in southwest Oregon to the northern Coast Ranges of California, and through the Sierra Nevada to central California and western Nevada (*585*). Red fir habitats are characterized by long winters with heavy snow and short, dry summers. Precipitation, about 80 percent of it as snow, varies from 30 to 60 in. Maximum temperatures seldom exceed 80° F. and very rarely reach 90°, and minimum temperatures may be —25° F. or lower. Best development is on glacial moraines or unglaciated areas with deep soil (*1055*). The species will occur on a variety of sites from about 5,000 to 9,000 ft. in elevation, except on flats where water stands, or on windswept slopes with shallow, rocky soils (*585*).

Red fir is intermediate in tolerance, being much less tolerant than white fir or Douglas-fir (*1367*). It reaches maturity at about 200 years, and its maximum longevity is between 350 and 400 years (*279*). Its dense foliage and exuding resinous bark blisters make it susceptible to fire damage even though the thick bark of older trees offers protection from heat. The abundance of snow in most stands causes injury from bending and breakage (*279*). Snow bending also often results in sweep in butt logs. Selection cutting results in much windthrow, but otherwise the tree is fairly wind-firm (*585*). It is subject to frost cracks, and one of its most common defects is shake (*1182*), in which wind has a major role.

The foliage is sensitive to smoke and other air pollution, so that the species is not suitable for planting in cities or in the vicinity of heavy emissions of soft coal smoke (*279*). The firs as a group are highly sensitive to injury from sulfur dioxide (*1249*).

The pathology of red fir is characterized by dwarfmistletoe damage; a conspicuous, yellow, witches' broom rust; and a large amount of decay cull.

Seedling Diseases.—Red fir seeds have a relatively low viability, with the percentage sound (44 percent) being the lowest among the 10 fir species listed in the Woody-Plant Seed Manual (*1*). Since the species is seldom planted, little is known of its seedling enemies. It is subject to snow damage, and to the brown felt blight (*Herpotrichia nigra*) that develops on foliage under snow. The gray mold blight caused by *Botrytis cinerea* can cause minor damage to seedlings and the lower parts of saplings (*151*).

Smith and Bega (*1323*) describe severe damage to coniferous nursery stock, including red fir, in California nurseries (see *Pinus lambertiana*) as a result of mid- to late-season attack of roots by *Sclerotium bataticola* (*Macrophomina phaseoli*).

Foliage Diseases.—Compared with the other firs, red fir has had few needle pathogens reported on it, and none are of economic importance. One of the most common is *Virgella* (*Hypoderma*) *robusta*, which has concolorous pycnidia that turn black after discharge, and which form two rows, one on each wing of the needle. *Lirula* (*Hypodermella*) *abietis-concoloris* can cause a heavy shedding of non-current year's needles of red fir, and forms dark-brown pycnidia in the groove on the upper surface of the needle. It is not nearly so severe on red fir as on white fir. *Lirula* (*Hypodermella*) *punctata* is occasionally found on red fir and is distinguished by having small, elliptical, waxy pycnidia in one or two scattered rows (*323*). *Lophomerum* (*Lophodermium*) *autumnale* occurs abundantly following attack by *Virgella robusta*, and has no pycnidia.

The needle rust *Pucciniastrum goeppertianum*, with its II and III stages on species of *Vaccinium*, produces, on red fir, hypophyllous, cylindric aecia with delicate peridia and yellow aeciospores (*46*). *Melampsorella caryophyllacearum* causes a conspicuous brooming, giving an upright habit to the dwarfed shoots, and causing a yellowing and premature shedding of needles. Its II and III stages are on species of *Cerastium* and *Stellaria* (*149*). Peterson (*1105, 1106*) gives good accounts of the broom rusts of spruce and fir, and mentions the latter as locally damaging to red fir in California (see also *Abies concolor*).

Herpotrichia nigra, the brown felt snow blight, produces a webbing over foliage that has remained long under snow (*151*).

Stem Diseases.—The most important single disease of red fir is

27

the fir dwarfmistletoe, *Arceuthobium campylopodum* f. *abietinum*. It causes extensive damage in stands from sapling size through maturity. It lowers vigor, deforms and stunts, creates entrance courts for decay fungi, weakens the trunk at its cankers, and causes mortality (*585, 1241*). The manner in which this parasite invades the tissues of California red fir is described by Scharpf and Parmeter (*1242*).

The most characteristic feature of dwarfmistletoe damage to red fir is the abundance of "flagging," resulting from the death of many branches scattered throughout the crowns. The rapid killing of branches, so distinctive of dwarfmistletoe attack of red fir, is considered to be the result of weak canker fungi such as *Valsa abietis* killing the bark overlying the dwarfmistletoe swellings. The dwarfmistletoes are known to be parasitized by four fungi: *Wallrothiella arceuthobi, Septogloeum gillii, Metasphaeria wheeleri,* and *Colletotrichum gloeosporioides.* Parmeter et al. (*1085*) provide access to the literature on the first 3 fungi, and describe, for the first time, the Colletotrichum blight. *C. gloeosporioides* is one of the many synonyms of *Glomerella cingulata,* representing its conidial stage. It causes leaf diseases of many species of trees (see *Ficus* and *Liriodendron*). On *Arceuthobium campylopodum* f. *abietinum* it forms brown to black lesions, usually at shoot nodes. These later involve the entire shoot. The surface becomes covered with numerous acervuli surrounded by ragged, yellow fringes of epidermis. This fungus kills shoots of *A. americanum* also (*1006*).

Valsa (Cytospora) abietis can cause cankering and death of branches and stems weakened by other causes (*1616*), and is considered by many to be of some consequence as a disease of red fir. *Aleurodiscus amorphus* can produce cankers on suppressed trees. Its flat, irregular fruiting bodies serve to identify it (*587*).

Root Diseases.—Only two fungi, *Fomes annosus,* mainly, and *Armillaria mellea,* typically cause killing root diseases of red fir. Their chief role, however, like that of the less common *Poria subacida,* is as root and butt rotters, extending many feet up the trunk, and in leading to windthrow and wind breakage.

Trunk Rots.—Heart rots that enter through wounds, especially fire scars, cause extensive losses in mature stands (*793*). Cull in such stands often ranges from 30 to 50 percent of the gross volume. Kimmey and Bynum (*799*) describe the rots of red and white fir. They list, in order of importance, the following white rot fungi which, together, cause about four-fifths of the decay loss in red and white firs: *Pholiota adiposa, Fomes annosus, Echinodontium tinctorium,* and *Armillaria mellea.* Brown cubical rots make up the other one-fifth of the decay loss, and they are caused by *F. pinicola, Polyporus sulphureus,* and *P. schweinitzii.*

While frost cracks and miscellaneous injuries lead to some decay, most butt rot fungi infect through fire scars or other basal wounds. *Echinodontium tinctorium* (see *Abies grandis*), however, enters almost exclusively through branch stubs and open knots, and its conks may appear at these points in great numbers. Kimmey (*793*) gives cull tables and pertinent descriptive data on the main rots and their indicators for northwestern California. He has also developed a method of applying cull indicator factors to white and red fir in the Sierras that provides cull estimates that are within

28

0.5 percent of the cull actually measured on cut trees (796).

The ring scale fungus, *Fomes pini*, rarely occurs on the true firs but is the most commonly fruiting heart rot fungus on Douglas-fir (793).

In allowing for defect in red fir in California, in addition to the deductions made necessary by decay, Robinson and Sanford (1182) found the following conditions necessitating a percentage deduction from the volume table figures in use: limby tops, likely to be left on the ground, 4 percent; shake, 3 percent; and breakage, 1 percent.

Mycorrhizal Relations.—Only one fungus, *Cenococcum graniforme*, has been reported to form mycorrhizae with red fir (1442).

Noble fir

Abies procera

Largest and finest of the true firs, noble fir is a clean-boled, round-topped tree with superior wood qualities (279). Its range is restricted to Washington and Oregon, where it is most abundant on the west side of the Cascade Range between 1,400 and 6,000 ft. elevation, extending from the Canadian border to the northern end of California. Small patches occur in the Coast Range in southwestern Washington and northwestern Oregon (1345). Noble fir occurs almost entirely in the superhumid climatic zone with average precipitation from about 70 to 103 in. per year, of which less than a fourth falls from April through September. Annual snowfall varies from 80 to 103 in. The climate of the range is generally mild, with average annual temperatures ranging between 24° and 62° F., and extremes between —17° and 105° F (1345). The tree has proved hardy when grown in the Northeast (279).

Noble fir is not exacting with respect to soil texture or fertility, but ample moisture is essential. Neither aspect, topography, nor soil depth are major factors in its distribution. Compared with other firs and many other conifers, noble fir is intolerant (1367). It grows rapidly, in this way competing well with associated species (592), and probably has the longest life of any of the true firs, growing well up to 300 years, with maximum longevity probably over 700 years (1367). The species is sensitive to fire, but the wet climate of its range minimizes this danger. Over its normal span of life the disease impact to noble fir is light, from seedling to sawtimber tree, and from roots to shoot tips.

Seedling Diseases.—Like the other firs, noble fir has a relatively low seedling germination, usually under 50 percent (1). When snow covers the ground before seed fall, seedlings that germinate the following spring, while still in snow, seldom survive (1345). The gray-mold blight caused by *Botrytis cinerea* causes some loss of seedlings. *Herpotrichia nigra*, the brown felt snow mold, also damages and sometimes kills seedlings.

Foliage Diseases.—Several needle-cast fungi attack the older foliage of noble fir, all of which are described briefly under *Abies concolor*. These are *Virgella robusta*, *Lirula abietis-concoloris*, *L. punctata*, *Lophodermium piceae*, and *Lophomerum autumnale* (323, 328), the last following *V. robusta* in a secondary role. The brown felt snow mold fungus already mentioned will also sometimes cover needles in the lower crown that remain long under snow (*151*).

Six rusts attack the current year's needles. *Pucciniastrum goeppertianum* has its II and III stages on *Vaccinium*. *P. epilobii* has its II and III stages mainly on *Epilobium*. The Pucciniastrums have yellow aeciospores. *Uredinopsis pteridis* and *U. struthiopteridis*, both with white aeciospores, have their II and III stages on ferns (*432*).

Peridermium ornamentale is a needle rust that Arthur (*46*) includes under *Pucciniastrum goeppertianum*. Others question this relation (*149*), and some consider that, although *Peridermium ornamentale* has been reported from many fir species including noble fir, it may really be confined to *Abies lasiocarpa* (*8*).

Peridermium rugosum, mainly a grand fir needle rust, has also been reported on noble fir and Arthur (*46*) considers that it probably belongs to a species of *Milesia* on ferns.

The eastern fir tip blight caused by *Rehmiellopsis balsameae* has attacked shoots and foliage of noble fir planted in eastern Massachusetts (*1514*).

Stem Diseases.—The fir dwarfmistletoe, *Arceuthobium campylopodum* f. *abietinum*, occasionally damages noble fir, causing brooming, distortion, and growth reduction, but has little economic impact on this species (*505*).

Aleurodiscus amorphus causes cankers on suppressed trees and produces flattened, irregular fruiting bodies (*151, 587*).

Melampsorella caryophyllacearum, the yellow rust witches' broom, occasionally attacks noble fir. Its II and III stages are on *Cerastium* and *Stellaria*. Peterson (*1105*) gives a good account of the many symptoms and effects of this rust, and devotes an illustrated leaflet to the fir broom rust (*1106*).

Dasyscypha agassizii and *D. arida* are saprophytes that produce conspicuous yellow-orange apothecia on dead bark.

Root Rots.—There are virtually no killing root diseases of noble fir, and the only strictly root and butt rot fungi considered important are *Polyporus schweinitzii* (*623*), *P. tomentosus*, *Poria subacida*, and possibly *Stereum chailletii*. *P. subacida* probably causes the greatest butt rot loss.

Trunk Rots.—The principal trunk rot fungus is *Echinodontium tinctorium* (*622*) (see *Abies grandis*). Others are *Fomes pini* (*622*), *F. nobilissimus* (*890*), *F. pinicola* (*623*), and *F. robustus*. These become important only in overmature timber, causing significant loss in younger stands only when they have suffered damage from wind, fire, or logging. Several other fungi rot dead sapwood and the heartwood of dead trees.

Mycorrhizal Relations.—Only *Russula delica* has been reported to form mycorrhizae with noble fir (*1442*).

Miscellaneous Pathology.—The significance of the discolorations in noble fir and western hemlock aircraft lumber was determined by Englerth and Hansbrough (*417*), who describe nine types of discoloration that are not indicative of decay, and eight types that indicated weakening defects.

Noble fir lumber often becomes stained during the drying process. The wood becomes unevenly reddish-brown, and the discoloration is regarded as due to the oxidation of certain cell contents, and does not weaken the wood (898).

A common but not serious stain of the wood is caused by *Cera-tocystis piceae* (1277). The mycelium produces a very light brown discoloration, or none at all (732).

Rocky Mountain maple

Acer glabrum

The Rocky Mountain or dwarf maple is a shrub or small tree up to 30 ft. in height. Little (872) recognizes two varieties: the type form, var. *glabrum,* which extends from the Black Hills of South Dakota, west to southeastern Idaho and southeastern Oregon, and through the Sierra Nevada and the Rocky Mountains to southern California and New Mexico; and var. *douglasii,* which extends from southern Alaska to the Inland Empire and Pacific Northwest states. Rehder (1154) recognizes two additional varieties: var. *rhodocarpum,* the fruit of which stays bright red until fully ripe; and var. *tripartitum,* with its very small trifoliolate leaves. This species is intolerant and grows mostly on moist sites along streams and ravines at from 5,000 to 6,000 ft. in the North, to 8,000 to 9,000 ft. elevations in the southern mountains (1137).

Foliage Diseases.—The most common leaf spots are those caused by *Septoria aceris,* a fungus that goes under many synonyms (8); *Phyllosticta minima* (436); and the blackspeckled tar spot caused by *Rhytisma punctatum.* These all occur on many maple species (see *Acer saccharum*) and are described and illustrated by May (939).

In the southern Rocky Mountains the leaf blister caused by *Taphrina bartholomaei* (994) has been reported on this maple by Keener[3]. He also mentions that erinosis, a mite-induced, brilliant red crust of hypertrophied plant cells that can be mistaken for a fungus, occurs on this species, as well as on the other maples commonly recorded in the literature. Boyce (151) mentions erinose specifically on Rocky Mountain maple in the Northwest.

Shaw (1278) lists collections of *Phyllosticta minutissima* from many northwestern states, and gives its synonymy and literature references.

One of the commonest of the twig fungi considered to cause dieback and twig cankering is *Valsa sordida* (imperfect stage *Cytospora chrysosperma*). It is most likely a weak parasite and invader of damaged tissue (see *Populus*).

Cryptosporella acerina—a fungus with pulvinate stromata and 1-celled, hyaline, ellipsoid to short-fusiform conidia—fruits on branches of this maple, but is likely secondary.

The common *Nectria cinnabarina* occurs on dead bark of *Acer glabrum,* but while often implied to be parasitic, its role is virtually always that of a saprobe. Its conspicuous, orange-red sporodochia are characteristic of this fungus.

To many wood-destroying fungi the wood of this maple is a con-

---

[3] Personal communication from Paul D. Keener, deceased, formerly plant pathologist, University of Arizona, Tucson, Ariz.

genial habitat. Shaw (*1278*) lists 15 species of *Polyporus* alone, on *Acer glabrum*. However, the basidiomycetes that actively decay the heartwood or inner wood of living trees are principally *Fomes igniarius* in the main trunk, and *Polyporus dryadeus* and *P. squamosus* in the butts.

The ring nematode *Criconemoides annulatum* is known to feed externally on the roots of *Acer glabrum* in Canada (*1222*).

Bigleaf maple

Acer macrophyllum

Bigleaf maple is the only large, commercially important maple in the Pacific Coast region. It extends from the mountains of southern California to the southern tip of Alaska, where it grows best along the very humid, west-facing ravines and moist, low areas of the Northwest. It thrives along the Coast under conditions of cool summers, long frost-free seasons, and abundant precipitation. It has a particular affinity for permanent water courses, but soil type is not of great importance. Its silvical characteristics have been described by Ruth and Muerle (*1233*).

This species is commonly used as a shade tree in the Pacific Northwest, where it forms a broad, dense crown (*955*). It varies greatly in size and form. Ordinarily mature trees approximate 50 ft. in height and 18 in. in diameter, maturing by 150 years, with a longevity approaching 300 years. A proposed variety, occurring near Longview, Washington, is known as Kimball maple (*594*).

Growth is fast for the first 40 to 60 years. The tree is rated as tolerant (*54*). It has a wide, shallow root system. It is readily damaged by fire (*279*).

Extensive damage to foliage of bigleaf maple in the Sierra Nevada, California Coast Ranges, and southern Oregon mountains has been attributed to late frost[4]. The time, locales, and exposed position of the most-damaged parts of the crowns, all pointed to late frost as the cause.

The principal diseases of bigleaf maple are the trunk rots following wounding; a disease of unknown cause, that kills leaves and twigs (*1233*); and Verticillium wilt where the tree is used as an ornamental.

Foliage Diseases.—Although many fungi will form lesions on living leaves, none are regarded as economically important. The more common ones, with references to their occurrence, are: *Cercosporella aceris* (*939, 1278*), *Rhytisma acerinum* and *R. punctatum* (*1277*), *Septoria aceris* (*8*) (see May (*939*) for photo), and the powdery mildews *Uncinula bicornis* (*8*), *U. circinata* (*939*), *Microsphaera alni*, and *Phyllactinia guttata* (*1153*).

May (*939*) refers to the leafspot caused by *Illosporium maculicola* as bigleaf brown spot. Spots may develop up to 3 in. in diameter. They are usually zoned, with an indefinite margin, and older parts break out, leaving holes. May mentions the similarity of this

---

[4] Personal communication from W. Willis Wagener, deceased, formerly pathologist, USDA Forest Service, Pacific Southwest Forest and Range Experiment Station, Berkeley, Calif.

disease to the one caused by *Cercosporella aceris*, and believes the two fungi may be identical.

A bacterial leaf spot of bigleaf maple (*Pseudomonas aceris*) and other maples occurs in California. Spots range in size up to ¼ in. and have yellowish margins (*939*). It has affected nursery plants and foliage hanging over water. Macerating the tissue in water will disclose the motile bacteria, and, if a suitable stain is used (*194*), will show their rod shape and polar flagella (*43*).

Stem and Vascular Diseases.—The common hardwood target canker caused by *Nectria galligena* (*47, 170*) occurs in the Northwest, and the saprobe *N. cinnabarina* occurs widely, producing its orange-red sporodochia on dead bark.

The only killing disease of any importance is Verticillium wilt (*1216*) (*V. albo-atrum*), a soil-borne disease responsible for the death of many ornamental bigleaf maples. A green ring or partial ring of vascular discoloration in the outer sapwood, which readily yields the causal fungus in culture, is a prime diagnostic symptom. Bedwell and Childs (*88*) reported widespread occasional killing of bigleaf maple by Verticillium wilt throughout Washington and Oregon.

The European mistletoe, *Viscum album*, has been found on bigleaf maple in California (*718*).

Root and Trunk Rots.—Almost three-fourths of the 115 fungi listed by Shaw (*1277*) as occurring on bigleaf maple are rot fungi. The great majority of these are saprobes decaying dead wood. However, *Fomes annosus* and *Armillaria mellea* are considered important root rot fungi in the Northwest, and *Fomes applanatus* and *F. connatus* are rated as important butt rotters in that area. In the absence of wounding, decay is seldom serious except in overaged trees. When wounded or cankered, however, bigleaf maple wood rots readily, being prey to dozens of species of decay fungi that can reduce a tree to a hollow shell (*279*). It is of interest that many typically conifer fungi such as *Fomes annosus, F. pinicola,* and *Stereum chailletii* attack this hardwood, and that many predominantly eastern species such as *Polyporus berkeleyi* and *P. dryadeus* attack this and a few other western species.

Miscellaneous Pathology.—Bigleaf maple is the only one of the western maples reported to be attacked in nature by nematodes. A swollen, stubby, galled condition of the roots caused by *Meloidogyne* spp. has been reported from Oregon (*1222*). May (*939*) also reports that *M. incognita,* applied experimentally, produced galls on Japanese maple (*Acer palmatum*).

A disease of bigleaf maple, with virus-like symptoms, resulting in the death of leaves and shoots (*939, 1233*), occurs throughout the coastal mountains of California and into southern Oregon. The cause has not yet been determined. Wagener[5] reports a curling and browning of foliage that is worse in certain years than others. He is inclined to regard the trouble as a climatic effect rather than a virus, although lack of research on it leaves this a conjecture.

---

[5] Personal communication from W. Willis Wagener, deceased, formerly pathologist, USDA Forest Service, Pacific Southwest Forest and Range Experiment Station, Berkeley, Calif.

Boxelder

Acer negundo

The boxelder borders streams and lakes from Canada to Florida, and extends westward in a zone from eastern North Dakota to central Texas. While its typical habitat is moist, its ability to thrive also on dry sites has made it a major tree of the Prairie states (*279*). While usually a fairly short tree, rarely over 50 ft. high at maturity, specimens over 3 ft. in diameter have not been rare. The biggest reported was 73 ft. high and 5 ft. in diameter. Trees on good soils may grow an inch in diameter per year for 15 to 20 years and then markedly drop off in growth. Longevity ranges from 60 to about 100 years.

Boxelder has in the past been used in the Midwest and Prairie states for shade and windbreaks (*1*), but its short life, susceptibility to heart rot, and tendency to ice damage in older spreading trees have somewhat discouraged its use (*279*), and among the large number of shelterbelt species examined for root rot in Oklahoma and Texas by Wright and Wells (*1627*) boxelder is not even mentioned. However, this species is still in use as a shelterbelt tree further north. Croxton (*310*) did not rate this species high in susceptibility to ice damage but his basis was small and the sizes of the trees studied were not specified.

The tree has been planted widely even in the Inland Empire and the West Coast. *Acer negundo* var. *californicum* is a quick-growing tree widely distributed along water courses at low elevations in California, and for a while was popular as a shade tree in interior valleys. Occasional trees of this variety have variegated leaves (*955*).

The pathology of boxelder is characterized by several leaf spot diseases, susceptibility to Verticillium wilt and wood rots, very high sensitivity to certain herbicides, and a unique red fungus stain of the wood of living trees.

Foliage Diseases.—Some of the leaf diseases mentioned in connection with *Acer rubrum* and *A. saccharum* affect boxelder also. Prominent among these are the sharply defined spots caused by *Phyllosticta minima* (*436*), which is particularly disfiguring in Ohio and neighboring states; the much more irregular anthracnose (*Gloeosporium apocryptum*) ; tar spot (*Rhytisma punctatum*) ; the concentric-zoned bulls-eye spot (*Cristulariella pyramidalis*) (*1523*), and the small, discrete, reddish-tan spot caused by *Septoria aceris*. These are described and illustrated by May (*939*). He also reports three species of powdery mildew fungi to occur on the maples: *Microsphaera alni, Phyllactinia guttata,* and *Uncinula circinata* (*1153*). *P. guttata* is known on boxelder in New Mexico.

In addition to the above leaf parasites that attack many species of *Acer*, there are several others that virtually confine their attack to boxelder. These include mainly *Phyllosticta negundinis; Cylindrosporium negundinis; Septoria negundinis; Cercospora negundinis* (*260*), which produces brownish-red, cracked, scabby spots having whitish areas and black fruiting bodies (*939*) ; and some others that require scrutiny of the literature (*8*) for one to become acquainted with their complicated synonymy (e.g., among species of *Ascochyta, Phleospora, Piggotia,* and *Macrophoma*). While seldom of more than mycological interest, the above leaf pathology is outlined here to provide an indication of the lush habitat of the foliage of some species of *Acer* for fungi, especially toward the end of the growing season.

Ascochyta negundinis (*1383*) causes circular, white spots, sometimes with light brown margins, 3 to 7 mm. across, and similar on both leaf surfaces. Pycnidia are scattered, mostly epiphyllous, light brown, producing conidia that are hyaline, somewhat unequally 2-celled, oblong with bluntly rounded cells, mostly 8.5–10μ × 2.9–3.6μ.

The bacterial leaf spot of maple that occurs primarily on *Acer macrophyllum* and is known only from the West, is caused by *Pseudomonas aceris.* Ark (*43*) succeeded in inoculating leaves of *A. negundo* and its var. *californicum* with this organism, by spraying foliage with a bacterial suspension.

A distortion, dwarfing, and blighting of the foliage of several hardwoods, notably boxelder, in the northern Great Plains area, in recent years has caused much concern. Investigations showed the trouble to result from the drift of 2,4-D sprays applied in connection with weeding field crops. This drift produced symptoms on boxelder up to 10 miles from the source (*1114*).

Shaw (*1277*) lists only a few fungi on boxelder in the Pacific Northwest, two of which are dark, surface molds of no economic importance.

Stem and Vascular Diseases.—A widespread twig-inhabiting fungus, *Physalospora obtusa,* goes under a large number of imperfect stage synonyms, notably *Sphaeropsis malorum* and *S. negundinis* (on boxelder). It is, at the most, a weak pathogen, although a common inhabitant of dying and dead twigs, in many states. Tehon and Daniels (*1386*) describe the conidial stage of this fungus and three others that they report to be associated with twig cankers in Illinois. The additional species are *Phacidium negundinis, Coniothyrium negundinis,* and *Leptothyrium maximum.* In each case they annotate what they consider to be the distinguishing characteristics of these fungi. Also, among the inhabitants of senescent and dead twigs are two species of *Cytospora* described only from boxelder, *C. annulata* and *C. negundinis.*

The only notable killing disease of boxelder is Verticillium wilt (*V. albo-atrum*), and while so rated by some pathologists, this disease has not been as severe on boxelder as on ornamental trees of *Acer platanoides, A. saccharum, A. saccharinum,* and *A. rubrum.*

A canker of the stem caused by *Eutypella parasitica* generally retains the bark, which bears the long-necked, black beaks of the fungus perithecia. Concentric zonation is common, with trunk distortions, white to buff mycelial fans under the bark, and decay of the sapwood beneath the canker (*351, 939*).

A brown felt, parasitic on scale insects, is formed on stems of boxelder by *Septobasidium cokeri, S. filiforme, S. patoullardii*[6], and *S. pseudopedicellatum* (*292*).

Root and Trunk Rots.—Boxelder proved moderately susceptible to *Phymatotrichum* root rot (*P. omnivorum*) following inocula-

---

[6] Reported by Arthur S. Rhoads, pathologist, Jacksonville, Fla.

tions in Texas, but can be considered able to survive long enough for shelterbelt planting in the root rot belt (*1379*).

The root rot caused by *Rhizoctonia crocorum*, the imperfect stage of *Helicobasidium purpureum*, has blighted seedlings in Texas. Wefts of purplish mycelium at and below ground level, with small, embedded sclerotia, are diagnostic (*1555*).

The black carbonaceous, crustose fruiting bodies of the ascomycete *Ustulina vulgaris* commonly form on stumps and logs. This fungus causes decay of the butts of trees, often entering dead companion sprouts (*211*). Many other common hardwood decay fungi have been reported rotting dead wood of boxelder (*8*), but the only species considered true heart rotters are *Fomes fraxineus, F. fraxinophilus, F. geotropus, F. scutellatus,* and *Polyporus glomeratus* (*1067*).

It is worthy of note that the thorough searches that led to the United States Index of Plant Diseases (*8*) failed to disclose reports of *Armillaria mellea* on boxelder, although the fungus is known to be a common root and butt rot fungus of other maple species.

Miscellaneous Pathology.—Boxelder is the only species known to harbor an interesting red stain of the wood of living trees caused by *Fusarium reticulatum* var. *negundinis*. This fungus is placed in *F. roseum* by Snyder and Hansen (*1328*). Toole (*1414*) found this stain so common in wood of this species in Mississippi that boxelder wood could be characterized by it. He also successfully inoculated living trees with it. Batra and Lichtwardt (*77*) found the stain regularly associated with Cerambycid beetles and the galleries of other insects, but itself did no damage to the wood. They determined the color to be due to scarlet-colored crystals formed as a result of infection by the *Fusarium*.

Potassium deficiency symptoms have been produced and described in code for several hardwoods, including *Acer negundo,* by Perala and Sucoff (*1095*).

Seven species of nematodes, each in a different genus, have been reported from boxelder (*1222*).

Norway maple
Acer platanoides

A European exotic, the Norway maple has become one of America's most widely planted street trees. Early growth is fast, and the form and most other characteristics of the tree are desirable (*279*), but the main reason for its popularity is its capacity to obsorb many urban impacts such as those induced by pavement, moderate levels of air pollution, dusts, and dry soil. It is also smaller at maturity than many other maples (e.g. *Acer rubrum, A. saccharum* and *A. saccharinum*) and thus is better adapted to many urban situations. Usually mature by 60 years, most trees do not live more than 80 years.

Norway maple transplants well, will grow on a wide variety of soils, and withstands ice and snow damage better (*310*) than any other maple. It was also resistant to damage from salt spray accompanying a hurricane, when red maple was badly injured (*1632*). Its adaptability and sturdiness have given it a planting range covering the entire United States east of the Great Plains, except for South Florida, and also much of the Pacific Coast.

There are many varieties of *Acer platanoides* (Rehder (*1154*) names 10), which differ from each other in many ways, including shape of crown and the size, color, shape, and lobation of leaves.

May[7], in commenting on the pathology of Norway maple, considers the main diseases to be leaf anthracnose, Verticillium wilt, and bacterial wetwood of the woody cylinder. He also states that winter freezing damage is common when Norway maple is planted in the colder parts of the Northeast and Lake States.

Foliage Diseases.—Several of the leaf spot or blotch fungi briefly annotated under *Acer saccharum*, and described by May (*939*) and others also occur on Norway maple. These include anthracnose (*Gloeosporium apocryptum*) (*939*), Phyllosticta spot (*P. minima*) (*436*), tar spot (*Rhytisma acerinum*) (*928*), gray mold spot (*Cristulariella depraedens*) (*928*), bull's eye spot (*C. pyramidalis*), Septoria spot (*S. aceris*) (*939*), and leaf blister (*Taphrina acerina*) (*994*). Occasionally other leaf fungi have been reported (*8*) but those mentioned above are the main species, not only on Norway maple, but also on several other species of *Acer*.

The bull's eye spot resulted in premature defoliation in 1960 in Asheville, N. C. Berry and Thompson (*105*) report several trees heavily infected and defoliated three times, while nearby, lightly infected trees kept their leaves until November. Trees of *Acer saccharum* and *A. saccharinum* near the diseased Norway maples appeared free of infection.

The commonest physiogenic leaf diseases, aside from those related to air pollution, are frost killing, where this maple has been planted in the coldest parts of the East, and a leaf scorch widely regarded as due to heat and drought. A folding and puckering of leaves of Norway maple occasionally occurs, and the cause of it is unknown (*939*).

Stem and Vascular Diseases.—Verticillium wilt (*V. albo-atrum* or *V. dahliae*) (*532, 1216*) is the main fungus enemy, and Norway maple is the most susceptible of the maples to this soil-borne disease. This wilt is rated as a major shade tree disease on elm and maple in the Northeast (*1640*). Greenish streaks in the outer sapwood, appearing as a ring or partial ring in stem cross section, are diagnostic, but lack of such streaking does not preclude the wilt. Sufficient vessel plugging and toxin production may occur, with infection of roots and lower trunk, to produce wilting of parts of the crown without evident streaking in the branches. The wilting, usually sudden, may involve only a branch or two or the entire crown. The causal fungus is easily isolated from streaked parts of the wood. Caroselli (*224*) gives a good account of this disease on maples.

Seven fungi from the rhizosphere of three Norway maple trees showed marked antagonism in vitro, to *V. dahliae* from maple. The most effective were *Aspergillus fumigatus*, *Trichoderma lignorum*, *Gliocladium roseum*, and *Penicillium funiculosum*. In vivo, the antagonistic effects were temporary (*240*).

---

[7] Personal communication from Curtis May, formerly pathologist, USDA Agricultural Research Service, Beltsville, Md.

The common "target" Nectria canker disease (*N. galligena*) (*47, 170*) affects Norway maple, but the incidence is far lower with this species than with sugar and red maple. The tiny, red, balloon-like perithecia around the canker margins are diagnostic. Dead branches will often bear the larger orange-red sporodochia of *N. cinnabarina* (*Tubercularia vulgaris*), a saprobe that often inhabits senescent or dead branches and stems (*1091*).

Wetwood, resulting from massive bacterial infection of the woody cylinder that produces a highly alkaline reaction in the wood, is not unusual in this species. This condition, as it occurs in many genera, is described by Hartley et al. (*605*). Where this infection reaches the surface a slime flux will often develop and persist (see also *Ulmus*).

The bleeding canker of maple (*Phytophthora cactorum*) (*717, 987*) produces long lesions that ooze a red to black fluid, and results in a blackening of the wood beneath. *P. cinnamomi* (*1510*) has also been isolated from basal cankers of Norway maple, some of which were not distinguishable from *P. cactorum* infections. Yet Crandall and Gravatt (*303*) report this maple susceptible to *P. cambivora* but resistant to *P. cinnamomi*.

Fusarium solani, a fungus associated with cankers on *Liquidambar*, *Liriodendron*, *Populus* and *Acer saccharum* (*1613*), has also been isolated from basal cankers on Norway maple.

Pirone and Carter (*1120*) report a disease of a Norway maple characterized by bright green discoloration of the outer sapwood underlying dead areas of bark. A fungus was isolated, with black pycnidia bearing alpha and beta conidia, that they named *Phomopsis acerina*. Comparisons with other species of *Phomopsis* from Norway maple are provided. The affected tree, in New Jersey, was also being actively root-rotted by *Polyporus lucidus*.

The *Cytospora* stages of *Valsa ambiens* and *V. sordida* often appear on damaged or weakened twigs (*254*). Boyce (*151*) gives a good account of the habit and characteristics of some of the *Cytospora* cankers.

Root and Butt Rots.—The most common root rot is caused by *Armillaria mellea*. It is specifically described in the available literature dealing with maple diseases (*928, 939*). Even so, while it is probably seldom the primary cause of death, it readily penetrates the roots and butts of weakened trees. The black, shoe-string-like rhizomorphs and the mycelial fans under the bark are diagnostic.

Another root rot, much less common, is caused by *Xylaria mali*, an aggressive pathogen of the apple (*1555*). The species of *Xylaria* produce a black, carbonaceous fungus crust, and black zone lines in the rotted wood. The stroma is erect and protruding, with a sterile base. The perithecia have dark-brown, 8-spored asci.

Norway maple was rated highly susceptible to *Phymatotrichum* root rot in Texas tests (*1379*).

Miscellaneous Pathology.—In the past many Norway maple street trees have succumbed to leaks of manufactured illuminating gas into the soil. Such leaks of toxic gases can be detected by digging a hole beneath the tree, placing one or two young potted tomato plants in it, covering with a tight lid, and observing for wilting of the tomatoes after 24–48 hours.

This species is very susceptible to heavy attacks by a very large,

38

gray, bark louse, the Norway maple aphid, which can cause the death of lower branches, and from a distance the damage could resemble maple wilt. Even casual observation, however, would disclose the bark covered with these large, soft-bodied insects.

Nematode species in 6 genera have been identified within the root zones of Norway maple trees in North·America and Europe (1222).

Norway maple showed much greater tolerance to chlorine ions than did sugar maple, in studies of road salt damage to maples in New England (see *Acer saccharum*).

Sycamore maple

Acer pseudoplatanus

A native of Europe and western Asia, the sycamore maple is a large tree, capable of growing to 100 ft. in height, vigorous in growth until mature, with a spreading habit, making it attractive for shade or ornament on large areas having no overhead impediments. It is adapted to exposed situations (1154) and those near the seashore. While the leaves are typically dark and leathery, Bailey (53) mentions some foliage with white and yellow spots or blotches. Among the nine varieties recognized by Rehder (1154) are forms that differ mostly in size, color, configuration and hairiness of foliage, and in color of fruit.

In Europe the sycamore maple is a timber tree valued much as Americans value the sugar maple (279). However, in the United States the tree is not as hardy as Norway maple, it is shorter-lived, and is too spreading for many purposes. It has been planted successfully throughout the United States except for northern New England and New York, the Lake States and the central and northern Great Plains, and Rocky Mountain areas (279). It thus has a somewhat more southerly range than Norway maple. Sycamore maple was relatively uninjured by salt spray accompanying a severe September hurricane in New England (1632).

Spaulding's list (1337) of disease fungi for this host tree is the same as that of the Index of Plant Diseases in the United States (8). Of these, the only pathogens of any consequence in the culture of this tree are *Verticillium albo-atrum* (532), a soil-borne wilt fungus; *Phyllosticta minima*, a leaf spot fungus common to all American maples and capable of epidemic spread (436); *Cristulariella pyramidalis*, cause of bull's eye spot (1119, 1523); and *Phytophthora cactorum*, the bleeding canker fungus (717). All of these are described by May (939) and by Marshall and Waterman (928), and have been annotated herein under *Acer saccharum* and other maples.

In addition occasional sycamore maples have been noted with crown gall (*Agrobacterium tumefaciens*) (151); the very common and mostly saprobic *Botryosphaeria ribis* (*Dothiorella gregaria*) (550) on twigs and branches; the saprobic coral fungus *Nectria cinnabarina* (1091), with its orange-red sporodochia; and two species of *Valsa, V. ambiens* and *V. sordida*, which are usually observed in their imperfect (*Cytospora*) stages (8). In spite of reports on the aggressiveness of the Cytosporas on maples in the

United States, they are probably largely secondary invaders of damaged or senescent tissue.

Nematodes in the root zones of trees of this species include *Helicotylenchus paxilli* in the United States, *Longidorus maximus* in Germany, and *Pratylenchus penetrans* in the Netherlands (*1222*).

Red maple
Acer rubrum

Red maple is seldom a highly regarded species to the forester because it is too often of poor form, hollow, decayed, discolored, or disfigured by injury. However, it is a major component of forest stands over much of the East, and it can attain good size and freedom from defect on good sites. Such clear material has a good market for furniture. It is a variable species, and while Rehder (*1154*) recognizes six varieties, Little (*872*) recognizes only one, var. *drummondii*, other than the type form. Red maple is noted for its brilliant red to orange fall coloration.

Occurring throughout the East, from Canada through Florida, and west to the Great Plains, red maple is one of our most common trees (*740*). Its variety, the Drummond maple, grows in the lowlands of the Atlantic coastal plain and major river valleys. The species is limited only by cold in the far North, and by dryness in the Prairie states. It is a pioneer species and yet is shade-tolerant (*54*) and can probably thrive over a wider range of soil types, textures, moisture, pH, elevation and species composition than any forest species in North America.

Chandler (*244*) rates red maple low as a soil builder, based on a foliar calcium content of only 0.91 percent. It is also low in nitrogen. While the tree may grow fast early in life, with seedlings often growing a foot and sprouts over 3 ft. in height per year, this species is short-lived, with few stands exceeding 150 years old (*279*).

Red maple is a prolific sprouter but can be difficult to propagate from cuttings. It can be reproduced by layering. Its seeds germinate soon after falling, and Hutnik and Yawney (*740*), who brought together the information on the silvical characteristics of red maple, consider the species the least exacting in its requirements for germination of any American forest tree species. It resists damage from flooding (*583, 907*), and resists drought by rapid and deep extension of roots (*1440*). The maples, including red maple, were rated intermediate with respect to amount of damage after a severe glaze storm in Pennsylvania. Major damage was sustained by 41 percent of the black cherry, 16 percent of the red maple, and 5 percent of the hemlock. Red maple is very sensitive to fire, and to salt water and salt spray (*1632*).

McKee (*911*) placed "soft maple" among the species most resistant to air pollution in an area near Houston, Texas, that is subject to sulfur dioxide emissions. However, red maple has shown the distinctive intervenal pattern of sulfur dioxide injury near other sources of the gas.

According to Sparrow and Sparrow (*1332*), the sensitivity of red maple to gamma radiation from a cobalt-60 source was low among a group of 12 coniferous and hardwood species (see *Picea glauca*).

This species is a preferred deer food (740), and browsing can almost completely suppress reproduction where deer populations are high. It is also sensitive to several herbicides. May (939) shows a photograph of damage to this species from 2,4-D.

The pathology of red maple is characterized by many leaf diseases of minor importance; many damaging canker diseases; Verticillium wilt; some of the abiotic general declines reported for sugar maple, but to a lesser degree; and in particular a high susceptibility to decay and other cull that mark it as a highly defective species (557). May (939) and Marshall and Waterman (928) have given good illustrated accounts of the diseases of shade and ornamental maples.

Foliage Diseases.—The following common leaf fungi annotated under sugar maple also are known to damage red maple foliage: *Gloeosporium apocryptum, Phyllosticta minima, Rhytisma acerinum, R. punctatum, Cristulariella depraedens, Septoria aceris,* and *Uncinula circinata.* The leaf blister species that distort red maple foliage are *Taphrina dearnessii* (974) and *T. letifera* (750). These last two are so similar that Mix (994) questions the validity of separation.

An epiphytotic of *Phyllosticta minima* on red and sugar maple was recorded by Fergus in Pennsylvania (436). He shows good photographs of the appearance of the spots.

A very conspicuous leaf spot of red and silver maple is caused by *Venturia acerina (Cladosporium humile).* Both the leaf symptoms and the fruiting structures of the fungus are well illustrated by Plakidas (1121).

The abiotic leaf disorders reported for sugar maple also affect red maple. One conspicuous leaf condition called erinose, sometimes confused with fungus disease, and occurring notably on red maple and northeastern dwarf maple, appears as a patchy, brilliant-red, felty crust, typically at vein axils. It is caused by a proliferation of cells of the lower epidermis induced by mites.

One of the common leaf spots of red maple that affects no other maple is caused by *Monochaetia desmazierii* (*M. monochaeta*). The spots are brown or gray, often indefinite, frequently zonate, with punctiform pustules, and five-celled, elliptic, olivaceous conidia (558, 536).

Stem Diseases.—Most of the canker diseases mentioned under sugar maple also affect red maple. In the Northeast, Nectria is the most common, with Eutypella cankers not uncommon. In the Midwest *Hypoxylon pruinatum* (887) (= *H. mammatum*) appears occasionally (see *Populus*), and saplings in some localities may develop large numbers of Schizoxylon cankers. A Hypoxylon canker on red and sugar maple was described from Ontario (111). Finally placed as *Hypoxylon mammatum* by Miller (978), it has been called *H. blakei, H. morsei,* and many other names.

Strumella canker (110), which is primarily an oak disease (see *Quercus*), has occasionally affected red maple, beech, and hickories. The fungus produces the black, powdery conidial masses of *Strumella coryneoidea* on the canker surface, and the apothecia of *Urnula craterium* on stumps.

The canker-forming Nectria on red maple is *N. galligena* (170, 879) (see *Betula alleghaniensis*). *N. cinnabarina* is simply a sap-

41

robe, conspicuous mainly because of its large, coral-pink sporodochia.

Among the so-called canker-rot fungi, red maple is afflicted with these combined effects by *Daedalea unicolor* (*205*) and by *Stereum murrayi* (*342*). As described under sugar maple, these cankers are characteristic and are always accompanied by considerable decay behind and beyond cankers.

The bleeding canker caused by *Phytophthora cactorum*, and described under sugar maple, also affects red maple. Toole (*1412*) reported forest trees of this species attacked in North Carolina and Tennessee where they exhibited prematurely red foliage, dwarfed leaves, very long irregular cankers, and reddish exudation. Later Campbell and Gallegley (*216*) reported *Phytophthora heveae* from the soils of this same area. *P. cinnamomi* has been reported associated with a strictly basal canker of red maple.

The lens-shaped annual canker in the Northeast, described by Wood and Skelly (*1613*) as probably caused by *Fusarium solani*, occurs on red maple, but not as frequently as on sugar maple.

A small discomycete, *Dermea* (*Dermatea*) *acerina* (*1352*), produces its dark apothecia on dead branches of red maple throughout the East. While commonly reported, there is no evidence that it is pathogenic.

Reid and Cain (*1156*) have demonstrated and illustrated that the maple branch saprobes *Valsa myinda* and *Cryptodiaporthe myinda* are distinct species, and also applied a proper nomenclature to these organisms.

A branch tumor associated with a species of *Phomopsis* is described by Brown (*178*).

The eastern mistletoe, *Phoradendron serotinum* (= *flavescens*) (*1580*) commonly develops on red maple throughout the warmer and moister parts of its range.

Three species of *Septobasidium* (*S. fumigatum, S. mariani*, and *S. pseudopedicellatum*) produce brown felts over scale insects on stems and branches of red maple, according to Couch (*292*). In addition, A. S. Rhoads [s] reports *S. castaneum* and *S. sinuosum* on red maple in Florida.

The importance of branch stubs in leading to a variety of cull and degrading defects is stressed by Shigo (*1291*) and by Bryan (*180*). The bending live branch can also be a source of damage. Grant and Spaulding (*530*) bring out that the bending that accompanies the weight of ice and snow can cause axillary cracks that serve as the infection courts for Nectria cankers. Other cankers also probably start in this way. In this connection, it may be significant that there is far less cankering of any of the maples in the South than in the North.

Vascular Diseases.—The diseases referred to under sugar maple as wetwood (*603*) and as Verticillium wilt (*532, 1216*) also affect red maple. The sapstreak disease (*641*), a vascular mycosis of sugar maple and yellow-poplar, is not known to affect red maple.

Root Diseases.—Red maple is seldom killed or seriously damaged by root disease. *Armillaria mellea* can enter through root or butt

---

[s] Personal communication from Arthur S. Rhoads, pathologist, Jacksonville, Fla.

wounds and destroy root and trunk wood, but it kills only trees already weakened from other causes (*826*). Other fungi known to cause root and butt rot of red maple, aside from the main trunk rotters, are *Polyporus spraguei, P. sulphureus*, and *Ustulina vulgaris*.

Trunk Rots.—Lists of the many trunk rot fungi attacking maple are available (*8, 939*). Certain of these deserve specific mention. Much of the rot in red maple in the Northeast is caused by *Polyporus glomeratus* (*210, 740*). On living trees it produces only sterile conks, but fertile sporophores form on dead and down trees. It occurs also in the Lake States.

Another leading heart rotter of red maple is *Fomes igniarius*. This well-known fungus attacks many hardwoods, and red maple ranks among its favorite hosts. Conks indicate extensive decay. Ohman and Kessler (*1050*) provide an illustrated account of the decay caused by *F. igniarius*, and standard texts (*81, 151*) emphasize its importance and diagnostic characters.

Fomes connatus forms a small, whitish conk, generally at an injury, which soon develops a green moss on the top. This fungus is usually confined to maple, occurring wherever maples grow, and the moss is virtually certain to be found on any such conk that is not very young (*151, 639*). *F. connatus* appears occasionally on other hardwoods.

Stereum murrayi, already mentioned in connection with cankers, occurs widely over the North, mainly in maples and birches (*342*). It may form a sunken, thick-lipped canker, retaining the bark, or it may not form a canker. The rot can be extensive. The sporophores are small, thin, and shelving, and may form on old canker margins or at the center of younger ones.

In their suggestions for making cull deductions in red maple, Spaulding, Hepting, and Westveld (*1343*) suggest a linear deduction of only 3 ft. where a conk of *Fomes connatus* occurs, but virtually complete loss of the tree if it bears a conk of *F. igniarius*. Swollen knots and seams indicate at least "black heart," if not active decay. They mention that red maple should generally be culled heavily.

Shigo (*1290*) studied the fungi surrounding, and in advance of, rot columns of *Fomes igniarius* in living trees, and found that a high-pH "wetwood" zone surrounded the columns and that several nonhymenomycetous fungi and certain bacteria colonized the surrounding area. The fungi were mostly species of *Phialophora, Trichocladium* and *Acrostaphylus*.

Shigo (*1298*) also found that, in red maple, branch stubs were more important as infection courts for decay fungi than were parent stumps. Of 210 of the 324 living sprouts sampled for fungi, 86 yielded hymenomycetes, 107 bacteria, 85 *Cytospora decipiens*, 90 *Phialophora* spp., 52 *Hypoxylon* spp., and 52 *Trichocladium canadense*.

Fungi capable of causing either rot of the central cylinder or rot at wounds of living *Acer* spp. include *Fomes connatus, F. robustus, F. scutellatus, Polyporus curtisii, P. cuticularis, P. dryophilus, P. farlowii* (in the Southwest), *P. fissilis, P. glomeratus, P. graveolens, P. lucidus, P. obtusus, P. robiniophilus*, and *P. squamosus*. Since Overholts (*1067*) does not cite the species of maple upon which these fungi were fruiting they are placed here, under *Acer rubrum*, for convenience, and because *A. rubrum* is the most widely distributed species of maple.

Red maple in northeastern Pennsylvania ranged in cull from an average of 13 percent in 12-inch trees to 46 percent in 24-inch trees. Of associated species only beech and sweet birch were more defective (*740*).

The volume deduction due to rot in sawtimber stands in North Carolina was computed for several hardwood species (*557*), with the cull percent due to rot in yellow-poplar and white oak 4 percent, sweetgum 5 percent, and in red maple 38 percent.

Campbell (*204*) studied decay transmission from parent stubs and dead companion sprouts to residual stump sprouts of the northern hardwood species. Of six tree species studied the highest incidence of this stump or stub rot was in red maple. Even so, such rot transmission was only occasional rather than frequent, as it is in the oaks. No one particular fungus was blamed for most of the red maple sprout rot.

Miscellaneous Pathology.—Many of the complex degenerative maple troubles described under the Miscellaneous Pathology of sugar maple are wholly or very largely confined to sugar maple. This is true of the insect-induced Wisconsin blight (*826*), the troubles of sugar-bush maples, the northern Michigan decline (*786*), and to a great extent the general eastern decline. (*674*). The New England roadside problem (*824*) involves red maple to a lesser degree.

Increment borings in red maple produced discoloration of the wood to the same extent as reported for sugar maple, namely, a narrow brown to black radial band, one to two feet in vertical extent (*669*).

The succession of mold and stain fungi that develop on red maple pulpwood in New Hampshire are described and named by Shigo (*1286*). *Ceratocystis coerulescens* was usually the first fungus to infect the ends of the bolts.

Wounds tend to heal slowly because of a tendency to cambial dieback following injury. Injuries in late winter and spring also bleed, and this interferes with healing.

A localized ring shake of hemlock and certain hardwoods, including red maple, is ascribed to sapsuckers by Shigo (*1292, 1295*). Discolorations also streak the wood from such injuries.

A flower blight of red and silver maple is caused by the discomycete *Ciboria acerina*. The inflorescence is killed and seed formation thus prevented (*939*).

A species of dodder (*Cuscuta gronovii*) has been reported on seedlings of red maple in New York (*8*).

Nonmycorrhizal roots of red maple are usually long and slender, in contrast to the typically beaded short roots infected with endotrophic mycorrhizal fungi. Red maple mycorrhizae are illustrated by Vozzo and Hacskaylo (*1486*).

The defects of many Piedmont hardwoods, including red maple, were studied by Bryan (*180*). The types of defects and the extent to which each contributed to the heavy degrade in these hardwoods are evaluated. Internal and external views of many of the defects are provided.

A large number of nematodes in 12 genera were identified either from roots or within the root zones of red maple trees (*1222*); but their significance with respect to plant damage was not known. A later tabulation by Ruehle (*1224*) of nematodes associated with red maple lists 22 species in 16 genera.

Silver maple

Acer saccharinum

Silver maple is distributed throughout the East except for the southern parts of the Gulf States, most of Florida, and the northern parts of the Lake States (*279*). Considered intermediate to tolerant of shade (*54*), it grows scattered on sheltered sites, particularly in the moist soil of lowlands and along watercourses. It is not a preferred forest species, but has had wide use as a shade tree mainly because of its very rapid growth for the first 30 to 40 years and its short-boled, spreading habit.

Since silver maple leaves are silvery beneath and deeply cleft, selections have been propagated making use of the "cut-leaf" and other interesting features, and Rehder (*1154*) lists five varieties, in addition to the type.

Despite the growth rate and growth habit advantages, silver maple is not a desirable shade tree. Its thin bark makes it readily scarred by mowing machines or by fire. It is consistently severely attacked by scale insects, which results in crowns full of dead twigs and branches that become unsightly and must be pruned out if a tree is to be attractive. The wood is weak and breaks easily under ice and snow, putting it near the top of Croxton's ice-damage susceptibility listing (*310*). In addition, the tree is short-lived, seldom with a longevity over 100 years; it is commonly rotten or hollowed, and its susceptibility to injuries and its sprouting potential ultimately result in much unsightly "feathering" along trunk and branches. This species is notorious for having its roots penetrate the joints of underground piping, causing major obstruction.

Foliage Diseases.—Like some of the other maples, this species' foliage is subject to spotting by many fungi. Those leaf pathogens that May (*939*) describes or illustrates include *Cristulariella depraedens* (gray-mold spot), *C. pyramidalis* (bull's eye spot), *Gloeosporium apocryptum* and *G. saccharinum* (anthracnose), *Phyllosticta minima*, *Rhytisma acerinum* and *R. punctatum* (tar spots), *Septoria aceris*, *Taphrina carveri* (leaf blister), and the powdery mildew fungi *Phyllactinia guttata* and *Uncinula circinata* (*1153*). Some annotations concerning these spots or spot fungi are made in the next section, *Acer saccharum*.

Venturia acerina (*1121*) (*Cladosporium humile*) is also a common spot fungus, mainly of red maple, but also of silver maple. The appearance of the spots in nature and illustrations of the fungus are shown by Plakidas (*1121*). The spots vary greatly in size, and when young are round to angular, with a pale green halo. Older spots are angular to suborbicular, with irregular margins surrounded by a pale green halo. The upper surface is dark red-brown, the lower lead-gray. Older spots are zonate.

Most of the more common maple leaf diseases, and many diseases of other organs are described and illustrated by Marshall and Waterman (*928*).

Stem Diseases.—The only noteworthy stem disease of silver maple is Verticillium wilt (*V. albo-atrum*) (*939*). Green streaks or a green ring or partial ring in stem cross-section of the outer sapwood, are diagnostic. Silver maple is not as susceptible to this wilt as Norway maple.

The common hardwood "target" canker caused by *Nectria galligena* (*47, 170*) occurs on silver maple, but not nearly as commonly as on red and sugar maple. In addition to this parasite, that produces its small, red, balloon-like perithecia along the canker edges, another *Nectria, N. cinnabarina,* will grow saprophytically on maples, usually producing large, conspicuous orange-red sporodochia on the dead bark (*1555*).

Crown gall (*Agrobacterium tumefaciens*) occasionally affects this tree in the Midwest, and south to Texas. Warty excrescences on stems, trunk or root collar should be suspect. However, a species of *Phomopsis* produces warty galls on maples, also, and Brown (*178*) has pointed out the confusion involving crown gall and *Phomopsis* gall.

At least two species of *Septobasidium* (*S. burtii* and *S. pseudo-pedicellatum*) produce a brown, felty thallus over scale insects on branches of this maple (*292*).

In the Midwest the common mistletoe, *Phoradendron serotinum,* often parasitizes silver maple, but does little harm.

Valsa sordida, usually reported under the imperfect stage name *Cytospora chrysosperma,* is often associated with twig blight and dieback (*151, 254*). Its role on maples is generally either secondary or entirely saprobic, following other damage.

Root and Trunk Rots.—*Rhizoctonia solani* can kill seedlings. Wefts of mycelium around the roots and the characteristically branched hyphae in culture are diagnostic (*1555*).

Silver maple is rated as highly susceptible to *Phymatotrichum omnivorum* root rot (*1379*) in tests in Texas.

The charcoal root rot (*Macrophomina phaseoli,* imperfect stage *Sclerotium bataticola*) has been mentioned specifically as attacking silver maple seedlings in Illinois (*8*).

Shoestring root rot (*Armillaria mellea*) is common, and not only will rot dead roots and butts but will often give the coup-de-grâce to silver maples already in a weakened condition from other causes (*928*). The very similar fungus *Clitocybe tabescens* has attacked this maple similarly in the South (*1168*).

Other decay fungi that are known to rot the heartwood or inner sapwood of living silver maples include *Fomes applanatus, F. connatus, F. igniarius, Hydnum erinaceus, H. septentrionale,* and *Polyporus obtusus.* Many other wood rot fungi can attack the heart and sapwood of dead trees, or dead parts of living trees, and since silver maple is very prone to injury, many fungi can contribute to the weakening and hollowing of trees of this species. May (*939*) lists the principal fungi rotting species of *Acer,* and the type of wood they usually decay.

Miscellaneous Pathology.—The inflorescences of silver maple can be destroyed, and seeds aborted, by the discomycete *Ciboria acerina* (*939*).

46

Since silver maple is so often used as a street tree, whenever one dies suddenly, or more gradually but with full crown involvement, it is well to suspect Verticillium wilt (928) or soil-borne toxic gas (939). Methods for detecting gas injury are available (see *Acer platanoides*).

May (939) shows a good photo of frost beak in silver maple. This is a healing reaction to a frost crack.

Hart (598) has demonstrated that sapwood of silver maple, discolored as a result of wounding, is similar morphologically to normal heartwood, but differs chemically in having a higher pH, higher ash content, and also a higher moisture content.

Potassium deficiency symptoms have been produced and described in code for several hardwoods including *Acer saccharinum* (1095).

Galleries of the Columbian timber beetle yielded *Hansenula* sp., *Graphium* sp., *Ceratocystis* sp., *Fusarium tricinctum*, *F. oxysporum*, and *F. solani*, although these fungi were of minor significance in wood staining (Kabir, 768).

Five species of nematodes, each in a different genus, have been identified in association with the roots or root zones of trees of this species in the United States (1222).

Sugar maple

Acer saccharum

Sugar maple, commonly known in the lumber trade as hard maple, is one of the most valuable trees in eastern North America. Its sap produces the maple syrup of commerce, its shade and lovely fall coloration grace much of the northern landscape, and its wood, especially in its birds-eye or curly form, is highly prized for furniture, paneling, flooring and many other uses. It occurs throughout the East except for the southern Piedmont and Coastal plain, but its commercial range extends only from southern Canada through the Lake, Central, and New England States to the upper elevations of the Southern Appalachian Mountains (513). The tree can withstand extreme cold, but cannot successfully compete in the heat and dryness of most of the South. It thrives only on fertile, moist, well-drained soils.

A soil-builder, with a fairly high calcium content in its foliage (244), sugar maple occurs mostly on soils of pH 5.5 to 7.0. It is very tolerant of shade (54), and responds very well to release. Downs (391) found a 100 percent increase in radial growth following release in North Carolina. It has a deep, branching root system and a compact, oval crown. Growth is typically slow, and stands can live to ages of 300 to 400 years. Reproduction by sprouts or root suckers is common. The species is windfirm, frosty-hardy, and moderately resistant to ice damage (310). Downs (390) rated damage following a severe glaze storm in Pennsylvania and New York, and found that 15 percent of the sugar maple was badly damaged, as compared with a like percentage of birch and beech, but 41 percent of the black cherry and only 5 percent of the hemlock were badly damaged.

Botanists recognize from three to five varieties of sugar maple.

In addition, three described species, Florida maple (*Acer barbatum*), chalk maple (*A. leucoderme*), and black maple (*A. nigrum*) could be regarded as varieties of *A. saccharum*. Godman (*513*) gives a very good account of the silvical and related characteristics of the sugar maple, and Kriebel (*816*) points out patterns of genetic variation in the species.

With respect to the onset of fall coloration of sugar maple, Ouelette and Bard (*1064*) found that the great majority of trees that took on fall coloration prematurely had been materially injured in some way, with the type of injury ranging from sunscald to frost cracks to heart or root rot.

Sugar maple is seldom planted, except as an ornamental. Field plantings usually have a low survival. The tree does not compete well with sod, and often needs an overstory nurse crop (*513*).

The main elements of the pathology of sugar maple are the following: many non-limiting leaf diseases; many fungus canker diseases that are locally damaging; the vascular diseases known as Verticillium wilt, sapstreak, and bacterial wetwood; rots and stains, many of which are associated with tapping for sugar, logging injuries and branch stubs; and a series of widespread declines not mainly of fungus origin that have gone under the names of maple blight, maple decline, maple dieback, roadside maple disease, and other vague names. The causes of most of these troubles have been determined.

May (*939*) has published a useful bulletin on the more specific diseases of shade and ornamental maples, and Marshall and Waterman illustrate many of these (*928*). University of Wisconsin Bulletin 250 on Wisconsin maple blight (*1595*) contains a wealth of reference material to some of the less well-defined troubles to which sugar maple is subject.

Seedling Diseases.—Seed germination is typically delayed because of dormant embryos, and some stratification for a short time is recommended. The seedlings are subject to few enemies in the nursery (*1*). However, *Rhizoctonia solani* has occasionally caused damage, and groups of seedlings were killed by *Sclerotium bataticola* causing basal lesions in an Illinois nursery. With the latter disease the seedling pith was hollowed out and lined with small, black dots (*360*).

A condition called sore-shin can affect maple nursery seedlings. Lesions of unknown cause develop on one side at the ground line, and differ from heat lesions in having no particular orientation with respect to the sun (*360*).

Foliage Diseases.—May (*939*) has given particular attention to this group, and while many additional fungi and other agents discolor sugar maple leaves, he gives descriptive accounts mainly of the following:

Anthracnose (*Gloeosporium apocryptum*). Small to large, circular to irregular necrotic areas, turning brown, purplish or black. On sugar maple large, green- or red-brown lesions occur along or between the veins, often extending to leaf margins. Cooke (*284*) further describes the lesions, and the characteristics of the fungus, under the synonym *Microstroma apocryptum*.

Phyllosticta spot (*Phyllosticta minima*). Fairly discrete spots, which on sugar maple have a narrow purplish border. Small, black pycnidia contain tiny, unicellular conidia.

Tar spots (*Rhytisma acerinum* and *R. punctatum*). In *R. acerinum* numerous, small, black spots coalesce to produce large, black, thickened areas of the leaf. In *R. punctatum* the many small spots occur in groups, but tend not to coalesce. Both fungi produce rod-shaped conidia in the spots on attached leaves (*1352*).

Bull's-eye spot (*Cristulariella pyramidalis*) (*1523*). Forms yellow-gray spots with light-brown, concentric rings on the upper surface, and brown spots without rings on the lower. Tiny globose, hyaline spores are produced on pyramidal conidiophores. This fungus has severely attacked *Acer platanoides* foliage in North Carolina, while leaving *A. saccharum* and *A. saccharinum* unaffected (*105*).

Gray-mold spot (*Cristulariella depraedens*). Spots are irregular, grayish, and often without a definite margin. Appears late in summer.

Leaf blister (*Taphrina sacchari*). Causes domed blisters, curling, twisting, and other leaf distortion, and also necrosis. It is easily identified, but is not common (*751*).

Septoria spot (*Septoria aceris*). Produces small, reddish-tan spots with an irregular, indefinite border. The conidia are narrowly elongate and multiseptate.

Powdery mildews (*Microsphaera alni*, *Phyllactinia guttata* and *Uncinula circinata*) (*1153, 1352*). Whitish, superficial fungus growth, particularly severe on sprout leaves, under humid conditions, and late in the season. Black perithecia form on and in the fungus mat in the autumn.

A few other fungi are associated with leaf spots on sugar maple, particularly *Actinopelte dryina* (*863*) (see *Quercus*), *Mycosphaerella* spp., and *Venturia acerina* (*1121*). The *Venturia* (*Cladosporium humile*) produces spots that are brown above and gray below, are zonate, and irregular in outline (see *Acer saccharinum*).

Tehon and Stout (*1391*) give a key to 8 species of *Diplodia*, some on leaves, that occur on *Acer* spp.

The physiogenic leaf troubles include mainly the following:

Individual sugar maples, beeches, and ashes are subject to leaf scorch particularly under conditions of bright sunlight, after prolonged cloudiness or drying winds. The leaves become bronzed in irregular areas, usually starting at the margins (*928*).

A twisting, cupping, and curling can result from herbicide sprays of the 2,4-D or 2,4,5-T types. While sugar maple can be so injured, it is considered fairly resistant to herbicide damage, as compared with many other hardwoods (*513*).

A condition called tatterleaf, in which major areas of the leaves drop out with a shot-hole effect, has been reported from several parts of the country. May (*939*) shows a good photo of this condition and mentions a possible relation to frost prior to full budbreak in the spring.

Stem Diseases.—Nectria canker (*Nectria galligena*) (*170, 639*) affects many hardwoods and is common on sugar maple in the North. Its "target" cankers with concentric rings of exposed, typically firm, bark-free ridges of callus (*661*) are distinct from the other maple cankers. Most cankers have a small branch stub in the center. Grant and Spaulding (*530*) concluded that the fungus enters mainly through cracks in the top of a branch axil, sprung by weight of ice or snow (see also *Betula alleghaniensis* and *Juglans nigra*).

According to Lohman and Watson (*879*) many early collections of *N. galligena* were erroneously referred to *N. coccinea sensu* Wr. The latter species does occur on sugar maple in New England, but their reports showed it only on dead bark and only on sugar maple. They do not record *N. coccinea* as a canker fungus in the East.

Eutypella canker (*Eutypella parasitica*) (*351*) develops only on sugar maple, red maple, and boxelder. While concentric zonation is evident, the bark adheres to the wood, and decay accompanies infection, often leading to breakage. A canker can also greatly deform a trunk.

Schizoxylon canker (*Schizoxylon microsporum*) occurs on suppressed red and sugar maples in the Lake States, and is of minor importance. The lesions are typically irregular and knobly, with the outer few callus rings bark-covered, and white mycelial fans develop beneath the bark at the canker margins. Davidson and Lorenz (*351*) fully describe both Eutypella and Schizoxylon cankers and their causal fungi.

Bleeding canker (*Phytophthora cactorum*) is typified by elongate lesions, up to several feet in length, that occur mainly on the trunks of ornamental maples in the East and the West (*717, 987*). Areas of dead bark surrounding bark fissures are often sunken and of varying size, and secrete a red to blackish fluid. The bark beneath the canker is reddish-brown, with the edges greenish. The wood surface beneath becomes darkly stained. Bleeding canker is considered the most serious disease of sugar maple in parts of southern New England (*1640*). Caroselli (*223*) illustrates and describes this disease and mentions that when the reddish-brown exudate dries, it takes on the appearance of dried blood. He also mentions that a vertical arrangement of trunk cankers is much more common than a peripheral distribution.

A wood-destroying fungus, *Stereum murrayi*, can cause deeply sunken lesions that retain the bark and lack the concentric zoning of many of the other cankers (*342*). The margins are swollen, trunk distortion is common, and the woody cylinder beneath is rotten. Another of these so-called canker-rot fungi, *Daedalea unicolor*, can infect a sugar maple trunk, decay the inner wood, and gradually work outward through the sapwood, reaching the cambium and forming a canker on the side at which it entered. By this time the rot extends 3 to 5 ft. above the canker. Campbell (*205*) found this canker mostly in Vermont.

Polyporus glomeratus (*209*) can cause cankers with sterile conks, similar to those caused by the two canker-rot fungi just described. Silverborg (*1306*), in his northern hardwoods cull manual, provides good illustrations of the canker and sporophore, and describes the disease as follows: "This conk or canker is difficult to recognize, but is one of the most serious causes of heart rot in hard maple and red maple in the Adirondack Region. The associated heart rot is white to light-brown and spongy and contains numerous particles of black, gritty material. . . . Abnormal callus tissue forms around the infected branch stubs, resulting in prominent, swollen, woody knobs."

A stem gall or swelling, often of considerable size, is common in Pennsylvania, New York, and the Lake States. It is described by Davidson and Campbell (*341*) as a conspicuous outgrowth, always on the main trunk, within 8 ft. from the ground, not cankerous, and with the wood beneath stained reddish to greenish-black. The cause was not determined. Another small gall, often on branches of red and sugar maple, is called maple tumor by Brown (*178*). Encircling tumors can kill branches. A *Phomopsis* species was isolated and tumors produced with it.

A small, lens-shaped, annual canker has been described from many parts of the East. The trunk and branches may be peppered with these lesions. Wood and Skelly (*1613*) concluded that fall infection by *Fusarium solani* was the cause. While this fungus may have a direct role in this disease, as it does with cankers on *Liriodendron*, *Nyssa*, and *Populus*, Ward et al. (*1509*) concluded that this particular syndrome, in Pennsylvania, was also related to site characteristics, and that the heavily cankered trees were on soils that were shallow, reaching to an impervious layer, and the A horizons contained a higher clay content and more pore space than did soils supporting less cankered trees.

Bier (*111*) described a small, sunken, bark-covered canker of sapling red and sugar maples in Ontario, caused by *Hypoxylon mammatum* (*H. blakei*, *H. morsei*) (*978*). He illustrates the conidial and perithecial fruit bodies that appear on the canker and adjacent dead twigs.

Hymenochaete agglutinans develops a brown thallus that can cause a branch that it is decaying to adhere firmly to a healthy stem, sometimes killing the bark at the union.

Shigo (*1293*) has pointed out that gnawing by squirrels initiated large numbers of annual cankers on sugar maple in New Hampshire. Sapsuckers also damage the bark, and the released sap serves as a food base for molds that blacken the trunk (*1051*).

Among the fungi that cause limited cankers at tap holes, *Valsa* (*Cytospora*) *leucostomoides* is particularly prominent in Vermont (*1344*).

Hepting et al. (*669*) found that Nectria cankers developed around increment borer holes in sugar maple in North Carolina and markedly retarded their closure.

Bark killing of sugar maple, referred to as sunscald or sunscald cankers, has been common in Canada and the Northeast, particularly when an understory of these shade-tolerant trees is exposed following logging. Orientation toward the south and west and lack of repeated callus killing are often sufficient symptoms for diagnosis.

Reid and Cain (*1156*) demonstrated and illustrated that the maple branch saprobes *Valsa myinda* and *Cryptodiaporthe myinda* are distinct species, and also applied a proper nomenclature to these organisms.

The fungus *Cryptostroma corticale*, considered the cause of the sooty-bark disease of *Acer pseudoplatanus* in Europe, is a bark saprophyte on *Acer saccharum* in the Lake States. Kessler and Ohman (*788*) state that an asthma allergy caused by the spores has affected papermill and other woodworkers handling sugar maple bolts and logs in this country. They mention observing sporulation especially on the trunks of trees killed by the sapstreak disease (see Vascular Diseases), and give citations to the literature dealing with the mycological and medical aspects of the fungus. Protein extracts of spores have produced a strong skin reaction in humans.

The common mistletoe *Phoradendron serotinum* occurs on sugar maple in the Middle West.

Vascular Diseases.—Sap flow may start from any type of timely wound to sugar maple, commonly from frost cracks. Bacterial contamination may then result in widespread infection of the sap within the tree, a condition common to many kinds of trees and referred to as wetwood. Sugar maples are seldom killed by this type of infection. However, toxic products of the infection can kill shoots or kill bark that the exuding sap flows over. The woody cylinder usually has a watersoaked appearance, a strongly alkaline reaction, and a sour odor. Where internal pressure results in outflow of sap, slime flux may develop, and additional bark killing follows. Insects are often attracted to the yeasty flux, and dark molds flourish on fluxing lesions. Hartley et al. (*603*) give a full account of wetwood, as it occurs on a number of species and genera.

One of the common shade tree killers is Verticillium wilt (*V. albo-atrum*) (*532*). It is less damaging to sugar maple than to Norway maple. An entire tree or just a branch or two may first wilt, and then the condition progresses or sometimes remains arrested. Infection takes place largely through the roots, and the best diagnostic symptom is the greenish streaking of the outer sapwood extending upward and ultimately out into the limbs. The causal fungus can be isolated from these streaks. Rudolph (*1216*) gives a full account of this disease as it attacks many kinds of plants, and Caroselli (*224*) provides a detailed account with respect to maples, particularly sugar maple. The question of how much of the Verticillium wilt complex should be attributed to *V. albo-atrum* and how much to *V. dahliae* is yet to be resolved.

Another vascular mycosis described and named "sapstreak" by Hepting (*641*) caused an epidemic dying of sugar maple following logging in North Carolina and later was found killing this species in the Lake States (*1049*) and in the Northeast (*716*). The disease is distinguished by thinning crowns, with dwarfed, chlorotic foliage, followed by death. The sapwood appears watersoaked, with greenish, gray, and reddish streaking extending radially in flame-like patterns. The cause, *Ceratocystis coerulescens* (*641, 732*), is easily isolated and is characteristic in culture.

Some trees killed by sapstreak in the Lake States have been reported by Kessler and Ohman (*788*) to support fruiting by *Cryptostroma corticale* (see Stem Diseases).

Ohman and Spike (*1052*) found that the sapstreak disease so degraded the lumber of infected trees in the Lake States that it was worth little for anything other than pallets or pulpwood.

Root Diseases and Mycorrhizae.—Sugar maple is not often damaged by strictly root diseases. *Armillaria mellea,* a fungus common to the roots of most hardwoods, has, however, given the coup-de-grâce to many weakened or badly injured trees, as well as caused butt rot (*674, 1595*). Its black, flattened rhizomorphs may be seen on the outside of roots, and where root injury affords an opening, rot may begin and extend, to cause major damage as a root-collar cambial pathogen. Other fungi known to attack sugar maple roots, but lacking the diagnostic black rhizomorphs of *A. mellea*, are *Polyporus lucidus* (*1118*) and *Pholiota adiposa*.

Ustulina vulgaris, an ascomycete that rots stumps and the butts of sprout hardwoods, can also rot the wood of the roots. Campbell and Davidson (*211*) give good descriptions and illustrations of its attack on sugar maple.

In the course of the study of an insect-induced maple blight in Wisconsin, Riffle (*1170*) studied the nematodes associated with sugar maples. He found a large number of genera and species, including some known to be parasitic to plants and others suspected of parasitism. He determined species in *Criconema, Criconemoides, Hemicycliophora, Paratylenchus, Tylenchorrhyncus, Helicotylenchus, Meloidogyne, Trichodorus, Xiphinema, Leptonchus*, and *Triplonchium*. Additional information on the nematodes in maple blight and maple dieback areas in Wisconsin is provided by Riffle and Kuntz (*1173*). Occasional high populations of nematodes in some of these genera were also identified by Hibben (*674*) in connection with a widespread decline of sugar maple in New York (see Miscellaneous Pathology), but he did not associate them causally with the decline.

Ruehle (*1222*) lists a large number of nematodes associated with the roots of sugar maple. Another tabulation by Ruehle (*1224*) lists 8 species of nematodes in 8 genera associated with sugar maple in Tennessee.

Sugar maple proved highly susceptible to *Phymatotrichum omnivorum* in tests in Texas (*1379*), but this fungus is no threat within the native range of the species.

Trappe (*1442*) mentions only one fungus, *Cortinarius rubripes*, as forming ectotrophic mycorrhizae with sugar maple. Kessler (*785*) describes an endotrophic mycorrhiza of this species characterized by what he calls beaded rootlets. Arbuscle development was common in cortical cells, but vesicle production was rare. A phycomycete that developed an extra-matrical mycelium that invaded partially decayed organic matter in the soil was associated.

Trunk Rots.—Many fungi rot the woody cylinder of sugar maple (*8*). May (*939*) has selected the more prominent species and given an indication of the type of wood attacked and the extent of decay to be expected. Some of these have already been mentioned in connection with canker formation and root rot.

With respect to attack on sugar maple the following additional decay-fungus reference material is useful:

Armillaria mellea (*848, 939, 1041*)
Collybia velutipes (*1196, 151*)
Corticium vellereum (*1041*)
Daedalea unicolor (*205*)
Fomes applanatus (*151, 639*)
Fomes connatus (*639, 1041*)
Fomes igniarius (*639, 1041, 1050*)
Hericium erinaceus (*151, 639*)
Pholiota adiposa (*151*)
Pholiota spectabilis (*1041*)
Pleurotus ostreatus (*151, 425*)
Polyporus glomeratus (*209, 210*)
Polyporus sulphureus (*151, 639*)
Steccherinum septentrionale (*1041*)
Stereum murrayi (*342*)
Ustulina vulgaris (*211, 1041*)

Nordin (*1041*), working in Ontario, found that 35 percent of his sugar maple infections followed frost cracks, 33 percent from dead branches and stubs, 20 percent from scars, and 7 percent from roots. While 28 species of fungi were identified with decay, the most important were *Armillaria mellea, Corticium vellereum, Fomes connatus, F. igniarius, Pholiota spectabilis, Polyporus glomeratus, Steccherinum septentrionale,* and *Ustulina vulgaris.* He gives good descriptions and photographs of decays and sporophores. His percentage of cull in sugar maple rose from 30 percent at age class 40 to 57 percent at age class 320.

Shigo states (*1297*) that in many cases the way is prepared for hymenomycete attack of the woody cylinder of living hardwoods by prior invasion by other fungi and by lower organisms. He has published a series of papers in support of his position, dealing largely with northern hardwoods.

A study of top rot following ice damage in the Northeast indicated black cherry decay to extend three or more times further from the breaks as did decay in sugar maple (*212*). The riddled condition of the rotten wood precluded getting a good appraisal of the fungi involved.

In connection with decay transmission from parent stump to attached sprout, Campbell and Davidson (*211*) noted that only *Ustulina vulgaris* followed this path, and also Nordin's (*1041*) few cases of such stump-to-sprout decay involved only this fungus. *Armillaria mellea* was, however, commonly isolated from parent stumps at ground level by Campbell (*204*). While some decay can develop in the butts of sugar maples of sprout origin, via the parent stump or dead companion sprout stubs, the incidence of such rot is much lower than in oak and in some other northern hardwoods (*204*).

Nordin (*1046*) developed net volume tables for sugar maple in Ontario. Depending upon the locality, decay varied with tree diameter. Decay cull rose at one area from no decay at 8 in. in diameter to 17 percent at 15 in. in diameter. At another area the cull/age curve ran downward from 60 percent cull at 10 in. in diameter to 35 percent at 21 in. in diameter. Other trends of cull as related to tree diameter were still different.

Decay and degrade following logging in the Upper Peninsula of Michigan was intensively studied by Hesterberg (*673*). The volume of cull increased with width of logging wound and with time. He put dollar values on losses associated with logging injury 10 to 20 years after logging. He also developed tree risk classes based on recognizable wound types and sizes. There are interesting parallels in his scar age and scar width relationships to rot with those of Hepting (*640*), working with Appalachian oak, and Toole (*1417*), with some Delta hardwoods. Reduction in value with increase in cull also has parallels with the decay risk classes developed for Appalachian oaks by Hepting et al. (*662*), and with financial loss associated with decay in southern pine by Hepting and Chapman (*657*).

Some suggestions for estimating cull in sugar maple have been prepared by Spaulding, Hepting, and Westveld (*1343*), making use of external indications. Conks of *Fomes connatus* called for culling only 3 linear ft., while those of *F. igniarius* indicated a serious percentage loss. In general, surface defects called for less

54

deduction in sugar maple than in yellow birch.

Shigo (*1291*) stresses the importance of branch stubs in hardwoods, including the maples, as pathways of entrance for rot and canker fungi, stain organisms, and other defects. He considers branch stubs as "the beginning of trouble for most trees."

In Ontario, Basham and Morawski (*73*) reported that sugar maple had a rot cull loss of 6 percent, and required a stain deduction of 23 percent. The commonest fungi isolated were *Polyporus glomeratus, Pholiota spectabilis, P. adiposa,* and *Fomes igniarius.*

Good, et al. (*517*) studied the progressive changes in decay in sugar maple trees by comparing total activity of the "decay community" (as measured by CO_2 output of excised samples), water content, pH, and the identity of the predominant organisms. The pattern across a zone infected with *Fomes igniarius* was very different, in all respects, from the pattern across regions harboring no basidiomycete flora.

Stains.—Many disturbances to sugar maple sapwood tend to result in brown, green, reddish, or grayish stains. Some of these have already been mentioned in connection with disease, such as stem gall, Verticillium wilt, and sapstreak. Perhaps the most common stain in the living tree is called mineral streak. Scheffer (*1244*) found this extensive disfiguring maple stain to be typically olive to greenish-black, high in ash content, and to effervesce with hydrochloric acid. The direct cause has not yet been determined. The color is due to dark phenolic globules in the ray cells and other living parenchyma cells.

Sapsucker pecking leads to much of the sapwood streaking or "black heart" in Lake States sugar maple. This injury, and to a lesser extent that caused by rodents, leads to sap flow with the result that *Fumago* sp. and *Pullularia pullulans* (*477*) turn the lower bark black. Thus, Ohman and Kessler (*1051*) consider black sooty bark a good indication of bird-peck and sapwood streaking.

Basham and Taylor (*74*), isolating from "normal" heartwood, found 98 percent of the attempts sterile. Of the cultures made from discolored wood with no evident rot, 31 percent yielded fungi and 7 percent yielded bacteria. With decay, wood yielded fungi in 49 percent and bacteria in 4 percent of the isolation attempts. *Trichocladium canadense* was the fungus found most often in discolored wood. Others were *Nodulisporium* sp., *Phialophora* spp. (many were *P. melinii*), and *Corticium vellereum.*

The common hardwood blue stain fungus *Ceratocystis coerulescens,* that also causes the sapstreak disease of sugar maple and yellow-poplar, can widely infect sugar maple lumber, imparting a gray stain to the wood and a black surface molding (*1201*). The succession of mold and stain fungi that develop on sugar maple cut for pulpwood in New Hampshire are described and named by Shigo (*1286*). *C. coerulescens* was usually the first fungus to infect the ends of the bolts.

Ceratocystis acericola fruits on the inner bark of sugar maple in Ontario (*545*).

Another lumberyard stain of sugar maple wood turns it gray but is not caused by a fungus. Globules in ray cells similar to those mentioned in connection with mineral streak appear to produce the coloration.

Increment borings made in sugar maple by Hepting et al. (*669*) resulted in a band of brown discoloration, slightly more than the width of the hole and from 1 to 2 ft. in vertical extent. Plugging the holes had no effects on the staining, which is regarded as an oxidant reaction resulting in conversion of cell contents to phenolic compounds. Many of the borings, made in four forest regions, developed localized decay as well as wood staining.

Miscellaneous Pathology.—In recent years many disorders of sugar maple have claimed the attention of pathologists. Some disorders have been localized but alarming, and others more widespread. Such names as maple blight, maple decline, and maple dieback have been applied, denoting general recession maladies rather than leaf spots, cankers, rots, etc. For convenience, these decline troubles might be put into five categories: (1) the New England and Lake States roadside maple problem; (2) the general maple decline of the Northeast; (3) the insect-induced sugar maple blight of northern Wisconsin; (4) the sapstreak disease of North Carolina and the Lake States; and (5) the pathology of sugarbush maples.

The New England roadside problem is limited to the immediate roadside and its drainage areas, being particularly serious in New Hampshire and neighboring states. Lacasse and Rich (*824*) define the symptoms as premature foliar coloration, marginal leaf scorch, defoliation, and death. Salt, applied to roads in winter, was an early causal suspect. However, Holmes (*702*) did not succeed in inducing this syndrome by the addition of sodium chloride during the winter months for 7 years, and indicated doubt about the extent that road salt harms maples in Massachusetts. Nevertheless, Lacasse and Rich (*824*) laid stress on sodium chloride because: (1) they found maple particularly sensitive to sodium; (2) that of 4 genera studied, only maple translocated sodium; and (3) the concentration of sodium in the leaves, twigs, and sap of maples within the windrow of plowed snow was much higher than in areas further from the road. Some investigators feel that salt has a prominent role, but that other factors are involved, including road widening, asphalt sprays on shoulders, automobile exhaust, snowplow injury, and the aging of many of New England's roadside trees.

New unpublished findings in one Northeastern State demonstrated clearly that road salt was an important cause of the decline of roadside trees, mainly sugar maples, where drainage conditions directed the brine to the root zones.

Kotheimer et al. (*809*) determined the role of several ions in the maple decline related to road salt application. In sugar maples chlorine ion levels were significantly correlated with damage ratings and attained levels several times higher than sodium levels, except in terminal decline. *Acer platanoides* showed much greater tolerance to chlorine ions than *A. saccharum*.

The widespread sugar maple decline of the Northeast has been given particular attention in New York. Welch (*1547*) gives the symptoms as: twig and branch dieback involving mainly the upper crown, but often the lower also; foliage showing chlorosis, premature coloration, dwarfing, cupping, or abscission; and cankers not specifically involved. Hibben (674) found declining maples of all sizes, and in a wide variety of situations. He did much isolating, inoculating, and grafting, but was unable to implicate a fungus, a nematode, or a virus. He concluded that this New York decline seems similar to declines of other hardwoods in the Northeast, and that specific biotic factors, such as Armillaria root rot, play only a minor role. He believes that a succession of dry growing seasons, together with other recent climatic changes (651) are probably involved in the complex of factors that have led to the decline of many eastern hardwood species. In this respect, there are many parallels between the conclusions drawn by Hibben regarding sugar maple decline, those of Ross (1193) with respect to ash dieback, and some of the interpretations of Staley (1348) regarding oak decline.

In the course of Hibben's work on decline of sugar maple in New York he isolated many fungi and nematodes, and although none had an aggressive role, he has provided an account of those organisms that he found associated with declining maples (675), listing species of *Cephalosporium, Cytospora, Massaria, Myxosporium, Phoma, Pyrenochaeta,* and *Valsa,* as well as *Armillaria mellea,* and nematodes in the genera *Helicotylenchus, Hemicycliophora, Xiphinema,* and *Tylenchus.*

The maple dieback described by Griffin (544) in Ontario, Canada, is probably the same as what has just been described as a general decline in the Northeast. Maples and other species had been declining during the 1950's. However, during the 1960's, recovery, except among severely affected trees, was general. Although the cause was not determined with certainty, Griffin concluded that neither fungus pathogens nor insects were involved and that the condition apparently resulted from "adverse environmental factors," thus putting it along with ash dieback, oak decline, and similar maladies.

The Wisconsin maple blight claimed attention first in 1957 when thousands of sugar maples of all sizes died in Florence County. Although confined within a 25,000 square mile area, the sudden death of a species on a major scale caused such alarm that a coordinated multiagency attack was made on the problem. The results of this work by pathologists, entomologists, and foresters have been summarized particularly well in two publications (826, 1595). All studies support the view that the maple webworm did the main damage, but its attack was preceded by the maple leaf-roller because the webworm lays its eggs only in rolled leaves. Other events accompanied these attacks, including Armillaria root rot and periods of below-normal soil moisture. The webworm defoliation occurred at a critical time in the summer—early enough for a reflush of growth, and yet so late that much of the new growth failed to harden off properly and so was killed by cold fall weather.

The sapstreak disease (641), already mentioned under vascular diseases, is considered one of the elements in recent declines of sugar maple in Michigan. In that State, Kessler (786) reports still another maple decline that differs from the Wisconsin blight in affecting only large trees and in lacking any relation to webworms or leafrollers.

Sugar-bush maples suffer from a variety of troubles of their own, including their share of the many maladies of sugar maple already mentioned. These tapped trees are subject to maple borer; various cankers (*669, 1032*) that form at the holes, particularly one caused by *Valsa leucostomoides* (*1344*); heavy stains of the wood, root and trunks; rots; and swellings resulting from poor closure of tap holes (*714*).

Rough-bark is a bumpy condition of sugar maple described by Lorenz and Christensen (*887*) as a long-continued callus response to minor injuries. It is very possible that there is a relation of this condition to the injury by squirrels, sapsuckers, and some of the annual canker fungi mentioned earlier. Such lumpiness can greatly reduce the value of sugar maple lumber.

A localized ring shake of hemlock and certain hardwoods, including sugar maple, has been ascribed to sapsucker activity by Shigo (*1292, 1295*). In addition to the shake, there are discolorations of the wood, extending as streaks vertically from the injuries, that have the appearance of those from other mechanical injuries.

Miller (*974*), in his account of the ascomycetes of Georgia, lists many fungi, mostly saprobes, from the leaves and twigs of species of maple. Few of these ever attain economic consequence.

Pith flecks in sugar maple are abnormal wood features caused by the feeding of certain fly larvae on cambial tissue. They degrade lumber, as described and illustrated by Ward and Marden (*1508*).

According to Sparrow and Sparrow (*1332*) the sensitivity of sugar maple to gamma radiation from a cobalt-60 source was low among a group of 12 coniferous and hardwood species (see *Picea glauca*).

California buckeye

Aesculus californica

Metcalf (*955*) describes the California buckeye as a "strikingly beautiful flowering tree—used as an ornamental in hot, dry valley and foothill areas where it requires little care." A spreading shrub-like tree that grows rapidly in the brushy foothills of coastal and interior mountains, it prefers full sunlight rather than partial shade. Its habitat conditions are much like those of *Pinus sabiniana* (Digger pine). It is short-lived, with an estimated longevity of 100 years (*1367*).

The dry habitat of California buckeye is probably one of the factors involved in the small fungus flora reported for this species. A similar relationship occurs with fungi and dry-site pines in arid parts of the West. This buckeye, according to W. W. Wagener[9], has an extraordinary capacity to survive in dry environments. He has noted the continued survival of trees—in the low, dry, California foothills—the foliage of which often had turned brown from drought by July 4.

The leaves are sometimes distorted and buckled by the yellow leaf blister fungus *Taphrina aesculi* (*994*).

The common powdery mildew *Phyllactinia guttata* (*151, 1153*)

---

[9] Personal communication from W. Willis Wagener, deceased, formerly pathologist, USDA Forest Service Pacific Southwest Forest and Range Experiment Station, Berkeley, Calif.

and some secondary twig fungi (8) have been reported. The pericarp (ovary envelope) of fruits has occasionally been attacked by the anthracnose fungus, *Gloeosporium carpigenum;* and the common hairy mistletoe of the West Coast, *Phoradendron villosum* subsp. *villosum* (1580), occurs on branches, although the buckeye is not a favorite host.

Rankin (1143) mentions a witches' broom of this species, but provides no further information on it.

This buckeye is one of the earliest hardwoods to lose its leaves, and under unirrigated conditions, leaf fall may start in middle or late summer.

Ohio buckeye

Aesculus glabra

A relatively small tree, not important as a forest species, the Ohio buckeye is largely confined to those parts of the Central States region that are drained by the Ohio and Mississippi Rivers. It thus occurs from western Pennsylvania to Kansas, south to northeast Texas, with another south-extending arm running through central Tennessee to northern Alabama and Mississippi. This is an area of moderate rainfall and moderate temperatures. However, this tree can withstand severe winters and hot summers.

Ohio buckeye is a moist-soil, mostly streambank species, and where it occurs on drier sites it is mainly only a shrub 4-5 ft. high. Leafing out early, this tree is subject to frost damage on foliage. It withstands ice and snow loads well, and it is not subject to sunscald. The silvical characteristics of Ohio buckeye have been compiled by Merz (953). He mentions that the seeds and bark are poisonous to some animals.

Rehder (1154) describes 4 varieties, differing from each other in foliar characteristics. In general, Chadwick[10] considers that the Ohio buckeye has most of the same diseases as *Aesculus hippocastanum,* but as an ornamental is less subject to disease than the horsechestnut. He considers leaf blotch and leaf scorch, the latter involving a physiogenic response to heat and drought along streets, the main diseases. Air pollution may also be involved in leaf blighting (see *Aesculus hippocastanum*).

A leaf rust of the Ohio buckeye only (which occurs in the western part of this tree's range), long known as *Aecidium aesculi,* has been established by Baxter (84) as *Puccinia andropogonis,* with its telial stage on *Andropogon gerardi.*

The very common leaf blotch (*Guignardia aesculi*), a powdery mildew, and the common physiogenic leaf scorch of buckeye are described under *Aesculus octandra. A. glabra* differed in susceptibility to blotch, from light to severe, depending upon the variety, at the Morton Arboretum in Illinois (1013).

A small leaf spot with immersed pycnidia bearing long, narrow, multiseptate conidia has been attributed to *Septoria glabra,* a name possibly synonymous with *S. aesculi* and *S. hippocastani* (932). The spots can merge to blight major areas of the leaf.

[10] Personal communication from L. C. Chadwick, professor of horticulture, Ohio State University, Columbus, Ohio.

The common eastern leafy mistletoe, *Phoradendron serotinum* (*P. flavescens*), occurs generally on this one buckeye species, but damage is negligible.

Fungi capable of causing either rot of the central cylinder or rot at wounds of living *Aesculus* spp. include *Fomes applanatus, F. connatus, F. densus,* and *Polyporus squamosus* (*1067*).

Horsechestnut

Aesculus hippocastanum

The horsechestnut is mostly a native of southern Asia, in an area extending from northern Greece to the Himalayan Mountains. It is widely used in Europe and southern Asia as a street tree, and for this purpose was introduced into the United States from Europe early in the 18th century (*279*). A full-crowned, spreading, densely-foliaged tree (*1353*) that reaches a height of 80 ft., this species has at least eight named varieties (*1154*), among which are pendulous forms, very erect forms, and others with special foliage characteristics, including a variegated variety.

Horsechestnut withstands ice, snow, and wind well, and adapts itself to a wide range of sites in cultivation. Frost can cause slitting or tearing of the leaves between the veins (*151*). This species was virtually uninjured from salt spray associated with a New England hurricane (*1005*).

The horsechestnut has no serious disease enemies other than the development of unsightly foliage from midsummer on, as a result of the well-known fungus leaf blotch, and some sensitiveness to the heat, dryness, and polluted air of cities. This latter physiogenic leaf scorch, so obvious in European cities, especially Paris, may stunt one tree while leaving its neighbor virtually untouched. This striking tree-to-tree variation, together with other evidence, suggests that a photochemical oxidant type of urban air pollution is probably involved in the common scorch of *Aesculus* species along city streets.

Foliage Diseases.—The most prominent disease of this species, leaf blotch (*Guignardia aesculi*), is described under *Aesculus octandra* (*1353*). The imperfect stage is a *Phyllosticta* to which many specific names have been applied, the most common being *P. paviae*. This blotch and the physiogenic scorch account for some prejudice against horsechestnut. Neely and Himelick (*1013*) rate *A. hippocastanum* among the species of *Aesculus* most susceptible to blotch.

Since some trees are markedly resistant to scorch while adjacent horsechestnuts are badly stunted, there is an opportunity here for grafted selections to provide scorch-resistant clones of this species.

Another common leaf spot is caused by *Glomorella cingulata* (*1483*). Petioles, midribs, and veins turn brown. Acervuli are often formed before leaf fall. The closeness of association with veins distinguishes anthracnose from leaf blotch, the latter browning large, irregular areas of the leaf. The *Colletotrichum* (imperfect) stage bears acervuli with hyaline, 1-celled conidia 4–5μ × 14–21μ and dark multiseptate setae (*1115*). The *Glomerella* stage only appears on overwintered leaves on the ground.

Unimportant leaf diseases include the buckeye powdery mildew

(*Uncinula flexuosa*) (*1153*)—see *Aesculus octandra;* and the small buckeye leaf spot (*Septoria hippocastani*)—see *A. glabra*.

Stem Diseases.—Two killing diseases of street trees of many deciduous species have been reported attacking horsechestnut but not any of the native species of *Aesculus*. These are Verticillium wilt (*V. albo-atrum* and probably *V. dahliae*) and bleeding canker (*Phytophthora cactorum* and possibly *P. cinnamomi*). Both are annotated under *Acer saccharum*. These two diseases only occasionally affect the horsechestnut and in no way limit its culture.

The coral fungus, *Nectria cinnabarina*, often mistakenly assigned a pathogenic role, is largely a saprobe on this species. Its large, coral-colored sporodochia appearing on dying twigs give the impression of primary parasitism, but attack is almost always secondary to other damage. *Diplodia aesculi*, the probable imperfect stage of *Physalospora mutila*, has a similar role. *P. mutila* is known mostly as a black rot and canker fungus of *Malus* in the Pacific Northwest.

Miscellaneous Pathology.—Several fungi have been reported attacking the pericarps or seed coats of the horsechestnut (*8*). While of no importance, they are of mycological interest.

Many fungi can rot the wood of living trees, but collections too often fail to specify the species of *Aesculus* involved. *Collybia velutipes* in the East (*8*), and *Pleurotus* sp., *Stereum purpureum*, and *Trametes hispida* in the West (*1277*), have been reported attacking *A. hippocastanum*. Seymour (*1276*) also lists this species as a host to *Fomes applanatus*, *Pleurotus sapidus*, *P. ulmarius*, and *Polyporus squamosus*.

Horsechestnut is rated moderately susceptible to Texas root rot (*1379*).

Yellow buckeye

Aesculus octandra

The yellow buckeye is typically a tree of the eastern mountains from southwest Pennsylvania and Ohio through the southern Appalachian chain to north Alabama and Georgia, and along much of the Ohio River drainage almost to its junction with the Mississippi River. Paradoxically, it is essentially a bottomland species in the upper part of its range, and an important associate of the northern hardwoods on high mountain slopes and cove heads in the southern mountains. Its silvical characteristics have been compiled by Carmean (*222*).

Yellow buckeye is one of the first trees to leaf out and begin shoot growth in the spring. It grows to very large sizes with a clean trunk, and in virgin stands of high-elevation species in the Southern Appalachian Mountains, it is often the species with greatest height and diameter. Its dominant position in these old stands that include maple, beech, and yellow birch, is also testimony to its long life. It is tolerant (*54*), thrives in deep, moist soils of north slopes or otherwise cool environment, but is sensitive to heat and drought.

Rehder (*1154*) lists two varieties, *Aesculus octandra* var. *virginica*, with red flowers, and *A. octandra* var. *vestita*, with densely tomentose leaves and branches.

The yellow buckeye is subject to few diseases, and none of them are important economically or likely to be lethal. Easily the most conspicuous is the leaf blotch (*Guignardia aesculi*) to which all of the eastern species of *Aesculus* are subject (*1013*). Lesions develop on both petioles and leaves. They are of irregular outline (hence the name blotch) and may appear anywhere on the leaf, enlarging in size until by mid- to late August most of a buckeye's foliage may have turned brittle, brown, and distorted, with some leaves starting to fall (*1353*). Only the *Phyllosticta* stage of the fungus appears while the leaves are still on the trees. Leaf blotch is so common and extensive that in mid- to late summer, buckeye trees can often be identified in the woods at a distance by the blighted foliage. Yet, striking as late as it does, blotch does not seem to affect growth noticeably.

A small, dingy, gray leaf spot, usually with a purple border and bearing long, narrow, 1- to 2-septate conidia, is caused by *Cercospora aesculina* (*260*).

Another leaf disease of buckeye that may occur about the same time as the leaf blotch and is commonest on the leaves of sprouts is the powdery mildew *Uncinula flexuosa* (*1143*). The white, surface mycelium grows mostly on the undersides of leaves, and bears the exposed black perithecia (*1153*).

The fungus *Botryosphaeria ribis* (*550*), an active twig blight and canker organism on a few hardwoods (see *Cercis*), occurs on dead twigs of the yellow buckeye as a saprobe.

In the leaf scorch of the buckeyes that appears so commonly on street trees and has been attributed to heat and drought, there is a regular pattern of brown scorching that develops first near the leaf center and extends outward mainly between the veins. Air pollution should also be suspect as a possible cause of this widespread condition in urban environments.

Yellow buckeye is relatively free from fungus defects of the wood. Only *Polyporus squamosus* (*8*) and *Collybia velutipes* (*222*) have been specifically reported in connection with rot in living trees of this species, although doubtless many other sap rot fungi attack the dead wood.

Ruehle (*1224*) lists 5 species of nematodes in 5 genera, associated with yellow buckeye in Tennessee.

Red buckeye

Aesculus pavia

The red buckeye is a shrub or small tree (reaching a maximum height of about 30 ft.) that grows near the sea along the Atlantic Coastal Plain from southern Virginia to northern Florida, and from central Texas north into the Mississippi Valley in a strip through Oklahoma to southern Illinois (*872*). It grows mostly on wet sites, has handsome red flowers, and makes a fine ornamental in coastal areas. It spreads readily by underground runners (*274*). The seeds have some curious toxic and other medicinal properties, and an extract of them will stupefy fish (*279*).

Two varieties are recognized by Rehder (*1154*); one, *A. pavia* var. *atrosanguinea,* with dark red flowers; and the other *A. pavia* var. *humilis,* that grows very low and is sometimes prostrate.

The pathology of this species is much like that of *Aesculus glabra,* except that the leaf rust on *A. glabra* is known only on that tree. The diseases of the red buckeye that are annotated elsewhere are the leaf blotch (*Guignardia aesculi*)—see *A. octandra;* the gray leaf spot (*Cercospora aesculina*)—see *A. glabra;* and the buckeye powdery mildew (*Uncinula flexuosa*)—see *A. octandra. A. pavia* was rated very high in susceptibility to blotch at the Morton Arboretum in Illinois (*1013*). A leaf spot (*Mycosphaerella punctiformis*) that is very common on many hardwoods is reported from Georgia by Miller (*974*) on *A. pavia.*

Susceptibility to Texas root rot is rated as moderate (*1379*).

Ailanthus

Ailanthus altissima

The ailanthus, or "tree-of-heaven," is a native of China (*872*), and while not a desirable street tree, it has escaped cultivation and commonly occupies yards and other urban sites where few other trees could grow. It may be seen in towns and cities or along roadsides anywhere in the country except for the coldest parts of northern States and the West. It has very long compound leaves, and its staminate flowers have a disagreeable odor.

Ailanthus grows very rapidly, and can attain a height of 70 ft. The wood is weak and brittle, and the tree is messy in the fall and smelly in the summer. Rehder (*1154*) recognizes three varieties, based on color and habit of foliage. Ailanthus can withstand the droughts, pavement, heat, fumes, and other adverse factors common to cities. It prefers a neutral to alkaline soil (*1119*) and moderate winter temperatures. Large numbers of ailanthus trees have been planted for shelterbelt purposes in Texas and Oklahoma, and the tree has done fairly well there. In that area, Wright and Wells (*1627*) state that ailanthus appears to be one of the best of the tall tree species that can be recommended for growth on Texas root rot infested soil.

It is noteworthy that in Croxton's list of 37 tree species (*310*), arranged in order of susceptibility to damage from ice accumulation, the least susceptible of all was ailanthus. The 42 ailanthus trees observed suffered no damage in his study. This is a tribute, not to any particular strength of ailanthus wood, but to the absence of fine twigs on this species. Its thick, few-branched shoots present few foci about which ice can accumulate.

Ailanthus also was relatively uninjured following heavy salt spray associated with a New England hurricane (*1632*).

Along with the catalpa tree, ailanthus is among the few which annually shed some of their branches (*932*). It can send sprouts up from the roots (*1627*), a nuisance characteristic for farmers.

While many fungi have been reported as pathogenic to ailanthus, the tree suffers little from disease, and its pathology need rarely be a consideration in its culture.

Foliage Diseases.—The leaf fungi reported are anthracnose (*Gloeosporium ailanthi*) in the South; *Cercospora glandulosa,* widespread; *Phyllosticta ailanthi,* occasional on small, discrete,

63

round spots; and a smudgy, black, surface mildew (*Dimerosporium robiniae*).

The *Cercospora* spot occurs mostly in the South; its diameter varies from 1-6 mm.; it is grayish-brown to almost black, and often falls out, leaving the leaf ragged. The spores are acicular, with indistinct septa (*260*).

The petioles may bear the fungus *Leptothyrium petiolarum*, which has superficial, dark, shield-shaped pycnidia that contain hyaline, 1-celled conidia (*62*).

Stem and Vascular Diseases.—Many fungi inhabit dying and dead twigs and branches, but few of these are primary pathogens on ailanthus. Those which have this potential include *Botryosphaeria ribis* and its variety *chromogena* (*550*); two species of *Diplodia; Fusarium lateritium* (*1610*); *Nectria cinnabarina* (*1555*); *Nectria* sp. (probably *N. galligena*); *Phoma ailanthi; Physalospora obtusa*, which appears mostly in its conidial stage, called *Sphaeropsis ailanthi* as applied to ailanthus; and *P. rhodina*. Specific references to some of these fungi are not provided here because of their lack of impact on ailanthus culture.

If ailanthus can be said to be subject to a major disease it would be Verticillium wilt (*V. albo-atrum*). About 1936, many trees of this species were killed by this soil-borne wilt in Philadelphia, with the wood streaks and foliage wilt symptoms as described under *Acer saccharum* (*1119*). Rudolph (*1216*) gives a good account of this disease.

Root and Trunk Rots.—Some cases of shoestring root rot (*Armillaria mellea*) on ailanthus have been reported from New York (*1119*).

While this tree is rated as moderately susceptible to Phymatotrichum root rot in Texas (*1379*), it is considered one of the most satisfactory for planting in the southern parts of the Texas root rot belt. Wright and Wells (*1627*), in a tally of Texas root rot losses from 1937 to 1942, involving 25 tree species, found the average annual mortality loss for ailanthus to be only 0.4 percent.

The five additional wood decay fungi reported on ailanthus (*8*) are all typically rotters of dead wood, and their occurrence on living trees is thus largely associated with wounds. None are true heart rot fungi. *Daedalea ambigua* and *Fomes applanatus* can cause localized wound decay in *Ailanthus* (*1067*).

Mimosa-tree

Albizia julibrissin

This small, multistemmed tree, known in the United States as the mimosa-tree, and often listed as "silktree," is native from Iran to China (*872*), and has been widely planted in this country from Long Island, New York, to Florida and west to Texas and California. The first record of the cultivation of this tree in North America was in 1831 (*1411*). It grows rapidly, has graceful, fernlike leaves that fold at night or in the rain, and colorful flowers. It has escaped cultivation and has shown a remarkable capacity to thrive under unfavorable soil conditions. Individuals vary greatly in deepness of flower color and in hardiness. A hardy strain, var. *rosea* (*1154*),

64

will grow in southern New England, and two wilt-resistant varieties, var. *Charlotte*, with light colored flowers, and var. *Tryon*, with deeper red flowers (*503*), have been developed by Toole and Hepting (*1434*) and released to the nursery trade.

The mimosa-tree reproduces readily from seed or cuttings. Root pieces take root more readily than stem cuttings. Toole (*1410*) describes the rooting characteristics of mimosa-tree cuttings.

The normal life span of this tree is only about 50 years. The population of mimosa-trees has been literally eradicated from many cities and other areas of the South, as a result of a Fusarium wilt disease discovered in 1935 in Tryon, N. C. It has no other serious disease enemies, but it is often defoliated by the mimosa webworm, and sometimes girdled by rodents or by an accumulation of vine growth around the base of the trunk.

The only leaf disease of the mimosa-tree in this country is caused by *Cercospora glauca*, that produces an angular, dark brown spot 3-10 mm. in diameter, sometimes with a pale center. The conidia are produced on the underside of the leaf, are subhyaline to pale olive, linear, and multiseptate (*260*).

One disease, mimosa wilt (*Fusarium oxysporum* f. *perniciosum*), dominates the pathology of this species. In 30 years, the wilt has swept from one known center in North Carolina, over much of the tree's range, at least from New York and New Jersey to Florida, and west to Mississippi. The wilt is also known in Russia, Argentina, and Puerto Rico. Infection is through the roots; a dark wood ring forms, consisting of the gum-filled springwood vessels and xylem parenchyma of the last year's growth, and trees usually wilt and die within a year of symptom onset. There is no recovery. Hepting (*638*) first described the disease and its cause; Toole (*1409*) determined many phases of the biology of the fungus, and the development of the disease; and Gill (*502*) showed that either the nematode *Meloidogyne incognita* or *M. javanica* would facilitate infection by *F. oxysporum* f. *perniciosum*.

Toole and Hepting (*1434*) developed, by selection and propagation, lines of the mimosa-tree virtually immune to the wilt. After 25 years of exposure to wilt by first inoculation, and then being planted in the field around the stumps of wilt-killed trees, the two resistant varieties released to the nursery trade have stood up remarkably well (*503*). However, Gill (*504*) found that several trees of cultivar *Tryon* ultimately died of wilt at Tifton, Georgia, and one tree of the other named cultivar, *Charlotte*, showed unmistakable evidence of wilt at Winder, Georgia, where trees of cultivar *Tryon* remained unaffected. It is surprising to none who work with Fusarium wilts that sooner or later lines of this wilt fungus would appear that could wilt the selections made and distributed. Boyce (*151*) and Gill (*504*) both point out that breeding trees against lethal pathogens virtually requires achieving complete, sustained immunity, and this compounds the breeding and progeny testing problems.

Different races of the wilt *Fusarium* attack *Albizia julibrissin* and *A. procera* (*1413*). In inoculation experiments (*1409*), *A. lophantha*, grown as an ornamental in California, and the white-flowered *A. kalkora* were very susceptible to the wilt; *A. lebbek* succumbed to one line of the fungus; and *A. thorelii* and *A. pudica* seemed immune. In addition to testing these species of *Albizia*, Toole (*1409*) also inoculated seedlings of the native leguminous species *Cercis canadensis, Gleditsia triacanthos* and *Robinia pseudoacacia,* and failed to induce the wilt in them.

Fusarium oxysporum f. *perniciosum* rarely produces its salmon-colored sporodochia on diseased trees, but other fusaria, notably *F. lateritium,* will commonly produce similar sporodochia erupting from the bark of trees dying of wilt or other causes, often while the bark is still green. These and several other fungi that fruit on the mimosa-tree mainly as saprobes are described by Snyder, Toole, and Hepting (*1329*).

A limb canker has been attributed by Fowler and Stevenson (*475*) to *Nectria cinnabarina.* The coral-colored sporodochia of the imperfect stage, *Tubercularia vulgaris,* have appeared around these lesions. In addition, Fowler, Stevenson and others (*8, 1329*) have reported, on mimosa-trees, several other fungi that are not regarded as pathogens.

Injured or wilt-infected mimosas, or their senescent or dead branches, may support the yellow, pycnidial stromata or the clustered, brown perithecia of *Thyronectria austro-americana,* which contain muriform ascospores. This fungus causes a vascular wilt of *Gleditsia japonica,* a canker disease of *G. triacanthos* (*1270*), and is weakly pathogenic to *Albizia julibrissin.*

The common hardwood twig and branch fungus *Botryosphaeria ribis* (*Dothiorella gregaria*) (*550*), that is an aggressive canker-former on some hardwoods, notably *Cercis canadensis,* appears as a saprobe on *Albizia.*

Although *Physalospora rhodina,* a common fungus with a *Diplodia* conidial stage, and stoutly elliptical 2-celled conidia, has fruited on dead branches of the mimosa-tree, it has not been aggressive on this host, as it has on many crop plants around the world (*1484*).

Two species of *Septobasidium* (*S. castaneum* and *S. leprieurii*) produce brown felts over scale insects on branches and stems (*292*).

A root rot of the mimosa-tree caused by *Ganoderma* (*Polyporus*) *curtisii* has occurred in Louisiana, that Edgerton (*403*) considered responsible for wilting and killing. This fungus has a "varnished" top to its pileus, and differs from *Polyporus lucidus* (*Ganoderma lucidum*) mainly in always having a stipe, and in the bright ochraceous color of the pileus top. E. R. Toole [11] killed 50 percent of a set of mimosa-tree seedlings, within 3 years, by inoculation with *Polyporus lucidus,* and 75 percent within 5 years. Attempts by Toole (*1429*) to kill mimosa-trees by inoculation with *Corticium galactinum* were unsuccessful.

Rhoads reports killing by Clitocybe root rot (*C. tabescens*) in Florida (*1168*), and Raabe (*1141*) reported attack by *Armillaria mellea* in California.

Gill (*502*) reported on two species of *Meloidogyne* attacking roots and stunting mimosa-tree seedlings, and has records of additional species of this genus that infest the roots of this tree. *Paratylenchus projectus* and *Pratylenchus crenatus* have also been identified from the root zones of mimosa-trees in New Jersey (*1222*).

---

[11] Personal communication from E. Richard Toole, formerly pathologist, USDA Forest Service, now at Mississippi State University, State College, Miss.

Miller (*976*) reported a witches' broom of this tree in Georgia that resembled the virus-caused brooming disease of *Robinia* (*529*).

Lebbek

Albizia lebbek

The lebbek is called "woman's tongue" in the tropics because of the chattering sound made by the large pods in the wind. Introduced to the Florida Keys from Egypt about 1900, this tree is probably native to tropical Asia (*872*). It escaped cultivation in south Florida and now occurs generally in that area of the State. Its leaflets and pods are much larger than those of *Albizia julibrissin*, the mimosa-tree. The pods are particularly high in tannin. The tree is not only a showy ornamental, but its white, soft wood offers a prospect for tropical hardwood forestry in south Florida. While lebbek will grow under a wide range of soil conditions, it is not hardy and will not survive more than occasional freezing temperatures.

Lebbek has proved susceptible to Fusarium wilt (*F. oxysporum* f. *perniciosum*) in inoculations. This disease is described under *A. julibrissin*. While one isolate of the fungus wilted all trees inoculated, another failed to wilt any (*1409*). Some trees developed streaking of the last sapwood ring, but did not wilt. Lebbek is thus regarded as less susceptible than most of the species of *Albizia* tested by Toole (*1409*). No reports of wilting of lebbek in the field have yet been recorded, even though mimosa-trees have been dying of Fusarium wilt in Florida for many years.

A rust, *Sphaerophragmium acaciae* (*930*), is common in Florida, but is of no importance to the vigor or appearance of the tree. It produces small, yellow-green spots 0.5 to 1 mm. in diameter, on the upper leaf surface, and uredia and telia on the lower surface. Sori sometimes occur in concentric rings. Pods may also have small rust spots. The teliospores are light brown, 4- to 8-celled, and have ornate, spiny appendages.

The algal leaf spot caused by *Cephaleuros virescens* develops into a green scurf as velvety, reddish-brown to orange, cushionlike patches form. If the bright.sporangia do not form, the spots may appear greenish or brownish as a result of the dense, hairy processes (*1555*).

Rhoads (*1168*) reports killing by Clitocybe root rot (*C. tabescens*) in Florida.

The burrowing nematode *Radopholus similis* and the root rot nematode *Meloidogyne* sp. have been identified in roots of lebbek in Florida (*1222*).

Tung

Aleurites fordii

The tung tree, native to central and western China, where it has been planted since antiquity, was introduced into the United States in 1905. It produces one of the best oils for paint, linoleum, and printer's ink, and is now grown in a belt 75 to 100 miles wide, from northern Florida and southern Georgia to southern Louisiana, with the principal production centers highly localized. The tree can be grown satisfactorily in some localities north of the current tung belt, but commercial oil production is only feasible in the belt. Potter and Crane (*1130*) give an excellent account of tung production in this country.

The tree grows rapidly to a maximum height of about 40 ft., and when mature is likely to be as broad as tall. It has wide, dark green leaves, and in early spring its clusters of whitish, often tinted flowers are very attractive. Longevity is only about 30 years.

The tung tree has been recommended for street planting in California (*947*).

Tung is very exacting in climatic and soil requirements, needing uniformly warm days and nights, at least 45 in. of rainfall, evenly spaced over the year, and winter chilling for 350 to 400 hours at temperatures of 45° F. or lower. Trees in good condition and thoroughly dormant can withstand temperatures close to 8° F. Once trees have been stimulated to activity, they are very cold-sensitive and liable to injury by ground temperatures of 23 to 28° F. (*1130*). Tung requires soils that are deep, well-drained and well-aerated, and easily penetrated by roots. Slightly acid, sandy loams are best.

In general, tung is not bothered much by diseases involving pathogens. It is, however, subject to several mineral deficiencies, a few fungus leaf diseases, one major root rot, a bark virus, and a number of other minor tree problems as well as some diseases of the nuts.

Foliage Diseases.—Zinc deficiency results in uneven growth, sickle-shaped leaves with a loss of color between veins (*1130*). Copper deficiency (in Florida) results in chlorosis, dwarfing, "cupping," and marginal burn (*379*). Manganese deficiency results in "frenching," which is a narrowing, thickening, and crinkling of leaves (*378*). Leaf composition as it is related to the mineral nutrition of tung in the United States is described by Drosdoff (*394*).

The main fungus diseases are an angular leaf spot (*Mycosphaerella aleuritidis*) and thread blight (*Pellicularia koleroga*). The first causes reddish to almost black, irregular spots 6 to 10 mm. in diameter, and probably occurs wherever tung is grown. Its imperfect stage is *Cercospora aleuritidis* (*260*). The second, which goes also under the synonym *Corticium stevensii*, kills foliage and the leaves are left hanging by fungus threads (*1130, 1408*).

Pellicularia filamentosa (*Corticium microsclerotia*) causes web blight, a seedling disease of occasional occurrence. Forms of this fungus attack a wide range of plants, first producing spots that enlarge and have a scalded appearance, and then the whitish mycelium grows over the leaves, petioles, and other exposed organs, killing them (*1555*).

Southern root rot (*Pellicularia rolfsii*) sometimes blights seedlings, appearing first as a white weft around the base of a plant. The weft may eventually form a crust with embedded brownish sclerotia (*1555*).

A ring spot (*Mycosphaerella websteri*) first appeared in epidemic proportions on the leaves of young seedlings in Mississippi in 1960. Its imperfect stage is *Cercospora websteri*. The spots were

68

large, concentric zones, often confluent, and produced abundant conidia (*1467*).

Other minor leaf diseases include a bacterial spot (*Pseudomonas aleuritidis*) ; the common Glomerella spot and blight (*G. cingulata* (*1483, 1555*) ; an anthracnose import, *Gloeosporium aleuriticum* (*1337*) ; and a *Phyllosticta* that is probably the spermatial stage of the angular spot fungus *Mycosphaerella* (*Cercospora*) *aleuritidis* (*260*).

Stem Diseases.—A black, sunken rot canker (*Physalospora rhodina*) has killed young trees back almost to the ground line in several nurseries. The following spring, the killed shoots were ashen-colored and bore perithecia of the perfect stage, (imp. stage *Diplodia theobromae, D. natalensis*) (*831*). Voorhees (*1484*) gives a fine account and illustrations of the life history and taxonomy of this fungus.

A twig and stem canker and dieback caused by *Botryosphaeria ribis* (*550, 1352*), which has perithecia resembling the *Physalospora,* also has been reported occasionally attacking tung in several States. This disease, as it affects the sister tung species *Aleurites montana* in Nyasaland, is described by Wiehe (*1579*).

Additional stem diseases include a branch canker caused by the angular leaf spot fungus (*260*), a *Cephalosporium* (*8*) involved in a problem called "collar girdle," and a surface brown felt that forms over scale insects caused by *Septobasidium pseudopedicellatum* (*292*).

Root Diseases.—The main root disease is the rot caused by *Clitocybe tabescens* (*1168*). Attacks have originated from the stumps of native trees being rotted by this fungus. New orchards attacked by *C. tabescens* have suffered the loss of many trees (*1130*). The fungus kills the cambium of the root collar, producing mycelial fans under the bark, and rots the roots. Its habit of working out from hardwood stumps, killing by rotting roots and by cambial necrosis, and even many elements of the morphology of the fungus, are similar to *Armillaria mellea*. However, the mushroom lacks an annulus and the fungus lacks the flat, black rhizomorphs of *A. mellea*.

Tung is somewhat susceptible to Texas root rot (*1379*) and to *Phytophthora cinnamomi* (*1659*), and seedlings can be attacked by root knot nematodes (*Meloidogyne* sp.). These, however, are not important diseases in the tung belt.

Miscellaneous Pathology.—Several fungi attack the nuts (*8, 1130*), but this handbook does not deal with the diseases of orchard products.

A disease responsible for rough bark is caused by a virus. Large (*832*) describes and illustrates "rough bark." A light, bronze bark discoloration is followed by small, widely-spaced blisters. Later the bark turns dark and cracks into small, irregular segments.

The condition known as "wetwood" (*603*), in which bacteria multiply enormously in the vessels, producing a very alkaline condition of the wood, sometimes breaks through the bark to form a slime flux in tung trees. Wetwood shortens the life of many of the trees affected.

The few wood-rot fungi reported on tung in this country are wound saprobes or scavengers of moribund or dead parts of trees, and are not factors in the pathology of tung.

Red alder
Alnus rubra

The red, or Oregon, alder is the most abundant and most useful hardwood of the Pacific Coast region. Growing from Alaska south along the coast to Santa Barbara, California, these trees are common features on moist slopes or in stream bottoms, occurring typically in groups, sometimes intermixed with conifers (*279*). Red alder sprouts vigorously. It is not found on bottoms subject to consistent overflow (*1614*).

Red alder is used as a nurse crop for more valuable species, since it is short-lived, fire-resistant although thin-barked, and acts as a soil builder. Soil under red alders, in mixture with conifers, had markedly higher levels of nitrate nitrogen than soil under a stand of pure conifers (Li, et al. (*860*)).

Red alders are also cultivated for shade and ornament. The tree self-prunes well in the forest. Longevity is generally under 100 years (*1614*). Abundant soil moisture and rich soil are requisite for optimum growth (*1367*). The general climatic conditions for red alder are termed humid to superhumid and are like those for *Abies grandis*. Its temperature extremes range from 0 to 105° F. Red alder requires full sunlight after its first 2 or 3 years.

There are nodules on the roots of the alders, which are reported to have a role in nitrogen fixation. The conclusion that the alder nodules contribute to soil nitrogen is supported by the work in Canada showing that under *Alnus rugosa* soil nitrogen may be built up at the rate of 150 kilograms per hectare per year (*1354*).

The cause of alder nodules was first wrongly attributed to the genus *Plasmodiophora*. Further investigation has shown that whereas legume nodules are caused by bacteria of the genus *Rhizobium*, the nodules on *Alnus*, *Eleagnus*, and *Myrica* are caused by actinomycetes (*1091*). The generic name, *Frankiella*, applied to these actinomycetes has been preempted by a fungus (*8*) ; and the name *Schinzia* (*1614*), also applied to the nodule organisms according to Ainsworth (*17*), is a *nomen dubium*—meaning a name of uncertain meaning or description.

Rodriguez-Barrueco and Bond (*1444*) refer to the alder nodule-inducing agents as simply "nodule endophytes," and point out that although inoculations were successful, using ground-up nodules, the endophytes themselves have never been grown in pure culture. They report that plant responses indicated that nodules induced by *Alnus rubra* inoculum were effective in nitrogen fixation.

The alders tend to have a pathology of their own. While some of the rot fungi and saprobes inhabiting dead wood and bark are common to many tree genera, most of the leaf pathogens attack only species of *Alnus*. Heart rot in trees over 40 years old is the major disease impact, according to Worthington (*1614*), who compiled the silvical characteristics of red alder.

The presentations at a symposium on the red alder, in 1967, have been published and provide a wealth of information on the biology of the alders (*1444*). Among the topics discussed, of special interest to the pathologist are the rhizosphere microflora, two types of ectotrophic mycorrhizae, nodule endophytes in the genus *Alnus*, the resistance of red alder to root rot infection by *Poria weirii,* a review of the relationship of *Hypoxylon fuscum* with *Alnus* in the Northwest, the requirement and role of cobalt in *Alnus rubra,* and deficiency symptoms and fertilizer effects on alder.

Foliage Diseases.—A large number of fungi produce spots and blotches on alder foliage, principally *Cercosporella alni; Gnomonia alni; Gnomoniella tubiformis* (on fading leaves only)—a fungus with at least 10 synonyms; *Hypospila californica (365)*; and *Septoria alnifolia (406)*. Shaw *(1278)* provides references to descriptions of all of these and also other alder fungi. None of the leaf pathogens are economically important.

Other leaf diseases are the common gray mold, *Botrytis cinerea (1555)*; the rust *Melampsoridium alni (46)*, with hypophyllous, cylindric aecia, and the *Larix* stages (II and III) unknown in North America; *Microsphaera alni (1153)*, a prodigious, ubiquitous, powdery mildew that strikes late in the season; and *Taphrina japonica (994)*, a typical leaf blister and curl that is known in North America only on red alder.

Stem Diseases.—While there is a very large fungus flora on the senescent and dead bark and wood of red alder *(1277)*, few of these organisms behave as primary pathogens.

Didymosphaeria oregonensis is associated with a trunk and branch canker of young trees of three species of alder in the Northwest. Goodding *(519)* describes and illustrates the canker and the fungus. The cankers form bands, often swollen, around stems on which the bark becomes rough. Dark perithecia, opening by a minute pore, appear around the active edges of lesions. They contain 8–spored asci, with 1–septate, greenish ascospores.

The "gluing fungus," *Hymenochaete agglutinans (151)*, in addition to cementing a dead branch to a living one and covering the bark with its yellow-margined brown felt, can kill the cambium beneath, forming a canker on the live branch. It also will rot dead sapwood.

Several species of *Nectria* have been reported on red alder *(1277)*. One that can form target cankers is the aggressive *N. galligena (47, 170)*. This fungus has at times been identified as *N. coccinea* or *N. ditissima (879)*. *N. episphaeria* on red alder and many other hardwoods, grows on the stromata of sphaeriaceous fungi, and is not a plant parasite. *N. cinnabarina,* with its characteristic large, coral sporodochia, is a secondary invader of dying twigs. Another saprobic species that occurs on dead alder bark is *N. (Creonectria) pithoides,* which is distinguished by the barrel shape of the red perithecia when dried *(1266)*.

Root and Trunk Rots.—A great many basidiomycetes and some ascomycetes rot the dead wood of red and other alders. With few exceptions, these are sapwood rots, wound rots, rots of dead parts of living trees, of slash, and of senescent and dead trees. While red alder remains quite free from rot when uninjured, up to an age approaching 40 years, it becomes very subject to decay thereafter. The important hardwood heart rotter *Fomes igniarius* is considered by many as the main cause of cull in these older trees *(1614)*, although a great many decay fungi have been collected from red alder *(1277)*.

Red alder is subject to root rot by *Armillaria mellea*, but this is not a major disease. This alder was also highly susceptible to Texas root rot in Texas tests (*1379*), but the tree could not be grown in the root rot belt of the Southwest anyway.

Hypoxylon fuscum causes a white rot (see *A. tenuifolia*).

Mycorrhizae are known to be formed by *Cenococcum graniforme* (*1442*).

Root nodules possibly caused by an actinomycete have been already mentioned. Becking (*86*) has succeeded in cultivating alder root-nodule tissue containing the endophyte.

Miscellaneous Pathology.—The catkins of alders have long been known to have an interesting fungus flora of their own. *Taphrina occidentalis* and *T. amentorum* both cause tonguelike enlargements of the bracts of female catkins (*994*), with the latter causing the greater enlargement.

Ciboria alni on overwintering seeds and *C. amentacea* on fallen catkins are *Sclerotinia*-like discomycetes. An excellent, illustrated account of this group of fungi is provided by Whetzel (*1559*).

Sitka alder

Alnus sinuata

The Sitka alder, considered a uniquely distinct species by Sudworth (*1367*), is mostly a shrub in the Pacific Northwest, reaching tree size only as it approaches Alaska. It extends into the United States in an area from Washington to western Montana, south to northeastern and western Oregon and northern California (*872*). It grows in moist bottoms and lower courses of mountain streams and boggy flats, mostly in humus-covered and rich, but rocky, soils. It grows mainly at elevations above 3,000 ft. in the Northwest.

There is much similarity in pathology between Sitka alder and the other alder species. For example, among the more common pathogens annotated under *Alnus rubra* the following also occur on *A. sinuata*: the leaf spot fungi *Cercosporella alni; Septoria alnifolia;* and *Gnomoniella tubiformis,* the last a fungus with a *Septoria*-like stage that develops on attached leaves and forms a perfect stage on fallen leaves; and the common powdery mildew *Microsphaera alni.*

The Septoria spot (*S. alnifolia*) was reported particularly abundant on Sitka alder in central Idaho in 1942, although not previously reported from Idaho (*406*).

Among the stem fungi annotated under *Alnus rubra*, the following are known to have a similar habit on *A. sinuata*: *Didymosphaeria oregonensis, Nectria galligena,* and *N. cinnabarina.*

Fomes igniarius is considered the main cause of heart rot south of the Canadian border; and *Cenococcum graniforme* the only reported mycorrhiza-former (*1442*).

The catkins develop tonguelike projections as a result of infection by *Taphrina occidentalis*, and the roots develop nodules as described under *Alnus rubra.*

A few leaf spots, twig saprobes, and rot fungi occur on Sitka alder, particularly in Alaska, that do not occur on the other species of *Alnus*, but they are of only mycological interest.

Baxter (*82*) considers that *Poria ferrea* causes more rot in Sitka alder in Alaska than does *Fomes igniarius*.

Thinleaf alder

Alnus tenuifolia

The thinleaf alder is a tree of the heads of mountain streams, boggy slopes, gulches, high meadows, and lakes, in mucky but stony situations, mainly with saturated soil, from Alaska and British Columbia, south through the Rocky Mountains to northern New Mexico (*1367*). Another southward extension from British Columbia runs through eastern Washington and Oregon and close to the headwaters of streams along the western slopes of the Sierra Nevada to central California, mainly at 6,000 to 7,000 ft.

The tree is small, often shrubby, and seldom exceeds 30 ft. in height and 5 in. in diameter. Sudworth (*1367*) records maximum ages of approximately 40 years and mentions this tree's need for full sunlight. One variety, *occidentalis*, is recognized (*1154*), based largely on foliage characters.

To present a separate account of the diseases of thinleaf alder would be unduly repetitious. Of nine of the leaf fungi mentioned under *Alnus rubra*, five are known to occur on *A. tenuifolia*, the exceptions being the *Cercosporella, Hypospila, Botrytis,* and *Taphrina* leaf species that occur on *A. rubra*, but have not been reported from *A. tenuifolia*.

Similarly, all of the stem fungi mentioned under *A. rubra* have been observed on *A. tenuifolia* excepting *Nectria galligena* and *N. pithoides;* and the same is true of all of the root fungi, mycorrhizae, and tubercle organisms except that *Armillaria mellea* and the *Ciboria* species on *A. rubra* seeds and catkins, are not known on *A. tenuifolia*.

From the published accounts available (*8, 1277*), no economic or noteworthy pathogens occur on *A. tenuifolia* that have not already been mentioned under *A. rubra*.

Hypoxylon fuscum is a widely distributed inhabitant of *Alnus* spp. throughout the North Temperate Zone. It causes a rapid white-type rot of the wood of dead or dying alders. It is probably a weak parasite, possibly contributing to the killing of trees. It has been studied in detail by Rogers (*1444*), especially on *Alnus tenuifolia*.

Cenococcum graniforme forms mycorrhizae with thinleaf alder (*1442*).

Serviceberry

Amelanchier spp.

The members of this genus have many common names, mostly serviceberry, juneberry, or shadbush. Little (*872*) recognizes seven American species, and a glance at the synonymy of these species shows the confusion that has been typical of nomenclature in this genus. For example, 23 botanical names have been applied just to *Amelanchier utahensis*. The species of *Amelanchier* discussed here grow chiefly in low, moist situations and near streams. With respect to *Amelanchier* pathology, attention here is given only to the four species mentioned below.

Amelanchier alnifolia, the saskatoon or western serviceberry, is typically a shrub, but grows to 30 ft. in height and 8 in. in diameter on its best sites (*1367*). It thrives in alluvial bottoms, prairies, benches, and mountain meadows on good and poor soil, from western Minnesota northwest to Alaska, and westward to southern Oregon, Utah, and Colorado (*872*).

A. arborea, downy serviceberry, long known as *A. canadensis,* occurs widely throughout the East, from the Northeast and Lake States southward into Oklahoma, and across to northern Florida. Usually shrubby and irregular, reaching a maximum height of 30 ft., its main foliage characteristic is the dense tomentum on the underside of young leaves. *A. arborea* resisted salt-spray damage following a New England hurricane (*1632*).

A. florida, the Pacific serviceberry, grows from Alaska, along the Pacific Coast to western Washington and northwestern California. Mostly a shrub, under 30 ft. high, it has stout upright branches.

A. laevis, the Allegheny serviceberry, is a spreading, small tree, reaching 40 ft. in height. It is common throughout the East, from Maine through the Appalachian Mountains to Alabama, and scattered through the Lake States and Central States (*872*).

The pathology of species of *Amelanchier* is fairly simple, being dominated by the aecial stages of many species of *Gymnosporangium* rusts on fruits, stems, and leaves; a sooty fungus witches' broom; a fungus leaf blight; and the bacterial fire blight disease. The remainder of the pathogens on *Amelanchier* species are of little consequence and seldom reported.

A simple and effective means of presenting the information on the 13 *Gymnosporangium* species, their affinities and effects, is by reference to the United States Index of Plant Diseases (*8*), the supplemented edition of Arthur's rust manual (*46*), and Kern's *Lists and Keys of the Cedar Rusts of the World* (*784*). These rusts will therefore *not* be dealt with here. Almost half of the species of *Gymnosporangium* have their aecial stages on organs of *Amelanchier* species.

In considering other elements of *Amelanchier* pathology, it is obvious that far more is known about the diseases of the saskatoon serviceberry (*A. alnifolia*) than any of the other species. Therefore, in annotating the more important diseases, other than those caused by species of *Gymnosporangium,* we have considered them as referring to *A. alnifolia* except as otherwise noted. Indications will also be given of any susceptibility to these diseases on the part of *A. arborea* (*A. canadensis*), *A. florida,* and *A. laevis.*

Foliage Diseases.—The witches' broom caused by *Apiosporina collinsii* is both a twig disease and a leaf disease, and affects all four *Amelanchier* species. Perennial mycelium in the twigs results in shoot proliferation (brooming). An olive to black, sooty fungus growth develops on the underside of leaves, which bears globose, black perithecia in late summer (*1555*). The development and taxonomy of *A. collinsii* are described and illustrated by Kennedy and Stewart (*783*). They believe that the black knot fungus, *Dibotryon morbosum* (see *Prunus* spp.), should be placed in the genus *Apio-*

sporina, and find that the differences between *D. morbosum* and *A. collinsii* mainly concern the development and location of a stroma from which the ascocarps arise.

One of the effects of fire blight (*Erwinia amylovora*) is to cause a sudden wilting and blackening of the leaves (*619*). No other *Amelanchier* disease produces this effect. An association of blighting leaves, with the blossom blight, twig blight, or canker phases of this bacterial disease is often obvious (see *Malus*).

Another well-known leaf parasite that occurs on *Amelanchier alnifolia* is the powdery mildew *Erysiphe polygoni* (*619, 1153*), best known for its attack on legumes.

Fabraea maculata causes a common leaf and fruit spot, or blight, on pear, quince, *Amelanchier,* and other rosaceous plants (*1352, 1555*). The spots are first very small and purple, then enlarge up to ¼ in. and become brown. Later each bears a raised black dot, the acervulus, in the center. The conidia are distinctively cruciate, ciliate, and 4-celled.

Monilinia (*Sclerotinia*) *gregaria* produces a leaf spot and fruit rot in the West. Young leaves are attacked, the margins rolling upward so that the leaves may appear tubular. A *Monilia* stage forms on the inner surfaces. Later, after leaf fall, "mummies" form and produce tiny apothecia in the spring (*318*).

Other leaf spots have occasionally been reported, particularly with *Phyllosticta* stages on spots on attached leaves and with *Mycosphaerella* stages on fallen or overwintered leaves. Some connections between the spermatial, conidial, and perithecial stages of such species doubtless remain to be made.

Stem Diseases.—The common Apiosporina sooty witches' broom has been mentioned under leaf diseases. Another brooming disease is caused by *Taphrina amelanchieri* on *Amelanchier alnifolia* in California (*994*). A *Fusicladium* species has also been reported as forming witches' brooms on *A. alnifolia* in Washington (*8*).

Three stem fungi occur on the eastern species *Amelanchier arborea,* and to some extent on *A. laevis.* These include the common target canker fungus *Nectria galligena* (*170*), the saprobic *N. cinnabarina,* with its large coral-colored sporodochia, and the brown, funnel-shaped *Thelephora albido-brunnea,* that surrounds the stems and root collars of young trees, but does little harm. This species can be distinguished from the other dimidiate and reflexed species of *Thelephora* by its even and pale hymenium and its thick spongy pileus (*195*).

A disease called blister canker (*Nummularia discreta*) affects many rosaceous trees and a few others. It is a major apple disease as well as a disease of *Amelanchier alnifolia* east of the Rocky Mountains, especially in the valleys of the Mississippi and Missouri Rivers. It has killed thousands of trees. Cankers up to 3 ft. long form on limbs and stems. These lesions become mottled as a result of intermixed living and dead bark. The nailhead-like stromata that bear immersed, black perithecia appear scattered over the cankers. The stromata also bear hyphae that support the conidia (*1555*).

The bacterial fire blight (*Erwinia amylovora*), so serious on pear and apple, has been mentioned under leaf diseases. It also causes cankers, covered with bark that is shrunken, off-color, sometimes blistered, and with gum oozing out. Cracks are common around the edges of "holdover" cankers, and in wet weather, bacteria appear on the canker surface in pearly viscid drops. Fruit spurs often protrude from the centers of cankers (*1555*).

Tympanis amelanchieris, a twig fungus of *Amelanchier* species, repeatedly collected in Idaho, produces small, erumpent, gregarious apothecia that are cespitose, and mostly in groups of 2 to 8; typically grayish-pruinose to black. Illustrations and descriptions are provided by Groves (*552*).

A. alnifolia proved moderately susceptible to Texas root rot following inoculation (*1379*).

Fomes scutellatus can cause a wound rot in living trees, and *Daedalea unicolor* is a common saprobe on *Amelanchier* (*1067*).

Reports of mycorrhizae on *Amelanchier* are lacking.

Pacific madrone

Arbutus menziesii

One of the heath family, the madrone, or madrona, is one of the most common native trees of the Pacific Coast. It is a broadleafed evergreen, typically broad-crowned, often multiple-stemmed or misshapen, reaching a height of about 80 ft. on its best sites. The largest known one is 30 ft. 9 in. in circumference. Records of longevity are lacking but the species doubtless exceeds 100 years of age. Its silvical characteristics have been compiled by Tarrant (*1378*). Its range extends through the humid to superhumid areas of the West Coast from parts of Vancouver Island, British Columbia, to San Francisco, and in patches southward to the vicinity of Los Angeles. It also occurs along streams and in cool valleys and canyons (*1367*) in moist areas in the Sierra Nevada Mountains in northern California, up to an elevation of about 6,000 ft.

Madrone is tolerant (*54*), and is known to withstand temperature extremes between —6° to 115° F. Its soils are mostly slightly acid and with a wide range in texture. Once established, moisture requirements for madrone are not high, and the species is rated as drought-resistant (*1378*), resistant to high temperatures, and to wet, freezing conditions. It is sensitive to fire, and fire-killed trees often resprout from the roots. Its pathology is characterized by many leaf spots, a leaf rust, a spot anthracnose, a tar spot, and a basal canker, with only the canker seriously affecting its culture in occasional situations.

Foliage Diseases.—Many leaf fungi have been reported on madrone. Being an evergreen, the opportunities for fungus colonization of foliage in various stages of senescence are enhanced. *The United States Index of Plant Diseases* (*8*) describes many fungi, simply as "on leaves," and still others in association with a leaf disease. The latter include the fungi described below:

Ascochyta hanseni, leaf spot, common in California and Texas; with black pycnidia and hyaline, 1–septate, ellipsoid conidia, slightly constricted at the septum.

Cryptostictis arbuti (*1654, 1655*), leaf spot, common in Oregon and California. Spots irregular, becoming several centimeters in diameter, often involving most of the leaf; dark brown with purplish-black border. Spots fall out in angular pieces. Acervuli bear fusoid conidia, slightly curved, typically 5–celled, with a bristle at each end (*136*).

Didymosporium arbuticola, leaf spot. General. Spots brown with purplish to reddish margins, 3-6 mm. in diameter. Acervuli hypophyllous, with a grayish epiderm. Conidia ellipsoid, 1–septate but occasionally 3-septate, dark brown in mass. Zeller (*1654*) describes and illustrates this disease and fungus.

Elsinoë mattirolianum, spot anthracnose. Spots small, abundant, raised, and tending to fall out leaving a "shothole" condition. It produces a *Sphaceloma* imperfect stage and is particularly common in southern California on both *Arbutus unedo,* the strawberry tree (*752*), and *A. menziesii.*

Exobasidium vaccinii, red leaf spot and gall. General (*1654*). Small, red, blisterlike galls with spores packed in a dense layer on the underside. The galls may become sizable, bladderlike enlargements of soft tissue (*1555*).

Mycosphaerella arbuticola, leaf spot. General (*1654*). Spots are typically small, discrete, and abundant, with light centers and deeply hued margins. Spots bear subepidermal perithecia (on overwintered leaves) that are globose–lenticular with 8-spored asci, containing hyaline, ellipsoid, 2–celled spores. Sometimes this disease virtually defoliates madrone.

Phyllosticta fimbriata (*1278*), leaf spot. Common in California. Small spots bearing black pycnidia with 1-celled, hyaline conidia. May have a *Mycosphaerella* as its perfect stage.

Pucciniastrum sparsum (II, III), a rust with the 0 to I stages known only from Europe on *Picea excelsa* (*46*). Uredia and telia hypophyllous, on discolored spots on *Arbutus.* Teliospores in epidermal cells, singly or in a layer, ellipsoid, and vertically septate.

Rhytisma arbuti, speckled tar spot. General. Aggregated clusters of slightly raised, tarry-looking spots. One-celled, allantoid conidia produced in pycnidia early in the season. The swollen tissues later become sclerotia and may produce apothecia which contain long, narrow ascospores and paraphyses. Zeller (*1654*) considers this fungus the most common and damaging of the leaf diseases of madrone, particularly on overwintered, attached foliage.

Bonar (*135*) describes an irregular, dark brown leaf spot that can involve a major part of the leaf, that has a purplish black border. Spot tissue tends to fall out in irregular pieces. Conidia are borne in acervuli, and are fusoid, typically 5-celled, the end cells hyaline, and the others almost opaque. It is caused by *Disaeta arbuti.*

Stem Diseases.—The only stem disease important to madrone is a basal canker caused by *Phytophthora cactorum,* that also affects *Cornus nuttallii.* It is described by Stuntz and Seliskar (*1364*). First reported in the area around Seattle, Wash., it is now known to extend into California. Crowns thin because the new leaves may remain small, or turn brown and die. By the time these symptoms are obvious, extensive basal cankering has occurred. The lesions become evident as sunken areas with watersoaked-appearing bark. The bark becomes brown to purplish-black, and the outer sapwood also becomes discolored. A definite margin, and sometimes a crack, surrounds a canker. Cankers appear to originate at the ground line. A black liquid often oozes from the surfaces of the cankers.

Wagener and Cave (*1497*) mention upward canker extension in madrone, in a pattern of bluntly wedge-shaped areas of dead tissue. There are many similarities between the basal canker of madrone and the bleeding canker of maple (see *Acer saccharum*), and both are caused by the same organism. Inoculations on *Acer macrophyllum* (*1364*) produced symptoms similar to those on madrone, but the disease has not been reported on this western maple in nature.

A remarkably cryptose, nodose canker, characterized by many varied partly-healed, seamy, irregularly swollen-lipped lesions, has been found on madrone by W. W. Wagener in scattered locations in Sonoma and Mendocino Counties, California.[12] The cause is not known.

J. R. Parmeter[13] also reports a canker of madrone in California, occurring in long, narrow streaks that may extend for several feet along main branches. Infected bark becomes a dark, wine red, and the cambium beneath dies. Parmeter has isolated a *Phomopsis* sp. but has not yet demonstrated its pathogenicity.

Miscellaneous Pathology.—Shaw (*1277*) gives a very complete list of the rot fungi associated with madrone. Most of these fungi attack dead wood, but some cause true heart rot, in the sense of rotting the normal, inner wood of living trees. The list includes *Fomes igniarius, F. cajanderi* (*F. subroseus*), and *Poria subacida*. Most of the decay fungi that Shaw (*1277*) lists have been reported from British Columbia.

A small discomycete, *Aleurodiscus diffissus*, occurs harmlessly on the bark of madrone (*1278*).

Lemke (*858*) describes *Aleurodiscus macrocystidiatus* and *A. succineus* from the lower surface of dead branches of madrone. They are both saprobic.

A species of *Sebacina* will produce felts that may invest the bark of stems, but do no damage (*908*).

Madrone is rated moderately susceptible to Texas root rot (*1379*) following inoculation.

A decline disease of madrone in coastal Central California, first noted about 1925, has killed hundreds of trees since. Although W. W. Wagener[12] reports that the symptoms are much like those of the virus disease "quick decline" in California, sprouts from cut stumps appear normal. The cause is not yet known.

Yellow birch

Betula alleghaniensis

Most valuable of the American birches in amount, size, and usefulness, yellow birch reaches up to 100 ft. in height, 4 ft. in diameter (*4*) and 300 years in age (*500*). Rated intermediate in tolerance (*54*), it is the most tolerant of the birches. It is a tree of the cool, moist North, and the rich soils of the higher elevations of the

---

[12] Personal communication from W. Willis Wagener, deceased, formerly pathologist, USDA Forest Service, Pacific Southwest Forest and Range Experiment Station, Berkeley, Calif.

[13] Personal communication from J. R. Parmeter, plant pathologist, University of California at Berkeley.

eastern mountains, extending southward to Georgia. Its commercial range extends southward and eastward from Newfoundland, and includes northern New England, northern New York, and the upper parts of the Lake States.

Yellow birch is hardy, enduring temperature extremes from −40° to 100° F. It thrives on flats and lower slopes up to 2,500 ft. in elevation, in New York and New England, whereas it is an upper slope tree at elevations above 3,000 ft. in the southern Appalachians. Its soils are largely well-drained loams. Redmond (1148) experimentally demonstrated the strong predilection of yellow birch roots for loam as contrasted to sand.

The root system is typically shallow, giving a tendency to windthrow. The loose bark is highly flammable, and the main bark is easily killed by fire, logging impacts, or abrasion and other injuries. Godman (515) describes and illustrates a winter sunscald in yellow birch in Michigan. This condition is believed to be caused by rapid freezing of bark tissue after it has been unseasonably warmed by the sun.

Gilbert (500), who compiled the *Silvical Characteristics of Yellow Birch,* states, in connection with its weaknesses and enemies, that it may be described as a very sensitive tree.

Croxton's (310) list of species rated as to susceptibility to ice damage ranks yellow birch at the top; its injury is so severe because of the ice load that accumulates as a result of the abundance of fine twigs. Salt spray exposure in September manifested itself as late spring refoliation and dieback (1005).

According to Sparrow and Sparrow (1332), yellow birch was more sensitive to gamma radiation from a cobalt-60 source than most species of a group of 12 hardwoods and conifers tested (see *Picea glauca*).

The pathology of yellow birch is characterized chiefly by the following: birch dieback, post-logging decadence, Nectria canker, two species of *Poria* that rot the woody cylinder and are also often associated with cankers, and three species of *Fomes* (with *F. igniarius* by far the most important) that rot the heart of living trees.

Seedling Diseases.—Shigo and Yelenosky (1299) review what is known about the diseases and insects affecting yellow birch seeds and seedlings. Although the literature yielded little on the subject, they found a weevil that distorts and destroys a large percentage of the cones in New Hampshire, and a fungus species of *Coniothyrium,* probably *C. olivaceum,* associated with seedling chlorosis. The fungus occurs in and on the seed before it falls, and was particularly abundant on seeds in weevil-injured cones.

The generally low viability (0 to 34 percent) of yellow birch seed and related factors have been studied in Canada (1152) and in the United States (1).

Abnormal germination followed by twinning can occur.

Foliage Diseases.—A rust, *Melampsordium betulinum* (II, III), occurs on the underside of leaves with the internal telia forming a slightly raised crust that is at first yellow, and later is very dark. The rust is common locally in moist situations in the North, but rarely damaging.

Two common powdery mildews, *Microsphaera alni* and *Phyllactinea guttata* (1153, 1555), appear on leaves, particularly sprout foliage, midway or later through the growing season.

Taphrina carnea (*994*), a fungus widely distributed on birch in Europe as well as eastern North America, causes thickened, yellowish to red, leaf-curl lesions. Although an unnamed species of *Taphrina* (*8*) has been reported causing a leaf blister on yellow birch in New England, Mix (*994*) does not mention it in his *Taphrina* monograph.

Two other leaf diseases sometimes spot the foliage late in the growing season, the anthracnose (*Gloeosporium betulae-luteae*) and a small spot (*Septoria betulicola*).

A very distinctive yellow line pattern (*1273*), sometimes aptly called "tiger stripe," is a manifestation of a virus in the foliage. It is considered likely that the virus involved causes known diseases of other hosts, some of which are non-woody.

Stem Diseases.—Nectria canker (*N. galligena*) (*47, 170*) is the most damaging stem disease of yellow birch. The heavily cankered hardwood stands that Spaulding (*1335*) urged be converted to softwoods were mostly yellow birch. There is abundant literature on this disease (*151*), with some of the more important early papers that dealt with its attack on eastern hardwoods using the names *N. coccinea* or *N. ditissima* (*1340*) for the cause. Lohman and Watson (*879*) ultimately established the proper nomenclature for many American Nectria species. The "target" Nectria cankers on birch expose ridges of bare wood, and many bear their perithecia in bark crevices around the canker edges (*639*). Lortie (*888*) produced perithecia of *N. galligena* in culture. He has also stressed that this fungus can cause a twig blight and subsequent crown dieback—conditions seldom attributed to it in the past.

Nectria cinnabarina (*1555*) is a saprobe on dead bark and wood, and its coral sporodochia are characteristic. *N. mammoidea*, which produces red perithecia on bark and wood not associated with cankers, also occurs as a saprobe on yellow birch in New England (*879, 1266*).

Hypoxylon mammatum (*H. pruinatum*) (*978*) that causes a major killing disease of *Populus* spp. (*36*) also is known to produce cankers on yellow birch in the Lake States. The fruiting-bodies are small, crustlike growths of a few millimeters in diameter, which form on cankered bark, and bear a grayish bloom of spores when young.

The so-called "gluing fungus," *Hymenochaete aggulutinans*, will spread from a dead branch to a living one, cementing the two together with its mycelium and brown felt, and often producing a girdling lesion on the living stem (*151*).

Bleeding canker (*Phytophthora cactorum*) (*717, 987*) produces long, dark, often narrow trunk lesions that exude a red to black liquid (see *Acer saccharum*).

A witches' broom of yellow birch in New England is caused by the subcuticular, perennial mycelium of *Taphrina americana* (*994*).

The heart rot fungus *Stereum murrayi* can cause elongated cankers with depressed centers and with the bark remaining attached (*342*). Cankers can also result from trunk infection by *Poria laevigata* (*Fomes igniarius* var. *laevigatus*) (*214*). The common trunk rot fungus *Poria obliqua* produces only sterile clinkerlike conks on living trees (*208*), emerging from cankerlike wounds with swollen edges. These two *Poria* cankers are referred to later in the discussion of trunk rots of yellow birch. Another of these so-called canker-rot fungi affecting yellow birch is *Daedalea unicolor* (*205*). Its effects are described under *Acer saccharum*.

Large burls of unknown origin form on the trunks and provide unusual figured wood (*887*).

Arnold (*45*) describes, from the Northeast, a canker and twig blight of yellow birch caused by a new fungus species, *Diaporthe alleghaniensis*. Greenwood shoots blacken toward the ends, and expanded leaves have blackened areas on veins and petioles. In August living shoots have cream-colored discolorations of periderm. Later, many depressed cankers form at nodes. Some girdle, others develop late callus. The bark adheres to the wood. The fungus is the only species of *Diaporthe* known on yellow birch and is distinguished by the narrow, cylindrical ascus with truncate apex and by the narrow, cylindric-ellipsoid ascospores with variable position of the single septum.

Root Diseases.—The ubiquitous *Armillaria mellea* causes a common, soft, white root rot, with black zone lines in the rotted wood and black rhizomorphs on the roots. A unique manifestation of this rot in New Hampshire on yellow birch is what Shigo (*1295*) calls "collar crack." Vertical cracks, from a few inches to several feet long, develop at the bases of yellow and paper birches. They weaken a tree, leading to windthrow, or even girdle it, resulting in chlorotic foliage and then death. Shigo concluded that *A. mellea* rots the upper roots and butt, and then the cracks form, and finally some of the main trunk rotters, for example, *Pholiota* species, *Fomes igniarius* and its variety *laevigatus,* and *Poria obliqua,* continue to decay the trunk after *A. mellea,* strictly a root and butt decayer, has rotted as far as it can extend.

Although much is known about the trunk rots of yellow birch, little is reported concerning root rots other than that caused by *A. mellea. Polyporus spraguei* and *Poria subacida* are among those additional fungi known to rot roots and butts of this species.

Redmond (*1149*) intensively studied the roots of yellow birch, their sensitiveness to temperature changes, the condition and flora of the rootlets, and their mycorrhizae. Five species of phycomycetes, including the known mycorrhizal fungi *Mortierella alpina* and *Endogone spragnophila,* and a large number of other fungi were isolated from the rootlets, including the mycorrhizae. Redmond illustrates normal and collapsed yellow birch mycorrhizae.

Athough Trappe's review (*1442*) mentions reports of mycorrhizae on many species of *Betula*, there is no listing of such fungi specifically on *B. alleghaniensis. Cenococcum graniforme* has been reported on this species (*1441*).

The phanerogamic root parasite *Comandra umbellata* sometimes attaches itself to the roots of sweet birch and yellow birch, but does little damage. It has small, alternate, entire, mostly sessile leaves on stems less than a foot high, with small panicles of whitish flowers.

Trunk Rots.—Although a great many fungi can rot yellow birch wood (*8*), most of them decay only dead wood. Some, while mainly saprobic, can extend some distance into the heart or inner wood of living trees. These include mainly *Fomes applanatus, F. fomentarius, F. pinicola, Polyporus betulinus,* and *P. lucidus.*

The principal economic trunk rot fungi in the United States appear to be *Fomes igniarius* and its resupinate variety *laevigatus* (syn. *Poria laevigata*), *Pholiota* spp., *Polyporus hispidus, Poria obliqua, Stereum murrayi,* and the root and butt rotter *Armillaria mellea.* All of the major birch decays are described in standard forest pathology texts (*81, 151, 725*), and their mycological characteristics and keys to their identification provided mainly by Overholts (*1067*), Baxter (*81*), and the papers of Josiah Lowe and his associates.

Basham and Morawski (*73*), working in Ontario, found rot cull in yellow birch to reach 10 percent of the merchantable volume by age 130 years, and 17 percent by age 170. Cull from staining was about twice that from rot in most of the older age classes. By far the commonest decay fungus was *Stereum murraii* (sic.), followed by *Pholiota adiposa, Fomes igniarius* and its variety *laevigatus, F. fomentarius,* and *Flammula alnicola.*

True, Tryon, and King (*1453*) describe the cankers, rots, and sporophores produced by *Poria laevigata* (*Fomes igniarius* var. *laevigatus*) and *Poria obliqua* on mature yellow birch in West Virginia. *P. laevigata* causes large, irregular cankers on large trees. They are always bark-covered and lack any distinct callusing at the margins. Sterile, hard, dark, cracked, mycelial mats often form on dead branches, over the canker face, and on dead trees. Campbell and Davidson (*214*) established that such birch cankers and decay, and the fruiting of this brown, perennial, resupinate fungus after death of the tree, all are manifestations of *P. laevigata.* They also inoculated yellow birch and sweet birch with this fungus and produced typical infection.

Poria obliqua produces the protruding, sterile, clinkerlike masses on wounds or cankers with protruding, swollen edges so commonly seen on the birches. Campbell and Davidson (*208*) also established the connection attributing the sterile conk fungus and its heart rot to *Poria obliqua,* which fruits only on dead or down trees that had been undergoing decay while alive by the clinker fungus. The sporophores of *P. obliqua* are also brown, but differ in many ways from *P. laevigata* including being thin, annual, and having much larger pores than the latter (*1453*).

The three articles referred to in the preceding two paragraphs should be consulted with respect to questions concerning the heart rots of birch, since they go into considerable detail on the characteristics of the conks, rots, and sterile fungus tissues of these two common and interesting birch fungi. Spaulding, Hepting, and Westveld (*1343*) pointed out that a sterile conk of *Poria obliqua* (erroneously referred to as *Fomes nigricans* at that time) on a living yellow birch in New England meant that the tree was from 50 to 100 percent cull, and the later work of True, Tryon, and King (*1453*) in West Virgina bore out these findings.

Lavallee and Lortie (*840*) found that, in Quebec, although broken branches and branch stubs were indicators of internal defect, mechanical injuries were more important indicators of decay. They developed a "pathological classification" of yellow birch based on external evidence of internal decay and discoloration.

Fungi capable of causing either rot of the central cylinder or rot at wounds of living *Betula* spp. include *Fomes connatus, F. robustus, Polyporus spraguei,* and *P. squamosus (1067).*

In Ontario, many fungi were found to cause decay in living yellow birch that have not been reported in this connection in the United States *(73).* By far the leading cause of cull there was *Stereum murraii* (sic.), followed by *Pholiota adiposa, Fomes igniarius,* and *Flammula alnicola.* In all, 23 hymenomycetes were isolated more than once. Rot cull reached 22 percent and stain deduction 33 percent by age 260 years.

The New England paper *(1343)* presents additional suggestions for estimating cull in yellow birch where such indications as conks, sterile conks, butt scars, seams, and rotten knots are in evidence.

Shigo *(1290)* studied the fungi surrounding, and in advance of, rot columns of *Fomes igniarius* in living trees and found that a high-pH "wetwood" zone surrounded the columns and that several non-hymenomycetous fungi and certain bacteria colonized the surrounding area. The fungi were mostly species of *Phialophora, Trichocladium,* and *Acrostaphylus.*

Shigo *(1288)* stressed the importance of logging wounds as major courts of infection for decays and extensive discolorations in northern hardwoods, and presented external and internal views of logging scars and their effects on yellow birch.

Miscellaneous Pathology.—The biggest impact yet suffered by yellow and paper birch was noticed first in the 1930's in the Maritime Provinces of Canada, and is referred to as birch dieback. It appeared in an ever-widening area southward and westward through Maine, New Hampshire, Vermont, and into New York *(661).* Thousands of square miles of birch stands, mostly yellow birch, were destroyed and yet extensive research has failed to establish the cause. A full account of this sudden decline is provided by Clark and Barter *(266).* First the foliage becomes thin, with chlorotic or curled leaves at the shoot tips. Twigs then become bare because of lack of sufficient vigor to refoliate. Then branches and parts of the crown die, below which a bunching of foliage develops that tends to be confined to the lower crown. Death usually takes place within 3 to 5 years after the onset of symptoms *(1149).*

In the course of the research on birch dieback, some seemingly minor virus diseases were discovered. However, one virus disease was shown to be able to debilitate young birch trees, and it has been considered as the possible triggering mechanism to the dieback, with insects, climatic factors, and environmental influences then taking over and causing the main damage *(97).*

René Pomerleau, with long experience as a forest pathologist in Quebec, Canada, recently visited the author and presented the following explanation for this widespread decline of birch. He states that, (1) most yellow and paper birch trees are shallow-rooted, (2) long winter periods without snow occurred in 1923, 1932, 1938, 1942, and 1943 at least in the area around Quebec City and probably much more generally, and (3) that the freezing of birch roots, in the absence of snow cover over the soil, results in both rootlet breakage associated with soil heaving, and the failure of roots in frozen soil to absorb sufficient moisture to compensate for evaporation from stem and shoots. Deeply-rooted species, Pomerleau maintains, can absorb moisture from below the solid "ice lens," and thus show minimal effects from soil freezing in the absence of snow.

The above account is a paraphrasing and abridgement of a much longer account sent by Pomerleau following his visit, but it records his point of view, which is at variance with the published views of others, as an explanation for birch dieback. Pomerleau concludes with the statement, "Since 1946 young birch trees are growing normally and older trees not heavily affected have recovered." This "frozen soil" theory is presented as Pomerleau's, to complete the record on the nature of the genesis of birch dieback. He supports the common view that the bronze birch borer, root rot fungi and other agents attacking birch during the dieback sequence, are most likely secondary invaders.

The syndrome of birch dieback is not greatly different from that of post-logging decadence, in which hardwoods decline as a result of stand opening (582). The rate and seriousness of this decline are in proportion to the intensity of the cut. The heavier the volume cut, the heavier the mortality of residual trees. However, while birch dieback spreads to envelop and destroy over a huge area, post-logging decadence is a localized decline.

A condition called wetwood, common to many genera of trees, generally results from massive bacterial invasion of the woody cylinder, or infection by *Torula ligniperda,* usually producing an alkaline state of the wood. The effects of wetwood on tree health are complicated, and for some species are not known (603). Dark discoloration accompanies wetwood in the birches, and an alkaline wetwood zone appears in advance of some birch heart rots (1290).

A study of defects following increment boring (669) included yellow birches in the Northeast, the Lake States, and Pennsylvania. The mean vertical extent of the red-brown discoloration that invariably followed varied from 29 in. in Pennsylvania to 84 in. in the Lake States. From 20 to 25 percent of the borings led to decay that extended mostly from 13 to 16 in. vertically from the holes.

The succession of mold and stain fungi that develop on yellow birch pulpwood in New Hampshire is described, and the organisms identified, by Shigo (1286). *Ceratocystis coerulescens* was usually the first to infect the ends of the bolts.

Shields and Atwell (1285) found that *Trichoderma viride* almost completely inhibited decay of yellow birch sapwood blocks inoculated simultaneously with this mold and either *Polyporus hirsutus, P. versicolor,* or *Stereum purpureum. P. adustus* was checked only if the blocks were first inoculated with the mold.

A stain in yellow birch lumber, termed "black line stain" by Hansbrough (589), is localized in the vessels, forming parallel black lines of varying lengths. He considers the stain of fungus origin, but the organism has not been identified.

Many fungi are involved in the blue-staining of hardwood lumber (1252). A deeply penetrating yellow stain, which starts as a moldy, surface spotting on birch and some other hardwood lumber, is caused by a member of the *Penicillium divaricatum* group (725).

A localized ring shake of hemlock and hardwoods, including yellow birch, is ascribed to sapsuckers by Shigo (1292, 1295). In addition, discolorations develop above and below these injuries.

The thelephoraceous basidiomycete *Solenia ochracea* (1278), with its small, cylindric pilei, sometimes forms harmless patches on the bark of living trees.

Ruehle (*1224*) lists 9 species of nematodes in 9 genera, associated with species of *Betula* in the Southeast.

Sweet birch

Betula lenta

The sweet birch, also commonly known as black birch or cherry birch, occurs from near sea level in New England, through New York and Pennsylvania, and southwestward through the eastern mountains into the Southern Appalachians, where the species occurs between 2,000 and 4,500 ft. in elevation. Its preferred sites are moist, loamy, northerly or easterly slopes. Sweet birches grow to 80 ft. in height and to a maximum diameter of 5 ft. Mostly a small tree, its longevity is seldom much over 100 years, with a known maximum of 265 years. The silvical characteristics of sweet birch have been compiled by Leak (*844*).

This species is intermediate in tolerance (*54*), very sensitive to fire, winter hardy, and moderately drought resistant. While the network of fine twigs provides many loci (*310*) for ice accumulation, Downs (*390*) found the birches and maples about equally damaged, whereas black cherry suffered far more from ice.

Sweet birch can exude sap copiously in the autumn as well as in the spring.

Sweet birch is relatively free from disease. Its main fungus enemy is Nectria canker. Few foliage diseases attack the species. Heart rots, however, take a toll at an early age.

Foliage Diseases.—The commonest of the leaf spots is anthracnose (*Gloeosporium betularum*). It has been reported epidemic on *Betula nigra* in Indiana, and is described by Van Hook and Busteed (*1469*) (see *B. nigra*).

A small, discrete spot bearing pycnidia with long, septate spores is caused by *Septoria betulicola*. The two common powdery mildews *Microsphaera alni* and *Phyllactinia guttata* (*619*) may appear by midway through the growing season, chiefly on sprout foliage.

Although Mix's monograph (*994*) makes no mention of a *Taphrina* on *Betula lenta,* a leaf blister caused by an unnamed *Taphrina* species has been reported from New England (*8*).

Stem Diseases.—The common Nectria canker *(N. galligena)* (*170, 879*) of eastern hardwoods is the most damaging disease of sweet birch (*47*). Grant and Spaulding (*530*) consider that the bending of twigs under the weight of ice and snow make axillary cracks through which the fungus commonly enters, and that this accounts for the branch stub usually found in the middle of a Nectria canker. The tiny, red perithecia can be found under bark near the edges of the perennial cankers formed by this fungus. Nectria cankers sometimes lead to infection by *Poria obliqua* (*1453*).

Although *Nectria coccinea* Fr. *sensu* Wr. has also been reported in association with birch cankers, Lohman and Watson (*879*) consider this a saprobe, and point out that many early reports of *N. coccinea* were probably *N. galligena*. Another *Nectria (N. cin-*

nabarina) is saprobic on branches, and is characterized readily by its coral sporodochia, representing the imperfect stage, *Tubercularia vulgaris*.

The gluing fungus, *Hymenochaete agglutinans* (*151*), will often cause a dead branch being rotted by it to become cemented to a living branch by its mycelium and brown felt, and thus cause the death of the interface bark of the living branch.

Trunk Rots.—Many fungi can rot the dead wood of sweet birch, but few rot the heart of living trees. The chief heart-rotters are *Fomes igniarius, F. igniarius* var. *laevigatus* (*Poria laevigata*), and *Poria obliqua*. The latter two produce cankers, rot the central woody cylinder, produce sterile fungus thalli on living trees, and brown resupinate conks on dead trees that had been decaying while alive. They both occur on several species of *Betula*, and are discussed in some detail under yellow birch (*Betula alleghaniensis*). The decays of yellow birch and sweet birch are similar, and for the most part involve the same fungi (*214, 1290, 1453*).

Fomes robustus (*890*), which produces conks similar in outward appearance to *F. igniarius*, and in the past was often mistaken for it, has been repeatedly reported on living sweet birch and river birch but not on the common northern birches (*8*).

Miscellaneous Pathology.—A red stain of the heartwood accompanies heavy infection by *Torula ligniperda*. This fungus is known best as a stainer for its association with a "wet redheart" of paper birch (*213*). However, there is a good possibility that the *Torula*, as a stainer of birch, may be secondary to a bacterium (*603*).

Increment borings made in sweet birch trees in Pennsylvania that were split and examined 10 years later showed a brown, discolored radial band with a mean vertical extent of 27 in. Forty-four percent of the borings had developed decay that had progressed an average of 12 in. vertically (*669*).

The fungi reported as forming mycorrhizae with sweet birch are *Boletus scaber, Cenococcum graniforme*, and *Hebeloma crustuliniforme* (*1442*).

Sweet birch proved moderately susceptible to Texas root rot in Texas tests (*1379*), but would never be planted in that unsuitable climate.

The nematodes occurring in or around the roots of *Betula lenta* in New Jersey were *Criconemoides macrodorum, Hemicycliophora* sp., and *Hoplotylus femina* (*1222*).

River birch

Betula nigra

The red, or river, birch is a tree of streambanks, the shores of lakes, and swampy areas throughout the East, except for the tidal lands of the Atlantic and Gulf Coasts (*279*). It extends from southern New England to northern Florida, west to east Texas, north through the Mississippi Valley to southern Minnesota, and eastward, occurring commonly in all States of this huge block except Michigan and most of New York. In spite of its affinity for water, it is seldom a component of the creekbanks of the Southern Appalachian Mountains. It is the only "southern" birch, being widely distributed along the rivers of the South (*593*) ; while of the other birches, only sweet birch and yellow birch reach the South, occurring in the Appalachian Mountain chain, and only at the higher elevations.

River birch is typically short-boled, often of poor form, with several major ascending branches. Its soils are usually alluvial, and its affinity to water is much like that of sycamore, black willow, and alder. It grows fast when young, is usually a medium-sized tree, but can grow to heights of 100 ft. with diameters up to 5 ft. in the lower Mississippi Valley. A specimen 4 ft. in diameter has been reported from Maryland (*4*). Older trees may have bark an inch thick.

River birch usually has a short life, is notably intolerant (*279*), and is somewhat paradoxical with respect to soil water. While it is a riverbank tree, it was only average in resistance to flooding in a Kentucky study of the flooding reaction of 39 species (*583*). Curiously also, it will grow well as an ornamental even on dry soils (*593*). Stumps sprout prolifically.

River birch is usually free from serious disease unless old or damaged, but is frequently injured or killed in the Central States by cakes of ice carried downstream in spring thaws.

Miller (*974*) reports 18 ascomycetes from river birch in Georgia, mostly from senescent or dead leaves and stems of river birch, and none of which enter into the economic pathology of the species.

Foliage Diseases.—The principal leaf disease of river birch is anthracnose (*Gloeosporium betularum*). This leaf blight was reported epidemic on river birch in Indiana during 1932 and 1934 (*1469*), and is known to disfigure the foliage of *Betula lenta* and *B. papyrifera* also. It produces rounded spots, 2 to 3 mm. across, with blackish margins. Its acervuli are amphigenous, brownish, cupulate, with hyaline, obovate, 1-celled conidia about $6\mu \times 10\mu$ in dimension (*1352*).

Another discrete spot is attributed to *Phyllosticta betulina*, and a leaf mold to *Cladosporium caducum*.

A common powdery mildew (*Phyllactinia guttata*) (*619*) occurs widely on the birches, including river birch.

Stem Diseases.—While river birch is subject to the common Nectria canker of hardwoods caused by *N. galligena* (see *Betula alleghaniensis*) (*170, 879*), it is of less importance on this species than on other birches. Very likely this is explained by the fact that river birch, being to a large extent a southern tree, is not as subject as the more northern species to the axillary cracking resulting from the weight of ice and snow, which Grant and Spaulding (*530*) consider to provide the main infection courts for this *Nectria* species. This common northern disease is notably infrequent in the South, except in some mountain areas.

Nectria cinnabarina (*1555*), a saprobe, often produces its coral sporodochia on the dead bark of branches.

The common eastern leafy mistletoe *Phoradendron serotinum* is common on river birch in the South, because of the predilection of both the tree and the parasite for low, wet sites.

Septobasidium pseudopedicellatum (*292*) inhabits the bark of branches, living on scale insects, and producing foliose, gray to brown crusts or patches of varying extent, and is not harmful to the tree.

Trunk Rots.—River birch is subject to most of the rot fungi that attack other birches (see *Betula alleghaniensis*), but their incidence varies with tree species. The heart rotters are less common and the saprobes abundant on river birches. *Fomes robustus* (see *Betula lenta*) is particularly conspicuous in its fruiting on river birch, while reports of the canker-rot fungi, so common on the northern birches (see *B. alleghaniensis*), are notably lacking.

Miscellaneous Pathology.—The losses from defect in southern hardwoods, as determined by Bryan (*180*), show river birch to yield little clear lumber, because of a large number of minor defects that would not necessarily cause the trees to be considered culls.

The thelephoraceous basidiomycete *Solenia ochracea*, with its cylindric pilei, sometimes forms harmless felty patches on the bark of living trees (*1278*).

River birch proved very susceptible to *Phymatotrichum* root rot (*P. omnivorum*) in Texas tests (*1379*), but it is not grown in the root rot area of the Southwest.

The aments of river birch are attacked by the discomycete *Ciboria betulae* (*1565*) that produces brown to black mummified sclerotia from which the apothecia arise in the male catkins on the ground.

The only fungus reported as forming mycorrhizae with river birch is *Cenococcum graniforme* (*1442*).

It is notable that almost all of the American tree and shrub species in the Betulaceae excepting *Betula nigra* are attacked by one or more of the many species of *Taphrina* that cause leaf blisters, witches' brooms, and other distortions of active tissue (*994*).

Ruehle (*1224*) lists 7 species of nematodes in 7 genera associated with river birch in Georgia.

Paper birch

Betula papyrifera

Paper birch, also called white birch, is a tree of cold climates, and is one of the few species that is transcontinental in range. It extends continuously across Canada from Newfoundland to Alaska, and penetrates the United States in quantity only in the Northeast, southward to Pennsylvania, in the Lake States, and in northern Idaho and Montana. It develops best in northern New England. The silvical characteristics have been compiled by Hutnik and Cunningham (*739*).

Paper birch is intolerant (*54*), but grows well on a wide variety of soils, mostly podzols, sandy to stony loams, and even on bog soils. These soils range from acidic to highly calcareous, and average a little drier than most within its range. Walker (*1504*) considers that white birch can restore exchangeable potassium in K-deficient soils. It grows to timberline in the Northeast, will not tolerate situations where the mean July temperature reaches 70° F., is winter hardy, can be heavily damaged by deer browse and by fire, and is subject to damage by ice accumulation because of its many fine twigs (*310*). It can also be seriously damaged by sea spray or temporary immersion of roots in salt water (*1632*).

Trees mature in about 75 years and seldom live over 150 years (*279*), but will occasionally reach an age of 200 years. Individuals may grow to 30 in. in diameter and 100 ft. in height on the best sites (*739*), although the trees in mature stands typically average only about 10 in. in diameter. The roots of large trees are shallow but spreading, making the trees windfirm. Cuttings of paper birch can be rooted.

There are many varieties of paper birch. Some are horticultural selections, but several are Canadian or western wild variants. Thus, following Little (*872*), the commonest western form is called *Betula papyrifera* var. *commutata,* but the United States Index of Plant Diseases (*8*) calls this *Betula papyrifera occidentalis.* However, in this handbook, the pathology of the entire species is considered together.

Paper birch was moderately susceptible to sulfur dioxide injury near two ore-reducing plants in Canada. It could survive much nearer these plants than any of the conifers, but was more sensitive to the gas than some other deciduous trees (*522*).

The pathology of this short-lived species is dominated by Nectria canker, two heart rot fungi, stains of the wood of living trees, birch dieback, and the decline following stand-opening referred to as post-logging decadence. Up to 50 years of age, paper birch is generally free from disease unless injured.

Foliage Diseases.—The leaf spots of paper birch are caused by the following fungi: *Cylindrosporium betulae* in the East, *Gloeosporium betulae-papyriferae* in the East, *G. betularum* in the Lake States and Colorado, *Septoria betulae* in Wisconsin, and *S. betulicola* nationwide (*8*). None of these spots is of more than mycological interest, and therefore no further reference to them is provided.

The leaf rust, *Melampsoridium betulinum,* and the common powdery mildew, *Phyllactinia guttata* (see *Betula alleghaniensis*), also occur on paper birch in all parts of its range in the United States. Shaw (*1277*) uses the name *P. guttata* for this fungus in the West, and this name is used for it throughout this book. It is also commonly known as *P. corylea.*

Taphrina carnea causes thickened, yellowish to red leaf curl lesions in New England. *T. flava* causes small (up to 5 mm.), yellow to brown or red-brown blistered spots in New England and the Lake States (*994*). *T. boycei* causes small, unthickened spots, pale yellow on both sides on *Betula occidentalis* (*993*), the water birch of the West—the nomenclature of which has been somewhat confused with the western form of paper birch (*872*).

Stem Diseases.—There are several cankers of paper birch, and all have been described under either *Acer saccharum* or *Betula alleghaniensis.* They include those caused by *Nectria galligena, Daedalea unicolor, Poria laevigata, P. obliqua,* and *Stereum murrayi.* The latter four are also heart rot fungi and are known from both the East and the West. The saprobic role of *N. coccinea* and *N. cinnabarina* is as described for the other birches.

The basal cracking, termed "collar crack" by Shigo (*1295*) and attributed to *Armillaria mellea,* and the developments that follow this rot are described under yellow birch.

A witches' broom is formed by *Taphrina americana* in New England and the Lake States (*994*).

Root Diseases.—The most common root rot is caused by *Armillaria mellea*. While not often a primary killer, its joint role with "collar crack" in leading to windthrow, its part in birch dieback, and its association with logging wounds are typical of the way this fungus teams with other agents to damage yellow birch and paper birch.

A root rot of paper birch seedlings has been attributed to *Phytophthora cinnamomi* in a Maryland nursery well south of the tree's native range (*304*).

Corticium galactinum, a well-known root rot fungus, has been reported rotting wood of paper birch, but not as a root-rotter of living trees (*1561*). It may, however, also have this potential.

Paper birch proved moderately susceptible to Texas root rot in Texas tests (*1379*).

Ruehle (*1222*) lists 7 species of nematodes on the roots of, or under, paper birches in Canada, and one species in Maine.

Mycorrhizal formation by *Cenococcum graniforme, Boletus scaber* and its variety *fusca,* and *Cortinarius* sp. has been reported (*8, 1442*).

Trunk Rots.—The most important of the heart rots of living trees are those caused by *Fomes igniarius, F. igniarius* var. *laevigatus (Poria laevigata), Poria obliqua, Daedalea unicolor,* and *Stereum murrayi.* All but the first cause cankering in addition to their primary role of causing decay in living trees. All of these fungi are annotated and documented under either sugar maple (*Acer saccharum*) or yellow birch (*Betula alleghaniensis*). The yellow birch account deals with the amount of cull to be expected from these rots and refers to literature on the extent of rot to be expected from them. This information is applicable to paper birch also.

Shigo (*1290*) studied the fungi surrounding, and in advance of, rot columns of *Fomes igniarius* in living trees, and found that a high pH "wetwood" zone surrounded the columns, and that several non-hymenomycetous fungi and certain bacteria colonized the surrounding area. The fungi were mostly species of *Phialophora, Trichocladium,* and *Acrostaphylus.*

Fomes applanatus, while a heart rotter mainly of beech, will also sometimes rot the heart of the birches and maples for distances up to at least 6 linear ft. from a sporophore (*1343*). It is mainly a wound decay fungus in living trees and a rotter of dead material. Many other fungi can act in this dual capacity of saprobe and wound decay agent.

Hydnum (Steccherinum) ochraceum (*984*), with a resupinate, toothed, ochraceous sporophore characterized by its tough texture, mainly rots dead wood, but can cause a wet, soft, white rot in living birches and also in trees of other genera.

The ascomycete *Ustulina vulgaris* has been isolated from butt rot in paper birch. It produces carbonaceous, crustose, black fruiting bodies on exposed, decaying wood of stumps (*211*).

In Ontario (*73*), the cull from decay reached 8 percent of the merchantable volume by age 120 years. The deduction for stains was less than for yellow birch or sugar maple, never exceeding 14 percent. The main rot fungi were *Fomes igniarius, Stereum murraii, F. igniarius laevigatus, S. purpureum,* and *Peniophora cinerea,* in that order.

Miscellaneous Pathology.—The widespread and serious decline in the Northeast and Canada known as birch dieback has affected yellow birch primarily, and to a lesser extent, paper birch. Dieback has caused the virtual disappearance of these birches in some areas. A documented account is provided under *Betula alleghaniensis*.

The problem of post-logging decadence (*582*) and the similarity in symptoms with birch dieback are brought out by Hutnik and Cunningham (*739*), with special reference to paper birch. Thinning or partial cutting in older stands, unless done with due attention to avoiding undue exposure of the remaining stems, leads to a drop in vigor, dying back of branches, and often death of residual trees.

A red staining of the heartwood, referred to as "red heart" by Campbell and Davidson (*213*), is commonly associated with heavy infection by *Torula ligniperda*. Hartley et al. (*603*) cast some doubt on this fungus being the primary cause, because of concomitant involvement of an easily overlooked bacterium.

Siegle (*1303*) has shown that the common red heart of white birch is a result of enzymatic oxidation. He identified pyrocatechol, coniferyl alcohol, pyrogallol, and catechin as substrates for the staining process. The red-brown color of the wood is due to the oxidation products of the phenols involved. Fungi produce the phenol oxidases. However, Siegle questions the ability of *Trichocladium canadense* to cause red heart.

The succession of mold and stain fungi that develops on paper birch cut for pulpwood in New Hampshire is described and the organisms named by Shigo (*1286*). *Ceratocystis coerulescens* was usually the first fungus to invade the ends of the bolts.

A localized ring shake of hemlock and certain hardwoods, including paper birch, is attributed to sapsuckers by Shigo (*1292, 1295*). Discolorations extend well above and below these injuries.

Some of the birches are particularly subject to fasciation. The author, as well as Boyce (*151*) and Carter (*233*), have observed birch branches that became broad, flattened, twisted, and contorted. This condition has been suspected to be related to overfertilization.

Gray birch

Betula populifolia

Reaching its best development in moist situations along streams and the banks of swamps and ponds, gray birch is the smallest of the northeastern birches. Mainly a tree of New England and New York, it extends from New Brunswick, Canada, southward through eastern Pennsylvania. Like pin cherry and the aspens, it helps to quickly vegetate burned or abandoned land, and may be found as a temporary component on a wide variety of soils, wet or dry, and either sandy, gravelly, or loamy (*279*).

Gray birches seldom grow over 40 ft. tall and 18 in. in diameter (*593*), and in the second-growth stands (in which they are a common component) gray birches are most likely to be under 8 in. in diameter and no more than 30 ft. tall. Of record size is a tree in Maryland,

60 ft. tall and over 2 ft. in diameter (4). A prolific sprouter, the gray birch typically appears in clumps The light seeds carry well and bring about the early population of abandoned land. Rehder (1154) describes three varieties of this species.

Gray birch is hardy but short-lived, and like all the birches, subject to glaze (310) and other storm damage, because of its abundance of fine twigs. Its silvical features are much like those of paper birch. It is very intolerant (54), generally giving way to more tolerant associates. Along with paper birch, gray birch has been killed or severely injured by exposure to salt spray and temporary immersion in salt water (1632).

Foliage Diseases.—During some years, an insect called the birch leaf miner, *Fenusa pusilla*, which has a preference for gray birch and paper birch, will virtually defoliate trees early in the season (297, 1260) and can overwhelm any evidence of leaf disease. No leaf disease of birch causes damage so spectacular as that caused by certain birch leaf-feeding insects.

The fungi pathogenic to leaves of gray birch are of little importance. Minor spots are caused by the anthracnose, *Gloeosporium betulicola* (8), and by *Septoria betulicola* (1278). The common powdery mildew *Phyllactinia guttata* (619) has a particular affinity for sprout leaves. The leaf rust *Melampsoridium betulinum* (46) (see *Betula alleghaniensis*) can become quite severe locally in moist situations, and a yellow leaf blister (*Taphrina flava*) (994) has been reported from many localities in New England and the Lake States on gray birch and paper birch.

Stem Diseases.—The stem diseases of gray birch are essentially the same as those of the other birches, but possibly because of this tree's short life none of them develop as conspicuously as they do on yellow birch and paper birch.

Nectria canker (*N. galligena*) will produce its flaring "birch type" lesions on gray birch. While this canker is typically bark-free and of the target type, the Nectria cankers on birch tend to be more irregular (928) than the symmetrical Nectria target cankers so common on black walnut and red maple. See yellow birch (*Betula alleghaniensis*) for fuller annotation.

Nectria coccinea, mainly a saprobe, has also been reported from gray birch. However, it does not fruit in association with cankers. In view of the early confusion of *N. coccinea* with *N. galligena*, reference to Lohman and Watson (879) is advisable in cases of question.

Carter (233) states that birch trees (species unspecified) weakened by the bronze birch borer or by some other agent are often attacked by *Melanconium betulinum*. Invading the bark, it causes cankers, easily seen because on branches with gray or green bark the diseased bark turns red-brown and is dotted with raised, black fruiting bodies. These acervuli form simple conidiophores, and dark, 1-celled ovoid to ellipsoid conidia.

The canker-rot fungi *Poria laevigata*, *P. obliqua*, and *Daedalea unicolor* are described under yellow birch, and do much more damage to that species than to gray birch.

Trunk Rots.—The early senescence of gray birch leads to excessive defect while trees are still small and fairly young. A large number of fungi will rot the central cylinder of maturing or damaged trees. Among the commonest are the three canker-rot fungi mentioned above. Other common heart rotters and their effects on cull are as follows (*1343*) :

- *Fomes igniarius*—a conk usually means the loss of all or most of the tree.
- *Fomes connatus*—rot seldom extends more than a foot or two in each direction from a conk.
- *Fomes applanatus*—in gray birch, this fungus, mainly a saprobe, may lead to rot extending 2 or 3 ft. in either direction from a conk.
- *Fomes fomentarius*—while the hoof-shaped, large-pored conks of this fungus are common on dead birch, its rot seldom extends more than a foot or two into the wood of the living bole, above and below the point of entrance
- *Fomes pinicola*—like *F. fomentarius,* this is largely a saprobe on the birches and other tree species of the Northeast.

Taxonomic treatments of these and other species of *Fomes* have been provided most recently by Lowe (*890*) and also by Overholts (*1067*). Accounts of the fungi and the rots they cause are provided by Boyce (*151*), Baxter (*81*), and Hubert (*725*).

Many other fungi attack the wood of dead birches, notably *Polyporus betulinus,* but they cause little loss in living trees.

Miscellaneous Pathology.—Gray birch was rated very susceptible to Texas root rot (*1379*), but is not grown in the root rot belt.

There have been no specific mycorrhizal associations reported for gray birch (*1442*), although some specific fungi are known to form mycorrhizae with certain of the other species of *Betula.*

Ruehle (*1222*) lists 8 species of nematodes as occurring on the roots of, or in the soil under, gray birch in North America.

Potassium deficiency symptoms have been produced and described for several hardwoods including *Betula populifolia* (*1095*).

American hornbeam

Carpinus caroliniana

The American hornbeam is a wide-crowned, bushy tree rarely over 30 ft. tall or over 18 in. in diameter. The largest reported is almost 2 ft. in diameter and 70 ft. tall (*4*). The branches take erratic forms. The bark is typically furrowed, ridged, smooth, firm, and gray, thus giving rise to one of the common names, "bluebeech." Another common name is ironwood because of the hardness of the wood.

The range is virtually that of *Betula nigra,* and both species also have an affinity for riparian sites (*279*) and moist bottom lands. Also, like river birch, it reaches its highest development in the South Atlantic States. American hornbeam is shade loving and ranks among the most tolerant of our North American trees (*54*). A member of the birch family, it differs from the birches in flowering in that its staminate catkins are not formed until the spring of the year in which they mature (*279*).

Although they are moisture-loving trees, American hornbeam, river birch, and sycamore are only moderate in resistance to flooding (*583*). This hornbeam species is very windfirm, and it is notably resistant to major damage from insects and diseases. It sprouts prolifically from stumps.

Foliage Diseases.—Many fungi cause necrotic spots, discolorations, and mildews, mostly late in the season, but none are damaging.

Clasterosporium cornigerum causes a common spot, upon which dark, creeping hyphae produce erect, often swollen, conidiophores, with 2- to several-septate, solitary, apical conidia (*62, 1352*).

Another common spot is caused by *Sphaerognomonia carpinea* (imperfect stage—*Gloeosporium robergei*). This sphaeriaceous fungus has unbeaked perithecia, formed when the leaves are on the ground, that have a black, adhering periderm, no paraphyses, and 8-spored asci with 1-celled hyaline spores.

Other less common spots that have been reported on *Carpinus* are caused by *Cercoseptoria caryigena, Cylindrosporium dearnessii, Gnomoniella fimbriella* (that produces small, black stromata), and some species of *Phyllosticta* (*8*).

Powdery mildews, mostly on sprout foliage and mostly occurring late in the season, are caused by the common species *Microsphaera alni* and *Phyllactinia guttata.* The former has terminally branched perithecial appendages and the latter unbranched, proximally bulbous appendages (*1555*).

A leaf curl, starting early in the season, involving small areas or entire leaves, without apparent thickening of the leaf, is caused by *Taphrina australis* (*994*).

Stem Diseases.—*Carpinus caroliniana* is remarkably free from stem diseases. The common European canker fungus, *Nectria galligena,* occasionally produces its characteristic bark-free target cankers on this species (*170*).

A trunk and branch canker that occurs widely on this tree is caused by *Pezicula* (*Dermatea*) *carpinea* (*1352*), a discomycete that is reported as a wound parasite on *Carpinus betulus* in Germany (*1091*).

Carpinus caroliniana is a favorite host to species of *Septobasidium.* Couch (*292*) lists 7 species that produce their brown felts on scale insects infesting the bark of branches of this tree. These fungi are not harmful. The species reported on *Carpinus caroliniana* are *S. apiculatum, S. curtisii, S. filiforme, S. hesleri, S. langloisii, S. pseudopedicellatum,* and *S. sinuosum.*

The small, thelephoraceous fungus *Aleurodiscus oakesii* fruits on small, roughly elliptical, often sunken areas of bark, but it causes no cambial necrosis. It is particularly common on the outer bark of white oak, where it causes a condition known as smooth patch (*825*).

Several species of *Hypoxylon* occur on dead bark of *Carpinus* but are not known to cause cankers. One, *H. mammatum* (*H. morsei*) (*978*), has been associated with sugar maple cankers in Canada, and, under the synonym *H. pruinatum,* is known widely on aspen, and it may have some potential for weak parasitism to *Carpinus.*

Stereum murrayi, a heart rot fungus of *Acer, Betula, Fagus, Malus,* and *Ostrya,* also occurs occasionally on *Carpinus.* Where the fungus has entered or worked its way out to the bark, it can produce sunken lesions with the bark attached. The thin, foliate fruiting bodies appear on these lesions (*342*).

Other Diseases.—*Carpinus caroliniana* was moderately suscepti-ble to Texas root rot in Texas tests (*1379*).·

A seedling root rot in a Missouri nursery was attributed to *Rhizoctonia solani*.

Armillaria mellea can rot roots of *Carpinus* but is not known to kill trees.

Hydnum (*Steccherinum*) *ochraceum* can rot roots and butts.

The only rot fungi that attack *Carpinus* and are considered heart rotters are *Fomes applanatus, F. igniarius, Hydnum ochraceum, Stereum gausapatum,* and *S. murrayi*. The other rot fungi reported on *Carpinus* (*8*) are decayers of dead wood.

The only fungus reported to form mycorrhizae with this species is *Cenococcum graniforme* (*1442*).

A nematode, *Pratylenchus scribneri*, highly parasitic to amaryl-lis in Florida, has also been known to attack *Carpinus caroliniana* in that State (*1222*).

Hickory

Carya spp.

A general account of the silvical characteristics of the com-mercial hickories is provided by Nelson (*1026*), and much of the following silvical material pertinent to the pathology of this genus is drawn from his account. Of more than 30 species of hickory in the Eastern United States, only eight are considered of commer-cial importance. These eight include (1) true hickories: pignut hickory, *Carya glabra;* shellbark hickory, *C. laciniosa;* shagbark hickory, *C. ovata;* and mockernut hickory, *C. tomentosa;* and (2) pecan hickories: water hickory, *C. aquatica;* bitternut hickory, *C. cordiformis;* pecan, *C. illinoensis;* and nutmeg hickory, *C. my-risticaeformis*.

Following silvical digests of the seven most abundant of these species, the pathology of the hickories is discussed by causes; men-tion is made of how each pathogen affects the different hickory species, rather than that of arranging the pathology under each hickory species. Without doubt, most of the hickory diseases af-fect more species of *Carya* than specific reports would indicate. This arrangement, used also for certain other large tree genera, permits an appreciation not only of the diseases known to attack a species, but also of those likely to do so, but so far unreported on that species. The many reports of fungi, indicated as simply on "hickory" or on "*Carya*", have made it difficult to provide ef-fective host coverage at the species level.

The Index of Plant Diseases in the United States (*8*) lists 133 fungi and 10 other causes of disease on species of *Carya*. Most of the fungi are saprophytes, but a few are damaging to foliage, or produce cankers, or cause trunk or root rots. The fungi considered wholly or largely saprobic are not included in this account.

A series of publications dealing with the characteristics, prop-erties, uses, and other information on the hickories is available from the USDA Forest Service, Southeastern Forest Experiment

Station. They are the reports of a selected group of contributors known as the Hickory Task Force. Excellent bulletins are also available on the diseases and insects of pecans (*1056, 1057, 1113*).

Carya glabra, pignut hickory. Although officially called pignut hickory (*872*), five other hickory species have been called "pignut" in certain sections. The taxonomy of the species is complicated, and as with most true hickories, the wood is bought and sold simply as hickory (*1025*). Reaching its best development in the Ohio Valley, pignut hickory is the commonest hickory of the Southern Appalachian Mountains. It is found throughout the East, from southern New England to Florida, westward through Louisiana, north through Arkansas and Missouri, and through the Central States into southern Michigan.

Pignut hickory inhabits dry ridges and hillsides and also grows on moist mountain and Piedmont sites. It sprouts prolifically. It is intermediate in tolerance, and since hickory foliage has a high calcium content, it is considered a "soil improver" (*244*). It can grow to over 120 ft. tall and to diameters of over 5 ft. (*4*). Maturing at 200 to 300 years, maximum longevity is about 400 years (*279*). The tree is deeply and pronouncedly taprooted, windfirm, slow growing, easily injured by frost and fire, and degraded by sapwood streaks following sapsucker injury. It is readily subject to injury following flooding (*583*).

The wood is tough, hard, resilient, and heavy. Its major disease enemy is the canker and rot caused by *Poria spiculosa.* It strongly resists ice damage.

Carya laciniosa, shellbark hickory. The bark resembles that of shagbark hickory, but there are many means of distinction (*279*). This tree has a restricted range, extending from western New York west to southern Iowa, south to central Arkansas, eastward to the Cumberland Plateau in Tennessee, and northeastward, remaining mostly west of the Appalachian Mountains except for the western North Carolina mountains and some isolated pockets in the Piedmont (*279, 954*). It is typically a bottom land species, occurring in pure groves or mixed with other species on loamy areas occasionally subject to inundation. It requires moister sites than other true hickories (*1026*). It will sometimes grow on fairly dry sites, including upland slopes, in the northern part of its range. Shellbark hickory will self-prune well and can grow to over 130 ft. tall, but seldom exceeds 3 ft. in diameter (*279*). It has a long taproot; is windfirm; slow growing; subject to frost damage, drought injury, fire damage, and sapwood streaking following sapsucker injury. It is a very tolerant tree and is considered by some as exceeded in tolerance only by sugar maple, beech, and pignut hickory (*954*), although Baker's (*54*) tolerance table rates all the hickories as intermediate. It is resistant to ice damage and has no major disease enemies. It was readily damaged by high water in a Kentucky reservoir (*583*). The wood is tough and heavy, with approximately the properties of the other true hickories.

Carya ovata, shagbark hickory. The most distinctive of the hickories, with its loose, recurved plates of bark, shagbark hickory is the most widespread and most important commercially (*279*). It grows from southern New England southwestward through the Piedmont, the Southern Appalachian Mountains, and westward throughout the Southern States, except for the Atlantic and Gulf Coastal Plains, and northward from Louisiana to the southern part of the Lake States, including the area so bounded (*1024*). The tree is rugged, tends to fork one or more times, and can reach heights in excess of 130 ft. and diameters over 3 ft.

In the North, shagbark hickory grows mainly on upland slopes, while farther south it is more prevalent on deep, moist, alluvial soils. Thus, it is a north- and east-slope species in the Ohio Valley and a river bottom tree in Louisiana and Mississippi (*1024*). Its foliage has a high calcium content (*244*), giving it properties that improve soil. It grows slowly, although fast for a hickory, and its longevity seldom exceeds 200 years. Shagbark hickory sprouts prolifically from stumps and root suckers, has a long, strong taproot, is moderately tolerant, and is easily injured by fire. It resists damage by ice. Following flooding of a Kentucky reservoir site, it was one of the species most readily injured or killed (*583*). Humans and wildlife eat the sweet nuts.

Shagbark hickory is tough, resilient, firm, and heavy. Its main disease enemies are the canker and rot caused by *Poria spiculosa,* and dark streaks that usually downgrade the sapwood. In general, it is relatively free from major diseases.

Carya tomentosa, mockernut hickory. Largely a southern species, mockernut hickory is one of the most important commercial species. Its large, hairy, terminal buds, and coarse, hairy leaves are distinctive, and its high proportion of white sapwood enhances its value and has led to the oft-used names white hickory or white-heart hickory (*1022*). It becomes abundant through Virginia and the South Atlantic Coast, extending into Florida, where it is the commonest of the hickories. It extends westward to east Texas except right along the Gulf Coast, and north through the other Southern and Central States, into southern Michigan. It is abundant, and reaches its best development, in the interior river valleys and deep fertile soils of the Ohio River basin, and it is also the only hickory found in the predominantly pine forests of the sandy coastal plain belt of the South (*1022*).

Mockernut hickory tends to be intolerant and seldom reaches 100 ft. in height or 3 ft. in diameter, but it can grow to ages approaching 300 years (*279*). It sprouts prolifically, is not easily injured by the weight of ice, but is very subject to frost damage when young. It is readily damaged by fire because of the poor insulation afforded by the hard, flinty bark.

The wood has the hard, heavy, tough characteristics of the true hickories, and it furnishes the bulk of the hickory cut commercially. Not subject to severe loss from disease, its main fungus enemy is *Poria spiculosa,* which causes both a deep canker and heart rot.

The nuts are consumed by humans and are sweet, tasty, and large.

Carya aquatica, water hickory. Considered together in this account are both the species *C. aquatica,* which occurs in wetlands from southeastern Virginia throughout the South to Texas and Oklahoma, and the hybrid with *C. illinoensis* called bitter pecan (*C.* X *lecontei* Little) which grows mostly in the Mississippi and tributary bottom lands of the deep South, mainly in Louisiana, Mississippi, Arkansas, Missouri, and Texas (*872*). The hybrid is not common, even in the Mississippi Delta. Typical water hickory produces small, flattened, very bitter nuts, and in the Delta it is almost invariably also called bitter pecan, although the true bitter pecan is *C. X lecontei* (*1140*).

Water hickory predominates in the first bottoms of southern rivers, particularly in the Mississippi Delta, on low, very poorly drained flats subject to overflows of long duration. It is a medium to large tree and is difficult to distinguish from the sweet pecan (*Carya illinoensis*) except for the bitter taste and other unique characteristics of the nuts (*1140*).

It grows to diameters of over 3 ft. and to heights of over 100 ft. (*4*). It is generally considered intolerant but is tolerant in the seedling stages. It has an unusually long dormant season that enables it to withstand late spring flooding (*1026*).

Water hickory and pecan have so many characteristics in common that they are cut and sold together as "pecan," whereas the other species of *Carya* in the southern bottom lands are sold as "terrace hickories" (*1140*).

Although water hickory is not unusually defective, heart rot fungi tend to spread faster in the trunks of this species than in associated oaks and other lowland species. It also tends to support more mistletoe than any of its associated "Delta" hardwood species (*1140*).

Carya cordiformis, bitternut hickory. This is the only member of the pecan group (Apocarya) common to the Northeast, and it is probably the most abundant and most uniformly distributed of the hickories. It occurs throughout the East, from southern New England to southern Georgia, across to east Texas, north to the southern part of the Lake States, and across the Central States. Nelson (*1023*), who compiled the silvical characteristics of bitternut hickory, points out the wide range in sites, climate, and species associates of this hickory. It is, however, generally a moist-site species and is moderately tolerant, reproduces abundantly from stump sprouts and root suckers, is frost-hardy, and self-prunes well. Of all the hickories, bitternut is least susceptible to frost damage (*1026*).

The high calcium content of the foliage of this species (2.5 percent ovendry weight) puts it near the top in Chandler's (*244*) list of soil-improving species.

Bitternut hickory grows to diameters of over 4 ft. and to heights of over 170 ft. (*4*). Its low ratio of sapwood to heartwood is a disadvantage commercially. It is readily damaged by fire because of the low insulating capacity of the hard bark. This hickory is not subject to any unusually severe disease and has much the same troubles as most hickories, including the "mineral" streaks and sapsucker-induced streaks that low-grade the wood.

Carya illinoensis, pecan. This tree, with its many commercial varieties, is known largely for its nuts. They are sweet and have a high food value, and extensive orchards throughout the mid-South and the deep South produce the nuts in quantities that make pecans a major economic commodity. The natural range, which is much more restricted than the planted range, extends down the Mississippi Valley from Illinois and Indiana, and not far east of it, to the Gulf of Mexico, westward to central Texas and northward embracing most of Arkansas, Oklahoma, and Missouri.

A tree of the well-drained loams of the bottom lands, this species is never found naturally on dry soil, although planted trees will do well when not in river bottoms (279). Pecan grows fastest and is the largest of the hickories, reaching heights of 180 ft. (1026) and diameters exceeding 6 ft. (7). Sprouting is common from stumps and roots. It is intolerant, and sensitive to cold, to fire, and to drought. It sustained visible damage from air pollution in Texas, presumably from sulfur dioxide, but was not killed (911).

Like the other "pecan hickories," the wood is not particularly strong and yet its uses include those generally reserved for the strong true hickories.

The extensive pathology done on this species is a result of its intensive culture for nuts. This account, however, does not feature the pathology of the pecan from the point of view of nut production, but rather as a forest and ornamental tree. Good general accounts of the diseases of pecan have been prepared by Cole and others, and they appear in three inclusive publications (277, 1057, 1113).

Seedling Diseases.—Seeds of the pecan hickories remain dormant until spring, and germinate from April to June. In this group, germination may be over 80 percent, leading often to thickets of water hickory. They well withstand shade and competition once established. Nelson (1026) states that because water hickory has a long dormant season it can withstand some late spring flooding.

Bitternut hickory seedlings withstand frost better than other hickories.

Pecan seedlings are subject to bark killing near the ground line, referred to as "sand burn," and caused by the excessive summer temperatures reached by encircling sand.

A spot anthracnose fungus (*Elsinoë randii*) causes an important nursery blight of pecan and can become a limiting factor in the production of budded stock in wet seasons (1056). Small, reddish lesions form on both leaf surfaces, those on the upper surface becoming gray. Tissue falling out of the spots produces both a "shothole" effect and ragged leaf margins (1555).

Foliage Diseases.—In dealing with this group of diseases, it is well to consider Cole's analyses (275, 276) of the pecan Gnomonias, which provided the material for the following four paragraphs.

Several species of *Gnomonia* have been reported on *Carya* but the spores of only two of them (*G. caryae* var. *pecanae* and *G. nerviseda*) bear gelatinous appendages. The perithecia of *G. setacea* occur scattered over the surface of fallen hickory leaves with no evidence of *Leptothyrium* pycnidia among them, and its var. *macrospora* has 4- to 8-spored asci, the spores septate, and without septal constrictions. *G. nerviseda*, strictly a pecan fungus, has 8-spored asci, constricted spores, produces its beaked perithecia mostly around and on veins, and has intermingled, hypophyllous *Leptothyrium* pycnidia.

A *Gnomonia* on living pecan leaves in Florida has asci with usually 2 and sometimes 1, 3, or 4 spores and is not known to have a conidial stage.

Wolf (1596) described the anthracnose caused by *Gnomonia caryae* (imperfect stage *Leptothyrium caryae*). In late summer conidia are produced on large, red-brown areas that are dull brown below and are without definite borders. The perithecia, formed on fallen leaves in the spring, are scattered over the leaf surface, produce guttulate spores 25–33μ long and 5μ wide, without appendages; compared with *G. nerviseda,* that has spores half as long, appendaged, and occurring typically about veins. Anthracnose affects only the hickories, while *G. caryae* var. *pecanae* attacks sweet pecan.

Cole (*275*) described the liver spot fungus (*Gnomonia caryae* var. *pecanae*), that causes dark brown, circular spots along and about the midrib and veins of pecan leaves. While the ascospores of both this fungus and the vein spot fungus, *G. nerviseda,* have gelatinous appendages, the former measure 20–28μ long $\times$ 3–5μ wide, with perithecia 300–350μ wide $\times$ 150–250μ high, excluding beaks. The latter's spores are 14–15μ long $\times$ 4–5μ wide, with perithecia 250–275μ $\times$ 160–185μ.

Liver spot (*Gnomonia caryae* var. *pecanae*) is sometimes accompanied by *G. nerviseda* and *Mycosphaerella caryigena,* and attacks trees of low vitality. A *Leptothyrium* stage to *G. c. pecanae* appears in late summer, grouped on pecan leaves, and scattered over the leaf in the hickories. The conidia are elongate, and 0-, 1-, or 2-septate. Cole (*275*) relates the hickory form to *L. caryae* (*G. caryae*) and the pecan form to *L. c. pecanae* (*G. c. pecanae.*)

The *Gnomonia* from Florida, with two-celled ascospores, previously mentioned, was later described by Demaree and Cole (*371*) as *G. dispora.* Known only in Georgia and Florida on pecan, it causes spots, tan to black, that show on both sides of the leaf. The spots enlarge rapidly and tend to be circular, but are often blocked out by veins and midrib. A spot may occupy three intervenal spaces. Beaked perithecia (no conidia) appear in July, and they afford easy separation from the somewhat similar spotting caused by *Cercospora caryae.*

Vein spot (*276*) attacks the rachis, petiole, and veins of pecan resulting in severe injury or premature defoliation. The imperfect stage, *Leptothyrium nervisedum,* appears in late summer and the perfect stage, *Gnomonia nerviseda,* appears on lesions on fallen leaves in the spring. It is known from Mississippi to Texas and Arkansas and has many similarities to pecan scab, but unlike scab it does not attack shoots or nuts (*1056*).

Pecan scab (*Cladosporium effusum*) is a limiting factor in nut production in parts of the South. Attacking rapidly growing tissue, it produces elongated, olivaceous lesions along veins and on the underside of leaves. Lesions coalesce and leaves may become black. On resistant varieties, such as Stuart (*1056*), and on the hickories, attack is later and there is a lesser tendency for spots to coalesce. Scab is easily confused with vein spot (*276*) on pecan, but the latter is not known on the other species of *Carya.* The *Cladosporium* conidia are dark, whereas those of *Leptothyrium* are hyaline. Scab is known to damage the foliage of *C. aquatica, C. cordiformis, C. illinoensis,* and *C. tomentosa.*

The fungus *Microstroma juglandis* causes a leaf spot or white mold, as well as witches' brooms on pecan, hickory, and walnut. It is described under *Juglans nigra.* It has been reported from *Carya aquatica, C. cordiformis, C. glabra, C. illinoensis, C. ovata,* and

C. tomentosa. A variety, *juglandis,* causes a widespread catkin blight of pecan.

Wilson (*1587*) gives an illustrated account of brooming and galling of *Carya ovata* in Arkansas. He found *Microstroma juglandis* fruiting consistently on the foliage of brooms, and early in June the undersurface of broom foliage had turned white from the sporulation of this fungus. The formation of short shoots, with swelling accompanying inhibition of apical extension, together with callus growth resulted in decided swelling and galling of stems. The brooms are associated with these swellings. Many shagbark hickories had broken over at trunk galls.

Cercospora caryae produces numerous, minute, white to dark spots that finally cause the entire leaf to turn brown. Confined to pecan, the fungus produces hypophyllous fascicles of hyaline 1- to 4-septate spores with constrictions, nearly straight, 15–80μ × 4–6μ in dimensions. *C. fusca,* also on pecan, produces larger spots and is mostly epiphyllous. A fungus with thick-walled conidia, sometimes known as *C. halstedii,* causes a leaf blotch of hickories. It is not regarded as a *Cercospora* by Chupp (260). It is the conidial stage of *Mycosphaerella dendroides.* Chupp's monograph (*260*) should be consulted in attempts to understand the *Cercospora* and *Cercospora*-like fungi on *Carya.*

Mycosphaerella dendroides (*Cercospora halstedii*) causes a leaf blotch of all of the species of hickory and pecan in the South, and also occurs in the North. Starting in June on older pecan foliage, blotching works upward and outward through the tree. By harvest time, the trees may have lost three-fourths of their foliage. Yellowish diseased areas show first on the upper leaf surface, becoming dark brown, without being sharply delimited (*1056*). The spots on the lower leaf surface are occupied by a dense growth of conidiophores and conidia, colored brown to greenish. The conidia are light brown, recurved, multiseptate, and with prominent vacuoles (*370*). The pycnidia are probably what has been called *Phyllosticta convexula.* "The conidial stage," Chupp (*260*) says, "is characterized by thick-walled conidia, *Alternaria*-like in outline. Therefore, it is not a *Cercospora.*" The pycnidial and conidial stages are formed on attached leaves during the summer, and the perfect stage forms on attached foliage but matures on fallen leaves in the spring.

Another common *Mycosphaerella* on pecan is *M. caryigena.* It is also known from *Carya cordiformis.* Sometimes called downy spot, because of "frosty" spots on the lower leaf surface (*1056, 1057*), its imperfect stage has been known as *Cercosporella caryigena* or *Cylindrosporium caryigenum.*

Spotting of injured or senescent leaves can be caused by *Monochaetia monochaeta* (*M. desmazierii*) (*558*). Mostly an oak fungus, it causes brown to gray spots typically with indefinite margins, and often zonate or concentrically divided. The conidia are 5-celled, elliptic, and with the three intermediate cells olivaceous, guttulate, and only slightly constricted at the septa. It is rather widely known on *Carya glabra, C. ovata, C. tomentosa,* and sometimes other hickories (*624*).

The common powdery mildews, *Phyllactinia guttata* on true hickories in the North, and *Microsphaera alni* on *Carya tomentosa* and sometimes on pecan, are widely distributed but do little damage (*1153*).

Thread blight (*Pellicularia koleroga* = *Corticium stevensii*) is a southern disease affecting a wide variety of orchard and ornamental crops (*1555*). It is a minor disease of pecan. The fungus winters as sclerotia on twigs and petioles, and in late spring produces a threadlike mycelium that grows over the lower surfaces of leaves, killing them and causing premature defoliation, often leaving foliage hanging by silky fungus threads. Fruiting patches on leaves are white and then buff. They produce tiny, delicate spores in summer. Tims (*1408*) and Weber (*1527*) give accounts of the symptoms of thread blight.

Clasterosporium diffusum produces subcircular to irregular spots with indefinite margins on pecan in Texas (*620*). The spots are uniformly brown on both surfaces. Dark brown hyphae run through the tissue or creep over either leaf surface, or aggregate into conidiophores. The conidia are curved, clavate, multiseptate, brownish, and $4-5\mu \times 45-135\mu$.

Tehon (*1384*) has described *Hypoderma caryae* as a fungus producing shiny, black, hysterothecia on the fallen petioles of *Carya glabra* in the Northeast. They are large and long and are oriented parallel to the petiole axis in ashen to white spots of variable size.

A leaf spot of pecan, in Alabama and Georgia, is caused by *Cristulariella pyramidalis* (*834*), a fungus known mainly to attack maple foliage (see *Acer platanoides* and *A. saccharum*).

A greenish to brown scurfy algal leaf spot of pecan, mostly in Florida, is caused by *Cephaleuros virescens* (*1599*).

Spot anthracnose (*Elsinoë randii*) can be severe on nursery tree foliage (see Seedling Diseases).

Some of the lesser fungus leaf spots on *Carya* include those caused by *Septoria hicoriae* on *C. cordiformis* and other species in Texas, *S. caryae* on pecan in Texas and on *C. ovata* and other hickories further north, *Phyllosticta caryae* on the hickories (not on pecan) throughout the East, *P. subtilis* widespread on many hickories, *Marssonina juglandis* (*Gnomonia leptostyla*) on hickories in the North, *Fusarium carpineum* on *C. cordiformis* in Wisconsin, *Hendersonia davisii* on *C. tomentosa* in Wisconsin. *Pestalotia sphaerelloides* on *C. aquatica*, *P. uvicola* on pecan, and *Ceratophorum uncinatum* on *C. cordiformis* and *C. tomentosa* in the South and Central States. The curious fungus *Actinopelte dryina* (*863*), described under the diseases of *Quercus*, will make small, circular, very discrete spots on hickory, and the fungus has been specifically reported on *Carya* in Illinois (*1385*).

A leaf-dwarf condition of the foliage, known as littleleaf, is occasional from North Carolina to Mississippi, but its cause is not known.

Pecan rosette, a bunching of at-first mottled, then narrowed and crinkled foliage, is a result of zinc deficiency. It has been noted from the southeastern Piedmont to California. Rosetted limbs often die back from the tips.

A physiogenic leaf scorch of pecan can follow a combination of low fertility and low soil moisture.

Stem Diseases.—The most damaging and widespread disease of the true hickories, from the forestry standpoint, is the canker-rot

102

caused by *Poria spiculosa* (*220*). Spiculosa cankers, with thick, deep, callus folds, appear as rough circular swellings on the bole, usually with depressed centers. An old branch stub can generally be found in the center, with the branch wood replaced by brown, sterile fungus tissue (*1416*). The brown, flat *Poria* fruiting surfaces do not form on living trees, but develop under the bark of dead or down trees, ultimately pushing out the bark and exposing the sporophore (*215*). Spiculosa cankers are indicative of extensive decay of the inner woody cylinder.

In manner of fruiting on dead or down stems, and in general appearance and position of sporophores, *Poria andersonii* on *Carya* somewhat resembles *Poria obliqua* on species of *Betula*. Spore and cultural differences are provided by Campbell and Davidson (*210*).

While hickories are not favorite hosts to *Nectria galligena* (*170*), the perennial target cankers it causes, that shed the bark and often bear tiny, red, balloonlike perithecia on the dead bark near the advancing margins, may be found occasionally on any of the northern hickories (*47*).

The fungus associate in the beech bark disease, *Nectria coccinea* var. *faginata,* has been reported from northern hickories, but while this fungus will grow on dying patches of bark it does not form target cankers (*879*).

The coral fungus, *Nectria cinnabarina* (*1555*), with its large, coral-pink sporodochia, grows on senescent and dead hickory or pecan branches but is not a primary parasite.

Another of the common hardwood cankers that sometimes occurs on northern hickories is caused by *Strumella coryneoidea*. Typically an oak fungus, it causes long, sunken, perennial cankers that retain the bark that adheres to rotted wood beneath, and that support over their surfaces very dark cushions of sterile, 1-celled conidia (*110*). The perfect stage is *Urnula craterium*, a fingerlike to funnel-shaped discomycete that commonly fruits on stumps and logs (*338*), but not on living trees.

Also on northern hickories and oaks, a gall-forming fungus species of *Phomopsis* can produce warty excrescences ranging from small twig galls to very large trunk burls (*177*). They can be confused with the crown-galls that are formed on pecan by *Agrobacterium tumefaciens*. Crown-gall (*1056*) is common and often economically important on pecan, and Brown (*177*) succeeded in inoculating pecans, although she failed to successfully inoculate hickories with the bacterium.

The bunch disease, a virus brooming disorder of pecans and hickories, is characterized by large and numerous witches' brooms on individual trees, made up of dense growth of willowy shoots (*1056*). Occurring from North Carolina southward, occasional trees are heavily and systemically affected and die prematurely (*220*). It can be easily differentiated from the brooming caused by *Microstroma juglandis,* since the latter fruits as small, white sporodochia on the leaves involved in the brooms (*151*). On *Carya ovata*, brooms caused by this fungus have been reported up to 3 ft. in width (*1555*).

A stem canker of pecan in Louisiana and Texas is ascribed to *Microcera* (*Fusarium*) *coccophila*. However, this fungus lives on insects, and its role as a canker-former could be questioned. Also living on bark insects on hickory are many species of *Septobasidium* (seven species on *Carya tomentosa,* and just one, *S. alni* var. *squamosum,* on pecan) (*292*). The Septobasidiums produce brown felts over scale insects. Still another type of fungus, *Myriangium duriaei,* grows on scale insects on pecan. Its perithecia are superficial, as locules in a valsoid stroma, and its ascospores are muriform.

The very common twig fungus *Botryosphaeria ribis* (*Dothiorella gregaria*) (*550, 1555*), with its clusters of black perithecia, is often indicted as a twig pathogen of many hardwoods, including *Carya* spp., but it is generally saprophytic. On trees of a few genera, notably *Aleurites* and *Cercis,* it is a serious pathogen. On pecan, a form of this fungus, *B. berengeriana,* is said to cause some twig dieback.

A twig blight of *Carya ovata* in Michigan is caused by *Rosellinia caryae* (imperfect stage *Dothichiza caryae*). Sunken lesions on otherwise vigorous twigs, with a leaf scar typically in the center, bear abundant, black, dome-shaped, nonostiolate pycnidia, with fusoid, one-celled spores, and Indian-club-shaped conidiophores. Bonar (*134*), who described the canker and the fungus, got the superficial carbonaceous perithecia to form on twigs in test tubes.

Other twig fungi that live essentially as saprophytes on *Carya* spp., but occasionally are given canker status, are *Physalospora obtusa, P. rhodina* (*1484*), and the chestnut blight fungus *Endothia parasitica.*

The eastern leafy mistletoe *Phoradendron serotinum* (*P. flavescens*) is very common on the southern, lowland species, notably *Carya aquatica* and *C. illinoensis.*

Root Diseases.—Shoestring root rot is as cosmopolitan on species of *Carya* as it is on most hardwoods, but it is not aggressive except on weakened trees. It has, however, been troublesome on pecan in California (*8*). A fungus very similar in appearance and mode of attack, *Clitocybe tabescens,* has killed pecan and scrub hickories in Florida (*1168*). In the reports on pecan, this fungus has sometimes been given the synonym *C. parasitica.* Unlike *A. mellea, C. tabescens* does not produce flat, black rhizomorphs and does not have an annulus.

In Texas and Arizona, two root rots have caused some damage to pecan but have not been harmful to other *Carya* spp. elsewhere. One is Texas root rot (*Phymatotrichum omnivorum*), to which pecan is moderately susceptible (*1379*), and the other is violet root rot, caused by *Helicobasidium purpureum* (imperfect stage *Rhizoctonia crocorum*). The latter invades roots from the soil, turning them reddish or violet and killing them. Small, dark sclerotia are embedded in the purplish to brown fungus surface mat, which may form on the stem in wet weather (*1555*).

Root knot nematodes (*Meloidogyne* spp.) have been observed on pecan but damage has not been recognized as generally important.

Hendrix and Powell (*635*) report that species of *Pythium,* especially *P. irregulare,* and nematodes, especially *Meloidogyne incognita,* are capable of reducing the fine-root system of large pecan trees, resulting in symptoms of low vigor in the foliage and poor shoot and root growth. They mention the relative freedom of pecan from root diseases.

The sting nematode, *Belanolaimus euthychilus,* has been identified on *Carya cordiformis* in Florida, and 6 species of nematodes,
in several genera, have been reported as associated with *Carya
ovata* in North America (*1222*). A later tabulation by Ruehle
(*1224*) lists species of *Criconemoides, Trichodorus,* and *Xiphinema*
associated with *Carya* spp. in the Southeast.

Mycorrhizal Relations.—The mycorrhizal associations reported
(*1442*) are as follows: on *Carya* spp.—*Boletus edulis* and *Cenococcum graniforme;* on *C. illinoensis*—*Russula aeruginea, R. foetens,*
and *Xerocomus chrysenteron;* and on *C. laciniosa*—*Laccaria och-
ropurpurea.*

Trunk Rots.—A very large number of fungi will rot the woody
cylinder of living hickories and pecans. Some rot heartwood, others
rot dead or senescent sapwood. The main trunk rot fungi of the
North include *Fomes applanatus, F. connatus, F. igniarius, Hydnum (Steccherinum) septentrionale, Poria andersonii* (*210*), and
Poria spiculosa (*220*). Others include *Daedalea ambigua, Fomes
densus, F. everhartii, F. geotropus, F. marmoratus, Hydnum erinaceus, Pleurotus ostreatus* (*425*), *Polyporus cuticularis, P. fissilis,
P. delectans, P. graveolens, P. hispidus, P. lucidus* and its stipitate
form *P. (Ganoderma) curtisii, P. obtusus, P. zonalis,* and many
species of *Poria.* Information on these rot fungi are available in
several publications (*8, 151, 220, 1067*).

Toole (*1417*) was able to have identified 86 percent of the decay
fungi he isolated from the wood behind fire scars in water hickory
(*Carya aquatica*). *Schizophyllum commune,* also known to cause
saprot in injured pecan, *Polyporus lucidus,* and *Stereum complica-
tum* fruited early on the fire scars of this species. Isolates from the
decaying woody cylinder above scars yielded *Hydnum erinaceus,
Pleurotus ostreatus, Polyporus delectans, P. fissilis, P. hispidus, P.
zonalis,* and *Poria corticola.* The rate of decay upward from the
scars was mostly slower for water hickory than for red oaks, overcup oak, sugarberry, ash, or sweetgum, but *Polyporus fissilis* and
Pleurotus ostreatus spread rapidly in water hickory. True heart rot
did not develop until 10 years after wounding.

Campbell and Verrall (*220*) consider *Poria spiculosa,* which produces a soft, white heart rot, to be the most widespread and damaging disease of hickory. Cankers resulting from spiculosa infections indicate extensive decay (*215*). However, while this disease
is easily recognizable in the field, isolation of fungi from random
decaying hickories, as done by Toole (*1417*), may show that in the
aggregate many fungi exceed *P. spiculosa* in destroying wood of
living hickories.

Bryan (*180*) studied defect in many Piedmont hardwood species
and found *Poria spiculosa* particularly common in hickories and
oaks. Hickories led all species in incidence of bird-peck (44 percent
of his trees showed peck), and peck accounts for much of the sapwood streaking that causes degrade in hickory. He gives data on,
and illustrations of, many common hickory defects.

A large number of hickory and pecan fungi rot only dead wood.
While no attempt is made here to list them all, some of the most
common, in addition to many of the trunk rotters listed above, are
Favolus alveolaris on *Carya tomentosa;* and *Fomes pinicola, Poria
ambigua, P. canescens, P. semitincta, P. unita,* and several species

of *Trametes* on different species of *Carya* (*8*).

Miscellaneous Pathology.—Some of the essentially harmless fungi that live on twig and branch insects have already been mentioned under "Stem Diseases."

Four fungi are known to live on hickory bark but cause no necrosis or other pathology. *Solenia ochracea* (*1278*) is a thelephoraceous fungus with small, cylindric pilei, that forms harmless patches on the bark in the Northeast. *Myriangium tuberculans* (*M. curtisii*) is an ascomycete that causes black spots on the bark of pecan. Its perithecia are really locules in a dark stroma. *Carya glabra* is reported as supporting on its bark *Rosellinia aquila,* an ascomycete with almost free perithecia borne in a light fungus weft, and *Melanconis juglandis* var. *caryae,* an ascomycete with small, black acervuli that, in wet weather, develop spore horns of olive-gray conidia.

Hickory logs not milled soon after cutting are subject to degrade and cull from insects and fungi (*220*). In the South logs may be stored only for the three coldest winter months without appreciable loss. Both decay and staining become worse when insect attack takes place. Both ambrosia beetles and lyctus powder-post beetles attack hickory. Hickory sapwood and heartwood also have no appreciable natural resistance to decay. Therefore logs that must be stored are commonly sprayed with a fungicide-insecticide solution, and lumber is dipped in antistain chemicals (*220*).

The main defects in hickory veneer logs are bird (sapsucker) peck, insect boring, "mineral" stain, bark pockets, knots, ring shake, and cracks resulting from differential internal stresses expressed immediately following felling (*897*).

Red hickory wood, indicating either normal or pathological heartwood, is often discriminated against. Extensive tests have shown such wood to be as strong as white hickory sapwood (*3*).

Spanish moss (*Tillandsia usneoides*), although not parasitic, and using the trees only as a substrate, will often accumulate to such an extent on pecan and water hickory as to damage by smothering (*1056*). Lichens, which do no harm, are common on pecan branches (*1057*).

Winter injury causes sunken and cracked areas of branches of mainly vigorous-growing young trees. Freezes have led to abnormal flowering in pecan (*278*), and sunscald may kill bark on the south or southwest sides of trees (*1057*).

American chestnut

Castanea dentata

The American chestnut, eliminated as a commercial species by a fungus blight, once made up more than one-fourth of all hardwood sawtimber in the Southern Appalachian Mountains. It surpasses any American tree in number and diversity of uses. It grew from Maine to Alabama and westward almost to the Mississippi River. Trees over 100 ft. high and over 6 ft. in diameter were not uncommon in the southern mountains. These hollow veterans were several hundred years old (*196*). Chestnut is suited to a wide variety of soils and grew well all through the mountains, the Piedmont, and the Ohio River Basin areas.

Chestnut did not often grow in pure stands but was a component of many forest types, preferring mountain slopes and coves. It is only intermediate in tolerance (54). The bark and wood are high in tannin, the wood is durable, and the nuts are preferred food for game and humans. Its strong sprouting capacity coupled with the incapacity of the blight fungus to destroy roots (540) has kept the species alive in spite of the repeated killing of successive generations of sprouts. Chestnut was moderately sensitive to fire, quite easily damaged by ice (310), and subject to injury from extremes in temperature. The chestnut was already receding from the Piedmont in the 19th century (196), very likely as a result of root attack by the fungus *Phytophthora cinnamomi* (304). The blight then followed, and by 1930 had sealed the doom of the chestnut as a commercial species by extending its advance infections virtually over the range of the tree.

The pathology of American chestnut, aside from Phytophthora root rot and the blight, consisted mainly of a few weak twig fungi, some minor leaf diseases, and a large number of important butt and heart rot fungi that made hollow shells out of most overmature trees. A common, decorative commercial grade of chestnut wood, often riddled to the point of weakness, was called "sound and wormy," indicating that there were stain-lined galleries of the chestnut timber worm in the wood (297), but no decay.

Foliage Diseases.—No leaf disease of chestnut can be considered major. The arrangement below puts these diseases in approximate order of their importance in appearance and health of leaves in midsummer. All of them are known on the eastern chinkapins, as well as on chestnut.

The common powdery mildew fungus *Phyllactinea guttata* (151, 1153), with its bulbous, unbranched perithecial appendages, and also *Microsphaera alni*, with branched appendages, can be very copious, particularly on sprout leaves and in dry weather late in the summer.

Actinopelte dryina (863) causes very small spots in great abundance, and in wet summers can virtually ruin the foliage by August. It is mainly a disease of the red oaks and is described under *Quercus*.

A small, brown-bordered spot called eye-spot (*Marssonina ochroleuca*) (151) can be very conspicuous. The circular, sharply delimited, sunken grayish spots bear conidia with two cells of unequal size, in acervuli on the spots.

Monochaetia monochaeta (*M. desmazierii*) (558, 624) causes brown to gray circular spots up to ½ in. in diameter, typically with indefinite margins and often concentrically zonate. The conidia are 5-celled, elliptic, and with the three intermediate cells olivaceous. These spots can expand and rapidly involve the entire leaf (536).

Cylindrosporium castaneae (*C. castaneicolum*) is likely the conidial stage of *Mycosphaerella maculiformis*, the latter stage appearing on fading leaves. Stevens (1352) states that *Phyllosticta maculiformis* is also an imperfect stage of the same fungus. The foliage of many tree species is spotted by this fungus, particularly in the North.

Two species of *Phyllosticta*, *P. castanea* and *P. fusispora* have

107

been described by Ellis and Everhart from *Castanea* foliage. They cause small, circular spots in which the small, black pycnidia are embedded.

Occasionally the uredia and telia of *Cronartium quercuum* (*46*) will appear in abundance on the underside of chestnut or chinkapin foliage. It is likely that the "forma specialis" of this rust is the *cerebrum* or *fusiforme* type rather than the strictly deep-South cone rust forma *strobilinum*. These three formae are not distinguishable morphologically on the telial hosts, except as described under *Quercus* spp.

Stem Diseases.—The chestnut blight, a canker disease, is the only plant pathogen to have virtually eliminated its host. Except for recurrent sprouting, occasional seedlings, isolated orchards in the West, and a few heavily blighted veterans at high elevations in the southern mountains, the chestnut and a large proportion of the chinkapins, which are more resistant to the blight than chestnut trees, have been destroyed. From the time of its discovery in New York in 1904, the disease spread rapidly and 30 years later every stand of chestnut in the East was under attack or already killed out. While diligent efforts are still being made to seek out and propagate from any American chestnut tree showing evidence of strong resistance to the blight, so far no tree of *Castanea dentata* is known to have withstood the blight sufficiently to warrant strong optimism (*381*).

Chestnut blight cankers are caused by the fungus *Endothia parasitica*. Infection is through wounds. The fungus spreads through the inner bark and cambium leaving fan-shaped, buff-colored mycelial wefts. Two spore stages are formed on the bark: the perithecial stage, with reddish, perithecial groups dotted with ostiolar openings, and the conidial stage, which in wet weather oozes long, coiled tendrils of conidia from pycnidia (*534, 535*). Some cankers enlarge so rapidly that a stem is encircled without any callus forming. On other trees, considerable callusing takes place as healing takes the lead temporarily over fungus spread. Root bark is highly resistant to attack, even after inoculation (*540*), and this accounts for the persistence of sprouting.

Highly susceptible to blight, in addition to *Castanea dentata,* are *C. sativa, C. pumila* and the other eastern American chinkapins, and post oak, *Quercus stellata* (*262*). The Asiatic species *C. crenata* and *C. mollissima* are resistant. The fungus grows as a saprophyte on many forest species in the genera *Acer, Carya, Quercus,* and *Rhus* (*151*).

Two additional species of *Endothia* grow as saprophytes on chestnut and other species. These are *E. gyrosa* and *E. radicalis* (*E. fluens*). They are distinctive in culture as well as being not pathogenic or only very weakly so (*1283*).

An extensive literature has been built up on the chestnut blight. Good summaries appear in standard texts (*81, 151, 725*), and a more recent assessment of the past and future of the American chestnut with respect to the blight has been made by Diller and Clapper (*381*). A history of the blight over a 50-year period is provided by Beattie and Diller (*85*).

Strumella coryneoidea causes a canker, mainly of oaks (see *Quercus*) in the North, but is not uncommon on hickories, and in the past occurred also on chestnut. The cankers have concentric, sunken flutings, and retain the bark, which is firmly attached to rotted wood beneath. Very dark cushions of sterile, 1-celled conidia develop on the bark. The perfect stage, *Urnula craterium (110, 338)*, fruits only on dead wood on the ground or on stumps.

Mainly a cause of twig blight of oaks in the North and in the Appalachian Mountain chain, *Sphaeropsis quercina* (perfect stage *Physalospora glandicola*), known widely as *Diplodia longispora,* was just as common on chestnut. Shoots commonly die for a foot or more back, while foliated, so that these "flags" become very conspicuous in summer, looking much like cicada twig killing. Larger stems can be attacked through wounds. Black, globoid pycnidia with dark, 1-septate conidia break through the bark *(151)*.

Both *Cryptodiaporthe castanea* and *Botryosphaeria ribis* can cause twig blights and cankers on shoots of both native and Asiatic chestnuts *(471)*. *C. castanea* produces small, black pycnidia with hyaline, typically 2-celled, slightly unequally fusoid conidia, and erumpent, beaked perithecia with ascospores much like the conidia, but with a small appendage at each end. *B. ribis* is as described under *Cercis canadensis*. Fowler *(471)* describes both fungi and a *Diplodia* sp. as they appear on Asiatic chestnut species.

In parts of the South and the Ohio River Valley, the eastern leafy mistletoe, *Phoradendron serotinum (P. flavescens)*, grew in the crowns of chestnut trees.

American chestnut and the European *Castanea sativa* have been demonstrated to be susceptible to the oak wilt disease *(Ceratocystis fagacearum)*.

Root Diseases.—The dying of chestnut and chinkapins in the southern Piedmont and on other clayey soils of the lower elevations in the South, dating back to early in the 19th century, is considered by many to have characteristics similar to the ink disease of chestnut in Europe *(304)*. The European root disease is attributed in part to *Phytophthora cinnamomi* and in part to *P. cambivora* (see *Fagus sylvatica*). Crandall et al. *(304)* record the evidence indicating that the recession of *Castanea* spp. prior to the blight was due to Phytophthora root rot *(P. cinnamomi)* and point out the susceptibility of members of the genus *Castanea,* as compared to the resistance of some other hardwoods.

The fungus advances along roots and root collars in wedge-shaped streaks, turning the invaded bark tissues brown or green and girdling roots and stems. Root lesions exude an inky-blue exudate that stains the soil close to the roots. This disease can spread rapidly among young trees in a newly invaded area and has hampered the growing of the native and Asiatic chestnuts for root stocks in the Southeast, as well as proved a serious disease in nurseries raising as diverse crops as black walnut *(Juglans nigra)* and Fraser fir *(Abies fraseri)*.

The causal species of some of the bleeding canker Phytophthoras attacking hardwood trunks, e.g. of maples and oaks, may prove to be very close taxonomically to the chestnut root rot Phytophthora(s) of Europe and North America. An account of early chestnut recession, as well as other diseases of hardwoods and conifers, attributed to *Phythophthora cinnamomi* is given by Gravatt and Crandall *(533)*.

Shoestring root rot (*Armillaria mellea*) can attack chestnut of very low vitality, and rhizomorphs can often be seen also on healthy vigorous roots. Long (*883*) gives a detailed account of the killing of weakened oak and chestnut by *A. mellea*. *Fomes annosus* has been reported as a root and butt rot of chestnut in Michigan. However, none of the basidiomycete root rots have been important as killing agents with chestnut. Among the other species of this root rot group that can deeply penetrate and rot roots of large chestnut trees are *Polyporus berkeleyi*, causing a sweet-smelling soft rot; *P. spraguei*, a brown rot; and *P. sulphureus*, a brown cubical rot (*151*).

The American chestnut is rated as extremely susceptible to Texas root rot (*Phymatotrichum omnivorum*), and the chinkapin moderately so (*1379*).

Only *Amanita pantherina* and *Cenococcum graniforme* have been reported to form mycorrhizae with American chestnut (*1442*).

Species of nematodes in 4 genera have been identified from chestnut (*1222*).

Trunk Rots.—Like most of the hardwoods, living chestnut is subject to decay by dozens of fungi. They are largely the same species as decay oak. Since chestnut is a ring-porous wood with a high proportion of true heartwood, it tends to support many true heart rot fungi, as apart from those which decay the heartwood of dead or down trees, and the rotters of dead sapwood and slash.

The decay fungi that cause the most cull in chestnut are the trunk rotters *Fomes everhartii, F. ohiensis, Hydnum erinaceus, Pleurotus ostreatus, Polyporus croceus, Stereum frustulatum,* and *S. gausapatum;* and the root and butt rotters *Polyporus berkeleyi, P. spraguei,* and *P. sulphureus.* While conks help identify decays, they are usually absent from living trees, and if they occur they may not be associated with the main decay column. A few rots can be identified macroscopically as to cause, such as *Polyporus berkeleyi* by the sweet smell and *Stereum frustulatum* by its pockets; but only pure cultures will provide certain identification for most decays. Anyone working with the identification of the decays of chestnut and the oaks would be well advised to consult Overholts (*1067*) ; the works of Josiah Lowe on *Fomes, Polyporus,* and *Poria;* the standard tests (*81, 151, 725*) for conk and rot descriptions; the work of Davidson, et al. (*343*) on cultural identification of the oak rot fungi; and that of Nobles (*1038*) on cultural identification of wood-rotting fungi in general.

Miscellaneous Pathology.—Since chestnut had been the chief source of vegetable tannin for heavy leathers and had a multitude of other uses, it was imperative to know how long the supply would last after death of the main stands. Many studies were devoted to this subject, chiefly beginning with Baxter's (*78*) bulletin and ending with the report of Cruikshank, Hepting, Toole, and Roth (*311*). The latter was a complete analysis of chestnut supply, deterioration rate, and the state of the extract industry. Issued in 1951, it correctly forecast the virtual end of the industry by 1960 and showed curves of rate of deterioration for different States. Baxter (*79*) has provided an account of the fungi that are known to rot chestnut wood in North America and abroad, and a list of 183 basidiomycetes reported on *Castanea*.

Ciborinia hirtella, a fungus characterized by hairy apothecia that develop on fallen plant material in the spring, attacks the leaves and the bark of small twigs of *Castanea* spp. *(76).*

Golden chinkapin
Castanopsis chrysophylla

Also called giant chinkapin, the golden chinkapin is a West Coast, broad-leaved evergreen that can grow to heights well over 100 ft. and diameters over 6 ft. Its maximum longevity is estimated as about 500 years *(1367).* It thrives in western Washington, Oregon, and south to central California and also occurs in parts of the Sierra Nevada. It grows mostly along the western mountain slopes, from low to moderate elevations in Oregon to elevations mostly between 7,000 and 10,000 ft. in California. It grows in valleys, ravines, and canyons, typically on dry, gravelly soils *(1367).* It is tolerant *(54),* and its climatic requirements are much like those of *Abies concolor* in the Northwest and those of *Pinus jeffreyi* in central California. The prickly burs and nuts resemble those of the eastern *Castanea pumila.* The leaves, however, are entire.

The tree form of this species is almost confined to the north coast of California, and northward, below 2,000 ft. in elevation. W. W. Wagener[14] states that the tree form grades into var. *minor,* over a wide range in California and Oregon, from 1,000 to 6,000 ft. in elevation. The high elevation *Castanopsis* shrub in the Sierras and southern California is *C. sempervirens.*

The golden chinkapin is remarkably free from disease, and the species has fortunately escaped the chestnut blight even where it was growing in close proximity to early, and since-eradicated, blight infections on *Castanea sativa* and a probable *C. sativa* X. *C. dentata* hybrid in Oregon in 1930 *(87).* Inoculations in the East have shown that the golden chinkapin will take the disease, but it is resistant *(725).* Shaw *(1277)* lists only 11 fungi reported from this tree, and the chestnut blight fungus is not among them.

Foliage Diseases.—Even the commonest leaf fungi do little harm and appear mainly on older foliage or after leaf fall.

Dothidella janus, a leaf-spot fungus with eight synonyms, is discussed by Cooke *(283).* Widely distributed in the far West on *Castanopsis* and *Quercus,* it also is known from Florida on evergreen oaks. It has a *Phyllosticta* imperfect stage, and its perithecia occur in a sunken stroma and produce 2-celled, hyaline ascospores.

Coronellaria castanopsidis blotches old leaves, and it fruits on the underside of fallen leaves as sessile, waxy, brownish apothecia *(769).*

Gloeosporium castanopsidis and *Sphaerulina myriadea* have been described on old leaves in California.

Taphrina castanopsidis causes concave-convex distortions referred to as "leaf blister" *(994).*

The common powdery mildew *Microsphaera alni* can cause dis-

---

[14] Personal communication from W. Willis Wagener, deceased, formerly pathologist, USDA Forest Service, Pacific Southwest Forest and Range Experiment Station, Berkeley, Calif.

tortion and damage late in the season.

Miscellaneous Pathology.—A few saprobic fungi are known to inhabit twigs. Bedwell and Fowler (*90*) sought out the fungi on *Castanea* and *Castanopsis* in the West, and they concluded that on the latter genus all those found were secondary, and only capable of adding to damage already inflicted by other agents, or becoming aggressive on trees growing under adverse circumstances.

The golden chinkapin is also a poor medium for wood-destroying fungi, with remarkably few reported even on the dead wood (*8, 1277*). A few more common saprobic basidiomycetes have been found than are reported in the literature.[15]

A root and butt rot is caused by *Armillaria mellea* and by *Ganoderma oregonense* (*1067*). The mushrooms and black rhizomorphs of the former and the "varnished-topped" conks of the latter are of diagnostic value.

Fomes igniarius (*1050*) is the most aggressive of the true heart rot fungi known to attack golden chinkapin.

Only *Cenococcum graniforme* has been reported as a mycorrhizal fungus of this species (*1442*).

Horsetail casuarina

Casuarina equisetifolia

A native of tropical Asia and Australasia, the horsetail casuarina is also known as Australian-pine or beefwood. Introduced long ago into Florida and southern California, it is now naturalized in these subtropical areas of the United States and has been widely grown in the southern part of Florida for ornament, windbreaks, hedges, and to stabilize shifting sand. It grows very rapidly, produces bark suitable for tanning and dyes, and it has been used experimentally in the making of paper pulp, although neither bark nor wood is so used in the United States.

This species grows rankly under a wide variety of soil conditions, excluding swamps. It is very subject to cold and frost damage but withstands salt spray well. It is generally free from disease, but intervals of cold weather have resulted in much dieback of trees of all ages even in some subtropical parts of Florida.

The *Equisetum*-like foliage of this tree is not known to be subject to disease anywhere in the world. Spaulding (*1338*) mentions some major pathogens to which the species is subject in parts of the world other than North America, including southern root rot (*Sclerotium rolfsii*), Phytophthora root rot (*Phytophthora cambivora*), the seedling blight caused by *Macrophomina phaseoli* (*Sclerotium bataticola*), the bacterial wilt caused by *Pseudomonas solanacearum,* and a few others. A virus brooming disease occurs in parts of Central America that is causing the weakening and death of large numbers of this casuarina (*1548*).

In parts of Florida, according to Rhoads (*1168*), the root rot caused by *Clitocybe tabescens* is so damaging to the horsetail casuarina that the usefulness of the species is destroyed. He provides a

---

[15] Personal communication from Lewis F. Roth, professor of plant pathology, Oregon State University, Corvallis, Oreg.

photograph of a *Casuarina lepidophloia* tree killed by this fungus and illustrates the root collar lesions, the fungus felts beneath the bark, rotted roots, and the mushrooms of *C. tabescens* on several woody hosts. Except for the lack of flat, black rhizomorphs and lack of an annulus on the mushrooms, this fungus together with its mode of attack is very similar to *Armillaria mellea*. The whitish, perforated mycelial mats that occur under the bark are considered of diagnostic value.

Armillaria mellea has been reported to kill the horsetail casuarina in California, but this root rot is not highly destructive to casuarina.

Old casuarinas have been observed to be attacked by either *Fomes applanatus* or its close southern relative *F. marmoratus*. Overage trees along highways and near homes have proved to be hazards because the combination of root and butt rot, with the high winds common in Florida, will often result in large casuarinas breaking over or uprooting.

Root knot nematodes are common on the roots of casuarinas in Florida, but their damage potential has not been assessed. There have been few reports of other types of nematodes (*1222*). Ruehle (*1224*) lists 4 species of nematodes in 4 genera, associated with the horsetail casuarina in Florida.

The only fungus reported to form mycorrhizae with *Casuarina* spp. is *Hymenogaster cerebellum* (*1442*).

Catalpa

Catalpa spp.

There are two native species of catalpa, and the main elements of their pathology are so similar that the diseases of the two are here considered together.

Southern catalpa (***Catalpa bignonioides***) is also known as common or eastern catalpa. Grown widely over the entire East as an ornamental, its native range is along streams and other moist sites from southwestern Georgia and Florida to Louisiana. It is intolerant, damaged easily by fire, resistant to ice breakage, and very adaptable as to site. It is not as hardy as the northern catalpa. It grows mainly to heights of 20 to 40 ft. and diameters from 12 to 24 in. The trunk is short, often crooked, and the crown is made up of crooked branches. The commonest cultivated variety is *nana*, which has a broad, dense, umbrellalike head.

Northern catalpa (***Catalpa speciosa***) is also known as hardy or western catalpa. It also is widely cultivated in the East, Midwest, and the West Coast. Its native range was restricted to the area from southern Indiana to western Tennessee, and to northeastern Arkansas. It grows to heights over 70 ft. and, unlike the southern catalpa, has no recognized varieties (*1154*). A northern catalpa in Maryland reached a diameter of 6 ft. (*4*). The species is intolerant, and resists ice breakage (*310*) because its lack of fine twigs minimizes ice loading. The catalpas are about average in their capacity to resist damage from flooding (*583*). Northern catalpa recovered well after heavy exposure to salt water and salt spray during a hurricane (*1632*).

At the turn of the century, this tree was so highly regarded in its native habitat that Hall (*584*) wrote, "A few years trial on the plains sufficed to prove its good qualities for that region. It was easily propagated, grew rapidly on prairie soil, had good form, was drought resistant, had few insect or fungus enemies, and above all was a lasting timber, adapted to many uses." He shows excellent photographs of how well-planted *Catalpa speciosa* can do on the best sites of its native habitat.

The catalpas have very durable heartwood and thus are very useful for wood to be used in contact with the ground.

The most significant aspects of the pathology of the catalpas are as follows: Attack of nursery stock by nematodes, Verticillium wilt of street trees, and Texas root rot in the southern Great Plains area.

Seedling Diseases.—Catalpas have been attacked occasionally by parasitic fungi in nurseries. In the South and East root-knot nematodes (*Meloidogyne* spp.) have frequently been damaging (*360*), and powdery mildews are also common, particularly late in the season.

Pythium ultimum, Rhizoctonia crocorum, R. solani, and *Sclerotium rolfsii* have been known to attack catalpa seedlings in the Great Plains. *P. ultimum* caused a seedling root rot over a span of many weeks. It typically, but not always, produces oospores in culture, is well described by Middleton (*957*), and is discussed by Campbell and Sleeth (*219*) as the cause of a major disease of guayule.

Rhizoctonia solani (*Pellicularia filamentosa*) (*1555*) usually occurs only in the mycelial or sclerotial stages. It produces small, irregular, brownish-black sclerotia on a whitish thallus on basal lesions that sometimes develops the *Pellicularia* (*Corticium*) stage.

Rhizoctonia crocorum (*Helicobasidium purpureum*) produces a brownish-violet, fruiting felt on the attacked seedling, and on the ground around it. It, also, produces sclerotia (*1091*).

Sclerotium (*Pellicularia*) *rolfsii* causes a disease called southern root rot, which is similar to the two preceding species. It produces white wefts of mycelium around the seedling base, spreading fanwise, and also growing in and on the surrounding ground if moist. Sclerotia are formed in abundance. They are first white, then reddish to brownish. Westcott (*1555*) gives a good account of this fungus and the other common pathogenic species of *Pellicularia*.

Another seedling disease in the Midwest is called black root rot (*Thielaviopsis basicola*). Living in the soil, the causal fungus enters nematode wounds. The disease can be severe on heavy, cold soils, with abundant humus. Hyaline conidia are produced endogenously and expelled from the tips of branched conidiophores. Short, cylindrical chlamydospores, with a thick, brown wall are borne serially on the ends of hyaline mycelial branches. Asci are rare and are completely enclosed within round, brown ascocarps (*1352*).

Foliage Diseases.—None of the catalpa leaf diseases are important except for attacks by two powdery mildews (*Microsphaera alni* var. *vaccini* and *Phyllactinia guttata*), mostly late in the season and mostly on sprout leaves or nursery stock (*619*).

An anthracnose fungus, *Gloeosporium catalpae*, like most of

114

this group makes small, discrete brown spots with hyaline, ovate spores on needle-shaped conidiophores produced in acervuli on attached leaves.

Cercospora catalpae causes gray to brown circular spots, 1-4 mm. in diameter, often with a darker border. Fruiting is hypophyllous, as globular, brown stromata with dense fascicles, bearing pale olive-brown, long, narrow, multiseptate conidia (*260*).

Phyllosticta catalpae (*P. bignoniae* ?) is a common cause of summer spotting. It can easily be distinguished from the other spotting fungi by the small, black, subcuticular, scattered pycnidia; bearing ovate, hyaline conidia 5-7μ $\times$ 2-5μ (*1352*). Its perfect stage may be *Didymosphaeria catalpae*, which fruits on fallen leaves.

Other leaf fungi on catalpas include a species of *Ascochyta*, a spot anthracnose *Sphaceloma* (La.), and a surface, dark, sooty mold caused by *Capnodium axillatum*. An *Alternaria* sp., common on spots of both catalpas, may be a secondary invader (*8*).

In dry areas of the Great Plains and the West, catalpas can develop chlorosis due to mineral deficiencies resulting from soil alkalinity, as in iron-deficiency lime-induced chlorosis.

Stem Diseases.—The main killing disease of ornamental catalpas is Verticillium wilt (*Verticillium albo-atrum*) (*224, 412, 1216*). Carter (*231*) shows a photograph of a very severely wilted and defoliated catalpa which, in subsequent years, recovered and had not since shown wilt symptoms. This disease has been discussed under *Acer saccharum* and *Olea*. Recovery, as portrayed in Carter's photograph, can take place especially in ring-porous woods like catalpa and elm, if the vigor of the tree enables it to put a new ring of summerwood and springwood outside the infected ring, and if the common difficulty of radial spread of the fungus within the xylem is sufficient to keep it "sealed" into the enveloped infected ring.

Catalpas as street trees are commonly killed by Verticillium wilt. Often the ring or partial ring of discolored outer sapwood xylem is enough for diagnosis. If not, cultural identification of the fungus is quite simple.

Botryosphaeria ribis (*1555*) is one of the most common saprobes attacking dead hardwood branches of trees of many genera. Yet under some conditions and with some tree species, it can be an aggressive parasite. It causes a particularly fast-spreading, lethal canker of *Cercis* and constitutes redbud's principal pathogen. It has been considered as a cause of twig blight of southern catalpa out of its range.

Root and Trunk Rots.—*Catalpa speciosa* was rated intermediate in inoculation tests with respect to susceptibility to Texas root rot (*Phymatotrichum omnivorum*). Although this tree has never reached the stature as a Great Plains plantation species that Hall (*584*) envisioned for it, it has been used to some extent in the windbreak program. In following the performance of windbreak species planted in root rot soils of Texas and Oklahoma, Wright and Wells (*1627*) rated *C. speciosa* moderately susceptible. However, only 5 of the 800 trees checked had died of root rot over a 5-year period.

Seedlings have been destroyed by the violet root rot caused by *Helicobasidium purpureum* (*Rhizoctonia crocorum*) (*1555*). The disease is briefly described under *Melia azedarach*.

Armillaria mellea has been known to inhabit the roots of *C. speciosa* in the Northeast, but not as a primary pathogen.

Only a few wood-destroying fungi attack catalpa, and most of these rot only dead sapwood. However, *Collybia velutipes* can rot bole heartwood as a wound parasite, much as Roth (*1196*) has described its activity in snow-damaged *Liriodendron*. Von Schrenk (*1481*) devoted most of his discussion of catalpa diseases to the importance and behavior of *Polyporus versicolor* as a virulent heart rotter of wounded catalpa. He also described a brown, cubical butt rot of the *P. sulphureus* type, and gave it the provisional nomen nudum *Polyporus catalpae*. It is no longer possible to determine the identity of his fungus.

Miscellaneous Pathology.—Weddell (*1528*) described extensive cankering of 23-year-old planted *Catalpa bignonioides* trees in Georgia, that developed as a result of a curious "recreational" sequence. Fishermen like to use as bait the catalpa worm, which feeds on foliage. They beat the trunks to make the worms fall. These contusions then become infected by *Hypoxylon rubiginosum*, which will not invade uninjured bark. Weddell illustrates the cankering that followed. Hail damage has also led to decay in catalpa, in a similar manner.

In considering the diseases of catalpa on a world.basis, it is of interest to note that Paclt (*1068*) lists 93 fungi and six other diseases and injuries recorded on *Catalpa* spp.

The common southern root-knot nematode *Meloidogyne incognita* has been reported to injure catalpa roots in Alabama (*1222*).

Deodar cedar

Cedrus deodara

Deodar cedar has become a familiar evergreen ornamental in warm or warm-temperature parts of the United States. Its pyramidal form; soft-hued, dark blue-green foliage; and the interesting spiral arrangement of the needles, which are densely fascicled on the spurs, have made it a favorite tree for many situations (*1154*). Its native habitat is in Temperate Zones, and moderate elevations of the western Himalayas, where the tree grows to 150 ft. high. The wood is used for many purposes, including distillation for cedar oil. It was introduced into the United States sometime prior to 1831 (*1*).

This species can be grown successfully on a wide variety of soils, but it is not hardy and can be planted with assurance only in California, where particularly beautiful specimens grow (*955*), and in the South. Hepting, et al (*664*), reported that following a sudden severe drop in temperature in the Southeast in 1950, without a satisfactory preceding hardening-off period, many Deodar cedars in the western Carolinas and northern Georgia, not over 20 years old, died down from the terminal at least 5 to 10 ft. This type of dieback is a common sight where temperatures drop to 10° to 15° F. Parker (*1080*), for this species, gives the limit of "summer resistance" to cold at 20° F. and "winter resistance" at 0° F. However, geographic races may occur in Asia that could provide strains better able to survive our cooler temperate regions (1).

The male and female flowers are borne separately on the same or different trees. Pollination takes place in the fall, and the cones do not begin to grow until spring and may not fully develop until the third year. The mature seed is soft and oily.

The species can be propagated by veneer grafting, or by cuttings of adventitious shoots (1).

Despite its lack of hardiness, and its consequent susceptibility to dieback from cold, this tree is remarkably free from disease in the United States.

Seedling Diseases.—Seeds germinate the spring following dispersal. Dormancy is not a factor. Mineral soil or ashes make the best seedbed, and full light is essential for seedling development. Yet, seedlings are very sensitive to drought (1).

While reports are lacking on the fungi responsible for damping-off in Deodar cedar, the species, being one of the Pinaceae, is quite susceptible to damping-off, in contrast to the resistance of trees of the Cupressaceae. In Italy a species of *Fusarium* causes a seedling root rot (1338).

Foliage Diseases.—The species is unique in not only having no foliage diseases worthy of note, but no fungi reported on its needles in the United States. In India and Pakistan severe foliage damage and witches' brooms are caused by the autoecious rust *Peridermium cedri* (1338).

Stem Diseases.—While most of the twig dieback in other than subtropical parts of the country is likely caused by cold, *Diplodia pinea* has been blamed for some cankering and dieback (186). In such diseases this fungus probably becomes established following injury from cold or some other impact.

Root Diseases.—Occasional cases of killing root rot have been associated with *Armillaria mellea* (8) and, in the South, with the closely related *Clitocybe tabescens* (1168). Artificial inoculation has shown the true cedars to be either moderately susceptible or resistant to *Phymatotrichum omnivorum* (1379).

Deodar cedar is susceptible to root rot by *Phytophthora cinnamomi* (1659), and, on heavy soils subject to becoming wet for long periods, damage can be expected, particularly in young nursery stock.

The root rot caused by *Polyporus tomentosus* damages this species in India (1338), and since the fungus occurs widely in North America it is likely that it also can cause damage in the United States.

Miscellaneous Pathology.—The only trunk rot fungus reported on Deodar cedar is *Fomes pini*. It is found occasionally in the United States (8), and also occurs on this tree in India (1096).

The only fungi listed by Trappe (1442), as reported to form mycorrhizae on Deodar cedar, are *Amanita pantherina* and *Scleroderma aurantium*.

Three species of nematodes have been reported associated with Deodar cedar in the United States; namely, *Meloidogyne* sp., *Pratylenchus penetrans*, and *Xiphinema americanum*. Several other species occur on this host in Asia (1222).

117

Sugarberry
Celtis laevigata

The sugarberry has also been referred to as hackberry, especially in the Mississippi Delta, but the name hackberry should be reserved for *Celtis occidentalis* (*872*). Sugarberry is abundantly distributed throughout the Mississippi River Delta, and tributary bottom lands of the South, being particularly common in the first bottoms. It is strictly a southern tree ranging from coastal Virginia to southern Florida, west to Texas and northward in the Mississippi Valley to the southern parts of the Central States (*872*). It grew as an occasional tree in virgin stands but now occurs in pure second-growth stands on almost any Delta site. It grows best on low, wet flats (*1140*).

Sugarberry is a medium-sized tree, with a wide crown and often pendant branches. It grows typically to heights of 60 to 80 ft. and to diameters up to 28 in. It is often planted for shade or ornament and has two named varieties (*1154*). It is not hardy and is easily injured by fire. Hepting (*637*) shows a photograph of a young stand of sugarberry in the Mississippi Delta 7 years after a ground fire burned through it.

Sugarberry was listed among the species most resistant to air pollution in the Houston, Texas, area (*911*).

The pathology of this species is very similar to that described for hackberry (*Celtis occidentalis*).

Foliage Diseases.—Most of the leaf diseases are minor and are as described for *Celtis occidentalis*. These include the spots caused by *Cercosporella celtidis*, *Cylindrosporium defoliatum* (and *C. celtidis*), and *Phyllosticta celtidis*.

In Texas sugarberry foliage is quite generally blighted by *Cylindrosporium defoliatum*, which first produces irregular gray blotches that often coalesce (*620*). In later stages the leaves often turn yellow and are shed prematurely. The acervuli are amphigenous but mostly on the upper surface. The spores are extruded in masses and accumulate on the leaf surface where they appear as white tufts. The conidia are cylindric, hyaline, 3- to 5-septate and $3-3.5\mu \times 30-42\mu$. The fungus is clearly distinct from *Cylindrosporium celtidis* Earle, which has been described as forming small spots on sugarberry in Alabama.

Three powdery mildews and one downy mildew attack the foliage. Of these, one powdery mildew, *Sphaerotheca phytophila* (*1153*), is particularly important since, together with gall mites, it is responsible for the witches' brooming disease described under hackberry. Two other powdery mildews on sugarberry foliage, *Uncinula parvula* and *U. polychaeta* (*1153*), do not cause brooming. They, also, are annotated under hackberry.

Kimbrough and Korf (*791*) point out that two distinct American species on *Celtis* have passed as *Uncinula polychaeta;* namely, *U. polychaeta* and *Erysiphe polychaeta*. They place the former in *Pleochaeta*, describe it, and call it *P. polychaeta*. Kimbrough (*790*) then describes and illustrates the development of this fungus as it occurs on *Celtis laevigata*. In discussing *Uncinula* spp. on *Celtis*, no mention of *U. parvula* is made by these authors.

The downy mildew is *Plasmopara* (*Pseudoperonospora*) *celtidis,* a phycomycete. Emerging from stomata, the monopodially branched conidiophores have branches at right angles and bear ovoid, subhyaline, unicellular conidia. These germinate either by zoospores or by the entire spore contents escaping and then producing a germ tube. Globose, brownish oospores are formed in the thallus.

Thread blight (*Pellicularia koleroga, Corticium stevensii*) can attack sugarberry, especially young trees. Its growth habit on foliage, sometimes causing blighted leaves to hang by fungus threads, is described under *Aleurites* and *Carya* spp. (*1408, 1527*).

Seedling Diseases.—The only seedling disease recorded, other than foliage diseases, is the root rot and damping-off of unhardened seedlings caused by *Helicobasidium purpureum* (*Rhizoctonia crocorum*). The fungus invades and rots roots, turning them purplish or violet. In wet weather the purplish mycelium grows up and covers the stem. As it darkens, the small, almost black sclerotia appear embedded in the mat (*1555*).

Stem Diseases.—Excepting for the witches' broom caused by the powdery mildew described under *Celtis occidentalis*, there are no noteworthy stem diseases of sugarberry.

Hypoxylon rubiginosum is a weak parasite and, as described under *Catalpa* sp., can cause limited damage as an inhabitant of injured bark. This fungus has at least 56 synonyms, according to Miller (*978*), having at one time or another been given almost every other possible *Hypoxylon* name.

Two species of *Septobasidium, S. burtii* and *S. sydowii* (*292*), produce brown felts over scale insects, and can result in twig lesions although growing on the insects.

Two species of *Phoradendron*, the common eastern *P. serotinum* (*P. flavescens*) and also *P. tomentosum* (*P. engelmannii*), parasitize sugarberry in the South (*1580*). The eastern species has short, staminate spikes, and glabrous to slightly hairy foliage. *P. engelmannii* is a Southwestern, Pacific, and Mexican species with long staminate spikes and tomentose foliage and internodes (*1445*).

Root Diseases.—The species of *Celtis* have proved resistant to Texas root rot (*Phymatotrichum omnivorum*) (*1379*). See *Celtis occidentalis* for comments on this root rot and the shoestring root rot (*Armillaria mellea*).

Trunk Rots.—At least twenty wood-destroying fungi have been reported on sugarberry and probably many more inhabit this species. Most either rot the wood of dead trees or dead wood in living trees. After felling and splitting 64 living, fire-scarred trees between 6 and 11 in. in diameter, 7 or more years after scarring, Hepting (*637*) was able to obtain only four pure cultures of rot fungi. These include *Fomes geotropus, Polyporus lucidus,* and *P. zonalis.* He notes that while injured sugarberry was very subject to infection, the decay extended only a very short distance up the bole, and ants or termites almost invariably nested at the head of the short decay column, making pure decay-fungus isolation difficult. None of the sugarberry trees he studied contained heartwood. He concluded that while fire-scar decay could weaken trees, making them subject to windthrow, they caused little cull before heartwood formation begins. He gives decay rates, photographs, and a descriptive section on decay following fire-scarring in young sugarberry.

Toole (*1417*) later studied decay following fire in 240 sugarberry trees from 4 in. to 20 in. in diameter. As in Hepting's (*637*) experience, he obtained relatively few pure cultures (20 percent of the rot samples yielded rot fungi and only 10 percent of these were identifiable). These cultures were of *Pleurotus ostreatus* and *Coprinus* sp. Toole worked with larger trees than did Hepting, and the heartwood or inactive central sapwood decayed more rapidly than the sapwood of very high moisture content in Hepting's younger trees. Thus, Toole found that the average rate of upward spread of rot from scars in sugarberry and overcup oak (*Quercus lyrata*) during the first decade after injury was 2 ft., exceeding the rates for all of the several other Delta hardwood species studied. Toole also gives suggestions for estimating extent of rot from basal wounds in the field and provides data on hollowing, butt bulges, and other characteristics related to such decay in sugarberry and associated species.

Lockard, Putnam, and Carpenter (*876*) describe the wide range of defects in southern hardwoods, and their illustrations and descriptions of outside and inside views of defects can aid in log grading. They discuss 22 log surface abnormalities and 14 log end abnormalities, but only some of these occur in sugarberry.

It would be difficult to assess the relative importance of the many species of rot fungi reported by Hepting (*637*), Toole (*1417*), and in the Index of Plant Diseases in the United States (*8*) on sugarberry, because in *Celtis* one cannot disregard as unimportant many of the fungi that are strictly saprobic on trees of most other genera. Until better means are developed to isolate trunk rot fungi of *Celtis* in pure culture, it will not be possible to appraise the importance of the components of the basidiomycete flora in causing economic loss in standing trees of this genus.

Fungi capable of causing either rot of the central cylinder or rot at wounds of living *Celtis* spp. include, in addition to those already mentioned: *Fomes marmoratus, Daedalea ambigua, Polyporus sulphureus, P. squamosus, P. robiniophilus,* and *P. cuticularis* (*1067*).

Toole and Gamage (*1433*) found sugarberry to be the slowest of five Delta hardwood species in healing over increment borer holes. Staining of the wood, 2 years after the boring, had extended 13 in. vertically in autumn borings in sugarberry and 6 in. in spring borings. Almost a fourth of the autumn borings and one-eighth of the spring borings led to decay, which extended vertically from 4 to 5 inches.

A nematode highly parasitic to amaryllis has been found also to attack the roots of *Celtis laevigata* in Florida (*1222*).

Hackberry

Celtis occidentalis

Hackberry is a somewhat ragged, medium-sized tree of minor importance for timber, but scattered widely throughout the East and into the Great Plains, except in the coldest parts of the northern tier of States and the deep South. In the South its range overlaps that of *Celtis laevigata*, sugarberry, a tree of the hotter parts of the South. It is shade tolerant. Krajicek (*811*), who assembled the silvical characteristics of hackberry, stresses its capacity to thrive under a wide variety of climatic conditions and on different soils. In the Great Plains an annual temperature spread of 140° F. is not uncommon. Hackberry is recommended for planting as a shelterbelt tree in the Texas root rot belt (*1627*).

Hackberry is typically a bottom land tree, occurring mostly in river valleys. It also grows well on soils high in lime, commonly appearing near limestone outcrops. However, it also occurs naturally on sand dunes and on a wide range of sites and aspects, particularly in the middle Mississippi Valley. It cannot withstand permanent flooding or heavy mud deposits, although it tolerates intermittent flooding well (*583*). However, when potted seedlings were flooded for 38 days and then drained, the roots rotted and the trees died. Among the 6 species tested by Hosner (*711*), the effect on hackberry was the most harmful.

On some alluvial soils, hackberry has been known to reach a diameter of 4 ft., a height of 130 ft., and an age of 200 years. Normal expectancy would divide these figures at least by two.

The main features of the pathology of hackberry are as follows: a large number of unimportant leaf spots and fungi that inhabit senescent or dead foliage; three powdery mildews, one of which produces numerous witches' brooms; and a predisposition to decay behind wounds. It is characteristic of trees of the genus *Celtis* to be attacked by fungi peculiar to this genus. Thus, of ten common leaf fungi, the specific names involve the prefix "celt" in seven. All six fungus inhabitants of senescent twigs use the prefix "celt" in the specific names (*8*).

Foliage Diseases.—Of the many leaf spots of hackberry, none has been of sufficient importance to mar the foliage until late in the season.

Cercospora spegazzini, causes somewhat circular spots 2–7 mm. in diameter, convex on one side and concave on the other, yellowish to gray, with hypophyllous, dense, dark fascicles that can cause a sooty appearance. Conidia are cylindric, subhyaline to olivaceous, 0–5- but mostly 3-septate, sometimes slightly curved, $4–5\mu \times 20–45\mu$ (*260*).

Cylindrosporium defoliatum causes irregular grayish spots 1–2 cm. in diameter, often confluent. The acervuli are mostly epiphyllous, bear cylindrical conidia that are hyaline, 3–5-septate, and $3–4\mu \times 30–42\mu$ in dimension (*620*). This fungus can lead to premature leaf fall.

Cercosporella celtidis produces one of the commonest of the hackberry leaf spots. Whereas in *Cercospora* the conidiophores are dark and the conidia at least pale olivaceous, in *Cercosporella* the structures and spores are hyaline throughout, and the multiseptate conidia are cylindric to filiform.

Mycosphaerella maculiformis causes a late-season leaf spotting of many tree species, including hackberry. The perithecial stages form on fallen leaves in the spring, but the imperfect stages, *Cylindrosporium castanicolum* and *Phyllosticta maculiformis*, appear on the spots on attached leaves (*1352*).

Phleospora celtidis produces a spot bearing imperfectly developed pycnidia, consisting mostly of modified host tissue, that bear thick, fusoid to elongate, multiseptate conidia.

Phyllosticta celtidis causes a common late-season spot that bears small, black pycnidia with small, single-celled, ovoid, hyaline conidia.

Septogloeum celtidis is reported as a hackberry spot fungus in New York. The acervuli are very small, subepidermal, erumpent, and pallid; and the conidia are oblong to fusoid, blunt-ended and 2- or more septate.

The most striking disease of hackberry is the witches' brooming caused by the combined action of two agents, one the gall-mite *Eriophyes* sp. and the other a powdery mildew fungus, *Sphaerotheca phytophila* (*1153*). The brooms are of two types, the open type consisting of irregular swellings at a branch base, from which stubby twigs arise; and the closed type resulting when the leader fails to develop normally, ultimately resulting in a compact broom of deformed twigs arising from a large, irregular gall.

The mites can cause leaf galls and warts on twigs, and the fungus grows over these organs. The mildew fungus also grows over and within diseased buds, and perithecia may be found within unopened buds. Sometimes powdery mildew species other than *Sphaerotheca phytophila* grow on areas populated by the mites. Conidia form as chains of one-celled oval spores (oidia) on conidiophores on the surface mycelium. The perithecia are dark spheres with unbranched, unhooked appendages, each of which contains only one ascus (*619*). Rankin (*1143*) gives a good account of this disease-insect brooming complex and provides references to original work on it. Carter (*231*) describes it from Illinois and mentions particularly the abnormal swelling of buds and the development of stunted shoots from swollen buds.

At least two other species of powdery mildew, *Uncinula polychaeta* and *Erysiphe polychaeta* occur on hackberry in the South. In *Uncinula* the perithecial appendages are hooked at the ends and several asci are contained in a single perithecium. Other species of *Uncinula* (*8*) have been reported from species of *Celtis* other than hackberry, so that careful examination would be required for specific determination. Heald (*619*) gives a good treatment of the powdery mildews, and Reed (*1153*) has monographed this family (Erisyphaceae). However, the most recent work on the powdery mildews on *Celtis* is reported here, under *C. laevigata*.

Carter (*233*) mentions a hackberry leaf disease that develops as isolated chlorotic islands mainly on leaves produced during the middle of the growing season. The islandlike areas are bordered by small veins and are variable in shape. First reported in Michigan, it is widespread on *Celtis occidentalis*. It can be so conspicuous that affected trees can be identified at a distance of several hundred feet. Experiments with the potato leafhopper indicate that this insect induces the disease, either by its own direct effects or by transmitting a virus. Judging from Carter's description, the injury pattern is much like that directly attributed to potato leafhopper injury on *Cornus* (*654*).

Hackberry trees, in Washington, D. C., and Urbana, Ill., commonly exhibit symptoms resembling those of *Abutilon* mosaic, in that the leaves have vein-limited chlorotic blotches. Affected leaves are in groups a few leaves back from the growing tips.[16]

Potassium deficiency symptoms have been produced and described for several hardwoods including *Celtis occidentalis* (*1095*).

Stem Diseases.—Although several fungi have been reported from the dead twigs and branches of hackberry, none is considered a primary pathogen. The witches' brooming described above, under leaf diseases, can also be considered a twig disease. Other brooming can be caused by the common eastern mistletoe, *Phoradendron serotinum*, that is easily identifiable by its leafy structure.

The brown felt thallus of *Septobasidium burtii* (*292*) grows over scale insects on living branches of hackberry, but by itself is usually harmless. It will sometimes lead to branch lesions.

Root and Trunk Rots.—The common shoestring root rot (*Armillaria mellea*) plays its usual role of an unaggressive surface root inhabitant until death or injury of roots leads to extensive root rot. The fungus will also extend a short distance up the trunk from rotting roots or basal wounds.

The species of *Celtis* are all resistant to Texas (*Phymatotrichum*) root rot, as demonstrated in inoculations (*1379*) and from field examinations of trees planted for shelterbelts in the Texas root rot area. Only 1.4 percent of the 10,385 planted hackberry trees observed in this area of Texas and Oklahoma over a 6-year period died of this root rot (*1627*).

The small number of rot fungi listed as occurring on hackberry in the United States Index of Plant Diseases (*8*) is not a fair indication of the rot fungus flora of this species. It is probable that if the decays of living hackberry had been studied as Hepting (*637*) and Toole (*1417*) studied sugarberry (*Celtis laevigata*), hackberry in the South would prove to have much the same rot fungus flora. The rot fungi reported specifically from hackberry include the heart rotter *Pleurotus ostreatus*, and the typically saprobic *Daedalea ambigua* and *Polyporus tulipiferus*. *Polyporus robiniophilus*, a cause of heart rot in *Robinia*, is also common in the Ohio River Valley on hackberry (*1067*). The conk is small, corky, white, turning smoky when dry, and may occur in clusters.

The wood of young hackberry, like sugarberry, is virtually all sapwood of high moisture content, so that the upward extension of decay from basal wounds is far slower than that of young oak and ash, which have a high percentage of heartwood even in the pole sizes.

Eastern redbud

Cercis canadensis

The eastern redbud, or Judas tree, is a small, spreading, often multiple-stemmed legume that extends from southern New England to northern Florida, throughout the East and South to the eastern edge of the Great Plains, extending northward to southern Wisconsin. It is particularly common as an understory tree beneath hardwoods in the rolling lands of the temperate South. It thrives

---

[16] Observations by Francis O. Holmes, retired, formerly virologist, Rockefeller Institute of Medical Research, Princeton, N.J., reported at 1967 Annual Meeting of American Phytopathological Society.

in rich, moist woodlands, and while doing best on limestone soils it also is abundant on the acid soils of the Piedmont. It seldom grows over 30 ft. in height or 9 in. in diameter, and usually is much smaller. Rehder (*1154*) recognizes four varieties in addition to the type, one of which has white rather than purple flowers. The tree is widely grown as a handsome ornamental.

Redbud is quite hardy, withstands wide ranges in temperature, and is tolerant of shade. Its pathology is dominated by three diseases: a leaf anthracnose, Botryosphaeria canker, and Verticillium wilt. Some notes on the pathology of western redbud, *Cercis occidentalis,* appear at the end of this account.

Foliage Diseases.—The principal redbud leaf spot is caused by *Mycosphaerella cercidicola,* and it is widely distributed. The spots are brown, circular to angular, from ⅛ to ¼ in. in diameter, often haloed, and they produce a *Cercospora* stage on attached leaves. Fascicles of conidiophores appear on both leaf surfaces, bearing 1- to 3-celled, obclavate, subhyaline conidia. Perithecia form on fallen leaves in the spring. Descriptions and illustrations are provided by Wolf (*1604*).

Cercospora chionea (*C. cercidis* Ray) is a midwestern species causing red-brown spots up to ½ in. in diameter. The margin is irregular, and fruiting is mostly epiphyllous, often showing as a white mold. The fascicles are dense, pale olivaceous near the base, and bear linear to cylindric, variously curved, hyaline spores with several indistinct septa (*260*).

Another leaf spot is caused by *Actinopelte dryina,* with its curious, inverse fruiting on aggregations of tiny spots (*863*). These spots, 3 to 5 mm. across, roundish, light brown, and with purplish borders, may, on *Cercis,* arise from tiny hypophyllous insect galls.

Other leaf spots are caused by *Ovularia cercidis,* that has simple, hyaline, erect conidiophores and ovoid solitary conidia; *Phyllosticta cercidicola,* that has tiny, black pycnidia bearing 1-celled, hyaline conidia; and *Macrophoma cercis* (*1391*), a lesser known species reported only from Illinois, that makes spots 8 mm. across, that bear abundant, dark brown pycnidia with spores 1-celled, hyaline, ovoid, $13-23\mu \times 4.5-7.7\mu.$

Stem Diseases.—By far the most serious disease of redbud is caused either by *Botryosphaeria ribis* or its variety *chromogena.* Both the fungus species and its variety occur on a wide range of woody plants; the species mainly as a saprobe, the variety as a parasite. The latter is called *chromogena* because it turns cornstarch paste purplish when grown on it (*1555*). The variety is particularly virulent on redbud, producing sunken, blackened, stem and twig lesions, that retain the dead bark. Sometimes they will callus over, at least in part. A tree may bear dozens of such lesions, and whole groves of redbud have been killed out by this disease. The fungus fruits in two imperfect stages and one perfect stage. The imperfect stages are a *Dothiorella* (*D. gregaria*) with very tiny, 1-celled spores that may serve as spermatia, and a *Macrophoma* stage with larger spores (*1555*). The perfect stage fruit body is a perithecium with a papillate ostiole, usually many together, interspersed with pycnidia on a black stroma with 1-celled, hyaline spores, 8 to the ascus (*1352*). There are many synonyms for *B. ribis.* Although the fungus has been authoritatively renamed

Botryosphaeria dothidea,[17] the name *B. ribis* continues in wide use.

Wester et al. (*1556*) found many cankers caused by *Botryosphaeria* on both redbud and on several species of *Tilia* in Washington, D.C. Isolates from any given host, whether *Cercis* or a species of *Tilia,* readily infected that host, but cross-infection was almost entirely negative, even among isolates from different species of *Tilia.*

A very good account of *Botryosphaeria ribis* cankering on redbud and on spicebush (*Lindera benzoin*), including descriptions of the fungus and spore dimensions, is provided by Watson (*1525*).

Alfieri (*21*) reported a limb blight of redbud in Florida, caused by *Corticium salmonicolor*, a fungus that also causes limb blights of apple, pear, and fig in the South (see *Ficus carica*).

Verticillium wilt (*Verticillium albo-atrum*) has been known to kill redbud occasionally, particularly in the Midwest (*412*). It is annotated under *Acer saccharum* and *Olea europea*, and the symptoms on redbud are virtually the same except that whereas streaking of the wood is often greenish in maple, it is likely to be brown in redbud.

Miscellaneous Pathology.—Redbud is rated as highly susceptible to Texas root rot (*Phymatotrichum omnivorum*) (*1379*), but the tree is not grown to any extent in the root rot area.

Edgerton (*403*) mentions the association of conks of *Ganoderma* (*Polyporus*) *curtisii* with root rot in older trees of redbud and other woody species. This "varnished-topped" stipitate *Polyporus lucidus*-like fungus was often found emerging from the ground around declining trees in Louisiana.

Rhoads (*1168*) reports three redbud trees attacked by *Clitocybe tabescens* root rot in Florida. This disease and its causal fungus have most of the characteristics of *Armillaria mellea*, except for the *Clitocybe*'s lack of flat, black rhizomorphs, and its lack of an annulus on the mushroom. Raabe (*1142*) lists redbud as "susceptible" to *A. mellea* rot in California.

The California or western redbud (*Cercis occidentalis*) has no diseases that have not already been described on the eastern redbud, excepting dodder. Some reports from Texas mention attack of the western redbud by dodder (*Cuscuta exaltata*), and the occurrence of *Mycosphaerella cercidicola* leaf spot, and the brown felts (*Septobasidium opiculatum* and *S. filiforme*) that grow on scale insects (*292*).

Metcalf (*955*) states that the western redbud species is widely distributed in the foothills of California, and he stresses the beauty of the tree particularly as it occurs in Lake County. However, in most of the State, this species cannot be grown as an ornamental unless left unirrigated through the summer months. The cause of its decline under summer irrigation is not known, but attack by species of *Pythium* or *Phytophthora* is suspected.[18]

---

[17] Correspondence with C. R. Benjamin, leader, Mycology Investigations, Agricultural Research Service, USDA, Beltsville, Md. He states that Arx and Müller (1954) in "Die Gattungen der amerosporen Pyrenomyceten" adopt the name *Botryosphaeria dothidea* (Mong. ex Fr.) Ces. and de Not,. and consider among the synonyms *B. berengeriana, B. ribis, Physalospora gregaria* (in part) and some other names.

[18] Personal communication from R. D. Raabe, professor of plant pathology, University of California, Berkeley, Calif.

The only nematodes reported from redbud are the pin nematode *Paratylenchus projectus* and the dagger nematode *Xiphinema americanum* (*1222*).

Saguaro

Cereus giganteus

The giant cactus, often referred to as *Carnegiea gigantea*, is considered a tree since it has a single main trunk, as compared with *Cereus schottii*, the senita, and *C. thurberi*, the organpipe cactus, both of which have many erect columnar branches emerging from or near the ground (*872*). All three species occur in southern Arizona, southeastern California and extend into Mexico. The saguaro is a conspicuous plant of the Sonoran Desert, growing to over 30 ft. in height and 16 in. in diameter, and to ages up to 200 years (*1035*). Saguaro seedlings that survive typically come up through paloverde (*Cercidium microphyllum*) trees or other "nurse" plants. Growth at first is very slow, and it may take a plant 10 years to grow the first two centimeters. Later growth is faster.

Niering, Whitaker, and Lowe (*1035*) wrote a penetrating analysis of the ecology of saguaro and analyzed factors contributing to the recession of this plant in many environments since 1900. In summarizing the situation, they state in part, "The center of maximum population density in the Tucson area is on the driest slopes of mountains, at low elevations; the finest stands of large individuals occur on some of the upper parts of valley plains or bajadas. Toward higher elevations in the mountains the population is limited by low winter temperatures, which periodically kill large proportions of the population by freezing. Down the bajada slopes the population is limited by the occurrence of finer soils and by other factors. The population is reproducing well on rocky slopes and in some bajada communities but is failing to reproduce on the finer soils of bajadas affected by grazing. The kill by freezing is a temporary catastrophe, for many younger individuals survive the freeze. Grazing subjects the population to a gradual disaster, with slow decline to disappearance resulting from failure of the saguaro to reproduce. When the effects of grazing are far advanced and rodent populations are high, as in parts of Saguaro National Monument, these effects are largely irreversible." Rodents feed on young saguaros with relish, apparently more for water than for food, and have dens in large plants.

The mortality of mature saguaros in an undisturbed stand is estimated at 0.7 percent per year. In some areas the rate is much higher. Death results mainly from root washout, windthrow, freezing, or from bacterial necrosis.

Certainly saguaro supports fewer recorded pathogens or otherwise destructive micro-organisms than any other American tree. In addition to the bacterial wilt, only crown gall and a few rot fungi attack the plant.

Bacterial necrosis (*Erwinia carnegieana*) is described by Lightle, Standring, and Brown (*862*). Small, light-colored spots, usually with water-soaked margins, appear on the surface of the integument of trunk and branches. Subsequently the soft tissues beneath become water-soaked and very dark. A brown liquid may exude. Rapid destruction of tissues accompanies "bleeding," but slower internal decay may proceed without it. The rotted tissues break up into chunks and fall to the ground leaving only bare stelar stands.

Lesions may girdle, leading to windthrow, or rot out the top, or rot one side resulting in a leaning plant. The necrosis kills quickly, often in 2 or 3 weeks, and the tree falls and disintegrates. Tunneling moth larvae distribute the bacilli through the plant (*166*). Some lesions become contained by callus. If not, the plant soon dies. Positive field diagnosis is based upon darkening and softening of subepidermal tissues, and on fluid flow. Many other desert plants are susceptible to the causal bacterium (*18*).

While the bacterial necrosis kills many saguaros, it is important to recognize the many other impacts on reproduction and young trees, as brought out by Niering, et al. (*1035*), in order to understand the stresses leading to recessions in the range and abundance of this tree. Robinson (*1183*) also discusses the many pressures leading to decline of the saguaro.

The pathogens of saguaro other than *Erwinia carnegieana* are not considered important. Crown gall (*Agrobacterium tumefaciens*) has appeared at the base of some plants. A cortical tissue rot has been attributed to *Hendersonia cerei*. A dry, white rot of exposed woody ribs is caused by *Poria carnegiea* (*80*), and a basal rot of woody ribs of branches and trunk is caused by *Fomes robustus*, a fungus with many formae that differ in host preference (*83*), and occur from East to West, and on conifers as well as hardwoods (*1067*).

Davidson and Mielke (*352*) illustrate and describe *Fomes robustus* and its light-colored decay in saguaro. It occurs mostly on the hard, barklike outer tissues at arm bases and on the main stem or ribs exposed by injury. This small and very rimose form of *F. robustus* was found on many other plants of the arid Southwest, in addition to saguaro.

Port-Orford-cedar

Chamaecyparis lawsoniana

The largest species of the genus *Chamaecyparis*, Port-Orford-cedar has one of the most restricted ranges of any American tree, growing naturally only along a 130-mile area from Coos Bay in southwest Oregon, to the area around Eureka, Calif., and from 10 to 40 miles inland (*618*). It occupies a variety of sites west of the Cascade Range summit, thriving on many types of soil, even in swampy areas and on dry ridges, but it grows best in deep, friable soils. The climate of its range is typified by mild and uniform temperatures year-round, with very wet winters and dry summers. Annual precipitation ranges from 35 to 100 in., but summers are dry, with July and August rainfall together amounting to less than 1 in. Mean annual temperature is from 43° to 46° F. with an extreme range from about 0° to 100° F. The tree grows from sea level to 5,000 ft. in elevation (*1367*).

This species is tolerant (*54*), especially when young, and also frosthardy, since it leafs out late in the spring; but it is sensitive to sudden changes in temperature and humidity (1367); and, particularly out of its range, it can be damaged by hard frosts, sun scorch, and drying winds (618). It is sensitive to fire when young but becomes resistant with age. It grows to sizes several ft. in diameter; up to 200 ft. high, with many trees over 300 years old; and it has a maximum longevity approaching 600 years (279). Port-Orford-cedar makes a handsome ornamental, and has been widely planted in the Northeast, Europe, New Zealand, and elsewhere. It can be reproduced by cuttings (1). Its wood is highly desirable for its machining qualities as well as the high durability of the heartwood (618). Lacking a taproot, it is subject to windthrow. When grown in other countries, as in Europe and New Zealand, it sometimes develops multiple stems and misshapen crowns.

The role of Port-Orford-cedar as an important forest and ornamental tree is definitely threatened by the increasing destruction by *Phytophthora lateralis* root rot. This fungus, together with *P. cinnamomi*, has put the future of this species in the West in grave doubt.

Seedling Diseases.—The seeds of Port-Orford-cedar spoil quickly under ordinary storage conditions (1). New seedlings are small and tender, and can be easily injured by heat (601) and by drought. Some tests have indicated first-year survival in the field to range from 21 to 72 percent, with little indication that fungi play an important role in early mortality (618). The species of *Chamaecyparis* and their close relatives are all resistant to damping-off (360). However, *Pythium ultimum, P. irregulare, Phytophthora cinnamomi*, and *P. lateralis* can cause seedling root rots. In the Pacific Northwest (1439) the two Phytophthoras have been very damaging to ornamental nursery stock that is past the seedling stage. They are annotated, under Root Diseases. Phomopsis blight (*P. juniperovora*) has caused damage to seedlings east of the Great Plains.

Foliage Diseases.—*Phytophthora lateralis* does its main damage as a root rotter, but it can also attack foliage directly (1447). Individual aerial infections usually begin on foliage hanging near the ground, and the diseased area spreads upward and laterally giving a triangular pattern (1446). A tree can die from foliage infection alone, but several years may be required for such killing. Sporangia form on foliage only in the presence of free water.

Phomopsis blight (*Phomopsis juniperovora*) has caused occasional damage to the foliage in the East and Middle West, with attack starting at terminal shoots or foliage and working inward.

Stem Diseases.—The stem diseases of Port-Orford-cedar have seldom become important, except for the cankers caused by *Phytophthora lateralis* spreading from foliage into branches, and the basal cankers formed during spread of this fungus upward from the roots (1446).

Phomopsis juniperovora has caused occasional twig blight east of the Great Plains, and from California, Wagener (1488) has reported isolated cases of the *Cupressus* canker caused by *Coryneum cardinale*. The latter is characterized by the fading and death of individual twigs or branches associated with girdling cankers. A disease with similar symptoms, including gummy cankers, and caused by a very similar fungus, *Monochaetia unicornis*, is common and damaging in New Zealand. An apical cilium on the spore of *M. unicornis* separates it from *C. cardinale*, the conidia of which are not ciliate.

A stilbaceous sooty mold, *Arthrobotryum spongiosum* (*700*), occurs on the twigs and branches of Port-Orford-cedar in northern California (*991*). It makes a thick, dark mat over the substrate.

Port-Orford-cedar has been shown by inoculation to be resistant to crown-gall (*Agrobacterium tumefaciens*), and the disease has not been a problem in the culture of this tree. Smith (*1318*) got only weak gall formation in 3 of 90 inoculations, with the remainder negative.

Root Diseases.—By far the most important disease of Port-Orford-cedar is the root rot caused by *Phytophthora lateralis*. Reported first in 1937, the disease spread rapidly within the native range of the tree, and by 1954 the seriousness of the epiphytotic had become obvious (*1438, 1439*). Trees of all age classes are susceptible, and the disease is now considered as beyond control (*1210*). Another damaging root rot was reported attacking this tree in 1950. It is caused by *Phytophthora cinnamomi*, is widely distributed in the range of Port-Orford-cedar, and the root and root-collar symptoms of the two diseases are identical (*1438*). Specific identity requires isolation of the fungi and identification in culture. Both fungi are soil-borne, and both attack and destroy the roots and spread into the base of the stem or trunk, giving the killed inner bark a cinnamon color, with a sharp line of demarcation between the killed and the pinkish white, healthy inner bark (*1438*). Characteristically the entire crown wilts slightly, fades, and gradually changes to yellowish, then bright red, and then brown (*733*).

Phytophthora lateralis has probably been the more aggressive of the two pathogens, and its combined attack on roots, foliage, and branches has made it the major threat. Yet Roth (*1210*) hesitates to "draw analogies" between these two diseases, whose causes, methods of spread, symptoms, and destructiveness are so similar. Campbell and Verrall have found *P. cinnamomi* associated with heavy mortality of young outplanted Port-Orford-cedar in Louisiana (*221*).

Atkinson (*48*) found *Phytophthora lateralis* pathogenic only to *Chamaecyparis lawsoniana; P. cinnamomi* to a wide range of trees and some herbaceous plants; and an unnamed species of *Phytophthora* pathogenic to *C. lawsoniana, Cornus nuttallii,* and several *Rhododendron* spp. Roncadori (*1192*) provides a nutrient comparison of some species of *Phytophthora*.

Clitocybe tabescens, a destructive, killing root rot fungus that is similar in appearance and activity to *Armillaria mellea,* has attacked Port-Orford-cedar in Florida (*1168*).

Both *Fomes annosus* and *Polyporus schweinitzii* have been identified with root rots of this species in Oregon, but they have not had any important economic impact.

Trunk Rots.—*Fomes pini* is the only heart rot fungus reported from Port-Orford-cedar. However, an important heart rot of this species is recognized in Oregon, but the cause has not been determined.

Trametes carbonaria can rot the charred wood of dead trees of

Chamaecyparis, Larix, Sequoia, Thuja, and *Tsuga,* and dead wood has also been attacked by *Trametes (Poria) isabellina, Polyporus dichrous, P. fragilis, P. volvatus, Poria albobrunnea, P. versipora,* and *P. xantha.* The dead sapwood can be decayed by *Polyporus abietinus* and *P. versicolor.*

Miscellaneous Pathology.—Rennerfelt (*1163*), in studying the resistance to decay of the heartwood of 22 conifers, mostly durable species, reported Port-Orford-cedar in his "highly durable" category. However, he had not identified the fungistatic or fungicidal principles.

Only 3 nematode species were reported by Ruehle to be associated with Port-Orford-cedar, namely, *Hoplotylus femina, Pratylenchus penetrans,* and *Rotylenchus robustus* (*1222*). A later tabulation by Ruehle (*1224*) reports the nematodes *Helicotylenchus dihystera* and *Xiphinema americanum* on Port-Orford-cedar in Louisiana.

Alaska-cedar

Chamaecyparis nootkatensis

A medium-sized, very slow-growing tree, Alaska-cedar occurs along, or close to, the Pacific Coast from southeast Alaska to western British Columbia and Washington, and along the western slopes of the Cascade Range to Oregon. It occurs also in the Blue Mountains of northeast Oregon and in the Siskiyou Mountains of northern California (*872*). It has a conical crown, drooping branches that make it resistant to snow damage (*22*), and ashy brown, fibrous, seamy bark (*279*). Trees from 15 to 20 in. in diameter are usually from 200 to 275 years old. The largest trees have been estimated by Sudworth (*1367*) to be from 500 to 600 years old, but cases of longevity of over 1,000 years are known (*22*). In the United States, this species grows mostly at elevations between 2,000 and 7,500 ft. in moist, rocky, or gravelly soils of fair fertility. Although it often occurs in basins, valleys, and mountain slopes, it makes its best development on thin organic soils, covering bedrock, at high elevations where seepage water is available (*22*).

The climate of the range is moderate to cool, with cool, humid summers and winters that are not often severe although temperatures will drop to −20° F. Mean annual precipitation ranges from 20 to 100 in. and temperatures change gradually. Alaska-cedar is not so tolerant as western redcedar and western hemlock, but more tolerant than western white pine and noble fir (*1367*). Through the sapling stages, this tree is sensitive to·fire and to winter drying (*22*). It has, however, few disease enemies and none are serious. The species of *Chamaecyparis* can be reproduced by cuttings (*1*).

Alaska-cedar is one of the British Columbia species included in Eades' extensive bulletin on decays and natural defects of these species (*401*). The paucity of knowledge of such defects and the lack of serious pathology in Alaska-cedar are implied in mention of no specific diseases or rots of this tree. However, Eades' account of the characteristics of the tree and its wood is useful.

Seedling Diseases.—No strictly seedling diseases have been reported. The seedlings of *Chamaecyparis* spp. have been regarded as moderately susceptible (*1*) or resistant to damping-off (*360*).

Foliage Diseases.—The brown felt blight caused by *Herpotrichia nigra* can mold foliage that remains long under snow. Both in the Pacific Northwest and Alaska, this tree is subject to a leaf rust, *Gymnosporangium nootkatense*, that is confined, in its II and III stages, to Alaska-cedar (*46*). Bright orange uredia form on the foliage, and the teliospores are produced in the uredo sori. Stages 0 and I are formed on the leaves of a very few species of *Malus, Pyrus, and Sorbus.*

A black surface mildew, reported only from Alaska, can discolor foliage. The cause has been ascribed to *Asterina cupressina*, which may be a synonym for *Caliciopsis thujina* (*450*).

Stem Diseases.—None have been reported. Three unusual saprophytic fungi have been collected from dead stems of Alaska-cedar only. *Gelatinodiscus flavidus* is a discomycete with apothecia gelatinous when fresh and very fragile when dry, that occurs on dead wood in Washington (*770*). *Tryblidiaria washingtonensis* is a discomycete with tiny, subcarbonaceous, black apothecia emerging from decorticated wood, in Washington (*769*). *Venturia lanea* has carbonous perithecia in clusters on small, whitish patches of surface mycelium on dead bark (*365*).

Root Diseases.—*Phytophthora lateralis,* so destructive to Port-Orford-cedar, can attack the roots of Alaska-cedar also, but few such attacks have been reported. *Poria weirii*, an important root rot fungus on Douglas-fir and some other conifers, is known more as a butt rotter than a root rotter of Alaska-cedar in the Pacific Northwest.

Rhizomorphs of *Armillaria mellea* have been found on the roots of dead and dying trees in Alaska, but death of these roots could have been attributed to unfavorable moisture conditions (*22*).

Trunk Rots.—No heart rot fungi are common in this species. However, its decay-resistant heartwood, particularly in old or damaged trees, has been attacked by *Fomes pini, F. pinicola, Poria lenis, P. weirii,* and *P. xantha.* Since fruiting of rot fungi on living Alaska-cedar is rare, certain identification of causal fungi usually requires culturing. *Merulius himantioides* has been reported as a wood decay fungus of this species in British Columbia (*1277*), and *Lenzites saepiaria* in Alaska.

Miscellaneous Pathology.—The durable heartwood has proved very resistant to decay by *Lentinus lepideus* and *Poria vaporaria,* but it was not outstandingly resistant against *Coniophora puteana.* The heartwood constituents isolated by Rennerfelt (*1163*) that were toxic to fungi, were nootkatin, carvacrol, chamic acid, and chaminic acid.

Atlantic white-cedar

Chamaecyparis thyoides

Atlantic white-cedar is a coastal species that grows on wet ground or in swamps, and sometimes on sandy soils, but usually on peat deposits, in patches or areas of many acres from Maine to Florida, extending as far as 130 miles inland. While more tolerant than many associated species, such as gray birch, baldcypress, and pitch pine, it is less tolerant than others, including red maple, blackgum, and sweetbay. Its soils are predominantly acid. The species, considered strictly a swamp tree, is rare whereever the peat is underlain by clay, or contains much silt or clay (873). It occurs in Maine where temperatures drop to −36° F. and also in Florida where summer temperatures over 100° F. are common. The shallow-rooted habit of the tree, characteristic of wetland species, makes it sensitive to windthrow. It cannot tolerate sustained drought, and because of its thin bark it is sensitive to damage by fire (808). It is also injured by snow and ice, salt-spray (1005, 1632), and flooding by fresh, brackish, or salt water (875). White-cedars have the capacity for long life, with reports of longevity as high as 1,000 years (873).

Seedling Diseases.—Although the tree is host to many saprophytes and minor leaf and twig diseases, few fungi successfully attack it and material loss from disease in the field is rare. While not particularly subject to damping-off (360), one disease, juniper blight, which is a leaf and shoot disease caused by *Phomopsis juniperovora* (570), is very common in nurseries and plantations, but not common in natural reproduction. This blight has been so damaging in some nurseries that the growing of white-cedar has been stopped (661).

Foliage Diseases.—A destructive leaf and tip blight, especially common in southern New Jersey, is caused by *Didymascella* (*Keithia*) *chamaecyparissi* (12). Korstian and Brush (808) considered it "intensely parasitic," causing the lower leaves to turn brown, and then gray, with the perithecia of the fungus evident as kidney-shaped areas on the upper side of the leaf.

Rust galls are caused by *Gymnosporangium fraternum* (0 and I stages on *Aronia*) from Maine to New Jersey; a tip blight is caused by *Monochaetia unicornis* (558) from New Jersey to Georgia; and the leaf cast caused by *Lophodermium juniperi* (323, 808) (*Lophodermina cupressi-thyoides*) (328). *Nectria thujana* has been found on dead foliage and was regarded by Hedgcock (625) as saprophytic. *Caliciopsis thujina* (*Asterina cupressina*), with its protruding, setose ascocarps, has been associated with dying foliage in New Jersey (450, 808).

Stem Diseases.—Spindle-shaped stem and branch swellings induced by *Gymnosporangium biseptatum* occasionally cause damage in New Jersey and Rhode Island. A dense, distorted, bunchy growth of branches (witches' brooms) is caused by *G. ellisii* from Maine to Florida (661). The former has, as its alternate hosts, species of *Amelanchier*, and the latter *Comptonia* and *Myrica*.

Botryosphaeria ribis in Georgia and the Carolinas and *Physalospora obtusa* in New Jersey have been reported causing twig blights, although the latter may well have been secondary. The bark of white-cedar is host to several fungi: *Aleurodiscus niveus* causes a flaking called "bark patch," and *Diplodia thyoidea* and *Nectria truncata* fruit on dead bark.

Root Diseases and Trunk Rots.—Among the root rots, this species is susceptible to attack by *Armillaria mellea* in the vicinity of hardwood stumps, by *Polyporus schweinitzii* in various situations involving root injury, and by *Fomes annosus* in the vicinity of conifer stumps or other trees already attacked by it. In western North Carolina a small, 25-year-old plantation of Atlantic white-cedar was destroyed by *F. annosus* over a period of very few years (*1431*), and it has also been been reported from the Lake States. *Clitocybe tabescens,* whose mushrooms and root damage have much the appearance of *A. mellea,* is reported to have killed trees of this species in Florida (*1168*). The species was moderately susceptible to *Phymatotrichum omnivorum* in Texas (*1379*).

There is a possibility that *Poria weirii,* an important root and butt rot fungus in the Northwest, can similarly attack Atlantic white-cedar, but if so it is not a factor in the management of this species.

The heartwood of Atlantic white-cedar is very resistant to decay. By far the most important fungus known to destroy its heartwood is *Fomes cajanderi* (*890*) (*Trametes subrosea, 808*). The rot, observed in trees as young as 40 to 50 years, is described by Korstian and Brush (*808*). They cite *Polyporus schweinitzii* as of less importance as a trunk rot and mention several fungi that rot the wood of dead trees.

Echinodontium ballouii is an interesting rot fungus known only from New Jersey and only on Atlantic white-cedar. It has a woody, blackish brown, rimose conk, with an acute sepia margin and an undulating, warty undersurface. The character of the rot is not known (*547*).

Mycorrhizal Relations.—Information is lacking on the nematodes and mycorrhizal associations of this species.

Desertwillow

Chilopsis linearis

The desertwillow, so called because of its willowlike leaves, is closely related to the catalpa, being one of the Bignoniaceae. It grows in the arid region of the Southwest that extends across southern California, southern Nevada, parts of Arizona and New Mexico, southwestern Texas, and southward into Mexico. It is intolerant, seldom grows over 20 ft. in height, has a narrow crown of slim, upright branches and a short, crooked trunk that may reach a diameter of 6 in. It is often merely a shrub, with many stems (*1367*). It grows on the borders of deserts and low, mountain water courses in relatively dry, well-drained, sandy to gravelly soils at elevations from sea level to 5,000 ft. (*1137*).

The wood is durable and used for fenceposts. The tree has been planted to a considerable extent for shelterbelt purposes. Of the 25 species in experimental shelterbelt plantings in Oklahoma and Texas, reported by Wright and Wells (*1627*), the desertwillow was by far the species planted in greatest numbers.

As one would expect in a dry habitat, few fungi thrive on desertwillow. Even so, considering the work done on desertwillow as a shelterbelt tree in the Southwest, it is surprising that only four fungi are reported on it in the United States Index of Plant Diseases (*8*).

An unimportant leaf spot is caused by *Phyllosticta erysiphoides*.

In Nebraska and Texas nurseries, some damping-off losses have resulted from *Pythium ultimum* (*219, 957*) and from *Rhizoctonia solani*. While the *Pythium* diseases flourish in wet, poorly drained soils with low oxygen, *Rhizoctonia* spp. will flourish in well-drained soils (*1555*). While the damage from the above two damping-off fungi can be confused, they are distinctive in culture—the *Pythium* being a phycomycete, and the *Rhizoctonia* the sclerotial form of *Pellicularia* or *Corticium,* a basidiomycete. *Pythium* spp. tend to strike earlier than *Rhizoctonia,* in nursery beds.

Particular attention has been given desertwillow with respect to Texas root rot (*Phymatotrichum omnivorum*), because of its potential usefulness as a windbreak tree in the root rot area of Texas and Oklahoma. While it was rated highly susceptible in inoculation tests (*1379*), it proved resistant in the field. Of 28,313 trees of this species observed for this root rot for 5 years, and reported on by Wright and Wells (*1627*), only 5 trees died of root rot, giving desertwillow the lowest annual loss among the 25 species studied. In their susceptibility rating table, they place desertwillow among the 6 species resistant to root rot and usable on most soil types in the Texas root rot area.

Fringetree
Chionanthus virginicus

The fringetree is typically a large shrub or small tree that may occasionally reach 40 ft. in height and 12 in. in diameter. It grows in deep, rich, moist soils, from New Jersey to Florida and westward throughout the South and the Ohio River Valley to Missouri, Oklahoma, and east Texas. Its value is as an ornamental. In late May or June, it produces drooping clusters of feathery, white, fragrant flowers. It is diœcious, and the staminate plant has the larger panicles and flowers but lacks the ornamental bluish fruit (*1154*) of the pistillate tree. The leaves turn bright yellow in fall, and shed early. A variety, *maritimus,* is pubescent over the lower leaf surface and the panicles.

Although the fringetree is most commonly found along stream banks and borders of swamps, it does well in cultivation under a variety of soil conditions. It is typically a southern tree and will seldom withstand rigorous northern winters except in protected sites. It is rated intermediate in hardiness, and it is unusually free from disease.

Four leaf spots and a powdery mildew virtually comprise the known pathology of the fringetree.

Cercospora chionanthi (*260*) produces large, dark brown to almost black, epiphyllous, circular to angular spots. Dense fascicles form on black stromata, with the brown conidiophores bearing pale olivaceous conidia that are obclavate to cylindric, sometimes slightly curved, and $4-5\mu \times 20-65\mu$ in dimension. It is known from New Jersey to West Virginia.

Phyllosticta chionanthi produces black pycnidia on small spots, with small, hyaline, ovoid conidia. Its distribution is also from New Jersey to West Virginia.

Two species of *Septoria* (*S. chionanthi* and *S. eleospora*) cause spotting of foliage. Ostiolate, globoid pycnidia bear filiform, multiseptate, hyaline spores. These species are not known to be damaging.

134

The common powdery mildew, *Phyllactinia guttata* (*619*), with its basally bulbous perithecial appendages, can cause some distortion and stunting of foliage.

Septobasidium curtisii forms a brown felt over scale insects on stems (*292*).

Fringetree is only moderately susceptible to Texas root rot (*1379*).

Many fungi have been described as inhabitants of dead branches, dead leaves, bark, and wood (*8*), but they are saprobes and of interest only mycologically.

The oriental fringetree (*Chionanthus retusa*) is also used as an ornamental in the East, and its pathology and hardiness are much the same as for *C. virginicus*.

The only nematodes reported associated with the fringetree are *Helicotylenchus erythrinae* and *Trichodorus porosus* (*1222*).

Camphor-tree

Cinnamomum camphora

The camphor-tree, a native of China and Japan (*53*), is a rugged, dense-topped, broad-leaved evergreen, that grows to a height of 40 ft. and 12 in. or more in diameter. It is used as a street tree in the parts of the country with warm or mild climates, from central and southern California, eastward along the Gulf Coast, and through the southern half of Florida. It has pendant, yellow-green leaves that emit a strong odor of camphor when crushed. It grows slowly, stands pruning well, and is quite frost-hardy for a subtropical tree (*955*). When temperatures on Florida's west coast were between 14° and 22° F. in 1962, the camphor-tree was one of the species that survived in the open without perceptible damage (*948*). However, hard freezes that year in the New Orleans, La., area, with temperatures reaching 12° F. and staying very low for a day or more, resulted in the death of many fine camphor-trees of considerable size.

This species is fairly free from disease but is subject to some foliage diseases and to at least two root rots.

In Japan, the camphor-tree has shown a fair degree of resistance to urban air pollution.

Foliage Diseases.—One of the commonest diseases in this country and in Japan is the anthracnose caused by *Glomerella cingulata*, which can cause a leaf spot, canker, or shoot blight. Ito (*745*) provides photographs and drawings of the disease on camphor, and of the single-celled, ovoid conidia produced in acervuli, and the 8-spored asci and their single-celled, ovoid ascospores. He concluded that what had been called *G. cinnamomi* Yosh. in Japan was identical with *G. cingulata*. It is also likely that the imperfect epithets *Gloeosporium camphorae* and *G. ochraceum* applied to leaf spot, canker, and dieback fungi in the United States represent the conidial stage of *Glomerella cingulata*. This fungus, as shown by Fowler (*472*) for *Magnolia grandiflora*, can cause a major leaf disease of several broad-leaved evergreens in the South. Ito (*745*) concluded that while young shoots of camphor were easily invaded and blighted by this fungus, mature leaves and stems were infected only through wounds. Attached infected leaves show circular to irregular brown spots of varying size, and they bear only the conidial stage. Sterile, black stromata may occur on the upper side of the spots. *G. cingulata* causes the common bitter-rot of apples (*1483*) and many other fruits (*619*).

Also common in this country is the algal leaf spot caused by *Cephaleuros virescens* (*1555*), a disease that can attack twigs also. A green, velvety scurf forms on the spots, and if sporangia form they appear as tiny, globular heads on fine, dense, reddish hairs. In rainy weather this also can do considerable damage.

A shot-hole spot-anthracnose (*Elsinoë* sp.) and a few other leaf diseases have been reported occasionally (*8, 1555*).

Microsphaera alni var. *cinnamomi* is a form of this common powdery mildew fungus reported on camphor from Louisiana.

Thread blight (*Pellicularia koleroga*) can result in the foliage being completely overgrown by brown, silky mycelial threads. Blighted foliage may hang from such threads. Spores and brownish sclerotia are formed in the surface fungus growth (*1408, 1527*) on leaves or shoots.

Stem Diseases.—Some green-shoot blight and twig cankering is caused by *Glomerella cingulata*, as described above. Another canker and dieback of twigs is caused by one or more species of *Diplodia*. At least two of the three *Diplodia* species on camphor (*D. tubericola* and *D. natalensis*), both of which have a wide variety of hosts, and possibly the third (*D. camphorae*), are synonymous, and they represent conidial stages of *Physalospora rhodina*. In camphor, as in other woody plants, the *Diplodia* stage, with its stout, dark, two-celled conidia (well illustrated by Voorhees, *1484*) produced in carbonaceous pycnidia, appears on living or dying twigs; while the *Physalospora* stage, consisting of aggregations of papillate, carbonaceous perithecia that bear 1-celled, ellipsodial, hyaline to faintly olivaceous ascospores, appears on twigs after death.

Hundreds of camphor trees have been killed by Verticillium wilt (*Verticillium albo-atrum* or *V. dahliae*), in the San Francisco Bay area of California. W. W. Wagener [19] states that the fungus has often been difficult to isolate from wilted parts of the crown, and many affected branches showed no discoloration. These problems in isolation and in lack of symptoms in aerial parts caused a long delay in gaining acceptance of this disease as Verticillium wilt (see also *Acer platanoides* and *Olea*).

The common eastern mistletoe, *Phoradendron serotinum*, sometimes grows in the camphor-tree.

Miscellaneous Pathology.—Both *Clitocybe tabescens* in Florida, and *Armillaria mellea* more generally (*8*) are reported to cause root rot in this species. Rhoads (*1168*) reported the former attacking the roots of 20 camphor-trees. Raabe (*1142*) lists the camphor-tree as susceptible to *A. mellea* in California. The many similarities of these two fungi and the diseases they cause make for confusion (*1167*) (see also *Aleurites fordii*).

The nematodes *Pratylenchus pratensis* and *Radopholus similis* have been identified attacking roots in Florida (*1222*).

---

[19] Personal communication from W. Willis Wagener, deceased, formerly pathologist, USDA Forest Service, Pacific Southwest Forest and Range Experiment Station, Berkeley, Calif.

The roots are only moderately susceptible to attack by Texas root rot (*1379*).

On mineral-deficient sands in Florida, a lack of normal leaf color is sometimes caused by manganese deficiency.

Citrus

Citrus spp.

The species of *Citrus* are native to tropical and subtropical Asia and the Malay Archipelago. A few species are commonly cultivated, and these have given rise to many varieties and hybrids. The delimitation of species is thus made difficult. In the United States the species most widely cultivated for fruit and ornamental use are **Citrus aurantifolia** (lime), **C. limonia** (lemon), **C. paradisi** (grapefruit), and **C. sinensis** (sweet orange). Additional members of this genus include citrange, citron, and tangelo. Bailey (*51*) gives a good descriptive account of the genus.

The common *Citrus* spp. raised in the United States are grown in the southern half of Florida and in the Southwest, from southern California eastward, in irrigated situations or moist bottom lands, through southern New Mexico, Arizona, and Texas. They are small evergreen trees, sensitive to cold, but often able to withstand limited durations of temperatures several degrees below freezing. The lemon and lime are particularly cold-sensitive.

Virtually no commercial varieties of *Citrus* are grown as seedlings, except that seedlings of some varieties or species are used to produce stocks with desirable stock characteristics, to support scions of the plant whose fruit or form is desired (*201*). Thus, a rough Florida lemon species makes excellent stock for trees to be grown on very poor or calcareous soil; and the sour orange, a cold-resistant species, has been used widely as a stock on which to bud sweet orange or other citrus forms, being adaptable to many soils and especially well fitted for low, wet soils where its immunity to foot rot (*Phytophthora* spp.) makes it particularly valuable. Cuttings of *Citrus* spp. can be rooted (*201*).

Citrus growing requires a drained soil profile at least 2 ft. deep to the water table, and preferably deeper, in Florida (*1309*). There are many facets to site requirements that are important in the success or failure of an orchard but that would not mitigate against the use of citrus trees for ornamental use.

This account does not deal with citrus trees from the standpoint of commercial fruit production, but rather with their health when used as occasional trees serving as shade and ornament. There are several good sources of material on citrus diseases. In preparing this section, Dr. Leo J. Klotz has been very helpful in indicating those diseases that can materially affect the health and appearance of citrus trees, and his Color Handbook of Citrus Diseases (*806*) together with the references he provides can well serve anyone faced with diagnosing the ills of these trees. Therefore, instead of doing a shorter and much less effective job than Klotz has already done, this citrus account will simply annotate the list of those diseases that make up the major pathology of citrus in the United States.

Foliage Diseases.—Some of the same species of *Phytophthora* (e.g. *P. citrophthora, P. hibernalis, P. parasitica,* and *P. syringae*) that cause gummosis of trunks and brown rot of fruit can blight leaves, shoots, and blossoms in moist, windy weather. The sporangia of *P. hibernalis* in the West detach and are readily blown about.

Citrus blast (*Pseudomonas syringae*), a bacterial disease, affects the leaves of oranges and grapefruit in a small area in northern California. Lesions start mostly in a break on the petiole wing and extend to the leaf base and the twig where later a lesion with a brown, dry scab or crust forms.

Sour orange scab (*Elsinoë fawcettii*) makes corky projections on fruit and raised scabby lesions, with accompanying distortion, on leaves of sour orange, lemon, tangelo, and occasionally grapefruit. It occurs in Florida but not in California.

Melanose (*Diaporthe citri*) consists of tiny raised dots of pustules made up of gum-filled plant cells. Often crusts form on fruit, most notably on grapefruit, and a stem-end rot is often induced. The foliage may be peppered with small dots.

Leaf and fruit spots caused by species of *Septoria* (mainly *S. citri* or *S. limonum*) in California appear as tiny pits or depressions. Alone or in combination with other leaf spot fungi, the *Septoria* species can be damaging to the grade of fruit but do not materially devitalize trees.

Fisher (*448*) describes two diseases caused by species of *Cercospora*—one which causes raised, greasy-looking blotches on foliage only (*C. citri-grisea*) and another which causes raised spots on foliage and fruit (*C. gigantea*). The latter, called tar spot, can be distinguished from greasy spot by a mahogany-red circle inside the periphery of the spot, when viewed with transmitted light.

Psorosis, a virus disease (*Citrivir psorosis*) that has six forms, produces symptoms on leaves, as well as on bark (see Stem Diseases). Many small, elongate, light-colored areas appear in the areas of small veinlets, along with some vein clearing. A definite pattern often emerges. Some insects and mites produce somewhat similar markings. Crinkly-leaf and infectious variegation are also manifestations of the forms of psorosis.

Stubborn disease, in California, mostly affecting navel oranges, is also a virus disease (*Citrivir pertinaciae*), that results in a brushy growth of twigs that bend down, then upward at the ends. The foliage tends to be short and broad, and bends noticeably upward from the midrib. The leaves also develop a premature, chlorotic autumnal coloring, and the fruit becomes acorn-shaped.

Tristeza, or quick decline, is another virus disease (*Citrivir viatoris*) of the South and California. It is transmitted by certain aphids and is very destructive. Trees appear as though injured by girdling or root rot. The foliage becomes ashen in color, and the leaves curl both upward and lengthwise. Then the leaves droop, the twigs die back, and as this proceeds the peripheral roots die and their bark sloughs off. There are good histologic diagnostic symptoms for tristeza (*806*). Ultimately tristeza results in death or in weak unproductive trees that merely survive.

The six principal metallic-ion deficiencies that affect foliage are as follows:

138

1. Exanthema or "ammoniation," caused by copper deficiency, in which foliage becomes thick and deep green;
2. Zinc deficiency or mottleleaf, resulting in irregular yellowing between the veins, and small leaves;
3. Manganese deficiency, in which the yellow colorations may be similar to zinc deficiency symptoms but may involve larger areas, and the leaves remain full-sized;
4. Magnesium deficiency, which results in a bronzing and is particularly troublesome in Florida;
5. Boron deficiency, in which the leaves take on a gun-metal coloration, with a corking and splitting of main veins and a sharp downward curling of the leaf;
6. Iron-deficiency chlorosis, in which the leaves turn yellow, except for the veins.

There are many other deficiencies and excesses that affect foliage mostly on orchard trees that receive intensive cultivation. Orchard trees are also subject to a large number of fruit and foliage troubles as a result of cyanide fumigation, copper sprays, and the use of herbicides.

Components of smog, mainly peroxyacyl nitrate and ozone, have been damaging to citrus in southern California (*652*).

The foliage diseases of citrus require expert diagnosis. Fortunately, where the fruit is not being marketed, they can often be ignored. However, since any individual tree might harbor such dreaded diseases as tristeza or the citrus canker (*Xanthomonas citri*) that was successfully eradicated from Florida, symptoms on any individual yard tree take on added significance.

Stem Diseases.—Brown rot gummosis, or foot rot, attacks the bark, producing a basal necrosis in which dead areas of bark remain firm, gum exudes and infiltrates the wood beneath, and eventually as the bark dries it cracks. The necrotic bark lesions extend below ground and out the roots. *Phytophthora citrophthora* and *P. parasitica* are the most common causes of this condition, although other species of *Phytophthora* are sometimes involved, depending to some extent on whether the condition develops in Florida or California.

Bark necrosis and gummosis also can result from attack by *Diplodia natalensis* (perfect stage *Physalospora rhodina*) (*1484*) and by *Botryosphaeria ribis* (*550*) (see *Cercis canadensis*).

Many virus diseases cause bark necroses, with gummosis at certain times of the year. These include several forms of psorosis, tristeza, exocortis, and cachexia (xyloporosis). Klotz (*806*) provides, in addition to color photographs and descriptions of the virus diseases, a table of citrus virus diseases giving the common name, investigators and their countries, dates of their work, scientific names of the viruses both according to Fawcett and to Holmes, distribution, vectors, citrus varieties attacked, and control measures.

Root Diseases.—In some parts of California *Armillaria mellea* (*806*) causes an important root rot of citrus, and in Florida its counterpart, *Clitocybe tabescens* (*1168*), causes a similar disease. *A. mellea* results in rapid wilting or general decline, with the main diagnostic evidence below ground or at the root collar. White, fan-shaped mycelial felts form beneath the bark, and purplish to brownish or black shoestring-like rhizomorphs form on the bark of decaying roots. The mushroom fruiting-bodies, each with an annulus, occur in clusters.

The effects of *Clitocybe tabescens* can be confused with those of Phytophthora foot rot in Florida. *C. tabescens* attacks a wide variety of woody plants (*1168*) in Florida, and in citrus it occurs mostly on rough lemon and sweet orange rootstock, but not on sour orange. While many aspects of the disease and the fungus are similar to *Armillaria mellea*, differences are pointed out by Rhoads (*1167*), consisting, in the case of *C. tabescens*, mainly in the lack of a fan pattern for the pitted mycelial felts that form under the bark; the lack of dark, flattened rhizomorphs; and the lack of an annulus on the stipe of the mushroom; all of which do occur with *A. mellea*.

Ganoderma lucidum has been asociated with a root rot of citrus in Florida (*403*).

Mention has been made earlier that *Phytophthora citrophthora* and *P. parasitica* are among the *Phytophthora* species causing a brown rot of fruit and blighting of leaves and other green tissues. These fungi, and also *P. megasperma, P. cinnamomi,* and *P. palmivora,* can also attack the bark, bringing about a basal trunk necrosis known as brown rot gummosis or foot rot. The main symptoms are as follows: dead areas of bark remaining firm;.gum exudation at certain seasons; gum infiltration of wood; a yellow, gummous marginal zone; and ultimately drying and cracking of bark (*806*). These several fungi produce symptoms and effects in citrus that somewhat resemble those of the *Phytophthora* bleeding cankers of species of *Acer, Quercus,* and other trees. The genus *Phytophthora* has been monographed by Waterhouse (*1510, 1511*).

Roncadori (*1192*) provides a nutritional comparison of some species of *Phytophthora.*

The roots of citrus species are known to be attacked by the burrowing nematode (*Radopholus similis*), the lesion nematode (*Pratylenchus vulnus*), and the citrus nematode (*Tylenchus semipenetrans*) (*1222*).

Miscellaneous Pathology.—Citrus has been given such intensive study that its pathology has been extensively explored. This compendium is not the place to attempt to do more than sketch this pathology, which is highlighted by foliage and fruit spots, blights, rots, and other defects; many systemic virus diseases; many *Phytophthora* bark necrosis diseases; bacterial diseases and serious root rots involving wood decay and bark necrosis; and mineral deficiencies, excesses, and nonbiotic injuries from sprays and other applied chemicals. It is fortunate that much published information is available on citrus troubles, such as the manual by Klotz (*806*), together with the literature references to specific diseases that he provides.

Polyporus (Ganoderma) lucidus and *P. zonalis* have been reported rotting the wood of living *Citrus* trees (*1067*).

Flowering dogwood
Cornus florida

The flowering dogwood, or cornel, is one of the most prolific and

140

beautiful understory trees of the East. While mainly a southeastern tree, it occurs from southern New England to central Florida, westward to the Great Plains in Texas, and northeastward to southern Michigan. This dogwood does well on a variety of sites, from streambanks to light upland soils, but it thrives best in moist soils of good tilth. Vimmerstedt (*1480*), who compiled the silvical characteristics of this tree, states that it occurs most frequently on soils of pH 6 to 7. It is well to note that dogwood, having one of the highest foliage contents of calcium (2.0 to 3.5 percent), is a prime soil builder and often creates its own high pH, as do redcedar and a few other high-calcium species (*244*). Its role as a soil builder is enhanced by the rapid rate at which its litter decomposes, as compared with low-calcium species such as oaks or pine.

The species is very tolerant (*54*), a prolific sprouter, easily reproduced by air layering, very sensitive to flooding (*583, 1078*) and to earth fills, sensitive to drought (*1480*), hardy, easily damaged by fire, and relatively free of disease when in the forest. Leaves will redden, curl, and cup in prolonged dry weather, and severe dieback can accompany long droughts. Typically a small tree, dogwood can grow to heights of 40 ft. and diameters up to 18 in. on its best sites.

The showy, so-called flower petals of this dogwood are really bracts with tiny flowers in the center. Typically the bracts are dead white, but clones with bright-pink bracts are available. Only vegetative propagation (*1093*) will assure continuation of a pink line such as variety *rubra*. There are four other varieties (*53*).

The National Horticultural Magazine of April 1953 presented a comprehensive review of the flowering dogwood, its silvical characteristics and its diseases, in four articles with a combined authorship of seven research workers.

Seedling Diseases.—The only strictly seedling disease reported for dogwood is a Pythium root rot in New Jersey. The Pythium diseases flourish in wet, poorly drained soils and will kill seedlings before they become woody or will rot their roots later in the summer. Cultures are required for *Pythium* identification (*957*). Dogwoods in the nursery may be attacked by any of the leaf fungi described below, but because of nursery watering they are particularly subject in the spring to the gray-mold Botrytis blight (*B. cinerea*) that can envelop and destroy whole plants (*1555*). Later in the season they are subject to the powdery mildew *Phyllactinia guttata*, that is characterized by straight, basally bulbous appendages on the perithecia (*619*).

Foliage Diseases.—A considerable literature has accumulated on the foliage diseases of dogwood, mostly because of the attention accorded this tree as an ornamental. Jenkins has concentrated on the *Elsinoë* spot anthracnose and, together with Miller and Hepting (*754*), has reviewed and illustrated several leaf diseases. Cox (*295*) has featured the *Elsinoë* and *Septoria* diseases and their control. Hepting (*649*) has brought together the main distinguishing characteristics of several flower and fruit diseases of dogwood. In another paper (*643*) he describes how severe some of these diseases can be if conditions favor them.

Only the principal foliage diseases are described below. Confusion in fungus synonymy among species in *Phyllosticta* and *Sep-*

toria has clouded the identity of some forms.

Spot anthracnose (*Elsinoë corni*) (*754*) is probably the most damaging leaf disease and occurs in all states that border on the Atlantic Ocean. Bracts ("flowers") become covered with purplish spots and become stunted and aborted. Foliage develops purplish spots of rounded but variable shapes with light, paper-thin centers that often fall out, producing "shot hole." Wrinkling and distortion are common.

Ascochyta leaf blight (*Ascochyta cornicola*) (*754*) produces small to large spots, often irregular in outline, with gray to tan centers and prominent borders outside of which tissue is discolored. Spotting is often followed by complete collapse, shrivelling, and blackening of the leaf. This fungus has also been called *Phyllosticta cornicola,* and *P. globifera* may also be a synonym.

Botrytis petal blight (*Botrytis cinerea*) (*754, 1555*) can also affect foliage and green shoots. A disease of wet, spring weather, it often follows frost damage. Irregular brown patches form on "petals." With high humidity, lesions become covered with a gray-brown, fuzzy mold that bears spores which shed in clouds with movement.

Septoria and Cercospora leaf spots (*Septoria cornicola, 754; S. floridae, 1386;* and *Cercospora cornicola, 260*) appear late, from mid-July on. Spots are often very numerous and are generally small and angular. The Septoria spots have sharp borders and are typically haloed. The Cercospora spots are brown, are larger, and lack sharp borders. *S. floridae* has hyaline, cylindric, 1- to 3-septate pycnospores, $16–22\mu \times 4\mu$. The *Cercospora* conidia are in a loose sporodochium, measure $20–70\mu \times 2–3\mu$, and have indistinct septa.

The *Phyllactinia* powdery mildew has been mentioned as a seedling disease. It is also common late in the season on sprout foliage. In addition to the perithecia, enormous numbers of oidia are formed in late summer.

Stem Diseases.—The principal trunk distase of ornamental dogwoods is a basal canker caused by *Phytophthora cactorum*. The foliage may appear stunted and/or color red prematurely, but the trouble stems from a basal lesion at or near the groundline (crown canker). This is typically a disease of ornamentals that often follows injuries such as those from lawn mowers or boring insects. The canker is sunken; the bark peels away, exposing the wood; and eventually the trunk is girdled. The canker sometimes bleeds, exuding a dark fluid (*1555*) that darkens the wood. Creager (*306*) gives a good description of the symptoms and seriousness of this disease on Long Island. He describes the canker face without bark as "parabolic in outline with zonation."

On forest trees the perennial target canker caused by *Nectria galligena* (*47, 170*) is the most common stem disease, although only occasional trees are affected. These zonate cankers, with conspicuous bark-free callus folds, develop tiny, red, balloon-shaped perithecia around the edges in wet weather.

Stem and branch cankers are also caused by *Elsinoë corni* that already was mentioned in connection with leaf diseases. Twigs become peppered with scabby spots that commonly bear the *Sphaceloma* stage of the fungus (*754*).

A twig blight and canker caused by *Botryosphaeria ribis* cause occasional dieback (see *Cercis*). Pirone [20] reports it as an important killer of dogwood branches and whole trees in the Northeast. Other stem diseases that have occasionally appeared are crown gall (*Agrobacterium tumefaciens*) in the North and mistletoe (*Phoradendron serotinum*) in the South.

A large number of species of *Septobasidium* produce brown felts that overgrow scale insects on branches. Couch (*292*) lists and describes a record number (10 species on one host species) as occurring on *Cornus florida*.

Species of *Cryptostictus* and *Myxosporium* have been mentioned in connection with twig blights, but they are minor disease fungi at best. Also in this role are the common *Sphaeropsis malorum* (*Physalospora obtusa*) (*1555*) in the North and *Diplodia natalensis* (*Physalospora rhodina*) (*1484*) in the South.

Root Diseases.—Root rots are not major diseases of dogwood. *Armillaria mellea* in the North and its counterpart *Clitocybe tabescens* in the South (*1168*) have the capacity to destroy roots of injured trees. *Corticium galactinum* (*1561*), a root pathogen of apple and other woody plants, has been reported on dogwood. White felts of this fungus may appear in soil fissures around infected trees.

Flowering dogwood proved extremely susceptible to Texas root rot (*Phymatotrichum omnivorum*) in Texas inoculations (*1379*), but this species is not adapted to the root-rot areas of Texas and Oklahoma.

Twenty-one species of nematodes, in 12 genera, have been identified in association with root systems of dogwood in New Jersey, but none of these was considered to be associated with injury.

Rotylenchus robustus was related to injury to dogwood in Rhode Island (*1222*).

Miscellaneous Pathology.—The important diseases of dogwood are mainly those affecting the flower bracts. These diseases have already been discussed since they also affect the foliage.

Both the spot anthracnose (*Elsinoë corni*) and at least one species of *Septoria* (*S. cornicola*) can badly disfigure the normally plump, bright-red fruits of the dogwood. The former causes a scabbiness, and the latter turns the fruit black and shrivelled.

Virtually the only rot fungi reported from dogwood are saprobes that attack only dead wood, although *Fomes scutellatus* has been identified from living trees. Dogwood suffers little from trunk rots until overmature, and no studies on the amount of cull and its causes have been run on this species.

Thick, tough, gray felts of the thelephoraceous fungus *Sebacina helvelloides* can invest the bases of dogwood and other trees in the Southeast. The bark, however, appears uninjured beneath such felts (*908*).

Pacific dogwood
Cornus nuttallii

A tree much resembling the eastern *Cornus florida,* Pacific dogwood differs in appearance mainly by its petal-like bracts that are

---

[20] Personal communication from P. P. Pirone, pathologist, New York Botanical Garden, N. Y.

somewhat pointed at their apexes. In the eastern dogwood the apexes are notched. The Pacific species is typically a small tree that grows up to 30 ft. in height and about 8 in. in diameter. It can be double these dimensions, particularly in the Puget Sound Basin and in the redwood region of California (279). It grows in moist, well-drained soils on low, gentle slopes in valleys and bottoms from British Columbia through western Washington and Oregon and in the coast ranges and western Sierra slopes of California south to San Bernardino. It grows slowly, reaching ages close to 150 years on good sites. It is a desirable ornamental and is described by Metcalf (955) as "one of the most beautiful of all native (California) broad-leaved species." He also states with reference to California in general that "it is difficult to grow and is rarely seen in cultivation." It is very tolerant (1367) and has most of the silvical characteristics described for *Cornus florida*.

Very few diseases have been reported for this species, and probably the only one worthy of note is the Phytophthora crown canker (*P. cactorum*) on ornamental trees (see *Cornus florida*). While *Cornus florida* is subject to a large number of disfiguring leaf diseases, *C. nuttalli* is host to few leaf pathogens. One of these is *Placosphaeria cornicola* (362). This disease turns leaves or parts of leaves bright red, then cinnamon colored. Leaves become mottled on both sides with many black stromata. These stromata are effused. The pycnidia are epiphyllous, 1–9 or more per stroma, and are indicated by pale-bordered perforations. The spores are hyaline, oblong, .5–.8μ × 2.5μ.

Mycosphaerella auerswaldii (1278), a fungus known only on *Cornus*, has been reported from British Columbia.

A common powdery mildew, *Phyllactinia guttata* (1278), may distort the foliage late in the season. The genus *Phyllactinia*, characterized by straight, proximally bulbous, perithecial appendages, is represented by only the one species (1153).

Three species of *Nectria* have been reported on Pacific dogwood, but only one, *N. galligena*, is an aggressive parasite. Fortunately, it is not common in the East or West on dogwood. It forms the typical concentric-zoned target cankers so familiar on many eastern hardwoods (170). The bark is not retained on the canker face, and the wood beneath is more likely to be sound than rotted.

There may be some question as to the identity of *N. coccinea*, a second *Nectria* reported on this dogwood species, because this name has often been applied to what Lohman and Watson (879) consider to be *N. galligena*. True *N. coccinea* is a saprobe on forest trees.

N. cinnabarina (1555), the third *Nectria*, is the common, saprobic, "coral-spot" fungus so cosmopolitan on hardwoods. It is distinctive because of its large, conspicuous coral-colored sporodochia, in addition to the red perithecia that form later on the same stromata.

As in the East, *Phytophthora cactorum* causes a fairly common basal cankering of ornamental dogwoods in the West. This disease is annotated and documented under *Cornus florida*.

An unnamed *Phytophthora* sp. is pathogenic to Pacific dogwood in British Columbia (48).

The ubiquitous *Armillaria mellea* can rot damaged roots but has no reputation as a killing disease of dogwoods.

Pacific dogwood's freedom from leaf and stem diseases also extends to decay fungi. Remarkably few cases have been reported. *Fomes igniarius* is easily the commonest trunk rot of living trees. The only other basidiomycetes listed by Shaw (*1277*) and other sources in addition to *A. mellea* are: *Merulius confluens, Peniophora cinerea*, and *Poria ferrea*. Shaw (*1278*) provides access to their descriptions.

Hawthorn

Crataegus spp.

The genus *Crataegus*, which is made up of a large number of species of spiny shrubs or small trees, ranks low as a forest tree. However, as a highly congenial host to many species of *Gymnosporangium* that have alternate stages on trees of importance, it commands the respect of the pathologist. Little (*872*) recognizes 149 species of *Crataegus*, and he mentions that C. S. Sargeant alone named about 700 species. Altogether, about 1100 specific names have been proposed in the genus. Virtually all occur in the East; only one, the western blackhaw (*C. douglasii*), is native west of the Rocky Mountains.

Little (*872*) gives an excellent, succinct account of the problems in the taxonomy of *Crataegus*. He concludes that "*Crataegus* is regarded as an unstable genus characteristic of openings and exposed areas, which has expanded and evolved rapidly following the clearing of the forests and the origin of vast new areas suitable for colonization. The variable, expanding populations probably produced numerous hybrids." Many of the variations that have developed now breed true. Little credits E. J. Palmer as having contributed greatly to giving some stability to *Crataegus* taxonomy.

The hawthorns occur mostly in abandoned fields or hedgerows or as suppressed understory trees in the forest. Even though *Crataegus* spp. occur often in exposed rocky or dry situations, they withstood heavy flooding in a Tennessee study (*583*). They abound from Canada to Florida and west to the Great Plains; in coastal plains, Piedmont, and mountains; and on a variety of sites depending upon the adaptation of the species, race, or hybrid. There are many attractive horticultural forms (*1154*), and some of these are used not only in the East but also in the West which is out of the natural range of hawthorns. Since identification is so difficult and undependable in many cases, this account of *Crataegus* pathology will generally refer to the genus as a whole and not to particular forms within it.

Since *Crataegus* is among the Rosaceae, its diseases tend to be those commonly found on apple and other rosaceous hosts. Therefore a glance at the list of its disease organisms (*8*) discloses such familiar apple pathogens as *Erwinia amylovora, Podosphaera oxyacanthae*, and *Gymnosporangium* spp. on leaves; *Botrytis cinerea, Glomerella cingulata, Venturia inaequalis*, and *Gymnosporangium* spp. on fruits; *Erwinia amylovora* and *Gymnosporangium* spp. on stems; *Armillaria mellea* and *Xylaria* spp. on roots; and, in addition to these "apple" fungi, many others that spot leaves and cause minor stem damage that are confined to species of *Crataegus*. From the economic point of view the fruit diseases could have an impact on game food supply, and any of the leaf and stem pathogens could damage ornamental values. However, in this account, except for Fabraea leaf blight, only the species of *Gymnosporangium* will be annotated: they not only constitute the main elements of hawthorn pathology but also result in much damage to junipers which serve as alternate hosts to many species. Arthur and Cummins (*46*) are followed in this account. Boyce (*149*) also treats these species in some detail in his work on host relations of forest-tree rusts. For accounts of the juniper rusts of the West, Peterson's key and descriptive notes are up-to-date and very helpful (*1109*).

Gymnosporangium betheli (0, I) has epiphyllous pycnia also on fruits, and hypophyllous aecia also on fruits of *Crataegus* species growing in the Rocky Mountains and the Pacific Northwest. The species makes irregular knot-like galls on *Juniperus occidentalis* and *J. scopulorum*.

G. *clavariiforme* (0, I) has pycnia epiphyllous and on fruits, and aecia hypophyllous and on fruits and stems. O and I are mainly on *Amelanchier* but occur on *Crataegus columbiana* in Oregon. The rust forms swellings and brooms on *Juniperus communis* in the East and West (*813*).

G. *clavipes* (0, I) has pycnia mainly on fruits, and aecia crowded on fruits and stems of species of *Amelanchier* and *Crataegus* throughout the country. It produces fusiform swellings on stems of *Juniperus communis* and *J. virginiana*.

G. *exiguum* (0, I) has pycnia and aecia that are both epiphyllous and on fruits. It is known only from southern Texas where it produces telia principally on the foliage of *Juniperus pachyphloea* and *J. virginiana*.

G. *floriforme* (0, I) produces epiphyllous pycnia and hypophyllous aecia only on *Crataegus spathulata* and produces small, globoid or reniform galls only on *Juniperus virginiana* in the Southern States.

G. *globosum* (0, I) produces epiphyllous pycnia and hypophyllous aecia on *Crataegus*, *Malus*, *Pyrus*, and *Sorbus* and produces telia principally on globoid stem galls of *Juniperus virginiana* throughout the East and South.

G. *hyalinum* (0, I) produces epiphyllous pycnia and hypophyllous aecia on small, gall-like, pear-shaped swellings at the leaf bases of *Crataegus* spp. in the Southeast. The telial stage is unknown.

G. *juniperi-virginianae* (O, I), a well-known cedar-apple rust (see *Malus pumila*), is not listed on a rosaceous host outside *Malus* spp. by Arthur and Cummins (*46*), but it has been reported on *Crataegus* spp. from Iowa (*8*).

G. *libocedri* (0, I) produces mainly hypophyllous pycnia and aecia, with aecia also on the fruit of many rosaceous hosts, including *Crataegus douglasii*. The telia form on foliage, causing distortion and witches' brooms on *Libocedrus decurrens* on the West Coast.

G. *nelsoni* (0, I) produces epiphyllous pycnia, and aecia hypophyllous and on fruits of several rosaceous tree hosts; it produces its telia on woody, globose stem galls of several *Juniperus* spp. in the Rocky Mountains.

G. trachysorum (0, I) produces epiphyllous pycnia and hypophyllous aecia on thickened spots of some *Cratageus* spp., and telia on abruptly fusiform or globoid galls of *Juniperus virginiana* in scattered areas throughout the South.

G. tubulatum (0, I) produces epiphyllous pycnia and mostly hypophyllous aecia on *Crataegus* spp. in the northern Rocky Mountains. Its telia form on irregularly globoid galls, mostly on *Juniperus scopulorum*.

See *Juniperus virginiana* for references to work by Kern and by Parmelee on *Gymnosporangium* spp. of the world and of eastern Canada respectively.

The hawthorn leaf blight, caused by *Fabraea thuemenii*, produces symptoms much like those in pear resulting from attack by *F. maculata* (see *Pyrus*). Small, dark-brown or reddish-brown spots with raised black dots are numerous over the leaves, which drop prematurely in August. Westcott (*1555*), who reports this disease to be widespread on hawthorn, states that in wet years trees may be denuded by *F. thuemenii* by late August. The conidia, which are 4-celled, cruciate, and appendaged, are distinctive, and are referred to the imperfect genus *Entomosporium*.

Fungi capable of causing either rot of the central cylinder, or rot at wounds of living *Crataegus* spp. include *Fomes applanatus* (*1067*), *F. langloisii*, *F. occidentalis* (on *C. douglasii*), *F. ohiensis*, *F. pomaceus*, and *F. scutellatus*.

Arizona cypress

Cupressus arizonica

Arizona cypress is a tree of the mountains of the Southwest and northern Mexico. It grows on moist, gravelly slopes. On the better sites it occurs in pure stands, mainly at elevations between 5,000 and 8,000 ft., in Arizona and New Mexico. Under good growing conditions the trunk is straight, has considerable taper, and may reach 80 ft. in height (*279*). The tree will also survive on rigorous sites along canyon walls where it may appear as a misshapen shrub. The bark is dark reddish brown and has flat ridges. The leaves have a disagreeable odor.

Growth is slow, the crown is compact, and longevity may reach 400 years. If grown in areas of the Southwest where soil moisture is adequate, it will grow 3 ft. in height per year for many years.

The tree is sensitive to fire. It will grow under a considerable range of soil conditions. Thus it has an important role in erosion control in the Southwest, for windbreaks in California, and as an ornamental for wide use in temperate parts of the world. Many varieties are recognized (*1154*) since variation in many aspects of form and color is great. The species has become popular through the South as a Christmas tree, and large numbers are raised each year for this purpose. Variability in the species probably extends to disease resistance since there is evidence of great tree-to-tree variation in resistance to the heavy attacks of both Cercospora blight and Botryosphaeria blight.

The pathology of Arizona cypress in the South centers around *Phomopsis juniperovora* blight in the nursery and *Cercospora sequoiae* blight and Botryosphaeria (Diplodia) canker on out-planted stock. Losses from all three can be heavy. In the Southwest the main pathological impacts on the species have resulted from mistletoe and rust in the forest and sunscald to ornamentals. Wagener (*1489*) gives a very complete account of the diseases of the American species of *Cupressus*. He stresses that freedom from disease in their native habitats is more a matter of an environment that is not conducive to pathogen development rather than an inherent resistance to disease. He also stresses that this tree does not thrive and appears to be particularly subject to disease in sections of the country where the humidity is much higher than that of its native habitat.

Seedling Diseases.—As with other species of *Cupressus*, the annual production of seed is high (*1*), but reproduction is scant. Cypress seeds are usually germinated without treatment, and the low and irregular germination percentage may be due to a factor of embryo dormancy (*1*). Scant reproduction in the field is largely due to the loss of seeds that fall on dry, barren areas or areas that are subject to flood-wash or other vicissitudes of nature.

The nursery diseases of Arizona cypress in the South, where this species is raised in quantity, are not like those of the pines. Instead of the damping-off and root-rot losses suffered by pines, the main impact on Arizona cypress has come from Phomopsis blight (*P. juniperovora*) and girdling by the lesser corn stalk borer (*455*). Phomopsis blight is considered by Hodges (*696*) to be the most serious disease of Arizona cypress seedlings. The distinctive feature of this blight is the death of shoot tips and sometimes entire seedlings, and the production of small, black pustules on the affected parts. Infected plants if outplanted can suffer much additional damage (*697*).

In Georgia a dying of terminals and laterals of Arizona cypress nursery seedlings in August and September of their first year was associated with *Sclerotium baticola* and a species of *Alternaria*. Their role in this blighting was not determined (*455*).

While the ubiquitous *Pestalotia funerea* has been reported to cause a seedling blight in Texas and California, proof of pathogenicity of this common conifer saprophyte should precede its acceptance as a pathogen.

Foliage Diseases.—The most important foliage disease in the South is caused by *Cercospora sequoiae* (*C. thujina*). Some loss also is caused by *C. sequoiae* var. *juniperi*. Hodges (*693*) has helped to clear up the taxonomy of four similar fungi in the genera *Cercospora* and *Stigmina* that attack the foliage of members of the Cupressaceae. Cercospora blight works from the inner parts of lower branches upward and outward and sometimes leaves only the fresh green tips of the new growth. It has caused much mortality and ruinous damage to Arizona cypress being raised for Christmas trees and ornamentals in the South (*696, 1586*).

Waterman (*1512*) discusses a foliage and shoot blight of *Cupressus* spp. in the South that she attributed to *Diplodia cyparissa*, and she suggests the likelihood that the fungus referred to as *Macrophoma cupressi* or *Sphaeropsis cupressi* may represent merely another growth form of *D. cyparissa*. A probable relation of this fungus to the shoot blight described by Luttrell et al. (*895*) (see Stem

148

Diseases) is suggested by the disease descriptions and taxonomic discussions in these two papers.

Phomopsis blight (*P. juniperovora*) is mainly a nursery disease, but it can attack foliage of field trees under moist situations (*696*). It has been recurrent and damaging in young plantings of Arizona cypress in Arkansas[21]. While *C. sequoiae* starts near the stem on the lower branches and extends upward and outward, *P. juniperovora* commonly starts at the tips of the lower branches and extends upward and inward (*906*).

A species of *Monochaetia* (reported as *M. unicornis*) has been associated with dying of foliage in the South, but the discussion of the range and habit of this species by Guba (*558*) might throw some question on the identification, and on pathogenicity to *Cupressus* foliage. See Stem Diseases, below, for reports of *M. unicornis* as a canker fungus.

A very minor needle blight is associated with *Stigmatea sequoiae*.

Stem Diseases.—The importance of specific stem diseases depends upon whether the region involved is the Southwest or the Southeast. In the South, as far west as Texas, *Macrophoma cupressi* has been reported to cause a damaging twig blight and canker in outplanted Arizona cypress. Luttrell et al. (*895*) describe a blighting of stem tips over the entire surface of young trees. Only unhardened tissue was attacked. The disease seemed identical with the one reported earlier by Waterman (*1512*). The imperfect stage of the fungus causing it could be interpreted as a *Macrophoma,* and it may be the same as *M. cupressi,* but they place it more correctly in *Dothiorella.* The perfect stage is a species of *Botryosphaeria.* Damage has been severe in some years and there is much variation in susceptibility among individual trees. In some areas this disease and Cercospora blight occurred together.

Occasional stem damage is done by *Phomopsis juniperovora,* but this is largely a seedling, shoot, and foliage disease (*568, 570, 696*).

In the Southwest, sunscald is a major disturbance, and it limits the use of the smooth-barked type of Arizona cypress for ornamental purposes. Minor stem diseases in the West include *Phoradendron bolleanum* subsp. *densum,* a sub-glabrous, compact mistletoe with straw- to wine-colored berries which reaches damaging proportions in Arizona, and *P. juniperinum,* a leafless species, less common on this tree (*1445*).

On typical Arizona cypress, the rust *Gymnosporangium cupressi,* with pycnia and aecia on *Amelanchier mormonica,* forms fusiform or globoid stem and branch galls that bear the telial stage (*886*). *Cupressus arizonica* var. *bonita* is also attacked. This disease has been rated as important, with respect to damage, only in central Arizona (*1489*), with very heavy damage sustained in some areas.

Boyce and Graves (*161*) report a canker caused by *Monochaetia unicornis* (*558*) on *Cupressus arizonica* in South Carolina and Georgia. Lesions up to 14 mm. long were produced by inoculation, and some bore apothecia of this fungus. *Juniperus virginiana* also proved susceptible (see also *Cupressus macrocarpa*).

Arizona cypress proved highly susceptible to crown gall in inocu-

[21] Personal communication from Charles L. Wilson, patholoist, USDA, Agricultural Research Service, Delaware, Ohio.

149

lation experiments (*1319*), but this is not a common problem in the field.

Wagener (*1489*) lists the species of *Cupressus*, with respect to field susceptibility to Coryneum canker (*Coryneum cardinale*), a major disease of Monterey cypress. Although he considered Arizona cypress not susceptible at that time, it has since proved subject to the disease, although damage is minor.

Root Diseases and Decays.—Rhoads (*1168*) considers Arizona cypress susceptible to the root rot caused by *Clitocybe tabescens* in Florida, where the fungus fruited on the roots of killed trees. This species is also considered moderately susceptible to Phymatotrichum root rot in Texas (*1379*).

When young trees of Arizona cypress were grown in a liquid medium and subjected to inoculation with *Phytophthora cinnamomi*, 23 percent of the root tips became infected, as compared with 54- to 92-percent infection of the roots of southern pine species (*1646*).

No important damage from decay to this species has been reported. Dead wood of Arizona cypress is decayed mainly by *Lenzites sepiaria, Trametes sepium, T. serialis,* and *Poria rimosa*. The first three cause brown carbonizing rots and the last, a white rot (*893, 1067*).

Ruehle (*1224*) lists 5 species of nematodes, in 5 genera, associated with Arizona cypress in Louisiana.

Monterey cypress

Cupressus macrocarpa

Monterey cypress in its native habitat is confined to a coastal strip only two miles long, below Monterey Bay in California, and thus has the most limited natural range of any American conifer (*1367*). Nevertheless, having proved to be a useful ornamental and windbreak tree, it has been widely planted in parts of Europe, South America, Australia, New Zealand, and other areas having a mild climate (*279*). It has a conical form when young and develops into a sturdy, graceful tree that withstands wind and salt spray. It is a very tolerant tree, yet grows well in full light. In its native range, temperatures range from just above freezing to about 90° F., with an annual rainfall of about 17 in. However, plantings of the species elsewhere have shown that it can endure a wider range of temperature (*1367*) and a much higher and a somewhat lower rainfall. It is not hardy, however, and temperatures as low as 10° to 12° F. killed many trees inland in California (*1489*). Peace (*1091*) reports it to resist damage from spring frosts under European conditions. Monterey cypress has a thin bark which offers little protection from fire. Its longevity probably exceeds 200 years (*1367*).

Monterey cypress had been particularly free from serious diseases in California until a canker disease, later attributed to *Coryneum cardinale*, was discovered in the San Francisco Bay area in 1928. Since that time, this one disease has taken a heavy toll, killing a large proportion of the trees in the Bay area, and extending over much of the western part of the state (*1488*).

150

Wagener (*1489*) gives a very complete account of the diseases of the American species of *Cupressus* (see *C. arizonica*).

Seedling Diseases.—Seeds are produced abundantly annually. Germination is somewhat slow and irregular, and, although seedlings may be abundant in some planted stands, they are rare in natural stands (*1*). A factor of embryo dormancy may be involved. Seedlings grow rapidly. Monterey cypress can also be grown from cuttings.

Damping-off is not the problem with *Cupressus* spp. and their close relatives in the Cupressaceae that it is with the Pinaceae. Nursery seedlings are, however, subject to attack by the cedar-blight fungus, *Phomopsis juniperovora*, which infects from the shoot and leaf tips, working inward and downward, and becomes evident by producing small, dark pustules on the diseased tissue (*570*). The reported infections on Monterey cypress have been in eastern nurseries.

Foliage Diseases.—No important foliage diseases of Monterey cypress have been reported from the West. Phomopsis blight (*570*) has caused damage to seedling foliage in southern nurseries, and *Cercospora sequoiae* (*C. thujina*) is responsible for severe blighting of foliage of young trees in species of *Thuja*, *Juniperus*, and *Cupressus* (including *C. macrocarpa*) (*693*). While this disease starts in the lower, inner branches and progresses upward and outward (*1586*), Phomopsis blight starts at the shoot extremities and works inward. Cercospora blight can kill small trees within 2 or 3 years.

Pestalotia funerea (*8, 1489*) has been reported on foliage. However, this fungus is generally on senescent or dead coniferous foliage and should not be accepted as a pathogen unless pathogenicity has been demonstrated.

Stigmatea sequoiae, a subcuticular ascomycete with a discoid ascocarp and very dark spores, occasionally occurs on needles.

Monterey cypress has suffered from lime-induced chlorosis if planted in western soils of high pH.

Stem Diseases.—The only important stem disease is the canker caused by *Coryneum cardinale*. Wagener (*1488, 1489*) gives full accounts of this disease, which since 1928 has taken a heavy toll of planted Monterey cypress from north of San Francisco to below Los Angeles, mainly in coastal counties. The disease has not been found in the native groves, although it occurs in planted trees within 2 miles of natural stands. The *Coryneum* canker is characterized by resinous, girdling lesions that mainly originate at branch or twig junctions. The black, pustular fruiting bodies appear on the lesions from 4 to 8 weeks after death of bark tissues.

An epidemic canker disease of this species kills many windbreak and other trees in New Zealand. The New Zealand disease parallels the American one in all respects but one. A cilium on the conidium of the New Zealand fungus has placed it as *Monochaetia unicornis* while the American pathogen, lacking this process on the conidium, becomes a species of *Coryneum* and has been called *C. cardinale*. A genetic line of *M. unicornis* that attacks *Cupressus* in Kenya has been connected with its perfect stage which has been named *Rhynchosphaeria cupressi* (*1010*). Guba (*558*) discusses these related fungi from *Cupressus* cankers in the United States, Africa, and

New Zealand.

Another canker, mainly of *Cupressus sempervirens* but occurring occasionally on *C. macrocarpa*, is caused by *Cytospora cenesia* f. *littoralis* (= *Valsa cenesia?*). Slightly sunken lesions have less resinosis than *Coryneum* canker and bear many stromata which ultimately develop into simple, locular structures with yellow spore masses (*1657*).

A fungus occurring in the South and in California as a twig saprophyte or weak parasite, *Diplodia cyparissa*, may be related to a fungus, *Macrophoma cupressi*, reported to cause a twig blight and canker of Monterey cypress in California (*1512*). The possible relation of *M. cupressi* to a species of *Botryosphaeria* causing a twig blight on Arizona cypress and additional information on *M. cupressi* are discussed under *Cupressus arizonica*.

Phomopsis juniperovora causes a blight of shoots as well as foliage in southern nurseries (*570*).

While Monterey cypress has proved to be highly susceptible to crown gall (*Agrobacterium tumefaciens*) in inoculations (*1319*), this disease has had little impact in nature.

Root Diseases and Trunk Rots.—Some root and butt rot in older trees has been caused by *Armillaria mellea* (*1489*) and by *Coniophora puteana*, but neither fungus causes important damage. *Polyporus basilaris* (*1067*) causes a brown, carbonizing trunk rot only of this tree species, and *Steccherinum* (*Hydnum*) *ochraceum* and *P. cutifractus* can rot the dead wood.

Monterey cypress was considered moderately susceptible to *Phymatotrichum omnivorum* root rot in Texas tests (*1379*).

It is worth mention that the roots of Monterey cypress are severely attacked by *Phytophthora cinnamomi* and *P. cactorum* in New Zealand, and that a large number of the windbreak trees in parts of the North Island having heavy clay soils have been killed by these root rots and by *Monochaetia* canker (*510, 1027*).

Mycorrhizal formation with Monterey cypress has been attributed to *Rhizopogon rubescens* and *Scleroderma aurantium*, but pure-culture-synthesis confirmation is lacking. Trappe (*1442*) is dubious of the validity of this report of ectotrophic mycorrhizae by these 2 fungi[22].

Miscellaneous Pathology.—A harmless epiphytic alga, *Trentepohlia aurea* var. *polycarpa*, forms a bright-vermilion mantle over the windward side of bark and twigs of Monterey cypresses in the direct path of fine mist from wind-driven ocean spray near Carmel, Calif. (*1489*).

Italian cypress

Cupressus sempervirens

Italian cypress is a handsome tree, typically spreading, or erect and columnar, and it has been planted as an ornamental or windbreak tree since ancient times. It is a native of southern Europe and western Asia (*1154*), and its pyramidal varieties are commonly seen in the formal gardens of the Mediterranean area. It

---

[22] Personal communication from James M. Trappe, USDA Forest Service, Pacific Northwest Forest and Range Experiment Station, Corvallis, Oreg.

has thin, fissured bark, making it sensitive to fire, and it cannot be grown where it is subject to freezing temperatures. Rehder (*1154*) recognizes many varieties, some of which have horizontal or spreading branches instead of a columnar (var. *stricta*) habit. In the United States this tree is mainly grown in California but also is grown in the Deep South. Its deep-green foliage is in contrast to the pale-green foliage of *Cupressus arizonica* (*279*).

The main features of the pathology of Italian cypress are its susceptibility, especially when young, to the needle blights caused by *Cercospora sequoiae* and *Phomopsis juniperovora* and to attack of needles or shoots by three species of *Coryneum* and by *Diplodia cyparissa.*

Wagener (*1489*) gives a very complete account of the diseases of *Cupressus* in America. He considers Italian cypress along with Arizona cypress among the western species that fare badly unless grown in a warm, dry climate.

Seedling Diseases.—Seeds germinate slowly and irregularly (*1*). Damping-off is not the problem with members of the Cupressaceae that it is with the Pinaceae, although some losses can be expected under very moist conditions in soils with pH over 6.0. The only fungus specifically reported to attack Italian cypress seedlings in the United States, causing a blighting, is *Fusarium solani* in Texas (*8*).

Foliage Diseases.—A needle blight of species of *Thuja, Cupressus,* and *Juniperus,* caused by *Cerospora sequoiae* (*C. thujina*), has been particularly destructive to Italian cypress in the South (*692*). It first attacks the inner parts of lower branches and progresses upward and outward. It can kill small trees in a year or two (*1586*), whereas Phomopsis blight (*P. juniperovora*), to which young Italian cypresses are also subject in the East, attacks from the shoot extremities inward (*696*). Hodges (*693*) has helped to clear up the taxonomy of four similar fungi in *Cercospora* and *Stigmina* that attack the foliage of members of the Cupressaceae.

Phomopsis occulta is a saprobe occurring on senescent or dead branches of Italian cypress in California and Texas (*570*).

Coryneum berckmanii (see below) attacks foliage as well as non-woody shoots in Oregon. In Alabama a *Coryneum* with 3-septate conidia (*C. asperulum*) was associated with dead terminal leaves, buds, and shoots of Italian cypress. Pathogenicity was not investigated (*882*).

Stem Diseases.—Italian cypress is moderately subject to the severe *Coryneum* canker disease (*C. cardinale*) that mainly attacks Monterey cypress (*1489*). Gummy, girdling cankers, usually with a twig axil at the center, bear black pustules of the *Coryneum* on dead bark a few weeks after necrosis. In California attacks on Monterey cypress have preceded attacks on Italian cypress (*1488*). The disease is not considered a threat to the culture of the latter species in the United States, but a dieback of Italian cypress in the south of France is now attributed to it (*830*).

Still another species of *Coryneum* can cause damage to Italian cypress in the United States. *C. berckmanii,* which vigorously attacks *Thuja orientalis* in nurseries and home gardens of the Pacific Northwest, has also attacked Italian cypress in Oregon. It blights small branches, starting on the young scale leaves of the terminal branchlets. The blighted shoots turn reddish brown, and the foliage later turns gray and often drops from the plant. Black pustules bearing 5-septate conidia appear on attacked shoots. Milbrath (*968*) describes this disease and points out differences between *C. berckmanii* and *C. cardinale.*

A canker, mainly of *Cupressus sempervirens* in Calitornia but sometimes attacking *C. macrocarpa,* is caused by *Cytospora cenesia* f. *littoralis* (=*Valsa cenesia*?). Slightly sunken lesions, with less resinosis than accompanies *Coryneum cardinale* infection, bear many stromata which ultimately develop into simple, locular structures emitting yellow spore masses (*1657*).

In Florida and Texas a twig blight, canger, and dieback have been ascribed to *Macrophoma cupressi.* It is possible that this fungus is a growth form of *Diplodia cyparissa* which has been collected from dead parts of twigs in Georgia and California (*1512*). The possible relation of *M. cupressi* to a *Botryosphaeria* causing a twig blight on Arizona cypress and additional information on *M. cupressi* are discussed under *Cupressus arizonica.*

Diaporthe eres, a very cosmopolitan saprobe that has gone under many synonyms both in *Diaporthe* (perithecial) and *Phoma* or *Phomopsis* (conidial), also occurs on the dead twigs of Italian cypress in the South and Southwest.

Other Diseases.—Rhoads (*1168*) found *Clitocybe tabescens* fruiting on roots of killed trees of Italian cypress in Florida and regards this tree as a host to this fungus, which in morphology and pathogenicity has much in common with *Armillaria mellea.*

Italian cypress was considered moderately susceptible to *Phymatotrichum omnivorum* root rot in Texas tests (*1379*).

Lenzites striata, mainly a subtropical species confined in habitat to the Cupressaceae, has been reported rotting the dead wood of Italian cypress in Florida (*1067*).

Flamboyant-tree

Delonix regia

Commonly known as royal poinciana, or flame-tree, the striking, red-flowered, handsome tropical flamboyant-tree is wide crowned, is rapid growing, reaches 20 to 40 ft. in height, and has graceful fern-like foliage and showy flowers with scarlet petals. It is planted for shade and ornament in frost-free areas, as in southern Florida and southern California. A native of Madagascar, it is now naturalized in south Florida and the Florida Keys.

Miami park authorities consider the flamboyant-tree one of the best species for planting in that area. In addition to its virtues of color, form, shade, and growth rate, it has shown exceptional capacity to withstand high hurricane winds with only minor damage (*947*).

While a species of *Gloeosporium* and a species of *Colletotrichum* have been observed on leaf spots in Florida, the foliage of this tree is rarely marred by disease.

Only two stem diseases have been reported. Crown gall (*Agrobacterium tumefaciens*) has appeared at the root collar of some nursery plants but is not common. The branch canker caused by

154

Botryosphaeria ribis var. *chromogena* has caused severe dieback in southern Texas, but the climate there is rigorous for this tree and the fungus may have been preceded by climatic damage. This fungus also occurs on the flamboyant-tree in Florida. *B. ribis* is discussed under *Cercis canadensis*.

The only serious disease of the flamboyant-tree is the mushroom root rot caused by *Clitocybe tabescens* (see *Citrus* spp.) [23]. Rhoads (*1168*), who has studied this disease intensively in Florida, reported it affecting 213 species of plants in 137 genera and 59 families in the Southeast. Many flamboyant-trees have been killed by this southern counterpart of *Armillaria mellea*. *C. tabescens* produces light-colored, pitted felts around roots and root collars, lacks the flat, black rhizomorphs of *A. mellea,* produces a soft root rot and collar necrosis, and clusters of mushrooms without annuli often arise at the base of dead or doomed trees.

In Texas this tree is subject to Texas root rot (*Phymatotrichum omnivorum*) (*1379*), but the root-rot belt is climatically unsuited to the flamboyant-tree anyway, being too far north.

Dodder (*Cuscuta* spp.) is known to damage *Delonix regia* and other hardwood species in nurseries in Tanzania (*690*).

Common persimmon
Diospyros virginiana

The common persimmon is a member of the ebony genus *Diospyros* which is composed of over 200 species of largely tropical trees (*53*) of which only *D. virginiana* and *D. texana* are native to North America. The Japanese persimmon, *D. kaki,* a species with large fruit, is grown to some extent in warm parts of the United States, mainly in Florida and California (*357*). *D. lotus,* another oriental species, is used as rootstock for *D. kaki* (*53*). The common persimmon is tolerant (*54*) and medium sized; it seldom reaches heights over 60 ft. or diameters over 12 in. It grows throughout the East, south of a line from southern Iowa to New Jersey, and extends to the Great Plains. It occupies mostly hot and fairly dry old fields and eroded or otherwise submarginal sites, and sprout clumps and thickets of persimmon can take over pasture lands in parts of the lower Mississippi Valley. It·is not particularly site demanding but nevertheless it makes only a scrubby tree on exposed, infertile sites. It grows to largest sizes in the Mississippi bottomlands and other southern loamy lowlands (*468*) and also grows well in protected areas of the southern mountains to elevations of 3,000 ft.

Persimmon is avoided by livestock and rabbits, and even sheep, goats, and deer will not browse the foliage (*279*). The ripe fruit is eaten by man, wildlife, and domestic animals, but if it is short of being fully ripe the fruit is extremely puckery. The pathology of persimmon is dominated by a highly lethal vascular wilt that has virtually eliminated the species in the Tennessee Basin where it constituted one of the most abundant tree species until the 1930's.

Persimmon was fairly resistant to flooding in a ranking of 39 species in a Tennessee study (*583*), rating near cottonwood in its

---

[23] Personal communication from George F. Weber, professor of plant pathology, University of Florida, Gainesville, Fla.

tolerance to high water. It is moderately resistant to damage from ice accumulation (*310*).

Foliage Diseases.—The native eastern persimmon has few leaf diseases, but these spots and blotches become very noticeable by early August because of the tendency of leaf or stem trauma in persimmon to result in black coloration and because yellowing and premature leaf fall are associated with some leaf spots. Most leaf pathogens are fungi in the genus *Cercospora*. Chupp (*260*) has cleared up many points in their taxonomy and synonymy and provides a key to 6 species of *Cercospora* on *Diospyros* spp. There appear to be at least 2 distinct species on *D. virginiana* leaves. *C. diospyri* (with *C. flexuosa* a likely synonym) occurs on indefinite spots or none, fruiting in effuse, olivaceous to black patches on the lower leaf surface with globular stromata and usually some mycelial fascicles. The spores are cylindric to obclavate, colored dark shades of brown, 1- to 5-septate, and $3–5\mu \times 20–100\mu$.

C. fuligniosa (*C. atra*) also fruits hypophyllously but on definite black spots that have a tiny red-brown center on the lower surface. Stromata may or may not occur, fascicles are usually loose. While the conidia are much like those of *C. diospyri,* the conidiophores of the latter are dark brown as contrasted with very light in *C. fuligniosa.* Still another *Cercospora* (*C. kaki*) fruits on thè upper surface on leaf spots on the Japanese persimmon (*260*).

Another primary leaf-spot fungus has been called *Gloeosporium diospyri,* but, as has been the case so often with hardwood leaf-spot Gloeosporiums and Colletotrichums, this is probably the imperfect stage of *Glomerella cingulata* (*1483*), the common apple bitter-rot fungus. It is particularly prevalent in the South not only as a leaf pathogen but also as the cause of twig cankers and fruit rot (*1555*). The leaf-spot stage has been described by Fowler (*472*) for *Magnolia grandiflora,* by Pierce and Hartley (*1115*) for *Aesculus hippocastanum,* and by Ito (*745*) for *Cinnamomum camphora.* Hyaline, 1-celled conidia appear in masses in acervuli on brown to blackish discrete spots. The *Glomerella* stage appears on fallen leaves in the spring.

A common powdery mildew (*Podosphaera oxyacanthae*) (*1153*) may appear on foliage in the late summer, and a *Ramularia* sp. (*62*) is reported to cause a leaf spot in Florida. *Fusicladium levieri* causes a leaf spot reported from Connecticut to Florida. It produces dark, short conidiophores with conidial scars. The conidia are dark, 1- to 2-celled, usually pyriform, and are pushed off the ends of the conidiophores.

A very common, black, irregular spotting of persimmon leaves any time after midsummer, often accompanied by early yellowing and defoliation, appears to have no organism associated with it.

Stem Diseases.—The Cephalosporium wilt of persimmon (*C. diospyri*) must be regarded as ranking with chestnut blight, Dutch elm disease, elm phloem necrosis, and mimosa wilt as among the most devastating biotic hardwood tree diseases known. It has eliminated the persimmon from one of its main habitats, the central basin of Tennessee, where the disease was first found, and has killed large numbers of these trees south to Florida and west to Oklahoma. While the disease killed on an epidemic scale in the Tennessee Valley in the 1930's and 1940's, its destruction slowed down and by 1954 Toole and Lightle (*1436*) reported on the lack of evidence of active wilt in many states where dead and dying persimmons were earlier a major feature of the landscape.

The principal work on the disease and insect aspects of the wilt was done respectively by Crandall and Baker (*302*), and Crandall (*301*) described the causal fungus. The disease is characterized first by rapid wilting of foliage. A cut into the wood shows dark vertical streaking all through the sapwood, not only in a given annual ring. This appears as stippling or blackish arcs in cross-section. Pinkish spore masses form under the bark of recently killed trees. The *Cephalosporium* is easily isolated from the streaked wood.

Internal factors involved in the wilting of persimmon by *C. diospyri* and the pathological anatomy of wilting trees have been studied by Wilson (*1589*). Wilson (*1591*) also has studied the elimination of persimmon from Arkansas pastures by inoculation with the wilt fungus.

There are a few twig diseases of persimmon worthy of mention, but they do little damage. *Botryosphaeria ribis*, which causes a major canker of *Cercis canadensis*, can cause some dieback and twig blighting of persimmon, but, as with most hardwoods, it is likely to be mostly secondary.

Crown gall (*Agrobacterium tumefaciens*) causes some basal necrosis of young persimmon in Florida.

As with *Botryosphaeria ribis*, three species of *Physalospora* (*P. abdita*, *P. obtusa*, and *P. rhodina*) have been considered to be causes of twig blights of persimmon. On most hosts these fungi are secondary but, like *B. ribis* on *Cercis* and *P. rhodina* on tung (*Aleurites fordii*), they can be aggressive on some species in some areas. An example of the problems in understanding the taxonomy and life history of the *Physalospora* species is Voorhees' (*1484*) study on *P. rhodina*. Clusters of black, carbonaceous perithecia with erumpent ostioles and hyaline, subovate ascospores are some of the characteristics of the genus. Conidial stages are in *Diplodia* or one of the closely related imperfect genera.

Myriangium duriaei is parasitic on scale insects. It is dark, with a valsoid stroma, superficial perithecia, and muriform spores.

Persimmon is sometimes host to the eastern mistletoe *Phoradendron serotinum*.

Root Diseases.—Root diseases are not a problem with persimmon, except as the wilt disease can spread from tree to tree through root grafts. Root knot nematodes (*Meloidogyne* sp.) can attack the fine root system in sandy soils but harm only seedlings. The species is only mildly susceptible to Texas root rot (*Phymatotrichum omnivorum*) (*1379*). Tuckahoes, or Indian bread (*Poria cocos*), are masses of fungus tissue that form on the roots of many trees, including persimmon, and range up to several inches in diameter (*1597*). Little damage results from tuckahoes on living roots, although the fungus can cause a brown, cubical butt rot in many species (*343*).

Butt-rot fungi attacking persimmon, such as *Polyporus lucidus* and *P. spraguei* (*1543*), can extend a short distance into the roots but cause no necrotic disease.

Trunk Rots.—A large number of fungi will rot the dead wood

157

of persimmon, and fallen trees rot away remarkably fast. *Schizo-phyllum commune,* which normally has small fruiting bodies, develops copious numbers of very large sporophores on persimmon logs and dead snags.

Hepting (*637*) rated persimmon the soundest of the many fire-scarred Delta hardwood species that he studied. Only half of the scarred trees showed any decay, and the others had an average height of decay only 0.2 foot above the scars. Scars averaged 11 years since the fires.

The principal fungi known to rot the inner cylinder or exposed dead wood of living persimmon trees include *Daedalea ambigua, Fomes geotropus, F. marmoratus, Hydnum erinaceus, Lentinus tigrinus, Pleurotus ostreatus, Polyporus curtisii, P. lucidus,* and *P. spraguei.* Weir (*1543*) mentions repeatedly observing cases of butt rot in fire-scarred persimmon in Indiana caused by *P. spraguei.* This fungus produces a common, brown, carbonizing rot of certain hardwoods, particularly oaks and chestnut.

Hepting and Blaisdell (*656*) emphasize the very low percentage of decay cases in persimmon following fire in the Mississippi Delta compared with other species studied. They point out that this resistance to wound decay in persimmon and sweetgum appears to be associated with the capacity of these two species to form hard, dark, gum-filled zones extending from 2 to 10 mm. from the sap-wood surface inward over the face of the wound. This zone proved impervious to the wood-destroying fungi used in tests on the decay resistance of this barrier.

Miscellaneous Pathology.—If the seasoning of persimmon sap-wood lumber is retarded, the wood often develops a dark-brown to deep-gray color. Scheffer and Chapman (*1246*) provide means of avoiding this stain. Hubert (*722*) describes a grayish-olive stain of stored hardwood crossties or logs, including persimmon, attributed to *Lasiosphaeria pezicula,* an ascomycete fungus.

Russian-olive
Elaeagnus angustifolia

The Russian-olive, or oleaster, is a small tree or shrub with lanceolate leaves that are dull green above and silvery below. The twigs are silvery and often are spiny. Introduced from southern Europe and Asia, it has become naturalized in many parts of the West and eastward to New England. It was widely used in the northern Great Plains States as a shelterbelt tree and as an ornamental, but it is no longer considered suitable for planting in the Great Plains area. It is winter hardy, is very drought resistant, is salt-tolerant, and does well in alkaline soils (*1137*), although it is not suitable in the Texas root-rot belt.

Southern root rot (*Pellicularia (Sclerotium) rolfsii*) is known to kill seedlings in Texas nurseries. White wefts appear at stem bases and spread up the stem and out over the ground under moist conditions. Small, tan sclerotia form in these wefts, often in water droplets. The wefts become tan with age and may form a crust on the ground (*1555*).

Thread blight, a disease caused by a related fungus, *Pellicularia koleroga,* can injure Russian-olive in the South (see *Aleurites*).

A common leaf spot of Russian-olive is caused by *Cercospora elaeagni* (*C. carrii*). Spots are circular, 1–2 mm. across, with a definite brown border and a whitish to brown center. They may be inconspicuous on the under surface of a leaf because of the dense tomentum (*620*). There may be some yellowing beyond the spot itself. Fruiting is epiphyllous on small, brown stomata. Conidia are acicular to clavate, hyaline, slightly curved, indistinctly multiseptate, and measure $2.5–4\mu \times 30–150\mu$ (*260*).

Another small leaf spot is caused by *Septoria argyraea*. It is common over the range of Russian-olive in the Midwest and Great Plains States. Its long, very narrow, hyaline, multiseptate conidia are formed in black, globose, immersed pycnidia and are diagnostic.

A leaf rust, *Puccinia caricis-shepherdiae*, occurs occasionally on *Elaeagnus angustifolia* in the northern Plains States and Canada. This rust, and also *P. coronata* var. *elaeagni*, is fairly common on *E. commutata*. *P. caricis-shepherdiae* has its O and I stages on *Elaeagnus*, and its II and III stages on species of *Carex*. Aecia are hypophyllous in large, indefinite groups and are cupulate. Aeciospores are globoid and measure $17–26\mu \times 19–29\mu$.

Carter (*230*) describes a basal canker of Russian-olive in Illinois caused by *Phytophthora cactorum*. The infected bark is depressed, the inner phloem is very dark colored, and the underlying wood is brown to black with some dark streaking above the cankers in the last springwood vessels. Amber to brown, gummy exudate develops. Thus, the symptoms are similar to those exhibited by this fungus in causing cankers of *Acer, Arbutus, Cornus, Fagus, Prunus, Quercus, Ulmus,* et al. The pathogen is distributed countrywide, but it tends to strike individual trees rather than causing widespread damage. A foot rot and gummosis, caused by a *Phytophthora* sp., have also been reported from Arizona (*8*).

As in the case of most hardwoods, *Nectria cinnabarina* has been cited as a cause of twig blighting, but almost invariably this common organism is secondary (*879*) and follows injury from drought, cold, or some other agent.

A serious disease of unknown cause has resulted in heavy mortality in plantings of Russian-olive in the intermountain area of Washington, Idaho, and Oregon. The first and most characteristic symptom is an arrested development of the buds, which remain in a partially opened condition and then gradually desiccate. By the following year the affected part dies and the arrested bud development continues down the stem until the root collar is reached and then the plant dies. Another symptom is the development of small, brown, necrotic lesions just outside the phloem, and mostly on the undersides of branches. Miller (*973*), who investigated soil and site relationships and isolated extensively from diseased tissues, was unable to determine the cause. He considered that the diseased plants showed the type of dieback characteristic of winter killing of apricot trees.

Occasional trees have died from Verticillium wilt (see *Acer* and *Ulmus*) in the West. In the South crown gall has been identified as affecting Rusian-olive, and in the Midwest hairy root has been reported. These two tumors are caused by *Agrobacterium tumefaciens* and *A. rhizogenes*, respectively.

Although Russian-olive is rated as quite resistant to Texas root rot (*Phymatotrichum omnivorum*) in the mass tests of Taubenhaus and Ezekiel (*1379*), this was not the case when this tree was field planted for shelterbelt purposes in the Texas root-rot belt of Texas and Oklahoma. Thus, Wright and Wells (*1627*) reported that 9 percent of 16,818 trees of this species studied in that area died over a 6-year period: an annual loss of 4.5 percent. They put Russian-olive in the category "susceptible to root rot, not usable on any soil type" of the root-rot belt.

Root nodules, presumably formed by *Rhizobium* sp., have been reported on this tree in Washington.

No fungi have been reported involved in mycorrhizal association with Russian-olive nor have any nematodes been reported from the roots.

Eucalyptus

Eucalpytus spp.

The species of Eucalyptus are broadleaf evergreen natives of Australia where they are the dominant feature of the vegetation (*1094*). There are about 540 recognized species and 150 varieties, ranging from shrubs 10 ft. high to giant trees 300 ft. high. These many species include forms adapted to a wide variety of environmental conditions except those climates with rigorous winters, and they differ widely in tolerance, in durability and in other wood characteristics, and in resistance to disease and insects. Many species will resist damage from frosts. Almost all species produce a gum called kino; thus many eucalypts are called gum trees.

Eucalypts have been widely planted in tropical and subtropical parts of the world. Some planting has been done in Florida and other Deep South States, but eucalypts have not thrived in the Southeast. This is implied by Menninger (*947*), by his exclusion of eucalypts in his list of 46 tree species, all exotic, recommended for street planting in south Florida.

Eucalyptus trees were first introduced into California in 1853 and have been widely used there since, mainly for highway plantings and as windbreaks for citrus and other crops (*1094*). The species by far the most widely used there, especially throughout the lowlands, is the blue gum (*E. globulus*), which is grown as far north as Humboldt Bay. Manna gum, *E. viminalis,* also grows very tall and is more frost resistant than blue gum.

In describing "interesting" trees in California, Metcalf (*955*), after citing *E. globulus* and *E. viminalis,* also mentions *E. sideroxylon,* a tree with coal-black bark and blue-green foliage; *E. ficifolia,* a spectacular tree with broad, dark foliage and brilliant crimson flowers; three similar species with mottled tan and green trunks, which are drought resistant and frost resistant (*E. rostrata, E. tereticornis,* and *E. rudis*); the lemon-scented *E. citriodora* that has a silvery trunk and is limited to southern California because it is not hardy; *E. corynocalyx,* a tree that can withstand drought but not frost; and *E. polyanthemos,* a good highway tree with gray poplar-like leaves.

While much progress has been made in the bare-root planting of eucalypts in the United States and abroad, and while some direct seeding is done in Australia, for the most part the seedlings are grown in nursery beds and then transplanted into containers (tubing) before outplanting.

Eucalypts in general are not particularly subject to serious disease when a proper species selection has been made. The wood of some species, for example *E. gummifera* and *E. sideroxylon*, is very durable in contact with the ground (*1094*).

The described pathology of *Eucalyptus* spp. is only that pertaining to the United States (*1337*).

Seedling Diseases.—Damping-off can become a problem in the nursery under hot, moist conditions. A root-destroying seedling blight in California has been attributed to *Fusarium oxysporum* var. *aurantiacum*, a soil-borne fungus (*1610*).

Stem galls, sometimes called crown knot, form on some seedlings in the Southwest, and, while considered of non-parasitic origin, some consider it likely that crown knot is a virus disease.

Foliage Diseases.—While a number of fungi have been reported to cause leaf spots or to inhabit the foliage, none are considered important. They include three species of *Hendersonia*, *Monochaetia monochaeta* (*M. desmazierii*), *Mycosphaerella moelleriana*, *Phyllosticta extensa* (*P. eucalypti*), and a few other species (*8*).

On calcareous soils in dry parts of the Southwest iron-deficiency chlorosis (*806*) has been striking enough to be ranked as an important disorder of *Eucalyptus* by some observers.

Stem Diseases.—In addition to the galls mentioned under Seedling Diseases, some eucalypts are subject to crown gall (*Agrobacterium tumefaciens*). The latter disease, producing sublethal to lethal, warty stem excrescences, has been damaging enough on some species other than the common *E. globulus* to be rated an important disease in California.

The pathogenic form of *Botryosphaeria ribis*, var. *chromogena*, can cause cankers on branches and stems and some twig blighting in California. Small, black, clustered, subspherical pycnidia and perithecia form on the killed bark (*550, 1555*).

The gray-mold blight caused by *Botrytis cinerea* can invest the green twigs and foliage in the spring, resulting in blighting.

Root Diseases.—The shoestring root rot (*Armillaria mellea*) has killed many eucalypt trees in California and can be diagnosed by its flat, black rhizomorphs, the fan-shaped mycelial felts under bark in the root-collar area, and its typical, clustered, honey-colored mushrooms.

In Florida, Rhoads (*1168*) reports the killing of trees of several eucalypt species by *Clitocybe tabescens*, which is similar in most respects to *A. mellea* but lacks the flat, black rhizomorphs, forms non-fanshaped, pitted felts, and mushrooms without an annulus (*1167*).

Phytophthora cinnamomi has been reported attacking *Eucalyptus* spp. (*1659*), and *Phymatotrichum omnivorum* was parasitic to *E. longirostis* in Texas.

Poria cocos forms tuckahoes, also called Indian bread, on roots of eucalypts and trees of many other genera in Florida. These are tuberous masses of fungus tissue often several inches in diameter (*1597*). This fungus is not known to appreciably affect most of the trees upon which it forms tuckahoes on the roots, although it causes a heartrot of hardwoods throughout the Southeast (*343*).

Trunk Rots.—Only a few fungi have been reported to cause trunk or heart rots of eucalypts in the United States, and they are common species that cause such rots in many hardwoods. *Armillaria mellea* (*848, 1141*), *Polyporus schweinitzii*, and *P. sulphureus* (*151*) cause root and butt rots; the former is a soft, white rot and the latter two are brown, carbonizing rots. *Fomes applanatus*, mainly a saprot fungus, can make some inroads in the heartwood, and *F. robustus* is an effective heart-rotter in living trees (*1067*) of several genera, including *Eucalyptus*.

Miscellaneous Pathology.—The fungi reported to form mycorrhizae with eucalypts are *Boletus portentosus, Lycoperdon gemmatum, Pisolithus tinctorius, Scleroderma bovista, S. flavidum, S. verrucosum* (*1441*), and *Cenococcum graniforme* (*1441*).

Penfold and Willis (*1094*) give an account of the importance of suitable mycorrhizae for the success of growing eucalypts and stress the role of species of *Scleroderma*. They also point out that while a certain mycorrhizal fungus can greatly improve the growth and health of one eucalypt species it may have no effect on another.

A deeply penetrating blue-stain of the dead sapwood of some eucalypts is caused by *Ceratocystis pilifera* (*Endoconidiophora echinella*), normally a widespread and common sapstain fungus of coniferous trees in Europe and the United States (*732*).

Although several species of nematodes have been identified from the root zones of species of *Eucalyptus* in different parts of the world, none have been reported from North America and none have been proven to have caused injury (*1222*).

American beech

Fagus grandifolia

The American beech is a major component of the northern hardwood type, and may also be found in a lesser role throughout the East from Nova Scotia to northern Florida, westward to east Texas and northward, occurring occasionally west of the Mississippi River, in central Arkansas, and from eastern Wisconsin to northern Michigan. It will grow wherever moisture is fairly abundant in the upper soil, and thus beech may be found in river bottoms or at the highest elevations of the southern Appalachian Mountains. It grows to largest sizes in the Ohio and lower Mississippi River valleys, where it reaches over 120 ft. in height and over 4. ft. in diameter (*279*). Given its moisture requirements, beech grows in coastal sands, southern alluvial soils, rocky New England sites, mountain slopes, and is often among the species at timberline in the southern mountains. It seldom occurs on limestone soils, and its foliage ranks with the conifers in being very low in calcium (*244*).

Beech reproduces readily from seed, but most reproduction is either from stump sprouts, with sprouting capacity diminishing rapidly as stumps become larger than 4 in. in diameter, or from root suckers which often lead to beech thickets. Trees that develop from root suckers can grow to considerable size but usually remain small. The silvical characteristics of beech have been compiled by Rushmore (*1231*).

Beech is thin-barked and thus very sensitive to fire and subject to sunscald. Long frost cracks are not unusual in the North. Beech is one of the species most sensitive to flooding, ranking fifth out of 39 species in a Tennessee appraisal (583). It is readily injured by sulfur dioxide fumes, and its foliage shows the classic intervenal SO_2 necrotic pattern (151) if exposed to toxic concentrations.

Beech is very tolerant (54), proved resistant to damage from salt spray after a New England hurricane (1632), and was not readily injured by ice accumulation (234).

Hepting and Fowler (661) point out that beech does not tolerate sudden changes in its environment. Such changes may bring about damage from drought, heat, exposure, and winter injury. Beeches are particularly sensitive to disturbance from partial cutting in addition to being subject to logging wounds (1288). Beech trees left after logging often become stagheaded or die. This sequence is commonly referred to as beech decadence.

American beech is subject to many diseases and defects. In the Northeast its main enemy is the lethal beech-bark disease. It is also subject to cankering, to defects from branch stubs (1291), and to many heart rots and discolorations of the sapwood. There appear to be marked differences among individuals in susceptibility to bark diseases and insects. It is common in New England to see a fine, clean-boled beech standing beside a severely cankered, insect-infested, rough-barked, decadent tree.

Foliage Diseases.—Considering the range of beech and the amount of attention it has had from pathologists, few leaf diseases have been reported and none are important enough to adversely affect beech culture. All of the beech leaf spots develop late in the growing season. Only two leaf-spot fungi are common: *Gloeosporium fagi* and *Phyllosticta faginea*. *G. fagi* produces subcircular spots, fuscous above, olivaceous and vitreous below; acervuli, small, prominent, honey-colored; conidia, subovate, $7-8\mu \times 15-20\mu$, minutely 1- to 3-guttulate; conidiophores, fasciculate (1352).

Phyllosticta faginea may prove to be the spermatial stage of one of the two species of *Mycosphaerella* on beech, *M. fagi* and *M. punctiformis*. The perfect stages of these *Mycosphaerellas* form on fallen leaves in the spring.

Tehon (1382) described as *Coniothyrium fagi* a fungus from Illinois causing round spots 2–3 mm. across, light-brown above with a lighter center, bearing epiphyllous, carbonaceous pycnidia that abut the veins and produce non-septate, olivaceous, oval spores, mostly $3.5\mu \times 3\mu$.

Other beech leaf spots are caused by species of *Cercospora*, *Coccomyces*, and *Microstoma* (8).

Two common species of powdery mildews form on beech leaves in the late summer: *Microsphaera alni* with its multibranched perithecial appendages and *Phyllactinia guttata* with its bulbous-based, acicular appendages (619).

An unusual leaf disease affecting mainly beech and alder is the black, loose, sooty mold caused by *Scorias spongiosa*. The mycelium forms a thick, spongy, ultimately brittle, black mass. The perithecia are long stalked and round; the ascospores are 4-celled (1555). This fungus follows aphid or scale infestation of leaves and twigs.

Beech suffers from a leaf scorch considered to be due to hot, dry weather (*928*) ; a leaf mottle which, while appearing like a virus disease, has not yet been transmitted and has been damaged by extreme winter cold following drought (*151*).

Anyone working with beech foliage diseases should be aware of the thickened deformity (erineum) of the foliage that results from leaf mites in the genus *Eriophyes*.

Stem Diseases.—The principal stem disease is called the beech bark disease. Shigo (*1289*) provides a good, illustrated, succinct account of this destructive malady, which was first found killing beech in Nova Scotia, Canada, in 1920. The damage results from the sequence of beech scale insect (*Cryptococcus fagi*) infestation followed by infection with the weakly parasitic bark fungus *Nectria coccinea* var. *faginata*. The major early research was conducted by Ehrlich (*404*).

Wooly appearing, white, waxy material appears on the bark infested with the scale insects. A red-brown liquid often seeps down the trunk from heavily infested areas, and a slime-flux and necrotic areas often form. The fungus infects scale-infested and weakened bark, sometimes in large girdling patches and sometimes in long streaks. Both the white, sporodochia-bearing micro- and macro-conidia (*Cylindrocarpon*) and the red, lemon-shaped perithecia of the *Nectria* protrude from fissures in the bark. By the time the perithecia appear on killed bark, the scale insects have disappeared. The sequence from scale infestation to perithecial production ranges from 3 to 6 years. Ultimately the foliage yellows, new foliage emerges chlorotic, and the crown thins and dies. Many variations appear in the symptom complex. Other *Nectria* species are sometimes involved. Patches or streaks of bark may die and callus may form. Other insects inhabit living, dead, and dying bark (*1287*). The bark of some trees becomes roughened and cratered from cankers, insect feeding, and accompanying callus. This disease now occurs from eastern Canada southward and westward through the New England States and New York, and the beech scale insect is known as far south as Pennsylvania.

Shigo (*1296*) gives a penetrating analysis of the many biotic factors involved in the beech bark disease. He supports the view that several organisms other than the beech scale and *Nectria coccinea faginata* are closely associated with the disease and may play important roles in its etiology. As an example he cites another scale, *Xylococculus betulae*, a soft-bodied insect that lodges in the bark and has a protruding, hairlike wax tube through which a sweet liquid is secreted. Its feeding roughens the bark, and Nectrias other than *N. coccinea faginata* infect and cause small lesions surrounded by callus. These lesions then become suitable courts for infestation by the beech scale, *Cryptococcus fagi*. Thus, beech bark is a habitat for many scale insects and several species of *Nectria*.

Beech occasionally exhibits the typical bark-free, perennial target cankers caused by *Nectria galligena* (see *Acer saccharum*) ; and *N. cinnabarina* produces its large, coral-colored sporodochia, and sometimes red perithecia, in profusion on senescent and dead branches of beech. Lohman and Watson (*879*) provide means of separating the Nectrias on eastern hardwoods.

The bleeding canker caused by *Phytophthora cactorum*, described under *Acer saccharum*, occasionally affects beech in the Northeast.

Strumella canker (*S. coryneoidea*, perfect stage *Urnula crater-ium*), while mainly a disease of oaks (see *Quercus* spp.), also occurs occasionally on beech in the Northeast. Its cankers retain the bark, show concentric zonations, bear large, very dark, powdery, conidial pustules, and develop *Strumella*-caused wood decay beneath the canker.

One of the so-called canker-rot fungi, *Stereum murrayi*, attacks beech in the Northeast and causes sunken lesions that retain the bark and bear thin, foliate sporophores around the canker edge. Its decay typically extends 2 or more feet above and below the cankers, and the rotten wood has a distinctive sweet odor (*342*).

Two additional heart-rot fungi also produce irregular, callusing trunk cankers that retain the bark. In both, masses of hardened sterile mycelium can be seen within the cankered area, but the pro-duction of sporophores usually takes place only on dead snags and fallen trees. Both fungi, *Polyporus glomeratus* and *Fomes igniarius* var. *laevigatus*, are described and differentiated by Campbell and Davidson (*210, 214*).

Polyporus glomeratus causes a light-colored, spongy rot and pro-duces its sporophores, which may be stipitate, on the outside of the dead bark. *F. igniarius laevigatus* is a resupinate form of the type species and is sometimes called *Poria laevigata*.

In the South brown felts will grow over scale insects on beech branches. They may be formed either by *Septobasidium castaneum, S. cokeri,* or *S. curtisii* (*292*).

In moist, low-elevation parts of the South beech often bears the eastern mistletoe *Phoradendron serotinum*.

Root Diseases.—Beech suffers little damage from root diseases. *Armillaria mellea* rhizomorphs are not unusual on the roots of liv-ing trees. This fungus can cause a wound-decay of butts and roots, but it very seldom kills trees unless they are already weakened.

The squawroot or cancerroot, *Conophilis americana* (*1312*), is one of the broomrapes, a family of angiosperms that lack chloro-phyll, have bract-like leaves, and are parasitic on the roots of many plants. The squawroot is a clustered plant, 8 to 10 in. tall, with ovate to lanceolate leaves, a yellowish corolla, and an irregular, spathe-like calyx with the lower side split and the upper side with 3 or 4 toothlike lobes.

Another broomrape species is also called cancerroot or beech drops (*Epifagus virginiana*) (*1312*). While all *Conophilis* flowers are complete, *Epifagus* has many sterile ones toward the top of the spike. *Epifagus* is a dark-purplish, branching plant and has only a few leaves at the base of the plant. The upper lip of the corolla is notched. The impact of the broomrapes on their American tree hosts is not known, but it is considered slight. Gill (*506*) describes some broomrapes and their habit as root parasites.

Beech was only moderately susceptible to Texas root rot (*Phymatotrichum omnivorum*) in inoculation tests (*1379*), but this tree is not suited to the soils and climate of the Texas root rot belt.

The only mycorrhizal associations Trappe (*1442*) lists for Amer-ican beech are with *Cenococcum graniforme, Cortinarius cin-nabarinus,* and *Lactarius subdulcis.* Vozzo and Hacskaylo (*1486*) characterize the ectotrophic mycorrhizae of beech as short, stubby, and close together, with no root hairs. They illustrate beech mycorrhizae along with those of other eastern tree species.

None of the 6 species of nematodes in one list, identified from the root zones of trees of American beech, have been associated with root injury (*1222*). A later tabulation by Ruehle (*1224*) lists 8 species of nematodes, in 8 genera, associated with American beech in the Southeast.

Endothia gyrosa, a fungus with perithecia superficially resembling those of the chestnut-blight fungus (see *Castanea dentata*), often fruits on the bark of exposed roots. This fungus has a similar habit as a secondary invader of senescent oak bark killed from other causes. It is doubtful that it is ever more than a very weak parasite, although Weir (*1542*) infected beech and oak roots with pure cultures of *E. gyrosa*.

Trunk Rots.—Few trees are subject to decay by more species of fungi than beech. Not less than 10 species of *Fomes*, 5 of *Hydnum* (including its synonyms), 24 of *Polyporus*, 7 of *Stereum*, 11 of *Poria*, 4 of *Daedalea*, and a dozen or more species of agarics, other basidiomycetes, and ascomycetes (e.g., *Ustulina, Urnula, Xylaria*) attack beech (*8*). However, certain species predominate as causes of heartrot in living beech. These are described mainly in the compendia of Overholts (*1067*), Lowe (*890*), Boyce (*151*), and Baxter (*81*).

Fomes igniarius is probably the most common heartrot fungus of beech in the North that is capable of rotting the entire central cylinder (*1050*). Its variety *laevigatus* (*Poria laevigata*) is important further South (*214*). Shigo (*1290*) studied the fungi surrounding and in advance of rot columns of *Fomes igniarius* in living trees. He found that a high-pH "wetwood" zone surrounded the column, and that several non-hymenomycetous fungi and certain bacteria colonized the surrounding area. The fungi were mostly species of *Phialophora, Trichocladium*, and *Acrostaphylus*.

F. applanatus tends to be localized within a few feet of wounds. The other *Fomes* spp. seldom extend more than a few feet from sporophores.

The hydnaceous fungi (mainly *Hydnum coralloides, H. erinaceus*, and *H. septentrionale*) cause very complete destruction of wood, reducing it to a soft, wet mass. Their decay often results in hollows extending many feet through the central cylinder.

Polyporus spraguei and *P. squamosus* cause butt rots. Common butt and trunk rots are caused by *P. glomeratus, P. obtusus*, and *P. rheades*.

Stillwell (*1358*) found just one fungus, *Daedalea unicolor*, associated with the woodwasp *Tremex columba*, attacking the wood of the crowns of beech trees dying of the beech bark disease in New Brunswick, Canada.

The cankering effects of *P. glomeratus* and *Fomes igniarius* var. *laevigatus*, in addition to their heartrotting capacity, are described under Stem Diseases.

In an Ontario cull survey (*73*), the rot-cull percentage in beech reached 20 percent by age class 161–180 years and a stain deduction of 29 percent by age class 181 and over. The main rot fungi were *Polyporus glomeratus, Corticium vellereum, Fomes igniarius, Pholiota adiposa*, and *Armillaria mellea*.

166

Spaulding, Hepting, and Westveld (*1343*) made suggestions regarding cull deductions for beech in New England. They determined that a conk of *Fomes igniarius* indicated a 50 to 100 percent loss of commercial volume, and a single conk on the lower bole indicated a total loss. Cull from conks of *F. applanatus* extended 4 to 6 ft. from a conk. They state that beech is extremely deceptive in estimating cull by the appearance of the rot at a log end, because the rot columns tend to start and end abruptly, except *F. igniarius*.

Ustulina vulgaris (*U. deusta*) is a common invader of stumps and, sometimes, the butts of living beech and maple. It causes a white heartrot with prominent black zones. It is an ascomycete with black, carbonaceous fruiting bodies that form on stumps and logs. On beech they occur commonly on flat, cankered areas (*211*).

Shigo (*1288, 1290, 1291*) has paid particular attention to the discolorations in living beech wood. He deals with concepts of heartwood, pathologic heartwood, and other terminology used in connection with aging wood or darkened sapwood of living trees, as related to wounds and to bacteria and fungi other than so-called heartrot organisms. He believes (*1298*) that, in many cases, the way is prepared for hymenomycete attack of the woody cylinder of living hardwoods by prior invasion by other fungi and lower organisms.

Miscellaneous Pathology.—Shigo (*1286*) studied the succession of fungi on hardwood pulpwood bolts, including beech. *Ceratocystis coerulescens* (*732*), perhaps the most common sapstainer of hardwoods in the United States, was usually the first fungus to infect the log ends, and it was isolated 18 in. from the ends 5 weeks after cutting. The expanding, dark, mycelial patches on the exposed log ends were commonly overgrown by *Cephalosporium* sp., *Gliocladium roseum,* and *Trichothecium roseum,* which were responsible for changing the color of the ends from black to white.

Rough, black patches on the bark of trunk and branches, resulting in no injury, can be caused by *Dichaena faginea* (*1352*). It is one of the Hypodermataceae, and its rounded apothecia open by a slit. They are grouped in rounded spots, first sunken, then erumpent, that are dark brown and contain pyriform asci. The spores are 1-celled at first and are multicelled at maturity.

Increment borings in beech trees produced watersoaked narrow bands, the depth and width of the borings. These bands extended an average of one foot in each direction from the borings. In one series of tests, 85 percent of the borings led to decay, averaging 9 inches in vertical extent. Another series led only to a brownish band developing from each boring (*669*).

DeGroot (*369*) gives an account of fungi associated with American beech in New York.

European beech

Fagus sylvatica

The American and European species of beech are much alike, but in the former the bark is of a lighter color, the head is broader, and the leaves less shiny, turning clear yellow in the fall. The latter has a more ovate head and shinier foliage that turns reddish brown in the fall and may remain attached to the twigs throughout the winter (51).

The European beech, a major forest tree of central Europe, requires a loamy soil, preferably calcareous. It does poorly in sandy or swampy terrain. It is very tolerant, prefers north and east slopes, and grows to elevations over 3,500 ft. in Europe.

There are at least 45 varieties (1154), some dwarfed, others either pyramidal, pendulous, spreading, or with foliage deeply cut or purple in color, or varying in still other characteristics from the species type. Several of the forms are grown as ornamentals in North America.

The varieties most widely used in the United States have bronzed foliage and are commonly referred to as copper beech. They are grown mostly in the cooler parts of the East.

Peace (1091) emphasizes the sensitivity of European beech to spring frosts and to sunscald, if suddenly exposed by removal of overhead shade. He also mentions a high tolerance to lime, but on high-lime sites this beech can, nevertheless, develop lime-induced chlorosis. Peace gives a good account of the diseases of European beech, mainly as it grows in Europe. Since the account below refers only to diseases reported in the United States, Peace's work should be consulted for pathogenic disturbances of this species in the United States that may not be covered in this account.

In the United States the European beech has had few disease enemies and has proved a handsome ornamental except in the warmer and dryer areas.

There are no common diseases of the leaves (1091). The powdery mildew *Phyllactinia guttata* may appear following dry weather in late summer and the leaf deformity (erineum) induced by mites (*Eriophyes* sp.) sometimes affects this beech. The leaf scorch and mottle-leaf mentioned under *Fagus grandifolia* have also been observed to affect *F. sylvatica*.

The main stem disease is bleeding canker (see *Acer saccharum*). Caused by *Phytophthora cactorum*, a fungus that also can cause damping-off of European beech (1091), bleeding canker results in a basal cambial necrosis, exudation of a dark liquid, and a dark staining of the wood beneath the lesion. The ink disease of Europe, caused by either *P. cambivora* or *P. cinnamomi*, mainly affects European chestnut, but both fungi also attack beech. In the ink disease, root invasion results in death of roots and root-collar, and an inky, iron-tannate stain of the wood develops beneath and above the attacked areas. Thus, possibly three species of *Phytophthora* attack European beech in Europe, and possibly two in the United States.

The only other diseases reported for European beech in the United States are: a dieback with which a *Phomopsis* sp. is associated; another dieback with which the common dead-bark colonizer, *Nectria cinnabarina*, was associated, but whose pathogenicity is questionable; the attack of dead, exposed roots by the weak parasite *Endothia gyrosa*; and a nonlethal wound-rot of roots caused by *Armillaria mellea*. These diseases behave on this species like *Fagus grandifolia*.

Close to a record number of ectotrophic mycorrhizal associates (101 fungi) have been reported for *F. sylvatica* around the world,

168

but among this large number of fungi only one, *Tuber excavatum,* has been proved mycorrhizal with this species, by pure-culture technique (*1442*).

Common fig

Ficus carica

The genus *Ficus* is made up of over 600 species scattered over the tropical and subtropical parts of the world. One species, *F. laevigata,* is native to south Florida (*872*). Belonging to *Ficus* are such diverse-appearing plants as the common India-rubber house plant, the enormous banyan tree, the climbing ivy-like fig, and the common fig of commerce. Only the last, *Ficus carica,* produces an edible fruit. This species, a native of Asia, has been cultivated in California since early in the 18th century and in the Southeast since the earliest settlements. There are a great many varieties, about 30, being used for fruit production in the United States; the Smyrna types are the most widely grown. The common fig has escaped cultivation and grows wild from Virginia to Florida and Texas (*872*).

While fig growing is an important orchard industry in California and an imposing literature has been built up on it from that standpoint, the fruit aspect is not dealt with here. The fig tree is now common from Norfolk, Va. throughout the South, except in the mountains, and across the Gulf States and suitable areas of the Southwest. It grows well in soils that are heavy and uniformly moist, and where temperatures do not often go below 18° F., forming a small tree up to 30 ft. high or a large bush (*1312*). It fails in light, sandy soils, where it is usually prey to root-knot nematodes, and also does poorly on other soils that tend to be droughty. In the cooler parts of its range it may require the protection of a house or wall and often must be bent close to the ground and covered with straw or burlap during the cold months in order to survive the winter. In California the fig can be grown throughout the horticultural areas of the state. Fig is pollinated by highly specialized insects.

Bailey (*51*) provides a good account of fig culture in the American Southeast, South, and West. While largely from the point of view of fruit production, his information can be of great help to those maintaining fig trees as ornamentals. One of the most complete accounts of the fig, its culture and its diseases, is the book by Condit (*280*). In 1911 Edgerton (*402*) wrote a bulletin on diseases of the fig tree and its fruit.

The fig is generally propagated from hardwood cuttings, although new varieties are obtained from seeds. There is a growing interest in the fig as a street tree in California and the Gulf States, since it is deciduous and does not shade roads in winter, and since no special culture is necessary where moisture is adequate and the soil is deep. Its small size fits it well for use beneath electric wires.

Metcalf (*955*) mentions the use of the large, evergreen, glossy-leaved *Moreton Bay* fig (*Ficus macrophylla*) from Australia and the smaller, rusty-leaf fig (*F. rubiginosa*) as suitable for planting in open areas in southern California. Menninger (*947*) recommends the weeping fig (*F. benjamina*) and the thrips-proof type of *Ficus nitida* for street use in Florida.

This account deals only with diseases of *F. carica*. As would be expected with an exotic, often planted in areas climatically not suited to it, this tree has been attacked by many fungi that thrive on weakened or partly killed shoots. However, it also develops many leaf-spot diseases and molds, a mosaic virus disease, deficiency diseases, and suffers from soil salinity in parts of the West. The main limiting factors to fig culture are root-knot nematodes, which have been known for their damage to fig for several decades.

Foliage Diseases.—Thread blight (*Pellicularia koleroga, Corticium koleroga, Corticium stevensii*) is a disease of many Deep South species and is recognizable by dead leaves hanging by threads, mainly from the lower portion of the current season's growth. Tims, Mills, and Exner (*1408*) state that thread blight is the most important fig disease in Louisiana. Tims and his coworkers have reported on the leaf blights of fig, and anyone with a problem in the separation of these blights or confusion in nomenclature should consult reference *1408* and the literature it cites.

Also widespread in Florida, trees may be largely defoliated by thread blight, and the fruit may also be attacked. Sclerotia persist on the twigs and germinate and grow in the spring, with the fungus involving and killing shoots and foliage. Spores are produced in thin mats on leaf blades. Later, sclerotia again form. The fungus thallus appears as multithreaded strands, usually on the under surfaces of attacked organs (*1527*).

A web blight in the South is caused by *Rhizoctonia microsclerotia* (*8*).

Cercospora fici forms leaf spots 1–8 mm. long that have a grayish center and brown margin on the upper surface and are ferruginous on the lower surface. Fruiting is mainly epiphyllous, with black, globular stromata; dense fascicles; and pale, olivaceous conidiophores. Chupp (*260*) states that the narrow, obclavate conidia ($2–4\mu \times 30–180\mu$) and short, pale conidiophores separate this species from the other *Cercospora* spp. on *Ficus*. This fungus is widespread in the Southern States.

Another *Cercospora* (*C. bolleana*) commonly occurs on fig in the South. It has a perfect stage (*Mycosphaerella bolleana*) that forms on leaves overwintering on the ground. The *Cercospora* stage on the attached leaves produces brown, mostly angular spots ranging from tiny speckles to large, brown areas; thus, the common name "rusty-leaf." Stromata may form, the fascicles are dense, and the conidiophores are like those of *C. fici*. However, the conidia, $5–7.5\mu \times 20–65\mu$ (*260*), which are broadly obclavate, have blunt ends and are 1- to 5-septate; they can be easily separated from the conidia of *C. fici*, which are long and thin.

Glomerella cingulata (*1483*), a fungus causing a leaf anthracnose and fruit blight of many broadleaved species, attacks the fig throughout the South. Usually reported under a name of its imperfect stage, a *Gloeosporium* or *Colletotrichum* species (usually *C. gloeosporioides, 8*), this fungus causes a dieback of twigs of fig (*1555*) as well as large, circular leaf spots that become brown, sometimes bear black stromata, and produce pinkish spore pustules in wet weather. The *Colletotrichum* stage only may appear, producing

170

1-celled ovoid conidia in disc-shaped, waxy acervuli that bear long, dark setae around the internal perimeter of the acervuli (*62*).

Cerotelium (*Physopella*) *fici* is a common rust of fig and *Maclura pomifera* from North Carolina to Texas. Pycnia and aecia are unknown. This rust forms brown, hypophyllous uredia, the only stage seen in the United States. The telia are minute and white and have been seen only in India. The teliospores are in chains of 2 to 7 cells; the cells are broadly ellipsoid or oblong (*46*).

A sooty mold, consisting of a thick, black coating on the foliage, is formed by a species of *Capnodium* that grows over the surface following leaf attack by aphids, white-flies, or other insects (*1555*). Another heavy, black, moldlike growth in the Gulf States is caused by *Fumago vagans*, which also follows insects, growing on their secretions. The conidia are terminal, often in chains, and are multiseptate with cross and longitudinal septa. Barnett (*62*) states that species of *Fumago* are likely conidial stages of *Capnodium* and *Meliola*. However, Friend (*477*) has concluded that *F. vagans* is simply a mixture of *Aureobasidium pullulans* and *Cladosporium herbarum*.

Species in *Ascochyta*, *Eutypa*, *Alternaria*, and several other genera have been reported to cause leaf spots of fig, but they have not commanded the attention of the leaf fungi singled out for annotation above.

Fig mosaic is a virus disease known as *Ficus* virus 1, K.S.S., or *Marmor caricae*, according to Holmes. Known from the Southeast to California, it produces the yellow and light-green patterns characteristic of mosaic diseases (*1273*).

A little-leaf condition in California results from zinc deficiency.

Stem Diseases.—Fig is subject to crown gall (*Agrobacterium tumefaciens*) in the East and West. Rounded galls with a rough surface typically form near the ground line, but can appear anywhere along the stem, particularly at pruning wounds.

A twig blight and canker in California are caused by a form of *Fusarium lateritium* (perfect stage *Gibberella baccata*). The lesions bear the pinkish, corky sporodochia and 1- to several-septate macroconidia that are characteristic of this species. A variety, *mori*, is widespread on the related genus *Morus* (mulberry), and Wollenweber and Reinking (*1610*) include *Ficus carica* as a host of variety *mori* in Europe.

Phomopsis cinerescens (probably the same as *Libertella ulcerata* of Massee) causes a canker in California and in Europe. Small, radiating cracks develop from the infections, leading eventually to a large, cankered wound. Girdling may result. The fungus spores ooze out in tendrils. The pustules produce hyaline, curved, fusiform conidia with acute ends, $4\mu \times 55$–60μ (*932*).

The brown felts of *Septobasidium* spp. (*292*), which grow over the bodies of scale insects and sometimes result in a canker, have been reported from Mississippi.

Tims (*1407*) describes a limb blight of fig, apple, and pear in the Southeast, the cause of which has been called both *Corticium laetum* and *C. salmonicolor*. The American disease and the "pink disease" of the tropics are both considered by Tims to be caused by *C. salmonicolor*. A pink- or salmon-colored mat with basidia and spores forms over affected limbs, followed rapidly by sudden wilting and dying of the leaves. Pink mats may appear on leaves attached to affected limbs.

Sclerotinia sclerotiorum is responsible for a canker and twig blight in California and Texas. It produces a white, fan-shaped mycelium, evident on the surface in wet weather. Large, black sclerotia form in or on protected or continuously moist tissues, and apothecia form from these. Westcott (*1555*) gives a good account of the many kinds of diseases caused by this one fungus.

Twig cankers and dieback have been attributed to several fungi, most of which are known to have a largely secondary role in disease or to attack senescent shoots. These include *Botryosphaeria ribis* (see *Cercis*), *Physalospora rhodina* (see *Aleurites*), and *Nectria cinnabarina* (see *Fagus*). Others are *Macrophoma fici* (*1607*), *Diplodia natalensis* (*P. rhodina*), and *D. sycina* var. *syconophila*. *B. ribis* was considered the cause of heavy mortality in a fig orchard in Texas (*280*).

Root Diseases.—The fig is particularly susceptible to root diseases. It is damaged by *Armillaria mellea* (*848*) in California, by *Clitocybe tabescens* (*1168*) and *Sclerotium rolfsii* (*1555*) in Florida, and by *Rhizoctonia* sp. in Texas and is rated as extremely susceptible to Texas root rot (*1379*) in the Southwest.

In most areas the limiting factor in fig culture, however, is nematode damage. The high susceptibility to root-knot nematodes (*Meloidogyne*) of fig grown in light, sandy soils has long been known (*51*) both in the South and the West. In addition, fig roots have been reported subject to attack in California by the dagger nematode *Xiphinema index*, the fig-cyst nematode *Heterodera fici*, and four species of meadow nematodes (*1555*).

Ruehle (*1222*) lists 31 species of nematodes identified in association with *Ficus carica* throughout the world, many of which are responsible for some type of root injury.

White ash

Fraxinus americana

White ash is North America's largest, most common, and most useful ash species. The native range extends throughout the East from Nova Scotia to Minnesota, southward to east Texas, and eastward to north Florida. It requires fertile soil and a good supply of soil moisture, although it can obtain its needs from a wide variety of parent material, ranging from fine glacial till to limestone or shale (*1630*). The species tolerates soil pH from 5.0 to 7.5. It thrives best where nitrogen and calcium are particularly available.

Because the calcium content of its foliage is fairly high (*244*), white ash is a soil builder. Its fallen foliage is rapidly incorporated into the soil. Although seldom abundant or making up a large part of the stand, white ash is seldom absent from any of the forest types of the East that have fairly moist, well-drained soils. It is a component of 26 of North America's forest-cover types (*1630*). Although it will withstand temporary flooding (*583*), it is rarely found in swamps.

White ash is tolerant of shade when young, but becomes less tolerant with age, and is therefore usually classed as intermediate to intolerant, reflecting its later requirements (*54*).

According to Sparrow and Sparrow (*1332*), white ash was less sensitive to gamma radiation from a cobalt-60 source than most species of a group of 12 hardwoods and conifers tested (see *Picea glauca*).

This species was severely injured by stack gases from soft-coal consumption in Pennsylvania and from industrial processes in Texas, both of which emitted sulfur dioxide (*911*).

White ash is attacked by few major pathogens. It has suffered repeatedly in nurseries from a *Cylindrosporium* leaf spot, and its heartwood is subject to extensive decay by some common heartrot fungi if trees are old or wounded, exposing heartwood. However, the species was relatively free from disease impacts until trees began dying in great numbers in the 1940's, mainly in New York, from an apparently abiotic disturbance referred to as ash dieback.

Foliage Diseases.—Among the most common foliage diseases of many of the species of *Fraxinus* that occurs virtually wherever ash is grown is the leaf spot caused by *Mycosphaerella effigurata*. The fungus is polymorphic, consisting of a conidial stage (*Marssonina fraxini*)', a spermogonial and carpogonial stage (*Phyllosticta fraxini, Piggotia fraxini*), and a perithecial stage (*M. effigurata*) that develops over winter on fallen leaves. Common in the nursery (*1361*) and the forest, the lesions begin to appear as early as June, and are very small at first. Hundreds may develop on a single leaflet. The 2-celled, hyaline, cylindrical conidia form in tiny hypophyllous acervuli on these lesions. Later in the summer very dark, locular stromata form among the acervuli. These bear spermogonial locules that produce either tiny ($1\mu \times 2$–3μ), 1-celled spermatia or carpogonial locules which, after fertilization, will later form the perfect stage, producing 2-celled, hyaline ascospores. Wolf and Davidson (*1606*) give a very complete descriptive and illustrated account of this interesting fungus and not only indicate the diagnostic difficulties that the polymorphism presents, but also state that this fungus is generally accompanied by several other fungi that cause spots on the same ash leaf. The pathological anatomy of the associated diseased spots has been described by Cunningham (*315*).

The Index of Plant Diseases in the United States (*8*) places the various imperfect forms of *M. effigurata* under *Cylindrosporium fraxini*, although Wolf and Davidson (*1606*) reported the latter as a species separate from these forms. Obviously, the taxonomy and synonymy of some of the leaf-spot fungi on *Fraxinus* spp. need additional attention in order to clarify the conidial and spermogonial stages that accompany known perithecial stages. Reports of many of these are likely to continue to appear under imperfect-stage names, even when the perfect stage is known, since these imperfects are the stages that appear on the living leaves.

Another common leaf spot of ash is caused by *Mycosphaerella fraxinicola*, the spermatial stage of which is *Phyllosticta viridis*. Toward the end of summer, aggregations of small, hypophyllous pycnidia appear, while the upper side of the leaf may show only slight evidence of spotty discoloration. By the time the spots become necrotic, defoliation has begun. Wolf (*1603*) describes the symptoms, fruiting structures, and spores of this fungus. He had no evidence of a conidial stage. The perithecia develop in winter on fallen leaves. The ascospores of *M. fraxinicola* resemble those of *M. effigurata* in shape and septation, but the former measure $4-4.5\mu \times 8-10\mu$ and the latter, $3-4\mu \times 17-40\mu$.

A leaf spot or blotch anthracnose (*Gloeosporium aridum*) is widespread over the country on many ash species. Areas of the leaf, especially along the edges, turn brown, and premature defoliation can result (*661*). Large areas of the leaf become involved in *G. aridum* infection. However, being a late-season disorder, this leaf disease has not commanded the attention of the preceding two.

A rust of ash resulting in swollen and distorted gall-like structures (*661*) involving leaves and twigs, caused by *Puccinia peridermiospora,* is common east of the Great Plains. Epiphyllous pycnia and hypophyllous aecia, prominent and in crowded groups, form on the leaves of species of *Fraxinus* and *Forestiera.* The uredinia and telia form on leaves of *Spartina* spp. which are poaceous grasses (*46*).

The common powdery mildew *Phyllactinia guttata* (*151*) occurs widely on *Fraxinus* spp., except in the Southern States.

In the South *Cercospora fraxinites* causes some spotting; lesions are subcircular or irregular, 3–7 mm. in width, and dull gray-brown above. Fruiting is epiphyllous, as minute, black pustules. The subhyaline, narrowly linear, multiseptate conidia separate this species from the other Cercosporas occurring on species of *Fraxinus* (*260*).

Actinopelte dryina (see *Quercus*), mainly an oak fungus, has been reported on white ash from Illinois. It produces great numbers of very small spots that tend to become confluent (*863*).

Hibben (*676*) describes foliar symptoms that suggest a ringspot virus, and he was able to transmit the disease to bean (*Phaseolus*) and cowpea (*Vigna*). He mentions chlorotic areas with "green island" spots in chlorotic or reddish tissue and, also, chlorotic line patterns along veins of ash leaves. He later published a fuller account of his transmission studies with the ash ring-spot virus (*677*).

Stem Diseases.—White ash has no noteworthy stem diseases. Most fungi that have been mentioned as twig canker organisms, including species in *Diplodia, Haplosporella, Phoma, Macrophoma, Sphaeropsis,* and *Physalospora* (*1484*), are largely secondary and encroach into tissue weakened by abiotic influences as described here under ash dieback. However, *Cytospora annularis,* a fungus with allantoid, hyaline, 1-celled conidia that are extruded in tendrils from a valsoid stroma, is capable of primary attack of twigs and has been reported in many Eastern States. Ross (*1194*) demonstrated the capacity of *Cytophoma pruinosa* and *Fusicoccum* sp. to cause branch cankers.

In the Great Plains States *Dothiorella fraxinicola* has been reported on white ash and other *Fraxinus* spp.

Nectria galligena (*170*) occasionally produces its distinctive, bark-free "target" cankers on ash.

The olive tubercle bacterium, *Pseudomonas savastanoi,* causes galls and cankers of *Fraxinus excelsior* in Europe (*1091*) and was isolated from a galled tree of this species in Washington, D.C. Although it has not been reported from *F. americana* in this coun-

174

try, isolates from the Washington tree produced cankers on white ash following inoculation by Brown (*176*). She named the ash form var. *fraxini*, since it failed to infect olive and the olive form failed to infect *Fraxinus*. Ash and olive both belong to the family Oleaceae.

Root Diseases.—In the Great Plains States hairy root (*Agrobacterium rhizogenes*) has been reported frequently from young white ash. Unlike the somewhat similar crown-gall disease, hairy root involves the protrusion of a great number of small roots either from the base of stems or from the roots (*1555*). In the earlier literature (*619*) hairy root was mistakenly regarded as a form of crown-gall (*A. tumefaciens*).

White ash was rated highly susceptible to Texas root rot (*P. omnivorum*) in inoculation tests (*1379*).

Twenty-six species of nematodes, in 16 genera, have been reported from roots or root zones of white ash (*1222*). Only one of these, *Meloidogyne ovalis*, has been associated with injury to roots, having been described by Riffle (*1171*) as a new species of root-knot nematode. Most of the others were uncovered by Ross (*1195*) in his search for possible pathogens in connection with his investigation of ash dieback in New York.

Trunk Rots.—Most of the decay fungi collected from ash trees have been saprobes or wound rots. However, some of the most aggressive heartrot fungi attack older trees of this genus and cause extensive cull, including hollowing. The true heartrotters of the North that cause cull in white ash include *Fomes fraxinophilus, F. igniarius, Pleurotus ostreatus, Polyporus spraguei,* and *P. sulphureus* (*1067*).

Pandila (*1071*) found slight differences in the wood-decaying capacity of 4 dikaryons of *Fomes fraxinophilus*. Both monokaryotic and dikaryotic cultures showed variation in intensity of oxidase reaction.

Working with fire-scarred white and green ash in the Mississippi Delta, Hepting (*637*) found that decay spread upward from the scars at an average rate of 1.5 in. per year, the rate depending upon the fungus involved. Thus, *Lentinus tigrinus* spread at a rate of 3.0 in., while most other ash fungi rotted upward at a linear rate of 2.0 in. per year. He illustrates heartrot and hollowing in scarred ash. His most common decay fungus was *Lentinus tigrinus,* followed by *Fomes geotropus, Pleurotus ostreatus, Polyporus lucidus, P. tephroleucus* (his white hymenomycete I), and *P. zonalis.* Later, Davidson et al. (*350*), working with several similar but unidentified ash cultures from Hepting's earlier Delta work and from other sources, succeeded in identifying them as *Fomes johnsonianus,* which causes a white, laminated rot.

Campbell and Davidson (*211*) report isolating *Ustulina vulgaris* from a butt rot of white ash. This ascomycete typically rots stumps and forms black, carbonaceous, crustose fruiting bodies.

Shigo (*1290*) studied the area surrounding rot columns of *Fomes igniarius* in several hardwoods, including white ash, and found that several non-hymenomycetous fungi, as well as bacteria, occur in the discolored areas of high pH around such columns. He is exploring the role of this type of advance infection by non-decay organisms on decay by so-called true heartrotters.

Fungi mentioned by Overholts (*1067*) as capable of causing either rot of the central cylinder or rot at wounds of living *Fraxinus* spp. include *Fomes annosus* (*1139*), *F. applanatus, F. connatus, F. densus, F. igniarius, F. torulosus, Polyporus cuticularis, P. fissilis, P. hispidus, P. lucidus,* and *P. sulphureus.*

Miscellaneous Pathology.—Starting in the early 1940's, a dieback and recession of white ash and, to some degree, of green ash, has been taking place. This is occurring mainly in New England and New York and, to a lesser extent, westward to Michigan. By 1960, approximately 37 percent of the white ash in New York State was considered by Silverborg et al. (*1308*) to be dead or dying. In general, the upper and outer twigs show symptoms first, following failure of their buds to open. Some foliage of affected trees emerges yellow green in color and abnormally small. As some twigs and branches die, others exhibit chlorosis, dwarfing, tufting, a progressive thinning of foliage, and ultimately a reduction in width of annual wood rings. Ross (*1194*) and others have given much attention to cankers that form on the branches and main stem of some cankered trees. While Ross does not consider these cankers to be responsible for the onset of ash dieback, he does feel that they contribute to the death of large portions of the crown. While Ross isolated many fungi from ash lesions, four were particularly common, and two (*Cytophoma pruinosa* and *Fusicoccum* sp.) proved to be capable of causing typical dieback cankers on ash.

The background of ash dieback and the problems involved in uncovering its cause have been sketched by Brandt (*169*), Silverborg et al. (*1308*), and Ross (*1194*). Ross mentions the parallel drawn by Hepting (*651*) to the 20th-century declines of maple, birch, sweetgum, ash, oak, and other species and the likelihood of a relation to climate change; Ross has evidence that ash dieback may well be related to drought effects. The reports of Toole (*1418*) on sweetgum blight, Hibben (*674*) on maple decline, Staley (*1348*) on oak decline, and Ross (*1194*) on ash dieback strengthen the evidence that climatic factors have an important role in these disturbances. Favorable rainfall is reported to have alleviated most of the hardwood declines, and with adequate rainfall Ross (*1194*) was unable to obtain infection following inoculation with his ash dieback canker fungi.

In summarizing his extensive investigations of ash dieback in New York, Ross (*1195*) postulated that this decline "is induced by periods of low rainfall, with the fungi acting primarily as secondary invaders that accelerate death of the tree through severe stem and branch cankering."

Croxton (*309*) demonstrated that large-scale, color aerial photography is a useful tool in surveying for ash dieback. The ash trees can be identified in mixed stands, and the extent of decline also shows up well.

Shigo (*1286*) included white ash in his observations on the succession of fungi on hardwood pulpwood bolts in New Hampshire. *Ceratocystis coerulescens* was usually the first to infect the log ends. The expanding mycelial patches commonly were soon overgrown by several other fungi that were responsible for changing the color of the stained ends from black to white.

176

Gyrodon merulioides has been reported (*1442*) to form mycorrhizae with white ash.

Oregon ash
Fraxinus latifolia

Oregon ash is the only Pacific Coast species of *Fraxinus* suitable for timber. In the forest it produces a tall, straight trunk which may reach 30 in. in diameter and 75 ft. in height and has a longevity approaching 250 years. It thrives at the lower elevations along the many streams and bottoms draining the west side of the Coast Ranges and the Sierra Nevada Mountains, mainly on rich, deep, light soils (*1367*).

Its best development is reached in the Willamette Valley of Oregon (*279*). This ash has been planted in parts of the Eastern United States and Europe where the climate is not too rigorous.

Some of the principal leaf fungi of white ash have also been reported on Oregon ash. These include *Mycosphaerella effigurata* and its imperfect stages (*Cylindrosporium fraxini* or *Marssonina fraxini*, and *Piggotia fraxini* or *Phyllosticta fraxini*) (*8, 1277*), *Mycosphaerella fraxinicola* (*1277*) (spermatial stage probably *Phyllosticta innumera*, which may be synonymous with *P. viridis*) (*135*), and *Phyllactinia guttata* (see White Ash for annotations of these fungi).

Shaw (*1277*) lists the fungi that he could confirm as occurring on Oregon ash. These include the pathogens already mentioned and some saprobic leaf, twig, and wood fungi.

No notable aspects of the pathology of this species have been reported. Some fungi have been listed by Wright [24] as occurring on Oregon ash that are in addition to fungi listed in the Index of Plant Diseases in the United States (*8*) and Shaw's compendium (*1277*) as occurring on Oregon ash. These include the leaf fungus *Cylindrosporium californicum;* the twig fungi *Cytospora ambiens* and *Nectria cinnabarina;* and the well-known ash heartrotter *Fomes fraxinophilus.*

Green ash
Fraxinus pennsylvanica

The green ash is native throughout the East from the Great Plains to the Atlantic Ocean, except in southern Florida. It is so called because the lower leaf surface is almost as bright green as the upper. Natural stands are virtually confined to bottomlands, particularly along streams, yet the species has done well when planted on many upland soils. Wright (*1631*), who compiled the silvical characteristics of green ash, mentions its predilection for a ready moisture supply; its tolerance to soil alkalinity, if under pH 8; its tendency to be intolerant to shade; the marked differences in performance and hardiness among certain geographic lines;

---

[24] Personal communication from Ernest Wright, formerly pathologist, USDA Forest Service, Pacific Northwest Forest and Range Experiment Station, Portland, Oreg.

177

and the response of green ash to soil amendments. Since green ash is climatically better suited to the Great Plains than white ash and tolerates a higher soil pH, it has been used as a shelterbelt tree. Among 25 species reported on by Wright and Wells (*1627*) that were experimentally planted for shelterbelts in Texas and Oklahoma from 1937 to 1942, more green ash trees were planted than any species other than desert-willow. Out of 39 species studied in a flooding experiment in Tennessee (*583*), green ash was fifth in capacity to resist damage from high water.

The pathology of green ash is much like that of white ash, but some differences will be pointed out below.

Foliage Diseases.—All of the leaf diseases mentioned on white ash except the *Actinopelte dryina* fungus spot and the virus ring spot, have been reported from green ash. While a few additional leaf spots and another powdery mildew (*8*) have been reported from the latter, these additional leaf pathogens have only occasionally been reported and do not rank in importance with those mentioned under white ash.

Stem Diseases and Trunk Rots.—The stem organisms reported from white ash illustrate fairly well the noteworthy fungi known to attack green ash. *Fomes fraxinophilus* is of greater importance with green ash than with white ash because both this heartrot fungus and green ash are particularly prevalent in the Central and Lake States. Another point of note is that green ash is the only species of *Fraxinus* reported (from Colorado) subject to Verticillium wilt (*V. albo-atrum*).

A study by Hepting (*637*) of decay following fire in Mississippi Delta hardwoods included dissection, analysis, and culturing from 101 white and green ash trees. The results of this study are reported under *Fraxinus americana.*

Toole (*1417*) later dissected 122 green ash trees, in the Mississippi Delta, that had been fire-scarred from 6 to 54 years before. He describes the relation of fire-scar butt rot to age of wound, butt bulge, hollowing, and other features. The average annual rate of decay in green ash was 1.5 in. per year. Only *Lentinus tigrinus* (4 cases) and *Fomes igniarius* (1 case) were isolated from decaying heartwood. Both of these fungi rotted the wood upward at a rate of slightly over 3.5 in. per year. *Fomes meliae* is common on green ash stumps in Louisiana.

Root Diseases.—In inoculation tests green ash was rated less susceptible to Texas root rot (*Phymatotrichum omnivorum*) than white ash (*1379*). In the field tests already alluded to, involving 25 tree species in the Texas-Oklahoma root-rot belt, the 19,434 green ash trees planted stood up well; their mean annual loss to root rot was only 0.5 percent over a 6-year period. Wright and Wells (*1627*) classified green ash in their "intermediate susceptibility" category, as possibly usable for shelterbelts on sandy sites of the root-rot belt.

Root-knot nematodes (*Meloidogyne* spp.) have been found infesting seedlings in Oklahoma.

Miscellaneous Pathology.—Dodder (*Cuscuta* sp.) has occasionally parasitized green ash in nurseries.

Ash dieback (see *Fraxinus americana*) has taken a toll in the Northeast of green ash as well as white ash. Losses to the former species have been far less, perhaps because the green ash is less abundant than white ash in the main area of the decline.

Velvet ash
Fraxinus velutina

Velvet ash is the principal ash of the southern Rocky Mountains, extending from southern Texas across southern New Mexico and Arizona, and into Utah, Nevada, and southern California (*872*). It grows near streams, in canyon bottoms, and around desert water holes and lakes. It may occur on dry benches. It occurs mostly on gravelly, loamy, or sandy soils (*1367*) up to 6,000 ft. in elevation. It will also grow under arid conditions and in alkaline soils where, according to Preston (*1137*), few trees survive. It is very intolerant of shade.

Velvet ash grows to about 30 ft. in height, 18 in. in diameter, and more than 150 years in age on its better sites. The tree is generally symmetrical in shape, but is highly variable. Rehder (*1154*) recognizes three varieties in addition to the type, differing mainly in leaf characteristics. He considers variety *toumeyi* a particularly good street tree for dry climate areas. Variety *glabra,* the Modesto ash, is susceptible to anthracnose, resistant to Armillaria root rot, and not affected by powdery mildew or rust in California.

Only a few of the pathogens of the genus *Fraxinus* have been reported from velvet ash. Among the leaf diseases, *Mycosphaerella effigurata, M. fraxinicola,* and *Gloeosporium aridum* can cause spotting. See *Fraxinus americana* for their imperfect-stage relationships.

The ash anthracnose (*G. aridum*) on velvet ash in California can make trees very unsightly. It infects leaves and tender shoots as they emerge in the spring, turning them brown. The brown lesions on older leaves often have white areas near the margins. Petiole attack will cause a leaf to fall. As much as half of the foliage of some trees, mostly in the lower crown, has been killed (*271*) (see also *Fraxinus americana*).

The leaf and twig rust of ash, *Puccinia peridermiospora,* also attacks this species (see *Fraxinus americana*).

Root-knot nematodes have been reported on seedlings from Arizona.

The only heartrot fungus reported to attack velvet ash is *Fomes fraxinophilus* (*151*).

The western mistletoe *Phoradendron tomentosum* subsp. *macrophyllum,* occurs on this species in the warmer parts of its range (*1580*).

Ginkgo
Ginkgo biloba

The ginkgo, or maidenhair tree, is a unique plant. It is the only member of its family, Ginkgoaceae, and is not closely related to any other plant family in the world. A living remnant of an ancient vegetation, the remainder now recognizable only in fossils, it has been imported from the Orient, where it now exists only as planted individuals (279). It has been successfully grown as a street tree throughout the United States except in the coldest parts of New England, the Lake States, and the Great Plains. Pirone (1119) considers among its assets as a street tree its tolerance to a wide variety of soil types, ease of transplanting, ability to withstand city environmental conditions, and a remarkable freedom from diseases and insects. There is evidence, however, that ginkgo is as sensitive as most other gymnosperms to gamma radiation and as sensitive to the common air pollutants, sulfur dioxide and ozone, as most other street trees (918).

The ginkgo is dioecious, and it is advisable in many situations to plant only the male tree, since the hulls of the fruits of the female emit a very foul odor as they burst from the nuts.

Rehder (1154), who starts his manual that describes thousands of cultivated trees and shrubs with ginkgo as species number 1— the most primitive—mentions five varieties. One is fastigiate, one is pendulous, and the others have unusual leaf characteristics. Metcalf (955) has a high regard for the performance of ginkgo in California.

Ginkgo trees, typically asymmetrical when young, achieve a more conical form later and may grow to over 100 ft. in height and several feet in diameter. Ginkgo trees do not produce viable seed until they are more than 20 years old, but they can continue to reproduce to ages over 1,000 years. Major (918) gives an interesting account of the ginkgo tree, with emphasis on its leaf chemistry and the nature of its high resistance to plant pathogens and insects.

Ginkgo proved very sensitive to temporary immersion of its roots in salt water during a New England hurricane (1632).

Except for a few wood-decay fungi, the pathology of ginkgo consists of two minor leaf diseases, a seed rot, a rare form of edema, and a high susceptibility to Texas root rot. It is considered less susceptible to disease, in general, than any tree grown in the United States.

An occasional anthracnose of foliage is caused by *Glomerella cingulata* (1483, 1555). Usually seen in its imperfect stage, this fungus has repeatedly been placed in either *Colletotrichum* or *Gloeosporium*, depending upon whether or not the observer saw setae, and has been assigned a species epithet depending upon the host. Some of the other tree genera, species of which have conspicuous spots caused by this fungus, are *Aesculus, Cinnamomum, Ficus, Citrus, Magnolia, Malus,* and *Pyrus.*

It is not unusual late in the season for ginkgo foliage to develop the small, circular spots caused by *Phyllosticta ginkgo.* The spots appear as irregular, ashen areas with dark reddish-brown borders, often originating at the leaf margins and extending inward toward the petioles. Older lesions bear a few dark pycnidia. A golden-yellow tinge develops in tissues adjacent to the necrotic area (1129).

Pythium vexans has been isolated from the root zone of ginkgo in the Southeast (633).

Root-knot nematodes (*Meloidogyne* sp.) have been reported associated with seedlings in Mississippi, and several species in sev-

180

eral genera have been identified from the root zones of ginkgos (*1222*).

Although all gymnosperms are to some extent susceptible to Texas root rot (*Phymatotrichum omnivorum*), ginkgo is the only species out of 87 tested that was given a rating of "extremely susceptible" by Taubenhaus and Ezekiel (*1379*).

Several common, saprobic wound-rot basidiomycetes have been reported from ginkgo, but only one heartrotter of living trees, *Fomes connatus*, has been associated with this tree. This is mainly a decayer of *Acer* spp., but is known from several other genera. The soft, wet, white conks almost invariably have green moss on their upper surfaces.

Rusden (*1230*) has described the formation of masses of edemaceous tissue, giving the appearance of fungus tissue, that extruded between the bark fissures near the base of the trunks of ginkgos growing in a wet situation. This watersoaked tissue seemed to replace the cambium in the affected lower bole, and the crowns of the tree were dying. The trouble was ascribed simply to drowning of roots.

Adams et al. (*14*) have been investigating the nature of disease resistance in ginkgo, following the work of Major et al. (*919*), reporting on the isolation of alpha-hexenal, an inhibitor to fungus growth, from ginkgo leaves. In the later work, spores of four common pathogens were sown on ginkgo leaves. All fungi developed and grew over the leaf epidermis, and appressoria were formed. However, no infection pegs were produced. Swellings of the plant cells developed beneath the appressoria, and staining techniques indicated some cell wall changes at these points. Mechanical pressure is also known to induce such staining differentials in ginkgo and other plants.

Johnston and Sproston (*760*) pursued investigations of the nature of disease resistance in ginkgo, with particular attention to the role played by the cuticle. They concluded that the waxy cuticular layer inhibits infection-peg formation and thus "holds the secret" of why ginkgo leaves so effectively resist common pathogens.

Honeylocust

Gleditsia triacanthos

The honeylocust is an intolerant, leguminous tree of the rich alluvial flood plains of the major rivers of the Central States, the Deep South, and the eastern edge of the Great Plains. In the South Atlantic States it appears only in the westernmost portions. Honeylocust also grows on many hot, dry sites including limestone soils and spoil banks in Kentucky and Tennessee, and it is noted for its drought resistance. Geographic lines from the drier parts of its habitat have been useful for shelterbelt plantings. Southern races planted in the North tend to harden off so late that they are subject to frost injury there.

Funk (*493*), who compiled the silvical characteristics of honeylocust, stresses the need for good soil tilth and depth, the tolerance to salinity and alkalinity (preferable pH range between 6 and 8),

181

and the wide range of climatic conditions under which the tree grows. Since it casts only light shade and appears to have soil-building properties, it makes a useful pasture tree. No reports have been found, however, of anyone seeing nodules on the roots of this legume or on the roots of the leguminous Kentucky coffee-tree, *Gymnocladus dioicus.*

Honeylocust, particularly the thornless, podless form known as the Moraine locust, is commonly planted as a lawn and street tree. Rehder (*1154*) lists five varieties, one of which, var. *inermis,* is widely cultivated. Most seedlings grown from thornless honeylocust trees are themselves thornless.

Midwestern honeylocust stock planted on Nantucket Island, Mass., grew to large trees (*1270*), indicating a resistance to salt spray.

In the Houston, Texas area, honeylocust was visibly damaged but not killed by air pollution, presumed to be due mainly to sulfur dioxide (*911*).

Of the 37 species listed in his survey, Croxton (*310*) placed honeylocust and ailanthus as the species most resistant to ice damage. Of the 39 species listed in a Tennessee survey (*583*), honeylocust rated about average in resistance to flood damage.

This species is subject to few diseases, none of which interfere with its culture except in isolated situations.

Foliage Diseases.—Compared with most hardwoods, honeylocust has very few leaf diseases, none of which mar the tree. In the Midwest *Cercospora condensata* commonly causes very small spots that appear as grayish specks with brown margins. Dark stromata bear dense fascicles and septate conidiophores. Conidia are obclavate, plainly multiseptate, and $4-6\mu \times 40-115\mu$. Chupp (*260*) notes that there has been some confusion between this species and what had been called *C. seymouriana* (*C. olivacea*). He considers the latter species a *Helminthosporium.*

A widely distributed, tarry leaf-spot disease of *Gleditsia* is caused by *Linospora gleditsiae.* Affected leaflets may have their lower surface virtually covered with flat, black acervuli bearing 1-celled, hyaline conidia that measure $1-1.5\mu \times 3-5\mu$ and form on a thin palisade layer seated upon the epidermal cells. Miller and Wolf (*981*) illustrate the disease and the fungus. They describe the perithecia as having blunt, cylindrical beaks that project from the upper surfaces of overwintered leaves under trees from mid-May until August. The asci are 8-spored, and the spores are filiform, hyaline, non-septate and average $3\mu \times 70-90\mu$.

The ubiquitous *Glomerella cingulata* in its imperfect (*Colletotrichum*) stage occasionally occurs on leaves. The only other leaf fungi reported are the common powdery mildew *Microsphaera alni* (*1555*) and the very rare rust *Ravenelia opaca;* the latter having curious teliospore heads that are illustrated by Arthur (*46*). It is known only from one location in Illinois.

Stem Diseases.—The most noteworthy disease of *Gleditsia triacanthos* is a canker caused by *Thyronectria austro-americana.* Seeler (*1270*) describes this disease in detail and also describes a highly virulent vascular wilt of *G. japonica* caused by the same fungus. The wilt stage of the disease involves the formation of a darkened, current wood ring, typical of other vascular wilts of trees. He describes the symptoms of the canker disease of *G. triacanthos* as follows: elongated, depressed lesions; yellowing and defoliation following girdling; red-orange discolored bands in the wood surrounding the canker; and abundant hyaline mycelium in the wood beneath the cankers. Following death of a tree, yellow-brown pycnidial stromata emerge from the lenticels and later produce clusters of perithecia. The pycnospores are single-celled and extrude in tendrils. The ascospores are uniquely muriformly septate. This fungus is also weakly pathogenic to the mimosa-tree (see *Albizia julibrissin*).

Seeler (*1271*) has monographed the genus *Thyronectria*, only one species (above) of which is known to be a pathogen in North America.

Schoeneweiss (*1258*) reported long cankers on the stems of 4-year-old thornless honeylocust trees (*G. triacanthos inermis*) at an Illinois nursery. In some cases the lesions extended from the ground line to the shoot tip. Fruiting bodies of *Cytospora gleditschiae* occurred in the cankered bark, and cultures from them produced inoculum that successfully produced typical lesions when introduced into bark.

Physalospora obtusa (*1555*), usually in its *Sphaeropsis* stage, is sometimes involved in twig dieback, but in a partially secondary role.

The witches'-broom virus disease that strikes mainly *Robinia pseudoacacia* has also been observed affecting honeylocust (*529*). This disease has been described in detail on *Robinia*, but very little attention has been given to it on *Gleditsia*, although it has been reported on this host from Ohio, Kentucky, and West Virginia (*8*). Caused by *Robinia virus* I, according to Smith, or *Chlorogenus robiniae*, according to Holmes, this systemic disease results in tight or loose brooms of dwarfed leaflets. Symptoms may be so severe that a small tree of sprout origin may be all broom and may resemble a small juniper tree, or one or more brooms may be scattered through the crown of a larger tree, among normal-appearing branches, or a tree may be a virus carrier without displaying any obvious symptoms (*531*).

A collar rot of honeylocust in California has been attributed to *Phytophthora citrophthora* (see *Citrus*).

Three species of *Septobasidium* are known to produce their brown felts over the bodies of scale insects in the South (*292*).

The eastern mistletoe *Phoradendron serotinum* occasionally parasitizes honeylocust.

Root Diseases.—Some diseases and insects that have an affinity for *Albizia* also attack *Gleditsia*. Examples are Thyronectria canker and the mimosa webworm. Somewhat in this category are *Ganoderma* (*Polyporus*) *lucidum* and the similar but stipitate form *Ganoderma* (*Polyporus*) *curtisii*. Both have been reported, on occasion, to cause extensive root rot and some killing of *Albizia julibrissin* and *Gleditsia triacanthos* ·(*8*). While the incidence of these root rots as killing diseases is not high, infection may be severe, and conk production on any individual tree may be prolific. Parris (*1087*) describes and illustrates the killing of honeylocust in Mississippi by *G. lucidum* and the production of conks from the root system.

Wright and Wells (*1627*) reported on the fate of 5,942 honey-locust trees planted for shelterbelt purposes in the *Phymatotrichum* root-rot belt of Texas and Oklahoma. An annual average loss of 2 percent of these trees took place over a 6-year period. They classed this species as "susceptible to root rot, not usable on any soil type" in the Texas root-rot belt. Taubenhaus and Ezekiel (*1379*) classi-fied it as "extremely susceptible."

Honeylocust is susceptible to hairy root (*Agrobacterium rhizo-genes*) (*1555*) and the root rot caused by *Xylaria mali* (see *Malus*).

Trunk Rots.—The heart-rot and wound-decay fungi of honey-locust are not unusual. The several species of *Fomes* and of *Poly-porus* and the few other wood-destroying fungi listed (*8, 1276*) for honeylocust have no distinctive affinity for this host, and de-scriptions are readily available (*1067*). Fungi cited by Overholts (*1067*) as capable of causing either rot of the central cylinder or rot at wounds of living honeylocust include *Fomes applanatus, F. marmoratus, F. meliae, Polyporus curtisii, P. lucidus,* and *P. sul-phureus.*

Toole (*1417*) dissected 39 fire-scarred honeylocust trees of mer-chantable size in the Mississippi Delta. All but one were decayed, and the maximum length of the decay column (444 inches) ex-ceeded that for any other of the 12 species studied.

Kentucky coffeetree

Gymnocladus dioicus

The Kentucky coffeetree occurs as solitary individuals in the richer bottomlands of the Midwest, extending over approximately the same range as that given for *Gleditsia triacanthos*. It is a legume that grows to over 100 ft. in height and to more than 2 ft. in diameter. It produces large, coarse, heavy pods and is intol-erant of shade. Nodules have not been observed on the roots. A tree in Cleveland, Ohio, reached 4 ft. in diameter (*4*). The tree leafs out late in the spring and sheds its foliage early in the fall (*279*). Its wood is durable in contact with the ground.

This species is remarkably free from disease, and ranks along with *Ginkgo biloba* as having the fewest diseases reported among the trees included in the Index of Plant Diseases in the United States (*8*).

A leaf spot caused by *Cercospora gymnocladi* occurs generally over the range of the tree. Chupp (*260*) states that the large, dark-colored, thick-walled, obclavate, multiseptate conidia are more characteristic of *Helminthosporium* than of *Cercospora*.

Another leaf spot (*Phyllosticta gymnocladi*) has been reported from Illinois. Epiphyllous, black pycnidia with 1-celled, elliptical, hyaline spores occur on small circular spots. The spores measure $4.5–9\mu \times 4–6.5\mu$ (*1387*).

A leaf spot caused by a species of *Marssonina* has been reported from Nebraska. The fungus has pale, discoid acervuli with hyaline, 2-celled, ovoid to fusoid conidia produced on very short conidio-phores.

A sooty blotch (*Gloeodes pomigena*) forms on branches but does no harm. Clusters of short, dark hyphae form a superficial thallus, and the pycnidia form in this matrix. Westcott (1555) describes the blotch as it occurs on fruit and cites the fungus on forest-tree twigs as an important source of inoculum for fruit infection.

Kentucky coffeetree is rated resistant to Texas root rot by Taubenhaus and Ezekiel (1379). Taking this together with its native range extending into the Great Plains region made this tree an early favorite for shelterbelt planting. However, when Wright and Wells (1627) followed the performance of 11,741 Kentucky coffeetrees planted in the root-rot belt of Texas and Oklahoma for 6 years they found an annual mortality from root rot of 2.6 percent. They then classified this species as "susceptible to root rot—not usable on any soil type" of this area.

Polyporus lucidus is known to cause both root and butt rot (1067).

American holly
Ilex opaca

The typical American Christmas holly grows from Massachusetts, where it is a shrub, south to central Florida along the Atlantic Coast and the Piedmont, extends westward into West Virginia and Ohio and southward throughout the South to southeastern Texas (872). It is very tolerant and responds well to release. It does well as a timber tree only in deep, fertile soils of the South, and it grows to 40 or 50 ft. in height and up to 2 ft. in diameter only in the rich bottomlands of Arkansas and east Texas (279). Longevity may exceed 100 years. The leaves remain attached for 3 years and shed in the spring.

The native holly has often proved difficult to transplant despite the prolific lateral root system accompanying the taproot. The tree is dioecious; so only the female plants should be chosen for berries. Transplanting should be done in the dormant season. The trees then should be severely pruned and most of the remaining leaves removed to reduce transpiration until the tree is newly established (279).

There are many other species of *Ilex* in the United States, and all are native to the East and South (872). In addition to numerous hybrids of *Ilex opaca,* there is a variety, *subintegra,* with almost entire leaves and a variety, *xanthocarpa,* with yellow berries (1154).

Ilex opaca was one of the tree species least damaged from salt spray (1005, 1632) associated with a hurricane.

Foliage Diseases.—Since holly retains its foliage for several years it is not surprising that it is subject to attack by many leaf fungi. These fall into four general categories: the leaf-spot fungi (14 species), the black mildews (6 species), the powdery mildews (2 species), and one rust.

The most common and widespread of the leaf spots are caused by *Cercospora pulvinula* (*C. ilicis-opacae* is a less common *Cercospora* on holly) (260); *Phacidium curtisii,* a tar spot (1119); *Phyllosticta opaca;* and *Physalospora ilicis.*

The fungi that cause dark surface specks and molds on foliage and that can often be rubbed off are *Asterina ilicis* and *A. pellicu-*

losa (black mildews), *Capnodium elongatum* (sooty mold), *Englerulaster orbicularis* (black spot, black mildew), *Lembosiopsis brevis* (black mildew), and *Microthyriella cuticulosa* (black speck) (*1276*).

The powdery mildews are the two common species *Microsphaera alni* and *Phyllactinia guttata* (*P. corylea*) (*1153*).

The rust *Chrysomyxa ilicina* is known from the southern Appalachian area only and is the only rust on holly. Pycnia and aecia are unknown. The telia usually arise in the uredia and are flattened and waxy. The teliospores are catenulate and irregularly ellipsoid (*46*).

In the Northeast, *Ilex opaca* is subject to a serious leaf and twig blight caused by *Corynebacterium ilicis*. The bacterium is a Grampositive, non-motile rod that can be detected by macerating tissue and using a suitable stain (*194*).

The holly leaf miner, an insect, causes more destruction of holly foliage than any of the leaf diseases.

Stem Diseases.—A glance at the twig and stem·fungi of holly reveals many common saprobes (*8*). It is for this reason that they are so often indicated as "on branches" rather than stipulating pathogenicity in some way. Holly is virtually free of primary stem pathogens. *Fusarium solani*, known to cause cankers on many hardwoods including species of *Populus*, *Acer*, and *Liriodendron*, can cause a twig dieback (*1119*), and *Botryosphaeria ribis* (*550*) and the two common species of *Physalospora*, *P. obtusa* and *P. rhodina* (*1484*), can be weakly pathogenic on holly twigs.

Several species of *Septobasidium* produce brown felts over scale insects on holly branches (*292*).

Pirone (*1119*) mentions some of the holly dieback problems.

Miscellaneous Pathology.—Few of the remaining holly diseases are noteworthy.

A root rot is ascribed to *Clitocybe tabescens* in Florida (*1168*) (see *Aleurites fordii*).

Very few trunk decay fungi have been reported for holly. They include *Fomes australis* (possibly a synonym for a subtropical *F. applanatus*) (*1067*); *Polyporus ilicincola* and its synonyms, which have been placed in *P. pargamenus* by Overholts (*1067*); *Poria incrassata; Pleurotus ostreatus;* and the ascomycete *Ustulina vulgaris* (*U. deusta*) (*211*). Several species of *Stereum* are known to rot dead branches (*8*).

A purple leaf blotch has been attributed to drought and to nutritional deficiencies. However, unseasonable cold can produce purpling in some plants and may be involved in the holly purpling.

Holly is also subject to lime-induced chlorosis.

A blight of the male inflorescences of holly in New Jersey has been caused by *Botrytis* sp. (*50*). Flower clusters, peduncles, and small twigs were killed in mid-June in the Rutgers plantings of *Ilex opaca* var. Tom Brown.

Rhizoctonia solani (*1555*) caused a leaf rot of cuttings in a Maryland nursery.

None of the many species of nematodes known to occur in the root zones of *Ilex opaca* have been associated with injury to roots (*1222*). Nevertheless, several nematode species have been associated with decline of hollies in general, and Sasser et al. (*1236*) found several cultivars of *Ilex crenata* to be highly susceptible to attack by *Meloidogyne incognita, M. javanica,* and *M. arenaria* but highly resistant to *M. hapla.*

Those interested in the culture and the problems of raising holly would do well to consult the official publication of the American Holly Society.

Butternut
Juglans cinerea

The butternut is a medium-sized tree that, while never abundant, may be found in moist, loamy areas throughout the East from Canada to north Georgia and north Mississippi although it is absent in the Atlantic Coastal Plain and Gulf Coast Plain and is virtually absent in the Piedmont. Clark (*263*), who compiled the silvics of butternut, stressed the very wide range in climate over which the tree grows and therefore the many forest associations in which it is found—mostly as scattered individuals. However, it seldom grows on soils other than those that are deep, moist, and of good tilth. It produces an oily, edible nut.

Butternut is intolerant and generally is short boled, but it can reach a height of over 100 ft. and a diameter of 3 ft. in fertile coves and bottomlands. Typically the tree grows fast when young but is short lived, with few trees surviving past 75 years.

Like its sister species *Juglans nigra,* the roots of butternut exude a substance called juglone that is toxic to many other trees, ornamentals, and crop plants (*1119*). As a consequence the species of *Juglans* are usually found as solitary spreading trees (see *J. nigra*).

Butternut sprouts vigorously from stumps, is very sensitive to fire, and, while subject to storm damage, is windfirm.

Butternut has few disease enemies that have economic impact except for Melanconis canker and an average complement of wood-rot fungi.

Foliage Diseases.—A common anthracnose leaf spot is caused by *Gnomonia leptostyla,* which is an ascomycete that also disfigures the foliage of *Juglans nigra.* Irregular to subcircular dark spots appear scattered over the leaflets early in the summer (*1143*). Infection can be heavy enough to blight most of a leaf and can cause it to drop prematurely (*108*). Acervuli of the conidial stage, *Marssonina juglandis,* occur as black specks on the underside of the lesions (*1091*). Over winter, the conic, short-beaked perithecia of the *Gnomonia* stage form on fallen leaves. The ascospores are fusoid, curved, hyaline, septate, and $4\mu \times 18–22\mu$ (see also *Juglans nigra*).

Cercospora juglandis, mainly a leaf-spot fungus of *Juglans nigra,* also affects butternut. Large, brown blotches without a distinct border may occupy half or more of a leaflet (*260*). Fruiting is hypophyllous, stromata are lacking, and the 0- to 2-septate conidiophores are pale brown. The conidia are subhyaline, cylindric, often catenulate, 1- to 5-septate, and $3–5.5\mu \times 20–85\mu$.

A very widespread downy spot of hickory, walnut, and butternut foliage is caused by *Microstroma juglandis* (*M. brachysporum*), a fungus also capable of causing witches' brooms (see *Juglans nigra*).

Leaf spots on butternut have been attributed to *Actinothecium juglandis* in New York and a species of *Cylindrosporium* in Minnesota.

Stem Diseases.—The principal disease of butternut is a twig and branch dieback caused by *Melanconis juglandis*. While this is chiefly a butternut disease, it affects some other *Juglans* spp. but does not affect *J. nigra*, the common black walnut. Graves (*539*) considers *M. juglandis* to be mainly responsible for the gradual decline, limb by limb, of butternut trees over much of the Northeast and possibly over most of the tree's range, ultimately leading to death. He stresses that disease progress is slow: no sudden wilting of foliage occurs nor does any well-defined lesion or canker form on the infected branches.

Branch dieback is accompanied by a change in bark color from the normal dark greenish-brown, to red brown, and then to gray. As it dies the bark becomes studded with small, dark, smooth papillae, which burst open, exposing the black, pustular acervuli of the fungus. This stage is known as *Melanconium oblongum*.

New short sprouts appear, but they also soon die; ultimately, the trunk itself is involved and the dead gray branches give a stag-headed appearance to the dying tree. Yet, from Graves' (*539*) inoculation results, the fungus involved must be considered only a weak parasite that needs a weakened host to permit its development.

Acervuli are at first small, rounded, blackish, pimply elevations irregularly scattered on recently killed bark. They burst through the epidermis, revealing irregular openings with inky black masses of conidia within, which in saturated air may ooze out in black tendrils. The spores are asymmetrically ovoid, very dark, non-septate, and average $9\mu \times 19\mu$.

The perithecia form later in bark fissures in and about the acervuli. Following incubation in a moist chamber, the long, black necks of the perithecia protrude. The ascospores are 2-celled. A black pycnidial stage also was formed but only in culture. It produced tiny, oblong, hyaline, non-septate spores.

The common perennial target canker caused by *Nectria galligena* (*170*) may be found on the trunk and branches of butternut, but it is much less destructive to this species than it is to *Juglans nigra*. Its bark-free, dead callus folds and tiny, red, balloon-like perithecia are distinctive. Many of the reports of other Nectrias on butternut, including *N. coccinea* and *N. ditissima*, may well have been cases of *N. galligena* (*879*). *N. cinnabarina* is a saprophyte, and its coral-colored sporodochia are characteristic.

A witches' broom of butternut and other *Juglans* spp., cause unknown, may be virus caused with a possible relationship to the virus-caused brooming disease of *Carya* spp.

Root Diseases.—Root-knot nematodes (*Meloidogyne* spp.) have been identified from the roots of several species of *Juglans*, including butternut, but little is known of the effects since the occurrence of a few galls does not imply serious impact (*1222*).

Trunk Rots.—A wide array of rot fungi can cause wound decay in butternut (*8, 1276*). The main heart rot fungi appear to be *Fomes igniarius* and *Polyporus sulphureus* (*1143*). Since butternut seldom occurs in commercial quantities, its decays have not had the attention given those of most other commercial hardwoods. Its rot-fungus flora, however, is not distinctive.

Black walnut
Juglans nigra

One of the most valuable hardwood species is the black walnut. It produces the common, dark-hued "walnut" of the furniture industry and occurs widely throughout the East, except for the colder parts of the Northeast and Lake States; the southern parts of the Gulf States, including almost all of Florida; and the Mississippi Delta region. Brinkman (*173*) has compiled the silvical characteristics of black walnut. It grows in climates with 140–280 frost-free days per year, with annual precipitation from 25 to 70 in., and with mean temperatures from 45° to 67° F.

The site requirements of black walnut are much more exacting than the climatic. Soils must be deep, well drained, well watered, and nearly neutral in reaction. In hilly areas the preferred locations are cool slopes near streams, stream bottoms, benches, and fertile coves at elevations under 4,000 ft.

The species occurs as scattered trees or as small groups of trees. It is intolerant (*54*) : many woody and herbaceous species will not grow within the root zone of black walnut or butternut trees because of a toxic principle, called juglone, that poisons these trees upon contact with walnut roots (*175, 1261*). The identification of the extremely toxic principle isolated from hulls and roots of *J. nigra* as juglone was reported by Davis (*355*). Even black walnut seedlings fail in black walnut root zones in areas where normal competition appears not to be a factor. White, red, and shortleaf pines and several other species are affected by the juglone principle, but, conversely, many species are not so affected. If in the nursery walnut is followed by rhododendron in the same ground, the latter grows very poorly (*360*). The effects of black walnut and black locust on Ohio pastures are discussed by Smith (*1320*).

Black walnut is windfirm and remarkably resistant to ice damage. Croxton's (*310*) study of ice damage to 37 species of street trees included 48 black walnut trees. None of the walnut were badly damaged after a major ice storm, and only two were moderately injured. The heartwood of this species is durable in contact with the ground and decay resistant in the living tree.

Seedling Diseases.—The most important of the nursery diseases is Phytophthora root rot. Identical symptoms are caused both by *P. cactorum* (*305*) and *P. cinnamomi,* and both may occur in the same nursery (*304*). The first appearance of the disease is a wilting of the more succulent parts of the tops, followed by death of the seedlings. Examination reveals most of the roots to be dead and decaying, and dark-colored discoloration extends up the stems an inch or more (*360*). The causal fungi can be readily isolated and identified (*1510, 1511*).

Southern root rot (*Pellicularia rolfsii, Sclerotium rolfsii*) has also killed seedlings in the South (*427*). White mycelial strands and wefts appear at the base of the stem and over the adjacent soil or just below the soil surface. Sclerotia form in the wefts (*1555*).

They are typically spherical, first white, then brownish, and can be so numerous as to form a crust. The roots are killed and rotted by this fungus.

If black walnut seedlings have their roots damaged or pruned in nursery operations, it is common for one of the root rots mentioned to develop, resulting in death of the plants.

Root-knot nematodes (*Meloidogyne* spp.) (*259*) also may be prevalent, mainly on sandy soils, and can stunt seedlings. *Pratylenchus musicola* (*P. coffeae*), a lesion or meadow nematode, has been associated with roots in California. Christie (*259*) refers to these nematodes as vagrant parasites because of their transient association with the host.

Foliage Diseases.—The most damaging leaf disease is the anthracnose caused by *Gnomonia leptostyla*. The irregular, subcircular spots may be small or large and merge to cause large necrotic areas. Yellowish leaf tissue usually borders these spots. Current shoots and the hulls of nuts are also attacked, resulting in dark, shrivelled meats. Berry (*107, 108*), who has determined the etiology and control measures for this anthracnose, states that it may become quickly epidemic in wet weather, causing the loss of most of the foliage as early as late July. He considers black walnut to be particularly susceptible, although the fungus also attacks other *Juglans* spp. He provides good illustrations (*107*). Primary (spring) infection results from ascospores and subsequent infections from conidia (*Marssonina*) produced in acervuli. The conidia are colorless, crescent shaped, and 1-septate. The information on this disease that appears under *Juglans cinerea* also applies to *J. nigra*.

Cercospora leaf spot (*C. juglandis*) is not uncommon on black walnut (see *J. cinerea*), and a *Cladosporium* scab has been reported from Minnesota.

One of the commonest of the black walnut spots is caused by *Cylindrosporium juglandis*. It is very widespread on *Juglans* spp., East and West, but has not been reported on butternut (*J. cinerea*). The spots bear pale, discoid acervuli with very short, simple conidiophores, and hyaline, cylindric to filiform, 2- to 3-septate conidia.

A downy leaf spot or white mold is caused by *Microstroma juglandis*. It is characterized by small, white sporodochia bursting through the epidermis of the leaves, with hyaline, 1–celled, clavate conidiophores bearing hyaline, 1–celled conidia terminally on short sterigmata much in the manner of basidiospores on a basidium (*62*). As leaves approach full size in the late spring, a white, powdery coating appears on the lower leaf surface. Large angular lesions, ultimately becoming brown and dry, result from infection. Wolf (*1598*) describes the disease and illustrates the fungus fruiting body, conidiophores, and conidia, and Cooke (*284*) also describes the fungus.

The common powdery mildew *Microsphaera alni* may become abundant on foliage as autumn approaches.

A widespread bacterial blight of *Juglans* spp., including black walnut, is caused by *Xanthomonas juglandis* (*392*). Irregular, black spots appear on leaves and petioles, and young fruits may be spotted or killed and older fruits, spotted (*1091*). Black, necrotic patches on shoots often girdle them. Catkins are also blighted. Pollen from such catkins can spread the disease (*44*). The bacteria also overwinter in the buds and in shoot cankers.

On walnut, *Phleospora multimaculans* (*620*) produces subcircular, dark-brown spots 1–3 mm. across with a darker border on the upper surface. They may be so numerous as to virtually cover the leaf and can cause defoliation. Pycnidia are hypophyllous, 30–45μ across, with spores cylindric, somewhat curved, hyaline, 1- to 4-septate, and 3.5–5μ × 20–50μ. It is known mainly in Texas on *Juglans nigra*, *J. regia*, and *Platanus occidentalis*.

A yellows-type disease, cause unknown, has appeared in several states.

Stem Diseases.—As already mentioned, young shoots can be infected by the leaf organisms *Gnomonia leptostyla* and *Xanthomonas juglandis*.

The most important stem disease is the perennial target canker (*661*) caused by *Nectria galligena*. Brandt (*170*) gives a general account of this serious disease of many hardwoods, and Ashcroft (*47*) presents a detailed, illustrated account as it affects black walnut. In the southern Appalachian region, walnut trees, especially if not on optimum sites, may bear dozens of the flaring, bark-free, fluted cankers per tree on the trunk and branches. These cankers can cause ruinous defectiveness and stunting or sometimes can kill trees.

While *Nectria galligena* attacks trees in many hardwood genera, it is particularly virulent on black walnut. Also, as determined by the author, isolates from black walnut proved particularly aggressive in cross-inoculations to several different hosts, and black walnut proved particularly susceptible regardless of the host from which the fungus was isolated. The fungus fruits as tiny, bright-red, balloon-like perithecia around the advancing margin of cankers, usually in moist crevices under bark scales (see also *Betula alleghaniensis*).

From the work of Lohman and Watson (*879*), it seems likely that some of the older *Nectria* collections named *N. coccinea* or *N. ditissima* should be referred to *N. galligena*. Booth (*140*) has monographed the genus *Nectria* mainly with respect to European forms, and he discusses the problems of taxonomy and nomenclature among these three specific epithets.

The common eastern leafy mistletoe, *Phoradendron serotinum*, occasionally parasitizes black walnut.

Two types of brooming disease affect black walnut. In one, single, isolated brooms appear to result from localized stimuli of mutagenic origin. However, a bunch disease has also been observed that is similar to the systemic brooming in *Carya* spp. in which large numbers of brooms occur per tree and the trees may be killed. The latter type has been ascribed to a virus (*220*). This systemic brooming or "bunch disease" virtually wiped out the culture of Japanese walnut (*J. sieboldiana*) in the eastern United States. The English walnut is regarded as less susceptible, and the native black walnut still less so.

A *Cytospora* has been mentioned as a cause of cankering of black walnut in Arizona.

Miscellaneous Pathology.—Black walnut proved highly susceptible to Texas root rot (*Phymatotrichum omnivorum*) following inoculation (*1379*). The average annual loss to this disease was only 0.6 percent among the 9,083 planted black walnut trees followed for 6 years by Wright and Wells (*1627*) in Texas and Oklahoma. Both on loose sand and on firm sand, the percentage loss among walnut trees was far less than with most other species tested. Thus, while they consider black walnut intermediate in susceptibility, they regard it as possibly usable for shelterbelts on sandy soils in the root-rot belt.

Little is known of the heartrots of black walnut. The main ones are probably those caused by *Fomes everhartii* (*1067*), *F. igniarius* (*1143*), *Polyporus hispidus* (*1067*), *P. spraguei* (*1067*), and *P. sulphureus* (*1143*). Others capable of causing either rot of the central cylinder or rot at wounds of living *Juglans* spp. include *Fomes praerimosus* (in Southwest), *F. robustus*, and *Polyporus obtusus* (*1067*).

Many wound-rot fungi and saprobes can rot the sapwood of black walnut, but the durable heartwood is uncongenial to fungi.

Hart (*598*) has demonstrated that sapwood of black walnut discolored as a result of wounding is similar morphologically to normal heartwood but differs chemically in having a higher pH, higher ash content, and higher moisture content.

As already indicated, the hulls and nuts are attacked by some of the foliage fungi.

Burls of black walnut, which are overgrowths of unusual grain pattern, are highly prized for furniture stock.

Root-knot nematodes have been reported to attack black walnut. Other nematodes found in the root zones have not been associated with root injury (*1222*).

Injury to black walnut by use of the increment borer has resulted in the formation of open wounds up to 18 in. long (*265*). Although the investigator did not open the trees, it is likely that extensive internal discoloration resulted because the wounds resulted in copious exudate that supported the growth of microorganisms.

English (Persian) Walnut
Juglans regia

Juglans regia, a tree of the Himalayas and China, is grown extensively in the warmer parts of Europe and in California, mainly for nut production. The wood is also useful for cabinet work. It is the common thin-shelled walnut of commerce. To a minor extent, it has been grown in the eastern United States from Pennsylvania to Georgia. In the East, however, the climate has not been well suited to this species, and this, together with disease losses mainly from the virus "bunch disease" (see *Carya illinoensis*), has virtually stopped its culture. There are at least seven varieties (*1154*), many of which are used effectively as ornamentals, and several hybrids have been produced. Some forms have very narrow leaflets and are shrubby or otherwise differ markedly from the type.

In California, the English walnut is widely used as a street tree along the coast and is grown in thousands of acres of orchards

(*955*). Its light-green, compound leaves have fewer and larger leaflets than the native walnuts, and the bark is smooth and gray-green, instead of rough and furrowed as in the native species of *Juglans*.

Trees for nut production are largely grafted, using rootstocks from either the native California *Juglans hindsii*, or "Paradox" hybrids, or even stocks of *J. nigra* or the Chinese wingnut, *Pterocarya stenoptera*. The choice of rootstock material is governed to a large extent by disease and soil factors. Thus, *J. regia* rootstocks are susceptible to Armillaria root rot and *J. hindsii* stocks are highly resistant. Yet to crown rot, the former is highly resistant and the latter is susceptible. These relationships of kinds of rootstock and effects on walnut culture are well described by Serr and Rizzi (*1274*). The general care of English walnut in California, with information supplied on deficiency diseases involving zinc, manganese, and copper, is summarized by Rizzi et al. (*1181*).

English walnut is considered very susceptible to damage from late spring frosts in Europe (*1091*).

Trees used as ornamentals are commonly ungrafted and are raised simply from *J. regia* seedlings. Such trees are likely to be intolerant to heavy soil conditions and high salt concentrations, susceptible to Armillaria root rot and crown gall, and resistant to crown rot.

Foliage Diseases.—Foliage diseases annotated under *J. nigra*, which also occur on *J. regia*, are caused by the following fungi: *Cylindrosporium juglandis* in the East and West; *Gnomonia leptostyla* in the East and West; *Microstroma juglandis* in the East and West; *Phleospora multimaculans* in Texas; and the bacterium *Xanthomonas juglandis* in the East and West.

In addition, the foliage of English walnut trees on the West Coast is subject to a few additional fungus diseases, some deficiency diseases, a freckle spot of unknown origin in Oregon and Washington, and leaf galls in the Northwest, due to blister mites (*Eriophyes tristriatus*) that produce a condition that could be confused with a fungus disease (see *Acer rubrum*).

In Washington and Oregon, *Ascochyta juglandis*, *Phyllosticta juglandina*, and *P. juglandis* occasionally spot leaves. The literature sources containing descriptions of these fungi are provided by Shaw (*1278*).

Stem Diseases.—While there is much in common between the foliage diseases of the different *Juglans* spp., this is not the case with the stem diseases. The latter are caused largely by West Coast pathogens, and by soil conditions peculiar to that region.

J. regia is particularly susceptible to branch wilt, a disease caused by *Hendersonula toruloidea* (imperfect stage *Exosporina fawcetti*) that first appeared in California in the 1930's. Leaves wither and die in midsummer, and then remain attached late into winter. Both bark and wood are killed, and the fungus extends down branches, colors the wood beneath gray to brown, and ultimately spreads to larger branches. Partial exfoliation of bark occurs along the affected branches and exposes sooty layers in the inner bark that are composed of the 1-celled, dark conidia. Infection starts at a wound, often a sunscald injury (*1593*).

A bark canker of English walnut was discovered in California in

1955. Irregular, dark-brown, necrotic areas appear in the bark of the trunk and "scaffold" branches. They start as small, circular spots in the cortical tissue. Typically shallow, the cankers deepen if cracks develop. Dark sap oozes from the lesions, which are likely to squirt sap if punctured. Wilson et al. (*1594*) have designated the cause as *Erwinia nigrifluens,* a bacterium closely related to the fire-blight pathogen, *E. amylovora.*

Melaxuma is a canker that somewhat resembles the bacterial bark canker, but it almost always occurs at crotches between the trunk and scaffold branches. Its cause is referred to *Dothiorella gregaria,* the imperfect stage of the common *Botryosphaeria ribis* (see *Cercis canadensis*). Those fungi which tend to appear only in the vegetative and imperfect fruiting stage are likely to be known by the conidial-stage names long after the perfect stage has been discovered.

Crown gall (*Agrobacterium tumefaciens*) has occurred in the East and West on English walnut. Warty excrescences form at the root collar (*619*). Both *J. hindsii* and *J. regia* rootstocks are susceptible, but the disease has yet to be found on Chinese wingnut (*Pterocarya stenoptera*) seedlings used as rootstocks for walnuts.

Diplodia juglandis occurs widely on branches of *Juglans* spp. and has been reported associated with dieback. However, in many cases, species of *Diplodia* in this role have been essentially saprobic and have proved to be the imperfect stages of either *Physalospora abdita, P. obtusa,* or *P. rhodina* (*1484*).

Melanconis juglandis has been reported causing a canker and dieback in the East (see *J. cinerea*). However, evidence for a strongly pathogenic role for this fungus is lacking (*539*).

A leafy mistletoe, *Phoradendron tomentosum* subsp. *macrophyllum,* will sometimes parasitize English walnut in California (*1580*).

Root Diseases.—The most important of the root rots is the shoestring root rot (*Armillaria mellea*). Ornamental English walnut trees raised from seed can be expected to be very susceptible, whereas those trees established from scion grafts of *Juglans regia* onto stocks of the native *J. hindsii* are highly resistant. White, mycelial fans around the root collar and the flat, black rhizomorphs on the roots (*151*) are diagnostic in the absence of the mushroom clusters (*848*).

Crown or collar rot is caused by *Phytophthora cactorum.* The rot starts below the ground with irregular, dark-brown or black cankers and soft, spongy areas at the crown. A black fluid accumulates in cambial cavities (*1555*). This fungus causes the ink disease of *Castanea* and *Fagus* in Europe (see *F. sylvatica*). Fortunately, *J. regia* rootstocks and seedlings and the Paradox hybrids resist attack by *P. cactorum,* whereas *J. hindsii* is very susceptible (*1274*).

In an eastern nursery, seedlings of *Juglans regia* were destroyed by a collar rot caused by *P. cinnamomi* (*304*). Trees of this species have also been attacked on the West Coast and in other parts of the world (*303*).

Root-knot nematodes (*Meloidogyne* spp.) have been reported on walnut in the West, but a more important pathogen to English walnut in California is the small, sedentary, ectoparasitic root nematode *Cacopaurus pestis*. Christie (*259*) states that affected trees are characterized by gradual reduction in size and number of leaves, twigs, and nuts. He cites G. Thorne as concluding that these nematodes had a contributing cause to this condition. Serr and Rizzi (*1274*) show a photograph of a debilitated, infested tree on *J. regia* rootstock, and a very healthy neighboring tree on nematode-resistant Paradox rootstock.

Miscellaneous Pathology.—As in the case of most orchard crop trees raised on sandy soils, many deficiency diseases, mainly involving boron, copper, manganese, and zinc, have been reported (*8, 1181*). These problems, however, are not common with individual trees but more often result from the heavy demands of orchard culture.

Sunscald is a common form of injury and may be followed by infectious diseases, particularly limb blight.

A graft-incompatibility problem, which involves delay and failure of unions and is referred to as "black line," is common when *Juglans hindsii* is used as a rootstock for *J. regia*. When used as a stock for *J. regia*, Paradox (the hybird of these two species) may also result in the black-line condition (*1274*).

Common Juniper
Juniperus communis

Generally a low, prostrate bush but attaining heights up to 25 feet in New England and Canada, the common juniper is transcontinental in range—from Newfoundland to Alaska—and extends along the mountains of the Pacific Northwest southward to central California, along the Rocky Mountains into the Southwest, from North Dakota through the Lake States and Central States, and from New England to Georgia (*872*). A number of shrubby varieties (12, according to Rehder, *1154*) have been recognized, including the widespread old-field type that is called *Juniperus communis* var. *depressa*. Also, erect and fastigiate types are known, as well as those with pendulous branches, others with bluish foliage, and others with golden-yellow new growth. The common juniper grows in alkaline soils of limestone valleys and also in acid soils. It can tolerate a wide range in soil texture, soil moisture, and air temperature extremes. It is a hardy shrub, commonly occupying worn-out fields and rocky terrain. Yet in north Georgia in 1950, *J. communis* with its varieties were severely injured by a sudden, severe November freeze (*664*).

Common juniper is more subject to injury from salt spray than eastern redcedar (*1005*), but trees of both *Juniperus communis* and *J. virginiana* were either uninjured or recovered well after heavy salt spray accompanying a New England hurricane (*1632*). Although the evergreens in general are particularly subject to damage from air pollution, the junipers are fairly resistant and can succeed in some polluted areas where other conifers fail (*52*).

Seedling Diseases.—No nursery diseases other than Phomopsis blight (see Foliage Diseases), and no strictly seedling diseases have been reported for the common juniper. It is seldom raised from seed, except when trees are required in quantity for erosion control or to provide food plants for wildlife (1). Horticultural use of special clones requires vegetative reproduction. Some junipers are subject to damping-off, but losses to junipers and their close relatives from this disease ordinarily are negligible (360). An unspecified species of *Juniperus* has been reported a host to *Phytophthora cinnamomi* (1659).

Foliage Diseases.—There are several conspicuous needle blights of the common juniper. Phomopsis blight (*P. juniperovora*) kills shoot tips or entire shoots or seedlings, starting at the shoot ends. It is a widespread disease of species of *Juniperus* and related genera, and the causal fungus is first evident as very small, black, conidial fruiting bodies on recently killed leaf tissue (696).

Another leaf blight is caused by *Stigmina juniperina*. Hodges (693) has intensively studied four similar fungi from *Juniperus* and related genera, and found fungi going under the name of *Cercospora sequoiae* var. *juniperi* on *Juniperus communis*, and *Exosporium glomerulosum* on *J. communis*, to be really *Stigmina juniperina*. In addition to *S. juniperina* on common juniper, Hodges also described *Stigmina glomerulosa*. This fungus has had several synonyms, the commonest being *Coryneum juniperinum* and *E. glomerulosum*. The spore variations and fruiting pustules of Hodges' four fungi are illustrated in his paper (693).

Of the five species of *Gymnosporangium* (46) occurring on common juniper, two affect foliage and twigs and the others are twig and stem pathogens. *G. cornutum* produces large telia on leaves and on twigs that may exhibit fusiform swelling. It occurs on *J. communis depressa* in the Lake States and northern Rocky Mountains; and has its 0 and I stages on *Sorbus* spp. *G. davisii* produces small, inconspicuous telia, mostly on leaves; occurs on *J. communis depressa* in Maine and the Lake States; and has its 0 and I stages on *Aronia* spp.

Many secondary or saprobic fungi occur on the common juniper. The only additional fungi that could be aggressive enough to cause damage to foliage are *Asterina cupressina*, which causes a black, surface smudge; *Chloroscypha juniperina*, a discomycetous needle-blight fungus; *Dothidella juniperi*, an ascomycetous leaf-spot fungus; and *Herpotrichia nigra*, a brown-felt blight that damages coniferous foliage remaining too long under snow. *Lophodermium juniperi* (328) may produce hysterothecia in profusion on dead needles, but there is no evidence that it is parasitic (323).

A needle disease is caused by *Didymascella tetraspora* (see *J. scopulorum*).

Stem Diseases.—The most conspicuous stem diseases are caused by species of *Gymnosporangium* (46, 784) and by Phomopsis blight (*P. juniperovora*). The latter has been mentioned under Leaf Diseases. A secondary *Phomopsis* (*P. occulta*) occurs widely on dead twigs (570), and *Coccomyces juniperi* and *Diplodia pinea* are minor twig fungi on the common juniper.

Gymnosporangium clavariiforme produces large, terete telia on long, fusiform branch swellings; occurs almost wherever the common juniper grows except in the South; and has its 0 and I stages mostly on *Amelanchier* spp. *G. clavipes* produces hemispheric telia on small, fusiform twig swellings, occurs mainly in the South, the East, and the Lake States, and has its 0 and I stages mainly on the

196

fruits of species in a large number of genera of the Malaceae. *G. tremelloides* produces telia on fusiform galls, occurs on *Juniperus communis depressa* in parts of the northern Rocky Mountains, and has its 0 and I stages on *Sorbus* spp. (*46, 784*).

Krebill (*813*) found that, in addition to the usual swollen-shoot symptoms of infection with *G. clavariiforme* in common juniper, witches' brooms are also formed in the Rocky Mountains. He also discusses occurrence of the rust in Wyoming, Utah, and Idaho and describes the difficulties in taxonomic separation of this species and *G. gracile*, recently identified as a cause of witches' brooms of juniper in the Southwest.

See *Juniperus virginiana* for resistance tests of several junipers against the cedar-apple rust, *Gymnosporangium juniperi-virginianae*.

Root Diseases.—The common juniper is subject to killing by annosus root rot (*Fomes annosus*). If this shrub was of greater economic importance we might know more about the aggressiveness of *F. annosus* to the common juniper, as compared to the very susceptible *Juniperus virginiana*.

Poria cocos produces its tuberous tuckahoes on the roots in Florida, but little damage is associated with it on juniper (*1597*).

Moderate susceptibility to *Phymatotrichum omnivorum* has been established by inoculation in Texas (*1379*).

The nematodes *Hemicycliophora* sp. and *Paratylenchus* sp. have been reported from root zones but were not associated with injury (*1222*).

Trunk Rots.—*Fomes juniperinus*, sometimes under the synonym *F. earlii*, is the only heart-rot fungus reported to attack the common juniper (*1067*). Boyce (*151*) provides a good description of the rot and good photographs of this fungus. Its sporophore is orange colored to black and much cracked; the advanced decay is a decided pocket rot with yellowish fibers lining the pockets.

Mycorrhizal Relations.—Only *Cenococcum graniforme* has been reported as an ectotrophic mycorrhizal associate (*1442*). The mycorrhizae of the Cupressaceae are almost all endotrophic.

Rocky Mountain juniper
Juniperus scopulorum

A widely distributed species, Rocky Mountain juniper will tolerate a great range of temperatures and adapts well to dry climates. It occurs throughout the drier lower mountains and foothills of the West and can be found naturally in every western state except California and Texas (*672*). It is not, however, as xerophytic as several other western junipers. It is a shrub on exposed sites and can be a tree up to 40 ft. high on deep soils in sheltered situations (*1367*). In addition to withstanding drought, the species can endure temperature extremes of —35° to 100° F. Average annual precipitation in the areas occupied ranges from 12 in. in the Southwest to 26 in. in the Puget Sound area. Calcareous and alkaline soils are preferred, and in parts of northern Arizona the soils of the pinyon-juniper type typically have a pH of 8.0. Rocky Mountain juniper will commonly occupy areas where the soil is shallow, stony, and erosive, with a cemented subsoil. The elevational range varies greatly with latitude, from zero to 3,000 ft. in the Pacific Northwest, to from 3,500 to 6,000 ft. in much of the Rocky Mountain area, and up to 9,000 ft. in the Southwest (*672*).

Rocky Mountain juniper is shade tolerant when young but needs full light later, or it loses much of its crown. Even some of the pines (for example, ponderosa, limber, and lodgepole pine) are considered more tolerant than this juniper (*54, 833*). Trees of this species are long lived, with ages of 250 years not uncommon (*1367*). Certain relict trees may be very much older.

The pathology of this juniper is characterized mainly by high susceptibility of seedlings, in particular, to Phomopsis blight and to attack of foliage, shoots, and stems by many species of *Gymnosporangium*. Two species of true mistletoe are common on it in the Southwest. Neither root diseases nor trunk rots are known to cause much damage to this species.

Seedling Diseases.—Junipers and their close relatives seldom sustain important losses from damping-off (*360*).

Rocky Mountain juniper has not been raised extensively in nurseries, although stock is sometimes grown for erosion control and wildlife food. *Rhizoctonia solani* has caused damping-off in Texas, and Phomopsis blight (*P. juniperovora*) can destroy seedlings (*569, 580*). In the case of eastern redcedar, Hodges and Green (*697*) have demonstrated that, in addition to killing seedlings in the nursery, the survival of outplanted seedlings was markedly reduced by partial Phomopsis-blighting of foliage. Hahn (*569*) reports that attacks on *Juniperus scopulorum* nursery stock in Texas have been as severe as on *J. virginiana* at the same nursery. Wright and Slagg (*1625*) also found both species very susceptible in Great Plains nurseries. However, Rocky Mountain juniper raised in the Dakotas was free of Phomopsis blight (*569*).

In some West Coast nurseries, juniper cultivars Tam and Pfitzer have developed magnesium-deficiency symptoms that were very similar to the symptoms of Phomopsis blight (*606*). These cultivars are varieties of exotic junipers.

The root-lesion nematode *Pratylenchus penetrans* has injured seedlings of Rocky Mountain juniper in a Great Plains forest nursery, where populations had reached a high level. Fumigation resulted in healthy seedling production (*1097*).

Foliage Diseases.—Phomopsis blight (*570*) (*P. juniperovora*) can attack the leaves and shoots of trees in the field, but this disease does not thrive under the dry conditions prevailing on most juniper sites. It seldom damages trees over 4 years old (*580*). *Pestalotia funerea* has been observed widely in association with dying and dead foliage of Rocky Mountain juniper, but it is likely that it plays a secondary role, invading tissue that is dead or dying of other causes. *Apiosporium piniphilum* has caused a surface, sooty mold in the Northwest and *Dimerium juniperi*, a surface smudge on leaves and green shoots in Southwest (*365*).

Gymnosporangium juniperi-virginianae, the cedar-apple rust, produces its telia on subgloboid or kidney-shaped foliar galls; has been reported from Illinois to Colorado on Rocky Mountain juniper; and has its 0 and I stages on *Malus*. On this host, the galls can be considered to be made up of stem tissue. This rust has been a problem to the apple industry in many states. See *Juniperus virginiana* for resistance tests against this rust.

Peterson and Wysong (*1101*) describe the damage to *Juniperus virginiana* and *J. scopulorum* caused by *Cercospora sequoiae* in the Great Plains. Foliage at the base of branches in the lower crown is attacked first. In some cases only a tuft of healthy foliage remains at the ends of shoots. Some windbreaks have lost most of their junipers from this disease.

Pantidou and Darker (*1072*) recognize three species of *Didymascella* (*Keithia*) on the needles of junipers: *D. oxycedri* (spores $17–25\mu \times 9–13\mu$), with epiphyllous apothecia, on *Juniperus oxycedrus; D. tetramicrospora* (spores $15–17\mu \times 11–13\mu$), with epiphyllous apothecia, on *J. scopulorum;* and *D. tetraspora* (spores $16–25\mu \times 13–17\mu$), with hypophyllous apothecia, on *J. communis*.

Stem Diseases.—The most conspicuous of the stem diseases are caused by species of *Gymnosporangium* and by two true mistletoes. *G. betheli* produces telia on irregular knot-like twig excrescences, occurs mainly in the central and northern Rocky Mountain area, and has its 0 and I stages on the leaves and fruit of *Crataegus* spp. *G. nidus-avis* produces witches' brooms, and the telia form only on leafy (non-woody) twigs. It occurs throughout the Rocky Mountains from Canada to New Mexico. Its 0 and I stages are on *Amelanchier* spp. *G. nelsoni* produces telia on globoid or reniform woody galls. *G. nelsoni* is widespread through the Rocky Mountains and has its 0 and I stages on many genera of the Malaceae. Kern (*784*) provides lists and keys to the juniper rusts.

Two mistletoes, *Phoradendron bolleanum* subsp. *densum* and *P. juniperinum* subsp. *juniperinum,* occur on this species (*1580*). *P. bolleanum densum* (*454*) is a leafy, smooth to slightly hairy, compact plant with straw- or wine-colored berries and is mainly a southern Rocky Mountain form. *P. juniperinum* subsp. *juniperinum* (*1445*) is leafless, has straw- to wine-colored berries, and extends from the central Rocky Mountains into Mexico. Wagener (*1491*) pointed out that low temperature is a limiting factor in the northward spread of *P. bolleanum densum*.

Hawksworth (*611*) has reported the rust *Uredo phoradendri* on *Phoradendron juniperinum* subsp. *juniperinum* in Arizona and New Mexico. Uredia are localized on the shoots, which are girdled and killed beyond the point of infection.

Shaw (*1277*) lists *Gymnosporangium inconspicuum* on Rocky Mountain juniper in British Columbia and *G. nidus-avis* from the Inland Empire states and British Columbia. The latter forms witches' brooms, dwarfing the shoots, and has its 0 and I stages on *Amelanchier* spp. and *Cydonia vulgaris*.

Although Arthur (*46*) does not give *Juniperus scopulorum* as a host for the common eastern rust *Gymnosporangium globosum,* Boyce (*149*) does, and he mentions that *J. scopulorum* is as likely to be as severely attacked as *J. virginiana*. *G. globosum* produces telia on globoid branch galls, occurs almost entirely east of the Great Plains, and has its 0 and I stages on at least 90 species of *Crataegus* and on *Malus* and *Pyrus* spp.

Phomopsis occulta (*570*) is a harmless twig fungus, not to be confused with *P. juniperovora*. Both occur on many of the same hosts and, sometimes, even on the same plants.

Rocky Mountain juniper is susceptible to crown gall (*Agrobacterium tumefaciens*) (*1318*), but in nature this disease occurs rarely.

Root Diseases.—Root diseases have little impact on this species. In Texas, *Phymatotrichum omnivorum* has been shown to attack it successfully following inoculation, but when planted in infested areas in Oklahoma and Texas losses were small, and the species was rated among those more resistant to this root rot in the field (*1627*).

The nematode *Pratylenchus penetrans* has been reported under Seedling Diseases.

Trunk Rots.—The fungi known to cause heart rot attack only old or badly damaged trees. They are *Coniophora corrugis, Daedalea juniperina, Fomes juniperinus, F. roseus, F. texanus, Poria rimosa,* and *Trametes serialis*. Some of these can be distinguished easily, but others require culturing for certain identification.

Mycorrhizal Relations.—No mycorrhizal fungi are reported (*1442*).

Eastern redcedar

Juniperus virginiana

Eastern redcedar grows throughout the East, occurring naturally in every state from the Great Plains eastward to the Atlantic Ocean. It grows in the mountains and the plains and on a wide range of sites and soils: from the fertile limestone Great Valley of Virginia to heavy, infertile acid soils in the Piedmont and the sands of the Atlantic Coastal Plain. The species is considered intolerant to shade (*54*) and, being slow growing, is subject to being crowded out by pine and hardwoods. Although it grows naturally on soils from pH 4.0 to 8.0, it is not especially tolerant to alkali, rating in the least alkali-tolerant class among drought-hardy species (*1360*). Eastern redcedar can withstand climatic impacts: it is drought hardy, cold hardy, and it holds up well during very hot summers. It ranks high in survival among conifers used in Great Plains shelterbelt plantings (*1583*). Trees have withstood January temperatures as low as —52° F. (*1080*).

Although typically a tree of stony fence rows, dry gravelly slopes, and abandoned farm land, it also grows in soils that are wet much of the year. It recovered well following submergence in salt water during a hurricane (*1632*), and it was fairly resistant to salt spray (*1005*). Wells (*1550*) points out that eastern redcedar is a component of a salt-spray climax on the North Carolina coast.

Redcedar withstands snow weight reasonably well, but is only moderate in resistance to ice damage (*310*). Where the soil is deep and where root rot is not a factor, many redcedars grow to 130 to 150 years, and some had a longevity exceeding 300 years (*279*). The heartwood is very durable, making eastern redcedar a valuable wood for use in contact with the ground.

There are at least 25 varieties and formae (*681*).

Although the evergreens in general are particularly subject to damage from air pollution, the junipers are fairly resistant and will succeed in polluted areas where many other conifers fail (*52*).

200

In spite of its hardiness in many respects, eastern redcedar has serious enemies in fire, disease (*661*), and insects. In addition to sustaining injury from many leaf blights and leaf and twig rusts, most of the redcedar in the Southeast and some other areas has a brief life span because of annosus root rot. Redcedar is also a problem to apple orchardists by harboring the cedar-apple rust.

Seedling Diseases.—The most serious disease of eastern redcedar in nurseries is Phomopsis blight (*P. juniperovora*) (*360*). Shoot tips or entire tops of seedlings die, and the fungus fruiting bodies appear as small, black dots on recently killed leaf tissue (*696*). Phomopsis blight has been a problem in most nurseries raising eastern redcedar (*568, 697, 1625*). Hodges and Green (*697*) divided planting stock into four lots that ranged from no Phomopsis infection to over 50 percent of the tops dead of the blight. Survival after three growing seasons ranged from 83 percent for the healthy planting stock to 3 percent for the stock with the tops half or more dead.

Peterson (*1098*) refers to Phomopsis blight as the most damaging disease of eastern redcedar in Great Plains nurseries. He, like Hodges, found a much lower survival among outplanted seedlings with Phomopsis infection than among those apparently free of the disease.

Another disease of redcedar, caused by *Cercospora sequoiae*, has been reported by Hodges (*696*) from several southeastern nurseries. With this disease, browning starts with the oldest and lowest foliage and proceeds upward and outward. In late stages, only the tips remain green. This is the opposite from the course of events with Phomopsis blight, where tips blight first. Bretz (*172*) reported this same disease from Missouri and commented on the "ash-brown" color of foliage, defoliation, unusual development of juvenile needles, and the numerous sporodochia and conidia as described by Kelman et al. (*780*).

Some junipers have sustained losses to seedlings from damping-off, but with the junipers and related genera damping-off is generally negligible (*360*).

The root-lesion nematode *Pratylenchus penetrans* became abundant in the soil of a Great Plains nursery and injured redcedar and Rocky Mountain juniper. These nematodes also damaged redcedar hedges where populations became high (*1097*). Ruehle (*1224*) lists 5 species of nematodes in 5 genera that are associated with eastern redcedar in the Southeast.

Foliage Diseases.—Two foliage blights have already been mentioned under Seedling Diseases. Both of them can also cause major losses to redcedar in the field, but Phomopsis blight is not serious in trees over four years old (*580*). In the case of *Cercospora sequoiae* blight (*696*) damage to Christmas tree plantings in parts of the Southeast has been so severe that many have been abandoned (*778, 780*). Four leaf fungi with mutual structural similarities occur on *Juniperus* and related conifers, and this has complicated identification of needle fungi from these hosts. Their identities have been established and their synonymy worked out by Hodges (*693*). They are *Cercospora sequoiae* (see *Juniperus scopulorum*), *C. sequoiae* var. *juniperi*, *Stigmina juniperina*, and *S. glomerulosa*. Anyone attempting identifications of these or related

201

fungi on the junipers, cedars, and their close relatives should consult Hodges' paper.

Phomopsis occulta is an inhabitant of dead and dying foliage, and has, at times, been confused with the highly pathogenic *P. juniperovora*. Their separation is discussed by Hahn (*570*), who also gives the distribution and hosts of the latter (*568*).

Eastern redcedar is host to many species of *Gymnosporangium*, some of which involve foliage and others, twigs and branches (*46, 784*). Those producing the telial stage on redcedar foliage are *G. davisii* (rare on eastern redcedar), with its 0 and I stages on *Aronia* spp.; *G. exiguum* in southern Texas, with 0 and I stages on *Crataegus* spp.; *G. exterum* with its 0 and I stages on *Porteranthus* spp., from Virginia to Maine; *G. floriforme* in the Deep South, with 0 and I stages on *C. spathulata;* and *G. juniperi-virginianae*, the widespread cedar-apple rust, with its 0 and I stages on *Malus* spp., and producing its familiar reniform foliage- and twig-galls on redcedar. Its telial spore horns are longer and rounder than those of the common cedar-hawthorn rust *G. globosum* (*928*), a strictly caulicolous (stem) rust.

Himelick and Neely, in the last of three papers on the subject (*680, 681, 1012*), list the junipers that were resistant and those susceptible to the cedar-apple rust, based on observations at the Morton Arboretum in Illinois. They studied native and exotic species of *Juniperus*. Of the 3 native species discussed herein, they listed 10 varieties or forms of *J. communis* as resistant and none as susceptible; no forms of *J. scopulorum* as resistant and 8 forms as susceptible; and 8 forms of *J. virginiana* as resistant and 17 as susceptible.

Coccodothis sphaeroidea (Keithia juniperi) (*982*) occurs widely on the foliage of eastern redcedar. It has an exposed, carbonaceous ascocarp with 8-spored asci. Other species referred to *Keithia (Didymascella)* have 2- or 8-spored asci (*1073*).

A few additional fungi, including the ubiquitous *Pestalotia funerea,* have been reported on the foliage of eastern redcedar (*8*), but they are either minor pathogens or saprobes. *Lophodermium juniperi* will produce hysterothecia in great profusion on dead and dying foliage, but there is no evidence of parasitism (*323, 328*).

Stem Diseases.—The genus *Gymnosporangium* dominates the stem pathogen flora on eastern redcedar. The more common and often disfiguring species, all with the telial stage produced in stem or branch tissue, are *G. clavipes,* on small fusiform swellings with 0 and I stages mainly on the fruits of malaceous hosts; *G. globosum.* producing short, flat telial horns on globoid galls (*928*) with 0 and I stages on the leaves of malaceous hosts; *G. effusum,* on fusiform swellings with 0 and I probably on *Aronia;* and *G. nidus-avis,* a very widely distributed species that produces witches' brooms and has its 0 and I stages on *Amelanchier* spp.

In addition to the more widespread species of *Gymnosporangium* on stems, there are some that are more restricted geographically: *G. corniculans* produces telia on irregularly lobed gall-like excrescences, has its 0 and I stages on *Amelanchier* spp., and is a Northeast and Lake States rust; *G. exterum* produces telia on fusiform swellings, has its I stage on *Porteranthus* spp., and occurs only from Virginia to Kentucky; *G. bermudianum* has I and III stages on globose to subreniform branch galls and occurs mainly along the Gulf Coast; and *G. trachysorum* has telia on widely fusiform or globoid swellings, is roughened with warts and ridges, has 0 and I stages on *Crataegus* spp., and occurs in the South Atlantic and Gulf Coast States.

Kern (*784*) has provided lists and keys of the "cedar" rusts of the world, and Parmelee (*1082*) has provided an account of the species of *Gymnosporangium* in eastern Canada that is useful with respect to telial hosts (*Juniperus* spp.) to the varietal level, aecial hosts, life history notes, distribution, biology, descriptions, and nomenclature.

Valsa juniperi has been reported from eastern redcedar a number of times by Hedgcock (*625*), who suspected it to be parasitic. If so, it is a weak pathogen. It fruits on the bark.

Dothiorella gregaria (*Botryosphaeria ribis*) is occasionally associated with branch cankers on conifers, including eastern redcedar. *Caliciopsis nigra* (*450*) is occasionally associated with galls and is distinguished by the hair-like protrusions of its fruiting bodies.

Three species of *Physalospora* and several other fungi occur on dead branches but are not likely to be confused with the noteworthy pathogens of eastern redcedar. A species of *Cistella* with small, light-colored apothecia occurs on *Juniperus* in Virginia (*237*).

Eastern redcedar proved susceptible to crown gall following inoculation with *Agrobacterium tumefaciens* (*1318*), but this disease is not a problem in the field.

When inoculated, *Monochaetia unicornis* (*558*) formed cankers on redcedar and Arizona cypress in Georgia (*161*).

Root Diseases.—Eastern redcedar's greatest enemy over much of its range is the root-rot fungus *Fomes annosus*. On this host this fungus causes strictly a root rot, often completely destroying the living bark and sapwood of the roots right to the root collar, but hardly extending at all into the trunk, and never rotting heartwood. Dwyer (*400*) pointed out the increase in incidence of annosus root rot in relation to tree diameter, reaching 37 percent in the 2.7- to 4.5-inch diameter class, after which the number of trees available for study rapidly dropped off. The yellow, stringy rot, the irregular, whitish conks under the duff at the ground line, and the dead trees scattered through redcedar stands are diagnostic (*661*). Miller (*983*) in an early paper on the attack of eastern redcedar by *F. annosus* indicated that little loss may be anticipated if the trees are exposed to full sunlight. Subsequent experience by others has not supported this optimistic view.

Poria cocos forms large, tuberous sclerotia on the roots, called tuckahoes (*1597*), but appears to do little harm.

Polyporus juniperinus rots buried roots and has been considered as a cause of trunk rot (*628, 1143*). *Fomes subroseus* (*F. cajanderi*) rots the dead wood of living or killed trees (*1067*).

The heartwood of eastern redcedar is rarely decayed unless trees are very old.

Trunk Rots.—The most conspicuous of the heart-rot fungi in living eastern redcedar is *Daedalea juniperina*. Large trees may show the corky, daedaloid conks of this cubical-rot fungus under many dead branch stubs. Overholts (*1067*) regarded *D. westii* as agreeing with his concept of *D. juniperina*. Other heart-rot fungi

203

reported include the orange-topped *Fomes juniperinus* (*151*), which causes a decided pocket rot, *F. pini*, and *F. texanus* (*1067*). All of these trunk rots except *F. pini* are confined to *Juniperus* spp.

Mycorrhizal Relations.—No fungi have been reported to form mycorrhizae with eastern redcedar, but three other species of *Juniperus* have each had one fungus so reported but unproved by pure culture technique (*1442*). Ectotrophic mycorrhizae are rare on the Cupressaceae.

Miscellaneous Pathology.—*Aleurodiscus nivosus* results in a nonpathogenic flaking of outer bark of living trees, called smooth patch or bark patch, and has flat, irregular fruiting bodies (*858*).

Crapemyrtle
Lagerstroemia indica

The colorful crapemyrtle is a native of Asia, introduced into North America in the 18th century. It is widely planted along the streets and lawns of the South from Maryland to Florida, and west to Texas (*872*). It is hardy as far north as Baltimore but grows to its full stature as a small tree with large, colorful, pink, purple, or red flowers only in the Deep South, and up the Atlantic Coastal Plain to southeastern Virginia. In the southern mountains and much of the Piedmont, it tends to die back to the grqund following cold winters, and then to resprout. A white-flowered variety, var. *alba*, has been described (*1154*).

Crapemyrtle is not demanding as to site, as shown by the variety of situations in which it has been placed and has grown well. However, it does require almost subtropical to tropical conditions to grow dependably for decades, producing a tree up to 25 ft. high, with its smooth, tan bark, and a great profusion of blooms. In California, it blooms best in the interior valleys, but it is occasionally planted in coastal areas (*955*).

Only a few well-defined diseases affect the crapemyrtle, and only one of them seriously. Some foliage, shoots, and inflorescences can become disfigured with a prolific growth of powdery mildew.

Three powdery mildews have been reported: *Erysiphe lagerstroemiae* throughout the host's range, *Phyllactinia guttata* in Alabama, and *Uncinula australiana* in Louisiana. The *Uncinula* species as it occurs in America may be our *E. lagerstroemiae*.

The *Erysiphe* species has been reported as an *Oidium* for many years because the conidia are oidia and because the perfect stage has been found only in Florida, where it was described by Erdman West. This is the common and widespread powdery mildew of crapemyrtle and it affects no other host. It appears on young shoots in early spring, spreading to leaves and the inflorescences. Affected parts become covered with a conspicuous, white, dusty coating. Leaves become stunted, twigs develop a stubby appearance, and many flower buds may fail to develop. Diseased leaves and buds may shed early in the summer, and the trees leaf out again more normally later in the season (*1555*). The other mildew species strike later in the season and do little damage.

Species of *Capnodium* may form, on the foliage, a harmless but disfiguring, black, surface, sooty mold that grows on aphid honeydew secretion.

204

A leaf spot common on *Camellia* also occurs on crapemyrtle. It is caused by *Pestalotia guepini*. It forms numerous, tiny, black fruiting bodies scattered over papery, gray spots. The spores are olivaceous, 5–celled, with 1 to 4 divergent and sometimes branched setae (*558*). While the parasitism of many species of *Pestalotia* is questionable, *P. guepini* is a true pathogen.

Cercospora (*Mycosphaerella*) *lythracearum* (*260, 620*) produces circular spots 3–10 mm. across, gray to brownish, and often with a green fringe or yellowish halo in an otherwise browned leaf. Fruiting is amphigenous, with dense fascicles, olivaceous, non-septate conidiophores, and conidia that are indistinctly septate, pale olivaceous, and $2–3.5\mu \times 20–85\mu$. The perfect stage develops over winter on fallen leaves. Other species of *Cercospora* occur on other *Lagerstroemia* spp., so that reference to Chupp (*260*) is advisable to obtain certain identification within this genus.

Although *C. lythracearum* and *M. lythracearum* are considered synonymous in the United States Index of Plant Diseases (*8*), Westcott (*1555*) considers the latter as the perfect stage of *C. punicae*, a pomegranate fungus, and mentions that it had earlier been considered the perfect stage of the crapemyrtle species *C. lythracearum*.

One *Phyllosticta* (*P. lagerstroemiae*) has been reported spotting leaves and blighting shoot tips in Louisiana and Texas.

Two thread blights affect the foliage in the Deep South. One is caused by *Corticium* (*Pellicularia*) *koleroga* (see *Ficus carica*) (*1408*) and the other by *Rhizoctonia ramicola*.

The former produces shiny, silk-like threads on leaves and branches; small, brown sclerotia on twigs of most plants; and basidial mats on the lower leaf surfaces. The *Rhizoctonia* causes a similar disease that results in tan spots with purplish margins on leaves and necrotic lesions on petioles. It also results in abscission and the matting or hanging of abscissed leaves by fungus threads, but sclerotia are apparently lacking in *R. ramicola*. This fungus blights the foliage of many perennial ornamental species in Florida (*1555*).

A manganese deficency has resulted in yellowing of foliage in Florida.

Many crapemyrtle trees in Louisiana bear on their stems and branches rough tumors of all sizes that have the appearance of crown gall as it occurs on *Prunus* spp. and other hosts. They cause ugly deformations and kill some stems.

Crapemyrtle twigs that are senescent or dead may bear the familiar black stromata of *Botryosphaeria ribis* (see *Cercis canadensis*) or *Physalospora obtusa*.

A root rot of crapemyrtle in Florida has been ascribed to *Clitocybe tabescens* (see *Aleurites fordii*), but it does not commonly harm this tree over most of its range. Crapemyrtle is rated moderately susceptible to Texas root rot (*1379*), but is not grown in the root-rot belt.

European larch
Larix decidua

Although the native range of European larch is confined to a small area of mountainous country in south-central Europe, it has been planted widely over Europe, including the British Isles and elsewhere, and importations to the United States go back to colonial times (282). The tree has been planted both as an ornamental and in rows and stands in Canada, the Central States, and the northeastern parts of the United States, and it has become naturalized locally in Connecticut and New York (872). The form is regularly pyramidal, becoming flat-topped by an age of about 50 years in North America. Ages of 65 and 70 years are not unusual in the Northeast (282, 735). There are recognized varieties, at least one of which has pendulous branches (1154). This deciduous species thrives in a mild climate with moderate rainfall but can tolerate a considerable range in soil moisture and texture. However, since it typically has a long taproot, deep soil of intermediate texture serves the tree best (735).

European larch is hardy, in that it is not subject to winter killing. However, when planted in moist frost pockets, repeated dieback from late spring frost makes trees bushy and can eventually kill them. Peace (1091) considers this species *very susceptible* to spring frosts under European conditions. In dry situations it can stand low temperatures much better than on wet sites. Since the wood is brittle, the species suffers from ice and snow damage. Hunt (735) gives a good account of the performance of European larch in the Eastern United States.

Following exposure to salt spray in an early autumn New England hurricane, European larch was one of the species most severely damaged (1632).

The pathology of European larch in North America has been dominated by the occurrence of larch canker in New England, and by the appearance of five species of *Dasyscypha* on stems and branches. *Valsa kunzei*, causing a canker, is also worthy of note.

Seedling Diseases.—Very little is known about the seedling diseases of European larch in North America. It is known to be attacked by *Phytophthora cinnamomi* (304), and, since some of the larches in North America are known to be attacked by *P. cactorum* (1458) and *Rhizoctonia solani* (8), it is likely that European larch is subject to damage from these fungi as well as from *Pythium* spp. and the usual array of organisms that consistently cause damping-off and root rot in other conifers in North America (360).

In New Zealand, European larch seedlings are attacked by *Cylindrocladium scoparium* and *Rhizoctonia solani*, both causing damping-off; by *Pythium ultimum*, causing damping-off and root rot; and by *Phytophthora cinnamomi*, causing root rot and collar canker. Since all of these organisms cause seedling diseases to conifers in North America, they are likely capable of attacking European larch there. Gilmour (510) gives an excellent account of diseases of native and exotic species in New Zealand.

Foliage Diseases.—A striking defoliation of European larch saplings has taken place in Maine, and a species of *Cladosporium*, indicated by a black-green mold, was associated with the needle blight. Neighboring *Larix laricina* was unaffected. Campana and Rosinski (202), who reported this attack, give an account of *Cladosporium* spp. on species of *Larix*.

Melampsora paradoxa (*M. bigelowii*) is a common needle rust of larches and is known to occur on European larch. It produces aecia on the needles and forms stages II and III on species of *Salix*. The shedding of needles is rarely severe enough to affect growth.

Hypodermella laricis (*323*), which causes a severe needle disease of European larch in Europe, has also been damaging to *Larix laricina* in the United States, but there have been no reports of damage to *Larix decidua* in North America. *Lophodermium laricinum* also occurs on *L. decidua* in Europe, but in the United States it has been observed only on *L. laricina*, on which it does no harm. It fruits on fallen needles.

Although *Meria laricis* is an important needle disease of *Larix occidentalis* in the United States, it has not been reported on *L. decidua*. In New Zealand (*510*), this fungus has severely attacked *L. decidua*.

Stem Diseases.—European larch is host to five species of *Dasyscypha* in the United States. Four of them (*D. ellisiana, D. calycina, D. oblongospora,* and *D. occidentalis*) are essentially saprophytes that live on dead twigs and branches of larches and other conifers. The fifth, *D.* (*Trichoscyphella*) *willkommii*, has had much attention in the United States and in Europe because it has a prominent role in causing larch canker, a serious disease in Europe. Frost injury and other climatic impacts are considered by many to also have essential roles in the severely cankerous condition with which *D. willkommii* is associated (*151*). Hahn and Ayers (*579*) reported cankering of several species of *Larix*, following inoculation with *D. willkommii*, in the absence of frost injury or other trauma. They emphasize the primary nature of this pathogen. The parasitism and taxonomic aspects of this fungus in the United States have been studied intensively by Hahn and Ayers (*574, 577, 578*), and these investigators worked out many phases of the biology of the other Dasyscyphas (*567, 574, 575, 576*), some of which inhabit European larch.

Whether *D. willkommii* can be considered a North American fungus now depends upon the success of the periodic attempts to eradicate the American infections, all found on European larch in eastern Massachusetts, starting in 1927 (*474*). A re-survey of the infected area in Essex County, Mass., by Tegethoff in 1965 (*1380*) disclosed no evidence of the larch-canker pathogen.

Peace (*1091*), in summarizing views on the cause of larch canker, gives both frost and *D. willkommii* prominent roles and mentions great differences in susceptibility to larch canker among provenances of European larch.

Valsa (*Cytospora*) *kunzei* var. *kunzei* has been associated with cankers on European larches on poor sites in several states (*1519*). The lesions are resinous and are generally at branch bases.

In the Northeast, Hahn (*572*) reported that *Phacidiella pseudotsugae* (conidial stage *Phacidiopycnis pseudotsugae*) occurs as a saprophyte and branch-canker parasite of European larch, white pine, balsam fir, and Douglas-fir. Smerlis (*1315*) puts this fungus in the perfect-stage genus *Potebniamyces*. The disease is a minor one in the United States, but elsewhere it is reputed to be damaging (*572*) and is referred to as Phomopsis disease of conifers.

Lavallee (*838*) describes a *Leucostoma* canker of larches in Canada (see *Larix laricina*).

Other Diseases.—The pocket rot caused by *Fomes pini* and the red heart rot caused by *Stereum sanguinolentum* have been reported from European larch in the United States (*1337*). Many fungi attack this species in Europe, and *F. annosus* has done particular damage in thinned plantations there. A. H. Maxwell[25] has observed European larch severely debilitated by *F. annosus* and *Polyporus schweinitzii* in the North Carolina mountains.

Many species of nematodes have been isolated from roots and root zones of European larch, mainly in Europe. Little, if any, damage has been associated with the occurrence of these nematodes around the roots (*1222*).

Mycorrhizal Relations.—Thirty-four species of fungi have been reported to make mycorrhizal association with *Larix decidua* (*1442*). Of these, six have been proved by pure-culture techniques.

Tamarack
Larix laricina

This medium-sized deciduous conifer extends from New England, New York, and Pennsylvania westward through the Lake States. Further north it extends across the continent from Nova Scotia to Alaska. Average January temperatures within this extensive area range from –22° to 30° F. Tamarack is known to withstand temperatures in the field from –79° to over 100° F. (*1188*). Parts of the range have less than 10 in. of rainfall equivalent, and others have over 55 in., but in the United States its range receives moderate precipitation and much of it is snow. Because of its capacity to withstand many adverse soil and climatic conditions, tamarack is commonly found in peat bogs, swamps, and organic or muck soils, and also on thin soils with textures from heavy clay to coarse sand. Most of the tamarack's range is fairly flat. Elevations up to 1,700 ft. are reached in the Canadian Rockies and Alaska and up to 4,000 ft. in eastern North America (*1188*).

Tamarack is very intolerant (*54*), is subject to damage by fire on lowland sites, and its shallow roots, though often extensive, make it subject to windthrow. No taproot is formed in swamp sites. Flooding, mainly as a result of beaver dams, can cause the death of sizable areas of trees (*1188*). Denyer and Riley (*377*) describe a dieback and mortality of tamarack in Canada caused by high water.

Stand ages of over 100 years are common, with 150 to 180 years consdered overmature. Trees 240 years old, and one individual of 335 years, have been found on Isle Royale in Lake Superior (*1188*).

Tamarack is host to many pathogens, but none causes disease serious enough to have an economic impact on its culture.

Since the larches lose their foliage in winter, and, since air pollution tends to be particularly damaging under winter air-inversion conditions, larches are injured less by such pollution from industrial stack gases than are evergreen conifers.

Seedling Diseases.—The seeds need high moisture for germination, and although tamarack is a swamp species, its seeds will not

---

[25] Personal communication from A. H. Maxwell, North Carolina Forest Service, Edwards Forest Nursery, Morganton, N.C.

germinate under water (*395*). The seedlings are small and easily killed the first month or two after emergence. According to Roe (*1188*), damping-off causes most of the loss and is followed by mechanical injury, drought, drowning, and insect attack.

Although specific mention is made of such nursery pathogens as *Rhizoctonia solani* and *Phytophthora cinnamomi* in connection with damping-off and root rot of other species of *Larix*, such reports are lacking for tamarack. It is likely, however, that the common conifer damping-off fungi also attack this species. Vaartaja (*1458*) has demonstrated the strong pathogenicity of *P. cactorum* to tamarack in the laboratory.

Foliage Diseases.—The only common foliage diseases are rusts (*46*) and they do little damage. *Melampsora paradoxa (M. bigelowii)* produces aecia on the needles of several species of *Larix* and stages II and III on *Salix* spp. It is transcontinental in range. The aecia of *M. medusae* have been considered almost confined to the needles of tamarack, and stages II and III are on *Populus* spp. However, since Ziller (*1668*) proposes considering *Melampsora medusae* and *M. albertensis* synonymous, we can consider about 20 other conifers as hosts of this rust. It is essentially a rust of New England and the Lake States.

Melampsoridium betulinum produces aecia on larch needles in Europe and stages II and III on *Betula* spp. in New England, the Lake States, and abroad. Despite reports from Wisconsin and Connecticut, Boyce (*149*) points out reasons for questioning whether the aecial stage of *M. betulinum* has been found in North America. Some premature shedding of needles accompanies the needle rusts, but, with the larches being deciduous anyway, the rust impact is negligible.

The needle-cast fungus *Hypodermella laricis* has attacked tamarack in Ontario, Canada, and other larches in Canada and the United States. It can spread through the crowns of large trees, killing needles and shoot spurs, and has the potential for local damage (*323, 1254*). *Lophodermium laricinium* fruits on fallen needles in Ontario and Quebec, Canada. It causes no damage. Its ascospores are filiform, whereas *H. laricis* has clavate ascospores.

Fallen needles of tamarack in Michigan have supported the small, waxy apothecia of *Phialea acicularum*.

Larches can withstand repeated defoliation and survive, whereas even a single complete defoliation will commonly kill a nondeciduous conifer (*151*).

Stem Diseases.—Tamarack is essentially free of stem diseases. Tests in Europe established the susceptibility of this species to the European larch-canker disease, in which *Dasyscypha willkommii* has a role (*151*), but the development of larch canker in Massachusetts, since arrested, was confined to the European species, *Larix decidua*.

Lavallee (*838*) reported cankers on branches and stems of native and exotic larches, in Quebec, older than 13 years, that were caused by *Leucostoma (Cytospora) kunzei*. Lavallee states that Waterman's (*1519*) description of her fir-canker fungus, which she called *Valsa kunzei* var. *kunzei*, corresponds with his *Leucostoma*. Regardless of which generic name is the proper one, the organisms seem to be the same. Cankers were most common on lower branches, in groups of two or three, and eventually girdled the stems. Lesions were sunken, retained the bark, and bore the multiloculate pycnidia characteristic of *Cytospora*.

Tamarack is host to non-pathogenic species of *Dasyscypha*, including *D. calycina*, *D. oblongospora*, and *D. occidentalis* (*574*). Their yellow-orange apothecia appear mostly on the bark of dead branches. H. Robak[26] states that the name *D. calycina* should be dropped because of the confusion existing among *D. calycina* Schum., *D. calycina* Fries, and *D. calycina* Fuckel. He feels that the continental European *D. calycina* Fries should be called *D. hahniana* or *D. willkommii* var. *hahniana*.

The discomycete *Aleurodiscus amorphus*, with it flat, irregular apothecia, may appear on the bark of senescent trees (*587, 858, 1276*).

Tympanis laricina produces its clustered, black apothecia on the dead bark of several larch species in the United States and Canada (*552*).

Valsa (*Cytospora*) *abietis* also fruits on dead branches, and either perithecia or pycnidia may appear (*1616*). *Aleurodiscus weirii* grows on dead bark in the Lake States (*858*).

The eastern dwarfmistletoe *Arceuthobium pusillum*, while causing important damage to black spruce, is a minor pathogen of red spruce, white spruce, and tamarack (*505*). Its shoots are only 12 to 20 mm. high and are scattered along the branches.

On tamarack, the dwarfmistletoe brooms (*A. pusillum*) are small and occur only where tamarack is growing in mixture with infected black spruce. Sometimes large brooms occur randomly on tamarack and, like similar occasional large brooms on pines, Douglas-fir, and other conifers, are not caused by a pathogen but are genetically aberrant shoots.

Root Diseases and Trunk Rots.—The root- and butt-rot fungi reported on tamarack include *Armillaria mellea* (*887*), *Corticium galactinum*, and *Polyporus schweinitzii*. They are not aggressive killers on tamarack. The principal heart-rot fungi are *Fomes officinalis* and *F. pini*, with *F. pinicola* and *F. roseus* in a minor role as rot fungi of living trees (*1276*). *Polyporus borealis* causes a white, cubical rot of tamarack in Canada.

Ruehle (*1222*) indicated that only 3 species of nematodes have been associated with tamarack roots, and injury has not been ascribed to them. Sutherland (*1370*) showed that seedlings of tamarack in Canada were excellent hosts to *Pratylenchus penetrans* and to *Tylenchus emarginatus* but a poor host to *Paratylenchus projectus*.

Mycorrhizal Relations.—The fungi reported to form mycorrhizae with tamarack are *Cenococcum graniforme*, *Gomphidius maculatus*, and *Hygrophorus pseudoleucorum* (*1442*).

Western larch
Larix occidentalis

A very tall, deciduous conifer with short, horizontal branches,

---

[26] Personal communication from H. Robak, pathologist, Forest Research Institute of West-Norway, Stend, Norway.

western larch is the largest species of *Larix* and is now considered a commercially desirable species. It occupies high valleys and slopes, from British Columbia southward through the Inland Empire in an area bounded by the Rocky Mountains on the east and the Cascade Range on the west (*279*). The climate of the range is cool, with an average precipitation of 28 in., very little of which falls in summer. Temperature extremes range from −49° to 107° F. (*133*). Soils are mostly deep loams and sands, but they are also commonly gravelly, with pH in the range of 5.5 to 6.4. The species occupies a middle elevational zone of 2,000 to 5,000 ft. It is one of North America's most intolerant species (*54*). The thick-barked, older trees are very fire resistant and take over large areas from which many of the associated species have been eliminated through repeated fires. It is also a common associate in the mixed conifer forests of the Inland Empire.

Western larch is hardy, resistant to damage from ice and snow, sensitive to fire when young but very resistant when older, sensitive to late spring cold because it leafs out as early as April (*133*), and resistant to windthrow because of a deep, extensive root system. However, ring shake resulting from wind is fairly common. This species proved to be one of the least sensitive of the conifers to chronic air pollution by sulfur dioxide (*1249*), probably because the foliage is shed before winter, when air inversions intensify fume damage. Young foliage is sensitive to fluorine and sulfur dioxide, and the two types of injury can be distinguished (*850*).

The tree is long lived and often attains ages of 300 to 500 years, with the largest trees exceeding 700 years (*133, 1367*).

Of the pathogens of western larch, dwarfmistletoe causes the most damage, with the needle blight caused by *Hypodermella laricis* probably next in importance. *Meria laricis* causes a less important needle blight. Other points of special interest in the pathology of western larch are the large number of root-rot fungi that can attack it and the many polyporaceous fungi that decay the dead wood.

Shearer and Mielke (*1284*) have provided an annotated list of the diseases of western larch, together with 27 citations to literature dealing with the pathogens of this species.

Seedling Diseases.—In the field, first-year losses of seedlings are often very high. The early losses are attributed by Boe (*133*) largely to fungi. Later in the season, as the stems harden, the main losses are attributed to drought. Survival following drought is best among seedlings that have been exposed to the sun and is poorest among shaded seedlings, because the roots of the former penetrate the dry soil layer, while the roots of the latter are nearer the surface.

While larch seedlings are subject to damping-off, the tree has not been grown in quantity in nurseries, and thus little has been reported on its nursery diseases. The gray-mold blight caused by *Botrytis cinerea* can be damaging to succulent seedlings under conditions of sustained high humidity (*1529*). *Rhizina undulata* causes a root rot of seedlings up to several years old, of many coniferous species, including western larch, and can reach damaging proportions on burned areas (*1533*). Weir (*1540*) has reported both *Thelephora terrestris* and *T. caryophyllea* (*195*) growing around the stems and foliage of western larch seedlings. They are usually harmless, possibly mycorrhizal, but occasionally smother seedlings by their copious thallus development.

Foliage Diseases.—Leaphart and Denton (*850*) describe in detail the needle discolorations of western larch, classifying them as normal colorations, fungus diseases, climatic-induced colorations, noxious fume damage, and insect attack. While this species has many needle diseases they have not had an important impact on western larch except for periodic attacks by *Hypodermella laricis*. In 1913 Weir (*1531*) reported heavy successive defoliations of this species in Idaho caused by "a needle cast fungus," and wrote "the epidemic nature of this fungus is remarkable." It is highly likely that this was a case of attack by the needle-blight fungus *H. laricis*, since Schmitz (*1254*) and others later described a similar disease from Idaho, with killing of shoot spurs a major effect. This blight is considered an important disease in certain areas. The spur-shoot mortality aspect is emphasized by Cohen (*272*).

Cohen (*273*) provides a full account of the pathology of *H. laricis* on western larch. He describes the mode of infection, host-parasite relationships, and fruiting of the fungus. He points out that vulnerability to infection diminishes rapidly as the leaves mature.

Lophodermium laricinum fruits mainly on fallen needles and causes no damage. It has filiform ascospores, whereas *Hypodermella laricis* has clavate ascospores (*323*).

Three rusts attack the needles of western larch: *Melampsora paradoxa* (*314*) (*M. bigelowii*) produces aecia on larch needles and stages II and III on *Salix* spp., and *M. medusae* and *M. occidentalis*, rusts of *Larix* spp. and *Populus* spp., have been reported on by Ziller (*1668*).

A striking early-season browning of western larch foliage caused by the moniliaceous fungus *Meria laricis*, a disease important to larch in Europe (*932*), has been reported in the Northwest (*406*). White specks of mold issue from the stomata on the lower needle surface. Although the disease has similarities with *Hypodermella laricis* and the fungus may have an ascomycetous affiinity (*932*), Ehrlich (*406*) emphasizes that it is a distinct entity. Hubert (*730*) has provided an account of the diagnosis and control of *Hypodermella* and *Meria* needle blights on western larch and mentions that the former causes shoot-spur killing, but the latter does not.

Stem Diseases.—The larch dwarfmistletoe, *Arceuthobium campylopodum* f. *laricis* (*505*), has short, bright, yellow shoots but is not morphologically distinguishable from other formae. This larch form is western larch's most important disease. The stunting, growth reduction, brooming, burl formation, spike-top formation, other debilitating effects, and outright killing have had major impacts on this species in many areas. Weir (*1537*) describes and illustrates the effects of this disease on western larch and other conifers. In his bulletin on the western larch dwarfmistletoe, Weir (*1536*) states that the principal defects of this tree, except for pitchy butt and shake, originate from this parasite and that closed stands suffer little but that open stands are subject to heavy damage.

In the Pacific Northwest, cankers caused by *Phomopsis pseudotsugae* in the upper crowns of western larch result in a bright yellowing of the tree tops referred to as "carrot-top" or "spike-top."

These tops then die. Wicker (*1576*) describes the disease and gives an account of the complicated nomenclature of the causal fungus (see *Pseudotsuga menziesii*).

Western larch has few important cankers. Five species of *Aleurodiscus* (*858*)—*A. amorphus, A. lividocoeruleus, A. spiniger, A. spinulosus,* and *A. weirii*—are saprophytic, on bark or wood, with *A. amorphus* occasionally producing shallow lesions on suppressed trees (*587*). Three species of *Dasyscypha—D. arida, D. calyciformis,* and *D. occidentalis*—are saprophytic on western larch, and a fourth—*D. willkommii,* which is associated with the larch canker of Europe—has been shown to be parasitic by artificial inoculation (*574*). *Tympanis laricina* produces its clustered, black apothecia on the dead bark of larch in the Inland Empire and Canada (*552*). *Valsa* (*Cytospora*) *abietis* fruits on dead branches (*1616*).

A tracheomycotic blue stain caused by *Ceratocystis minor,* introduced by bark beetles, rapidly kills the attacked trees (*732*). This fungus has been considered synonymous with *C. pseudotsugae* isolated in connection with infestation of western larch and Douglas-fir by the bark beetle *Dendroctonus pseudotsugae* (*1227*). *C. ips,* associated with attack of green western larch trees by the bark beetle *Ips integer,* behaves in a similar manner.

Root Diseases.—Western larch has seven notable root and butt rots, each of which is distinctive. *Armillaria mellea* (*848*), the shoestring root- and butt-rot fungus, is widespread on dead and dying trees and probably is responsible for some mortality. *Fomes annosus,* also widespread, probably hastens the decline of affected trees. *Polyporus berkeleyi* in the Northwest has a particular affinity for western larch, and it builds up in the debris around the bases of trees. It grows in this material and sends rootlike processes into the soil. It enters major wounds and rots mainly inactive wood. It establishes itself in the roots and does not extend far into the trunk (*1530*).

Polyporus tomentosus (*724*) is less common. It enters mainly at fire scars and causes a rot that resembles that of *Fomes pini.* It is less well known as a root-rotter of western larch than it is of other conifers. *Poria weirii,* the cause of yellow, laminated root rot has been reported, in its "annual" form, on western larch mainly in British Columbia (*190*). *Sparassis radicata* (*1538*) is widespread on western larch and other associated conifers, has a distinctive fruit body, makes a fungus root-stalk connection with the soil, and forms foliate mats under the bark. It does not extend into the bole. *Polyporus schweinitzii* causes mostly a butt rot and is seldom responsible for mortality. All of these rots can lead to windthrow or wind breakage.

Occasional root rot is caused by *Poria subacida* and by the trunk-rot fungus *Stereum sanguinolentum.*

Trunk Rots.—Western larch is host to many wood-rot fungi. Shaw (*1277*) lists 25 species of *Polyporus,* 14 of *Poria,* and 9 of *Fomes,* as well as members of other genera that attack the wood of this tree. Many decay only the wood of dead trees or dead parts of living trees.

Although any trunk-rot fungus can extend somewhat into the roots, the following are the more important heart-rot fungi that are largely confined to the bole:

Fomes officinalis (*F. laricis*), called the quinine fungus because of the bitter taste of the conk, is the main cause of heartrot in this species. However, its attack has been mainly in overmature trees, which it enters through large, broken tops or limbs (*145*).

Fomes pini is listed by Boyce (*145*) in second place among the heartrots of western larch. He describes and illustrates the large, swollen knots that give evidence of this rot and make the tree appear to be cankered.

The other fungi that extensively rot the trunks of older living western larch are *Polyporus sulphureus* and *Stereum sanguinolentum*.

Among those that are mainly rotters of dead trees or the dead wood of living trees are *Fomes nigrolimitatus* (*F. putearius* Weir) (*1532*), *F. pinicola,* and *F. roseus. Trametes carbonaria* will rot the charred wood of western larch (*1067*).

The extensive defect reported in early studies of western larch is largely a matter of overmaturity and damage. Future rotations should sustain much less loss.

Mycorrhizal Relations.—The fungi reported to form mycorrhizae with western larch are *Boletinus appendiculatus, B. cavipes, B. grisellus, B. ochraceoroseus, Boletus grevillei, B. luteus,* and *Cenococcum graniforme* (*1442*). The *Boletus* spp. have been confirmed by pure-culture technique.

Incense-cedar
Libocedrus decurrens

Incense-cedar is rarely a major component of any of the six forest types in which it occurs, but it grows, often singly, under moderate climatic conditions on both east- and west-facing slopes (mainly west) in the Cascade Range and the Siskiyou Mountains in Oregon, along the Coast Ranges and Sierra Nevada in California, and southward into Mexico (*1263*). Its altitudinal range is from about 1,000 ft. in elevation in Oregon to mainly between 4,000 and 7,000 ft. in California, where the best stands occur in the central Sierras. The tree is distinctive, compactly columnar, with yellowish-green foliage that has a pungent aroma when crushed (*279*).

The climate of the range is characterized by dry summers; an annual precipitation of 15 to 50 in., part of which is snow (*1263*); and annual temperatures that range from about −10° to 100° F. with a minimum of about −20° F. The species grows on a wide range of soils, reaching optimum development on moderately acid, deep, well-drained sandy to silt loams (*1263*). It grows slowly and lives long; ages of 300 to 500 years are common and longevity as high as 1,000 years has been reported (*279*). It is tolerant (*54*), sensitive to fire when young but resistant when the bark becomes thick. It sometimes suffers from drought at the southern end of its range and from winter injury following unseasonable cold periods. In northern Georgia, where incense-cedar has been grown as an ornamental, it was badly damaged by a sudden severe November freeze in 1950 (*664*).

While incense-cedar is noted for its durable heartwood, it is interesting that a heartrot, caused by *Polyporus amarus*, should be this tree's most destructive single enemy (*1263*). Other conspicuous, but seldom damaging, diseases are a brooming *Gymnosporangium* rust and a leafy mistletoe.

Seedling Diseases.—The seeds have the capability to germinate well in organic as well as mineral soil. A fair percentage germinates well without treatment which indicates that some seeds require no dormancy. Germination averages about 40 percent in the greenhouse or nursery (*1*). While field seedling mortality is frequently high, due mostly to cutworms and drought, little loss has been attributed to diseases. Incense-cedar has been reported as a host to *Phytophthora cinnamomi* (*1659*), a fungus that can cause damping-off and root rot.

Foliage Diseases.—The only foliage disease of any importance is the rust caused by *Gymnosporangium libocedri*. It causes stem and branch swellings and witches' brooms, and commonly kills small sprays of foliage. Telia are produced only on the incense-cedar leaves. The alternate hosts are many members of the Malaceae, and this fungus has been known to damage the foliage of pear orchards in Oregon (*151*).

Herpotrichia nigra can cause some brown molding of foliage that remained long under snow. None of the other fungi collected from foliage appear to have any economic importance. *Lophodermium juniperinum* produces hysterothecia in abundance on dead foliage but appears not to be pathogenic (*323*). *Camaropycnis libocedri*, an imperfect fungus (*236*); *Parksia libocedri*, a discomycete (*236*); *Pithya cupressi* (*1268*); and *Stigmatea sequoiae* occur on foliage or "branchlets" but are not damaging.

Stem Diseases.—A leafy mistletoe, *Phoradendron juniperinum* subsp. *libocedri* (*1580*), occurs throughout the range of incense-cedar. It grows on stems and branches. When abundant it can check growth or kill affected parts, but the effects on incense-cedar are seldom damaging. Wagener (*1487*) describes a stage of this mistletoe in the lower bole where, as the tree bark thickens, the leafy shoots are pushed out with increasing difficulty. Finally, they become smothered, after which the mistletoe plant adapts itself to the life of a complete parasite in the tree's tissues. The swellings that result can be several feet long and the ages of some infections have been estimated at over 400 years.

Typical crown gall (*Agrobacterium tumefaciens*), with its warty excrescences near the base of the stem, has been found on yard trees and nursery seedlings. The bacterium was isolated by Smith (*1317*) in California; and by inoculating with it he produced typical galls on other known hosts.

A species of *Botryosphaeria* is associated with occasional branch dieback.

Isolated cases of a canker that attacks mainly *Cupressus* spp., and is caused by *Coryneum cardinale*, occur on incense-cedar in California (*1488*). Yellowing and death of branches and tops result from resinous lesions at the base of the killed parts. The lesions bear black acervuli.

A stilbaceous sooty mold, *Arthrobotryum spongiosum*, on the surface of twigs and branches, occurs commonly in northern California (*991*). It makes a thick, dark mat over the substrate (*700*).

The other fungi occurring on twigs of incense-cedar are largely

215

saprobes and none are important. They include *Chloroscypha* (*Kriegeria*) *jacksonii*, *Parksia libocedri*, and *Tryblidiella macrospora* (*236*).

Root and Trunk Rots.—The cotton root-rot fungus *Phymatotrichum omnivorum* has attacked incense-cedar in Texas following inoculation (*1379*).

Only a few wood-destroying fungi attack the heartwood of incense-cedar, and only one of these is important as a cause of cull in living trees. Yet this one fungus, *Polyporus amarus*, is not only the most destructive agent to which the species is subject (*1263*), but it is confined to incense-cedar. In California alone, over 36 percent of the volume of this species is cull from this source (*1496*). *P. amarus* causes a brown pocket "dry rot" with the pocket effect often so decided that the term "peck" has been used, as it is in "pecky" cypress (*142*). *P. amarus* enters fire wounds, other wounds, and large branch stubs. It gives little evidence of its presence since conks and bark depressions, called shot-hole cups, are the only positive indicators and neither is common. A shot-hole cup is a pockmarked area on the trunk where a conk had grown; after the punky bark has been riddled by insects, woodpeckers seeking the insect larvae chop out depressions (*145*).

Boyce (*142*) gives a thorough account of dry rot of incense-cedar, the high losses it causes, entrance courts of the fungus, decay in relation to age, scaling practices, and detailed descriptions of the decayed wood and the conks.

Fomes pini occasionally rots the heart of living incense-cedar, but few conks have been seen on this tree. This rot is likely to occur in older trees that also have dry rot in them (*1496*). The brown, cubical root and butt rot caused by *Polyporus schweinitzii* occasionally occurs in living trees, and *F. pinicola*, *P. volvatus*, and sometimes other fungi can be found rotting the heartwood of dead trees.

Kimmey (*793*) rates incense-cedar as probably the most defective conifer in California. Using Dunning's (*398*) tree classes he assigns cull and breakage factors (*794*). Breakage remained at 2.2-percent loss (board-foot-volume basis) for each class, while rot cull ranged from 6 percent in Dunning's classes 1 and 6 to 20 to 30 percent in classes 3, 4, and 7 and to 68 percent in class 5.

Miscellaneous Pathology.—When incense-cedar heartwood, a low-density wood, was subjected by Rennerfelt (*1163*) to decay by three wood-destroying fungi in tests involving the heartwood of 22 coniferous species, it sustained the lowest average decay loss of any species tested. He lists the heartwood constituents of incense-cedar as carvacrol, hydrothymoquinone, thymoquinone, and libocedrol.

Anderson et al. (*23*) found hydrothymoquinone to be highly effective in preventing decay by *Lentinus lepideus*.

The ends of logs of incense-cedar may show a superficial reddish-brown stain, the cause of which has not been determined.

Sweetgum
Liquidambar styraciflua

The sweetgum ranks as one of the most important hardwoods in the United States. It is abundant, is valuable for its wood qualities and as an ornamental, regenerates readily by seed and by sprouts, and grows to a very large, handsome tree that is colorful in the autumn. In closed stands it self-prunes well, producing a clean-boled tree and, thus, a high percentage of clear lumber or veneer. The species extends from southern Connecticut to central Florida, west to eastern Texas, and northeastward to southern Indiana and Ohio (929). It may be found in any part of this vast range except for parts of the mountains where elevations exceed 1,800 ft. It grows in sandy soils of coastal areas, in Piedmont clays, in loessal soils along the Mississippi River, and in loams and alluvial soils. Its best development is on heavy alluvial soils.

In the past, heights of 150 ft. and diameters of 5 ft. were common in river delta and swamp margin sites of the Deep South, and one tree that grew on the coast of South Carolina was 200 ft. high and 7 ft. in diameter and produced over 8,000 ft. of lumber (929). The tree develops a long, strong taproot in the bottomlands, making it quite windfirm (279). It is hardy as far north as Massachusetts and can be grown on the Pacific Coast. It is now one of the most popular street trees being planted in California. Its outermost xylem yields a yellowish balsam known as American storax (498). Its characteristically star-shaped leaves turn red in the fall.

The tree is readily scarred by fire, but Hepting and Blaisdell (656) demonstrated that a gum-infiltrated zone usually forms on the wound surface and helps protect the sapwood from decay.

Two varieties, one with round-lobed leaves and a pendant form, have been described (1154).

Sweetgum resists damage from flooding and was in a class with the true swamp species in tolerating high water, among 39 species observed in a Tennessee River flooding project (583). However, salt water or salt spray proved damaging to sweetgum following a hurricane (1632). It was among the species that best resisted injury from air pollution, mainly from sulfur dioxide, in Texas (911).

This species has suffered severely from an apparently abiotic general decline called sweetgum blight, from about 1950 to 1960, over most of its range. Otherwise, it has had few disease enemies. A trunk canker has caused some losses, and much decay has followed fire injury. Damping-off of seedlings has been caused by *Pythium sylvaticum* (444).

Foliage Diseases.—One of the most common leaf spots is caused by *Cercospora liquidambaris*. These spots are angular to subcircular, 2–10 mm. in length, and dark brown, with a narrow, raised-line border. Fruiting is amphigenous. Conidia are obclavate to linear and are indistinctly septate (260). *C. tuberculans*, another leaf fungus, may or may not produce a discrete spot or slight discoloration on the upper surface. Fruiting is hypophyllous on small, brown tubercles. The conidia are cylindric and 1- to 5-septate (260).

Another common leaf spot is caused by *Septoria liquidambaris*. Black pycnidia are immersed in the spots and have narrowly-elongated to filiform, hyaline, multiseptate conidia.

The fungus *Actinopelte dryina*, known best as the cause of an oak leaf spot reaching epidemic proportions in some years, has often been noted on sweetgum. The spots are small, very numerous, brown, and epiphyllous, and they bear an arched scutellum borne on a stalk (*863*). Confluent spots can blight and distort a large proportion of a tree's foliage by August (see also *Quercus* spp.).

The leaf spots caused by *Leptothyriella liquidambaris* (*1391*) are brown, circular, 1–5 mm. across, concolorous, fragile, and collapsing with age. Pycnidia are sparse, epiphyllous, and 91–112μ across. Conidia are oval to oblong, virescent-hyaline, non-septate, 8.4–10.2μ × 6–6.8μ.

A few other fungi have been described from sweetgum leaves, but the only additional definite spot pathogen is *Exosporium liquidambaris*, reported from Texas.

Gloeosporium nervisequum, the imperfect stage of the sycamore anthracnose fungus, *Gnomonia veneta*, has been reported on sweetgum leaves in Mississippi and Texas. The conidial layer is subepidermal, on necrotic blotches, and erumpent, with acicular conidiophores and ovate, hyaline conidia (*1352*).

Gnomoniella georgiana is a fungus that fruits on dead leaves of sweetgum and *Nyssa* spp. on the ground or on the tree in Georgia. It has large, immersed, epiphyllous, somewhat beaked perithecia, with 8-spored asci and hyaline, oblong-ellipsoid, thin-walled ascospores (*980*). *G. amoena* var. *petiolorum* makes lesions on petioles (*974*).

Stem Diseases.—Trunk cankers and branch lesions are caused by *Botryosphaeria ribis* and its var. *chromogena*. Trunk infections result in bumps and ridges, and they degrade trees in the Deep South. Limited but adjacent patches of bark die from year to year, and storax flows from the lesions (*1424, 1437*). The clustered pycnidia, appearing as a multiloculate stroma with fusoid, 1–celled conidia, are referred to species of *Dothiorella*, usually *D. gregaria* or its synonym *D. berengeriana* (*1117*). The same stromata can give rise to the perfect stage, with its hyaline, elliptic, 1–celled ascospores. While Toole and Morris (*1424, 1437*) found their *B. ribis* disease only within 100 miles of the Gulf Coast, Pirone (*1117*) described his *D. berengeriana* disease from New Jersey and from Staten Island, New York (see also *Cercis*).

Pirone (*1117*) named his stem lesions disease "bleeding necrosis" and reported that the main symptoms were bleeding lesions on the trunk, reddish-brown discoloration of the sapwood 3 to 4 rings deep, and a dieback and wilting of the top that could lead to death in a season or less. His "bleeding necrosis" mortality may be a combination of sweetgum blight (see Miscellaneous Pathology) and Toole's *B. ribis* trunk lesion disease.

Myriangium duriaei and five species of *Septobasidium*, growing on scale insects infesting bark, have been reported on sweetgum. The felts they produce do not harm the tree. Many fungi inhabit dead branches, but only one of them, *Endothia gyrosa*, can be weakly pathogenic. It will sometimes fruit on exposed roots. Its reddish stromata are very noticeable when wet and appear superficially much like the chestnut-blight fungus, *E. parasitica;* but *E. gyrosa* differs in having short, cylindric to allantoid ascospores rather than the fusoid ascospores and mycelial fans in the bark that characterize *E. parasitica.*

Eastern mistletoe, *Phoradendron serotinum*, is common on sweetgum, especially in the Atlantic and Gulf coastal plains and bottom-

land areas. It is the only mistletoe in the East, north of Florida
(454), and it is not considered to have an economic impact on
sweetgum. *Nectria galligena* causes occasional cankers on sweetgum.

Root Diseases.—Sweetgum proved moderately susceptible to
Phymatotrichum root rot in Texas tests (1379). Rhoads (1168)
includes sweetgum among the hosts of *Clitocybe tabescens* in Florida, but few trees have been lost to it. Root-knot nematodes of the
genus *Meloidogyne* have been reported on this species on sandy
soils.

Toole [27] states that *Ganoderma* (*Polyporus*) *curtisii*, a stipitate,
orchraceous, "varnished-topped" form closely related to *Polyporus
lucidus*, can rot the roots of sweetgum, as reported by Edgerton
(403) for other species of trees.

The following nematodes have been reported associated with root
injury to sweetgum in Mississippi: root-knot nematodes (*Meloidogyne* sp.), lesion nematodes (*Pratylenchus* sp.), and stubby-root
nematodes (*Trichodorus* sp.) (1222).

Trunk Rots.—A large number of fungi can rot the wood of living
sweetgum trees. Most enter from basal scars caused by fire and by
logging. Hepting (637) reported on seven fungus species in the
Mississippi Delta that grew upward in the bole of sweetgum trees
from fire scars at rates of from 2 to 3 in. per year. They were
*Fomes geotropus, Lentinus tigrinus, Pleurotus corticatus, P. ostrea-
tus, Polyporus fissilis, P. lucidus,* and *P. zonalis.* Hepting, working
with young trees, and later Toole (1417), with larger trees, determined the relation of wound ages and other characteristics to
extent of decay. Toole also gives valuable aids in scaling out rot
defects and otherwise interpreting indicators of decay. In his
larger trees decay spread upward 0.9 ft. per decade.

Some of the other fungi known to aggressively attack the butt
and bole wood of living sweetgum trees are *Hydnum erinaceus* and
occasionally other species of *Hydnum, Polyporus sector,* and *P.
spraguei.* Additional fungi cited by Overholts (1067) as capable
of causing either rot of the central cylinder or rot at wounds of
living sweetgum trees include *Fomes connatus, F. marmoratus, F.
scutellatus, Polyporus calkinsii, P. curtisii, P. fissilis, P. graveolens,*
and *P. obtusus.*

Toole (1422) also studied the spread of decay from dead branches
in the Mississippi bottomlands. Out of 80 sweetgum branch wounds,
2 to 10 in. wide and dead from 3 to 25 years, rot had spread from
0 to 16 in. above the scars and 0 to 30 in. below. Only two fungi
were obtained in culture: *Lentinus tigrinus* and *Pleurotus corticatus.*

Toole (1420) found that 5 years after the surplus companion
sprouts were cut from a 55-year-old sweetgum sprout stand, no rot
had appeared in the attached residual stems, even when high V-
crotch twins had one stem removed. The stubs were inhabited by
one or more of nine fungi, with *Daedalea confragosa* predominat-
ing. After 10 years (1428), half of the residual trees dissected had
contracted rot from the attached cut stubs of the stems removed.

---

[27] Personal communication from E. Richard Toole, formerly pathologist,
USDA Forest Service, now at Mississippi State University, State College, Miss.

Toole considered that this decay was largely attributable to *Pleurotus ostreatus* and *Polyporus ulmarius*.

The volume deduction due to rot in sawtimber stands in North Carolina was computed for several hardwood species (*557*), with the cull percentage due to rot in yellow-poplar and white oak 4 percent, in sweetgum 5 percent, and in red maple 38 percent.

Scheffer (*1243*) describes the progressive effects of *Polyporus versicolor* on the physical and chemical properties of sweetgum sapwood, and Cowling (*293*) gives a detailed account of the biochemistry of the decay of sweetgum sapwood by both brown-rot and white-rot fungi.

Scheffer and Lindgren (*1251*) found that steaming unseasoned sapwood lumber makes it more subject to decay.

Stains.—In the living tree, stains not caused by hymenomycetes have been ascribed to two fungi, *Lasiosphaeria pezizula* and *Torula ligniperda*. A grayish stain can be caused by *Lasiosphaeria pezizula*, a fungus with free, thick, carbonaceous, hairy perithecia and multiseptate, elongate spores. A pink to red stain is caused by *Torula ligniperda* (*62*), a common dark to black fungus with catenulate conidia that seem to form without conidiophores.

The economically important stains are those that take place in logs and lumber. These blue stains, or sapstains, of sweetgum, listed roughly in order of decreasing importance in degrading logs and lumber, are caused by *Ceratocystis coerulescens, C. pluriannulata, C. moniliformis, C. capillifera* (*732*), *Graphium rigidum, Diplodia natalensis*, and *Pullularia* (*Hormonema*) *pullulans* (*284*). Papers by Davidson et al. (*337*) and Verrall (*1472, 1474, 1475*) and the *Ceratocystis* monograph by Hunt (*732*) provide much information on these and other stain fungi of sweetgum. Verrall (*1476*) also describes the fungi associated with ambrosia beetle galleries in sweetgum.

Scheffer and Hansbrough (*1248*) determined the effects on strength of several discolorations in sweetgum aircraft veneer. Figured heartwood and pathologic heartwood were of normal strength, but mineral streak, blue stain, and incipient decay lowered toughness somewhat.

Miscellaneous Pathology.—A general decline of sweetgum over most of its range that reached alarming proportions between 1950 and 1960, is now considered of abiotic origin. This striking crown thinning, often resulting in heavy mortality, was first described by Miller and Gravatt (*989*) in Maryland. Hepting (*645*) reported the trouble to occur from Delaware to Texas, and his decline rating system showed elms to be declining as much as sweetgum over the same area. The cottonwoods and willows also declined in the Mississippi bottomlands (*1418*). The sweetgum trouble has gone under other names, including "leader dieback," and has been studied by many pathologists, including Garren (*495*), Young (*1636*), Toole (*1418*), and Berry (*106*). Toole and Broadfoot (*1432*) concluded that, at least for the Deep South areas they studied, "the data strongly suggest that sweetgum blight is primarily a reaction to moisture shortages."

In the late 1950's a return to adequate rainfall stopped this decline in many areas, resulting in recovery of many trees that had lost part of their crowns.

Increment borings in sweetgum, opened 2 years later, disclosed stain behind all holes, extending an average of 10 in. vertically, with decay developing behind 80 percent of the holes when the borings were made in the spring. Autumn boring was less harmful (*1433*).

The defects in Piedmont sweetgum approaching sawlog size were described by Bryan (*180*). He computed the individual effect of each type of defect in reducing the amount of clear lumber that the trees could produce. Knots led all forms of defect in trees of this size.

Vozzo and Hacskaylo (*1486*) illustrate examples of beaded secondary roots of endotrophic sweetgum mycorrhizae, comparing them with the short, stubby, unbeaded non-mycorrhizal roots.

Filer and Toole (*445*) made 953 direct isolations from sweetgum mycorrhizae in the Mississippi bottomlands to determine the fungi involved. Twenty-six percent yielded species of fungi considered as possible mycorrhizal partners. While representatives of the ascomycetes, basidiomycetes, and deuteromycetes were isolated, no phycomycetes appeared. The mycorrhizal types were classified.

Filer and Toole (*446*) found that fumigation of nursery beds with methyl bromide improved sweetgum growth by reducing the population of soil-borne pathogens. The incidence of mycorrhizae was reduced, but they regenerated rapidly, and no harm resulted from fumigation.

Potassium deficiency symptoms have been produced and described for several hardwoods including *Liquidambar styraciflua* (*1095*).

Yellow-poplar
Liriodendron tulipifera

The yellow-poplar is one of the finest "soft hardwoods" of North America. It is not a true poplar, being one of the Magnoliaceae, and it is often called tuliptree because of its tulip-like flowers and tulip-shaped leaves. It is as straight stemmed as a spruce or fir and is remarkably self-pruning in closed stands. It occurs throughout the East from New England to Florida, west to Michigan, and southward to Louisiana.

Yellow-poplar grows on wet and sandy sites along the Atlantic Coast, on Piedmont clays, and to elevations over 4,000 ft. on loams or rocky slopes of the southern Appalachian Mountains. The rainfall in its range falls between 30 and 90 in. annually. It reaches optimum development in the deep, moist, loamy coves of the southern mountains. Mature trees can reach a height of 190 ft., a diameter of 10 ft., and ages over 300 years. The species is intolerant (*1154*), and trees, once suppressed, respond poorly to release (*391*). Given an equal start with its associated species, it will outgrow most of them, often equalling the height growth of white pine in the southern Appalachians. Diameters of 18 to 24 in. in 50 to 60 years are not uncommon (*1165*). Yellow-poplar is a soil builder and had the highest foliar-calcium content of any of the 27 species reported by Chandler (*244*).

Yellow-poplar seeds readily and sprouts prolifically, but experience with rooting stem cuttings has been mostly negative. The new shoots are seldom injured by frost, but saplings and poles and the tops of larger trees are commonly badly bent or broken off by ice and snow (*234, 1196*). The tree is very sensitive to flooding (*901, 1632*), and where earth fill covers roots to a depth of only a few inches even large trees may die. Yellow-poplar also reacts particularly adversely to grade changes, mainly in connection with construction work. Arborists have generally considered this species the least tolerant to poor soil aeration among a long list of common tree species (*1633*). Salt water or salt spray has been damaging (*1005, 1632*). The thin, firm bark of most young trees makes them easily damaged by fire (*1165*), but older trees were more fire resistant than the oaks (*1020*). In stands suddenly opened, yellow-poplar is highly susceptible to sunscald.

Yellow-poplar is unusually free from serious disease (*661*). Nursery seedlings are subject to Cylindrocladium root rot. Small or suppressed trees suffer some stem damage from cankers, caused mainly by species of either *Nectria* or *Fusarium*, and occasionally a large tree is killed by the virulent sapstreak disease. Top rots following ice breakage and butt and trunk rots from basal wounds result in a moderate amount of cull. The wood may develop a wide range of pastel coloration associated with injury or exposure, but only the browns are indicative of decay.

Seedling Diseases.—Yellow-poplar is one of the few hardwoods raised in quantity in nurseries for forest planting in the United States. Although the species is a prolific seeder, few seeds per strobilus are fertile, the rest being empty seed coats. Germination tests of stratified seed showed a high of 14 percent and an average of only 5 percent germinating (*1*).

Shipman (*1301*) found much higher counts of bacteria and actinomycetes, but lower fungal counts, in the soil rhizosphere around 1-year-old seedlings than in the surrounding soil.

The most important nursery disease is the root rot caused by *Cylindrocladium scoparium* (*296, 696*). The roots turn black and die, and basal-stem lesions may develop. This disease has limited seedling production in some Virginia and North Carolina nurseries. Infected stock has low survival, and mixing infected and healthy stock in buckets prior to planting can result in contamination of all of the stock and almost complete failure of the outplantings.

Kelman and Gooding (*779*) demonstrated the causal relationship of *C. scoparium* to root rot of seedlings of *Liriodendron tulipifera*, *Pinus strobus*, and *Abies fraseri*. In field inoculations only 43 percent of the inoculated 1-year-old yellow-poplar seedlings survived, compared with 84 percent of the uninoculated seedlings. They describe symptoms of the disease on this species as consisting of lateral root necrosis and dark-brown to black cortical lesions at the base of the stem and on the taproot.

Rhizoctonia solani has also caused some blighting of nursery seedlings. It can be distinguished in culture by its characteristic unfertile mycelium that is constricted at the branches (*1555*).

The nematode *Pratylenchus pratensis* has been associated with seedling roots in Texas; root-knot nematodes, *Meloidogyne* sp., have also been reported from this species. A tabulation by Ruehle (*1224*) lists 15 species of nematodes, in 12 genera, associated with yellow-poplar in the Southeast.

Foliage Diseases.—The many fungi affecting foliage tend to appear late in the growing season, and thus have little, if any, impact on growth or food storage.

Any time during the summer, dark, surface, sooty molds may appear, growing on aphid honey-dew, but having little effect on the foliage. *Capnodium elongatum,* with its 8-muriform ascospores and what has been considered its conidial stage, *Fumago vagans* (*2*), is one of the most common. Friend (*477*), however, considers *F. vagans* simply a mixture of *Aureobasidium pullulans* and *Cladosporium herbarum.*

Another leaf fungus that can appear any time in the season and that can cause much leaf damage, especially on sprout growth, is the common powdery mildew, *Erysiphe polygoni* (*1153*).*E. liriodendri* is a closely related species (*974*). Another powdery mildew is the cosmopolitan *Phyllactinia guttata,* that is common only on mature leaves, on sprout growth, and late in the season (*1153*).

A black, discrete tar-spot is referred to *Ectostroma* (*Xyloma*) *liriodendri.* This is one of the mycelia-sterilia. The leaf spot itself is probably mostly insect injury, and the black stroma may well be that of the discomycete *Rhytisma liriodendri.* However, *E. liriodendri* has been widely reported, while *R. liriodendri* is known only from Texas and California (*8*).

Reports of *Mycosphaerella liriodendri* and *M. tulipiferae* (*974*) have been based on the same imperfect stage. The conidial form has been called *Depazea tulipiferae* and the spermatial form, *Phyllosticta liriodendri* (*8*). Yet the very widespread leaf-spot fungus *P. liriodendrica* is known to be an imperfect stage of *M. liriodendri;* and *Cercospora liriodendri,* with its thick-walled 1- to 3-septate spores, is known to be the conidial stage of *M. tulipiferae.* Still another *Phyllosticta, P. macrospora,* occurs from Virginia to Pennsylvania.

Another common pathogen is *Gloeosporium liriodendri* (*905, 1119*), commonly causing a spotting that appears first with the beginning of fall coloration. This anthracnose fungus, referred to in the literature also as *Collectotrichum gloeosporioides,* is regarded by Ito (*746*) as simply another of the many host lines of *Glomerella cingulata.* Ito describes and illustrates the disease and the perfect and imperfect stages of the fungus as it occurs in Japan. The irregular, blotchy lesions produced by his inoculations are similar to the symptoms of this anthracnose as it occurs in the United States (see *Aesculus, Cinnamomum, Diospyros, Ficus, Magnolia, Mangifera,* and *Sassafras*).

Many other leaf-spot or leaf-blotch fungi are listed for yellow-poplar (*8*), but they are primarily of mycologic interest.

Stem diseases.—Sapling trees in the Appalachian region, especially if suppressed, are susceptible to cankers caused by *Nectria magnoliae.* These cankers may spread rapidly both vertically and around the tree, and the bark may become literally red with perithecia in wet weather (*661*). However, vigorous young trees can recover rapidly, healing out cankers that were spreading only a year or two earlier, but leaving a defective core of wood in the center of the bole (*1018*). *N. magnoliae,* described by Lohman and Hepting (*879*), has sometimes been mistaken for *N. galligena,* with which it has some similarities, but the former has smaller ascospores, averaging 13.1μ × 5.4μ.

Another canker is general in southern Ohio and eastward to Virginia and is caused by *Fusarium solani*. This canker differs from the Nectria canker in successfully attacking larger stems; in often appearing first as a long crack in the bark; in the outline of the necrotic area being typically irregular, rather than cleanly elliptical as in Nectria canker; and in lacking the red perithecia typical of Nectria cankers (*385*). *F. solani* also causes cankers on *Acer saccharum, Liquidambar styraciflua,* and *Populus* spp.

Cytospora leucostoma var. *magnoliae* may appear on senescent branches, its pimple-like pycnidia oozing light yellow spore tendrils in wet summer weather. It is a weak pathogen.

Dieback and associated cankering of young yellow-poplars has been reported from different parts of the South (*759, 1435*). Although several organisms, including *Botryosphaeria ribis* (*Dothiorella gregaria*), *Myxosporium* spp., and a bacterium, have been implicated to varying degrees, it is likely that these diebacks follow abiotic declines associated with drought (*1435*), defoliation, or other impacts and that the associated fungi play a minor role. The subsequent lack of aggressiveness of the fungi in the cases reported to date, taken together with the lack of sustained pathogenicity for any of the many associated "dieback" organisms tested, support this view. Both *B. ribis* and its variety *chromogena* have long been known in connection with minor branch lesions on *Liriodendron*.

The most lethal disease of yellow-poplar beyond the sapling stage is, fortunately, one that has been observed rarely. It is a vascular disease called sapstreak, involving rapid invasion of the living sapwood by a form of the common lumber blue-stain fungus *Ceratocystis coerulescens* (*Endoconidiophora virescens*) (*732*). This fungus was first reported by Hepting (*641*) as a killing, vascular pathogen causing the sapstreak disease of sugar maple. In both maple and yellow-poplar, sapwood infection appears, in transverse section, in flamelike, dark patterns extending radially from the inner wood. The fungus is readily obtained in culture, where it produces a musty, slightly banana-oil odor. New leaves emerge small, the crown thins, and large trees may die in a year or more after onset of visible symptoms. Sapstreak is now known on yellow-poplar from western North Carolina (*1208*) and eastern Tennessee and on sugar maple there, in the Northeast, and in the Lake States (*787*) (see *Acer saccharum*).

Verticillium wilt (*V. albo-atrum*) has been verified as a disease of yellow-poplar in Connecticut by Waterman (*1520*) and in Illinois by Engelhard and Carter (*412*). It is discussed under *Acer saccharum* and *A. platanoides*. While the pattern of sapstreak in stem cross-section is usually in radial flame-like projections and may involve the entire sapwood, in Verticillium wilt the green discoloration tends to conform to specific annual rings.

The common sooty blotch caused by *Gloeodes pomigena* grows on weakened or dead twigs. It has subcarbonaceous, dimidiate pycnidia with 1-celled spores.

Root Diseases.—Yellow-poplar has no major root diseases.

Armillaria mellea can kill badly weakened trees, and its rhizomorphs are common on the roots of old trees. Yellow-poplar is

224

considered moderately susceptible to Phymatotrichum root rot in tests in Texas (*1379*), but *P. omnivorum* is no problem within the native range of the species. Also in Texas, the nematode *Pratylenchus pratensis* has been isolated from roots.

Shipman (*1300*) studied the microflora in soil profiles of a yellow-poplar stand and found the highest counts of bacteria in the A_0 and A_1 horizons and the highest fungal counts in the B_2 horizon. He was not able to relate microbial counts to rate of tree growth.

Trunk Rots.—The fungi isolated most commonly by Hepting and Hedgcock (*663*) from butt rots and heartrots of sawlog-size yellow-poplar trees were *Pleurotus ostreatus, Hydnum erinaceus, Armillaria mellea,* and a species of *Hypholoma.* Others able to rot the "inner" wood, or heartwood, include *Fomes applanatus, F. connatus, F. everhartii, F. robiniophilus, Polyporus sulphureus, P. graveolens,* and *P. zonalis* (*1067*). Roth (*1196*) found that in one young stand, severely broken by the weight of snow, practically all of the rot developing from the wounds was caused by *Collybia velutipes.*

The volume deduction due to rot in sawtimber stands in North Carolina was computed for several hardwood species (*557*), with the cull percentage due to rot in yellow-poplar and white oak 4 percent, in sweetgum 5 percent, and in red maple 38 percent.

True (*1450*) studied the sprouting habits of yellow-poplar in relation to decay and found that over 80 percent of the sprouts originated within 1 in. of the ground, thus implying a low rot hazard from the parent stump. True (*1451*) also studied the fungus flora of stumps after thinning clumps of yellow-poplar. Only two of the fungi isolated, *Armillaria mellea* and *Pleurotus ostreatus,* were known to be heartrot organisms.

Rot in sprouts that was contracted from the decaying parent stump is discussed in detail under *Quercus, Acer,* and *Liquidambar.* Byler and True (*198*) studied "sprout rot" in yellow-poplar. They found that parent stumps were the infection source for 84 percent of the butt rot in yellow-poplar sprouts in West Virginia. As in the oaks, establishment of a heartwood connection between stump and sprout were prerequisite to such decay. The most common rot was variously colored and very limited in extent. It yielded a species of *Phialophora.* The fungus second in frequency was *Armillaria mellea.* Also, as in the oaks, high-origin sprouts and those from the larger stumps were particularly prone to decay.

Ginns and True (*511*) studied decay transmission from dead yellow-poplar companion sprouts to attached living stems. As in the oaks (see *Quercus* spp.), they found that a heartwood connection between dead and living sprout was prerequisite to the spread of decay through the union. The living stem was actively decaying in 26 percent of the sprout pairs studied.

Stains.—Hepting et al. (*668*) and Roth (*1199*) have described the many colorations to which yellow-poplar wood is subject. These include greens, reds, purples, blues, browns, grays, and black. Only the shades of brown indicated decay. The grays and black indicated internal and external infection by sapstain fungi, and most of the other colors were of abiotic origin and associated with some injury. A purplish color in the butt log of many trees is called "blue butt" and may be an oxidation stain. The abiotic stains proved to have no weakening effect on the wood.

Hepting et al. (*669*) found that increment boring yellow-poplar resulted in a blue discoloration extending about a foot above and a foot below the hole; that *Nectria*-cankering prevented closure of holes in suppressed trees; and that sapwood decay was active within 10 years of boring in 15 percent of the borings.

Roth (*1199*) isolated many types of bacteria from fresh, discolored yellow-poplar logs and lumber. When wounds were inoculated with them, the type and extent of discoloration that followed was no greater than from uninoculated wounds. Staining was more extensive from open wounds that held water than from those oriented to shed water.

The most important fungi causing sapstain of lumber of this species are *Ceratocystis coerulescens* and *C. pluriannulata* (*337, 1473*). *C. multiannulata* does not stain severely and is not economically important. Some of the other stain fungi of hardwoods, including *Graphium rigidum* (*905, 1252*), can attack yellow-poplar. A form of *C. coerulescens* isolated from sapstain in a yellow-poplar log, morphologically identical with the sapstreak-disease fungus isolated from sugar maple, failed to cause sapstreak when inoculated into sugar maples (*641*).

A grayish stain in living trees can be caused by *Lasiosphaeria pezizula*, a fungus with free, thick, carbonaceous, hairy perithecia and multiseptate, elongate-cylindric spores.

Miscellaneous Pathology.—A defect called blister shake is described by Tryon and True (*1454*) from West Virginia. This is a separation between rings, involving part or all of the distance around, with some wound wood having the appearance of bark within the separation. The authors suggest a weather sequence involving freezing and thawing as a possible cause and describe how blister shake differs from frost shake, frost blister, frost ring, frost canker, frost crack, and winter sunscald.

Clark (*264*) determined that endotrophic mycorrhizae can greatly increase the growth of yellow-poplar seedlings. This stimulation followed inoculating the soil of stunted seedlings grown in sterilized field soil, with root material containing an endotrophic mycorrhizal fungus.

Vozzo and Hacskaylo (*1486*) illustrate the difference between the endotrophic mycorrhizae of yellow-poplar, which are short, stubby, and without root hairs; and the non-mycorrhizal roots, which are long, slender, and delicate.

Gerdemann (*497*) has described vesicular-arbuscular endotrophic mycorrhizae formed on *Liriodendron* and on *Zea mays* by the phycomycete *Endogone fasciculata*.

Ike (*742*) has described the visual symptoms of N, P, and K effects in yellow-poplar seedlings, when applied in concentrations varying from minimal to excessive. Applied or withheld singly and in combination, these elements produced a variety of characteristic symptoms.

Tanoak
Lithocarpus densiflorus

The genus *Lithocarpus* appears to form a connecting link between the chestnuts and chinkapins (*Castanea* and *Castanopsis* spp.) and the oaks (*Quercus* spp.). The tanoak extends along the coast ranges from southwestern Oregon to southern California, in ravines and along streams from sea level to about 5,000 ft. in elevation. It grows slowly, to diameters up to 5 ft. and to ages over 250 years (*1367*). It is tolerant (*54*), reproduces copiously by seeds and stump sprouts, and is readily damaged by fire. The wood is dense and hard, and the bark is high in tannin.

While it may seem from the literature that tanoak is fairly free from disease, western authorities consider this seemingly good health to be an illusion resulting from lack of study of the pathology of this species.

Tanoak leaves support the II and III stages of a *Cronartium* species close to *C. quercuum,* a rust occurring on 2- and 3-needled pines.

Bonar (*136*) reported a leaf blight in California, caused by *Pestalotia castagnei.* He mentions abundant acervuli on the upper surface of leaves, which appear as black specks .5–1 mm. in diameter, with infection usually starting at the leaf tip and spreading to kill most of the leaf. Guba (*558*) considers this fungus to be *Pestalotia montellica,* a fungus with 5-celled conidia (the two end cells hyaline), that was originally described from Europe.

Another leaf spot is caused by *Ceuthocarpum conflictum,* a sphaeriaceous fungus with unbeaked, aggregated perithecia that have a clypeus and acicular, hyaline ascospores.

Several dark, sooty molds occur on the surface, mostly upper, of the foliage of this tree. Miller and Bonar (*991*) describe *Limacinia lithocarpi, Capnodium coffeae, Phaeosaccardinula anomola* (see *Umbellularia*), *Protopeltis lithocarpi,* and *Chaetasbolisia falcata.*

The remaining fungi reported from tanoak include a common fungus that stains dead sapwood green, and a few common wood rot fungi that attack dead wood (*8, 1277*).

Tanoak has been shown to be susceptible to oak wilt (*Ceratocystis fagacearum*Q in greenhouse inoculations in Missouri (*171*).

Cenococcum graniforme (*1441*) forms mycorrhizae with tanoak.

Kimmey (*793*) found tanoak to have a mean board-foot cull of 33 percent of the merchantable volume, based on a 90-tree sample of tanoaks of commercial size, in northwestern California. *Armillaria mellea,* one of the rot fungi of tanoak, has been known to cause ornamental trees of this species to break over at the base. Raabe (*1142*) lists tanoak among the California species most susceptible to *A. mellea* decay.

Tanoak has been host to *Phytophthora cinnamomi* in the West (*303*).

Osage-orange
Maclura pomifera

The osage-orange was originally confined to the rich bottomlands of the Arkansas and Red River Valleys (*279*). However, being hardy, drought resistant, durable in contact with the ground, and possessed of many other virtues as a wood, it became widely planted, and now hedges or specimen trees may be found over much of the country (872) except the coldest parts of the North and the West.

Typically, osage-orange is a small, thorny tree with an irregular crown. It may grow to 60 ft., with a stout, short, divided trunk that in exceptional cases may exceed 3 ft. in diameter. Adaptable to dry as well as moist sites, and to a wide variety of soils, the tree has been widely planted for shelterbelts and hedges, particularly in the Great Plains States. However, its high susceptibility to Texas root rot has caused osage-orange to be ruled out for planting in root-rot-infested soil in Texas and Oklahoma (1627).

Seedling Diseases.—In a Nebraska nursery, seedlings have been killed by damping-off and root rot caused by *Pythium ultimum* and *Rhizoctonia solani* (1555), although these common seedling pathogens have only occasionally caused losses to osage-orange (360).

Foliage Diseases.—A cottony leaf spot (*Ovularia maclurae*) is fairly common in the Deep South. The whitish surface mycelium bears short, stout, mainly simple conidiophores that bear ovoid, hyaline conidia, generally singly.

Phyllosticta maclurae makes a common, discrete spot and fruits by small, black pycnidia, with very small, hyaline, ovate conidia.

Sporodesmium maclurae can blight large areas of a leaf or kill it entirely, and it occurs widely. While the mycelium and conidiophores are poorly developed, the somewhat ovoid, dark conidia are large, short-stalked, and clathrate-septate (62, 1352).

A fungus generally referred to as *Cercospora maclurae* causes a large leaf spot in the South. Chupp (260) states that because of its thick-walled, *Alternaria*-shaped conidia, he considers it not a *Cercospora* but a species of *Pseudocercospora*.

Septoria angustissima, characterized by long, very narrow conidia, causes some late season spotting. In the Northwest, the common gray mold *Botrytis cinerea* (1555) has invested young stems and leaves during wet weather.

The rust *Physopella fici* develops in the leaves of *Ficus* and *Maclura*. Only uredia and telia are known. The uredia are hypophyllous, scattered, and cinnamon-brown after central dehiscence. The telia are also hypophyllous, tiny, whitish, and with the oblong teliospores in chains of two to seven cells (46).

Stem Diseases.—Osage-orange trees used as ornamentals in the Northeast have occasionally been killed by Verticillium wilt (*V. albo-atrum*) (see *Acer platanoides* and *A. saccharum*).

Two species of *Phoradendron* grow in the branches in the South and Southwest. The common eastern species, *P. serotinum* (*P. flavescens*), has slender, staminate spikes, and the rather few-flowered, nearly glabrous joints are only a few millimeters long. *P. tomentosum* (*P. engelmannii*) occurs in Texas and has stouter and longer, tomentose, staminate spikes with many-flowered joints up to 15 mm. long (1445, 1580).

Root Diseases.—The most important disease of osage-orange is Texas root rot (*Phymatotrichum omnivorum*). It appears odd that in view of the poor field performance in infested areas of Texas and Oklahoma (1627) that Taubenhaus and Ezekiel (1379) rated this tree as only slightly susceptible, following their inoculation tests; indicating it to be one of the most resistant of the 2,116 kinds of plants tested.

Wright and Wells (*1627*) studied Texas root rot losses over a 6-year period in shelterbelt plantings in Texas and Oklahoma. Of 25 tree species studied, the root rot loss to osage-orange (based on 13,851 trees of this species planted) was 6.8 percent and was exceeded only by losses to *Eleagnus angustifolia* and *Gymnocladus dioicus*. As a result of their study, they list osage-orange as not recommended for use on any soil type in the root rot belt.

Miscellaneous Pathology.—Osage-orange ranks along with black locust, catalpa, red mulberry, and black walnut, among the hardwoods whose heartwood is highly resistant to decay, and it is therefore useful in contact with the ground (*6*).

Hart (*600*) analyzed the morphological and chemical differences between sapwood, discolored sapwood, and heartwood of osage-orange and black-locust, and found that discolored sapwood, such as is associated with wounding, is very different from true heartwood.

It is notable that the Index of Plant Diseases in the United States lists only two wood-destroying basidiomycetes as reported on osage-orange; *Poria ferruginosa* and *P. punctata*. Both occur only on dead wood and both find their main habitat in the subtropical or tropical parts of the western hemisphere (*891*). *Fomes ribis* is known to attack bole wood exposed by wounding (*1067*).

Cucumbertree

Magnolia acuminata

The cucumbertree is never common, but it is widely distributed in cool, moist situations in eastern forests, from southern New York through the Appalachian Mountains, deep into Alabama, Mississippi, and Arkansas, and into Indiana, Ohio, and southern Michigan. It is the most hardy of the many tree-sized species of *Magnolia* (*279*). It is moderately tolerant, grows fast in the moist, deep soils of coves and lower slopes, matures by 100 years, and seldom lives over 150 years. The leaves have acuminate tips, the flowers are pale green and bell-shaped, and the fruit is knobby, erect, and roughly cucumber-shaped. The tree is symmetrical, with an ascending branch habit, and like its near-relative the yellow-poplar, it self-prunes well in closed stands, thus often being clean-boled. It also makes a handsome ornamental (*274*) and has been so used, successfully, well north of its native range. The cucumbertree is very sensitive to ground fire, but has no important disease enemies. In this connection, it is interesting that while the Index of Plant Diseases in the United States (*8*) lists 94 organisms on various species of *Magnolia*, only four are listed for *M. acuminata*, the commonest of the magnolias.

The seedlings are sometimes used as root stocks on which ornamental species and varieties of *Magnolia* are grafted (*279*).

The Nectria canker caused by *N. galligena* is common on cucumbertree in crowded stands or on unsuitable sites, particularly in the Southern Appalachian Region. It forms target cankers (*661*) with concentric rings of killed callus folds, and can cause defects and deformity although it seldom kills trees of this species. It is quite possible that *N. magnoliae*, now known only on *Liriodendron tulipifera* and *Magnolia fraseri,* can attack cucumbertree, and although *N. magnoliae* has smaller ascospores than *N. galligena* it would probably take cultural study for certain separation of these two species (*879*).

A common discomycete, *Pezizella oenotherae,* fruits on branches of cucumbertree and many other tree species, but its confinement to senescent and dead material makes it of no importance as a cause of disease. Another saprobe, *Tympanis magnoliae,* produces tiny, grayish, hard apothecia, up to 12 in a cluster, in erumpent groups. It is illustrated and described by Groves (*552*).

The only leaf spot pathogen reported on this tree is *Phyllosticta cookei,* a widespread spot fungus on several species of *Magnolia.*

Torula ligniperda can cause a pink stain of fresh wood (*1252*). Its chains of dark conidia, without conidiophores, are characteristic (*62*).

Increment borings in the cucumbertree led to bluish bands extending 32 in. vertically (*669*), and the approximate depth and width of the borer hole.

Fraser magnolia
Magnolia fraseri

The Fraser or mountain magnolia is a small tree growing in cool situations in the mountain areas from Virginia to Georgia (*274*). Distinctive features are the earlobe-like base of each leaf half and widespread branches. The clustered leaves are spatulate, and the flowers are large. Cool, moist soil and environment are required; this tree is not found under other conditions.

The only diseases conspicuous on this species are Nectria canker on small trees and powdery mildew on low foliage.

Sprout leaves, in particular, may be heavily attacked by the common powdery mildew, *Phyllactinia guttata,* a species with its perithecia having acicular, bulbous-based appendages (*1352*).

Phyllosticta magnoliae causes a large leaf spot bearing black pycnidia with small, hyaline, 1-celled conidia.

Nectria magnoliae causes cankers on small or suppressed trees of this species and on *Liriodendron* (*879*). It is not known to occur on any other species. It resembles *N. galligena* grossly, but differs in cultural characteristics. Trees that become dominant, or whose crowns become free, usually heal out what may have seemed earlier to be aggressive cankers (*1018*). In cool, moist weather the bark around active cankers may become pink with the abundant perithecia (see *Liriodendron*).

Phoma pedunculi and *Cytospora tumulosa* have been reported on branches in West Virginia, but are likely saprophytes or inhabitants of senescent tissue.

Southern magnolia
Magnolia grandiflora

A widely-known, beautiful, broadleaf evergreen, the southern magnolia, with its handsome, elliptical, dark, glossy foliage and its large, white, handsome flowers is a symbol of the South. Its natural range is from sea level to 500 ft., from southeastern North Carolina to central Florida and westward to southeastern Texas, commonly ranging 100 or more miles inland (95). Individual planted trees have thrived northward to Massachusetts, inland into the southern Appalachian Mountains to elevations of 2,500 ft., upward from the Gulf of Mexico to Missouri and Illinois, and in the West as far north as British Columbia. However, it is a warm-temperate to subtropical tree, and where temperatures commonly get below 15° F. or above 100° F. the foliage tends to die and the tree does not thrive (95). Some trees that harden off gradually in the autumn can take temperatures as low as 0° F. and show no damage. Other individuals are hurt easily by temperatures not that low, exhibiting extensive killing of leaves and shoots. Winter drought can cause extensive dieback or outright killing.

This species is tolerant when young, but becomes less so as it grows older. Growth is fairly rapid, with trees reaching heights of 80 ft. and diameters of 2 to 3 ft. in 120 years (279). Trees have been known to grow over 100 ft. high and with a diameter of almost 6 ft., but the ages of such veterans have not been determined. This magnolia generally grows on rich, loamy, moist soils, high in organic matter, near swamps or streams in the low country. Yet, when planted, it is notably undemanding with respect to soil type. It can be reproduced by grafting or rooting cuttings (1). Magnolia cannot withstand prolonged inundation. It is resistant to damage by salt spray. McKee (911) lists "magnolia" among the species most resistant to damage from air pollution in an area—about Houston, Tex.—exposed to emissions of sulfur dioxide.

While winter injury and several fungus leaf-spot diseases sometimes disfigure planted trees, especially those growing outside the native range, the southern magnolia is relatively free of damage from disease.

Foliage Diseases.—Small, epiphyllous, dark spots, often with gray centers, and often coalescing along midribs or leaf margins, are caused by the spot anthracnose fungus *Elsinoë magnoliae* (979). It produces its 3-septate ascospores by the midsummer of a leaf's second year. First-year leaf ascocarps are mostly sterile. Those on second year leaves are fertile. Sporodochia with one-celled spores (*Sphaceloma*) also appear.

Glomerella cingulata causes a striking, large, circular, epiphyllous, dark brown spot, sometimes with a pale yellow border. Sterile, dark fungus pustules form within some spots. This spot does not show before spring following a leaf's first summer, and therefore is not damaging. Fowler (472) describes and illustrates this disease.

Algal spots caused by *Cephaleuros virescens* may be as large as *Glomerella* spots. On magnolia leaves the alga forms velvety, reddish-brown to orange, cushion-like patches, but if sporangia are absent the spots appear greenish with reddish hairs (1555). This algal disease, as it occurs on *Magnolia* and *Citrus*, has been described in detail by Wolf (1599).

A badly disfiguring angular spot of *Magnolia grandiflora* and *M. virginiana*, caused by *Cercospora* (*Isariopsis*) *magnoliae*, is notable as a nursery seedling disease. The small spots, delimited by veinlets, become dark brown or black, bordered by a yellow halo, and can become very abundant early on first-year leaves. Hodges

231

and Haasis (*698*) describe and illustrate the disease and the fungus and discuss related taxonomy concerning the imperfect stage in one paper, and in a later paper (*699*) they establish connection between this stage and the perfect stage, which they named *Mycosphaerella milleri.*

Another small leaf spot occurring widely on trees in the genus *Magnolia* is caused by *Phyllosticta cookei,* a fungus with small, black, erumpent pycnidia producing 1–celled, hyaline spores.

Very dark surface mildews, growing mostly on aphid honey-dew on leaves and green shoots, are caused by the perisporiaceous fungi *Dimerosporium magnoliae* (2-celled ascospores) and *Meliola amphitricha* (appendaged perithecia and muriform ascospores) and by the dothidiaceous, loculate ascomycete *Trichodothis* (*Asterina*) *comata.*

The thread blight fungus, *Pellicularia koleroga* (*Corticium stevensii*), after overwintering as sclerotia on twigs and leaf petioles, produces a light, thread-like mycelium which grows over the lower surface of leaves, causing blighting and premature defoliation. The fungus can mat dead and hanging leaves together and can fruit as a mat on the leaves (*1555*) (see also *Aleurites* and *Ficus*).

The foliage is subject to lime-induced chlorosis in high-lime areas of the South (*312*).

Many other leaf spot and blotch fungi occur on southern magnolia (*8*), particularly on older leaves, and some are quite common. However, only those mentioned have been sufficiently damaging or conspicuous enough to get into the literature for other than mycologic reasons.

Other Diseases.—Southern magnolia proved moderately susceptible to Phymatotrichum root rot in tests in Texas (*1379*), and root knot nematodes (*Meloidogyne* spp.) were observed on this tree further eastward.

A white heart rot in living trees is known to be caused by *Fomes sclerodermeus* (*F. fasciatus*), which is similar to *F. fomentarius* of the North; the latter, however, has larger pores and spores (*890*). A brown rot resulting in hollowing is caused by *Fomes geotropus.* Johnson and Edgerton (*757*) describe the incipient decay by *F. geotropus* in magnolia as grayish-black, with greenish and reddish tinges when freshly exposed. Zone lines are conspicuous. The conk is applanate, with a thick, white context and a flesh-colored hymenium with long tubes (*1067*).

Fungi capable of causing either rot of the central cylinder or rot at wounds of living *Magnolia* spp. included *Daedalea ambigua, Fomes applanatus, F. geotropus, F. marmoratus, Polyporus calkinsii, P. curtisii,* and *P. sulphureus* (*1067*).

In the San Francisco Bay area of California, *Verticillium alboatrum* was isolated from the twigs of a yellowing southern magnolia tree (*903*). No vascular discoloration was evident.

A burrowing nematode, *Radopholus similis,* has been found in the rhizosphere of southern magnolia in Florida (*259*). Other nematodes associated with injury to magnolia roots in the Southeast are *Helicotylenchus* sp., *Meloidogyne* sp., *Pratylenchus* sp., and *Xiphinema* sp. (*1222*). A later tabulation by Ruehle (*1224*) reports the nematodes *Criconemoides* sp., *Helicotylenchus dihystera,* and *Hemicycliophora* sp. associated with *Magnolia grandiflora* in

Georgia.

A light blue interior stain may develop following kiln drying of the evergreen magnolias.

Sweetbay
Magnolia virginiana

The sweetbay is a small, moderately tolerant tree, occasionally reaching a height of 90 ft., with narrow leaves and small blooms (*274*). It grows in swamps or near water, mainly along the Atlantic Coastal Plain from Long Island, N. Y., to southern Florida, west to eastern Texas, and north to southern Arkansas (*872*). It may extend inland 100 or more miles. The tree is normally deciduous in late fall, but the foliage may persist until new leaves form in the spring. A variety, *australis,* with densely pubescent petioles and branchlets is recognized; a hybrid between *Magnolia virginiana* and *M. grandiflora* has been produced (*1154*).

Small, angular spots are caused by *Mycosphaerella milleri* (*Cercospora magnoliae*) (*699*). The *Cercospora* stage forms in early summer on attached foliage. *M. milleri* produces hyaline, 1-septate ascospores in black perithecia which form on overwintered, fallen leaves. *Mycosphaerella glauca* (*699*) causes large circular leaf spots commonly over one-half inch in diameter. The perithecia of this fungus may be found at any time of the year in spots on attached leaves, in contrast to those of *M. milleri.* No imperfect stage is known.

Gnomonia magnoliae (*8*), with beaked perithecia and septate ascospores, and *Guignardia magnoliae,* with non-paraphysate, fascicular asci and non-septate ascospores, are not responsible for leaf spots, but are commonly found on dead leaves on the ground. Hodges and Haasis (*698, 699*) and Miller (*975*) should be consulted in separating the leaf fungi of the magnolias.

A large, circular algal spot (*Cephaleuros virescens*), a small spot caused by *Phyllosticta cookei,* and the small, angular, brown fungus spot bordered by a yellow halo (*Cercospora magnoliae*—see above) are as described under *Magnolia grandiflora.*

Two other species of *Phyllosticta, P. glauca* and *P. magnoliae*—the latter causing a large spot—occur on sweetbay leaves.

Black surface molds grow mostly on aphid honey-dew and may be very conspicuous, although they do practically no damage. These include *Meliola amphitricha* and *M. magnoliae,* which have setose mycelium, and *Irene araliae,* which is without setae on its mycelium.

Miller (*980*) described *Didymosphaeria magnoliae,* a fungus with epiphyllous, aggregated perithecia and 1-celled, olivaceous ascospores, from sweetbay leaves on the ground. Its pathogenicity is unknown.

The flower petals can be rotted by *Sclerotinia gracilipes,* a species confined to sweetbay.

Septobasidium langloisii and *S. tenue* grow on scale insects that infest the bark, but the fungi do not harm the tree (*292*).

A light brown stain caused by *Cephalosporium pallidum* sometimes forms around tunnels of ambrosia beetle (*Xyleborus affinis*) galleries in the wood of sweetbay (*1476*).

A sting nematode, *Belonolaimus longicaudatus,* has been associated with sweetbay roots in Florida (*1145*). Species of four other genera of nematodes have been identified from soil in the root zone of sweetbay trees in Florida (*1222*), but were not associated with damage. Ruehle (*1224*) also reports a nematode species of *Helicotylenchus* associated with sweetbay in South Carolina.

Apple

Malus pumila

A native of western Asia and Europe, the apple now is grown widely throughout the United States and Canada. Varieties and hybrids suitable to local conditions have made this extensive culture possible. The tree has escaped cultivation in many parts of the Northeast. Little (*872*) states that *"Malus,* like its relative *Crataegus,* is a taxonomically difficult genus, with numerous intergrading variations and hybrids for which many scientific names have been given."

The many apple varieties vary in their response to most of the important diseases, and ratings have been published of their differing susceptibility to many diseases, including cedar-apple rust, scab, and latent virus (*1166*).

The pathogens and diseases of the apple can be counted in the hundreds, and reflect mainly the intensive culture of the tree for its fruit and the growing of the tree in virtually all parts of the country. As in the case of other trees grown for their fruit, such as citrus, pecan, walnut, and tung, this handbook does not discuss the numerous diseases of the fruit. But since fruit trees are used to some extent along streets or for ornamental purposes, an attempt is made to call attention to diseases that can impair or destroy their usefulness for these purposes.

The major apple growing States and the U. S. Department of Agriculture make available literature on apple diseases, and the Index of Plant Diseases in the United States (*8*) gives a helpful listing of apple pathogens and diseases reported in this country. With a few exceptions, the seriousness of any given apple tree pathogen varies greatly with the climate and soil of an area, and with the variety under consideration.

Foliage Diseases.—Apple scab, a disease of leaves and blossoms, and one of the most important and widespread causes of degrade in fruit, has long ranked at or near the top of the list of costly and damaging apple diseases. Caused by the fungus *Venturia inaequalis,* scab produces leaf spots that are typically circular, first brownish-gray and later olive-green or darker. Early spots may show the dendritic ramifications of the fungus. Spots can become diffuse or coalescing. In some cases infected leaves turn yellow and the scab infections appear as green islands. Infected leaves may drop early or develop a shot-hole condition as the lesions drop out. Ruinous scab spots, distortion, and cracking can affect the fruit, and lesions also develop on the shoots (*619*). The lesions on living organs bear the *Fusicladium dendriticum* conidial stage, in which stromatic cushions produce short conidiophores, and ovoid to truncate, lanceolate, 1-celled conidia. The perithecia, with 2-celled ascospores, form on infected overwintering tissue lesions on fallen leaves.

234

The very widespread cedar-apple rust (*Gymnosporangium juni-peri-virginianae*) produces a telial stage in the form of gelatinous spore horns emanating in wet weather from roundish galls involving the foliage of *Juniperus virginiana* and to a lesser extent *J. scopulorum*. Spores from these horns infect nearby apple trees. On the apple leaf the rust first shows as tiny, pale-yellow spots on the upper surface about 10 days after the cedar spore horns become fully developed. The spots tend to be circular and enlarge, becoming orange-colored; later the tissue beneath the spots swells and minute, tubular projections appear, which later split and recurve. These are the aecia, which produce the spores that infect the redcedar foliage. The indexes of varietal susceptibility in the apple are based on the amount of aecial production (*308*). Injury results from defoliation and from deformation of fruit. Fruit lesions also produce aecia.

In the East *Gymnosporangium globosum* also causes a leaf rust of apple and also alternates with the redcedar. In the West *G. libocedri* alternates between apple and incense cedar (*Libocedrus decurrens*). The aecia of these two species do not split into strongly revolute segments as in the cedar-apple rust (*46*), and neither are these two rusts as damaging to the apple.

A frogeye leaf spot, canker, and black rot of fruit throughout the East and in California is caused by *Physalospora obtusa,* and in the Pacific Northwest by *P. mutila.* For many years the former was known by its imperfect-stage name *Sphaeropsis malorum,* and the latter by the name *Diplodia mutila.* The leaf spots appear soon after bud-burst. Purple specks become circular brown spots up to 10 mm. across, sharp in outline, and with a raised margin. The spots enlarge with age, ultimately becoming concentrically zonate, with a gray center and brown rings (*619*). Black, erumpent pycnidia with colored, non-septate spores appear on the *Sphaeropsis* spots and with colored, 1-septate spores on *Diplodia* spots.

The powdery mildew of apple (*Podosphaera leucotricha*) (*619*) attacks the leaves, terminal shoots, blossoms, and fruit of many desirable varieties. A powdery coating of spores and mycelium appears on both leaf surfaces and may result in distortion, twisting, and cupping of foliage. It can attack as the buds unfold, and invest the new growth. Later in the summer black perithecia with multibranched ends on the appendages appear. The very similar *P. oxyacanthae* (*1153*) affects the foliage in the same manner as *P. leucotricha.*

In some sections of the country certain leaf diseases become locally common. In this category are the *Illosporium malifoliorum* spot in the middle-Atlantic States, the *Elsinoë piri* (*753*) spot anthracnose in the Northwest, *Cercospora mali* (*260*) spot and *Pellicularia koleroga* thread blight in the Gulf States, *Alternaria mali* leaf spot (*1456*) widely, and virus mosaic or infectious variegation in the East, Michigan, and the Far West. Mineral deficiencies, mainly iron deficiency in alkaline soils of the West, are typically localized problems. Fire blight and silver leaf are discussed under Stem Diseases.

Stem Diseases.—No disease has a greater total impact on the apple tree than fire blight (*Erwinia amylovora*). It is even a more severe disease of pears (*Pyrus*) and the quince (*Cydonia*) (*396,*

619). The blight of blossoms usually appears first. The blossoms shrivel and darken. The causal bacteria are typically spread from blossom to blossom by bees, and from the blossoms to leaves of the fruit-spurs. The leaves turn very dark to black, shrivel, and remain attached. The bacteria then penetrate twigs and branches from the infected spurs, and this results in twig blight and cankering. These cankers, usually sharply delimited, exude a milky ooze of bacteria in humid weather. Fruit blight is also common.

Silver leaf (*Stereum purpureum*) occurs widely on apple and plum in the East, the West, and the Lake States. By harvest time all or part of the leaves of affected trees appear to have a silvery-to-dull, leaden luster, as a result of air spaces formed between the epidermal and palisade cells. The causal fungus enters the tree through exposed dead wood, growing first in the heartwood, and then killing the sapwood. Toxins are produced that cause the foliar symptoms and ultimately kill branches or the whole tree. The fungus finally grows out of the dead bark in the fall to form small, flattened fruit-bodies that may appear purplish, bluish, or rose-colored. A brown heartwood discoloration of branches, trunk, or roots is characteristic (*619*).

Canker and dieback is caused by *Botryosphaeria ribis* (*858*) (see *Cercis*), *Glomerella cingulata* (*1483*), *Diaporthe eres* (including the syononymous *D. perniciosa* and *Phomopsis mali*), several species of *Septobasidium* which invest branches by their brown felts growing over scale insects (*292*), *Corticium laetum* and *C. salmonicolor* limb blights in the South (*1407*), *Cytospora* (*Valsa*) *leucostoma* in the Northwest (*447*). and some other fungi.

Bark-free concentric callus folds, and tiny, red, balloon-like perithecia characterize the canker caused by *Nectria galligena* (*170*). This stem and branch disease occurs widely throughout this country. *N. cinnabarina* (*1396*) causes a twig canker of apple, and grows as a saprobe on woody stems of most hardwoods. It is distinguished by its large, coral-colored sporodochia (*879*).

Some cultivars of the apple are very susceptible to crown gall (see Root Diseases). The author has seen some trees in North Carolina with large numbers of galls, mainly at pruning wounds. In these cases the bacterium was undoubtedly spread on pruning tools.

In the Southwest, Verticillium wilt (*V. albo-atrum*) (*1216*) affects the apple tree and presents an unusual symptom, namely, a "wet bleeding" of sapwood beneath and extending into the bark, in addition to the usual streaking in the outer sapwood (see *Acer platanoides*).

The European mistletoe, *Viscum album*, occurs on apple in California.

Root Diseases and Trunk Rots.—The apple tree is subject to many root diseases. The shoestring root rot (*Armillaria mellea*) (*619*) is one of the most damaging, particularly on the Pacific Coast. Its southern counterpart, *Clitocybe tabescens* (*1168*), kills occasional trees in parts of the South and Southwest (see *Aleurites*). In the Texas root rot belt of the Southwest, *Phymatotrichum omnivorum* can be very damaging, the apple being rated as extremely susceptible (*1379*).

Apple trees are susceptible both to crown gall (*Agrobacterium*

236

tumefaciens) and to hairy root (*A. rhizogenes*). Both diseases may occur on the same tree and in their early stages can be confused (*1555*). Heald (*396*) shows photographs of both diseases on young apple trees. However, his early account preceded the discovery that hairy root and crown gall were caused by different species of *Agrobacterium*, and were not manifestations of the same disease. The grafting knife and the pruning tool, as indicated under Stem Diseases, have been important means of spreading these bacteria. Crown gall appears as a tumorous, usually warty condition, typically at the root collar. In hairy root a great proliferation of fine roots extends from stem bases or roots or forms swellings on them.

A white root rot, notably of apple but also affecting some other trees (*151*), has been ascribed to *Corticium galactinum* (*285*). Reports of this rot of apple roots have come from Delaware west to Illinois, Missouri, Arkansas, and Oklahoma. Starting near the ground line, the fungus spreads rapidly out the roots and may girdle at the root collar, before the more distal roots are dead. Wefts, and later layers, of white mycelium appear on the root surface as the fungus penetrates the cambium and then rots the wood. The disease and the fruiting habits of the fungus are described by Cooley and Davidson (*285*). The whole tree generally dies at one time. This disease is said to spread from oaks to apple trees on recently cleared land.

In the case of *Xylaria mali*, which causes an apple root rot over much the same range as that for *C. galactinum*, the rot develops more slowly, and the disease is manifested in the top by weakening limbs on the side of the tree above the rotted roots. In *X. mali*, which rots roots of apple and honeylocust (*Gleditsia*), the wood is soft, spongy, dirty-white, and with black zone lines forming patterns. The mycelium on the roots changes from soft and white to crusty and black. The clustered fruiting bodies are very dark, club-shaped, and an inch or more high (*1555*).

In the Northwest the phanerogamic plant *Comandra pallida* (*506*) is known to parasitize apple roots.

A collar rot of apple of wide occurrence, but of scattered distribution, is caused by *Phytophthora cactorum*. This fungus is also described as causing a basal canker of madrone (*Arbutus*) on the west coast, bleeding canker of maple (*Acer saccharum*) on the east coast, and similar diseases of species of *Fagus, Cornus,* and other hardwood genera. The pattern of attack and the symptoms on apple are similar to those described under these other species or genera.

Sewell and Wilson (*1275*) report the death of maiden apple trees caused by *Phytophthora syringae,* and provide a comparison of the pathogen with *P. cactorum.*

The roots of apple have been reported invaded or attacked by the following nematodes: *Aphelenchus avenae,* in Maine; the root knot nematode *Meloidogyne* sp., mainly in the South; *Pratylenchus pratensis,* associated with a little leaf condition in California (*8*) ; and *P. vulnus* and *P. penetrans,* in inoculation tests (*259*).

Other root diseases of the apple include occasional attack of seedlings by *Rhizoctonia solani,* and by southern root rot, *Sclerotium rolfsii* (*1555*).

Rosellinia necatrix causes a white root rot in California. This is an ascomycete that forms surface mycelium, and large, round, dark, very superficial perithecia on affected parts.

A large number of fungi cause decay in the trunks of apple trees, mostly associated with sunscald, wounds, diseases, and senescence. Eide and Christensen (*407*) studied these trunk rots of the apple in Minnesota, and list 10 fungi identified as causes. None were unusual, and any of them might be found rotting the dead wood of many hardwood species.

Miscellaneous Pathology.—A glance at the Index of Plant Diseases in the United States (*8*) gives an appreciation of the attention that the apple has had from the pathologist. In addition to its many major fungus and bacterial diseases, the apple, like practically all intensively bred and cultured orchard crops, is subject to many locally important abiotic diseases associated mainly with weather and mineral deficiencies or excesses, and also to some additional but lesser virus and bacterial infections.

Apple trees resisted salt spray damage in New England (*1632*). In the Southwest, boron or zinc deficiency results in a rosetting of foliage, and iron deficiency results in chlorosis. Magnesium deficiency produces a leaf scorch in Maine. Several bark disturbances are related to climatic factors. Diagnosis of many apple diseases require a knowledge of the apple pathology of the locality in question.

Mango
Mangifera indica

Bailey (*53*) states that to millions of people living in the tropics the mango is of greater importance than is the apple to those in North America. From the fruit standpoint, however, only certain varieties are of high quality, and most of the trees raised in the United States produce inferior, fibrous types of fruit. Native to southern Asia, the mango has been widely planted in tropical parts of the New World including southern Florida and California. There are many forms of the mango tree, but typically it is erect, either with a broad, dome-shaped crown, or with a tall, more open crown, having ascending branches. It can grow from 70 to over 100 ft. high, and to diameters of over 7 ft.

The mango is evergreen, and growth is made in periodic flushes. Easily injured by frost when young, trees can withstand temperatures of about 27° F. for short durations when older. It is subject to a tipburn from salt spray. Mango is not exacting as to soil requirements. An annual rainfall of 30 to 50 in., with little of it during flowering, appears to be optimum. Moist weather during flowering, in Florida, has led to loss of most of the blossoms from the anthracnose disease. The dry weather in some parts of California has resulted in stunted trees.

Mangos grow from seed and are also reproduced by budding and grafting. There are innumerable varieties, most of which are important more for their fruit than from any ornamental value. The very sprawling habit of most mango trees makes them unsuitable for situations in which wide-spreading crowns are a disadvantage.

Mango trees suffering from zinc deficiency in Florida produce small, recurved, thickened leaves, often with some chlorosis. Twig dieback may follow. Copper deficiency causes weak terminal shoots,

238

defoliation, and dieback of the long, drooping, S-shaped branches.

Ruehle (*1218*) gives a good, illustrated account of the diseases of mango in Florida.

Foliage Diseases.—Only two diseases of mango could be considered important in the United States; these are (1) the ubiquitous anthracnose, flower blight, and twig blight (withertip) caused by *Glomerella cingulata;* and (2) the spot-anthracnose or scab caused by *Elsinoë mangiferae.*

G. cingulata is known best on mango under the imperfect-stage name *Colletotrichum gloeosporiodes.* The characteristics of this fungus on mango are like those on citrus, involving twig dieback, leaf spotting, and blossom blast—with pinkish spore pustules prominent in wet weather (*1555*). This disease is particularly severe in the South on many hosts, and is much less common in California, being governed to a great extent by moisture (*1218*). Many kinds of trees and lesser vegetation are attacked, and since the perfect stage is so often absent, the causal fungus has gone under the name of various species of *Gloeosporium* if setae were not observed in the acervuli, or *Colletotrichum* if they were (see also *Liriodendron*).

In mango scab (*Elsinoë mangiferae*) spots usually originate on the underside of the leaves, ultimately becoming visible above. They are circular or angular, generally smaller than anthracnose spots, and dark brown to black, with downy, olivaceous centers. On mature leaves the spots become raised and have narrow, brown margins and dirty-white centers. Grayish blotches also form on the shoots. Severe attacks cause crinkling, distortion, and early shedding (*1218*).

An algal leaf spot (*Cephaleuros virescens*) is common on the foliage of a large number of woody plants in the Deep South and in greenhouses there and further north. Reddish-brown fruiting-bodies form a scurf, and the underlying tissues may swell, crack, and become necrotic lesions. Wolf (*1599*) gives a good account of this unusual pathogen, and Ruehle (*1218*) describes it specifically on mango.

A powdery mildew (*Oidium mangiferae*) occurs in Florida and California, for which no perithecial stage has been described. On leaves and fruit it causes superficial, scattered blotches, up to an inch across, that are often purplish with a whitish bloom (*1218*).

Sooty molds in the genera *Capnodium* and *Meliola* often blacken the surface of leaves, but typically live on insect secretions and produce merely surface discolorations. The ascospores of *Capnodium* spp. have muriform septation and those of *Meliola* have septate ascospores, but are rarely muriform.

Many other fungi can cause leaf spots of mango, particularly *Lophodermium mangiferae, Microthyrium mangiferae, Pestalotia mangiferae,* and *Phyllosticta mortoni,* but they are of little importance to mango culture in the United States.

Zinc deficiency has produced a littleleaf effect on mango in Florida sands.

Stem Diseases.—Many fungi also occur on twigs and stems of mango, and the University of Florida herbarium lists many more than does the Index of Plant Diseases in the United States (*8*). However, none of them causes major disease in this country.

Three fungi that have gross similarities with respect to their prominent, black, clustered perithecia are *Botryosphaeria ribis* (*550*), *Physalospora abdita,* and *P. rhodina* (*1484*). It is doubtful that any of them are more than secondary invaders of mango twig bark tissue weakened or killed by other causes. *P. abdita,* as a saprobe, is commonly referred to in its imperfect stage as *Sphaeropsis* spp. (dark, nonseptate conidia) on oaks, maple, alder, and persimmon in the South. It is also likely that the *Diplodia* spp. (dark, 1-septate conidia) referred to as associated with twig blights and diebacks of mango are the imperfect stages of *P. abdita* or *P. rhodina*.

Couch (*292*) lists *Septobasidium lepidosaphis* and *S. pilosum* on mango; *S. pseudopedicellatum* has also been reported. The members of this genus all produce a brown, surface, felt thallus that feeds on insects and can indirectly result in injury to the twig tissue beneath. The leathery, non-poroid hymenium of this genus bears septate basidia.

Aleurodiscus candidus, one of the so-called bark-patch fungi, produces small, resupinate felts on the outer bark of living trees and on dead trees. The hymenium has no cystidia, the spore membrane is colorless, and the spore contents are colored.

Root and Trunk Rots.—Basidiomycetes that are considered root rotters of mango in North America include[28]: *Agaricus cheimonophyllus, Ganoderma mangiferae, G. argillaceum,* and *G. perzonatum.* The author cannot vouch for the legitimacy of these names.

Mango was considered moderately susceptible to Texas root rot in greenhouse tests (*1379*).

Although dead wood has been known to be attacked by many fungi, including *Pholiota martinicensis, Polyporus gilvus, P. sanguineus, Poria borbonica* (*891*), *Trametes corrugata* (*1067*), and *T. hydnoides,* there are no records of heartrot fungi attacking living mango in this country.

Ruehle (*1222*) listed 27 species of nematodes associated with roots or soil under the mango tree. Only one of these, the burrowing nematode, *Radopholus similis,* was from North America.

Cajeput-tree
Melaleuca leucadendron

A native evergreen of Australia, the cajeput grows to a medium size in the warm, temperate-to-subtropical areas of the United States, and is grown commonly in Florida and California as an ornamental. It has thick, spongy bark that peels off in thin layers. The leaves yield an oil used in medicine. Cajeput has been used for fixing muddy shores, and for planting in alkaline soils. It withstands salt spray, wind, drought, and slight frosts. The wood is durable (*53*).

Menninger (*947*) recommends cajeput for planting, in clusters, along wide highways in south Florida, and both Miami and Tampa park authorities rate cajeput as among the best species for street planting. Metcalf (*955*) describes cajeput among his Interesting Trees in California.

---

[28] Personal communication from George F. Weber, professor of plant pathology, University of Florida, Gainesville, Fla.

Cajeput seems to be unusually free of disease, not only in the United States, but elsewhere, including its native habitat. In this country the only disease record concerns some damping-off in nurseries in Florida due to *Rhizoctonia* sp. Spaulding's Foreign Diseases of Forest Trees of the World (*1338*) lists as causes of diseases of cajeput only *Fomes lignosus* (root rot) from Uganda, *Phyllosticta leucadendri* (leaf spot) from Australia, and *Puccinia camargoi,* the latter forming rust pustules on leaves of cajeput in Brazil.

The nematode *Hemicycliophora epicharis* was associated with cajeput roots in Florida (*1222*).

Chinaberry
Melia azedarach

The chinaberry tree, a native of southeast Asia (*872*), has been widely planted mainly for quick, dense shade, from southern Virginia to Texas. It has often escaped cultivation and is a common feature of farmstead vegetation in the southern Piedmont and Coastal Plain. Among its many other common names are chinatree and umbrella tree. The denser forms are sometimes called chinaball. A variety (*M. azedarach* var. *umbraculiformis*), with upright-spreading branches and a flattened head, is called the Texas umbrella-tree (*1154*). Chinaberry trees can reach heights of 30 to 40 ft. The wood is coarse but durable, according to Bailey (*53*).

Since the chinaberry is not demanding with respect to soil and site, it thrives in some of the most difficult situations, excepting in swamps or under other extreme conditions. Its rapid early growth and dense canopy made it an early favorite around cabin sites in exposed, hot, agricultural areas of the South. While it can briefly withstand temperatures approaching 5° F. if well hardened off, fully grown trees have been killed by cold. Hepting et al. (*664*), reporting on the effects of a drop to 8° F. on November 25, 1950, after a mild autumn in the Georgia Piedmont, state that "The chinaberry was the only tree in the woods visibly affected to the extent of dieback of large limbs."

The fruits contain a pulp with a poisonous narcotic, and children, poultry, and pigs are reported to have been poisoned by them (*546*).

Foliage Diseases.—Chupp (*260*) recognizes four species of *Cercospora* on *Melia* spp., but only two on *M. azedarach* in the United States. These latter are *C. meliae* and *C. subsessilis*. *C. meliae* occurs generally through the Gulf States, producing circular to angular leaf spots 0.5–2.5 mm. across, each with a white center, a narrow dark reddish border, with fruiting amphigenous. Fascicles, often dense, are produced on a stroma, conidiophores are pale, and the conidia are hyaline, acicular, and multiseptate. There are many sterile stromata. What was called *C. leucosticta* is now regarded as this sterile phase of *C. meliae*.

C. subsessilis, known from Mississippi to Texas, makes spots 2–5 mm. across, often zonate, tan to gray, with hypophyllous fruiting. The stromata are globular, the fascicles are dense, and the conidia are pale-olivaceous and narrowly cylindric, rather than acicular.

Two species of *Phyllosticta, P. azedarachis* and *P. meliae,* spot foliage in the Deep South but are of no importance.

The commonest leaf disease is the ubiquitous powdery mildew, *Phyllactinia guttata* (*619*), with its bottle-shaped perithecial appendages. It is most abundant in late summer.

A downy mildew reported as *Peronospora parasitica* is common in some areas.[29] This fungus, one of the Peronosporaceae, is a phycomycete with aerial, tree-like branching conidiophores, and in the case of *Peronospora*, with conidia that germinate from the side (*1352*).

The thread-blight caused by *Pellicularia koleroga* attacks chinaberry in Florida, and the symptoms are as described for *Cinnamomum* and *Ficus*.

Stem Diseases.—Chinaberry is host to many twig fungi. Most of them are readily recognized as common, secondary invaders of moribund tissue of many southern nonconiferous trees, and have been discussed under *Aleurites, Cercis, Ficus, Magnolia,* or *Mangifera.* This group of fungi includes *Botryosphaeria ribis, Fusarium lateritium, Glomerella cingulata, Nectria cinnabarina, Physalospora fusca, P. obtusa,* and *P. rhodina.* It is .likely that two other twig fungi reported on chinaberry (*Botryodiplodia meliae* and *Diplodia langloisii*) are simply imperfect stages of *P. rhodina* (*8, 1484*).

In addition to the above weak parasites, a twig blight caused by *Eutypella stellulata* has been reported from Oklahoma and Texas. This fungus is sphaeriaceous, with stalked asci in perithecia in a stroma on or in wood, rather than bark, and has 1-celled allantoid spores (*267*).

A stem canker has been referred to *Nectria coccinea.* Because of the confusion that has developed in the taxonomy of this genus (*879*) it is likely that this is the common bark-free target canker caused by *N. galligena,* a fungus similar to *N. coccinea,* that produces red perithecia in bark folds at the invading edge of the canker.

The common eastern leafy mistletoe, *Phoradendron serotinum,* sometimes parasitizes chinaberry.

Root and Stem Rots.—Chinaberry has been given the top rating of "extremely susceptible" to Texas root rot, following inoculation tests (*1379*).

Seedlings are susceptible to the violet root rot caused by *Helicobasidium purpureum* (*Rhizoctonia crocorum*). The roots are invaded from the soil and ultimately turn purplish. In very wet weather the colored mycelium may be evident at the stem base. Later the mycelium turns brown, and small, dark sclerotia can be found embedded in it (*1555*).

Root knot nematodes (*Meloidogyne* spp.) also attack chinaberry, but, except with seedlings, they have caused no recognizable damage to the trees.

A few common basidiomycetes attack the dead wood, but only one, *Fomes meliae,* rots the wood of living trees. However, even this fungus attacks only dead or "inactive" wood. It is particularly common on *Melia* and *Fraxinus,* but occurs also on the dead wood of

---

[29] Personal communication from W. A. Campbell, pathologist, USDA Forest Service, Southeastern Forest Experiment Station, Athens, Ga.

242

many other tree genera in the South. It forms a small, usually imbricate, dirty-white, often tomentose, corky sporophore (*1067*). Cultures of *Fomes* (*Polyporus*) *meliae* closely resemble those of *Polyporus palustris,* and McKay (*910*) has provided information on the characteristics that separate the two, in culture.

Fomes torulosus, which is considered by some to be a perennial form of *Polyporus gilvus,* can rot the wood of trees in a state of decline, or cause a rot of bole wood exposed by wounding.

White mulberry
Morus alba

The white mulberry is the silkworm mulberry of the Orient. It is a native of China, and has been cultivated in Asia for its edible fruits and for its foliage, which serves as forage for silkworm larvae. The species has been widely planted in the United States from New York to Kansas and south to Florida and Texas, and also in southeastern Washington (*872*). In the East it is now naturalized in many localities such as along roads, premises, and edges of woods. The tree is wide-spreading, with a round crown, and reaches a height of 45 ft. The trunk may reach a diameter of 2 ft.

The white mulberry is a very variable tree in form, leaf size, lobation, color, and other characters. Rehder (*1154*) recognizes seven varieties. *Morus alba* var. *tatarica* is a small tree, with a bushy head and small lobed or unlobed leaves, that is reputed to be the hardiest form of this species.

A curiosity among diseases is the popcorn disease of mulberry (*Ciboria carunculoides*), that occurs only in the South. Sclerotia of the fungus form in the carpels of the fruits, resulting in swellings that cause the fruit to resemble popcorn. The apothecia form from these sclerotia (*1560*).

Foliage Diseases.—The only noteworthy leaf diseases of *Morus* in the United States are spots caused by species of *Cercospora* and *Mycosphaerella.* Chupp (*260*) recognizes three species of *Cercospora* on *Morus* in this country: *C. missouriensis, C. mori,* and *C. moricola.*

C. missouriensis occurs in the Mississippi Valley, causing subcircular spots 2–10 mm. across, or coalescing to form large, dull-brown to almost black areas. Fruiting, occurring on stromata, is hypophyllous; the long, obclavate, multiseptate conidia are dark; and the fascicles are dense.

C. mori is known in North America only from Alabama, fruiting is hypophyllous on dark indistinct spots, stromata are virtually non-existent, fascicles are absent or 2- to 7-stalked, and conidia are colored.

C. moricola is widespread, fruiting on subcircular to irregular spots, with gray to tan centers and dark purple to black borders. Fruiting is amphigenous, the stromata variable, the fascicles very dense, and conidia hyaline, acicular, and with many indistinct septa.

A leaf spot of white mulberry caused by *Cercosporella mori* has been reported from Nebraska to Texas. This fungus genus differs from *Cercospora* in that in *Cercosporella* both the conidia and conidiophores are hyaline, while in *Cercospora* the conidiophores are always brownish.

The most widespread leaf spot of mulberry is caused by *Mycosphaerella mori*. Since the perfect stage forms only on fallen leaves the fungus has gone mainly under imperfect stage names, including *Cercosporella maculans,* and species of *Cylindrosporium, Phleospora, Septogloeum,* and *Septoria (8)*. The spots can become very abundant in wet, shady situations. Wolf (*1600, 1608*) describes this common mulberry disease well.

The spots are circular, brown, becoming fuscous to ochraceous, with a broad, dark border. Conidial fruiting is amphigenous, mostly hypophyllous. The spores form in gelatinous masses, appearing, on drying, as pinkish incrustations. Conidiophores are in fascicles. The conidia are curved, blunt, hyaline, multiseptate, $20-60\mu \times 5-8\mu$. The perithecia are epiphyllous, black, and appear on overwintered leaves. The ascospores are 2-celled, and $12-15\mu \times 3.5-4\mu$.

A bacterial leaf spot and blight (*Pseudomonas mori*) occurs generally, wherever the white mulberry grows. The bacteria can be readily plated from leaf lesions, or observed directly using Burkholder's (*194*) stain technique. They are motile rods with 1 or 2 polar flagella, and form no spores. Stevens (*1352*) mentions E. F. Smith's early experience with this disease in Georgia, and he also provides a description of the organism.

In Arizona, *Morus alba* var. *kingan* has developed a marginal leaf chlorosis and burning as a result of manganese deficiency.

Stem Diseases.—None of the stem diseases are considered generally damaging, except for the widespread twig blight caused by *Fusarium lateritium* var. *mori*. This is the imperfect stage of *Gibberella baccata* var. *moricola*. Cankers and blighted parts of shoots may produce the corky, pink sporodochia of the *Fusarium* stage. The conidia may be from 0- to 6-septate. Wollenweber and Reinking (*1610*) give the basis of varietal separation within both the imperfect and perfect stages. The *Gibberella* stage is comprised of groups of blackish perithecia, with ascospores smaller than those of the type species. These ascospores are oval to spindle-shaped, mostly 1- to 3-septate, and up to $20\mu \times 5.5\mu$ in dimensions. Usually the *Fusarium* stage only is seen in nature, following wet weather.

Nectria cankers are not uncommon. They are typically perennial target cankers, and bear small, red perithecia under bark crevices around the margins (*170*). Although usually ascribed in the past to *N. coccinea* it is likely that most if not all would now be placed in *N. galligena* (*879*) (see *Cornus florida*). *N. cinnabarina* (*879*), that produces large, coral-colored sporodochia on dead shoots, is probably a saprobe, being common on hardwoods in this role and seldom behaving as a parasite excepting possibly in the case of apple (see *Malus pumila*).

One or more species of *Cytospora* (*151*) have been reported associated with twig diebacks. The question of pathogenicity in these cases and in the cases of *Botryosphaeria ribis* (*Dothiorella gregaria*) (see *Cercis*) and *Myxosporium* sp. on mulberry remains to be proven.

Root Diseases.—Hairy root (*Agrobacterium rhizogenes*), a bacterial disease (see *Malus*), has affected white mulberry in Connecticut.

Armillaria mellea (848) attacks in its usual manner with hardwoods, in that while its rhizomorphs may occur generally on healthy root bark, pathogenic invasion and damage by A. mellea is almost always preceded by major root injury or other debility of the host.

White mulberry has been rated highly susceptible to Texas root rot (Phymatotrichum omnivorum) in inoculation tests (1379). M. alba var. tatarica, the Russian mulberry, was tested for planting as a shelterbelt tree in the root rot belt of Texas and Oklahoma, and based on 6 years of records it was considered "intermediate in susceptibility, possibly usable on sandy sites" (1627).

Also in Texas, the violet root rot (Helicobasidium purpureum, Rhizoctonia crocorum) has attacked the roots of seedlings and young woody plants (see Catalpa, Melia) (1555).

Root knot nematodes (Meloidogyne spp.) have attacked seedlings in the East and Southwest, but are not known to be serious pests of mulberry. Nematodes in 5 other genera have been listed by Ruehle (1222) as occurring on or around the roots of white mulberry.

Red mulberry
Morus rubra

The red mulberry is a short, native tree with stout, spreading branches, reaching a height of 60 ft. and having red fruits. It extends from New England across to southern Minnesota and Nebraska, south to Central Texas, and eastward to southern Florida. Its leaves are normally dark green, turning bright yellow in autumn (1154). It occurs occasionally singly or in small groups, mainly along stream banks and the deeper, moist soils of the South and the Central States. In the Mississippi Delta red mulberry is confined largely to "ridges" in first bottoms, being most common on the edges of these ridges where they grade off into flats. It is never a prominent species. It is used locally for fence posts because the heartwood is durable.

Variety tomentosa, the Lampasas mulberry, has leaves that are whitish-tomentose below and glossy above, and grows in Texas.

The red mulberry was listed among the species most resistant to sulfur dioxide air pollution in Texas (911).

Of the leaf pathogens annotated under Morus alba, the following have also been reported on M. rubra: Cercospora moricola, C. pulvinulata (in the Midwest only), Pseudomonas mori, and Mycosphaerella mori. The last is the most widespread and important, particularly on red mulberry, and has been described and illustrated by Wolf (1600, 1608) (see Morus alba).

In addition, the foliage of red mulberry has been attacked by some fungi not reported on white mulberry. Cerotelium (Physopella) fici (see Ficus) is one of these. It is a rust (46) occurring in the Deep South, virtually entirely in the uredial stage, on Ficus, Morus, and Maclura.

Two powdery mildews occur on red mulberry: the very common Phyllactinia guttata, with basally bulbous perithecial appendages; and Uncinula geniculata, very widespread on this species, having simple, hooked perithecial appendages. The species of the powdery mildews are described and keyed by Reed (1153).

Wolf (1601) gave the name "false mildew" to a disease of red mulberry caused by *Mycosphaerella arachnoidea*, which produces an effused, white, cobwebby coating that simulates the appearance of a powdery mildew. The affected leaf areas become necrotic by early autumn. The whitish mycelium bears a profusion of hyaline, septate *Cercosporella* conidia which are produced acrogenously, and arise singly. The black perithecia are formed in abundance in the hyphal wefts, just before and after abscission of the leaves.

A leaf spot has also been attributed to *Phyllosticta moricola* in Kansas and South Carolina.

Root knot nematodes (*Meloidogyne* spp.) have been isolated from red as well as white mulberry.

Few rot fungi have been reported from *Morus* and they are not distinctive, being species causing rot of dead wood of many hardwoods. These include *Fomes applanatus, Hymenochaete agglutinans, Polyporus gilvus,* and *P. hispidus.* Those cited by Overholts (1067) as capable of causing either rot of the central cylinder or rot at wounds of living *Morus* spp. include *Fomes applanatus, Polyporus robiniophilus, P. texanus, P. hispidus,* and two southwestern fungi, *P. farlowii* and *P. munzii.*

Water tupelo
Nyssa aquatica

The water tupelo occurs mainly in low, wet flats and in swamps on the flood plains of alluvial streams from southeastern Virginia to Texas. It is common along the rivers and swamps of the Atlantic Coastal Plain, exclusive of Florida, and along the Gulf of Mexico Coastal Plain from the western Florida panhandle to east Texas. Its penetration into the interior is mainly in the bottomlands of the Mississippi River and its tributaries, to the southern tip of Illinois (468). In the Mississippi Delta, water tupelo is confined to sites that are periodically or permanently under water (1140).

Water tupelo is seldom found more than 5 ft. above stream level, but can grow well in the Deep South wherever seepage has created ponds. The soils that support this species range in texture from plastic clay to silt loam. The tree grows to a height of 110 ft. and to a diameter of 4 ft., above its characteristic butt swell. It is intolerant but responds to release. Growth tends to be slow, but longevity approaches the old age of the commonly associated baldcypress (468).

Since the bark is thin, fire is a prime enemy. When the wet sites dry out in the fall, fires can be devastating, not only killing many trees, but scorching the trunks of others, leaving them exposed to internal decay, which is, fortunately, slow in this species.

When a southern Kentucky reservoir area was flooded (583), of the 39 species studied for flood damage, water tupelo was one of the least damaged.

Foliage Diseases.—The most conspicuous leaf disease of *Nyssa aquatica* and *N. sylvatica* is caused by *Mycosphaerella nyssaecola* (spermogonial stage *Phyllosticta nyssae*). It is mainly a disease of the Southeast, and is described in detail by Wolf (1605), who also named the perfect stage. By midsummer irregular, purplish blotches appear on the upper leaf surface; these blotches may reach a diameter of 3 cm. or even involve the entire upper surface. If, toward the end of the growing season, the lesions remain discrete, the intervening leaf areas acquire the purplish coloration characteristic of tupelo leaves in autumn. Premature defoliation follows heavy attack.

The lower surface beneath a lesion becomes brown and dotted with dark fungus structures, some being the spermogonia, which contain tiny, hyaline, unicellular rod-shaped spermatia, and others being perithecial primordia. The dark, globular perithecia mature in the spring on overwintered leaves on the ground. The ascospores are hyaline, 1-septate with the upper cell the broader, and 8–10μ × 3.5–4.5μ.

A rust, *Aplopsora nyssae*, occurs occasionally on *Nyssa aquatica* and *N. sylvatica*. *Aplopsora* is a monotypic genus for which only uredinia and telia are known. They are hypophyllous. The uredinia are scattered, tiny, and cinnamon-brown. The uredospores are brown and echinulate. The telia are gregarious, early naked, yellow, with teliospores in a single layer, cylindric, rounded at both ends, and with colorless walls (*46*).

The thread-blight caused by *Pellicularia koleroga* sometimes involves water tupelo foliage in the Deep South. It is characterized by nondiscrete leaf blighting, white fungus wefts, and the hanging of blighted foliage by fungus strands (see *Carya* and *Ficus*).

Stem Diseases.—There are no important stem diseases of water tupelo. Twig lesions are sometimes produced by *Fusarium solani*, as reported under *Liquidambar*. *Phoma nyssicarpa* has also been considered capable of blighting twigs.[30]

Septobasidium curtisii produces a brown felt over scale insects on the branches of living *Nyssa* spp.

Trunk Rots.—E. R. Toole has given much study to the fungi that are important in the decay of living timber trees of the Mississippi bottomlands. For water tupelo he has listed the following: *Lentinus crinitus, L. tigrinus, Lenzites betulina, Pleurotus ostreatus, Polyporus hirsutus, P. mutabilis, P. rhipidium, P. rigidus, P. sanguineus, Stereum fuscum, S. hirsutum,* and *S. lobatum*.[30]

Most of these fungi will be recognized as decayers of dead wood. However, such fungi can enter a tree via the large food base of dead wood exposed by fire-scarring and continue into and up the bole for varying distances, extending the cull loss. Others, notably *L tigrinus* and *Pleurotus ostreatus*, are vigorous heartrot fungi.

Stains.—*Ceratocystis coerulescens* and *C. moniliformis* have been specifically identified as causes of sapstain in logs and lumber of water tupelo.

Black tupelo
Nyssa sylvatica

Black tupelo has also been known very generally as black-gum, and is the most widely distributed species of *Nyssa*. From New England to Michigan it extends southward over the entire area

[30] Personal communication from E. Richard Toole, formerly pathologist, USDA Forest Service, now at Mississippi State University, State College, Miss.

east of the Mississippi River, and also west of the river from Missouri south to east Texas. *Nyssa sylvatica* var. *sylvatica*, typical black tupelo, grows in uplands and in alluvial bottoms, being the common "black-gum" of the East, from the mountains to the sea. *N. sylvatica* var. *biflora* is the swamp tupelo, and is limited to coastal swamps and estuaries, from Maryland to Florida, and along the east side of the Mississippi River from Tennessee to Louisiana (*468*).

Black tupelo in the Mississippi Delta is mostly on fairly well-drained, loamy "ridges," mainly in second or higher bottoms. It will tolerate occasional shallow overflow. In the uplands of the Deep South it occurs mostly on lower slopes and stream bottoms (*1140*). It also grows on the relatively dry lower slopes of the Appalachian Mountains and on the hot, dry hills of the Piedmont and the upper Coastal Plain. Its soils are mostly clays, loams, and silt loams. The swamp tupelo grows on wetter sites than typical black tupelo but not in the permanently or periodically wet sites occupied by water tupelo (*468*).

The lesser tolerance to flooding of black tupelo, as compared with water tupelo, was evident in a Kentucky reservoir flooding study (*583*). Black tupelo trees are very subject to sapsucker injury, and the wood is subject to rapid decay. They also are readily injured by salt spray (*1005*). The foliage takes on a rich red color in the autumn.

Foliage Diseases.—The curious hypophyllous fungus *Actinopelte dryina* (see *Quercus*) produces large numbers of very small, reddish-brown, discrete spots on leaves of *Nyssa*, *Quercus*, and some other deciduous species. A membranous scutellum with radiating hyphal strands bears conidiophores extending inward that bear subglobose, subhyaline 1-celled spores (*863*).

A much larger spot or blight, that may involve much or all of a leaf, is caused by *Mycosphaerella nyssaecola*. It is the commonest leaf disease of *Nyssa* (see *N. aquatica*).

A subcircular, brown leaf spot, with a gray, punctiform center bearing 3- to 12-septate conidia, amphigenously, is caused by *Cercospora nyssae* and is known only from Texas (*260*).

The leaf rust *Aplopsora nyssae* occurs widely but is not a serious pathogen (see *N. aquatica*).

Late in the season *Gnomoniella georgiana* (*980*) will produce its sunken, black, epiphyllous perithecia with long, cylindric, erumpent ostioles, on dead leaves on the ground or on the tree. The ostiole neck is not as long as illustrated by Stevens (*1352*) for *G. tubiformis*, but is about the length of the neck in *Gnomonia ulmea*.

Stem Diseases.—Annual branch cankers called "stem lesion" by Toole (*1423*) are caused by *Fusarium solani* (see *N. aquatica* and *Liquidambar*) in the Deep South. Some minor twig blighting has also been ascribed to *Botryosphaeria ribis* (see *Cercis*), *Didymella segna*, and *Phoma nyssicarpa*.

In the North, branch and stem cankers are caused by *Nectria galligena* (see *Juglans nigra*), and more rarely by *Strumella coryneoidea* (see *Quercus*). Nectria cankers expose callus folds of firm, dead wood. Strumella cankers retain the bark, and the wood beneath the lesions is invariably decayed (*661*).

Some cankering can result from the brown felts of *Septobasidium curtisii (292)* which grow over scale insects infesting branches.

The eastern leafy mistletoe *Phoradendron serotinum* is common on black tupelo in the South.

A seedling wilt in Missouri has been ascribed to *Phytophthora cactorum,* a common nursery pathogen *(305).*

Verticillium wilt *(V. albo-atrum)* has been reported a disease of black tupelo by Engelhard and Carter *(412)* in Illinois (see *Acer platanoides).* This fungus, however, has not been reported as causing disease in the forest.

Fungi cited by Overholts *(1067)* as capable of causing either rot of the central cylinder, or rot at wounds of living *Nyssa* spp. include *Daedalea ambigua, Fomes connatus, F. fraxineus, Polyporus fissilis, P. lucidus,* and *P. zonalis.* Others known to rot the bole wood of *N. sylvatica,* specifically, are *Hydnum erinaceus, Lentinus tigrinus (637),* and *Pleurotus ostreatus.* The dead sapwood is rotted by many species of *Polyporus* and *Stereum.*

Olive
Olea europaea

The olive of commerce is a small tree, mainly of the Mediterranean Region, which grows wild from Asia Minor to Morocco. It thrives on a wide variety of soils, provided they are well-drained, and makes a handsome, vigorous tree in many situations too dry for other fruits, provided the subsoil permits deep penetration of roots. In the United States, the olive succeeds only in California, and in restricted parts of Arizona, New Mexico, and Florida *(51).* In California, this tree has not only proved important for its fruit and oil, but, according to Metcalf *(955),* it is one of the hardiest and most satisfactory street and highway trees in that State.

The olive is small to medium in size, long-lived and grows slowly. Although its gray-green, narrow, oval leaves are resistant to wind, insects, and diseases, it can withstand temperatures below 20° F. for only a short period. The olive is favored by a clear, dry atmosphere. Summer rains or fog make trees subject to attack by a black scale insect *(Saissetia oleae).*

Most of the olive trees in California are of variety Mission, but there are many other known varieties, several of which also can be found in California *(51, 1581).* Propagation is, in most cases, from cuttings, but also sometimes by seed.

Foliage Diseases.—A leaf spot, in California, called peacock spot or ring spot, is caused by *Cycloconium oleaginum,* an imperfect fungus with coiled mycelium, and small, dark, 2-celled spores that are little different from the short hyphae. The spots are blackish, and are concentrically zonate. They occur mostly on old or weakened leaves *(1555).*

A brownish anthracnose spot, in California, is caused by *Gloeosporium olivarum.* The small spots bear acervuli without setae and with hyaline, 1-celled conidia.

Infection by *Cercospora cladosporioides* may result in definite, brown spots, or virtually no distinct spotting. Fruiting is hypophyllous and olivaceous; stromata are large and irregular; fascicles are dense; conidiophores olivaceous and somewhat septate; and the conidia are subhyaline, 1- to 5-septate, and cylindric *(260).*

In Florida and south Georgia, a black leaf spot is caused by *Asterina oleina*. The spot results largely from a surface mycelial development. Hyphopodia, acting like haustoria, penetrate the cuticle and parasitize the leaf tissues. The perithecium has a shield-shaped top and radially arranged, dark hyphae. Beneath the stroma is a single layer of dark 2-celled spores.

Stem Diseases.—One of the most well-known diseases of olive, in California and Europe, is the bacterial knot caused by *Pseudomonas savastanoi*. Warty excrescences, knots, or tumors form on leaves, branches, and trunks, which, when abundant, can weaken or kill trees. The bacteria, which multiply in these galls, infect through wounds or leaf scars. Variety *manzanilla* is the most susceptible of the olives grown in California. Brown (*176*) describes the bacterium, and also a variety of it (var. *fraxini*) which forms similar tumors on species of *Fraxinus* in Europe.

A similar bacterial knot disease of oleander (*Nerium*) occurs in Europe and in California, the cause of which has gone under the name *Pseudomonas tonelliana*. Later evidence (*1592*) showed this bacterium to be identical with *P. savastanoi* physiologically, serologically, and pathologically.

The most serious of the diseases of olive in California today is Verticillium wilt (*V. albo-atrum*), according to Wilhelm and Taylor (*1581*). All varieties are susceptible, and since cotton is also susceptible, cotton culture, particularly in the San Joaquin Valley, is involved in the spread and intensification of inoculum. Individual branches, sides of trees, or entire crowns may die in a single season. Yet entire trees rarely die, and boles often produce suckers that tend to remain uninfected.

Verticillium wilt results in the foliage becoming dull and lusterless in the spring. This is followed by defoliation and dieback, with the bark of affected branches turning bluish. Distinct vascular discoloration is generally absent. Some slight browning of the wood may appear, but this is not a reliable symptom. Wilhelm and Taylor (*1581*) found that living mycelium, active in the wood in winter and spring—as indicated by simple isolation of the fungus—tends to disappear in summer and fall, often when symptoms are severe. If new root infection can be prevented, trees can recover. Resistant lines have been identified.

Exanthema, or dieback, is a physiological disturbance of olive in California that is associated with deficiency of organic matter and poor drainage.

The dodder, *Cuscuta indecora*, commonly called bigseed alfalfa dodder, sends its leafless, yellowish vines in copious mats over its hosts which include olive, tomato, and sweetpea. This dodder is reported to cause a stem gall of olive, in addition to its normal attrition type of parasitism by means of its haustoria.

Root Diseases.—Shoestring root rot (*Armillaria mellea*) has killed olive trees in the Southwest, and is readily identified by the white mycelial fans under the bark at the root collar, and by the characteristic, flat, black rhizomorphs under the dead root bark.

The olive is rated as highly susceptible to Texas root rot (*Phymatotrichum omnivorum*) (*1379*), and both root rot nematodes (*Meloidogyne* spp.) and lesion nematodes (*Pratylenchus coffeae*) are known to parasitize olive roots in California.

The citrus nematode, *Tylenchulus semipenetrans*, also attacks olive roots in California (*259*).

Miscellaneous Pathology.—Paul Keener [31] reported that the olive in Arizona is very sensitive to injury from 2, 4-D weed killers. He also reported that an unspecified species of *Ganoderma* causes a wood rot of living trees in that State.

Bonar (*137*) describes, in detail, the fruiting body of *Polyporus oleae* as it occurred on olive trees in Berkeley, Cal. Imbricate sessile, coriaceous brackets, with a whitish to light pink pore surface having irregular to daedaloid pores, appeared on the trunks near the ground line, or emerged from the ground and connected to roots by cordlike rhizomorphs.

Eastern hophornbeam
Ostrya virginiana

The eastern hophornbeam is a small, regular tree, with thin flaky bark, occurring mostly singly throughout the East from southeastern Canada to northern Florida, and westward to the Great Plains, except in the Mississippi Delta. It occurs mainly along low ground and river banks in the Piedmont, and up to 5,200 ft. in the Southern Appalachian Mountains. It reaches its best development in Arkansas and eastern Texas, and is rare in the Atlantic Coastal Plain. Along with *Betula* and *Carpinus,* it is one of the Betulaceae.

The hophornbeam is tolerant, grows slowly, is very hardy, and the heartwood is durable in contact with the soil (*279*). It has hard wood and tough resilient branches that resist damage from wind, snow, ice, disease, and insects. However, it ranked third among 39 species in sensitivity to flooding in Tennessee (*583*). No serious diseases of *Ostrya* have been reported.

The only common leaf spot is caused by *Gloeosporium robergei*. It forms brown, discrete spots, a few millimeters across, that bear acervuli with 1-celled, hyaline spores, and no setae. Two species of *Gnomoniella*—*G. fimbriata* and *G. gnomon*—and species of *Cylindrosporium* and *Septoria* have been reported only rarely (*8*).

A rust, *Melampsoridium carpini*, known in northern New York, and in Europe and Japan, produces hypophyllous uredia loosely grouped on yellow spots. The telia are scattered, hypophyllous, with somewhat clavate, golden-brown, subepidermal teliospores. The O and I stages are lacking.

Taphrina virginica causes small, pale yellow, thickened areas, or curling of the foliage of *Ostrya*, widely through the East (*994*).

Westcott (*1555*) reports that powdery mildews, *Microsphaera alni* and *Phyllactinia guttata* (*P. corylea*), that are common on *Carpinus* also occur on *Ostrya*, and she also reports *Uncinula macrocarpa* on *Ostrya*.

Several species of the thelephoraceous genus *Aleurodiscus* have been reported. *A. oakesii* is common on the bark of standing *Ostrya virginiana* and *Quercus alba*, causing a flaking called bark patch. *A. botryosus* occurs on dead branches. These two amyloid-spored species are described by Lemke (*858*). *A. griseo-canus* has been reported from the Midwest and *A. strumosus* from Florida (*8*).

---

[31] Personal communication from Paul D. Keener, deceased, formerly plant pathologist, University of Arizona, Tucson, Ariz.

Ostrya is also host to many species of *Hypoxylon,* which fruit on dead stem and branch wood (*8*). The monograph of Miller (*978*) is recommended for identification, nomenclature, and synonymy in this genus.

Although *Botryosphaeria ribis* (*550*), *Diaporthe eres* (*1555*), and *Melanconis ostryae* appear on branches, their activity on *Ostrya* is saprobic.

An apparently systemic brooming disease of hophornbeam has appeared in several parts of Raleigh, N. C. The cause has not been demonstrated, but the symptoms and abundance of brooming on any given tree strongly suggest a virus origin.

Two true canker-forming fungi occasionally occur on *Ostrya* in the Northeast. *Nectria galligena* forms "target" cankers that shed the bark, while *Strumella coryneoidea* (*Urnula craterium*) cankers retain the bark. The bark on Strumella cankers bears black, powdery spore masses, and the wood decays behind the bark (*639, 661*).

Fusarium lateritium, a fungus that is saprobic on many woody plants but that also has many formae, e.g. on *Morus* and on *Pinus,* that cause cankers and dieback, was reported in a questionably pathogenic role on *Ostrya* twigs in Ohio (*8*).

Root rots have been attributed to *Armillaria mellea* and to *Clitocybe tabescens* (*1168*), but these fungi are not aggressive on *Ostrya.* Susceptibility to *Phymatotrichum omnivorum* was "moderate" in Texas tests (*1379*).

Poria obliqua, a fungus that causes mainly a heart rot of birch (see *Betula alleghaniensis*), also causes a similar rot of the heart of *Ostrya* (*151*). On living trees the fungus produces only a massive, clinker-like, aborted fruiting structure. On a fallen, rotted tree it will produce its brown *Poria* sporophore, on the underside of the snag.

Davidson et al. (*342*) reported on the cankers and decay associated with *Stereum murrayi* on beech, birch, maple, and *Ostrya.* They found decay in an *Ostrya* tree to extend 3 ft. above and below the canker. *S. murrayi* cankers were generally elongate, with depressed centers and swollen margins. Sporophores of the papery *Stereum* generally formed within the cankered area.

Fungi capable of causing either rot of the central cylinder, or rot at wounds of living *Ostrya* spp. include *Fomes connatus, F. igniarius,* and *F. ohiensis. Polyporus melanopus* fruits on the ground, attached to buried roots of *Ostrya.* It is stipitate, brown, and scurfy (*1067*).

Royal paulownia
Paulownia tomentosa

A fast-growing, deciduous ornamental from the Orient, the paulownia, or empress-tree, can grow to 40 ft. in height in 25 years. It bears large, showy, violet-colored flowers, and retains its clusters of large, ovoid fruit pods over winter. It has stout, spreading branches and make a dense shade. It is fairly hardy as far north as southern New England but is typically a tree of mild to warm regions. It sprouts prolifically from stumps and roots, and leaves on sprouts may be a foot or more wide. It is not demanding as to soil but does best on light loams (*51*). There are at least two described varieties, *pallida* and *lanata* (*1154*). The latter, when grown as far north as Montreal, dies back every year to the ground, and resprouts with shoots attaining a length up to 4 ft. and with leaves up to 2 ft. long (*51*).

Paulownia is not subject to any major diseases in the United States. The only common pathogen is *Phyllosticta paulowniae*, which produces small, uniform brown spots on the leaves. Two common powdery mildews, *Phyllactinia guttata* (*P. corylea*) and *Uncinula clintonii*, also develop on the foliage (*1338*), particularly on sprout leaves in late summer. *Ascochyta paulowniae* causes a leaf spot and produces hyaline, 1-septate, ellipsoid conidia in erumpent, unbeaked pycnidia.

A root rot is caused by *Armillaria mellea*. Tests showed paulownia to be resistant to Texas root rot (*1379*), suggesting its possible use as a shelterbelt tree in parts of the Southwest.

The twig fungi and root rots reported on paulownia in this country (*8*) are saprobes. However, *Polyporus robiniophilus* is a true heart-rot fungus that is known to decay the woody cylinder of living paulownia (see *Robinia*).

Avocado
Persea americana

The cultivated American avocado is generally regarded as native to Mexico, Central America, and parts of South America. While seedling trees may grow to a height of 60 ft., budded or grafted trees reach less than half that height. There are many named varieties, most of them with special attributes of site or climatic adaptation, disease resistance, size of fruit, shipping or marketing characteristics, or season of ripening. Orchard culture is practiced mainly in California and Florida and, to a lesser extent, in parts of the Southwest where temperatures do not fall below the middle twenties F.

Many consider the avocado a highly desirable ornamental, and for California and Florida, as Bailey (*51*) puts it, "The tree is worthy of a place in every dooryard for shade and ornament." The small, greenish flowers are produced in great abundance on loose axillary racemes. While it is not frost-hardy, Metcalf (*955*) mentions it as a distinctive, shiny-leafed, round-crowned tree widely used as an ornamental in southern California.

The preferred soil is a light, sandy loam. Whatever the soil, it must have good internal drainage if root rot is to be avoided. Slopes are desirable sites. In this country the tree goes into a semidormant state after the cool weather of winter. The culture of the avocado has much in common with citrus culture in California (*51*) with respect to propagation, fertilization, pruning, and watering.

Although many diseases have been reported for avocado, only one, Phytophthora root rot, is very serious; a few, including spot anthracnose and Armillaria root rot, are important; most are minor; and others affect fruit production or marketing and therefore are not dealt with here. Zentmyer et al. (*1661*), in their circular on avocado diseases in California, discuss only five diseases of the tree caused by pathogenic organisms, with Phytophthora root rot the most important. The others are Armillaria root rot,

Verticillium wilt, Phytophthora canker, and Dothiorella canker.

Mircetich and Zentmyer (*992*) found poor stands of avocado and *Persea indica* in the greenhouse to result from seed rot and root rot caused by *Rhizoctonia solani*. The pathogenicity of six isolates to avocado varied from none (citrus isolate) to highly pathogenic (avocado isolate). All were pathogenic to *P. indica*.

Foliage Diseases.—A green leaf scurf is caused by a leaf-spot alga, *Cephaleuros virescens*, in Florida. Velvety, red-brown to orange, cushiony patches are formed, and if the dense, reddish, hairy sporangia do not form, the spots remain green (*1555, 1599*).

An important leaf fungus in Florida, *Cercospora purpurea*, forms large, irregular, pale-brown spots or blotches, or necrosis without distinct margins. Fruiting is amphigenous; conidiophores olive-brown, multiseptate; conidia 1- to 9-septate and up to 100μ long (*260*).

Another cosmopolitan leaf fungus, occurring mainly in the South, is *Colletotrichum gloeosporioides* (*Glomerella cingulata*). This fungus causes a large leaf spot as well as a twig blight of many woody plants including citrus, magnolia, yellow-poplar, camphor, and privet. The disease is often referred to as withertip and is usually secondary to injury from some abiotic cause. Pink masses of 1-celled conidia, produced in acervuli with setae, are characteristic of the causal fungus.

A surface black mildew in Florida is caused by *Irene perseae*. Several other genera of black-mildew fungi occur on the closely related *Persea borbonia* (*8*). A powdery mildew (*Oidium* sp.) occurs in Florida.

A spot anthracnose, with typically small, epiphyllous spots, deep red coloration, and shot-hole effects is one of the most important avocado diseases in Florida. It occurs also in Texas. The *Sphaceloma* stage has an olivaceous coloration (*1555*).

Many deficiency diseases affect the foliage of avocado in both California and Texas. Zentmyer et al. (*1661*) provide suggestions for the diagnosis of deficiency diseases.

Stem Diseases.—The soil-borne vascular wilt fungus *Verticillium albo-atrum* (see *Acer*) is important in California, but not so serious as Phytophthora root rot. In the case of Verticillium wilt the leaves may wilt on one part of a tree or all over. Brownish streaks form in the wood of stems, roots, and branches. Mexican rootstocks are more resistant than Guatemalan (*1661*).

The only known virus disease of avocado is called sun blotch, because the lesions resemble sunscorch. The most consistent symptom, and the one most useful in diagnosis, is a streaking and spotting of the bark of twigs, limbs, and fruit (*1661*). The streaked areas may be depressed. Affected trees may bear clusters of leaves with a white or pink mottle or variegation. Some trees are symptomless carriers of the virus.

Dothiorella canker (*D. gregaria*, the conidial stage of *Botryosphaeria ribis* var. *chromogena*) (*550*) occurs on trunk and branches in California, and a similar disease occurs in Florida (see *Liquidambar*). A white powder exudes from the bark, and the outer bark cracks and drops off. Trees become unthrifty and may die back. Brownish discoloration of the shallow bark is followed by flaking (*1661*). The most severe manifestation follows attack of the lower trunk, and Guatemalan rootstocks have been girdled by these cankers. Inoculum is amply provided by fallen leaves. Mexican rootstocks are the least susceptible, and their use, together with high grafting, helps avoid losses from Dothiorella canker.[32]

A trunk canker of minor importance in California may be caused by either *Phytophthora cinnamomi* or *P. cactorum* (see *Arbutus, Citrus,* and *Cornus*).

Still another Phytophthora, *P. palmivora,* occasionally causes a seedling blight of avocado in California. The species of *Phytophthora* have been monographed by Waterhouse (*1511*). Seedlings in Florida have been killed by southern root rot (*Sclerotium rolfsii*) (*1555*).

In Florida the weak parasite *Physalospora rhodina* (*1484*), appearing mostly in its imperfect stage, *Diplodia. theobromae,* has been blamed for some dieback (see *Aleurites* and *Platanus*) and fruit rot.

Root Diseases.—The most important disease is the root rot caused by *Phytophthora cinnamomi.* This fungus thrives under conditions of poor soil drainage and excess soil moisture, because they aid spore formation, motility, and infection. Trees of any size can be affected. Zentmyer and his coworkers (*1661*) have subjected this disease on avocado to intensive study. Leaves emerge small, pale, or yellowish, and tend to drop early. New growth fails to appear. Branches die back, and the fruit crop diminishes. The feeder roots become black and brittle as they die. Lack of root regeneration leads to decline and death. In advanced cases it is difficult to find any feeder roots. The fungus can be isolated most readily by placing avocado fruit in a moistened soil sample, and if *P. cinnamomi* is in the soil, brown spots will appear on the fruit in 4 to 6 days. This technique is given in detail by Zentmyer, Paulus, and Burns (*1660*). Variety "Duke" rootstocks tend to resist Phytophthora root rot.

The shoestring root rot, caused by *Armillaria mellea,* occurs sporadically and is rated of only slight importance in California. Its southeastern counterpart, *Clitocybe tabescens* root rot, occupies a similar position in Florida. These two fungi are described and compared under *Citrus.*

Several species of *Pythium* (*957*) have, from time to time, been considered causes of root rot and decline of avocado in California, and *Sclerotinia sclerotiorum* (*1266*) as causing a collar rot; but these fungi do not rank in importance with the principal five described by Zentmyer et al. (*1661*) as causes of disease of avocado in California.

The avocado is resistant to root knot nematodes (*Meloidogyne*), but in susceptibility tests some damage to seedlings has been associated with soil infestation by burrowing nematodes (*Radopholus* spp.) and lesion nematodes (*Pratylenchus spp.*) (*259*). Ruehle (*1222*) lists many species of nematodes identified from roots or root zones of avocado. Avocado was highly susceptible to Texas root rot (*Phymatotrichum omnivorum*) in greenhouse tests (*1379*).

---

[32] Personal communication from George A. Zentmyer, professor of plant pathology, University of California, Riverside, Calif.

Miscellaneous Pathology.—A number of diseases affect avocado fruits, and many of these are mentioned briefly in the United States Index of Plant Diseases (8). A few are dealt with in greater detail in the California circular by Zentmyer et al. (1661) and other University of California releases.

Since avocado should be planted in well-drained soils, and since such soils, for example sands, tend to be low in certain essential minerals, avocados in both Florida and California have suffered from many deficiency diseases. Among these are a dieback in Florida from copper deficiency; a "little-leaf" rosette due to zinc deficiency in California; a "mottle-leaf" ascribed to mineral deficiency in California; and a tipburn regarded as possibly due to sodium chloride accumulation in poorly drained soil in both Florida and California (8).

Norway spruce
Picea abies

Norway spruce is a European species and the most important of the spruces of that continent. It is a fast-growing pyramidal tree with dark-green foliage that for many years has been grown widely in eastern North America and to some extent in the West but has escaped cultivation in parts of New England. In North America this tree occurs in most of the United States except the Gulf States. Rehder (1154) lists 30 cultivated varieties, with a wide range in form, foliar characteristics, and degree of pendency of branching.

Norway spruce in the United States has good form and grows well over a great range of soils (710) and has had therefore wide utility as an ornamental tree. It prefers a cool to moderately cold climate with air humidity higher than that typical of major parts of many of our western states. The tree is very hardy, and in tests reported by Parker (1080) it has withstood January temperatures as low as −72° F. However, there is great variability in hardiness depending upon provenance. It also stands high temperatures well for short periods, is tolerant, and is resistant to damage from ice and snow (310). It is very sensitive to fire, moderately susceptible to windthrow, and shoot tips are sometimes killed by late-spring frosts (279). Peace (1091) considers them very susceptible to spring frosts under European conditions.

In the United States, Norway spruce matures early, seldom exceeds 60 ft. in height, and does not often live past 100 years. This species was among those that either were uninjured or recovered well after heavy salt spray accompanying a New England hurricane (1632). However, salt applied to roads in New England has seriously damaged large Norway spruces immediately adjacent to the roads.

A comparison of the tolerance of Norway and Colorado blue spruce to the nematocide referred to as DBCP (857) indicated that after 12 weeks there were no differences between treated and untreated trees of either species at rates up to 172 lbs. DBCP per acre. Norway spruce was sensitive to fertilizer salt concentrations above 1.0 millimhos/cm. conductance.

Norway spruce is not subject to serious diseases in North Amer-

256

ica. Cytospora canker is quite common and can kill trees, and the life span for this tree is short compared to related native species. Insects, particularly spider mites, cause heavy damage to Norway spruce in the United States during certain years. In Europe the pathology of this species has had much attention, because many diseases have a major impact on the tree there, and the species is one of the principal timber trees of Europe.

Seedling Diseases.—In the nursery seedlings are subject to damping-off and root rot caused by *Fusarium* spp., *Pythium irregulare* (*1337, 1460*), *Rhizoctonia solani* (*1337*), *Phytophthora cinnamomi* (*304, 360*), *Sclerotium bataticola*, and *Cylindrocladium scoparium* (*296*). The foliage blight phase of *C. scoparium* infection, so spectacular with white pine, red pine, and some other species, rarely occurs with Norway spruce. Vaartaja (*1458*) has shown the pathogenicity of *Phytophthora cactorum* to this species in the laboratory. *Diplodia pinea* (*1513*) can cause a collar rot of seedlings, and *Ascochyta piniperda* (*538*) has blighted the young shoots of 4- to 5-year-old seedlings in a North Carolina nursery. *Botrytis cinerea* can cause a gray-mold blight of seedlings in wet spring weather (*538*). A yellowing and defoliation of white and Norway spruce at the Greenbush Nursery in Maine was associated with infection by a species of *Cladosporium*, but its pathogenicity has not yet been proved (*202*).

A disease of woody seedlings of many conifers called "basal stem girdle" results from excessive heat at the soil surface (*601*). Downward food movement is interrupted, resulting in swelling above the attenuated lesion area. As a result of soil surface heat non-woody seedlings can develop whitish lesions at the ground line that somewhat resemble damping-off symptoms (*601*).

Frost-heaving of seedlings has been reported where lack of mulch resulted in exposure of moist mineral soil (*710*).

A large number of nematodes in 12 genera have been found on roots, in roots, and in the soil around Norway spruce in North America and elsewhere in the world (*1222*). Sutherland (*1370*) showed Norway spruce to be an excellent host to *Paratylenchus projectus, Pratylenchus penetrans,* and *Tylenchus emarginatus.* See *Picea mariana* for further information on *T. emarginatus.*

Foliage Diseases.—In any case of widespread russeting, browning, and heavy shedding of needles, spider mites should be suspected, since Norway spruce is very susceptible to severe attacks. There are no major foliage diseases of Norway spruce in the United States. In the West foliage long under snow has been molded by *Herpotrichia nigra. Lophodermium piceae*, which causes a very important disease in Europe, is minor in North America, appearing only on old needles about to drop off from other causes (*323*).

Lophophacidium hyperboreum and *Sarcotrochila piniperda* cause snow blights (*1157*).

Stem Diseases.—By far the most important disease of ornamental Norway spruces in the United States is the canker caused by *Valsa* (*Cytospora*) *kunzei* var. *piceae* (*1519*). Basal branch cankers occur commonly on many conifers, but red and Norway spruce are particularly subject to girdling trunk cankers that are the more damaging. Copious resin flow is a major symptom. Jorgensen and Cafley (*765*) have studied this disease intensively in plantations of white and Norway spruce in Ontario and conclude the fungus to be a weak parasite, forming cankers mainly on unvigorous stems or branches and on trees with shallow roots. They suspect a relation between cankering and the roosting of birds. In Idaho Norway spruce is attacked by the larch dwarfmistletoe *Arceuthobium campylopodum* f. *laricis*.

The widespread hardwood canker fungus *Botryosphaeria ribis* sometimes uses dead coniferous twigs, including Norway spruce, as a substrate. Another harmless twig fungus is *Phoma piceina*.

The spruce yellow rust witches' broom, *Chrysomyxa arctostaphyli*, occurs occasionally on this species in the West. This rust has in the past been mistakenly considered synonymous with the yellow broom rust of fir, *Melampsorella caryophyllacearum*. This matter is explained further under *Picea engelmannii* and *P. rubens*.

A species of *Fusicoccum* has been reported to have caused much cankering of Norway spruce in Charlottesville, Virginia, following several dry years. Return to normal rainfall was accompanied by healing of the cankers[33].

Two species of *Tympanis*, *T. piceae* and *T. piceina*, occur occasionally on dead bark of Norway spruce (*552*).

Root Diseases and Trunk Rots.—Surprisingly little has been published on this subject in the United States. In Europe, Norway spruce is a prime target of *Fomes annosus*, which causes a major root rot in several countries. This fungus also has attacked this tree in Connecticut (*1337*).

Hosley (*710*) remarked on the freedom from root rot of even weakened Norway spruces in many planted stands in the Northeast. However, he found some cases of *Armillaria mellea* fruiting at the bases of living trees. *Polyporus schweinitzii* has also been known to attack this species in the United States (*1337*).

In planted Norway spruce in central New York, *Stereum sanguinolentum*, a major rot fungus of balsam fir, has caused extensive heart rot (*1180*) following pruning. In some trees both heartwood and sapwood had decayed, causing death.

Mycorrhizal Relations.—One hundred and two fungi have been reported to form mycorrhizae with Norway spruce. Of these, only 12 have been proved by pure-culture techniques (*1442*). The preponderance of literature on the structure and function of the mycorrhizal apparatus in this spruce is European.

Miscellaneous Pathology.—A rust of spruce cones, including those of Norway spruce in the Northeast, is caused by *Chrysomyxa pyrolae*, which produces aecia on the cones, aborting them, and stages II and III on species of *Moneses* and *Pyrola*.

Dead or senescent parts of Norway spruce cones are host to *Pestalotia* spp., possibly all referable to *P. funerea*. The cone scales may also harbor *Phoma strobiligena*.

Water-soaked areas occur in the heartwood of certain conifers including Norway spruce that probably have no connection with infections of any kind. Linzon (*868*) describes this type of wetwood in white pine.

Although not a North American report, it is deserving of mention that in Czechoslovakia (*243*) rod-shaped particles were found

---

[33] Personal communication from Caleb L. Morris, pathologist, Virginia Division of Forestry, Charlottesville, Va.

in the exudates of woody twigs of what the authors call "virus-diseased" Norway spruce trees. No virus disease had hitherto been reported among the gymnosperms.

Engelmann spruce
Picea engelmannii

A widely-distributed species, Engelmann spruce extends, often together with *Abies lasiocarpa*, southward from British Columbia and Alberta, Canada, to New Mexico and Arizona. This beautiful tree occurs on east slopes of the Cascades, through Washington and Oregon to northern California, and in the Rocky Mountains at high elevations (up to 11,000 ft.) from the Inland Empire, Utah, Wyoming, and Colorado to the Southwest (*19*). The crown of the tree has a narow, pyramidal form with deep blue-green foliage, and the trunk has little taper. Clusters of hanging branchlets give it a compact appearance, and open-grown trees are likely to have low living branches touching the ground. The needles emit an unpleasant odor when crushed (*279*).

Engelmann spruce occupies the highest and coldest forest environment in the Western United States. Mean annual temperatures range from 10° F. in January to 60°F. in July with extremes from −50° to 90° F. Frost may occur in any month. Snowfall is heavy, and precipitation ranges from 60 to 160 in. on the Pacific Coast to 25 to 45 in. inland (*19*). This species grows best on deep, well-drained loams, and does not develop well on soils that are either shallow, coarse, dry, or saturated. Good growth is commonly maintained for 300 years (*19*), and longevity is estimated at 500 to 600 years (*279*).

Demands for moisture are lower than for most associated species, and the tree resists winter-killing, possibly because of its high sap density (*75*). It is not resistant to summer drought, and its shallow root system makes it susceptible to windthrow (*19*). It is rated as tolerant by some (*54*) and very tolerant by others. Its thin bark makes it sensitive to fire.

Of 12 western conifers exposed to sulfur dioxide fumes from the ore smelter at Trail, British Columbia, Engelmann spruce was tenth in sensitivity. Of eight conifers exposed to similar fumes near Anaconda, Montana, this species was fourth in sensitivity (*1249*). It is less sensitive to the "red-belt" form of winter injury in Montana than associated pines and Douglas-fir (*1249*).

Nordin (*1042*) lists among the physiogenic diseases affecting spruce in Alberta, Canada: frost discoloration of foliage, frost cracks along the trunk, chlorosis due to unfavorable environment, flood injury resulting from beaver dams, hail damage, and lightning. Features of the pathology of Engelmann spruce in the United States are: high susceptibility of seedlings to damping-off; susceptibility to five needle rusts and one cone rust, all in the genus *Chrysomyxa*; attack by a common yellow witches' broom rust that is also in *Chrysomyxa*; and attack by a large number of root-, butt-, and trunk-rot fungi, which, in the aggregate, still fail to have Engelmann spruce considered a highly defective species.

Seedling Diseases.—Seed viability is good (69 percent), averaging higher than the germination percentage of associated species

(*1*). Engelmann spruce can also be reproduced by layering. Seedlings have a slow, feeble rooting habit and are thus very sensitive to heat (*19, 601*). Although drought, heat, cutworms, frost-heaving, damping-off, and rodents take their toll in the field, losses are no greater than those of associated species (*19*).

Rathbun-Gravatt (*1144*) concluded that poor germination of Englemann spruce resulting from damping-off fungi is due mainly to the destruction of radicles by fungi after emergence from the seed coat but before seedlings break through the soil. Such fungi can also decay unruptured seed. Emerging radicles were rotted by *Corticium vagum* (*Rhizoctonia solani*), *Pythium ultimum,* and *Fusarium sporotrichioides. Pestalotia funerea* and several other fungi failed to rot radicles. *Picea engelmannii* appeared more susceptible to seed decay than either of two pines (*Pinus resinosa* and *P. banksiana*) used in Rathbun-Gravatt's experiments.

Eliason (*408*) found that *Aphanomyces euteiches,* a root parasite of *Pisum sativum,* could cause damping-off of Engelmann spruce. He also isolated *Rhizoctonia solani* from diseased seedlings.

Both *Pythium debaryanum* and *Rhizoctonia solani* have caused damping-off in Texas, and *Pestalotia funerea* has been named as a cause of seedling blight. The last is a weak pathogen at best. *Fusarium scirpi* var. *acuminatum* (imperfect stage of *Gibberella acuminata*) has caused a snow mold of nursery trees in Colorado. In many cases of snow molds it is likely that suffocation preceded attack by the fungi.

Thelephora terrestris can grow copiously around seedlings and, while usually harmless, can smother foliage (*1540*).

The ring nematode *Criconemoides annulatum* has been found feeding externally on the roots of Engelmann spruce in Canada (*1222*).

Foliage Diseases.—The foliage of Engelmann spruce is subject to five needle rusts, and all are in the genus *Chrysomyxa* (*1237, 1239*). A sixth species attacks cones. *C. ledi* var. *cassandrae* has produced aecia on Engelmann spruce out of its range in the Lake States. Its II and III stages are on *Chamaedaphne calyculata. Chrysomyxa empetri* has been associated with this spruce in British Columbia (*1277*) and produces bright-orange uredia on *Empetrum nigrum* from New England to British Columbia. *C. ledi* produces aecia on spruce needles, and stages II and III on *Ledum* spp. from Connecticut to Nova Scotia to British Columbia. *C. ledicola* also produces aecia on the spruce needles, and stages II and III on *Ledum* spp. However, in *C. ledicola* the uredia and telia are epiphyllous and in *C. ledi* they are hypophyllous. *C. weirii* was considered by Arthur (*46*) to be a short-cycled form of the cone rust, *C. pirolata.* Savile (*1237*) doubts this. No pycnia and aecia are known for *C. weirii,* and its dull-orange, waxy telia are formed in spruce needles. This possible relationship of *C. weirii* to *C. pirolata* may be much like that of the short-cycled *Melampsora farlowii,* with its telia produced on species of *Tsuga,* to the long-cycled *M. abietis-canadensis,* which forms its aecia on *Tsuga* (*670*).

Three needle-cast fungi are known to attack Engelmann spruce. *Lophodermium macrosporum* (*L. filiforme*) has shiny, black hysterothecia of varying length and can severely defoliate understory trees or the lower branches of larger trees. It has been reported only from Colorado on this species of spruce (*323*) and on blue spruce. *L. piceae* appears only on old, senescent needles and is of no importance in North America, although it causes a major disease in Europe (*323*). *Bifusella crepidiformis* superficially resembles *L. macrosporum* but has bifusoid spores. In addition to the very conspicuous, wide, tarry, elongated spots that bear the ascocarps, with their 2-celled spores, a conidial stage also occurs, with clavate-to-cylindric spores $7-1.1\mu \times 4-7\mu$ (*1350*).

Herpotrichia nigra, the common non-pine, brown-felt snow mold, can damage foliage that has remained too long under snow (*1365*). While *H. nigra* occurs widely on western conifers outside the genus *Pinus*, Weir (*1534*) thought he found an additional species on Engelmann spruce in the Rocky Mountains. It had 5-septate ascospores, compared with 3-septate ascospores for *H. nigra*, so he named his new species *H. quinquiseptata*. However, Seaver (*1267*) concluded that *H. quinquiseptata* is based on the combined characters of two fungi—the mycelia and perithecia of *H. nigra* and the asci and spores of *Mytilidion* sp.—and thus there is no such species as *H. quinquiseptata*.

Dimerosporium (*Meliola*) *balsamicola* causes a sooty, surface mold on needles (*571*).

Stem Diseases.—Western spruce dwarfmistletoe *Arceuthobium campylopodum* f. *microcarpum* attacks Engelmann spruce in several areas in Arizona and New Mexico, especially where this tree is mixed with *Pinus flexilis*. It results in growth reduction, broom formation, and greatly accelerated mortality rates. Several other dwarfmistletoes occasionally occur on Engelmann spruce elsewhere in the West, but these are of no practical importance (*614*).

A common yellow witches' broom rust, *Chrysomyxa arctostaphyli*, is conspicuous on Engelmann spruce and can result in decay and mortality, but it is not often economically important. It has its telial stage on the bearberry *Arctostaphylos uva-ursi*. The hyperparasite *Cladosporium aecidiicola* (*777*) very commonly covers the aecial sori of the spruce broom rust. Peterson (*1105*) cites concentrated, damaging outbreaks of the spruce broom rust in southern Colorado and northern Arizona on Engelmann and blue spruce, and he presents data showing a marked correlation of broom rust with mortality in Engelmann spruce. The effects on growth were also determined.

Decay caused by *Fomes pinicola* and *Coniophora puteana* have been linked with stem damage by the spruce broom rust (*19*).

Valsa (*Cytospora*) *kunzei* causes a canker of Engelmann spruce in Colorado. Hawksworth and Hinds (*615*) found this fungus fruiting on diamond-shaped cankers from which resin flowed copiously. They suspect that hail damage may have preceded the attacks.

Swollen branch cankers bearing very numerous, black, papillate, spherical ascocarps, often devoid of spores, have been found on Sitka spruce (see *Picea sitchensis*) and have been very destructive to some young stands of Engelmann spruce in British Columbia. Funk (*486*) later found sporulating material and described the cause as the fungus *Botryosphaeria piceae*, with the black, gregarious ascocarps so characteristic of that genus.

Aleurodiscus amorphus, a so-called bark-patch fungus, is sometimes associated with shallow lesions on suppressed trees. It has flat, irregular apothecia (*587, 858*).

The saprophytes *Dasyscypha agassizii* and *D. arida* (*574*) in the West and *D. ellisiana* (*575*) in the East produce yellow-orange apothecia on dead bark. Among the other conspicuous saprobes are *Nectria cucurbitula*, with red perithecia; *Phomopsis occulta* (*570, 1277*), with two types of conidia; and *Rosellinia weiriana* which has very superficial, dark perithecia.

Davidson (*339*) has described a staining fungus, *Leptographium engelmannii*, that is important in a lethal tracheomycosis of Engelmann spruce following attack by the bark beetle *Dendroctonus engelmannii*. He also describes two other stain fungi, *Ophiostoma bicolor* and *O. truncicolor*, associated with this beetle, but of minor importance, and he mentions that the common sapstain fungus *Endoconidiophora coerulescens* has been isolated from beetle galleries near the ends of logs of Engelmann spruce.

Root Diseases.—*Armillaria mellea, Coniophora puteana, Fomes annosus, Polyporus balsameus, P. tomentosus* (*708, 724*), *P. dryadeus, P. schweinitzii, P. sulphureus, Poria subacida*, and *Sparassis radicata* have caused root and butt rots. All of these fungi have the capability of killing or leading to windthrow, but the only species that have a major potential for killing roots of Engelmann spruce in addition to rotting them are *A. mellea* (*848*), *F. annosus* (*151*), *P. dryadeus* (*885, 1539*), and *S. radicata* (*1538*). *S. radicata* has a thinly lobate sporophore with a large, perennial root stalk, and it attacks the bark first, then produces a brown, carbonizing rot of the root wood (*1538*). Hubert (*724*) gives ways of distinguishing *Polyporus tomentosus* rot from that of *Fomes annosus* and *Poria subacida*.

In a defect study in Colorado, Hornibrook (*708*) found the major root and butt fungi in mature and overmature trees to be *Polyporus tomentosus, Coniophora cerebella*, and *Armillaria mellea*, with *P. osseus* isolated only once. He describes the early and late stages of these rots and indicates deductions for defect for each. While decay made up 87 percent of all defect, butt rot made up only 14 percent, the remainder being trunk rot.

A yellow, stringy root rot caused by *Flammula alnicola* is common in Colorado and occurs occasionally on Engelmann spruce in Canada (*374*).

Trunk Rots.—Hornibrook (*708*) provides means of estimating trunk defect in mature and overmature Engelmann spruce and associated species in Colorado. Most of the cull was associated with specific indicators which, in order of importance, were conks, swollen knots, hollowing, decay evident in borings, crook and sweep, fire wounds, forks, cankers, frayed branch stubs, lightning scars, frost and wind cracks, and top injuries. Trunk rot made up 78 percent of the total defect and of this *Fomes pini* was responsible for 64 percent, and the remainder was accountable to *Peniophora luna, Stereum sanguinolentum, F. pinicola, Trametes serialis*, and *F. nigrolimitatus*. Descriptions of these rots and recommended scaling practices for them are provided.

Etheridge (*418, 420*) studied decay in subalpine spruce in Alberta, Canada. He cites earlier work of his own and others on decay in this group, which is made up of *Picea engelmannii, P. glauca* and its variety, *albertiana,* and *P. mariana.* Root rots made up 30 percent and trunk rots, 70 percent, of the decay cull. On a board-foot-volume basis, decay increased from 10 percent at 120 years to 16 percent at 190 years and to 26 percent at 310 years. The average pathological rotation was suggested at 190 years (*1042*). Etheridge (*418*) breaks down his data on the rot fungi and their role in decay, in part, as follows:

Fungus:	Total infections	Total decay volume
	Percent	*Percent*
White root and butt rots—		
Polyporus tomentosus	17	17
Flammula conissans	11	6
Unknown	6	3
Stereum sulcatum	0.5	0.3
Armillaria mellea	0.5	—
Undetermined	3	—
Brown root and butt rots—		
Coniophora puteana	5	2
Polyporus balsameus	0.5	0.2
Undetermined	4	1
White trunk rots—		
Fomes pini	15	34
Stereum sanguinolentum	19	14
Peniophora septentrionalis	8	11
Undetermined	5	7
Brown trunk rots—		
Trametes serialis	1	2
Omphalia campanella	0.5	0.2
Trametes heteromorpha	0.5	0.3
Lenzites saepiaria	0.5	0.1
Undetermined	1	0.3

Etheridge (*418*) describes the rots caused by the above fungi. The identity of some of them could be determined in the field, but many required culturing to identify the cause. Since the above table is based on three tree species, it does not accurately reflect the incidence of decay by fungi for any one. Etheridge[34] states that *S. sanguinolentum* was rare on Engelmann spruce, but *F. pini* caused a high proportion of the rot reported in this table.

The more important heart-rot fungi attacking Engelmann spruce in the Rocky Mountains of the United States are considered by some pathologists as *Fomes pini, F. nigrolimitatus,* and *P. tomentosus.* In parts of the Rocky Mountains *Echinodontium tinctorium, Hydnum coralloides, Fomes tenuis, F. officinalis, F. cajanderi (F. subroseus), Polyporus anceps, Poria isabellina,* and several other fungi are known to cause heart rot, occasionally, in this species (*1277*).

Mycorrhizal Relations.—The fungi regarded as forming mycorrhizae with Engelmann spruce are: *Amanita pantherina, Cenococcum graniforme, Lactarius deliciosus, Russula delica, R. emetica,* and *Suillus ruber* (*1442*).

---

[34] Personal communication from D. E. Etheridge, pathologist, Canada Department of Forestry, Forest Entomology and Pathology Branch, Sillery, Quebec.

Miscellaneous Pathology.—The rust *Chrysomyxa pirolata* produces aecia on spruce cones, has its stages II and III on *Moneses* spp. and *Pyrola* spp., and occurs in the East, West, and in Canada.

Mielke (*960*) studied the deterioration of beetle-killed Engelmann spruce in Utah and found the decay fungi to be as follows:

Rotting Trees

Standing and Down	Down
Armillaria mellea	*Lenzites sepiaria*
Fomes pini	*Polyporus alboluteus*
F. pinicola	*P. leucospongia*
F. nigrolimitatus	*P. ursinus (P. lapponicus)*
F. tomentosus	*P. abietinus*
	Stereum abietinum
	Trametes serialis
	T. variiformis

Coniophora corrugis also causes decay of dead sapwood of Engelmann spruce.

Gerry (*499*) describes red radial streaks in spruce wood resulting from abnormal medullary ray tissue, and also abnormal "giant" resin ducts.

Ips-infested Engelmann spruce is subject to staining by *Ceratocystis abiocarpa*, a new species earlier thought to be *C. penicillata* (*340*).

White spruce
Picea glauca

White spruce is a boreal species that, along with black spruce and tamarack, spans the entire North American continent in Canada. It dips into the United States in commercial quantity only in northern New England, northern New York, and the northern halves of Michigan, Wisconsin, and Minnesota. Nienstaedt (*1034*) presents a very good account of the silvical characteristics of white spruce. It grows in a cold climate with moisture conditions ranging from wet in Nova Scotia to semi-arid in Manitoba and on soils ranging from podzol clay to alluvial soils to peat. It does very well on the heavier soils and poorly on sandy soil. It will not thrive on very wet or very dry soil (see *Picea mariana*). A truly hardy tree, white spruce grows in areas of Canada and Alaska where the mean daily temperature is —20° F. For a conifer it can tolerate a wide soil pH range. White spruce soils are ordinarily between pH 5 and 7, but soils at 7.5 near the surface and higher at greater depths support the species. Lime-induced chlorosis has occurred in heavily limed nursery soils with a pH of 8.3 (*1034*). The altitudinal range of white spruce is from sea level along the Coasts to 5,000 ft. in the Rocky Mountains of Montana and Canada.

White spruce is a handsome, tolerant (*54*), medium-sized tree with blue-green foliage that has a disagreeable odor when crushed (*279*). This odor makes this tree undesirable as an indoor Christmas tree. It is shallow-rooted and subject to windthrow (*414*), sensitive to fire and flooding, and since it leafs out earlier than black spruce, it can be injured by late spring frosts (*1034*). It exhibits stunting, yellowing, and needle shedding, where phosphorus deficiency occurs on sandy worn-out soils, to a greater extent than several conifers associated with it in the Adirondacks (631). It is notably resistant to damage from salt spray (1632) and from ice and snow accumulations. There are many horticultural varieties useful as ornamentals in those North American and European areas with cold climates (1154). The largest trees have been estimated by Sudworth (1367) at between 250 and 350 years old, but in the Canadian Northwest trees up to 500 years old have been recorded (1034).

Wagg (1500) provides a monograph on the origin and development of white spruce roots. He discusses the many forms these roots take, including elongate-taproot form, restricted-taproot form, monolayered and multilayered forms, and many variations from normal.

Nordin (1042) gives a brief account of the physiogenic and pathogenic impacts to which western Canadian spruce, made up mostly of western white spruce, is subject. Among the physiogenic he mentions frost blight, frost cracks, chlorosis, flooding, hail damage, and lightning. Among the pathogenic he mentions damping-off, cankers, stains, root and trunk rots, snow blight, cone rust, foliage rusts, dwarfmistletoe damage, and tumors of unknown origin. In general, however, white spruce is not subject to serious disease impacts except for the important root and butt rots. Its pathology is characterized chiefly by rusts and root rots.

The drought resistance of white spruce seedlings is related to photoperiod (1459). This species has been injured by sulfur dioxide near oil refineries (869).

Mortality due to gamma irradiation has been found by Sparrow et al. (1332) to be related to interphase chromosome volume of shoot apical meristem cells. Tests were made with 12 species of trees on the harmful effects of 16-hour exposure to 50 to 18,000 r. of gamma rays from a cobalt-60 source. Since increase in injury was correlated with increase in chromosome volume, the order of species by most seriously injured first was *Picea glauca*, *Abies balsamea*, *Pinus strobus*, *Larix leptolepis*, *Sambucus canadensis*, *Taxus media*, *Thuja occidentalis*, *Quercus rubra*, *Fraxinus americana*, *Acer rubrum*, and *Betula alleghaniensis*. Hardwoods were damaged far less than conifers.

Shallow rooting, associated with a concentration of nutrients near the surface of sandy soils, has resulted in deterioration in plantations of white spruce in Quebec (1070). Summer drought had a role in this decline. Nutrient deficiencies on sandy soils also led to low volume production.

Seedling Diseases.—In the field, requirements for moisture, poor competitive ability with hardwoods and ferns, and smothering from hardwood leaves make early seedling development difficult. Seedlings growing on decayed wood do particularly well, are freer from damping-off, and may develop better mycorrhizal systems (1034). Snow blight (*Phacidium infestans*) can cause material losses in the nursery and the field when the seedlings have been under snow too long.

A striking and damaging disease of white pine, white spruce, and black spruce at the Chittenden Nursery in Michigan has been attributed to the root- and top-blight fungus *Cylindrocladium scoparium* (*33, 39*). Damage to white spruce has been light, compared to the other species mentioned.

A yellowing and defoliation of white and Norway spruce at the Greenbush Nursery in Maine was associated with infection by a species of *Cladosporium*, but its pathogenicity has not yet been proved (*202*).

Rhizina undulata caused some damage to white spruce and red pine seedlings in an area in a Maine nursery where slash had been burned (*336*). This fungus causes the roots to become rotted and matted.

Bloomberg (*128*) reported that white spruce seedlings died in patches when alfalfa hay was applied as a protective mulch at the Cranbrook Nursery in British Columbia, while no such dying occurred where this hay was not used. High *Rhizoctonia* sp. population followed application of the hay.

The snow blights (see Foliage Diseases) are important nursery diseases of white spruce in Canada.

In test tube tests of pathogenicity to the seedlings of many trees and non-woody plants, Vaartaja and Salisbury (*1464*) rate white spruce as moderately susceptible to attack by seven *Pythium* isolates (predominantly *P. debaryanum* and *P. ultimum*). Vaartaja and Cram (*1461*) found no evidence of pre-emergence damping-off of white spruce, inoculating with five fungi including *Rhizoctonia solani* and *Pythium* (*debaryanum* ?), but *R. solani* did cause a significant degree of post-emergence damping-off.

In experiments involving inoculation at time of seeding Whitney (*1569*) found *Rhizoctonia solani* and *Phytophthora cactorum* rapidly lethal to white spruce, but several other fungi including *Polyporus tomentosus* caused little mortality, and even that was slow in taking place. Vaartaja (*1458*) showed *P. cactorum* to be pathogenic, and *Fusarium* spp. are also known to attack white spruce seedlings.

The dagger nematode *Xiphinema americanum* has caused stunting and increased sensitivity to winterkill in greenhouse-raised seedlings of blue spruce and white spruce (*543*).

Root lesion nematodes *Pratylenchus penetrans*, heavily infesting the soil in which white spruce seedlings were growing in a Great Plains nursery, caused low vigor in the seedlings (*1097*). A large number of other nematodes have been found on and in white spruce seedlings (*1222*), and in the root zones.

White spruce seedlings in Canada proved to be excellent hosts to *Paratylenchus projectus, Pratylenchus penetrans,* and *Tylenchus emarginatus*, according to Sutherland (*1370*). He also discusses mycorrhizal aspects of nematode feeding. See *Picea mariana* for further information on *T. emarginatus*.

Foliage Diseases.—Five species of *Chrysomyxa* and one of *Pucciniastrum* cause needle rusts on white spruce in the United States, and additional species of *Chrysomyxa* occur in Canada (*1237, 1239*). These rusts result in the shedding of some of the new needles but would only have an economic impact on Christmas tree stock. *C. ledi* var. *cassandrae* produces aecia on spruce needles and stages II and III on *Chamaedaphne*. *C. chiogenis* has produced aecia on white and black spruce following needle inoculation, but

266

aecia have not been observed in the field. Stages II and III occur in the field on *Chiogenes* (*Gaultheria*) *hispidula*. *C. ledicola* produces aecia on spruce needles and stages SI and III on *Ledum groenlandicum*. *C. empetri* alternates between spruces and *Empetrum nigrum*. *Chrysomyxa weirii*, a short-cycled rust, has been reported on black and on white spruce in Quebec.

Pucciniastrum americanum in its II and III stages is widespread in the United States and Canada on *Rubus strigosus*, but aecia have been observed on white spruce, its only aecial host, only in Canada. *P. arcticum*, with stages II and III on other *Rubus* spp., occurs infrequently on white spruce, its only aecial host, in the United States and Canada.

Other needle diseases are very minor. *Lophodermium piceae* appears only on senescent needles and is of no importance in North America, although it causes a spruce disease of consequence in Europe (*323*). *Ascochyta piniperda* attacked young white and red spruce out of their range in a North Carolina nursery (*538*) and has also been reported in the Northeast. *Lophophacidium hyperboreum* and *Sarcotrochila piniperda* can cause a snow mold and blighting of needles on small trees and low branches of saplings (see *Abies balsamea*).

Ostreola consociata is a muriform-spored, lophiaceous fungus on white spruce needles in Quebec (*324*).

A new genus, *Lophomerum*, was erected by Ouellette (*1066*) to accommodate *L. darkeri*, a hypodermataceous fungus, on white spruce in Canada, and *L. septatum*, a similar fungus, on Sitka spruce in Oregon.

Stem Diseases.—White spruce has no major stem diseases. The eastern dwarfmistletoe *Arceuthobium pusillum*, which causes the most important disease of black spruce (*38*), is rare on white spruce except along the coast of Maine and in the Canadian Maritime Provinces. In Alberta, Canada, the lodgepole pine dwarfmistletoe *A. americanum* occasionally attacks white spruce. The plants of *A. pusillum* are less than an inch long, scattered along the branches; infections cause stunting, witches' brooms, and destruction of trees (*505*).

A canker often starting around the base of a branch and exhibiting copious resin flow is caused by *Valsa* (*Cytospora*) *kunzei* var. *piceae* (*1519*). Lower branches are the principal targets in white spruce, and trunk cankers are more common on red and Norway spruce. Jorgensen and Cafley (*765*) bring out the relation of drought to damage by this canker fungus in Ontario; and Ouelette and Bard (*1063*), in discussing a resinosis and canker of white and Norway spruce in Quebec, raise some questions concerning the nomenclature of the organism.

A common yellow witches' broom is conspicuous on many species of spruce, including white spruce, but does little damage. However, Peterson (*1103*), working with *Picea engelmannii*, has shown that the spruce broom rust, referred to commonly as *Peridermium coloradense* (*151*) to differentiate it from the fir rust, is really *Chrysomyxa arctostaphyli*, which has its III stage on bearberry, *Arctostaphylos uva-ursi*.

Tumors of the trunk, branch, or roots, with their origin at the pith, develop in epidemic proportions on white spruce along the seacoasts of northeastern America. Tsoumis (*1455*) describes them as varying from a few millimeters to a meter or more in diameter. He mentions extra wood rings on the tumor side, and traumatic resin canals. The cause is unknown, but insects, bacteria, and sea salt have been suspected.

Attacks on white spruce by the bark beetle *Dendroctonus piceaperda* lead to a lethal tracheomycotic blue-staining of the sapwood by *Ceratocystis piceaperda* (*1227*). An unimportant light stainer of spruce, fir logs, and lumber is *C. piceae* (*732*).

Two species of *Tympanis*, *T. piceae* and *T. piceina*, occur only occasionally on white spruce, inhabiting dead twig tissue (*552*); and three species of *Aleurodiscus*, namely, *A. amorphus*, *A. canadensis*, and *A. penicillatus*, fruit on dead bark or decorticated wood (*858*).

Root Diseases.—The Canadians have given much attention to the root rots of white spruce, since cull and windfall from this source cause much loss in Canada. Whitney (*1568*) found root wounds common on white spruce and highly correlated with rot infections. The percentages of his decay cases by kind of wound were: girdling *Hylobius* weevil wounds, 17 percent of the root-decay cases; non-girdling *Hylobius* wounds, 10 percent; root-crown injury, 9 percent; flooding, 7 percent; root cankers, 7 percent; dead root ends, 6 percent; compression wounds, 5 percent; animal trampling, 1 percent; and unknown, 38 percent.

Denyer and Riley (*375*), working with western white spruce (*Picea glauca* var. *albertiana*) in Alberta, found that root rot by *Polyporus tomentosus* and *Flammula alnicola* was responsible for 30 percent of the total decay volume, with some root rot also caused by *Armillaria mellea*, *Stereum sulcatum*, *Polyporus balsameus*, and a very few undetermined species.

Parker and Johnson (*1077*), working in the Prince George region of British Columbia, analyzed rot damage from the scarring of western white spruce. The root-rot fungi that entered through bole wounds were *Coniophora puteana* and *Corticium galactinum*. However, it is interesting that the following, mainly trunk-rot fungi, also entered, in a large percentage of cases, through root injuries: *Stereum sanguinolentum*, *Peniophora septentrionalis*, and *Fomes pinicola*. In the eastern Canadian Maritime Provinces, Davidson (*331*) reported *Corticium galactinum* and *Polyporus tomentosus* to be predominant root- and butt-rot fungi on white spruce.

Other root- and butt-rot fungi of white spruce are *Polyporus guttulatus*, *P. schweinitzii*, and *P. sulphureus*.

Nordin (*1042*) points out that in Canadian boreal spruce root rots made up 62 percent of the rot infections and accounted for 29 percent of the rot volume, while in subalpine spruce root rots made up 48 percent of the infections and accounted for 30 percent of the rot volume.

Whitney (*1569*) found that root rot caused by *Polyporus tomentosus* was a major cause of the slow decline and death of white spruce in patches of an acre or more in Saskatchewan. The fungus commonly entered roots at points of contact with infected roots. Injury by *Hylobius* weevils as well as soil factors (*1468*) were also associated with this "stand-opening disease." In culture, attack by

P. tomentosus was slow, following involvement of root tips. Whitney (*1570*) successfully inoculated small, woody roots by several methods. Death of planted white spruce in Quebec has also been attributed to this fungus. Gosselin (*525*) gives a major account of it on Canadian spruce, on both seedlings and large trees, and also discusses its taxonomy.

A yellow, stringy root rot of conifers in Canada, including white spruce, is caused by the agaric *Flammula alnicola,* erroneously referred sometimes to *F. conissans* (*374*).

Davidson and Redmond (*335*), working on decay in red and white spruce in the Canadian Maritime Provinces, found the principal root and butt fungus of white spruce to be *Corticium galactinum,* followed by *Polyporus tomentosus, Coniophora puteana,* and 10 other fungi. *C. galactinum* did not occur in the red spruce, but in that species, *Poria subacida* predominated. *Merulius himantioides* causes a brown cubical rot of white spruce in Canada.

Trunk Rots.—Parker and Johnson (*1077*) in their spruce and fir decay studies in British Columbia found *Stereum sanguinolentum* to be the main trunk-rot fungus in western white spruce, with *Peniophora septentrionalis* also commonly entering bole wounds, while the other fungi associated with wounding (*Coniophora puteana, Fomes pinicola,* and *Corticium galactinum*) seldom developed rot beyond the butt section.

In Alberta, Denyer and Riley (*375*) found that in addition to the fungi already mentioned as root-rotters decay of the main trunk was caused by *Fomes pini,* the predominant heart rot, and also by *Stereum sanguinolentum* and *Peniophora septentrionalis,* with occasional rot cases caused by other fungi.

Nordin (*1042*), in Alberta, found decay-cull percentage in boreal spruce to rise from 4.5 percent at age 120 to 12 percent at age 160. Decay indicators are not common enough to be of much use in estimating decay in this spruce.

In the Canadian Maritime Provinces, Davidson and Redmond (*335*) found that cull percentage due to rot reached its maximum at age 150 to 180 years, when it reached 22 percent in white spruce and only 5 percent in red spruce. Butt rot accounted for more loss than trunk rot.

Basham and Morawski (*73*), in Ontario, found that, as with black spruce, decay in white spruce was too low (under 7 percent maximum) to be a factor in management. Also, as with black spruce, the most important rot fungi were *Corticium galactinum, Polyporus tomentosus,* and *Fomes pini.*

In the Northeast and the Lake States *Fomes pini* is considered the most important heart-rot fungus in white spruce, with *F. officinalis, F. pinicola,* and *F. cajanderi* (*F. subroseus*) playing a smaller role (*1034*). *F. pinicola* is mainly a decayer of the wood of dead trees or damaged areas in living trees.

Mycorrhizal Relations.—Only *Cenococcum graniforme* has been reported a mycorrhizal associate of white spruce (*1442*). The mycorrhizal role of *Polyporus tomentosus* is greatly in doubt. This fungus is ultimately pathogenic to white spruce. While Gosselin (*525*) felt that he had evidence that this fungus is mycorrhizal, Whitney (*1572*) consistently failed to produce mycorrhizae with it when placed in flasks containing seedlings.

Miscellaneous Pathology.—An ascomycetous fungus, *Coryne sarcoides*, that is commonly associated with root- and heart-rot fungi in white spruce and other species (*1573*) was shown by Etheridge (*419*) to produce a substance antibiotic to *Polyporus tomentosus* and to *Coniophora puteana*. All three fungi were isolated from white spruce.

Riley and Skolko (*1178*) studied the rate of deterioration in spruce (mostly white spruce) on the Gaspé Peninsula of eastern Canada, that had been killed by the European spruce sawfly and the spruce budworm. Sapwood deterioration was much faster for the sawfly-killed trees than for those killed by the budworm. By the fifth year there was a 50 percent reduction in usable wood because of saprot, breakage, and red stain (early *Fomes pini* attack) in the sawfly-killed trees. The fungi responsible for most of the sapwood rot were *F. pinicola* and *Polyporus abietinus*, with *Stereum sanguinolentum* and *P. volvatus* much less important.

Following windthrow, white spruce and alpine fir deteriorated at about the same rate in British Columbia (*414*), but by the tenth year decay had destroyed 77 percent of the spruce wood and only 29 percent of the fir wood. In this study Engelhardt et al. (*414*) found that three fungi accounted for most of the decay: *Stereum sanguinolentum*, *Polyporus abietinus*, and *Fomes pinicola*. However, while *F. pinicola* accounted for 67 percent of the rot in white spruce after 10 years, it accounted for only 14 percent of the fir rot in that same time.

A cone rust of white and other spruces is caused by *Chrysomyxa pirolata*. Aecia are produced on the spruce cones and stages II and III on species of *Moneses* and *Pyrola*. The rust occurs from Canada and the Lake States south to Maryland.

Small clefts in white spruce wood in Alaska are attributed by Lutz (*896*) to collapse resulting from an imbalance between rate of water loss and water replenishment.

Nordin (*1042*) refers to burls and galls of unknown origin occurring on some white spruce trees in Canada.

Molnar and Silver (*999*) reported a high build-up of *Pullularia pullulans* in white spruce buds in a Canadian stand severely infested with the spruce budworm. They suspect that this fungus may have a deleterious effect on the infected buds. *P. pullulans* has often been suspected of having pathogenic potentialities, but experimental proof is lacking.

Black spruce

Picea mariana

Black spruce is an abundant boreal species that spans the North American continent in Canada from Newfoundland to the Bering Strait. However, its commercial range in the United States is virtually confined to far-northern New England and northern Michigan, Wisconsin, and Minnesota, with minor extensions southward. Heinselman (*632*) has compiled an excellent account of the silvical characteristics of this species. It grows in a cold, subhumid climate, withstanding winter temperatures below —50° F. in the far North and summer temperatures as high as 94° F. at the southeastern limit of the range. Precipitation is moderate, with more than half of it falling during the short growing season.

Black spruce can occupy either mineral or organic soils. In the United States, it occurs mainly in bogs and seepage accumulations. Peaty swamps commonly support this species, and most stands in these bogs make poor growth. The better stands in the United States are around bog margins, and on the Laurentian Shield in northeastern Minnesota, where the tree grows on very moist, heavy, mineral soils on gentle slopes and in lowlands. Although the best growth occurs on the deeper, better drained, moist, mineral soils, black spruce is usually a minor component of stands on these sites (854), being unable, there, to compete with associated species that grow faster (853).

Black spruce is mainly a small- to medium-sized tree, and it is shallow-rooted and very subject to windthrow (632). It is thin-barked, resinous, and is killed readily by crown or ground fires, but its semiserotinous cones often provide heavy reseeding after fire. Even though it is a wet-land species, it is notably vulnerable to flooding or to any unusual rise or fall in the normal water levels such as result from beaver dams and highway fills. The species is tolerant (54)—narrow-crowned, with drooping branches (279), thus suffering little from ice or snow accumulations—and lives to ages in excess of 200 years.

Drought has been found to be the cause of a conspicuous reddening and defoliation of young black and white spruce in both mucky depressions and well-drained sites over extensive areas in Saskatchewan. Denyer and Riley (376) describe and illustrate this damage.

Layering makes up much of the reproduction of black spruce, along with seedlings and a form of reproduction called "rootlings." Rootlings form from roots near the surface that produce buds capable of producing stems (855).

The pathology of black spruce in the United States is characterized by major attack by the only eastern dwarfmistletoe, by needle-shedding resulting from four needle rusts in the genus *Chrysomyxa*, and by a large amount of uprooting and wind breakage due to root and butt rots, resulting in the commonest cause of mortality in mature and overmature stands of this species.

Seedling Diseases.—Heavy first-year seedling mortality in the field can result from lack of early summer rainfall, from heat, flooding, moss encroachment (853, 1187), insect feeding, damping-off, and frost-heaving. The snow-blight fungus *Lophophacidium hyperboreum* (*Phacidium infestans*) and, to a lesser extent, *Sarcotrochila piniperda* (*Phacidium expansum*) can seriously damage seedlings. Both fungi attack *Picea abies, P. glauca, P. mariana*, and *P. rubens*. Boyce (151) gives a lucid account of the "snow blights" as they appear in the field. The complicated taxonomy of the causal organisms is clearly explained by Reid and Cain (1157), and by Korf (807). The snow blights become evident following snow-melt, by subepidermal apothecia forming on browned foliage after long periods under snow. In nursery beds these blights tend to develop involving patches of seedlings 2 ft. or more across.

Black spruce is subject to damping-off, seedling root rot, and heat lesions (601), as well as to "sore shin," the last a disease of

271

seedlings over one year old that is characterized by lesions on one side of the stem, and differing from heat lesions in being oriented in any direction, rather than just southerly (*360*). Vaartaja (*1458*) has shown the pathogenicity of *Phytophthora cactorum* to black spruce in the laboratory. *Fusarium* spp. are associated with damping-off in Quebec.

An important seedling root rot and top blight on several conifers, including black spruce, in Minnesota, is caused by *Cylindrocladium scoparium* (*33, 192*). Microsclerotia form in the root cortex and the needles. Symptoms include stunting and chlorosis, followed by the needles turning reddish brown, and then death of the seedlings (*193*).

At the Chittenden Nursery in Michigan, where heavy mortality to white pine was earlier attributed to a fungus-nematode complex, Anderson and Anderson (*32*) found that *C. scoparium* occurred there, and also that black spruce and red pine were also highly susceptible. Isolates of *Rhizoctonia* sp. did little, if any, damage to seedlings raised in inoculated soil.

Thelephora terrestris will grow around black spruce seedlings. It seldom produces growth so copious that it smothers the seedlings (*1540*), and it may well be a mycorrhizal fungus. Sutherland (*1370*) showed black spruce seedlings, in a Canadian nursery, to be very good hosts to *Paratylenchus projectus, Pratylenchus penetrans,* and *Tylenchus emarginatus.*

Tylenchus emarginatus fed and reproduced as an ectoparasite on the roots of seven conifer seedlings tested by Sutherland (*1371*). He describes the mode of parasitism on black and red spruce. He computed that one such nematode could cause 576 wounds on a seedling root in 24 hours. *T. emarginatus* did not feed on any of 10 soil fungi exposed to it.

Foliage Diseases.—The black spruce needle rusts are scarcely economic parasites, but they can cause enough defoliation to interfere with use for Christmas trees (*632*). Savile (*1237, 1239*) has given special attention to the taxonomy and host relationships of the genus *Chrysomyxa,* in which the black spruce rust species fall. *C. ledi* var. *cassandrae* produces aecia on spruce needles, and stages II and III on *Chamaedaphne calyculata. C. ledi* and *C. ledicola* produce aecia on spruce needles, and stages II and III on *Ledum* spp., from Connecticut north to Nova Scotia and west to the Lake States. In *C. ledi* the uredia and telia are epiphyllous and in *C. ledicola* they are hypophyllous. *C. chiogenis* has produced aecia following inoculation of black spruce needles and produces stages II and III on *Chiogenes (Gaultheria) hispidula.* The last species of rust has not been observed on spruce in the field. *Chrysomyxa weirii,* a short-cycled rust, has been reported on black and on white spruce in Quebec (see *Picea engelmannii*).

The snow blights caused by *Sarcotrochila piniperda* and *Lophophacidium hyperboreum* (*1157*) can materially damage the foliage of small trees and needles on the lower branches of saplings in the field.

Two needle-cast fungi (*323*) attack black spruce. One, *Lirula macrospora (Lophodermium macrospora, L. filiforme)*, which has shiny, black hysterothecia of varying lengths, can severely defoliate understory trees or the lower branches of larger trees, but it is known only from localized areas. Darker (*323*) mentions that in eastern America, *Naevia piniperda*, a fungus with innate, waxy apothecia, has always been found in association with *Lirula macrospora*. The other needle-cast fungus, *Lophodermium piceae*, appears only on old senescent needles and is of no importance in North America although it causes a major spruce disease in Europe.

A new phacidiaceous genus, *Micraspis*, has been erected by Darker (*325*) to accommodate the black spruce needle species *M. acicola* from Ontario.

Herpotrichia nigra, a common, brown snow mold of conifers in the West has been reported from the Canadian Maritime Provinces.

Stem Diseases.—The most damaging stem disease is the eastern dwarfmistletoe caused by *Arceuthobium pusillum*. Its preferred host is black spruce, on which it causes witches' brooms, stunts growth, and can lead to early death. The dwarfmistletoe shoots are only 12 to 20 mm. high, brownish green, and scattered along the branches (*505*). Anderson and Kaufert (*38*) fully describe the brooming responses of black spruce to dwarfmistletoe infection, and place this disease as one of the most serious affecting black spruce. Brooms can replace the entire crown of small trees.

Bonga (*139*) described and illustrated a most unusual witches' broom, caused by *A. pusillum*, with an open, ascending habit, and bearing distally, mature cones with viable seeds.

A common yellow witches' broom (*Chrysomyxa arctostaphyli*) is conspicuous on several species of spruce including black spruce (see *Picea glauca*).

Cankers attributed to *Valsa kunzei* have been reported on black spruce in Canada.

Dasyscypha agassizii and *D. calycina* (*574*) are saprophytic inhabitants of dead bark and fruit, conspicuously producing yellow-orange apothecia.

Attacks on black spruce by the spruce bark beetle, *Dendroctonus piceaperda*, lead to a lethal blue-staining of the sapwood. The blue-stain fungus is probably either *Ceratocystis piceaperda*, reported in such an association on white spruce by Rumbold (*1227*), or a related species.

Aleurodiscus lividocoeruleus fruits on dry, decorticated wood, and occurs widely (*858*).

Root Diseases.—Root and butt rots of black spruce are caused mostly by *Armillaria mellea* (*887*), *Coniophora puteana*, *Polyporus schweinitzii* (*887*), *P. tomentosus* (*724*), and *Stereum abietinum*, with many other fungi, including *Corticium galactinum* and *Polyporus borealis*, causing occasional root rot of this species (*8, 887*). It is chiefly these fungi, together with black spruce's shallow roots and lack of a taproot, that result in such heavy losses from windthrow and wind breakage in old or damaged timber. In Alberta, Canada, *Coniophora puteana* caused more butt rot in black spruce than in any other spruce. This information, supplied by Etheridge personally, does not show in his rot-fungus table reproduced here under *Picea engelmannii*.

A yellow, stringy root rot caused by *Flammula alnicola* and a brown, cubical butt rot caused by *Polyporus hirtus* occur occasionally in black spruce in Canada (*374*).

Gosselin (*525*) gives a full account of damage to Canadian spruce by *Polyporus tomentosus,* and also deals with the taxonomy and nomenclature of this organism.

Trunk Rots.—All of the fungi mentioned as root- and butt-rotters will invade the trunk, with *Armillaria mellea* making the least bole penetration. In addition, many other fungi chiefly rot the trunk, and can extend somewhat into the roots. The more important of these heart-rot fungi on black spruce in the Lake States (*887*) appear to be *Fomes pini, F. pinicola, F. cajanderi* (*F. subroseus*), and *Stereum sanguinolentum,* of which the first and last, together with the butt-rotters, become factors in the management of black spruce on upland sites at from 70 to 100 years, and in swamp stands between 100 to 130 years of age (*632*).

Lavalle (*839*), in Quebec, found that in black spruce broken tops were the main points of entry of trunk-rot fungi, with trunk wounds second. *Fomes pini* and *Stereum sanguinolentum* were the main rot fungi.

Basham and Morawski (*73*), in a major study across Ontario, found a maximum of only 3.4 percent rot-cull in black spruce, regardless of age class, in stands up to 220 years old. Seventeen Hymenomycetes were isolated more than once, with most of the rot accounted for by *Fomes pini, Polyporus tomentosus,* and *Corticium galactinum. F. pini* was the only fungus consistently associated with trunk rot, with *S. sanguinolentum* and *Peniophora septentrionalis* causing occasional decay. Much of the *F. pini* butt rot apparently originated from basal wounds or from roots. The authors provide descriptions of the wood attacked by the main fungi.

Mycorrhizal Relations.—The mycorrhizal associates reported for black spruce are *Cenococcum graniforme, Gomphidius septentrionalis,* and *Polyporus tomentosus* (*1442*). Gosselin (*525*) shows photographs of black spruce seedlings infected with *P. tomentosus,* revealing an ectotrophic mantle and Hartig network. He also found seedling root rot caused by the fungus, and felt that it could be both beneficial and harmful. However, Whitney (*1572*) consistently failed to produce mycorrhizae with *P. tomentosus* in flasks containing spruce or pine seedlings, and doubts a mycorrhizal capability of this fungus.

Miscellaneous Pathology.—A bunchy appearance of the crowns of some black spruce trees results from red squirrels clipping the cones. Sometimes, large bunches of these persistent cones accumulate in localized areas of the crown, giving the appearance of a witches' broom with cones (*632*).

A cone rust of black spruce and other spruces is caused by *Chrysomyxa pirolata.* Aecia are produced on the spruce cones and stages II and III on species of *Moneses* and *Pyrola.* The rust is known from Canada and the Lake States south to Maryland.

Etheridge and Morin (*424*) studied the bacterial and fungus flora of normal wood of living black spruce and balsam fir (see *Abies balsamea*).

Blue spruce
Picea pungens

One of the most beautiful conifers anywhere, blue spruce is widely grown as an ornamental in North America and abroad, but is minor as a forest species. Its silver-blue foliage, most distinctive while the trees are young, varies from tree to tree (*1368*), and clones with the bluest and longest needles are those most widely propagated. Rehder (*1154*) recognizes seven horticultural varieties. In nature, blue spruce occurs singly or in patches, at elevations of 6,000 to 10,000 ft., in moist, gravelly, fairly fertile soils, usually along stream banks, in restricted areas in the Rocky Mountains from Montana to Arizona and New Mexico (*279*). Although its widespread use as an ornamental implies adaptability to a variety of soils, sites, and climatic regimes, this species rarely does well planted in stands, except in its restricted optimum natural range. It does not thrive in the lower elevations of the South.

Colorado blue spruce is subject to winter drying, a condition brought about when unseasonable, warm, drying winds cause more water to be lost in transpiration than can be replaced when the soil is frozen or very cold.

Blue spruce is intermediate in tolerance (*54*), sensitive to fire, hardy, and grows slowly. It is very resistant to salt-spray injury (*1005, 1632*). Baxter (*78*) notes that species with bluish color, such as blue spruce and white fir, resist chinook conditions (cold followed by sudden rises in temperature) and winter drying, better than species with greener foliage. In nature, large trees over 400 years old have been reported, and a probable maximum longevity of 600 years is postulated (*1368*). While it is a prolific seeder, ornamental stock is obtained mainly by grafting, using stocks of Norway spruce or other spruce species (*279*).

For tolerance of blue spruce to the nematocide DBCP, see *Picea abies*. This species has been injured by sulfur dioxide near oil refineries (*869*).

Seedling Diseases.—Blue spruce is subject to damping-off, and a seedling root and collar rot caused by *Phytophthora cinnamomi* has caused losses in a Maryland nursery (*304*).

Large populations of the nematode *Xiphinema americanum* decreased root growth of blue spruce seedlings, and were particularly damaging in their effect on winter survival. A large percentage of the young trees in heavily infested soil died from winterkill (*543*).

Root lesion nematodes, *Pratylenchus penetrans*, heavily infesting the soil in which blue spruce seedlings were growing in a Great Plains nursery, caused low vigor in the seedlings (*1097*). Twenty-four other species of nematodes have been reported associated with the roots of white spruce. Few of these have been known to cause damage (*1222*).

Ferris and Leiser (*440*) determined the identity of plant pathogenic nematodes in 7 genera associated with nursery-grown blue spruce in Indiana. Although DBCP was used for control at dosages considered much too low for phytotoxicity, nevertheless, applications caused damage in many of the treated beds.

Blue spruce seeds were tested for germination capacity and germination speed after treatments with eight pesticides, applied before and after stratification. Only one pesticide, an organic mercury, reduced germination speed significantly when applied before stratification. Some, however, were very detrimental (two were lethal) when applied after stratification, and still others were harmless (*298*).

Foliage Diseases.—Three species of *Chrysomyxa*, a genus studied intensively by Savile (*1237, 1239*), cause needle rusts of blue spruce in the United States, and a fourth causes witches' brooms. *C. ledi* var. *cassandrae* produces aecia on spruce needles in the northern states and Canada, and stages II and III on *Chamaedaphne calyculata; C. ledi* and *C. ledicola* produce aecia on spruce needles in the northern states and Canada, and stages II and III on *Ledum groenlandicum.* These rusts can cause a moderate amount of shedding of the new needles. The rust hyperparasite *Cladosporium aecidiicola* often covers all of the rust sori on a given needle.

Lophodermium piceae, which has caused a serious disease of spruce in Denmark, is unimportant in North America because it occurs only on senescent needles about to drop from other causes, or in densely shaded or wet situations (*323*). *Lirula macrospora* (*Lophodermium filiforme*) occurs on blue spruce in Colorado.

Waterman (*1516*) reported *Rhizosphaera kalkhoffii* to be associated with a severe needle cast of 25-year-old blue spruce in a plantation in Connecticut. It is also known on blue spruce from Virginia. The small, round, black, surface pycnidia with their origins in stomatal openings are diagnostic. Some trees have lost all but the current year's needles as a result of infection.

In the West, the brown-felt snow mold *Herpotrichia nigra* can destroy foliage that remains too long under snow (*151*).

Stem Diseases.—In Arizona and New Mexico, blue spruce is subject to attack by the western spruce dwarfmistletoe, *Arceuthobium campylopodum* f. *microcarpum.* Damage can be severe in local areas. This forma resembles forma *cyanocarpum* in the tendency of the parasite shoots to be scattered along the branches rather than occurring in tufts (*505*).

A stem disease of some importance to ornamental blue spruce is the canker caused by *Valsa* (*Cytospora*) *kunzei* var. *piceae.* On this tree species, branch cankers and twig blight are much more common than trunk cankers. Resin flow may be heavy, and the cankers may bear small, black pycnidia (*1519*).

Ascochyta piniperda has been reported as causing a shoot blight of young red, Norway, and blue spruces, characterized by a downward bending of the attacked shoots (*538*). This fungus has killed many seedlings and 1- to 4-year-old trees in German nurseries. Symptoms, there, are a darkening, browning, and casting of young needles, with drooping shoot tips on the weaker plants and seedlings. The bent tips often bear dead needles on which pycnidia form, and these release spores in wet weather.

Phomopsis occulta (*570*) is a saprophyte, sometimes appearing on dead twigs. It is not associated with lesions or resin flow. Three species of *Dasyscypha, D. arida* (*576*), *D. ellisiana* (*575*), and *D. oblongospora* (*574*), occur on dead bark where they produce their yellow-orange apothecia.

Yellow witches' brooms caused by *Chrysomyxa arctostaphyli* occur in abundance on blue spruce in parts of Arizona. This rust, earlier called *Peridermium coloradense,* is now known to form stage III on *Arctostaphylos uva-ursi* (*1103*), and to be distinct from the fir rust *Melampsorella caryophyllacearum,* which has stages II and III on *Cerastium* and *Stellaria* (*46*). The aecial sori of the *Chrysomyxa* on spruce may be covered with the hyperparasite *Cladosporium aecidiicola*.[35] A *Nectria* sp. fruits on old brooms of the rust. Peterson (*1105*) gives a very good account of the spruce and fir broom rusts, and mentions that the spruce rust is particularly damaging to blue and Engelmann spruce in southern Colorado and northern Arizona.

Root Diseases and Trunk Rots.—In pathogenicity tests, blue spruce has been only moderately susceptible to Phymatotrichum root rot (*P. omnivorum*) (*1379*). *Armillaria mellea* (*848*) and *Polyporus tomentosus* (*724*) cause root rots in the native range of the tree but, while common, damage has been slight.

The principal heart-rot fungus is *Fomes pini*. Blue spruce trees are usually old before heart rot becomes a factor. Since the wood properties of blue spruce are poor, the tree is not of commercial importance for its wood and, therefore, the heart rots have not had much attention.

In addition to red heart (*Fomes pini*) and to the butt rots already mentioned, the fungi that are known to decay the wood of living trees are *F. pinicola, Polyporus borealis,* and *P. caesius.*

Mycorrhizal Relations.—Only *Cenococcum graniforme* is reported to form mycorrhizae with blue spruce (*1442*). Wright (*1618*) cites some unpublished work by Stoeckeler, conducted in North Dakota, to the effect that Rocky Mountain ponderosa pine appeared to be less responsive to mycorrhizae than jack pine or blue spruce at one nursery, while the reverse was true at another nursery. At the second nursery, a combination of acidification and inoculation resulted in an increase in the percentage of plantable ponderosa pine stock produced.

Red spruce
Picea rubens

Red spruce is one of the most important conifers in northeastern North America. It extends from Nova Scotia, New Brunswick, and Quebec, where it grows near sea level, southwestward to central New York and southward along the highest elevations of the Appalachian Mountains to North Carolina and Tennessee, where it is confined to elevations above 4,000 ft. It grows best in cool, moist situations, and withstands extremes from —30° to 95° F., with recorded extremes of —40° to 100° F. (*596*). Given adequate soil moisture and a pH of 4.0 to 5.5, red spruce will thrive on soils of various depths and textures, some of which are thin and largely organic. It is not a swamp species, but will grow close to marshes and sometimes in wet soil. Hart (*596*) makes a statement on red spruce that could be made for many tree species that grow in rigorous situations, "The tree occurs most commonly where conditions are not ideal for its own growth but are even less favorable for its competitors." The ecology of red spruce is described, and its silviculture and management discussed by Murphy (*1007*), by Westveld (*1558*), and many others (*596*).

Its thin bark and resinous secretions (spruce chewing gum was

---

[35] Personal communication from Paul D. Keener, deceased, formerly plant pathologist, University of Arizona, Tucson, Ariz.

once an article of commerce) of red spruce make it very sensitive to fire injury, and its shallow root systems make it subject to windthrow. It is tolerant to very tolerant, ranking about with balsam fir in this respect (54), and responds well to release. While the similar but exotic *Picea abies* does well as an ornamental in many urban and suburban situations, red spruce, like its common associate balsam fir, has not thrived except in environments very similar to those of its natural habitat. Estimates of longevity put the maximum age at about 400 years (596). Red spruce leafs out very late, and this characteristic minimizes the danger of damage from late spring frosts. In Connecticut, it was defoliated by salt spray from a hurricane (1005).

Pomerleau (1125) reported a severe winter browning of red spruce in Quebec, Canada, associated with abnormally warm March weather:

Seedling Diseases.—In nature, first-year spruce seedlings are subject to many destructive forces including dryness, heat at the soil surface, frost-heaving, fungi, and smothering or crushing by forest litter or snow. However, after the first year losses are light (596). In the nursery, seedlings are subject to damping-off and, while few named fungi have been reported specifically in connection with red spruce nursery diseases (*Rhizoctonia sp.* is one, 1), it is likely that some of the species of *Pythium, Phytophthora, Fusarium,* and other genera of fungi that are known to attack other spruces and other conifers also can cause damping-off and root rot in red spruce. One- to two-year-old seedlings sustained top damage, including an angular tip-bending, from *Rhizoctonia* sp. in West Virginia (835).

Ascochyta piniperda has blighted 4- to 5-year-old red spruce seedlings and young shoots in a North Carolina nursery (538), and blue spruce further north. The gray-mold blight caused by *Botrytis cinerea* has also caused damage to red spruce in the same North Carolina nursery (538).

In Canada, seedlings of red spruce proved to be good hosts to the nematodes *Paratylenchus projectus* and *Tylenchus emarginatus,* but were not hosts to *Pratylenchus penetrans* (1370). See *Picea mariana* for information on *T. emarginatus.*

Foliage Diseases.—The main foliage diseases are rusts, caused by six species of *Chrysomyxa* (46, 1237, 1239). *C. ledi* var. *cassandrae* produces aecia on spruce needles, and stages II and III on *Chamaedaphne calyculata. C. empetri* produces aecia on red spruce in Maine and the far North, and stages II and III on *Empetrum nigrum. C. ledi* and *C. ledicola* produce aecia on spruce needles, and stages II and III on *Ledum* spp. from Connecticut to Nova Scotia and west to the Lake States. In *C. ledicola,* the uredia and telia are epiphyllous; in *C. ledi,* they are hypophyllous. *C. roanensis* produces aecia on spruce needles, and stages II and III on *Rhododendron catawbiense* and *R. punctatum* in North Carolina and Tennessee.

Two needle-cast fungi (323) attack red spruce. One, *Lirula (Lophodermium) macrospora* (*L. filiforme*), which has shiny, black hysterothecia of varying lengths, can severely defoliate understory trees or the lower branches of larger trees, but it is known only from localized areas. Darker (323) mentions that in eastern

278

America, *Naevia piniperda,* a fungus with innate, waxy apothecia, has always been found in association with *L. macrospora.* The other needle-cast fungus, *Lophodermium piceae,* appears only on old, senescent needles and is of no importance in North America, although it causes a major spruce disease in Europe.

Snow-blight fungi will blight foliage that remains too long under snow. These fungi and the damage they cause in spruce are annotated under *Picea mariana.*

Stem Diseases.—Red spruce has no serious stem diseases. A common yellow witches' broom (*Chrysomyxa arctostaphyli*) is conspicuous on several species of spruce, including red spruce (see *Picea glauca*).

The eastern dwarfmistletoe, *Arceuthobium pusillum,* occurs mainly on black spruce and occasionally on red spruce, white spruce, and tamarack. The shoots are only 12 to 20 mm. high, brownish green, and occur scattered along the branches (*151, 505*). The only dwarfmistletoe in the East, this plant has not been a serious pathogen to any host but black spruce, except for some heavy infections in old stands of red spruce reported from Canada by Pomerleau[36].

Trunk and branch cankers, their limits often poorly defined, and exhibiting copious resin flow, are caused by *Valsa* (*Cytospora*) *kunzei* var. *piceae.* Waterman (*1519*) stresses the damaging effects of trunk cankers, which are particularly common on red and Norway spruce.

Among the common saprobic fungi occurring on dead wood or bark are *Dasyscypha abietis, D. agassizii* (*151*), *Pestalotia* spp., and *Phoma piceina* (*538*).

Attacks of red spruce by the eastern spruce bark beetle, *Dendroctonus piceaperda,* lead to lethal tracheomycotic blue-staining of the sapwood, as far south as North Carolina. Although *Ceratocystis piceaperda* has been reported only from white spruce (*1227*), this stain fungus, or one or more closely related to it, are the likely associates of the beetle on red spruce.

Aleurodiscus fennicus, A. penicillatus, and *A. piceinus* fruit on dead twigs in the United States and Canada (*858*), and *A. canadensis* causes a twig blight of red spruce in Canada[37].

Root Diseases.—Red spruce has not been subject to killing diseases of the roots. However, *Fomes annosus, Polyporus schweinitzii, P. sulphureus,* and *Pora subacida* are root- and butt-rot fungi that can weaken red spruce, making it especially subject to windthrow (*1002*) or wind breakage. *Polyporus tomentosus,* a common root-rot fungus of other spruce species, will also attack the roots of living red spruce (*525, 1570*).

Davidson and Redmond (*335*), working in the Canadian Maritime Provinces, found that the commonest root and butt fungus in red spruce there was *Poria subacida,* followed by *Polyporus tomentosus, Omphalia campanella,* and four other fungi. In their white

---

[36] Personal communication from René Pomerleau, pathologist, Canada Department of Forestry, Forest Entomology and Pathology Branch, Sillery, Quebec.

[37] Personal communication from René Pomerleau, pathologist, Canada Department of Forestry, Forest Entomology and Pathology Branch, Sillery, Quebec.

spruce, *P. subacida* appeared only once, whereas *Corticium galactinum* predominated.

Trunk Rots.—Many fungi can rot the heartwood of red spruce, but virtually all of them confine any significant decay progress to trees of old age or trees that have sustained major damage. Unlike its associate balsam fir, in which heart rots generally become of importance by the 70th year, in red spruce current volume loss from rot does not even come close to current gross increment until double this age.

Fomes pini (*1002, 1096*), *F. pinicola, F. roseus, F. cajanderi* (*F. subroseus*) (*890*), *Polyporus borealis, P. schweinitzii,* and *Poria subacida* are among the principal trunk fungi with *F. pini* (*596*), *Polyporus borealis* (*1005, 1143*), and *P. schweinitzii* (which may extend 10 feet up the trunk (*661*)) causing much of the ultimate decay in overmature red spruce. Many other fungi will invade injured areas of living trees and also rot the sapwood and heartwood of dead trees (*8*).

Mook and Eno (*1002*) found, in Vermont, a heavy incidence of *Polyporus borealis* butt rot in red spruce, and also some total culls due to *Fomes pini.* However, they did not consider these fungi as being responsible for observed mortality in the stands. *P. borealis* also rots red spruce in Canada.

Merulius himantioides causes a brown, cubical butt rot in Canada.

Davidson and Redmond (*335*) found that cull percentage due to rot, in the Canadian Maritime Provinces, reached its maximum at age 150 to 180 years, when it reached 22 percent in white spruce, but only 5 percent in red spruce. Butt rots accounted for more loss than trunk rots.

Mycorrhizal Relations.—Only *Polyporus tomentosus* has been reported probably making true mycorrhizal association with red spruce (Gosselin, *525*), but pure-culture confirmation is lacking. Gosselin shows improved growth and a Hartig net with *P. tomentosus* infection. Whitney (*1570*) failed to produce mycorrhizae in seedlings raised in flasks, and doubts that this fungus is mycorrhizal.

Miscellaneous Pathology.—A cone rust of red and other spruces is caused by *Chrysomyxa pirolata.* Aecia are produced on the spruce cones, and stages II and III on species of *Moneses* and *Pyrola.* The rust occurs from Canada and the Lake States south to Maryland. Cone scales will also serve as a substrate for *Phragmotrichum chailletii.*

Sitka spruce
Picea sitchensis

Sitka spruce, largest of the native spruces, grows fast, tall, with considerable taper, and commonly develops a buttressed base (*1367*). It hugs the fog belt of the Pacific Coast from northern California to southern Alaska, seldom extending more than 100 miles inland. The area occupied is classified as superhumid and, under the influence of the Pacific Ocean, the weather is characterized by equable temperatures, absence of extreme winter cold, high precipitation, and prolonged cloudiness (*1232*). The species reaches its optimum development on the Olympic Peninsula of Washington and on the Queen Charlotte Islands of British Columbia. Its altitudinal range is from sea level to 3,000 ft. Frosts occur over much of the range, and Sudworth (*1367*) notes that at its northern limit temperatures can drop to —35° F. Peace (*1091*) considers this species *very susceptible* to spring frosts under European conditions.

Most Sitka spruce soils are very high in organic matter, and of a fairly uniform texture. Given adequate soil and air moisture, the type of soil is not important to this species. Growth is poor, however, on swampy sites and on very thin soils, and this species gives way to others on the dry, east slopes of the coastal mountains (*1232*). In its "rain forest" Sitka spruce will outgrow most associated species. It is also tolerant (*54*), particularly when young. Trees as tall as 285 ft. have been measured, and while the commonly associated western hemlock dies out before 500 years, the Sitka spruces may live to between 700 and 800 years (*1232*).

Sitka spruce is shallow-rooted and heavy losses have been sustained by blow-down and breakage on the north and east sides of clear-cut areas since the heavy winds come mostly from the southwest. Many aspects of the silviculture of this species are influenced or dictated by the likelihood to wind damage (*1232*).

Sitka spruce is sensitive to fire, but severe fire damage is not common in the wet, coastal forests (*279*). It is fairly resistant to some herbicides used for hardwood control, being more resistant than western hemlock or Douglas-fir (*1232*). As an ornamental and a forest tree it has done well abroad where climates are cool and humid. The hot and dry summers of the eastern and middle-western United States have precluded any promise for Sitka spruce there.

Epicormic sprouts will develop along the bole, often prolifically, on road rights-of-way, but the species does not form stump or root sprouts. Layering can succeed, and cuttings can be rooted (*1232*).

The main disease problem with Sitka spruce is its high susceptibility to decay when injured. An interesting facet of the species' pathology is that it is attacked by seven species of the rust genus *Chrysomyxa*.

Seedling Diseases.—The seeds are small and light, and the germinative capacity of sound seed is high. However, while the percentage of seeds that are sound is generally over 90 percent for most species of *Picea,* Sitka spruce yields seed only about half of which are sound (*1*). After germination in the field, even short dry spells result in heavy mortality. Some losses due to frost-heaving take place when seedlings come up on exposed mineral soil.

Shea (*1281*) reports attack of the foliage of Sitka spruce seedlings in a nursery in the State of Washington, by *Rosellinia herpotrichioides*. Under moist conditions this fungus produces copious mycelial webbing over needles, and the very large perithecia are borne on the surface of the felts (*659*).

While little is known of the fungi capable of attacking young seedlings of Sitka spruce in North America, Buxton et al. (*197*) experienced spring damping-off, summer browning of foliage and roots, and stunting, in an English nursery. They conducted pathogenicity tests with 96 isolates of fungi occurring on seedlings or in the rhizosphere, and concluded that damping-off was caused by *Pythium* spp., browning by *Fusarium oxysporum,* and stunting by some isolates of *F. oxysporum* and *F. roseum.*

Vaartaja (*1458*) has shown the pathogenicity of *Phytophthora cactorum* to Sitka spruce in the laboratory, and Gilmour (*510*) reports *Pythium ultimum* and *Rhizoctonia solani* causing damping-off of Sitka spruce in New Zealand.

Foliage Diseases.—Sitka spruce needles are subject to infection by four species of *Chrysomyxa* (*1237, 1239*). Two other species attack cones and another causes yellow witches' brooms. *C. ledi* produces aecia on spruce needles in British Columbia, and stages II and III on *Ledum* spp. from Connecticut, to Nova Scotia, to British Columbia. *C. ledicola* also produces aecia on spruce, occurring in the Northwest, and stages II and III on *Ledum* spp. However, in *C. ledicola* the uredinia and telia are epiphyllous, while in *C. ledi* they are hypophyllous. *C. piperiana* (*Peridermium parksianum*) produces aecia on spruce needles, and stages II and III on *Rhododendron californicum. C. weirii* produces its dull-orange, waxy telia on Sitka spruce needles in British Columbia.

Two needle-cast fungi attack Sitka spruce. One, *Lirula macrospora* (*Lophodermium filiforme*), which has shiny, black hysterothecia of varying length, can severely defoliate understory trees or the lower branches of larger trees (*323*). The other, *Lophodermium piceae,* appears only on old, senescent needles and is of no importance in North America, although it causes a major disease in Europe (*323*).

The other minor needle casts are reported on Sitka spruce *Lophomerum* (*Lophodermium*) *septatum* (*1066*), in Oregon, and *Diedickia piceae,* in California.

Herpotrichia nigra, the common non-pine, brown-felt snow mold, can damage foliage that has remained too long under snow (*1365*). *Dimerosporium* (*Meliola*) *balsamicola* causes a sooty, surface mold on needles (*571*).

Stem Diseases.—The rust *Chrysomyxa arctostaphyli* causes conspicuous, yellow, compact witches' brooms, and has its telial stage on the bearberry, *Arctostaphylos uva-ursi.*

Swollen cankers on Sitka spruce and Engelmann spruce, bearing many black, spherical fruiting bodies often containing no spores, have been found by Funk (*486*) to be caused by a new species of *Botryosphaeria* (*B. piceae*). Only the perfect stage is known. The ascospores are large, filled with granular contents, hyaline in the ascocarp, but turning black as they germinate on agar.

Bark lesions on suppressed trees sometimes bear the flat, irregular apothecia of *Aleurodiscus amorphus, A. weirii,* or the closely related *Aleurocystidiellum subcruentatum. Aleurodiscus penicillatus* occurs in British Columbia (*858*).

A single collection of *Atropellis treleasii* was made in Alaska in 1899 from supposed Sitka spruce bark, and the fungus had not been reported thereafter for many years (*1656*). The fungus has more recently been found, commonly on Sitka spruce and western hemlock, in British Columbia, Washington, and Alaska, placed in a new genus, and named, illustrated, and described as *Discocainia treleasei* by Reid and Funk (*1160*).

A discomycete, *Cistella parksii,* with small, yellow-to-orange apothecia, grows on bark and decorticated wood of Sitka spruce and western hemlock in California (*237*).

The only report of dwarfmistletoe on Sitka spruce is a single case in an Alaskan stand where *Tsuga heterophylla* is heavily infected with *Arceuthobium campylopodum* f. *tsugensis* (*836*).

Large galls occur on the stems and branches of Sitka spruce and other spruces (*1563*) that, while disfiguring, do not result in death of the stem beyond the galls or burls.

Root Diseases.—There are no important, killing root diseases of Sitka spruce. However, of the root- and butt-rot fungi known to attack this host, it is likely that, working alone or in conjunction with other impacts, some root necrosis results from *Armillaria mellea*, *Fomes annosus*, and *Polyporus schweinitzii*. Other chiefly root- and butt-rot fungi include *Lentinus kauffmanii* (*113*), *P. berkeleyi*, *P. sulphureus*, and *P. tomentosus*. The annual form of *Poria weirii* also causes root rot in Sitka spruce (*190*). Since wind damage is so important with Sitka spruce, root- and butt-rot fungi contribute significantly to mortality from uprooting and breakage. Wright and Isaac (*1623*), working with injured Sitka spruce and associated species in Washington and Oregon, found *F. annosus* a leading wound-colonizer, whether the wounds were on roots, butts, or far up the bole.

Trunk Rots.—The Wright and Isaac study (*1623*) determined that rot following injury to the above species was more important east of the Coast Ranges than along the Coast, and provides data on the probability of decay and its rate of spread after injury. The more serious decay cases were those following butt wounds. The fungi causing decay following injury were as follows:

Decay cases

Fungus:	*Percent*
Fomes pinicola	34
Lentinus kauffmanii	11
Stereum spp.	7
S. sanguinolentum	7
Fomes pini	6
Polyporus guttulatus	2
Poria monticola	2
Coniophora cerebella	2
Fomes annosus	2
Hydnum sp.	2
Unidentified	25

While *Fomes annosus* led all decay fungi following injury in western hemlock (40 percent of the cases) and in the true firs (32 percent), it made up only 2 percent of the cases in Sitka spruce (*1623*).

Wright et al. (*1624*) found that half of the reserve trees injured by logging became decayed, and that in injured Sitka spruce trees this rot amounted to 43 percent of the gross increment after logging. They emphasized the importance of broken tops and sunscald, in addition to butt and bole scars, as injuries attributed to logging and leading to decay.

Bier and Foster (*120*) give aids for cruising overmature Sitka spruce on the Queen Charlotte Islands, Canada, and show that decay volume per tree rose from 0 at 200 years, to 4,000 board-feet at 700 years, with a culmination of net periodic increment at 250 to 300 years, and then a drop to two-thirds this maximum by 600 years. The same authors (*121*) stress the importance of decay by *Fomes pini* in that area, stating that it is responsible for 40 percent of the rot loss. It was the only fungus of the 31 species rotting living Sitka spruce in that area that consistently produced external conks indicating internal defect. The average 40-foot butt log with a conk on it, or above it, was 50-percent rotten. The average second 40-foot butt log with a conk on it, or above it, was 33-percent rotten.

A third paper by Bier and Foster (*122*) brings out the importance of computing loss in lumber grade as well as loss in log scale due to cull in assessing the real loss attributable to decay in Sitka spruce. Hepting and Chapman (*657*) dealt with this aspect of red heart in shortleaf and loblolly pine and found the total financial loss (cull loss plus degrade of discolored, but sound, red heart) on a percentage basis, to be much greater than loss from cull only.

Bier (*113*) describes a brown pocket rot of Sitka spruce that has some of the pecky characteristics of *Stereum taxodii* on *Taxodium*, *Polyporus amarus* on *Libocedrus*, and *Poria sequoiae* on *Sequoia*. It is caused by *Lentinus kauffmanii* and was fourth in importance in the Queen Charlotte Islands, after *Fomes pini*, *Polyporus schweinitzii*, and *F. pinicola*. While it can rot any part of the trunk, roots served as the entry point in 56 percent of the infections.

Bier et al. (*123*) bring together the entire subject of decay in Sitka spruce on the Queen Charlotte Islands, in a comprehensive bulletin, with good illustrations of many of the rots. The leading trunk rots were listed as *Fomes pini*, *F. pinicola*, *Poria microspora*, *Lentinus kauffmanii*, *Polyporus sulphureus*, and *F. officinalis*. *P. schweinitzii* and *Poria subacida* led the butt-rot fungi.

Englerth (*416*) studied decay in Sitka spruce in southeast Alaska. He found sporophores, except for *Fomes pini*, rare on living trees, and found no swollen knots with *F. pini* infections. Frost cracks or other injuries provided the only evidence of decay, aside from *F. pini* conks.

Infection courts of the various fungi occurring in Sitka spruce in southeast Alaska were as follows:

Fungus:	Total infections	Roots	Falling-tree scars	Broken branches	Dead tops	Frost cracks	Undetermined
				Percent of total			
Fomes applanatus	1	—	—	—	100	—	—
F. nigrolimitatus	2	—	—	—	—	—	100
F. officinalis	7	—	14	—	—	—	86
F. pini	11	—	—	100	—	—	—
F. pinicola	28	—	71	—	4	—	25
Lentinus kauffmanii	4	—	25	—	—	—	75
Polyporus borealis	41	85	12	—	—	2	—
P. picipes	1	—	100	—	—	—	—
P. schweinitzii	75	88	12	—	—	—	—
P. sulphureus	23	—	4	17	—	—	78
Poria subacida	1	100	—	—	—	—	—
Trametes serialis	1	—	—	—	—	—	100
Unknown fungi	18	—	24	—	33	6	41
All fungi	213	48	20	7	4	1	21

Kimmey (795) conducted an extensive study of cull in Sitka spruce, western hemlock, and western redcedar in southeast Alaska. He determined the causes and types of cull, cull indicators, and cull factors. He related the incidence of decay to elevation of stand, to age of trees, and to tree diameter. In Sitka spruce, the fungi responsible for cull, expressed in terms of the total cubic-foot rot-cull volume, were as follows: *Fomes pinicola,* 73 percent; *F. pini,* 9 percent; *Armillaria mellea,* 4 percent; *Polyporus schweinitzii,* 4 percent; *P. sulphureus,* 4 percent; *F. annosus,* 1 percent; *Trametes heteromorpha,* 1 percent; *F. nigrolimitatus,* 1 percent; *Lentinus kauffmanii,* trace; unknown rots, 1 percent. Sitka spruce had less cull than the other two species, per age class.

In addition to the heart-rot fungi already mentioned, the following fungi can also attack Sitka spruce: *Echinodontium tinctorium, Fomes subroseus, Polyporus berkeleyi, Poria microspora,* and a few others (1278). Many fungi can rot the dead wood of Sitka spruce, but *Ganoderma (Polyporus) oregonense,* with a reddish, "varnished" appearance to the top of its conk, *Lenzites saepiaria,* and the ubiquitous *Polyporus abietinus* are the most common.

Mycorrhizal Relations.—Twenty-one fungi have been reported to make mycorrhizal association with Sitka spruce (1442). None of these relationships, however, have been established by pure-culture technique.

Miscellaneous Pathology.—One of two cone rusts is caused by *Chrysomyxa monesis,* with aecia produced on Sitka spruce cones in the Queen Charlotte Islands, Canada, and stages II and III on *Moneses uniflora* from Alaska to Washington. Ziller (1662), who described this rust, had found striking differences in aeciospore markings from those of the other cone rust, *Chrysomyxa pyrolae,* a widespread rust of spruces, including Sitka spruce, which also has its II and III stages on *Moneses* spp. and several species of *Pyrola.*

The brick-red stain of Sitka spruce lumber, that can deeply penetrate the heartwood, is caused by a fungus with red-brown ascophore stalks, called *Ascocybe grovesii.* Although adopting the "brick-red" name, Davidson and Lombard (349) describe the stain and mention that the color caused by the fungus is from pink to cinnamon brown.

Hansbrough and Englerth (590) determined the significance of a large number of discolorations on the toughness of Sitka spruce lumber. Normal sapwood is usually creamy white, sometimes faintly tinged with red. The heartwood is also often very light colored, but more commonly is pinkish to reddish brown, with the reddish hues predominant. The terms they applied to colorations not materially affecting toughness are: included sapwood, vertical red streaks, radial red or "strawberry" marks, pitch inclusions, machine burn, brick-red stain, orange stain, and surface molds.

Discolorations indicating reduced toughness were: blue stain, yellow streaks, brown markings of any kind, white pits or pockets, and zone lines. The authors describe each of the above colorations.

Boyce (144) studied deterioration following the great Olympic Peninsula blowdown of 1921. Six years later the volume loss, on a board-foot basis, was: for western hemlock, 92 percent; Pacific silver fir, 74 percent; Sitka spruce, 46 percent; Douglas-fir 35 percent; and western redcedar, 7 percent. The main fungi identified as rotting Sitka spruce were *Fomes pinicola, Polyporus abietinus, F. applanatus,* and *P. fibrillosus.*

Pine
Pinus spp.

Some generalizations can be made about the pathology of the eastern and southern hard pines because their close phylogenetic relationship to each other has meant many features of pathology in common. These two- and three-needled pines are typically intolerant subclimax species. They have what might be termed a three-element root system, with a well-defined taproot, a lateral system not far below the surface of the ground, and sinker roots extending straight down from the laterals. Laterals extend rapidly, usually to an age near 20 years when extension slows markedly and proliferation goes on within the existing root zone (*916*). The root systems of pine seedlings are far less prolific than those of associated hardwoods, with root-length ratios of as high as 1:170 in the case of greenhouse-grown loblolly pine versus black locust (*810*).

Nursery seedlings can be expected to be susceptible to damping-off when the pH reaches 5.5 or higher, to root rots caused by *Rhizoctonia solani, Sclerotium bataticola,* and species of *Phytophthora, Pythium,* and *Fusarium* (*696*), and in cool regions by *Cylindrocladium scoparium* and *Diplodia pinea.* Hodges (*694*) lists a large number of fungi isolated from southern forest nurseries. High pH and high moisture can lead to heavy losses. High heat will also produce lethal lesions at the ground line (*360*), a condition often referred to as white spot (*601*).

Jones et al. (*761*) determined the fumigation dosages of methyl bromide that reduced the germination of longleaf, slash, and loblolly pine seed. Seeds maintained at high moisture content (e.g. 15 percent) were particularly subject to damage at the dosages commonly used for fumigating imported pine seed.

Wood treated with pentachlorophenol or related chemicals, used in the soil or for shade frames in nurseries, can damage pine seedlings (*439*). At least one widely used surfactant has been known to severely injure slash, loblolly, and shortleaf pine seedlings (*1327*). Freezing seedlings, not uncommon sometime between lifting and outplanting, will lower the survival of southern pine planting stock (*691*).

The foliage of these hard pines is susceptible to many needle rusts, all of them except for certain western *Melampsora* spp. (*1668*), in the genus *Coleosporium,* and all but very few having herbaceous alternate hosts. *Ploioderma* (*Hypoderma*) *lethale* and to a lesser extent *P. hedgcockii* (*328*), occur on most species, and cause some late-winter browning of older needles. The brown-spot fungus (*Scirrhia acicola*) is also general on this group. *Lophodermium pinastri* may be found fruiting on moribund or dead foliage of any pine species, and although it has often been cited as a pathogen, there is no North American experimental evidence yet to back the position that *L. pinastri* is pathogenic (*153, 323*). This fungus is widely regarded as a pine pathogen in Europe (*1091*). Similarly, *Pestalotia funerea* and *Pullularia pullulans* occur widely on healthy,

286

sickly, or dead pine foliage and greenwood shoots, and have often been indicted as pathogens, but in most cases proof is lacking that either is the primary cause of disease. *Diplodia pinea*, another ubiquitous pine-stem fungus blamed for much damage, is usually preceded by injuries (*1513*). Both *P. funerea* and *D. pinea*, when inserted into slits in very young red pine seedlings, and the latter also applied to uninjured seedling stems, produced lethal root and stem lesions (*299*).

The needles of the eastern hard pines are killed almost instantaneously when exposed to a temperature of 64° C. or higher, but at 52° C. they withstand 9 to 11 minutes of heat (*1019*).

Witches' brooms have often been reported on eastern pines, as well as on many other conifers, countrywide, usually occurring singly, and not obviously associated with any organism. These brooms are regarded as of genetic origin, through overstimulation of bud formation and budbreak at one site on a branch. Many stem rusts, all in the genus *Cronartium*, attack the eastern hard pines.

Fomes annosus and *Clitocybe tabescens* can kill roots, which results in tree mortality under certain circumstances, and *Polyporus schweinitzii* and *Armillaria mellea* will occasionally cause some root and butt rot in injured trees. *Fomes pini*, once it gains entry to the heartwood, can rot the heart of any pine. Its entrance, in the East, is mainly through branch stubs that expose heartwood (*657*), but in the case of eastern white pine, De Groot (*368*) reports that it can enter through leaders killed by the white pine weevil. Its decay goes under the common name red heart in the South.

Thelephora terrestris appears in the literature in many roles: as a smothering fungus, as a harmless symbiont, or even as a beneficient mycorrhiza-former. It can be any of these. In the North, or at high elevations in the West, where a conifer seedling may grow little more than an inch or two the first year, the smothering effect of the thallus of this fungus can be damaging, whereas, in the South, where pine seedlings often reach a height of 6 in. by midsummer, the fungus sporophore appears only as a small funnel around the stem base, with no smothering or girdling effect. Evidence of its mycorrhizal capacity is cited with the appropriate hosts.

All of the eastern pines are subject to the tracheomycosis resulting from blue stain and other fungi being introduced into the sapwood by bark beetles (*842*). The pine bark beetles, mostly species of *Ips* or *Dendroctonus*, carry specific stain fungi, mostly species of *Ceratocystis*, and the relationship of beetle to fungus is one of benefit to both, but fatal to the tree (*841*). The beetle is now considered as largely a vector, while it is the stain fungus in the sapwood that kills the tree.

The new roots of the hard pines are normally always transformed into ectotrophic or ectendotrophic mycorrhizae. While white pines may have many root hairs, few occur on hard pines in the field, and this means that absorption of minerals and water in the latter must take place largely through a fungus mantle (*181*). It is generally recognized, however, that some water, and even salts, may enter suberized root tissue.

The roots also support many species of nematodes, both in the rhizosphere, and on and in the roots (*1220*). Since many species of nematodes are fungus-feeders (*259*), the interplay among the many species of mycorrhizal fungi (*1442*) that can occur on any one tree's roots, and the many species of nematodes (*704, 1220*) commonly found on and in any one tree's roots, presents an enormous field for investigation that is of vital importance to a pine's development (*1225*).

The tiny, yellow apothecia of *Biatorella* (*Zythia*) *resinae* are common on any resinous part of a pine (*267*). The fungus lives on the resin and is harmless.

While the southern pines have many features of their pathology in common, there also are some marked and somewhat surprising differences, such as the following:

Of the major species, only loblolly does not take the common form of pitch canker (*Fusarium lateritium pini*).

While brown spot occurs on almost all species of the group, it is an important seedling disease only on longleaf. The only southern species not known to harbor brown spot is sand pine.

Only Virginia pine takes the autoecious short-cycled needle rust caused by *Coleosporium pinicola* or, so far as known, the stem rust caused by *Cronartium appalachianum*.

While loblolly and slash pines are hard hit by *Cronartium fusiforme*, longleaf and shortleaf are very resistant.

Of all the group, only slash and longleaf pines take southern cone rust (*Cronartium strobilinum*).

Whitebark pine
Pinus albicaulis

An intolerant, five-needled pine of the high elevations of the West, whitebark pine grows at from 5,000 to 7,000 ft., in British Columbia and Alberta, to 12,000 ft. in the Sierras of California. On the mountain summits and high slopes of the Inland Empire and the Cascade and Sierra Nevada ranges, it has a thick, squatty trunk with flexible limbs that occur mostly on the leeward side in situations where the tree is exposed to constant wind of considerable force. At lower elevations and on the better soils, it grows taller, more symmetrical, and up to 2 ft. in diameter (*279*). Its growth is very slow, and some 5-foot-high trees have been recorded as 500 years old. Maximum recorded longevity is 800 years. Needles may be retained from 4 to 8 years before being shed. The tree is very hardy, withstanding temperatures of from —60° to 100° F., and its soil-moisture requirements are moderate. It is very sensitive to fire. It often grows, although slowly, among bare rocks on shallow soils, with available moisture only near the soil surface (*1367*).

Foliage Diseases.—Since whitebark pine is seldom planted, except occasionally as an ornamental, little is known of its strictly seedling diseases. The foliage is reported subject to attack by both *Herpotrichia nigra* and *Neopeckia coulteri*. These fungi are generally considered the non-pine and the pine brown-felt snow molds, respectively (*8*), and they destroy foliage when needles remain under snow for long periods—a condition not uncommon for this species.

Lophodermium nitens and *L. pinastri* occur on needles. The former causes a casting of needles 3 or more years old, and the latter also invades senescent needles (*323*).

Bifusella linearis has been reported on *Pinus albicaulis* and *P. flexilis* at high elevations in southern California (see *Pinus strobus*) (*970*).

Whitebark pine, and especially Douglas-fir, in western Oregon and Washington, are subject to winter drying, to which the name "parch blight" has been applied. This occurs during brief periods in the winter when dry winds from the east sweep across the Cascade Mountains. Needles, and even twigs, can be killed, especially on the windward side, but mortality is not common (*151*).

Stem Diseases.—The main disease enemy is white pine blister rust (*Cronartium ribicola*), to which whitebark pine is extremely susceptible (*89, 251*). Its attacks have been severe enough to reduce the watershed protection value of this tree (*971*) in parts of Oregon, Washington, and Idaho. Control operations are often not feasible in the high, rigorous, exposed sites where most whitebark pine occurs, and species of *Ribes*, the alternate hosts of the rust, often thrive in abundance. *Ribes* bushes, at a considerable distance (*89*), contribute to the inoculum load reaching whitebark pine stands.

While whitebark bark develops a high incidence of blister-rust infections, canker enlargement tends to be slow, probably because of the low temperatures of the sites involved. Pathologists in the Northwest have estimated that as high as 1 or 2 percent of the whitebark pine population may be highly resistant to blister rust.

Three dwarfmistletoes attack this tree (*505*): (1) *Arceuthobium americanum*, the lodgepole pine dwarfmistletoe, in Montana; (2) *A. campylopodum* f. *cyanocarpum*, the limber pine dwarfmistletoe, widely over the tree's range; and (3) *A. campylopodum* f. *tsugensis*, to a limited extent. All three species cause swellings, retard growth, induce brooming, and lead to premature death. Other effects are defect and degrade in the form of hypertrophies, pitchy cankers, and large knots (*507*).

Branch cankers are caused by *Atropellis piniphila*, widely over the range of whitebark pine. This fungus also causes a blue-black staining of the wood beneath (*877*). *Dasyscypha pini* is a parasitic species forming branch and stem cankers somewhat resembling those caused by blister rust (*576*). The large, bright-orange apothecia are diagnostic. The yellow-orange apothecial cups of the saprophyte *D. agassizii* are common on dead bark and on blister-rust cankers, and the harmles *D. arida* and *Phoma harknessii* occur on twigs. Saprophytic species of *Tympanis*, sometimes refered to simply as *T. pinastri*, also occur on dead bark. Groves (*552*) refers to the species of *Tympanis* on whitebark pine as *T. confusa*, *T. pithya*, and *T. hypopodia*.

Root Diseases.—*Fomes annosus*, *Polyporus schweinitzii*, and *Poria subacida* have caused root and butt rot in old trees. While *F. annosus* and *F. pini* are not regarded as important in the culture of whitebark pine, *P. schweinitzii* causes an important brown cubical butt rot, and *P. subacida*, a spongy root rot that causes trees to break over.

Mycorrhizal Relations.—*Cenococcum graniforme* is reported as a mycorrhizal associate with whitebark pine (*1442*).

Knobcone pine
Pinus attenuata

Knobcone pine is a very intolerant, small, bushy tree with sparse, dull foliage and slender, horizontal branches ascending at the ends, occurring through the Coast Range of southern Oregon and California, and in the southern Cascades and northern Sierra Nevada. It matures at 40 to 60 years, and its longevity probably does not exceed 100 to 150 years. It is found singly or in small groups, usually on dry, exposed, steep, southeastern slopes on poor, rocky, gravelly, or sandy soils, and is next to Digger pine in being the least fastidious species, regarding soil moisture, of the Pacific Coast pines. It also grows in moist ravines. It is not particularly hardy, but endures temperatures between zero and 95° F., and its sites may have occasional snows, as well as rainfall up to 45 in. per year. Its altitudinal range is from about 1,000 to 5,400 ft. elevation. The heavy cones rarely open until a tree is killed or they are cut from it; then they open slowly (*1367*). The bark is thin and scaly, and the bole is thus subject to fire injury. The dry conditions under which most knobcone pines grow are not conducive to fungus dissemination or infection, and the tree suffers little from diseases.

Foliage Diseases.—Since this species is seldom planted, little is known of its seedling diseases. The foliage is occasionally discolored and killed by *Elytroderma deformans*, which is perennial in the twigs, and commonly results in killing new needles and producing the characteristic reddish "flags" of this disease (*248*). Short sections of needle are sometimes killed by *Davisomycella (Hypodermella) lacrimiformis*, a species confined to knobcone pine (*323*). In Oregon, the brown-spot fungus, *Scirrhia acicola*, produces needle lesions on this species. The everpresent *Lophodermium pinastri* occurs on senescent or dead needles.

Stem Diseases.—The most important disease of knobcone pine is western gall rust. The two autoecious round-gall forms, known as *Peridermium cerebroides* and *P. harknessii*, both fall under this common name, and both occur on this tree species. They are separated largely on gall characteristics as indicated under *Pinus radiata*. Peterson (*1110*) regards them as one species, *P. harknessii*. The stalactiform rust (*P. stalactiforme*) occurs rarely on knobcone pine, forming only slight, if any, swelling of the infected area. Still another stem rust, *Cronartium comandrae*, with its alternate stages on *Comandra* spp., occasionally attacks this species.

Knobcone pine is subject to local damage from western dwarfmistletoe (*Arceuthobium campylopodum* f. *campylopodum*) (*821*) which causes swellings on branches or stems, and also distortion, brooming, growth reduction, and sometimes killing. *A. americanum*, the lodgepole pine dwarfmistletoe, occurs occasionally on this tree in Oregon.

Trunk Rots.—The wood of living trees is subject to decay by *Fomes pini* entering through exposed heartwood; the butts and roots may be decayed by *Polyporus schweinitzii*.

Jack pine
Pinus banksiana

A species mainly of the Northeast and Lake States, jack pine thrives on light, sandy soils in the heavy snow country. It extends the farthest north of all the North American pines, and is almost transcontinental in its range. Its usual habitat is barren, sandy, or rocky land up to about 1,200 ft. in elevation. The species is very intolerant and, except on its best sites, is inclined to be small, scrubby, limby, and of inferior form. In parts of the Lake States, however, it grows to a sizable tree of good form (*279*). Jack pine is slow-growing, matures at about 10 years, practically stops growth at 80 years, and can live to about 200 years (*1215*). It is hardy, resisting well the impacts of weather, and in spite of its many enemies, it has none that, alone, is both widespread and serious. It is, however, sensitive to heat and, particularly, to fire. Many of its cones are serotinous, requiring dry weather or high heat to open (*1215*).

Rudolph (*1217*) describes lammas shoots and prolepsis in jack pine in the Lake States. The former represent flushes of leader growth in addition to the first, or "normal," shoot. The latter refers to the condition whereby, at the end of the normal seasonal growth, one or more lateral buds at the base of the terminal bud break dormancy and add another flush of growth. Rudolph asserts that production of lammas shoots and prolepsis are under genetic control, but that their incidence is related to latitude and other phenologic considerations.

Jack pine can be severely injured by hail, and 7 years after a hail storm there were dead trees, dead tops, thin crowns on the side that faced the storm, open and healed wounds, especially on the thin-barked upper parts—all traceable to the same year by annual-ring count (*1176*). Jack pine is also subject to severe damage where the water table rises above normal (*1036*). Soot-laden smoke emanating from a railroad roundhouse suppressed the growth of nearby jack pines (*867*).

The pathology of jack pine is characterized by a moderate susceptibility of seedlings to damping-off (*853*); frequent losses due to eastern and western gall rusts; susceptibility to "burn blight" in the Lake States; and the fact that the species is host to many leaf blights, cankers, and root rots that have little impact on its growth except in localized situations.

Seedling Diseases.—Rathbun-Gravatt (*1144*) concluded that poor germination of jack pine, resulting from attack by damping-off fungi, is due mainly to the destruction of radicles after emergence from the seed coat, but before seedlings break through the soil. Such fungi can decay unruptured seed. Emerging radicles were rotted by *Pythium ultimum, P. aphanidermatum, Pythiacystis citrophora, Phytophthora* spp., *Fusarium sporotrichioides, F. discolor sulphureum, F. arthrosporioides, Botrytis cinerea, Phomopsis juniperovora,* and some lines of *Corticium vagum* (*Rhizoctonia solani*) and *F. moniliforme.*

Fisher (*449*) found the following fungi to decay radicles just emerging from seed coats: *Botrytis* (*cinerea?*), *Fusarium* spp., *Pythium debaryanum, P. ultimum, Rhizoctonia* sp., *Sphaeropsis ellissi* (*Diplodia pinea*), and *Verticillium* sp.

Eliason (*408*) demonstrated the capacity of several *Pythium* isolates, mainly *P. debaryanum*, to cause damping-off of jack pine.

Seedlings in Canadian nurseries have been killed, singly and in patches, by *Scleroderis lagerbergii* (see *Pinus resinosa*).

Jack pine in the United States is moderately susceptible to damping-off and to snow mold (*Phacidium infestans* et al. see *Abies balsamea*), the latter, when a heavy blanket of snow persists for long periods. Seedlings beyond the 1-0 stage may yellow and die gradually, usually in patches, from attack by *Rhizina undulata*, especially on areas where brush has been burned (*360*).

Thelephora terrestris grows up around some seedlings, and while it is often referred to as causing a "smothering disease," it harms only slow-growing seedlings. It is now known to be a mycorrhizal fungus. Post-emergence damping-off, mildew, and unidentified root rots take a toll of seedlings the first 2 years (*1215*).

Test-tube pathogenicity studies with jack pine in Canada led to a rating of 19 species of fungi—isolated from diseased seedlings from many sources—with respect to disease potential. The most pathogenic fungi were *Rhizoctonia solani, Phytophthora cactorum, P. cinnamomi, Pythium debaryanum, Fusarium oxysporum, F. roseum*, and a species of *Helminthosporium* (*1462*). However, jack pine was put in the "resistant" class with respect to damage from 7 isolates of *Pythium debaryanum* and *P. ultimum*, along with Scots pine and northern white-cedar (*1464*). This work by Vaartaja and associates followed earlier test tube trials that established high pathogenicity to jack pine seedlings from isolates of *Pythium* spp. and *Rhizoctonia solani*, with less damage by several other fungi (*1461*).

Xiphinema americanum, a dagger nematode, is the only nematode reported on jack pine from the United States. A few others have been identified on and around jack pine roots in Canada (*1222*). Sutherland (*1370*) reported seedlings there to be good hosts to *Paratylenchus projectus* and to *Tylenchus emarginatus*, but not to *Pratylenchus penetrans*. See *Picea mariana* for further information on *T. emarginatus*. Multiple jack pine seedlings have been reported in Canada (*242*).

Foliage Diseases.—Foliage diseases are seldom serious. They include the rusts caused by five species of *Coleosporium*, with heavy needle killing by *C. asterum* not uncommon; the tar-spot needle cast peculiar to jack pine, which results in casting of year-old needles and is caused by *Davisomycella* (*Hypodermella*) *ampla* (*323*); and the ubiquitous *Lophodermium pinastri* of doubtful pathogenicity. Jack pine often suffers so severely from *D. ampla* attack that all needles drop off except those of the current season (*151*). Darker (*329*) describes a fungus from needles of jack pine, which he named *Davisomycella fragilis,* and which he says strongly resembles *Lophodermium pinastri*. He believes it likely that this similarity casts doubt on some of the past reports of *L. pinastri*. In his paper on *D. fragilis*, Darker (*329*) mentions six hypodermataceous fungi on the needles of jack pine in eastern Canada.

Ouellette (*1061*) describes, from Quebec, a small, black, hemisphaeriaceous ascomycete associated with chlorotic spots on living needles of jack pine. Identified as *Thyriopsis halepensis*, it produces black pycnidia and perithecia bearing ellipsoid, 1-septate, light-brown ascospores.

A microcyclic needle rust, morphologically indistinguishable from *Coleosporium pinicola* on Virginia pine, will defoliate jack pines in local areas in Ontario (*1159*). This rust is also known in Quebec.

Ouellette (*1062*) has demonstrated that *C. viburni*, previously known only in its II and III stages on *Viburnum* spp., forms its 0 and I stages on jack pine needles. He presents means of distinguishing this rust from *C. asterum* on jack pine.

Laut et al. (*837*) have reported the imperfect stage of the brown-spot fungus (*Lecanosticta acicola*) associated with needle blighting of jack pine and lodgepole pine in Canada (see *Pinus contorta*).

The snow-mold fungus, *Neopeckia coulteri*, will cause a brown-felt blight when deep snows have covered the lower branches of trees of any size for protracted periods (*151*).

Stem Diseases.—The eastern gall rust (*Cronartium quercuum*) (*630*), the sweetfern rust (*C. comptoniae*) (*25, 1341*), and the Comandra blister rust (*C. comandrae*) (*151*) all can distort or kill trees in proximity to their alternate hosts, with suitable microclimatic conditions. Emphasis has been given (*559*), however, to the fact that basal cankers of sweetfern rust on jack pine in Michigan had little effect on height or diameter growth, or mortality up to 15 years, and that the only damage was defect at the canker itself and, perhaps, a tendency to breakage due to decay or other weakening at the canker. Although Guilkey et al. (*559*) reported no reduction in growth and no mortality of 15-year old trees having basal cankers of *C. comptoniae*, Anderson and French (*35*) found a 58-percent mortality rate of inoculated 1-year-old seedlings, and less than 1-percent mortality with 2- and 3-year-old seedlings. They found mortality at all ages in the forest, with mature and overmature stands suffering 48- and 52-percent mortality, respectively, from sweetfern rust infection. The sweetfern rust is known to extend into northern Alberta and the Northwest Territories on *Pinus banksiana, P. contorta,* and on the alternate host *Myrica gale.*

The eastern gall rust (*Cronartium quercuum*) has been responsible for losses of over 25 percent in jack and Scots pine nursery stock, and has caused ruinous damage to plantations and natural stands (*31*). This rust has been reported to infect 40 to 50 percent of the young seedlings in some areas, and to cause considerable mortality from girdling and breaking at the galls on stems (*1215*). Weir (*1535*) stresses even heavier losses from this gall rust, especially in swampy areas, and he mentions the only occasional occurrence of the sweetfern rust. He presents an account of the pathology of jack pine as known in 1915.

The epidemiology of *C. quercuum*, as it occurs on Lake States jack pine, is described by Nighswander and Patton (*1037*).

The stalactiform rust (*Peridermium stalactiforme*), largely a western rust, causes a canker of jack pine in Minnesota (*34*), where it has resulted directly in mortality, led to bark stripping by rodents, and often resulted in infection by *Fomes pini.* In the field, *Melampyrum lineare*, an alternate host for this rust, was rust-infected near the stalactiform-rusted trees. Ouellette (*1060*) describes attack of jack pine by *Peridermium stalactiforme* in Quebec.

Western gall rust (*Peridermium harknessii*) has been reported on jack pine as far east as Quebec, Canada (*1102*) and the Maritime Provinces. Such a situation could mean a bridge for this fungus from the western hard pines to its appearance as the "Woodgate rust" on Scots pine in New York (*150*). Anderson and French (*28*) found that they could differentiate *Cronartium quercuum* from *Peridermium harknessii* on jack pine, since the aeciospores of the former produce germ tubes three times the length of those of the latter, on water agar. Although other investigators had failed to obtain infection of a scrophulariaceous host with aeciospores from the globose galls of the western gall rust, leading to the conviction that *Peridermium harknessii* is a strictly autoecious rust, Anderson and French (*27*) obtained infection of *Castilleja* with the globose western form from jack pine, making it appear that *Cronartium coleosporioides* has both heteroecious and autoecious forms. The latter they consider *P. harknessii.*

The distinction between *Peridermium harknessii* and *Cronartium quercuum* on pine was clearly demonstrated by Anderson (*26*), when he proved that galls of both the long- and short-cycled rust occurred on the same jack pine tree in northern Minnesota. Tests, including both length of aeciospore germ tubes (see above) and infection of oak, but not pine, by *C. quercuum* aeciospores and pine, but not oak, by *P. harknessii* aeciospores, show the two rusts on this tree to be physiologically distinct. For further information on the identity of *Peridermium* spp. see Peterson (*1110*).

Atropellis piniphila and *A. tingens* kill twigs on jack pine, and *Nectria cucurbitula, Dasyscypha calyciformis,* and *D. ellisiana* are secondary invaders of moribund or dead twigs. Witches'-brooms not associated with an organism occur on jack pine, as they do on other hard pines.

Scleroderris lagerbergii, a pathogen of many conifers in Europe, has been identified as attacking red pine and jack pine in Canada and the Lake States. Ohman (*1048*) describes the symptoms and a low-temperature technique essential to isolate the fungus. In jack pine, entire trees were killed above girdling, elongated cankers that extended above ground line for 4–6 in. The killed trees thus looked much as though attacked by *Armillaria mellea.* In red pine, however, there were many small, discrete cankers on stem and branches, with a few trees having long, spiral cankers on the stem, as branch cankers spread to stems. A yellow-green discoloration, characteristic of the fungus mat in culture, was observed in the cambial zones of recently killed pine stems.

From its western limits, eastward to western Ontario, jack pine is attacked by the dwarfmistletoe *Arceuthobium americanum* (*1215*). The main attack by this plant, in the United States, is on lodgepole pine, with damage to jack pine known only in Canada (*507, 508*). The parasitism of jack pine dwarfmistletoe by *Wallrothiella arceuthobii* is described by Dowding (*389*). *A. pusillum* occurs occasionally on jack pine in Canada (*821*).

Root Diseases.—Root-rot fungi known to attack jack pine include

Armillaria mellea (*887*), which also causes a root-collar resinosis and necrosis (*1090*), especially in the vicinity of hardwood stumps; *Fomes annosus*, which causes a killing root disease in the vicinity of pine stumps or diseased trees (*92, 764*); and *Polyporus schweinitzii* (*887*) and *P. tomentosus* (*1570*), which cause root and butt rots associated with wounding. None of these fungi is a common cause of disease in protected, managed, naturally-regenerated stands of jack pine. A yellow, stringy root rot, caused by *Flammula alnicola*, occurs occasionally on jack pine in Canada (*374*).

A brown root rot of dead jack pine is described by Davidson and Patton (*353*), from plantations in Wisconsin.

The succession of fungi populating wounded roots of jack pine has recently received intensive study (*815*).

Trunk Rots.—Trees that are mature or overmature, with branch stubs exposing heartwood, are subject to red heart (*F. pini*) (*887*). Wood in many stages of stain and decay from attack by this fungus, as well as jack pine wood stained by a non-wood-destroying fungus, has been intensively studied for the impact on utilization. Firm redheart had ample strength for most uses, and the decay did not proceed once the wood was put in service (*49*). *Fomes pinicola* is a common decay fungus of dead trees or dead parts of living trees (*887*).

Basham and Morawski (*73*), in Ontario, found the rot-cull percentage in jack pine to reach 10 percent by age class 121–140, 16 percent by age class 141-160, and 30 percent for ages over 160. Seventeen Hymenomycetes were isolated from these rots, with *Fomes pini* accounting for 73 percent of the rot volume; *Stereum pini* (*Peniophora pseudo-pini*), 18 percent; *Polyporus tomentosus*, 3 percent; and *Corticium galactinum*, 2 percent.

In a later study in Ontario, Basham (*70*) found only about 2-percent cull (merchantable volume basis) at 80 years, but then a rapid rise, so that at 160 years his cull percentages were 13 percent for eastern Ontario, 18 percent for central, and 20 percent for western Ontario.

Basham (*69*) found that two basidiomycetes, *Fomes pini* and *Peniophora pseudo-pini*, and three microfungi, *Tympanis hypopodia*, *Retinocyclus abietis*, and a member of the *Coryne sarcoides* complex, are the common heartrot fungi in Ontario jack pine. While only *F. pini* has been isolated from decayed wood, all five caused weight loss in tests, and all but *C. sarcoides* discolored wood. *T. hypopodia* was very antagonistic to *F. pini* on agar and on wood. Some lesser mutualistic effects were noted among the other fungi when one was introduced before another.

Mycorrhizal Relations.—The fungi reported to form mycorrhizae with jack pine are *Amanita pantherina*, *A. rubescens*, *Boletus luteus*, *B. tomentosus*, *Cenococcum graniforme*, *Gomphidius vinicolor*, *Lactarius quietus*, and *Suillus cothurnatus* (*1442*). None of these associations have been established by pure-culture techniques.

Wright (*1618*) cites some unpublished work by Stoeckeler, conducted in North Dakota, to the effect that Rocky Mountain ponderosa pine appeared to be less responsive to mycorrhizae than jack pine or blue spruce at one nursery, while the reverse was true at another nursery. At the second nursery, a combination of acidification and inoculation resulted in an increase in the percentage of plantable ponderosa pine stock produced.

Jack pine grown in Middle West high-lime, semi-arid soils, without good mycorrhizal development, turned chlorotic and died. Neither NPK fertilizer nor available iron corrected the condition, but the addition of unsterilized humus from a healthy stand produced normal growth. Only this treatment led to mycorrhizal development (317).

Miscellaneous Pathology.—Burn blight is a disease of red and jack pine mainly affecting planted trees in the Lake States. It causes a heavily-damaged stand to appear as though a fire had singed the upper parts of the trees. The disease results from attacks by the Saratoga spittlebug (*Aphrophora saratogensis*) debilitating the trees and introducing the fungus *Nectria cucurbitula* through its punctures. In the punctured bark the fungus produces necrotic lesions which result in the killing of shoots (555). There is a good possibility that *N. cucurbitula* is the fungus subsequently involved in a dieback of balsam fir in Canada, and for which the name *Thyronectria balsamea* was used (1147).

Basham (66) studied the deterioration of fire-killed jack, red, and white pine in Ontario and describes three stains, designated blue stain, brown stain, and orange-ring stain. He also lists the isolation of 17 "white sap rot" fungi and 10 "brown sap rot" fungi, and gives the roles played by the more important ones in the course of the deterioration process. Later isolates made by Etheridge[38] from a blue stain similar to Basham's, above, "answered the description of *Ceratocystis ips*."

Sand pine
Pinus clausa

Sand pine occurs along the Atlantic and, less frequently, the Gulf Coast of Florida; inland, mainly in the north-central part of the State, it occurs on light, sandy, infertile, and slightly acid soils derived from deep deposits of marine sand and clay (287). Like many species that occur on poor soils, sand pine grows faster and has better form on good soils, but the species can prevail over other pines on the more adverse sites on which it is generally found, while the reverse is true on the better sites.

While small sand pines are easily killed by fire, their resistance to salt-spray injury helps them succeed on the coast and off-shore islands.

Sand pine bears cones early (even on 5-year-old trees), prolifically, and annually. Like pond pine, the Ocala race of sand pine has serotinous cones that remain tightly closed for years unless opened by the heat of fire. The Choctawhatchie race has non-serotinous cones. Sand pine is often a limby, poorly formed, short-lived tree, with a longevity rarely exceeding 70 years (287).

Although it sometimes does not transplant well, and survival percentages are often low, once established, sand pine is quite re-

---

[38] Personal communication from D. E. Etheridge, pathologist, Canada Department of Forestry, Forest Entomology and Pathology Branch, Sillery, Quebec.

sistant to temperature extremes, drought, wind, insects, and disease, and tolerates shade quite well when young. Many millions of sand pine seedlings are now raised each year in Florida for planting in the sandhills.

Outplanted seedlings 2 to 3 years old, in the western Florida sandhills, have suffered some damage from the black root rot that is common in nurseries and is caused by *Sclerotium bataticola* and *Fusarium* spp. (*1313*); the main damage there, however, was to slash pine.

Only one needle rust, *Coleosporium vernoniae*, with its alternate stage on ironweed (*Vernonia*), has been reported on sand pine. While two of the common trio of southern pine needle-browning fungi, *Ploioderma* (*Hypoderma*) *lethale* and *P. hedgcockii*, can blight some older foliage of sand pine, the third fungus, *Scirrhia acicola*, has never been reported on this host.

The round galls of *Cronartium quercuum* are common, and limbiness, together with many galls of this rust, present an appearance much like galled Virginia pines; but as with the latter, the rust does little damage.

Atropellis tingens causes a minor canker, twig blight, and blackening of the wood beneath the canker (*877*).

Witches' brooms of the type not apparently associated with any organism, occur occasionally on sand pine.

Clitocybe tabescens and *Fomes annosus* can cause root rots (*1168*), and *Polyporus schweinitzii* is known as a killing root fungus in young stands in Florida.

Fomes pini can cause considerable red heart in stands over 40 years old, if large branch stubs are common.

The nematode *Meloidodera floridensis* has caused severe damage to sand pine in a small Florida nursery (*704*). Other nematodes reported associated with the roots of sand pine are *Belonolaimus euthychilus* and *Trichodorus atlanticus* (*1222*).

Since sand pine has not been raised in quantity in nurseries until recently, little is known about its nursery diseases, nematode associations, or mycorrhizal relationships.

Lodgepole pine
Pinus contorta

Lodgepole pine occurs over a wide range of sites and soils, because it is not exacting in soil or temperature requirements. It is intolerant of shade, occurs over an altitudinal range from sea level to 11,500 ft., and from wet, flat soils in the Cascades of Washington and Oregon to moderately acid sands or gravelly loams in the Sierras and Rocky Mountain ranges. It is considered by many to be made up of two forms: *Pinus contorta* var. *contorta*, a coastal form resistant to salt spray; and *P. contorta* var. *latifolia*, an inland or mountain form (*1376*). Critchfield (*307*) recognizes four subspecies.

Lodgepole pine occurs over a wide temperature range with extremes of −55° and 100° F., and over a wide precipitation range from under 18 in. of rain per year to where snow cover reaches a depth of 250 in. The tree is not particularly windfirm, especially on shallow soils, and its form varies from a scrubby tree of the coastal variety, with twisted branches (279), in the northwest part of Washington, to clean-boled trees, over 2 ft. in diameter, on its better sites in the Sierras and the Rocky Mountains. One individual tree 6 ft. in diameter has been measured (7). Growth culmination varies greatly with site, but does not exceed 200 years. Stands as old as 450 years have been recorded, and one individual that reached 600 years has been reported (1376).

Although lodgepole pine does not self-prune well, nevertheless, in dense stands where the stocking remains high over many decades, the boles are clean and straight. Open-grown trees are branchy. The species stands weather impacts well, but is sensitive to fire because of its thin bark. Its cones, while serotinous, needing the heat of fire to open, can also be severely damaged by fire (1376). At certain well-defined elevations in the mountains, lodgepole pine is subject to "red belt," a physiogenic foliage disturbance that develops when alternate chilling by cold valley air and warming by chinook winds result in a needle reddening. This needle blight is considered to develop because of excessive transpiration at a time when ground frost prevents a compensating uptake of moisture. Subsequent growth impact has been found to be proportional to the amount of foliage killed (1043).

Nordin (1043) has given a good account of the diseases of lodgepole pine in Alberta, and many of his findings would pertain to the diseases of this species in the Rocky Mountains of the United States. Others of his publications deal with fire damage, cull, and management aspects of lodgepole pine as they are affected by pathology (1040, 1044, 1045). Since lodgepole pine is host to so many fungi of little or no economic importance, the present account is limited to the more noteworthy diseases or fungi, and for lists or accounts of other organisms, suitable publications should be consulted (8, 1043).

Features of the pathology of lodgepole pine include susceptibility to many needle-cast fungi; stem cankering by *Atropellis* spp.; attack by many stem rusts, mainly *Peridermium stalactiforme;* attack by dwarfmistletoe, which causes the greatest disease damage to this tree; and susceptibility to a large number of fungi that stain and rot the wood of living trees.

Seedling Diseases.—The fungi known to attack seedlings are *Rhizoctonia solani, Phytophthora cactorum* (1458), *Pythium* spp., and the snow-mold fungus *Neopeckia coulteri. Thelephora terrestris* and *T. caryophyllea* (1540) can be conspicuous, but they are seldom damaging and *T. terrestris*, at least, is mycorrhizal. All of the rusts and needle blights discussed for this species can attack seedlings in the nursery or in the field. *Rhizina undulata* occasionally kills seedlings where slash burning has taken place. The ring nematode *Criconemoides annulatum* has been reported from the roots of lodgepole pine (1222).

Foliage Diseases.—Lodgepole pine has many needle diseases,[39] mainly those caused by *Davisomycella montana, Elytroderma deformans, Lophodermella (Hypodermella) cerina, L. concolor,* and *L. montivaga* (323, 328). All have been reported of some local im-

---

[39] Personal communication from John M. Staley reported that the species known as *Hypodermella medusa* on lodgepole pine is a "distinct and unnamed" species.

portance in the United States on lodgepole pine. *L. montivaga* is the only species to become epidemic in Canada *(1045)*. Current year's needles are subject to infection by all species, except probably *D. montana,* so that the loss in highly functional foliage can be severe on individual trees. The fungus *Mycosphaerella hypodermellae* can make spots on needles already infected with Lophodermella concolor.

Coleosporium asterum causes the heaviest needle rust, with *Peridermium weirii* occasional in Idaho, and *C. vernoniae* on specimen trees in Kansas and North Carolina. The rusts caused by *Melampsora medusae (albertensis)* and *M. occidentalis* are known to attack seedlings in the Pacific Northwest *(1668)*.

Naemacyclus niveus and *Lophodermium pinastri* are distinctive and general *(323)*, but essentially harmless. The brown-felt snow blight, caused by *Neopeckia coulteri,* will produce its cobwebby mold on foliage that has remained under snow for long periods *(151)*. *Ascochyta piniperda* has been reported on seedling foliage. *Hendersonia pinicola* occurs on living needles in Wyoming, and in the South, specimen trees have developed the bar-spot symptom of the brown-spot disease *(Scirrhia acicola)* *(1304)*. Laut et al. *(837)* have reported the imperfect stage of the brown-spot fungus *(Lecanosticta acicola)* from Manitoba, Canada, on lodgepole pine and jack pine. On the former, needle lesions were up to 3 in. long, discrete, and encircling the needles, although multiple lesions were often confluent. A gray-green zone surrounded a brown, necrotic area that bore the acervuli. They describe these structures, their manner of opening, and the successive formation of conidia from annellophores.

A disease resulting in a red-banding discoloration of foliage, blighting, and defoliation has occurred periodically in Idaho *(1280)*. Much confusion has surrounded the cause, which is now attributed to *Dothistroma pini* var. *linearis*. Thyr and Shaw *(1406)*, who named the variety, give a good account of the problems of identity of fungi appearing on red-banded needles, a second being *Leptostroma decipiens*. For a discussion of *D. pini*, its perfect stage, *Scirrhia pini,* and comparisons with *S. acicola,* see *Pinus ponderosa.*

Stem Diseases.—An important branch and trunk canker of the mountain form of lodgepole pine is caused by *Atropellis piniphila,* with *A. pinicola* occurring less frequently, but on both forms. Hopkins *(703)* gives a good account of the biology of *A. piniphila* on lodgepole pine. The black, irregularly discoid apothecia and the blue-black color of the wood beneath are indicative of Atropellis cankers. Their chief damage is malformation and local defect.

Cenangium ferruginosum (C. abietis) is a common twig fungus, of doubtful capacity to invade tissue not already weakened from other causes, and is now considered largely a saprobe *(542)*. *Diplodia pinea* is a weak twig parasite mainly following other injury on ornamental trees *(1513)*. *Tympanis confusa* is a saprophyte that produces small, black apothecia on dead bark *(552)*.

The stem rust cankers of lodgepole pine are caused by *Peridermium (Cronartium) stalactiforme (10, 1653)*, *C. comandrae (966)*, *C. comptoniae (25, 1341)*, and *P. harknessii (1653)* with alternate hosts, respectively, as follows: *Castilleja* and *Melampyrum* spp., *Comandra* spp., *Comptonia* or *Myrica* spp., none. The complicated host relations and taxonomy of these rusts and *P. filamentosum* have been clarified by Peterson (*1110*). Questions of long-standing concern are whether long-cycled forms of *P. stalactiforme* and *P. filamentosum* occur in association with certain aecial pine hosts but not with others, and along with *P. harknessii*, whether all three may have stages on the Scrophulariaceae that are indistinguishable from each other on that host (*1102*), just as *C. quercuum, C. fusiforme,* and *C. strobilinum* are almost indistinguishable on oak leaves. Thus the imperfect genus name *Peridermium* is preferred for any rust of this type where the telial association, if any, is in question.

Recent experiments in Canada clearly showed that while *Peridermium stalactiforme* from jack pine readily infected *Castilleja* and *Melampyrum,* producing telia, in no case did aeciospores of *P. harknessii* from jack pine infect these hosts (*1653*). The stalactiform rust is regarded by Ziller (*10*) as always heteroecious.

Working with the rusts on lodgepole pine, Hiratsuka et al. (*686*) found some clear differences in the cytology of the aeciospores and aeciospore germ tubes of *Peridermium harknessii* and *P. stalactiforme* of the *Cronartium coleosporioides* complex.

None of the stem rusts are consistently damaging to lodgepole pine over large areas. *Peridermium stalactiforme* can kill, but it mainly deforms; *Cronartium comandrae* is common and has proven serious to lodgepole pine in some areas over a mile from the closest *Comandra umbellata* (*966*). Krebill (*812*), by analyzing cankers on lodgepole pine in the Rocky Mountains, concluded that after remaining endemic for a century, Comandra rust became epidemic between 1910 and 1945, and then subsided to an endemic state for the next 10 years. This rust is currently causing concern in Tennessee, where it has been attacking *Pinus taeda* following introduction on *P. ponderosa* nursery stock.

P. filamentosum, called limb rust, is rare on lodgepole pine (*961*), almost never causes swelling, and even when it has encircled the trunk over a long area and killed many limbs along this area, as it often does to ponderosa pine, the main part of the tree may still be alive. *P. harknessii* makes round galls, is particularly damaging to lodgepole pine, and can kill thousands of seedlings in small areas in the field, and ruin the form of, or kill, larger trees (*1102*).

Data on major damage from individual outbreaks of Comandra rust have been reported by Peterson (*1104*). Mielke has described cankers of *Peridermium stalactiforme* up to 30 ft. long that still had not girdled, and mentions the rodent feeding, breakage, and other damage associated with this rust (*962*). Mielke doubts whether true *P. filamentosum* ever occurs on lodgepole pine (*961*). The very complex situation regarding the identity of the stem rusts of American western pines, and which are heteroecious, is greatly clarified by Peterson's paper on limb rust (*1111*), and his monograph of the pine stem *Peridermium* species of the world (*1110*).

The hyperparasite *Tuberculina maxima* is known to attack *Cronartium comandrae* and *Peridermium stalactiforme* on lodgepole pine in Alberta, Canada (*1132*). In the course of surveys for *T. maxima* there, a strain of *P. stalactiforme* with white aeciospores was discovered. Albino forms of several *Peridermium* spp. are known to date.

The most serious disease of lodgepole pine is caused by the dwarfmistletoe, *Arceuthobium americanum.* It is widespread and attacks trees of all ages, producing yellowing and death of foliage, stem and branch swellings, deformation, witches' brooms, and killing. In managing this tree species in many areas, it is essential to take dwarfmistletoe behavior into consideration (*507, 1040*). Hawksworth and Hinds (*616*), working with lodgepole pine in 25 stands in Colorado, determined the extent to which infection by *Arceuthobium americanum* reduced growth. Reduction in height and diameter averaged 0.7 percent per year since time of infection. Reduction in merchantable cubic-foot volume per plot averaged 1.9 percent per year. Such data established an economic base for control planning. This dwarfmistletoe species has been attacked by the hyperparasite *Colletotrichum gloeosporioides* (*1006*) (see *Abies magnifica*). Means of distinguishing this fungus from *Septogloeum gillii* and *Wallrothiella arceuthobii* are provided by Wicker (*1577*). *A. vaginatum* f. *cryptopodum* has been found on lodgepole pine in Colorado.

At least three other dwarfmistletoes are known to attack lodgepole pine, but they are of little or no importance in the pathology of this tree.

The hyperparasites *Septogloeum gillii* and *Wallrothiella arceuthobii* are sometimes factors in the natural suppression of dwarfmistletoe (*965, 1043*). Non-mistletoe brooms, that Hawksworth (*612*) calls stimulation brooms, develop from the increased growth of branches of residual trees after logging.

Aleurodiscus lividocoeruleus and *A. penicillatus* occur on dead twigs (*858*).

Robinson (*1184*) has determined the blue-stain fungi responsible for the tracheomycosis following attack of lodgepole pine by *Dendroctonus monticolae.* She isolated, from attacked trees, the blue-stain fungi *Ceratocystis montia* and *Leptographium* sp.; yeasts *Pichia pini, Hansenula capsulata, H. holstii,* and others; and found perithecia of the following stainers on the bark: *C. montia, C. minor, C. minuta, Ceratocystis* sp., and *Europhium* sp.

Root Diseases.—The main root-rotters of lodgepole pine are *Armillaria mellea,* which attacks chiefly at the root collar of seedlings (*1043*), and *Fomes annosus, Polyporus tomentosus,* and *P. schweinitzii,* which rot roots and butts in localized areas over the lodgepole range. The species is also moderately susceptible to attack by *Poria weirii* in the Northwest. Hornibrook (*708*) found the main root and butt fungi in a Colorado defect study to be *P. tomentosus, Coniophora puteana* (*C. cerebella*), and *A. mellea,* with *P. osseus* isolated once. He describes the early and late stages of the rots caused by these fungi.

Many lodgepole pine stands in Alberta, Canada, have been sustaining heavy mortality, due mainly to *A. mellea,* but with *Peridermium* rusts, game, and rodents contributing (*60*). Old hardwood stumps provided a major food base for *A. mellea* attacking pine, as pointed out also under *Pinus strobus.*

A yellow, stringy root rot caused by *Flammula alnicola* occurs occasionally on lodgepole pine in Canada (*374*).

Trunk Rots.—The heartwood of this species is subject to many stains and decays. Among the important basidiomycete stainers in Canada are *Fomes pini, Stereum pini, S. sanguinolentum,* and *Polyporus anceps.* These fungi, together with *Coniophora puteana,* are also heart-rotters (*375, 1043*). The lodgepole pine fungus, referred to by Denyer and Riley (*375*) as *S. pini,* is not this fungus, and it has not yet been determined (*1177*). Other fungi, including *F. roseus, F. cajanderi* (*F. subroseus*), *Polyporus osseus,* and *Poria microspora,* have been reported as heart-rotters of lodgepole pine but cause little loss in protected and managed stands.

Hornibrook (*708*), in a Colorado study in mature and overmature timber, found that decay made up 87 percent of the cull and that 64 percent was caused by *Fomes pini,* with the remainder attributed to *F. pinicola, F. laricis, Peniophora luna, Trametes serialis,* and the four butt-rot fungi attributed to Hornibrook under Root Diseases. He describes the early and late stages of the rots caused by these fungi, lists the indicators of decay, and recommends scaling practices for each.

The fungus *Coryne sarcoides* inhibited *F. pini, S. pini,* and *S. sanguinolentum* in woodblock culture, and may interfere with the isolation of decay fungi from trees (*1573*) (see also *Pinus banksiana*).

In connection with a cull study of lodgepole pine in boreal Alberta, Loman and Paul (*881*) determined that *Fomes pini* and *Polyporus tomentosus* were the main pocket trunk-rot fungi, *P. tomentosus* and *Flammula alnicola* were the main pocket root- and butt-rotters, and *Coniophora puteana* was the main brown, cubical butt-rotter. *Peniophora pseudo-pini* was the most frequently isolated fungus, but was always associated with a red heartwood stain.

Robinson-Jeffrey and Loman (*1185*), working with lodgepole pine in Alberta, determined the fungi responsible for heartwood stain and decay encountered in a cull survey. The most common isolates were *Peniophora pseudo-pini* and *Tympanis hypopodia,* both associated with red heartwood stain. The trunk rots yielded mostly *Fomes pini* and *Polyporus tomentosus,* often together. Roots and butts yielded *P. tomentosus, Flammula alnicola, Coniophora puteana,* and *Peniophora gigantea.* Several additional basidiomycetes were associated with trunk injuries.

Mycorrhizal Relations.—Twenty-five fungi are reported as forming mycorrhizae with lodgepole pine, but none were confirmed by pure-culture technique (*1442*).

In Oregon, Wright (*1619*) reported black mycorrhizac, caused by *Cenococcum graniforme,* to be the most common on lodgepole and ponderosa pine seedlings, but that shading increased the percentage of white mycorrhizae. Wet soil did not inhibit mycorrhizal formation.

Miscellaneous Pathology.—A decline in vigor of pole-sized lodgepole pine has been described from British Columbia, which has associated with it symptoms very similar to those of pole blight of western white pine, and the two maladies may well have the same genesis (*1075*).

Loman (*880*) determined the lethal effect of periodic high temperatures on the following lodgepole pine slash-decay fungi in Canada: *Stereum sanguinolentum, Coniophora puteana, Peniophora phlebioides,* and *Lenzites saepiaria.* The latter two withstood much higher temperatures than the first two.

The nonbasidiomycete fungi that occur in the normal-appearing stems of lodgepole pine have been studied by Bourchier (*141*) in relation to attack by *Stereum pini*. Species in 14 genera were isolated. He concluded that normal-appearing heartwood generally supports a major flora of microfungi.

Lodgepole pine has been damaged by sulfur dioxide from ore smelting. It is intermediate in position, with respect to sensitivity to smelter fumes, being exceeded by many conifers, and itself exceeding others (*1249*).

Coulter pine
Pinus coulteri

An intolerant tree of the dry, warm slopes and ridges of the coastal ranges and cross-ranges of southern and central California, Coulter pine generally occurs between 3,000 and 6,000 ft. in elevation. Although a smaller tree, it has a certain resemblance to ponderosa pine; however, the former's stiff, heavier foliage, stouter twigs, and very large cones easily distinguish it. The tree ordinarily grows to a height of 40 to 60 ft. with an irregular, open, heavily branched crown, maturing at about 100 years, with a probable longevity of 150 to 200 years. The large lower branches are long, bending downward, often to the ground, with an upward curve at the ends, and with immense bunches of erect, deep bluegreen, stiff needles concealing their extremities. The cones are very heavy and strongly armed with spines. The tree occurs singly, often in chaparral, sometimes in ravines, but mostly on dry, gravelly loams. It is hardy and drought-resistant (*955*), enduring a range of from 15° to 100° F., high or low humidity, and, in the inland mountains, withstanding almost arid conditions (*1367*).

Top-dying of Coulter pine on the Angeles National Forest in California followed a sudden winter drop to 21° F., with strong winds and very heavy snow. The trouble was confined to fully exposed tops of thrifty trees. Typical freezing injury to the cambium was obvious and there was a heavy flow of resin just below the limit of complete cambial kill (*1490*).

Seedling Diseases.—Coulter pine seedlings are subject to damping-off and root rot. Smith and Bega (*1323*) describe severe damage to coniferous nursery stock, including Coulter pine, in California nurseries (see *Pinus lambertiana*), as a result of mid- to late-season attack of roots by *Sclerotium bataticola* (*Macrophomina phaseoli*). *Pythium* spp., *Fusarium* spp., and *Rhizoctonia* spp. were also isolated from California nurseries.

Foliage Diseases.—The dying or dead foliage of Coulter pine has supported *Soleella* (*Bifusella*) *striiformis*, with its small, black hysterothecia arranged in rows along the stomatal lines, but its pathogenicity to the foliage of this species can be questioned (*323*). Although reports have listed some needle rusts as occurring on Coulter pine—the eastern species *Coleosporium carneum, C. delicatulum,* and *C. asterum* (*1276*) and the western *C. madiae* (*1277*)—Arthur and Cummins list none (*46*), and certainly none are important pathogens on this species.

Stem Diseases.—The western gall rust (*Peridermium harknes-*

sii) is an important disease of Coulter pine, especially in areas of persistent fog or humidity, ranking with dwarfmistletoe as the only two major parasites of this species. Galling is practically confined to the branches on this species (*1102*). Coulter pine is a host of the sweetfern rust, *Cronartium comptoniae*, on planted trees in New Hampshire.

Western dwarfmistletoe (*Arceuthobium campylopodum* f. *campylopodum*) sometimes attacks Coulter pine, producing its typical swellings, distortion, growth reduction, and occasionally killing.

Root Diseases.—The only root pathogen known to attack Coulter pine is *Fomes annosus*, with killing reported in its normal field habitat (*1498*), and also during an epidemic in a California arboretum (*92*). The only fungus reported as a mycorrhizal associate of this pine is *Cenococcum graniforme* (*1442*).

Shortleaf pine
Pinus echinata

Shortleaf pine is intolerant (*54*), matures at about 120 years, can live up to about 300 years, and prefers light-textured soils, but will grow well on clays with good internal drainage. On heavy soils with poor internal drainage, as in parts of the Piedmont, it is very subject to littleleaf, its most damaging disease. Otherwise, this species, like longleaf pine, is unusually free from serious diseases. The species extends from New Jersey to Florida, and west through parts of the Central and Southern States, and from Missouri to Texas. Largely a tree of the upper Piedmont, its commercial range extends from the lower coastal plain to the lower slopes of the Appalachian Mountains and other hilly terrain, and from New Jersey to Louisiana, Arkansas, and Missouri. This species will reproduce by seedling sprouts.

To a greater degree than any of the other southern pines, it withstands ice, wind, and sudden temperature changes. Flowers of shortleaf pine have been damaged by cold, and this phenomenon might explain some seed-crop failures (*1080*). A late spring frost killed about 30 percent of the shortleaf pine flowers in a Virginia Piedmont stand. On May 2, 1963, a low of 25° F. was recorded and evidence of flower killing was apparent within 5 days (*738*).

Seedling Diseases.—Nursery seedlings are subject to damping-off and root rot caused, individually or collectively, by *Rhizoctonia solani*, *Fusarium oxysporum*, and *Sclerotium bataticola* (*696*) in soils with pH above 6 and under moist weather conditions. A black root rot caused by the latter two fungi becomes severe only if the soil temperature remains above 90° F. for many hours, repeatedly (*695*). Shortleaf pine seedlings proved susceptible to *Phytophthora cinnamomi* root rot when the seedlings were grown in liquid culture (*1646*).

Campbell and Hendrix (*217*) reported several species of *Pythium* from southern pine seedbeds, and demonstrated that large populations of *Pythium* spp. propagules were associated with yellowing and stunting in some nurseries. In the greenhouse, *P. irregulare* reduced emergence of shortleaf pine seedlings by 58 percent, loblolly pine by 32 percent, and slash pine by 12 percent. *P. sylvaticum* was only weakly pathogenic. In a later paper (*218*), they show the in-

304

cidence of several *Pythium* and *Phytophthora* spp. in forest soils of the Southeast.

Although several species of nematodes occur commonly on seedling roots (*1219*), material damage in the nursery has not yet been ascribed to them. Conks of *Thelephora terrestris* commonly surround seedlings, but this fungus appears to be more of a helpful mycorrhiza-former than a smothering pathogen when seedlings grow rapidly. A chlorosis of shortleaf and loblolly pines in an Arkansas nursery was related to a high calcium content of the soil (*1584*).

Many species of nematodes have been identified in association with the roots of shortleaf pine, as seedlings in nurseries and from trees in the field, both healthy and with littleleaf disease. Ruehle (*1222*) provides access to the literature on these nematodes (see also Root Diseases).

Shortleaf pine seedlings normally have a curious bend at the ground line that has led many to believe that they are seedling sprouts following injury to the original seedling. Many aspects of the normal morphology, nutrition, physiology, and ecology of shortleaf pine, as well as their pathological anatomy and behavior, have been determined in connection with the research on littleleaf (*288, 289, 642, 749, 1204, 1641, 1642*), and would be useful to anyone working with this species.

Foliage Diseases.—The foliage seldom develops serious diseases, but can be attacked by at least eight species of needle rusts (*Coleosporium* spp.), often by *Ploioderma* (*Hypoderma*) *lethale* (*155, 328*), occasionally by *P. hedgcockii*, and by the brownish surface mildew caused by *Irenina* (*Meliola*) *pinicola* (*365*). The parasitism of *Lophodermium pinastri*, common on dead or senescent needles, has yet to be demonstrated (*153*).

Brown spot (*Scirrhia acicola*) is sometimes aggressive, and a needle curl has been attributed to water deficiency (*748*). A needle and fascicle dwarf of unknown cause has been described by Young (*1637*) and later reported on in more detail (*1638*). Young (*1638*) states that the abnormality in the new shoots of shortleaf pine planted in Texas, that he calls "dwarf fascicle," is characterized by lack of buds in the winter condition, and instead, blue-green bunches of sharp terminal needles. The latter became flared and sometimes turned red, purple, or yellow. Some branch tips had new fascicles that remained tightly packed and parallel. Another symptom was a restriction in "candle" development to a slender, whitish shoot, often curved, with needles that remained very short. Witches' brooms, arising from apparently localized genetic aberration, have been reported.

Stem Diseases.—Many twig and stem diseases are common, but none are consistently damaging. *Caliciopsis pinea* (*483*) and *Atropellis tingens* (*380*) will sometimes kill twigs and small branches, and following insect injury, pitch canker (*Fusarium lateritium* f. *pini*) has caused extensive twig blighting in parts of the Carolinas (*665, 667*). *C. pinea* can be identified easily by the hairlike ascocarp stalks that stick out from the small lesions, usually on branches. *A. tingens* can be distinguished by the blue-black discoloration of the wood beneath the canker face, and by the irregular black apothecia. Pitch canker, as the name implies, involves copious resin flow and a pitch-soaking of the wood from the canker face to the pith.

Diplodia pinea has caused damage to specimen trees injured or weakened by other causes (*1513*). *Cenangium ferruginosum* (*542*) and *Dasyscypha ellisiana* (*575*) are less common twig-canker fungi of questionable pathogenicity. Branches and stems often develop the relatively benign galls of *Cronartium quercuum* (*630*) and, rarely, the more lethal spindle-shaped galls of *C. fusiforme*. *C. comptoniae*, the sweetfern rust, has occasionally been reported from shortleaf pine (*25, 1341*).

Jewell and Walker (*756*) worked out the structural details of the round galls of *Cronartium quercuum* on shortleaf pine. Mycelium occurred in all gall tissues except the periderm. Xylem rays were more numerous and ray parenchyma longer and wider; vertical tracheids were short and abnormal in shape. Resin ducts were numerous and large in the galls. The parasite did not influence the host beyond the limits of mycelium.

Cronartium comandrae was reported by E. R. Roth [40] to have killed 29 percent of the trees in a young shortleaf pine plantation in Arkansas.

Tracheomycosis, following bark beetle attack, results from invasion of the sapwood by *Ceratocystis minor* and *Dacryomyces* sp. (*167, 1017*).

Littleleaf (*207*) is the most serious disease, occurring from Virginia to Alabama on soils that are poorly drained internally. It appears any time after an age of about 20 years, with foliage becoming yellowish and short. Then, after a few years of progressive shortening of shoot and wood growth, the trees die. Littleleaf results from a combination of factors, including persistent root attack by *Phytophthora cinnamomi* (*1641, 1646*), poor soil aeration, low fertility, and, possibly, a contribution from manganese toxicity and nematodes (*1219*).

Jackson and Hepting (*749*) showed that root starvation accompanying littleleaf in shortleaf pine results in the formation of deep cork-cambium, which sometimes almost reaches the cambium of roots. The result is dead "rough bark," in contrast to the smooth, reddish bark of small, healthy roots. Rough-bark formation in stems or roots is thus considered a reaction to starvation of outer-bark tissues, whether from age, disease, or injury.

Root Diseases.—Saplings and older trees are moderately susceptible to attack by *Fomes annosus*. Some planted stands that have been thinned, and occasional unthinned natural stands, have lost many residual trees from this root rot, but such losses with shortleaf pine have not been general (*762, 763, 1588*). Kuhlman et al. (*820*) demonstrated the colonization of shortleaf pine stumps by *F. annosus* and compared the rate of growth through stumps colonized by basidiospores, conidia, and mycelium grown in sawdust.

The root rot caused by *Clitocybe tabescens*, general on many woody plants, attacks shortleaf pine in Florida (*1168*), but is not considered an important forest disease.

Polyporus schweinitzii and *P. tomentosus* cause occasional root

---

[40] Personal communication from Elmer R. Roth, pathologist, USDA Forest Service, Southeastern Area, S. & P.F., Atlanta, Ga.

and butt rot (*660*), but are seldom limiting factors. Tuckahoes (*Poria cocos*), also called Indian bread, are common tuberous growths on sapling and larger roots (*747*), but no important damage has been ascribed to this interesting root fungus. *Torula marginata* is an inhabitor of "brown-patch" areas on roots, which are starved phloem areas being cut off by a cork cambium (*747, 749*). Campbell isolated many fungi associated with the roots of healthy and littleleaf-diseased trees (*206*), almost all of which were saprophytes. His isolation of *Phytophthora cinnamomi* came later, through the use of the apple as a culture medium (*207*).

Trunk Rots.—*Fomes pini* heart rot (red heart), entering shortleaf and loblolly pines almost solely through dead branch stubs, is rarely a factor under 80 years, but has been noted abundantly in an occasional stand as young as 40 years. Rot cull in uninjured stands is not ordinarily over 2 percent up to 70 years (*657*).

Ruehle (*1219, 1220*) found parasitic nematodes commonly attacking roots to include *Xiphinema americanum, Hemicycliophora vidua, Helicotylenchus dihystera* and *H. erythrinae*, and *Hoplolaimus galeatus*. These have been found in large enough numbers to make them suspect of having an impact on a tree's vigor. Other genera and species of plant parasitic nematodes found occasionally on shortleaf pine include *Criconemoides rusticum, Longidorus* sp., *Meloidodera* sp., *Meloidogyne* sp., *Paratylenchus* sp., *Pratylenchus zeae, Trichodorus christiei, Trophurus* sp., *Tylenchorhynchus claytoni*, and *Xiphinema chambersi* (see also Seedling Diseases).

Mycorrhizal Relations.—The fungi definitely shown, by pure-culture synthesis, to form mycorrhizae (*181, 182*) are *Amanita muscaria, Boletus communis, B. luteus, Laccaria (Clitocybe) laccata, Lactarius deliciosus, Lactarius* sp., *Leucopaxillus (Clitocybe) cerealis, Pisolithus tinctorius*. Additional fungi reported on shortleaf pine (*1442*) are: *Cenococcum graniforme, Leucopaxillus albissimus*, and *Boletus granulatus*. There is also a likelihood that *Thelephora terrestris* is mycorrhizal on shortleaf pine. Satisfactory seedling growth has been correlated with abundance of mycorrhizae (*972*).

Zak and Bryan (*1645*) have succeeded in isolating several mycorrhizal fungi directly from the roots of southern pines, including shortleaf pine. Zak (*1643*) suggested that mycorrhizae may play a role in protecting pine roots from attack by *Phytophthora cinnamomi*, and Marx and Davey (*931*) demonstrated the mechanisms by which ectotrophic mycorrhizae protected pine roots from invasion by this root-rot fungus.

Miscellaneous Pathology.—Symptoms of mineral deficiencies in seedlings are as follows (*689*):

N—Needles short, pale-green, not yellow. Growth stunted.

P—Seedlings greatly stunted. Lower needles reddened.

K—Seedlings greatly stunted. Needles blue-green, never yellow. Necrosis common, mostly around terminal meristems. Great irregularity in size.

Mg—Moderate stunting. Best symptom is top chlorosis of needles, with sometimes full needle involvement. Chlorotic tips later necrotic. Tip chlorosis only in Mg deficiency.

Pinyon pine
Pinus edulis

Pinyon pine is an intolerant, small, scrubby tree, usually occurring in scattered groups and open stands on dry foothills, slopes, and canyon sides of the southern Rocky Mountains from Wyoming and Colorado to Texas and Arizona at elevations between 5,000 and 9,000 ft. It is one of the four so-called nut pines, the seeds of which are edible. Its needles are mostly in clusters of two, distinguishing it from the other three nut-pine species. Although less tolerant to cold and drought than neighboring junipers, pinyon will, nevertheless, succeed on exposed slopes where the average annual precipitation is less than 13 in. and the annual range of temperature extends from —25° to 110° F. It is resistant to fire because of its insulated, furrowed, thick bark. Its best growth is on mesas and slopes, where the gravelly or sandy soil is moderately deep and rich (*279*).

Pinyon pine has an interesting pathology. Although some of its pathogens occur also on many other pines (for example, *Elytroderma deformans* and *Armillaria mellea*), others are confined to just certain nut pines of the Southwest (*Cronartium occidentale* and *Arceuthobium campylopodum* f. *divaricatum*), and still others are almost confined just to *Pinus edulis* itself (*Bifusella* (*Hypoderma*) *saccata* and *Coleosporium jonesii*).

Seedling Diseases.—Virtually nothing is known of the seedling diseases of pinyon. Seedlings are subject to frost-heaving on exposed, bare, cold slopes, and frost pockets, and they also suffer much damage from grazing. Nematodes have been isolated from around seedling roots, but identifications are not available.

Foliage Diseases.—Although pinyon has many foliage diseases, only one, Elytroderma needle blight (*E. deformans*), is economically important. This unique fungus maintains itself perennially in twigs; infects, reddens, and kills new needles mainly by direct infection from attached twigs; and produces "flags" of dead foliage, brooms, crown-thinning, distortion, and killing (*248, 861*). On pinyon, *E. deformans* causes as much needle-browning, disfiguring, and brooming as it does on *Pinus ponderosa*, the main host with respect to broom formation by this fungus.

Bifusella (*Hypoderma*) *saccata* mainly attacks older needles on the lower parts of trees. *B. pini* has also been reported on *Pinus edulis*, but it is generally considered confined to *P. monophylla*, and to have a resemblance to *B. saccata* on *P. edulis* (*323*). Paul Keener [41] collected a variant of the above two Bifusellas in Arizona, but it has not been described.

Two needle rusts, one confined to *Pinus edulis* and the other to *P. edulis* and *P. monophylla*, have caused enough damage to be rated important by some, but this rating is largely based on the marring of the appearance of trees, as a result of needle-spotting and needle-killing, and thus interfering with aesthetic values. One rust, *Coleosporium jonesii*, which also attacks *P. monophylla* in California, goes to *Ribes* spp., and the other, *C. crowellii*, is auto-

---

[41] Personal communication from Paul D. Keener, deceased, formerly plant pathologist, University of Arizona, Tucson, Ariz.

cious, with telia produced in the needles, and is thus rather unique and, in this respect, corresponds to *C. pinicola* on *P. virginiana*.

The rust hyperparasites *Cladosporium aecidiicola* and *Darluca filum* occur commonly in association with *Coleosporium crowellii* on pinyon needles in Arizona (777). The ascomycete *Endarluca australis* is indicated by Keener (775) to be the perfect stage of *D. filum*.

At the higher elevations in Arizona, the uredo sori of *C. jonesii* on *Ribes* are so heavily parasitized, that by the time the sori are formed they appear black and look like a leaf-spot fungus. The hyperparasites are mainly *Darluca filum* and *Cladosporium aecidiicola*.

Diplodia pinea has attacked this species out of its range in Kansas, but its role was very likely secondary.

Stem Diseases.—The pinyon blister rust (*Cronartium occidentale*) occurs generally and endemically in the Southwest, producing branch and trunk swellings near the ground (1355). While many trees are killed, the disease has not been rated of particular importance to the species. In some areas, thousands of infections have been traced to a single epidemic year (1494). Its alternate hosts are species of *Ribes,* on which *C. occidentale* produces uredia and telia that resemble those of *C. ribicola.* Staining techniques have proven successful in distinguishing the two rusts on species of *Ribes* (241), and Kimmey reported a method of visual determination that proved 93 percent effective in separating *C. ribicola* from *C. occidentale* on *Ribes* (792). A buffered-acid fuchsin stain, developed later, was very effective in differentiating the two rusts on *Ribes* (453).

The pinyon dwarfmistletoe, *Arceuthobium campylopodum* f. *divaricatum,* attacks all four nut pines (505), causing its characteristic swellings, brooming, distortion, growth reduction, and sometimes killing. It outranks in importance both *Elytroderma deformans* and *Verticicladiella wagenerii* as the major pathogen of pinyon.

Root Diseases and Trunk Rots.—A root disease caused by *Verticicladiella wagenerii* attacks ponderosa, Jeffrey, and pinyon pines in California, Colorado, and Arizona, and is particularly severe on pinyon. It spreads by root contact, causes a staining of the wood (not in the usual wedge-shaped patterns of the blue-stainers), and kills the roots. Typically, small groups of trees are killed by this disease (1499) (see also *Pinus jeffreyi*).

Armillaria mellea and *Polyporus schweinitzii* are root- and buttrot fungi of pinyon, but neither has become noteworthy as a pathogen on this tree. The principal heart rots are red-ring rot (*Fomes pini*) and the brown, crumbly rot caused by *F. pinicola. F. roseus* also occurs on this species.

Slash pine
Pinus elliottii

Slash pine (*Pinus elliottii* var. *elliottii*) is moderately tolerant, matures at 100 years, and can live to over 200 years. It mostly occupies sandy soils that are often underlain with poorly drained hardpan, and often thrives in hillocks in swamps, as well as on dry sites (286). It grows best on "pond" margin sites. Its northern limits in South Carolina and middle Georgia are sharply defined by the incidence of ice storms. Slash pine breaks over from the weight of sleet or snow (912) to a greater extent than any other southern pine, and many plantings north of the natural range, that grew very well for many years, have been destroyed by a single sleet storm that would not bother shortleaf pine. Slash pine is subject to killing by fire through the sapling stages, is moderately resistant to wind, and tolerates flooding. It does not thrive much north of its natural range because of ice and temperature limitations. The tree thrives along the Gulf Coast to Louisiana, extending inland extensively only in Florida, Georgia, and Alabama. The south Florida form is *P. elliotti* var. *densa*.

The main features of the pathology of slash pine are (1) susceptibility to damping-off under conditions of high pH and high spring moisture, and to black root rot in warm and unfumigated nursery soil; ·(2) major losses from fusiform rust in unsprayed nurseries and in young field stands; (3) a common destruction of leaders and other shoots by pitch canker; (4) frequent death from annosus root rot in thinned plantations; (5) heavy loss of seed from cone rust in Florida and the Gulf Coast; and (6) high susceptibility to ice breakage.

Seedling Diseases.—The fungus and nematode diseases of slash pine nursery seedlings and young transplants are almost the same as described for loblolly. These two tree species are commonly grown in the same nurseries and together account for over 90 percent of the forest nursery stock produced in the South. The damping-off, black root rot, and nematode problems involve largely the same organisms for both species.

Pythium spp., as nursery pathogens, are discussed under *Pinus echinata*.

A serious disease in 2- to 3-year-old outplanted trees in the west Florida sandhills proved to be due, in part, to the black-root-rot fungi *Sclerotium bataticola* and *Fusarium* spp. (1313). Slash pine seedlings also proved susceptible to *Phytophthora cinnamomi* root rot when grown in liquid culture and inoculated (1646).

Ruehle (1222) provides access to the literature on the many species of nematodes identified in association with the roots of slash pine, both from nurseries and from larger trees in the field.

Foliage Diseases.—The foliage seldom develops serious diseases, but can be attacked by five needle rusts, all species of *Coleosporium* (46). These rusts can be very conspicuous in the spring, but have little impact on growth. In late winter, attacks by *Ploioderma* (*Hypoderma*) *lethale* are often so severe as to turn trees completely brown (155). Yet, after the new growth emerges, the trees usually appear normal, and ring-growth observations indicate little effect of this brief period of browning on growth. *P. hedgcockii* causes a less common needle blight, and there is great tree-to-tree variation in susceptibility to both the Ploiodermas. *P. lethale* in the late winter, and brown spot (*Scirrhia acicola*), which may appear first in the fall, account for most of the severe browning of slash pine so noticeable in certain years (156). Unlike longleaf pine, seedlings of slash are not markedly checked in early height growth by brown spot.

310

Lophodermium pinastri, common on dying and dead needles, is not regarded as attacking foliage unless senescent or otherwise debilitated.

Stem and Root Diseases.—The most serious disease of slash pine is fusiform rust (*Cronartium fusiforme*), which disfigures and kills trees up to pole size and results in much stem breakage (*1477*). The galls typically taper at both ends and lack collars. However, some have a collar only at the inner end, while some have them at both ends, making such galls hardly distinguishable from those of *C. quercuum.* Peterson (*1110*) describes, in detail, the *Peridermium* stages of the pine stem rusts.

Fusiform rust can be an economic factor throughout the range of slash pine, with some of the greatest damage resulting from the rust being followed by *Dioryctria* larvae and the pitch canker *Fusarium.* Trees with stem cankers or branch cankers within about 15 in. of the stem are poor risks to survive until pulpwood size. The round galls of *C. quercuum* sometimes occur on slash pine, but this fungus is much less of a killer of stems than *C. fusiforme.* The latter is known to produce secondary sporidia, which are forcibly abjected from the sterigmata.

Although seedlings can be killed readily by *C. fusiforme* alone, there is some question as to how lethal this fungus is to stems several inches in diameter, in the absence of insect invasion. In this connection, Myren (*1008*) found a high percentage of rust galls infested, with the commonest insect invaders being the pitch moth, *Dioryctria amatella,* a chalcid wasp, *Eurytoma sciromatis,* and the deodar weevil, *Pissodes nemorensis.* He concluded that these insects served as infection courts for the many fungi found in the gall wood; namely, basidiomycetes in 13 percent of the galls, bluestain fungi in 30 percent, and fungi imperfecti in all galls studied.

A common, but minor, twig blight and canker, chiefly on lower limbs, is caused by *Atropellis tingens,* which darkens the wood beneath and produces distorted, blackish apothecia.

Another blight of twigs, small stems, and especially of leaders, is pitch canker (*Fusarium lateritium* f. *pini*). Slash pine is a major host, and in certain years has suffered greatly from deformation and killing of trees up through the sapling sizes (*102, 109*). It usually follows attack by pine shoot moths, but can follow any injury (*934*). The fungus prolongs the flow of gum from turpentine faces and other fresh wounds and is the chief cause of pitch-soaking behind faces and other wounds (*261*).

Turpentine faces being worked sometimes cease gum flow and become dry. Drying is preceded by flamelike patterns of pitch soak and cambial necrosis just above the top streak. This condition, called dry-face (*1259*), is associated with lowered vigor, excessive chipping and other injury, drought, and ultimately some invasion of staining fungi and other fungi that can produce toxic and plugging effects like the tracheomycosis following bark beetle attack (*1449*). During the extended dry periods in the 1930's and 1950's many slash pines that had dry-face went into a condition known as pitch streak. Streaks of cambium, many feet in length, died, and resin seeped from these streaks. The trees bronzed and later died. No fungi were indicted and the trouble is regarded as physiological (*269*).

311

The activities of blue-stain fungi following bark beetle attack; the course and extent of damage by the root rots caused by *Fomes annosus*, *Polyporus schweinitzii*, and *Clitocybe tabescens;* as well as the course of the heart rot known as red heart (*Fomes pini*) are as described for loblolly pine.

P. tomentosus, a root and butt fungus, the rot of which resembles that of *F. pini*, occurs occasionally on slash pine. Slash pines with basal rust cankers (*Cronartium fusiforme*) are particularly subject to *P. tomentosus* root rot. This relationship was demonstrated by Boyce (*160*), in several north Georgia stands. He found sporophores of the root-rot fungus on 13 percent of 92 basal-cankered trees sampled in 4 stands. Later studies in Georgia confirmed that *P. tomentosus* fruits readily enough at the base of infected trees, so that fruiting is a useful indicator of the incidence of infection.

Although slash pine does not develop littleleaf, its roots are readily killed by *Phytophthora cinnamomi* in liquid culture (*1646*). Slash pine's rapid rate of root regeneration on the light soils it usually occupies prevents decline leading to littleleaf, in spite of *Phytophthora* infection.

Nematodes attacking, or in association with, slash pine roots in the United States include *Belonolaimus gracilis*, *Dolichodorus* sp., *Hoplolaimus coronatus*, *Hoplolaimus* sp., *Tylenchorhyncus claytoni*, *Tylenchorhyncus* sp., *Xiphinema americanum*, and species of the other genera listed for shortleaf pine, with the exception of *Rotylenchus* (*704, 1220*). Nematodes have been shown to be associated with stunting of loblolly and slash pines in southern plantations. Four species, in four genera, fed and reproduced on these pines (*1225*). Parasitic nematodes found to be associated with the roots of south Florida slash pine include species of *Helicotylenchus* and *Xiphinema* (abundant), and *Meloidodera* and *Pratylenchus* (few) (*1220*). See also Seedling Diseases concerning nematodes.

Mycorrhizal Relations.—The fungi proved by pure culture to form mycorrhizae on slash pine are *Boletus betula*, *B. communis*, *B. luteus*, *Laccaria* (*Clitocybe*) *laccata* (*181*), and *Thelephora terrestris*. Others recorded by Trappe (*1442*) include *Boletinus decipiens*, *Boletus aeruginascens*, *B. bovinus*, *B. granulatus*, *B. grevillei*, *B. griseus*, *B. rubellus*, *B. rubricitrinus*, *B. scaber*, *B. variegatus*, *Cenococcum graniforme*, *Rhizopogon luteolus*, *R. roseolus*, *R. rubescens*, and *Scleroderma aurantium*.

Zak and Bryan (*1645*) and Zak and Marx (*1647*) succeeded in isolating several mycorrhizal fungi from the roots of southern pines, including slash pine.

Studies on the influence of mycorrhizae on seedling vigor of slash pine at four Louisiana nurseries showed that visible mycorrhizae are probably as important as seedling grade in determining survival after outplanting (*766*).

Miscellaneous Pathology.—A cone rust (*Cronartium strobilinum*) consistently ruins about 20 percent of the slash and longleaf pine cone crop in south Georgia and north Florida, extending into coastal Mississippi, and local losses often run to almost 100 percent. Rusted cones not only die, but result in a buildup in cone insects that then attack and ruin neighboring unrusted cones (*950*). On the oaks, uredia often become heavily attacked by at least two species of hyperparasites which, in some years, destroy over 90 percent of the sori in south Florida.

Matthews (*935*) found that the female strobili (conelets) are susceptible to infection by the rust sporidia from the time of emergence from the bud scales through the pollination stage. Spray programs, using ferbam, and spanning this brief but critical period, were effective in controlling cone rust.

A tipburn and killing of slash pines near electric power substations in Mississippi has been difficult to explain, but appeared to be associated with the use of weed killers nearby (*480*).

Little is known of the diseases of *Pinus elliottii* var. *densa*, the south Florida slash pine, except that it is very subject to pitch canker, usually following shoot moth attack (*109, 934*). Neither of the Cronartiums common on north Florida slash pine (fusiform rust and cone rust) are common on variety *densa*, and its many needle fungi have not shown evidence of being particularly damaging. *Clitocybe tabescens* has been isolated from the rotted roots of recently dead south Florida slash pine (*1168*).

Limber pine
Pinus flexilis

Limber pine is a relatively small, intolerant, western, five-needled pine, commonly bushy, or dwarfed, near timberline. It grows singly or in small groups throughout the higher eastern slopes of the Rocky Mountains from Alberta, Canada, to Mexico, and west to southern California. It occupies rocky slopes, ridge tops, foothills, canyon sides, and stream banks from 4,000 to 12,000 ft. in elevation (*279*). Although usually low and many-branched, the tree can be clean boled, up to 80 ft. tall, and up to 5 ft. in diameter. Limber pine grows slowly, maturing at about 200 years, with a longevity exceeding 400 years. A few exceptional trees in the Angeles National Forest in southern California exceed 1,000 years in age (*621*). The needles are stout, stiff, dark green, and tufting at the branch ends. A long tap root and flexible limbs make limber pine resistant to wind damage. Young trees, especially, suffer severely from fire damage (*279*).

Limber pine is hardy, enduring temperatures from −60° to 97° F., and will occupy areas where snow is abundant, and with annual precipitation between 15 and 30 in. It occurs typically in dry, rocky, shallow soil, on loose gravelly loam with little or no humus (*1367*).

The main elements of the pathology of limber pine are its moderate susceptibility to blister rust, considerable damage from two species of dwarfmistletoe, and more than occasional killing by *Armillaria mellea*.

Pinus flexilis, as discussed here, could be considered to refer to the typical species from northern New Mexico and southern California to Alberta; and to *Pinus strobiformis* (*872*), from southern Colorado and Arizona, south to central Mexico. Annotations referring to the latter form are so indicated.

Foliage Diseases.—Among the needle pathogens are *Bifusella linearis* (*323*), a tar-spot needle-cast fungus with long, very large, black stromata; *Coleosporium crowellii* (*313*), a very unusual autoecious species, with its telia on the pine needles; *Bifusella (Hy-poderma) saccata*, of uncertain pathogenicity, and with very large, shiny, black pycnidia (*323*); *Neopeckia coulteri*, the common brown-felt snow mold that is damaging to many species of *Pinus;* and in Colorado, *Hemiphacidium planum (807)*, an apothecial needle-blight fungus. Other hypodermataceous fungi reported on this species, but for which information is lacking on damage, are *Bifusella pini, Lophodermella montivaga*, and *Lophodermium pinastri. Bifusella linearis* occurs in California (see *Pinus albicaulis*).

Stem Diseases.—Limber pine is moderately susceptible to white pine blister rust, but less susceptible than *Pinus albicaulis, P. lambertiana*, or *P. monticola (251)*. Where highly susceptible species of *Ribes* were nearby, losses have been considerable, both in the West and where limber pine has been planted in the East and Middle West.

The principal disease of typical *Pinus flexilis* is caused by the so-called limber pine dwarfmistletoe, *Arceuthobium campylopodum* f. *cyanocarpum*, which is common from Montana to Colorado and California. The lodgepole pine species, *A. americanum*, sometimes attacks limber pine in the northern and central Rocky Mountains. Both species cause swellings, brooming, distortions, reduced growth, and result in a variety of defects and premature death (*507*).

The principal disease of the tree called southwestern white pine, *Pinus strobiformis*, a close relative of limber pine, is caused by *A. campylopodum* f. *blumeri*, which occurs from central Arizona and New Mexico southward. This parasite causes damage typical of the limber pine form.

Cenangium ferruginosum (542) can invade injured branch tissue, causing secondary damage. *Diplodia pinea (1513)* is a weak parasite on this species following insect or other injury. *Dasyscypha agassizzi, D. arida*, and *D. ellisiana* invade dead tissue. *D. ellisiana* occurs only in the East. All three species produce their characteristic yellow-orange apothecia on the bark (*575, 576*).

Root Diseases and Trunk Rots.—*Armillaria mellea* and *Polyporus schweinitzii* have caused root and butt rots widely over limber pine's range, and *Fomes pini* and *F. pinicola* are the commonest causes of heart rot—mainly in mature or badly damaged trees.

Where pines have been cut in a control campaign against dwarfmistletoe, in New Mexico, there has been some mortality among residual limber pines, from *Fomes annosus* attack.

The only fungus reported as a mycorrhizal associate of limber pine is *Gomphidius smithii (1442)*.

Spruce pine
Pinus glabra

Unusually tolerant for a pine, spruce pine grows mostly in association with other pines and hardwoods in moist soil, usually on terraces along streams, mainly from South Carolina to southern Louisiana, touching Florida only in the western panhandle. It requires a warm, humid climate to compete successfully and, under optimum conditions, grows fast, often coming up through other species, and can attain an age of 150 years (*279*). Spruce pine is

314

sensitive to cold, to drought, and, because the wood is weak, to wind. It is resistant to injury from flooding. It is not a common tree, even within its native range.

Two needle rusts, *Coleosporium minutum* and *C. vernoniae*, have been reported on spruce pine in Florida; the former has an alternate host in *Forestiera*, and the latter, in *Vernonia*. The three commonest southern pine needle-blight fungi also occur on spruce pine—*Ploioderma* (*Hypoderma*) *lethale*, *P. hedgcockii*, and *Scirrhia acicola*. *Lophodermium pinastri* is secondary, occuring on dead or dying needle tissue.

Cronartium quercuum produces its round galls on this tree but seldom to a damaging degree. *C. fusiforme* is not known to attack spruce pine.

Clitocybe tabescens has killed spruce pines in the neighborhood of hardwood stumps in Florida, and *Fomes annosus* killed trees in a California arboretum (*92*). *F. pini*, the ubiquitous red-heart fungus, attacks the heartwood of older trees.

Since spruce pine has little to recommend it as a forest or ornamental tree except for its resistance to fusiform rust, it has had little study with respect to its seedling diseases, its mycorrhizae, or its associated nematodes. The only mycorrhiza-former reported for it is *Cenococcum graniforme* (*1442*).

Jeffrey pine
Pinus jeffreyi

An intolerant tree, often associated with, and similar to, ponderosa pine, Jeffrey pine was at one time considered a variety of ponderosa that was more restricted in its range than the parent species. While the two species often occur together, Jeffrey pine can endure greater extremes of weather (*279*) with –25° to 100° F. considered to denote the range it can tolerate. The climate of its habitat in the California Coast Range and the Sierra Nevada is characteristically warm and dry in summer and cold and wet in winter, and its normal altitudinal range is from 3,500 to almost 10,000 ft., mainly around 5,000 ft. It is largely confined to California (*1367*), extending only slightly into border states where the sites are suitable. Although producing good stands with precipitation as low as 18 in. per year, best growth is where precipitation averages over 30 in. (*586*).

June frosts that hurt western white pine did not damage Jeffrey and ponderosa pine (*1080*), and Jeffrey is more frost-resistant than ponderosa (*586*). The latter situation probably accounts for Jeffrey's occurrence in and around flats regarded as frost pockets, while ponderosa occurs further up the slopes. Jeffrey pine will also grow on high, cold ridges in fir-type forests where ponderosa is absent. There is evidence, however, that the temperature minimum before serious damage for Jeffrey may be higher than for ponderosa (*586*).

The soils occupied by these two similar species are also much alike. They are typically well-drained, often derived from lava flows, granite, and serpentine. Jeffrey pine can thus tolerate low levels of calcium and molybdenum and high levels of nickel, chromium, and magnesium. The species is not found on poorly drained soils (586). It matures at about 150 years, and many trees reach ages of over 500 years. Cone production starts at 8 years and crops are commonly produced 4 to 8 years apart. The tree does not reproduce naturally by sprouting or rooting.

Ponderosa and Jeffrey pine are most sensitive to damage by fire early in the growing season. They can sometimes withstand complete killing of foliage in a late-season fire, and still recover if most of the twigs and buds remain alive. Survival estimates after late-season fires are most dependable when made a year after the fire (1495).

The principal disease of Jeffrey pine is attributed to dwarf-mistletoe, with several stem rusts also causing material damage. Other noteworthy features of its pathology include "spot" killing by *Fomes annosus*, localized susceptibility to Verticicladiella root disease, and a paucity of serious damage by heart rots.

Seedling Diseases.—Jeffrey pine has, in the past, not been planted widely, so little is known of its nursery diseases. It is susceptible to damping-off and root rot, and both *Rhizoctonia solani* and *Fusarium oxysporum* have been identified in association with Jeffrey pine seedling disease in California. Smith and Bega (1323) describe severe damage to coniferous nursery stock, including Jeffrey pine, in California nurseries (see *Pinus lambertiana*), as a result of mid- to late-season attack of roots by *Sclerotium bataticola* (*Macrophomina phaseoli*). The needle diseases and stem rusts of this species can attack young trees in the nursery, but sources of inoculum and microclimate would have to be suitable.

Foliage Diseases.—Remarkably few needle diseases or cankers of any importance have been reported on Jeffrey pine. Among the Hypodermataceae only two species, *Davisomycella* (*Hypodermella*) *medusa* and *Elytroderma deformans*, attack the foilage (323). The former is known to attack needles over 2 years old on susceptible individuals in local areas in interior stands, but along with *Lophodermium pinastri*, it is of little consequence as a primary pathogen (1493). The claims of major damage from *L. pinastri* have no experimental basis (1531), and no other basis except association, to support the view that this fungus was responsible for the initial decline in some reported cases of needle damage to Jeffrey pine.

Coleosporium madiae, with its alternate stage on certain of the Compositae, causes the only needle rust on this species. *Naemacyclus niveus* has caused occasional needle-casting but is of minor concern (323). It causes a discrete necrotic band, bearing a single dark pustule. Elytroderma needle blight (*E. deformans*) can be an important disease of Jeffrey pine locally, but seldom does extensive damage. Infected needles are red-brown in the spring and summer of their second year, forming the characteristic "flags" of this disease. Damage varies greatly from place to place and from year to year (248).

A minor needle blight of Jeffrey pine has been attributed to *Coryneum cinereum* by Dearness (364). *Neopeckia coulteri*, the pine brown-felt snow blight, will mat foliage that has remained too long under snow. The brown-spot fungus, in mild form, has occurred on Jeffrey pine out of its range in the Southeast.

Stem Diseases.—The only canker attributed to a non-rust is the so-called pruning disease with which *Cenangium ferruginosum* (*C. abietis*) is associated. However, this fungus is no longer considered a primary pathogen (*542*), and the twig blights attributed to it may have had their inception in injury due to weather or other impacts. *C. ferruginosum* has been reported killing limbs and small trees of Jeffrey pine on the western slopes of the Sierra Nevada. However, the tree is out of its main range where the limb-killing has been reported, and the fungus has fruited only on the dead parts of the branches. Thus, the current view of this fungus as a secondary invader of senescent branch bark may apply to Jeffrey pine.

The taxonomy and nomenclature of the stem rusts of Jeffrey pine make it difficult to determine the fungi to which this tree is susceptible. In a recent compilation by competent authorities, Jeffrey pine is listed as a host for *Peridermium filamentosum, P. harknessii, P. stalactiforme, Cronartium comandrae,* and *C. comptoniae* (*10, 1341*).

Peridermium stalactiforme causes a limb rust on Jeffrey pine, but Mielke says that one of the unresolved questions concerning the western stem rusts is whether this fungus, which has, as alternate hosts, members of the Scrophulariaceae, is the same as the *P. stalactiforme* that produces the very long cankers and limb rust on lodgepole pine (*962*). In spite of reports of *P. filamentosum,* which causes a strikingly characteristic limb rust of ponderosa pine (*961*), attacking Jeffrey pine (*149*), Mielke stated that the only certain host for this fungus at present is ponderosa pine (*962*). Jeffrey pine is also subject to an autoecious rust in Inyo County, California, that is very similar in action and appearance to *P. filamentosum* on ponderosa. Inoculations with the Inyo Jeffrey pine limb rust on *Castilleja* failed, while concomitant inoculations succeeded with *P. stalactiforme.*

Peterson (*1111*) summarizes the limb-rust situation by stating that this progressive type of crown kill can be caused by four rusts: *Peridermium stalactiforme,* and three dissimilar races of *P. filamentosum,* only one of which infects scrophulariaceous alternate hosts. The rust on the scrophulariaceous host has long aeciospore germ tubes. The other two autoecious races have short germ tubes. One, called the Inyo race, occurs mainly on Jeffrey pine in Inyo County, California (*1492*), while the other race, called Coronado or Powell, occurs widely through the Rocky Mountain region and differs in phenology and morphology (see also *Pinus ponderosa*).

There have been some questionable reports of Comandra rust (*C. comandrae*) on Jeffrey pine in the West, but Boyce (*149*) does not consider it a host. On planted trees in the East, the sweetfern rust (*C. comptoniae*) and *C. quercuum* have been reported on this species. Since Peterson (*1102*) mentions western gall rust (*P. harknessii*) as attacking only branches of Jeffrey pine, this leaves the Inyo race of *P. filamentosum* and *P. stalactiforme* as the main stem rusts on this species. However, unpublished communications indicate that western gall rust *is* common and important on this species.

The most serious disease of Jeffrey pine is dwarfmistletoe. The plant of this group that is important on this tree is the western dwarfmistletoe (*Arceuthobium campylopodum* f. *campylopodum*), which causes swellings, brooms, dead areas on trunks, reduction of growth, and which can practically kill out stands of saplings and poles (*803*). It occurs on Jeffrey pine mainly from southern Oregon to Baja California. *A. americanum*, the lodgepole pine species, has been reported occasionally on Jeffrey pine along the Pacific Coast.

Root Diseases.—Root rots of the species are caused by *Armillaria mellea, Polyporus schweinitzii,* and *Fomes annosus.* The first two cause occasional local damage, but the last can be of greater importance. With respect to Jeffrey and ponderosa pines, it has been noted that some dying from attacks of *F. annosus* occurs at some infection centers almost every year, but mortality is sporadic. Some dying attributed to bark beetles has very likely been started by weakening and killing by this fungus (*1498*). *F. annosus,* under the erroneous new name of *Cunninghamella meineckella,* has also been described as a root disease of Jeffrey pine reproduction (*1053, 1498*).

A killing root disease, caused by a species of *Verticicladiella,* occurs on Jeffrey, ponderosa, and pinyon pine in California, Colorado, and Arizona. It spreads by root contact and causes staining of the wood (not in the usual wedge-shaped patterns of blue-stainers), killing of roots, and thus, of trees. Typically, small groups of trees are killed by this unusual disease (*1499*).

Later, the above organism was named *Verticicladiella wagenerii* by Kendrick (*781*). The disease it causes affects *Pinus ponderosa, P. jeffreyi, P. monophylla,* and *P. edulis* in California. A similar, if not identical, disease was reported by Leaphart (*847*) in 1960 on *P. strobus* and *P. contorta* in Montana, and on Douglas-fir in California (*270*).

Smith (*1321*) says that although usually referred to as a root disease, pathogenesis in this case differs widely from that with *Fomes annosus* and *Armillaria* root rots. In the case of Verticicladiella disease there is little or no cambial invasion and little decay of the wood. The symptoms are much like those of the "vascular wilts" in xylem-staining, in confinement of the pathogen to the xylem, in the ultimate systemic nature of xylem involvement, and in several histologic characteristics.

Trunk Rots.—Although ponderosa pine heartwood is attacked particularly by *Polyporus anceps,* and red heart in many other pines of the West is caused by *Fomes pini,* neither fungus has been reported highly damaging to Jeffrey pine.

Mycorrhizal Relations.—Only two fungi, *Cenococcum graniforme* and *Boletus granulatus,* have been regarded as mycorrhizaformers and these have not been proved by pure-culture technique (*1442*).

Sugar pine
Pinus lambertiana

Aptly described as the tallest and most magnificent of all the pines (*279*), sugar pine is five-needled, moderately tolerant when young, hardy, and is confined to a narrow strip about 1,000 miles long from southwestern Oregon along the western slopes of the Sierra Nevada and Coast Ranges to lower California. The tree grows to over 200 ft. in height and over 15 ft. in diameter. It sustains its growth to old age (commonly over 300 years), and longevity may exceed 500 years (*1367*). Sugar pine grows at 1,000 to 2,000 ft. elevation in the Coast Range and from 6,500 to 9,000 ft. in the Sierras, mainly in loose, deep, moist, well-drained, sandy or gravelly loams and where the relative humidity is fairly high. Optimum rainfall is over 40 in. per year. The tree stands on a broad, shallow root system (*279*). It does not self-prune well (*470*).

Atmospheric moisture is essential to sugar pine, and in its early years it requires partial shade on the drier slopes. When older it becomes even more intolerant than ponderosa pine (*1367*). Young trees are easily damaged by fire, but the thick bark of older trees protects them. However, in proportion to diameter, sugar pine has thinner, denser bark, with poorer insulating capacity than the bark of associated conifers. Being tall, older trees are frequent targets of lightning. Snow-breakage is common with smaller trees. Sugar pine is intermediate in sensitivity to sulfur dioxide injury, being less sensitive than the true firs, Douglas-fir, and western hemlock, but more sensitive than the hard pines, western larch, and Engelmann spruce (*1249*).

A summary of the pathology of sugar pine by Harold Offord [42] follows: The principal leaf disease is a needle cast (*Lophodermella arcuata*), the chief stem diseases are blister rust and dwarfmistletoe, the main root diseases are the rots caused by *Fomes annosus* and *Armillaria mellea*. The main trunk rots are caused by *Fomes pini* and *Polyporus schweinitzii*, and the main seedling disease by *Macrophomina phaseoli*.

Seedling Diseases.—Among seedling pathogens, *Sclerotium bataticola* (*Macrophomina phaseoli*) is of particular importance as a damping-off and root-rot fungus. Smith and Bega (*1323*) describe severe damage to seedlings in California from this fungus during the warmer part of the growing season and consider it the most important pathogen of coniferous seedlings in that state. Ten West Coast coniferous species and two pine hybrids are known to be attacked. Damage followed the earlier period of damping-off due to *Pythium* sp. and *Rhizoctonia solani* and consisted in wilting of the newest growth, with some chlorosis, and a necrosis of the upper part of the taproot and below-ground portions of the stem. Lower roots usually appeared healthy. Losses to sugar pine seedlings in 1960 at one nursery averaged 50 percent. Additional losses in the nursery have resulted from attack by *Phytophthora cinnamomi*. Some cases of damping-off have been associated with *Fusoma parasiticum*.

Smith (*1322*) demonstrated that within 3 years after outplanting sugar pine nursery stock heavily infected with *Fusarium oxysporum* at the time of planting was entirely free of this fungus.

Foliage Diseases.—Sugar pine supports no important foliage parasites, and all of its needle fungi occur on older needles. They include *Bifusella linearis* with its large, long, black stromata; *Coryneum cinereum*, causing an uncommon condition referred to as needle scorch; *Lophodermella* (*Hypodermella*) *arcuata*, an occa-

---

[42] Personal communication from Harold Offord, formerly pathologist, USDA Forest Service, Pacific Southwest Forest and Range Experiment Station, Berkeley, Calif.

sionally aggressive needle-cast fungus largely confined to sugar pine and likely simply a form of *L. montivaga;* and *Lophodermium nitens,* a fungus capable of attacking needles 2 or more years old *(323)*. *L. pinastri,* sometimes reported as *L. pinicolum,* occurs occasionally on old or senescent needles *(328)*.

The brown-felt snow mold *Neopeckia coulteri* can kill foliage that has been under snow for long periods.

Stem Diseases.—Sugar pine's most important disease is blister rust *(Cronartium ribicola)*. One of the most highly susceptible species *(251)*, sugar pine sustains heavy losses in the vicinity of *Ribes* spp. only north of the 38th parallel *(804)*. Microclimatic conditions further south in California are seldom sufficiently favorable for completion of the cycle from telial germination to pine infection by sporidia for a major build-up of the disease *(651)*. The purple hyperparasite *Tuberculina maxima* commonly appears on blister rust cankers.

None of the other canker diseases of sugar pine are rated as particularly damaging. They include those caused by *Atropellis pinicola (877)* which darkly stains the wood beneath, and *Cenangium ferruginosum* which is no longer considered a primary pathogen *(542)*. The other fungi, though secondary or saprophytic, that sometimes appear on lesions following debilitating climatic, traumatic, or other impacts are *Cytospora pini, Phoma harknessii, Phomopsis pseudotsugae (1315), Neofuckelia pinicola* (on Atropellis cankers), and *Sclerophoma* sp.

One western dwarfmistletoe *(Arceuthobium campylopodum* f. *blumeri)* is limited to species of white pines, including sugar pine *(505)*. Although in earlier reports infected trees were said to be uncommon, this dwarfmistletoe is now regarded as a serious parasite on both young and old trees *(470)*. The mistletoe shoots are large, usually greenish, and grow in tufts on the branches.

Bluish witches' brooms, with which no pathogen has been associated, occur occasionally on sugar pine. Such brooms occur on most pine species in the East and the West. They apparently result from localized bud stimulation not induced by an organism.

Root Diseases.—Seedlings and trees of considerable size can be killed by *Armillaria mellea*. The disease is commonly called shoestring root rot, and the shoestring-like rhizomorphs on the roots and resinosis and mycelial fans at the root collar are diagnostic *(848)*. A root and butt rot is also caused by *Fomes annosus* which is responsible for killing trees of all ages in scattered groups *(94, 1498)*, usually centered about the initially infected stump or tree *(1053)*. A third root and butt rot is caused by *Polyporus schweinitzii*. This is more strictly a wood rot and kills mainly by weakening, leading to windthrow or breakage, whereas the other two root-rot fungi often kill through necrosis of the cambium at and below the ground line.

Trunk Rots.—The most important trunk rots *(151)* of sugar pine are a red-brown cubical butt rot *(Polyporus schweinitzii)*, a light-colored, stringy butt rot *(Fomes annosus)*, red-ring trunk rot *(F. pini)*, and a brown trunk rot *(F. officinalis)*. Many other fungi can rot the heartwood of sugar pine but are of lesser importance, including *F. pinicola, Lentinus lepideus, P. anceps, P. berkeleyi,* and *P. sulphureus*.

Mycorrhizal Relations.—The fungi reported to form mycorrhizae with sugar pine are *Boletus badius, B. granulatus, B. variegatus, Cenococcum graniforme, Lactarius deliciosus, L. sanguifluus,* and *Russula delica* (*1442*). The relationship has been proved by pure-culture technique only for *B. variegatus* and *B. badius.*

Singleleaf pinyon
Pinus monophylla

Singleleaf pinyon is a very intolerant, small, scrubby tree usually occurring singly or in scattered groups on dry foothills, slopes, and canyon sides from southeastern Idaho to northwestern Arizona and westward into southern and eastern California. It sometimes forms stands of considerable extent at the lower elevations of its altitudinal range of 2,000 to 7,000 ft. The foliage is pale yellow green with a whitish tinge and is unique in that the needles occur singly (occasionally in pairs). The seeds are edible. Growth is exceedingly slow, and longevity is usually between 100 and 225 years. The tree is hardy, withstanding poor soil, extreme cold, heat, and drought, but it is rarely straight, and even diameters of 10 to 12 in. are unusual (*279*). Its temperature range is from –2° F. in the Sierras to 122° F. in the Mojave Desert (*1367*).

W. W. Wagener [43] observed the killing of all sizes of trees, in spite of its reputation of cold-hardiness, in parts of the Nevada Sierras where temperatures went as low as –31° F. The bark and cambium of these trees had been killed to the ground line.

Seedling Damage.—The seedlings characteristically produce only juvenile needles for 6 or 7 years before putting forth normal foliage((*1367*). Seedlings may often be lost from frost-heaving, and seedling damage from grazing is common.

Foliage Diseases.—The leaf rust *Coleosporium jonesii*, while common on pinyon pine and widespread on its *Ribes* hosts, has been reported from singleleaf pinyon only in California. A so-called tarspot needle cast caused by *Bifusella* (*Hypoderma*) *pini* is fairly common, but it is unimportant because attack is limited to old needles in the lower parts of trees (*323*).

For a description of the strange conidia of the needle fungus *Furcaspora pinicola,* see *Abies concolor.*

Stem Diseases.—The pinyon blister rust (*Cronartium occidentale*) occurs generally and endemically in the Southwest, producing branch and trunk swellings near the ground (*1355*). While many trees are killed, the disease has not been rated as particularly important to the species. The fungus is widespread and causes mortality, but it rarely becomes epidemic on singleleaf pinyon. Its alternate hosts are species of *Ribes* on which the pinyon rust produces uredia and telia that resemble *C. ribicola.* Staining techniques have been successful in distinguishing the two rusts on species of *Ribes* (*241*), and Kimmey reported a method of visual determination that proved 93-percent effective in separating *C. ribicola* from *C. occidentale* on *Ribes* (*792*), A buffered-acid fuch-

---

[43] Personal communication from W. Willis Wagener, deceased, formerly pathologist, USDA Forest Service, Pacific Southwest Forest and Range Experiment Station, Berkeley, Calif.

sin stain developed later was very effective in differentiating the two rusts on *Ribes* (*453*).

The pinyon dwarfmistletoe (*Arceuthobium campylopodum* f. *divaricatum*) attacks all four nut pines (*505*), causing its characteristic swellings, brooming, distortion, growth reduction, and killing. It is abundant on singleleaf pinyon throughout its range, causing extensive damage. Whether the disease is serious depends upon the point of view. In some areas the elimination of singleleaf pinyon would be considered beneficial from the range- and water-yield viewpoints. Elsewhere the value of this tree aesthetically and for fuel, nuts, and fenceposts make it a desirable part of the flora. Dwarfmistletoe is this tree's greatest enemy.

Root Diseases and Trunk Rots.—A root disease caused by *Verticicladiella wagenerii* attacks singleleaf pinyon in California, particularly in the San Bernardino Mountains. It spreads by root contact and causes a staining of the root wood and necrosis of roots. Typically small groups of trees are killed by this disease (*1499*). Singleleaf pinyon is subject to red heart, also called red ring rot, caused by *Fomes pini*; to the brown crumbly rot caused by *F. pinicola*; and to the carbonizing, cubical root and butt rot caused by *Polyporus schweinitzii*. None of these fungi is a disturbing element in the normal culture of this species.

Mycorrhizal Relations.—The only fungus reported as a mycorrhizal associate of singleleaf pinyon is *Cenococcum graniforme* (*1442*).

Western white pine
Pinus monticola

A tall, stately, narrow-crowned tree of the mountains, with a range extending from British Columbia across Idaho, Montana, and Washington and southward into California, western white pine is a highly valued tree of the Northwest. This five-needled pine is moderately tolerant (*54*) and grows on a wide variety of soils with best development in deep, well-drained, medium-to-fine-textured soils of high water-holding capacity. It usually grows in mixed stands and occupies sites with a range in mean annual precipitation of from 15 in. in California to 60 in. near Puget Sound. Its altitudinal range is from 2,000 to 5,000 ft. elevation in the Northwest to 10,000 ft. in California. The tree matures at about 100 years but often grows to 200 years with a maximum recorded longevity of 500 years (*279*).

In the Inland Empire where this species is most abundant, the climate is characterized by a short summer season of scanty precipitation and low humidities with a high percentage of clear, warm days and winters with heavy snowfall and low temperatures. Extremes in temperature of this region range from —36° to 107° F. (*1549*). A combination of summer drought and dry sites has often led to damage to this species. Another important physiogenic disorder is the needle desiccation associated with severe winter injury. This condition, often called winter drying, is commonly associated with drying winds (chinooks) that cause excessive losses of moisture that cannot be replaced fast enough because of cold or frozen soil or trunks (*151*).

Western white pine endures shade when young but not later in life, and it does not recover well after suppression (*1367*). It is rated intermediate, with respect to its associated species, in sensitivity to fire. It is intermediate in sensitivity to sulfur dioxide injury, being damaged less readily than the true firs, Douglas-fir, and western hemlock, but being more sensitive than the hard pines, western larch, and Engelmann spruce (*1249*). Considerable damage to this species results from wind, snow, and suppression. Diseases, however, are now its greatest enemies.

Western white pine was the most sensitive of the pines to sulfur dioxide smelter fumes in the Upper Columbia River Valley. Foliage became yellowed and shed prematurely. Acute fumigation resulted in needle-reddening, involving all or parts of needles, or banding with browned tissue (*1249*).

Although a very desirable species to the wood-using industries, western white pine is beset with serious diseases. Blister rust and pole blight take a heavy toll. Shoestring root rot and annosus root rot are important killing root diseases. Several needle diseases brown and cast the foliage during certain years, and a large number of fungi as well as two forms of dwarfmistletoe cause occasional damage in specific situations.

Seedling Diseases.—Among the seedling diseases, *Rhizina undulata* has been locally damaging to northwestern species, including western white pine. Seedlings up to 5 years old can be killed in patches 2 to 4 ft. in diameter, particularly on burned areas (*151*). In nurseries species of *Fusarium* have caused damping-off and root rot. Blister rust (*Cronartium ribicola*) can be an important nursery disease. The snow mold *Neopeckia coulteri* can overgrow foliage and kill it where seedlings have been under snow for long periods. Many seedlings unprotected by snow cover succumb from frost-heaving and winter-killing. Seedlings may be surrounded and occasionally smothered (*1540*) by sporophores of *Thelephora terrestris*, but this fungus is seldom harmful to fast-growing seedlings and is sometimes mycorrhizal. Seedling mortality from drought is most acute on heavily shaded areas where root penetration is slow and unable to keep pace with receding soil moisture (*1549*).

Foliage Diseases.—A needle blight, often severe and leading to shedding of foliage over a year old, particularly in north Idaho, is caused by a species of *Lecanosticta* (*1280*). There are similarities between this fungus and the imperfect (*Lecanosticta*) stage of the brown-spot fungus *Scirrhia acicola* of the South and the East. The symptoms, which are primarily a spotting, blighting, and shedding of foliage in the lower crown, are much like those attributed to *S. acicola* (*158*) on eastern white pine in North Carolina and West Virginia. The complications in nomenclature as well as the complex host relations of fungi causing some of the needle blights of pine in the Inland Empire are clarified by Thyr and Shaw (*1406*).

Another Idaho foliage disease, called needle cast, attacks mainly in the upper and middle crown but may overlap the *Lecanosticta* blight on the same tree. The cast is caused by *Lophodermella* (*Hypodermella*) *arcuata* (*1280*). Affected needles are always those which were new the previous growing season or earlier. One or all needles in a fascicle may be affected, and these turn brown and fall, leaving only current-year's needles at the ends of the branches.

Two other fungi of the needle cast or tar-spotting type attack older needles on occasional trees. One is *Bifusella linearis*, capable of killing much non-current year's foliage, with its very long, conspicuous, black stromata (*323*) ; and the other is *Lophodermium nitens* which has black, elliptical, subcuticular hysterothecia (*323*) and, like its close relative *L. pinastri*, is probably saprophytic (*151, 372*).

Stem Diseases.—By far the most important disease of western white pine is blister rust (*Cronartium ribicola*) (*971*), particularly in eastern Washington, northern Idaho, and western Montana (*959*). In this area the highly susceptible alternate host plants (species of *Ribes*) are so abundant, the climate so suitable, and the pine so susceptible that heavy losses continue in spite of control efforts. Blister rust cankers usually have many good diagnostic characteristics. They also commonly support the purple hyperparasite *Tuberculina maxima* (*728*). Rodents, particularly squirrels and field mice, will often strip the spongy infected bark from the cankers (*727, 958*). A fungus that has been confused with *Dasyscypha agassizzi* and *D. calyciformis*, common saprophytes on coniferous tree bark, often fruits on dead areas on rust cankers. It has not been named (*126*). *Cryptosporium lunasporum, C. pinicola*, and many other scavenging fungi fruit on active blister rust cankers (*8*).

Caliciopsis pinea, a common but seldom damaging twig- and branch-canker fungus on eastern white pine, has proved to be so destructive to western white pine grown in New York that Funk (*485*) considers it a threat to the culture of the latter species in eastern North America.

The non-rust canker diseases are seldom important. *Dasyscypha pini* with its yellow-to-orange apothecia, *Atropellis pinicola* with its black apothecia and accompanying dark-stained wood, and *Cenangium ferruginosum* with small brown-to-black apothecia can be found associated with cankers and twig dieback (*372, 1656*). Of these, *A. pinicola* is the only aggressive pathogen (*877*). *Tympanis confusa* is another saprophyte that produces small, black apothecia on the bark (*552*).

Tracheomycosis involving bark beetle attack followed by bluestain fungus infection involves chiefly the destructive mountain pine beetle *Dendroctonus monticolae* and the fungus *Ceratocystis montia* (*1228*). *C. pilifera* (*732*) is a common blue-stainer of lumber.

Three dwarfmistletoes, *Arceuthobium campylopodum* formae *blumeri, laricis,* and *tsugensis,* produce swellings, brooms, and other distortions, but western white pine is not a congenial host, and since damage is local, the diseases are not important (*505*).

Septobasidium pinicola produces a brown, resupinate, effused, generally circular sporophore from 1 to 3 centimeters in diameter. It occurs on the bark of living *Pinus monticola* in the Inland Empire and on *P. strobus* in the Northeast, probably living on scale insects (*1324*), and is harmless to the tree. The smooth bark of young trunks and branches are often covered by brown, harmless patches of growth of *Septobasidium pinicola* (*1324*). Several fungi minor to this pine species occur on needles and shoots outside the tree's native range, and still others play a strictly saprophytic role (8, 1277).

Pole blight is a disorder second only to blister rust as this species' most serious disease (849). Trees, mainly in the 40- to 100-year age class, develop short yellow foliage concentrated at the branch ends. Later on, long, resinous, dead areas may appear on the trunk. The fungus *Europhium trinacriforme* grows in these necrotic streaks and can produce lesions when inoculated into trees. However, it is regarded as naturally entering lesions that had already formed in connection with pole blight (1074). As pole blight develops, the top dies, followed in a few years by the rest of the tree. The disease occurs from Disalto Creek in the St. Joe National Forest in Idaho, north into Canada (457). It appears not to be caused by a primary pathogen but results from rootlet deterioration in certain soils that are unable to meet the tree's water requirements, and it may be associated with climate changes involving a trend toward lower annual precipitation and higher temperatures (651). In the course of the pole-blight studies much has been learned about western white pine roots, their distribution, and their pathology (845, 846).

Leaphart and Wicker (852), in seeking an explanation for pole blight, grew seedlings of several western conifers in modified environments. Western white pine appeared least efficient in competing for soil moisture on all soil types used and was least able to adapt to soils having inadequate moisture and low potential for recharge. They postulate a relationship between these characteristics and the disposition of western white pine to pole blight.

McMinn (915) presents additional evidence that climatic factors are responsible for pole blight and points out that with the return of more normal temperatures and precipitation, pole blight is on the decrease, and pole-blight lesions have been callusing over in many cases.

Root Diseases.—Isolates of *Leptographium* spp. encountered in the pole-blight studies were shown capable of causing root lesions. These fungi are considered to have a role in decline from pole blight, because their virulence was inversely proportional to a tree's callusing capacity (851), and a badly pole-blighted tree would be a weakened, poorly callusing tree. Another inhabitant of the roots of western white pine is *Rosellinia helena*.

In connection with pole-blight research it was found that "logging shock" results in much mortality, and that while in the past almost all emphasis on logging damage was placed on above-ground injuries, modern logging does much damage to roots of residual trees (1054).

Among the root pathogens, *Armillaria mellea* ranks first (96, 405). Any of its many symptoms may be evident, including fading foliage, growth reduction, root-collar exudation of resin and subcortical mycelial fans, dead and rotten roots, and black rhizomorphs (848). Hubert (729) reported 64 out of 127 recently killed trees in Idaho root-rotted by *A. mellea*.

Fomes annosus is another root killer that is responsible for the death of individuals and groups. *Poria weirii* causes some mortality in eastern Washington, but its aggressiveness is minor compared with its attack on Douglas-fir. In its "annual" form it also occurs on western white pine in British Columbia. Dying of planted conifers, including western white pine, in Idaho has been ascribed to *Stereum sanguinolentum* (*726*), a common slash decay and heartrot fungus, resulting in "mottled-bark disease".

Poria subacida produces so-called feather rot of roots but does not kill trees. *Polyporus schweinitzii, P. tomentosus* (*724*), and *Sparassis radicata* (*1538*) can rot the roots and butts of western white pine but are not killers. Hubert (*729*) gives special attention to identification of the root rots of species in the western white pine type. Although at least eight fungi can rot the roots of this species, only the four mentioned in the preceding two paragraphs kill immature trees, and only the first two are significant for their capacity to cause mortality. Hubert (*724*) gives methods of separating the rots caused by *F. annosus, F. pini, Polyporus anceps, P. schweinitzii, P. tomentosus,* and *Poria subacida.*

Nematodes isolated from the roots of *Pinus monticola* include species of *Criconema, Criconemoides, Heterodera, Trichodorus,* and *Tylenchorhynchus.* All were reported from Idaho in connection with investigation of the pole-blight disease. Nickle (*1033*) concluded that the *Heterodera* sp. was interfering with mycorrhizal development and that *Trichodorous elegans* is parasitic to western white pine. The other nematodes were obtained from rhizosphere soil samples.

Trunk Rots.—The butt-rot fungi include all those mentioned above in connection with root rots and also *Polyporus sulphureus.* The most important causes of trunk rot in order are *Fomes pini* (*920*), *P. schweinitzii,* and *F. annosus.* Many other fungi are capable of causing decay in injured or overmature trees. An age between 100 and 120 years has been suggested as a "pathological felling age," since rot cull losses tend to become excessive in older trees. The cull situation in this species and the tree and stand factors that lead to decay are discussed by Weir and Hubert (*1545*). Average cull in Inland Empire western white pine stands is about 3 percent in stands 81 to 100 years old and about 20 percent in stands 181 to 200 years old (*29*).

Mycorrhizal Relations.—The fungi that have been reported to form mycorrhizae with western white pine are *Boletus granulatus, B. subaureus, B. subluteus, Boletellus zelleri, Cenococcum graniforme, Gomphidius ochraceus, G. rutilus, Russula delica, R. xerampelina,* and *Tricholoma flavovirens* (*1442*). None have been proved through aseptic procedures.

Applications of Phytoactin 1,000 times greater than the 200 p.p.m. applied to western white pine forests had no effect on the formation or maintenance of normal mycorrhizal systems of 6-year-old seedlings (*607*).

Miscellaneous Pathology.—Witches' brooms not involving a pathogen but similar to those occurring occasionally on most pine species also occur on western white pine. They result from a localized overstimulation of bud formation.

Basal scars are common on western white pine and are attributable mainly to bears, *Armillaria mellea* infection, fire, mechanical wounding, and pole blight (*997*).

Austrian pine
Pinus nigra

A hardy species introduced from Europe, Austrian pine has been used more as an ornamental than as a forest tree in the United States. A fast and vigorously growing tree of pyramidal form with full dark foliage, it matures at about 80 years, developing a flat top by then. Its longevity in the United States has not been recorded. It is hardy as far north as southern Ontario and New England, and it is not demanding as to soil, growing well in sands, loams, and clay. It often serves well as a windbreak since the dense foliage and stiff branches will withstand wind and heavy snow. Its capacity to withstand drought, to grow on land of low productivity, and to tolerate fill has led to its use in the fixing of sand dunes (*279*). It withstands the weight of ice very well (*310*) and when exposed to heavy salt spray in a New England hurricane was one of the species that was uninjured or recovered well (*1005, 1632*). Austrian pine has been damaged by air pollution in New Jersey.

Seedling Diseases.—Although little has been written of the nursery diseases of this species in North America, its seedlings are very probably subject to the common diseases of hard pine nursery stock (*360*). Damping-off and seedling root rots of Austrian pine are known to have been caused by *Rhizoctonia solani, Phytophthora cactorum* (*305*), and *Pythium debaryanum. Diplodia pinea* (*1513*) causes a collar rot of seedlings, and *Thelephora terrestris* may encircle seedlings but seldom harms them.

Low vigor in Austrian pine seedlings in a Great Plains nursery appeared to be due to heavy soil infestation by the dagger nematode *Xiphinema americanum* (*1097*). *Hoplolaimus coronatus* was reported attacking Austrian pine in Florida (*704*). The pine cystoid nematode *Meloidodera floridensis* and species of *Criconemoides, Hoplolaimus, Longidorus, and Pratylenchus* also have been identified on Austrian pine roots (*1222*).

Foliage Diseases.—Leaf diseases include the rusts caused by four species of *Coleosporium; Meloderma* (*Hypoderma*) *desmazierii* (*323*) which causes a fading, browning, and then graying of older needles; *Ploioderma lethale* which causes a similar browning; and *Scirrhia acicola* (*1304*) that produces its typical spots and some blighting. *Naemacyclus niveus* (*323*) produces its characteristic bar spots. *Dothistroma pini* causes a needle blight and partial defoliation, occasionally attacking red pine (*1397*) and often attacking Austrian pine severely, mainly in the Central States. For a discussion of *D. pini*, its perfect stage *Scirrhia pini*, and comparisons with *S. acicola*, see *Pinus ponderosa.*. Peterson (*1099*) states that *D. pini* is widespread and is causing serious damage to Austrian pine and ponderosa pine in windbreak, ornamental, and Christmas tree plantings in the central and southern Great Plains. He reported favorable spray control results with Bordeaux mixture.

Lophodermium pinastri occurs on dead and dying needles and is probably not pathogenic.

Stem Diseases.—The most common twig disease is called tip blight and is caused by *Diplodia pinea*. Scattered current needles or all needles on a twig may be stunted and browned, resulting from needle or shoot infection leading to lesions on the twigs. The most

327

pronounced symptom is the killing of current year's growth, year after year, all over a tree (*1513*). Peterson and Wysong (*1100*) stress the damage to *Pinus nigra*, *P. ponderosa*, and *P. sylvestris* caused by *Diplodia pinea* in the Great Plains area. Mainly a shoot blight of older, planted trees, it can also kill seedlings. They demonstrated that *D. pinea* does not need wounds in order to infect young shoots.

Atropellis tingens (*380*), *A. pinicola* (*877*), and *Fusarium lateritium* f. *pini* (*667*) cause minor twig blights. *Cenangium atropurpureum* (*238*), *C. ferruginosum*, and *Dasyscypha ellisiana* (*575*), while occurring on moribund or dead twigs, can be considered secondary in the absence of any proof of pathogenicity.

Cronartium quercuum will produce occasional round galls, and *C. fusiforme* its fusiform swellings, on Austrian pine. *C. comptoniae*, the sweetfern rust, has frequently been reported stunting and disfiguring trees of this species and is considered one of its major diseases (*25, 1341*). *C. comandrae* has also been reported on Austrian pine.[44]

Root Diseases.—Where Austrian pine has been planted in Texas and Oklahoma, losses from cotton root rot (*Phymatotrichum omnivorum*) have been light, but the species is recommended there only on sandy sites (*1627*). Nematodes are discussed under seedling diseases.

Fomes annosus has killed Austrian pines in New York, but few attacks have been reported.

Mycorrhizal Relations.—Although 35 species of fungi have been reported in mycorrhizal association with Austrian pine, none have been proved by pure-culture technique (*1442*).

Miscellaneous Pathology.—*Physalospora obtusa*, a fruit rot, canker fungus, and also saprophyte on many deciduous trees, has been reported associated with a cone and seed rot of Austrian pine and also as a saprophytic invader of twigs.

Longleaf pine
Pinus palustris

Intolerant, maturing at about 100 years, living to over 300 years, longleaf pine grows well on sands or clays and wet or dry sites but most commonly persists on those higher and drier sites where past fires have destroyed the more fire-sensitive pines and hardwoods. Its main range extends from eastern North Carolina through the South Atlantic and Gulf States to east Texas. Drought, high winds, and lightning take a heavy toll, and more often than not longleaf trees ultimately die from a complex of causes rather than a single one (*1501*). Yet this species' resistance to these hazards, its capacity to recover from ice-bending as compared with the easily broken slash pine (*912*), and its high resistance to fire and fusiform rust have resulted in its surviving in the unmanaged forests of the past over large areas of the South where other pine species could not.

Today fire control has increased the slash and loblolly component on many old longleaf sites because of their faster early growth, and

---

[44] Personal communication from A. F. Verrall, formerly pathologist, USDA Forest Service Southern Forest Experiment Station, New Orleans, La.

328

fire control has also greatly increased the amount of young oak which carries the alternate stage of the rust. This situation has meant that much forest that once was in longleaf free of fusiform rust is now in heavily rusted slash and loblolly pine.

Longleaf pine hardens off only slightly in autumn and is practically incapable of responding to low temperatures by hardening further (*1080*).

The frequent high losses of longleaf seedlings to ranging hogs in the Deep South deserves mention. The thick, living bark of the main taproot is heavily packed with starch and its conversion products, particularly in the spring, and these are prime food targets for these animals. Even in shortleaf pine such available carbohydrates make up one-fourth to one-third of the weight of root bark in the spring (*642*). Hogs have been observed to root up or kill as many as 8,320 2-year-old longleaf seedlings per acre, at a rate of 200 to 400 per day (*1501*).

Longleaf pine strongly resists most pathogenic and physiogenic impacts. Other than the role of brown spot in holding longleaf seedlings in the grass stage, the only diseases that occasionally reach economic importance in local areas are pitch canker, dry face of turpentined trees, annosus root rot in thinned plantations, cone rust in the far South, and littleleaf in north Alabama.

Seedling Diseases.—Nursery seedlings are subject to damping-off and to black root rot as described under loblolly pine (*696*). Longleaf seedlings differ from other pines in that they tend to assume a rosette habit often leading, on unmulched nursery soil, to little cones of piled sand about them (called sand-splash) or silt accumulations which, together with *Rhizoctonia solani* or occasionally other fungi, can produce a common type of damping-off characteristic of longleaf pine (*358*). The black root rot fungi (see *Pinus elliottii*) also rotted roots of longleaf pine in 2- to 3-year-old outplantings in the west Florida sandhills (*1313*).

Longleaf pine seedlings have proved susceptible to *Phytophthora cinnamomi* root rot when grown in liquid culture and inoculated (*1646*).

High populations of nematodes have been suspected of having a role in the stunting and yellowing of longleaf in several nurseries (*704*). The genera that have been most commonly found associated with longleaf roots are *Xiphinema* (including *X. americanum*), *Criconemoides* (including *C. rusticum*), *Helicotylenchus*, *Hemicycliophora*, *Hoplolaimus* (including *H. coronatus*), *Meloidodera floridensis*, and *Scutellonema* (*704, 1220*).

Literature concerning many other nematodes reported associated with longleaf pine roots is cited by Ruehle (*1222*). He demonstrated (*1221*) that longleaf, loblolly, and Virginia pine were poor hosts or non-hosts to *Pratylenchus zeae*.

Foliage Diseases.—Longleaf pine is so resistant to fusiform rust that this disease, destructive to loblolly and slash, is seldom a problem on longleaf either in the nursery or in the field. In contrast, brown spot (*Scirrhia acicola*), which is seldom damaging to slash and loblolly pine in the nursery, often browns large areas of unsprayed longleaf seedbeds. In Deep South nurseries much longleaf seedling foliage can be killed by brown spot in rainy years. While brown spot is a nursery disease of longleaf, its importance is largely due to the excessive killing of foliage of natural or planted seedlings in the field (*1304*). It is commonly fatal to seedlings less than 18 in. tall and can seriously retard the growth of others up to a height of 3 ft. It is a major factor, along with competing vegetation, low moisture, and low nutrition, in unduly prolonging the number of years that longleaf seedlings may remain in the "grass" stage.

Longleaf seedlings need to reach about 1 in. in diameter at the ground to start height growth. Where brown spot and site factors are severe, seedlings may not attain this inch in 10 or more years and so remain in what is called the grass stage. Fire greatly reduces brown spot and competing vegetation for about 2 years, and, since the so-called "asbestos" longleaf bud is often not injured by prescribed fire, burning is a method for inducing height growth (*1501*). Where many dead needles occur around infected seedlings, burning has been known to kill an undue proportion of the seedlings.

Saplings and larger trees will often have the scattered, harmless bar spots of brown spot on the needles, but they do not sustain the severe blighting characteristic of the virulent type of brown spot attack on seedlings.

For a discussion of differences between *Scirrhia acicola* and its imperfect *Lecanosticta* stage and *S. pini* and its imperfect *Dothistroma* stage, see *Pinus ponderosa*.

Ten species of *Coleosporium* cause needle rusts on longleaf pine, and yet there is no proof of a measurable impact on growth due to any of these leaf rusts. While *Ploioderma* (*Hypoderma*) *lethale* (*328*) often causes a late winter browning of the foliage of many of the southern pines (*156*), it is not known to attack longleaf. Even the ubiquitous *Lophodermium pinastri* finds longleaf a very uncongenial host. *P. hedgcockii* (*156*) and *Monochaetia pinicola* (*558*) have been reported on longleaf needles in Florida.

Stem Diseases.—While occasional stands of sapling longleaf have had many trees cankered by *Cronartium fusiforme*, any attack of longleaf by either this fungus or *C. quercuum* is a rare occurrence. Fusiform rust can generally be ignored in longleaf management. The pitch canker disease (*Fusarium lateritium pini*) (*102*), however, can cause much leader and twig killing, particularly in south Georgia and Florida, often in association with insect injury (*934*). It can usually be easily distinguished by the copious gum accumulation, either dripping or hardened around the cankered shoots and gluing the old and dead needles together, and also by the pitch-soaking of the wood, often to the pith.

Dry face of turpentined trees, as described under slash pine (*1449*), similarly affects longleaf. Also in connection with turpentining, where the pitch canker *Fusarium* succeeds in establishing itself behind a worked-out face, a heavy pitch-soaking of the wood can take place to various depths into the sapwood. While dry face and pitch-soaking of wood from fungus infection were common with heavily worked (turpentined) wood-chipped trees, both are much less common with conservative chipping practices involving bark chipping with acid stimulation (*1259*).

Other Stem and Root Diseases.—The following diseases behave and appear on longleaf much as they do on loblolly pine, under

330

which heading they are described: tracheomycosis from blue-stain fungi (*Ceratocystis ips* and *C. minor*), following attack by bark beetles; the course and extent of damage by the root rots caused by *Fomes annosus, Polyporus schweinitzii,* and *Clitocybe tabescens;* and red heart (*Fomes pini*). Although the losses to longleaf from *F. annosus* now seem to be lower than for slash or loblolly, this may simply be because there has been much less longleaf planted than the other two species, and this is a disease principally of thinned planted stands. *Polyporus palustris* is a common saprobe on longleaf stumps (*910*).

Nematodes occasionally found on longleaf roots in addition to those mentioned in connection with seedlings include *Aphelenchus fragariae* and species of *Belonolaimus, Longidorus, Meloidogyne, Paratylenchus, Trichodorus,* and *Tylenchorhyncus* (*704, 1220*).

In the heavier soils of the upper coastal plain of Alabama, where littleleaf is very severe on shortleaf and loblolly pine, even longleaf is affected, and *Phytophthora cinnamomi* is known to successfully attack its roots (*207, 1646*).

Mycorrhizal Relations.—*Boletus luteus* and *Laccaria* (*Clitocybe*) *laccata* have been demonstrated to make mycorrhizal association with longleaf pine in the South (*181*). Trappe (*1442*) also reports *Boletinus decipiens, Boletus granulatus, Cenococcum graniforme, Gomphidius vinicolor, Suillus cothurnatus,* and *Tylopilus conicus.*

Zak and Bryan (*1645*) succeeded in isolating several mycorrhizal fungi directly from the roots of southern pines, including longleaf pine.

Miscellaneous Pathology.—The cone rust caused by *Cronartium strobilinum* (*648*) attacks longleaf cones as well as those of slash pine, but it seems less destructive on longleaf. The other southern pines do not take this disease. Repeated surveys have shown about 20 percent of the cone crop lost each year in south Georgia and north Florida, with all cones rusted and destroyed on some trees near evergreen oaks in moist situations. The rust extends southwestward from the South Carolina coast along the Gulf Coast to Louisiana (see also *Pinus elliottii*).

Solutions of a ferric fungicide used for the protection of strobili against cone rust, as well as another organic iron compound, consistently increased pollen germination of longleaf pine (*936*).

Ponderosa pine
Pinus ponderosa

Ponderosa pine, the most widely distributed species of pine in North America, extends from British Columbia well into Mexico and from the Pacific Coast to Nebraska. In addition to the type, there is one variety, *arizonica,* and a Rocky Mountain form, *scopulorum,* that is sometimes listed as a variety; and also many geographic races that thrive under different soil and climate conditions (*316*). Ponderosa pine generally occurs in areas of relatively low rainfall (from 10 to 28 in. per year), especially where rainfall is low in the summer. There are areas where the rainfall may be less than 1 in. or even none at all in July and August. Mean temperatures in ponderosa pine types are between 42° and 50° F. with extremes from —37° to 107° F. Although ponderosa pine grows on soils with a wide variety of origins, textures, moisture, and pH, it does best on well-drained, deep, sandy, gravelly, or clay loams (*316*). Its altitudinal range is from near sea level to over 9,000 ft. in elevation. Seedlings in the Southwest often need some protection from the hot sun, but once out of the seedling stage the tree requires full sunlight (*1092*). The mature tree is massive, grows tall, majestic, and straight-boled, with a narrow crown. It matures at about 200 years and grows to ages up to 500 years (*1367*).

While ponderosa pines of cold-climate provenances can endure severe winter temperatures as a result of natural selection within a geographic race (*1079*), they still may suffer winter killing of foliage (*1490*) and crown top killing resulting in multiple stems when sudden major drops in temperature occur. The tree can be damaged by snow and is sensitive to noxious gases. It has suffered from fluorine (*11, 1279*), from sulfur dioxide, to which it is only moderately sensitive (*1249*), and from smog and ozone (*1084*). Ponderosa pine seedlings vary greatly in sensitivity to fluorine injury (*636*), and older trees also vary in degree of reaction to air pollutants. Young trees are readily killed by fire, and heavy mortality from fire has been sustained even in virgin timber. Fire scars are common on all sizes. The tree is unusually windfirm, but even so wind and lightning are among the most serious sources of damage to trees of sawtimber size (*316*). Ponderosa pine seedlings proved more sensitive to several herbicides than Douglas-fir. They were most resistant to damage in late summer and most sensitive in spring and early summer (*1028*).

The principal characteristics of the pathology of ponderosa pine are growth reduction, cull, and mortality from dwarfmistletoe; heartrot, mainly by *Polyporus anceps;* striking local damage from stem rusts, particularly *Peridermium filamentosum;* localized cankering of young trees by species of *Atropellis;* and sensitivity of the foliage to air pollutants and in some areas to Elytroderma blight.

Seedling Diseases.—Ponderosa pine seedlings in nurseries are subject to damping-off and root rots under wet soil conditions, high humidity, and in soils not sufficiently acid. *Pythium debaryanum, Rhizoctonia solani,* and *Fusarium* spp. have been isolated from diseased seedlings and are important damping-off fungi of ponderosa pine (*602*). Vaartaja (*1458*) has killed seedlings in the laboratory by inoculation with *Phytophthora cactorum.* A Fusarium root rot of nursery seedlings has been particularly damaging in the Pacific Northwest but has been subject to control by cultural measures (*1622*).

Rhizina undulata causes a root rot in trees up to 5 years old in local patches in the Northwest, particularly on burned areas (*151*). *Pestalotia funerea, Thelephora terrestris* (*360*),and *T. fimbriata* (*1540*) have been reported as seedling pathogens, but their capacity to cause disease is questionable even though the latter grows around seedlings. Spaulding infected soft-tissued ponderosa pine seedlings with *P. funerea,* but this fungus is a minor pathogen in nursery practice (*605*). Fisher (*449*) found the following fungi to decay radicles just emerging from seed coats: *Botrytis* (*cinerea?*), *Fusarium* spp., *Pythium debaryanum, P. ultimum, Rhizoctonia* sp., *Sphaeropsis ellisii* (*Diplodia pinea*), and *Verticillium. Pestalotia* sp. failed to cause rot of radicles. Smith and Bega (*1323*) describe severe damage to coniferous nursery stock, including ponderosa pine, in California nurseries (see *Pinus lambertiana*) as a result of mid- to late-season attack of roots by *Sclerotium bataticola* (*Macrophomina phaseoli*).

Species of *Melampsora* are reported by Molnar and Sivak (*1000*) and Ziller (*1668*) as attacking seedlings of ponderosa pine in the Pacific Northwest.

Many of the leaf diseases and rusts of ponderosa pine can become nursery diseases under suitable conditions for seedling infection. High temperatures at the soil line cause lesions that somewhat resemble damping-off (*601*). In mountain areas frost-heaving can destroy many seedlings.

Low vigor in ponderosa pine seedlings in a Great Plains nursery appeared to be due to heavy soil infestation by the dagger nematode *Xiphinema americanum* (*1097*). Root knot nematodes (*Meloidgyne* sp.) and the spiral nematode *Helicotylenchus lobus* have also been identified from ponderosa pine roots (*1222*).

Riffle (*1172*) provides an account of the plant-parasitic nematodes in marginal ponderosa pine stands in central New Mexico.

Foliage Diseases.—The most serious leaf disease is caused by *Elytroderma deformans* (*861*) which causes the foliage of large numbers of trees to redden and die. By virtue of its over-wintering in twigs, it readily reinfects new crops of needles giving rise to the "flags" of dead-needled shoots, to brooms, and often causing the tree crowns to become thin, ragged, short, reduced in vigor, and the trees thus prey to insects and other enemies (*248*). Needle cast diseases are also caused by *Lophodermella* (*Hypodermella*) *cerina* and *Davisomycella medusa* (*1493*), both with pale fruiting bodies, the latter being strongly pathogenic (*323*); and by *L. concolor*, *Naemacyclus niveus*, and *Lophodermium ponderosae* (*1346*). All of these needle diseases are particularly prominent in California, but rarely economically important. The brown spot fungus *Scirrhia acicola* browns parts of needles in the South (*1304*) and also in the West, where it commonly goes under the name of its imperfect stage *Lecanosticta acicola*. In Missouri it has ruinously damaged ponderosa pine plantations. A disease resulting in a red-banding discoloration of foliage, blighting, and defoliation has occurred periodically in Idaho (*1280*). Much confusion has surrounded the cause, which now is attributed to *Dothistroma pini* var. *linearis*. Thyr and Shaw (*1406*), who named the new variety, give a good account of the problems of identifying fungi appearing on red-banded needles, another of which is *Leptostroma decipiens*.

Funk and Parker (*492*) consider it premature to recognize varieties of *Dothistroma pini* on the basis of size of conidia and stromata as did Thyr and Shaw (*1406*), since *D. pini* has a wide range in spore dimensions. The former found the perfect stage which they named *Scirrhia pini* in British Columbia on seven species or hybrids of western pines and on a *Pinus echinata* x *taeda* hybrid.

They point out differences between *S. acicola* and *S. pini*. Ascostromata of the former may attain a length of 2.5 mm. and contain up to 18 locules, while those of the latter rarely exceed 0.5 mm. and usually contain 6 to 10 locules. *Lecanosticta* conidia, as in *S. acicola*, become brownish at maturity, while *Dothistroma* conidia, as in *S. pini*, remain hyaline (*1280*). (See also *Pinus radiata*).

Lophodermium pinastri, although common on dead and dying needles, can probably be ignored as a pathogen. *Neopeckia coulteri* develops under snow.

The needle discomycete *Hemiphacidium planum* is considered by Keener [45] to cause as much damage through killing foliage as *Elytroderma deformans* on ponderosa and pinyon pines in Arizona; however, Staley [46] finds it following *Hypodermella medusa. H. planum (807)* often accompanies *E. deformans* in brooms on ponderosa pine. Keener also considered *Coryneum cinereum* to be a widespread needle pathogen and to be identical with a fungus that is killing needles of ponderosa pine in California.

Coleosporium asterum is a minor needle rust in the Inland Empire (*46*).

Stem Diseases.—The fungus *Cenangium ferruginosum (C. abietis)* is often associated with dead branches, and this led to the name "pruning twig blight," especially in Washington, Idaho, and Montana (*1541*). However, it is becoming increasingly questionable as to whether this fungus has any real pathogenic potential (*542*).

Atropellis arizonica causes long cankers in Arizona and blackens the wood beneath, and *A. piniphila* causes similar cankers both in the Southwest and in the Inland Empire (*151, 877*). *Diplodia pinea* causes a tip blight in the East, as described under *Pinus nigra. Dasyscypha ellisiana,* when inoculated into small ponderosa pines in the East, proved mildly pathogenic on branches (*577*).

Several rusts are very damaging to ponderosa pine. In local areas in the Southwest and Utah, *Peridermium filamentosum,* called limb rust, kills out lower, middle, or top areas of crowns in striking fashion (*961*) by successive branch killing, without producing noticeable swellings. The rust appears to be in part autoecious and in part goes to alternate hosts in the Scrophulariaceae (*10*).

Peterson and Shurtleff (*1112*) give a thorough account of the mycelium of the limb rust fungi. These include three strains of *Peridermium filamentosum* and *P. stalactiforme* (see *Pinus jeffreyi*). With the limb rusts: (1) longitudinal spread is mainly hyphal growth through tracheids; (2) hyphae grow deeply into the sapwood; (3) mycelia avoid, rather than concentrate in, bark and outer xylem rings; (4) hyphae are much larger than those of other rust fungi.

Peterson (*1107*) provides a good illustrated account of damage from limb rusts. They attack only pines of the group *Ponderosae.* He points out that, "Unlike other pine rusts, limb rust is a systemic disease; infection can spread throughout a tree rather than being restricted to a canker or gall." At any one time a lower, midsection, or top of a trunk may be limbless, but the final effect is always death of the tree.

The western gall rust (*P. harknessii*) attacks ponderosa pine mostly in local areas from the Black Hills of South Dakota across to the Pacific Northwest, causing round and pear-shaped galls,

---

[45] Personal communication from Paul D. Keener, deceased, formerly plant pathologist, University of Arizona, Tucson, Ariz.

[46] Personal communication from John M. Staley, pathologist, USDA Forest Service, Rocky Mountain Forest and Range Experiment Station, Ft. Collins, Colo.

distortion, trunk lesions, and killing. In some areas of the Northwest thousands of seedlings per acre have been killed (*1102*). This rust attacks ponderosa pine also along the West Coast States into Mexico. An albino strain has been reported, in the aecial stage, in the Rocky Mountains.

While *Peridermium* (*Cronartium*) *stalactiforme* causes a stem rust of this species, it is primarily a rust of lodgepole pine (*10, 1653*). The infected areas on small stems are only slightly swollen and diamond-shaped, but on larger trees of some pines they become very long (up to 30 ft.) sunken lesions, usually with resinosis, and sometimes with the cankered wood blackened by concurrent infection with *Atropellis piniphila*. The stalactiform rust has stages II and III on species in the Scrophulariaceae (*10*), mostly *Castilleja* and *Melampyrum* (*1110*).

Cronartium comandrae attacks ponderosa pine through the Rocky Mountain States to California and Washington and eastward to Tennessee and Mississippi, causing slight swellings on branches and elongated cankers on trunks (*814*). Its alternate hosts are species of *Comandra*, and the snowshoe-shaped aeciospores on pine cankers easily distinguish this rust (*966*).

C. comptoniae, the sweetfern rust, also attacks ponderosa pine, mostly in the East and Lake States (*25, 1341*), out of its native range, but also in Montana. It causes some distortion and growth aberrations but is not as damaging as the other Peridermiums already described on this pine. *C. quercuum*, with its round galls and alternate hosts among the oaks, also has been reported on ponderosa pine in the East, South, and West. There is considerable doubt as to whether a *Cronartium* on oak in California is this rust.

Peterson (*1110*) has monographed the species of *Peridermium* on pine stems throughout the world and has indicated many of the relationships to *Cronartium* stages. This monograph and his paper on limb rust (*1111*) are particularly useful in determining the identity of the stem rusts of hard pines in western North America.

Ponderosa pine's most widespread disease is dwarfmistletoe (*41*). In the Southwest and Central Rocky Mountains *Arceuthobium vaginatum* f. *cryptopodum* is prevalent (*613*) and very damaging, and in California and the Northwest *A. campylopodum* f. *campylopodum* prevails (*803*). In Arizona dwarfmistletoe is one of the three main causes of mortality in this species (*316*). The typical symptoms are swellings; brooming; reduced vigor; reduction in growth, quality, and seed production; and killing, especially in sapling and pole stands. The two species of dwarfmistletoe are distinguishable by their different seasons of blooming and by characteristics of the mistletoe plants (*505*). *A. americanum* also occurs on ponderosa pine in several Rocky Mountain States, in California, and in Canada.

Dwarfmistletoe reduces height growth of ponderosa pine more than it reduces diameter growth. If height growth effects are ignored, volume reduction due to infection would be underestimated by 40 percent. Stunting of infected trees makes infested areas appear to be of poorer quality than they are (*252*).

Wicker (*1577*), in appraising the biological control of *A. campylopodum* f. *campylopodum* on ponderosa pine by *Colletotrichum gloeosporioides* (*Glomerella cingulata*), mentions two other parasites of dwarfmistletoe. They are *Wallrothiella arceuthobii*, which attacks pistillate flowers of spring-flowering species, and *Septogloeum gillii*, which causes an anthracnose.

Specific blue-stain fungi are generally distributed by specific bark beetles, and some of these fungi kill the trees into which the beetles carry them. Others are simply stainers of logs and lumber (*841, 1473*). *Ceratocystis ips, C. minor,* and *C. pilifera* have been isolated from ponderosa pine trees (*8, 1227*). *C. ips* and *C. minor* are known to be widely carried by species of bark beetles that attack living pines, while *C. pilifera* appears to be carried mostly to fresh lumber (*1473*). Mathre (*933*) describes the pathogenicity of *C. minor* to ponderosa pine in California.

Aleurodiscus penicillatus occurs on dead branches in Canada (*858*).

Root Diseases.—A killing root disease of ponderosa, Jeffrey, and singleleaf pinyon pines in the Southwest and California results from attack by *Verticicladiella wageneri* (*781*), an imperfect fungus that causes a diffuse dark staining of the root wood and kills the roots (*1499*) (see also *Pinus jeffreyi*). *Fomes annosus* causes an insidious lethal root disease of ponderosa, killing trees of all ages and usually resulting in groupwise mortality that is sometimes mistaken for bark beetle damage (*316*). Diagnosis in the absence of fruiting bodies or typically rotted roots can be difficult (*1498*). *F. annosus,* as a pathogen of ponderosa pine, was mistakenly referred to as a species of *Cunninghamella* in one major publication (*1053, 1498*).

Polyporus schweinitzii is another fungus of importance as a root and butt rotter, chiefly the latter. *F. annosus* also rots butts of ponderosa pine as well as acting as a killing pathogen. *Armillaria mellea* is a root and butt rotter but is rarely a primary killer of this species. It is considered more aggressive on other species including western white pine and Douglas-fir. Minor root and butt fungi of ponderosa pine are *P. tomentosus* and *F. nigrolimitatus*. In British Columbia the "annual" form of *Poria weirii* causes some root rot of this species (*190*).

Fomes annosus is becoming increasingly important as a killing disease in California, acting alone or in conjunction with bark beetles. Bega and Smith (*94*) provide host records and a map of the occurrence of *F. annosus* in that state. While attacks have been most frequent on ponderosa and Jeffrey pine, most of the coniferous species in the state have served as hosts to this fungus.

Where ponderosa pine was planted in shelterbelts in *Phymatotrichum*-infested soils in Texas and Oklahoma, losses from this root rot were very light with this species (*1627*).

Trunk Rots.—The most important heartrot in the southern Rocky Mountains and the Black Hills regions is western red rot, caused by *Polyporus anceps* (*P. ellisianus*) (*40*). *Fomes pini* is also a major heart rotter of ponderosa pine. Between these species, there are many points of difference in the appearance of the rotted wood (*151*) and the vastly different conks. These two fungi also occur primarily in different regions. *F. pini, P. sulphureus,* and *P. volvatus* are among the heartrot fungi most common from California north into the Inland Empire. *F. pinicola, F. officinalis,* and *F. roseus* can also rot the heart of living trees, but they are mainly confined to the dead wood behind scars.

Normal rotation ages should eliminate much of the heartrot that has been common in old stands, but even immature trees in the Southwest develop streaks of red rot (*P. anceps*) from dead branches. Broken branches and pruning wounds are not important pathways of infection for this fungus (*40*). It requires a period of "build-up" as a saprobe in dead branches kept moist by summer rains before it can invade the trunk. Where summers are dry *P. anceps* is seldom damaging.

In one Arizona area where red rot was studied in relation to tree-age classes, cull losses from this rot reached only 6 percent by age 160, the highest age class reported. Data from six areas in Arizona and New Mexico showed that from 70 to 80 percent of all defect (20 to 30 percent of the stand volume) was due to wood rots with *Polyporus anceps* the chief decay fungus. Both poor physiological condition and high age were accompanied by very high defect percentages (*1405*) in these merchantable stands.

Veluticeps berkeleyi, according to Gilbertson et al. (*501*), is a widely distributed wood-rotting fungus in North America, particularly common on ponderosa pine. It causes a brown cubical heartrot of living trees and a saprot in down timber. Isolates of the fungus have a distinctive odor similar to that of smoke-cured bacon or ham. The basidiocarps have a *Stereum*-like appearance, but the hymenial surface has fine teeth. They are mainly resupinate; if reflexed, the upper surface is brown, with almost-black, matted hairs behind the margin. The hymenial surface is shades of buff color.

Mycorrhizal Relations.—The following fungi have been reported to form mycorrhizae with ponderosa pine, although none of the associations have been established by pure-culture technique: *Amanita muscaria, A. pantherina, A. vaginata; Boletus edulis, B. granulatus, B. luteus, B. piperatus, B. tomentosus, B. (Xerocomus)* sp.; *Cenococcum graniforme; Cortinarius croceofolius; Gomphidius rutilus, G. vinicolor; Hygrophorous gliocyclus, H. karstenii; Laccaria laccata; Marasmius oreades; Russula delica (1442);* and *Xerocomus* sp. (*1618*).

When mycorrhizal fungi in Northwest nurseries were destroyed by soil fumigation or other chemical treatment, the 2–0 ponderosa pine stock was stunted and chlorotic due to lack of mycorrhizae (*1618*). When outplanted on a good site, seedlings without mycorrhizae did not grow as well as those with them. In Nebraska, where mycorrhizae on ponderosa pine seedlings raised in nurseries are often lacking, the outplanted stock grew poorly, but duff inoculations that resulted in the formation of mycorrhizae brought about improvement (*523*).

Wright (*1618*) cites some unpublished work conducted in North Dakota by Stoeckeler to the effect that Rocky Mountain ponderosa pine appeared to be less responsive to mycorrhizae than jack pine or blue spruce at one nursery, while the reverse was true at another nursery. At the second nursery a combination of acidification and inoculation resulted in an increase in the percentage of plantable ponderosa pine stock produced.

Wright (*1619*) in Oregon reported black mycorrhizae caused by *Cenococcum graniforme* to be common on seedlings of ponderosa and lodgepole pine, but shading increased the percentage of white mycorrhizae. Wet soil did not inhibit mycorrhizal formation.

Table-Mountain pine
Pinus pungens

Generally a small, limby tree, the Table-Mountain pine is largely confined to the dry, gravelly tablelands, ridges, and slopes of the Southern Appalachian Mountains. Along with pitch pine it can withstand the rigors of these sites and survive, taking well the impacts of ice, snow, drought, and wind. Estimates of longevity run as high as 300 years. Since it is not a major component of the forest, the species has not had enough study to clearly define its pathology.

Coleosporium delicatulum and *C. asterum* cause minor leaf rusts; *Ploioderma (Hypoderma) lethale* blights some foliage in the mountains of the Carolinas; and *Cronartium quercuum (630)*, *C. comandrae (966)*, and *C. comptoniae (25, 1341)* attack the species occasionally and locally.

Twig killing by a scale insect (*Matsucoccus gallicola*) results in "flagging" that can be mistaken for a twig blight, but careful examination with a hand lens will disclose the small scale insects under the bark at the base of an insect-killed shoot. When the scales sink below the level of the normal stem tissue, they leave the tiny, black pits that reveal *Matsucoccus* injury (see also *Pinus resinosa*).

A common twig blight is caused by *Atropellis tingens* which stains the wood darkly beneath the lesion (*380, 877*). *Dasyscypha ellisiana (575)* and *D. oblongospora (574)* have been collected on dead shoots of Table-Mountain pine, and the former is considered parasitic to some exotic conifers in New England but not to native species. *Cenangium atropurpureum* which fruits on dead twigs has a weak potential as a twig dieback fungus.

A remarkable fasciculation of cones of Table-Mountain pine has been reported from Pennsylvania (*437*). *Phytophthora cinnamoni* causes a damping-off of this species (*360*). The only mycorrhiza-former reported is *Cenococcum graniforme (1442)*.

Polyporus schweinitzii causes a root and butt rot, and *Fomes pini* causes a heartrot in older or damaged trees.

Monterey pine
Pinus radiata

Monterey pine is a California tree of very limited range, occurring only along the coast from near San Francisco to near San Luis Obispo. A minor species in the American forest economy, it is a major timber exotic, often referred to as radiata pine, in six countries on five continents. It is playing an increasingly important role as an ornamental in the bay areas that it occupies naturally in California. Its native stands occur in an area only 130 miles long, 6 miles wide, and from sea level to an elevation of 1,000 ft. It is intermediate in tolerance, being more tolerant of shade than most pines, and makes rapid growth, when not overtopped, for 30 to 40 years, slowing markedly after 50 to 60 years (*1047*), after

338

which it might be said to be mature. Older stands now are mostly less than 100 years old.

The climate where Monterey pine occurs is considered Mediterranean, with 17 to 28 in. of rainfall annually, much summer fog, frost a rarity, no snow or hail, and moderate summer temperatures. The average absolute maximum and minimum temperatures in the Monterey pine belt are 102° and 25° F., respectively. The tree does best on clay loam or sandy loam from shales, slates, granite, or marine sandstones (1047). As demonstrated by performance abroad, the tree can grow well over a very wide range of soils from the heaviest mottled clays of New Zealand's Northland to deep sands or pumice. However, the heavier soils have led to root diseases and deficiencies and are thus in many cases not suitable for Monterey pine (1369), although there are some good stands on heavy soils on both the North and South Island of New Zealand.

The species regenerates aggressively in California and elsewhere in the world. It is thin-barked and more susceptible to fire damage than ponderosa or Jeffrey pine. The even-aged stands that follow fire tend to be free of dwarfmistletoe but may be heavily infected with western gall rust. The tree resists injury from salt spray and is not normally exposed to ice, snow, or other rigorous climatic impacts.

Windthrow has been a major cause of loss to Monterey pine because of this tree's tendency to a low root-shoot ratio. The tree tends to develop a long and heavy trunk and crown but a restricted and shallow root system, even on fairly light soils. Where wind is not excessive the tree is fairly straight, but it is almost always limby. It is sensitive to frost, and multiple stems are common, particularly abroad where much leader killing has resulted from frost. In years when and in places where the tree never goes fully into winter dormancy, the danger from frost is more acute.

Offord (1047) has prepared an analysis of the pathology of Monterey pine in California, and his account has been freely drawn upon, supplemented by other records and information and by personal experience of the author with this tree overseas. Some new Monterey pine problems are being exposed along the Pacific coast as the tree is now being planted considerably beyond its natural range. Attacks by *Fomes annosus* (92) and *Cronartium comptoniae* (995), excessive damage from western gall rust (1047), cold damage and other problems not typical for Monterey pine have beset plantings outside the natural range. Offord sums up this matter by stating that successful planting of Monterey pine in west coast areas of North America is definitely limited by frost, midsummer heat, disease, and pests (1047).

Seedling Diseases.—There have been few nursery problems with Monterey pine in the United States. Seed viability is normally very high and growth of seedlings excellent, if not excessive, for the best quality planting stock. While damping-off and subsequent root rots do occur under conditions highly conducive to these diseases, they have not yet proved serious. In western Florida Monterey pine suffered severe losses from damping-off for several successive years.[47]

---

[47] Personal communication from A. Alfred Foster, formerly pathologist, Tennessee Valley Authority, Norris, Tenn.

At one nursery where several tree species were raised, *Rhizoctonia solani, Fusarium* sp., *Pythium* sp., and *Sclerotium bataticola* (*Macrophomina phaseoli*) were isolated from some seedbeds, but no serious losses occurred to beds in Monterey pine (*1047*). However, Smith and Bega (*1323*) point out the importance of this fungus as a root pathogen of coniferous seedlings in California. *Phytophthora cinnamomi* has been isolated from nursery stock in California, but this fungus has not been aggressive on the lighter soils that Monterey pine seedlings have been grown on in this country (*1658*). In New Zealand (*510*) Monterey pine is subject to damping-off by *Cylindrocladium scoparium, Rhizoctonia solani, Phytophthora cactorum, P. cinnamomi,* and *Pythium ultimum.*

Ziller (*1668*) has found Monterey pine to be very susceptible to *Melampsora* rusts in inoculation tests in British Columbia.

Rhizina undulata has been reported attacking this species (*151*) but is of minor consequence and tends to attack seedlings mostly where slash burning has taken place. *Botrytis cinerea* has caused a gray mold locally in Oregon (*1277*).

Foliage Diseases.—Compared with almost any other hard pine, Monterey pine has very few needle pathogens, and none of them do much more harm than rendering trees unsightly or affecting growth to a nominal extent, if at all. These organisms include *Coleosporium madiae* (alternate hosts are in the genus *Madia*), *Diplodia pinea* (*1513*), *Davisomycella* (*Hypodermella*) *limitata, Ploioderma* (*Hypoderma*) *pedatum, Naemacyclus niveus,* and *Lophodermium pinastri* (*323*). *N. niveus* is mentioned by Offord as probably the most widespread and damaging of these fungi (*1047*). *C. madiae,* an obligate parasite, and *P. pedatum,* probably a saprophyte (*323*), are interesting in that the former has been reported only on Monterey and Jeffrey pine and the latter only on Monterey pine. *Diplodia pinea* bothers this species little, and this may be due in part to the absence of hail or other contusion-type injury that usually gives this fungus moribund tissue to develop in. Although *D. pinea* is basically a shoot pathogen and wood stainer, it can infect through buds and needle bases in North America (*1513*).

A premature shedding of needles preceded by yellow banding and mottling has been on the increase in the San Francisco Bay area for some years. Drought, cold, poor soil drainage, and air pollution are considered to be contributory factors to this disorder (*1047*).

Scirrhia pini (*Dothistroma pini*) has been reported on *P. radiata* in British Columbia (see *P. ponderosa*) where Parker and Collis (*1076*) found it widespread on *Pinus contorta, P. monticola, P. ponderosa,* and on Vancouver Island on *P. radiata, P. muricata, P. pinaster, P. nigra calabrica,* and some hybrids. *P. radiata* was particularly badly damaged. In general young trees and the lower needles of large trees were most severely attacked. Small, chlorotic areas appeared on needles in the fall, followed by larger necrotic spots. In the spring bright red bands bearing small, black fruiting bodies appeared in the spots. Needles of all ages are attacked, and they are usually cast in summer and fall.

Stem Diseases.—The important stem diseases are rusts and dwarfmistletoe. Two morphologic forms of western gall rust attack

Pinus radiata. The round- to pear-shaped galls of *Peridermium harknessii* tend to shed the overlaying bark thus exposing the smooth naked wood well in advance of branch killing, while the round galls of *P. cerebroides* (a nomen nudum) seldom lose their bark while still active. *P. harknessii* always has a collar of dead bark at the proximal (or both) ends, while *P. cerebroides* rarely if ever has such a collar (*1047*). The validity of separation of these rusts at the species level is open to question. Both rusts infect from pine to pine, both make brooms and retard growth, and both can kill small trees in the case of stem infection. Peterson (1110), in monographing the *Peridermium* species on pine stems, considers *P. cerebroides* to represent simply a host-reaction variant of *P. harknessii.*

Boyce has taken the position that the Woodgate rust of Scots pine in the East is *P. harknessii* and that *P. cerebroides* can produce similar galls on Scots pine (*150*). However, Peterson's views on the lack of meaning of the "collars" and on the likelihood that these two rusts are conspecific are compelling.

Cronartium comptoniae (*25, 1341*) has severely damaged Monterey pine planted on Vancouver Island, Canada, in the vicinity of one of the alternate hosts, *Myrica gale,* with 95 percent of a 5-year-old stand infected (*995*). A *Cronartium* on oak in California (*150*) raises the possibility that *C. quercuum* may occur on California pine (*10*).

The pitch canker fungus (*Fusarium lateritium* f. sp. *pini*), following inoculations in the East, attacked Monterey pine transplants more vigorously and lethally than any of the eastern hosts used in earlier inoculations. The fungus produced abundant sporodochia on the lesions, whereas it has rarely been seen sporulating on a lesion on an eastern pine (*650*), and then covertly under small bark scales.

The western dwarfmistletoe (*Arceuthobium campylopodum* f. *campylopodum*) produces its fusiform swellings, brooms, and lethal effects on Monterey pine mainly in the sapling and pole sizes but can damage larger or smaller trees (*505*). The dwarfmistletoe shoots on this tree have a characteristic olive-green shade, and their clusters attract spittle insects (Cercopidae). Other observations confirm that dwarfmistletoe on Monterey pine is entomophilout and that trees weakened by dwarfmistletoe are highly susceptible to insect attack (*1047*). This dwarfmistletoe has been found on planted Monterey pine in Alameda County, California.

An association of blue stain with bark beetles holds true for Monterey pine. The species associates, however, as worked out for many bark beetles and staining fungi, have not been the subject of study with respect to this tree.

A blighting of new shoots, buds, and needles, sometimes resulting in resinous cankers and blue-staining of woody tissue, is caused by *Diplodia pinea* (see Foliage Diseases). In Australasia and South America this fungus is more destructive than it is in the United States, and through bole infection it kills tops as a tracheomycotic stain organism.

Root Diseases.—The root diseases of Monterey pine (aside from seedlings) are caused by *Armillaria mellea, Fomes annosus,* and *Polyporus schweinitzii.* Since oak stumps, which are well-known foci for this fungus, are common in stands of this pine, it is not surprising that some damage from *A. mellea* occurs. Losses, however, have been minor, and the elimination of large patches of this pine, as takes place occasionally in New Zealand from *A. mellea*, have not been observed.

Fomes annosus has been reported from time to time as a killer of Monterey pine, and the losses that took place in the Placerville, Calif., arboretum when this fungus became epidemic testify to the susceptibility of this species under Placerville conditions .(*92*). *Polyporus schweinitzii* has been associated with the dying of vigorous young Monterey pines in California and has often been collected from root- or butt-rotted trees. It appears that this ubiquitous root and butt rotter can assume an aggressive role as a primary root pathogen of this species (*151*). *P. tomentosus* also occurs on Monterey pine but is damaging more as a butt rot than a root rot.

Trunk Rots.—Heartrot losses in Monterey pine are low, as in the case of the southern pines, causing only about 2- or 3-percent cull except in overmature or badly damaged stands (*1047*). In addition to the butt rot fungi already named, heartrot is caused mainly by *Fomes pini,* with *Polyporus anceps* occasionally entering through dead branches or stubs.

Mycorrhizal Relations.—Some attention to the mycorrhizae of Monterey pine has been given by investigators cited by Offord (*1047*), and Trappe (*1442*) lists the following fungi as reputed mycorrhiza-formers on this species: *Amanita muscaria; Boletus granulatus, B. luteus, B. piperatus, B. subaureus; Cenococcum graniforme; Gomphidium rutilus, G. vinicolor; Inocybe lacera; Laccaria (Clitocybe) laccata; Lactarius deliciosus; Rhizopogon luteolus, R. roseolus, R. rubescens; Scleroderma aurantium,* and *S. bovista.* Only *Boletus luteus* and *Cenococcum graniforme* have been confirmed by pure-culture technique.

Miscellaneous Pathology.—Offord (*1047*) mentions a physiogenic brooming of Monterey pine in several California localities that appears to be very similar to an occasional brooming reported from time to time on several species of eastern and western pines. It is ascribed to localized bud stimulation not caused by a pathogen.

Deep wedges of pitch-soaked wood extend inward from pitchy trunk lesions of varying size on trees of up to sawlog size. These wedges look very much like those associated with infection by the pitch canker fungus in slash and longleaf pine (*261*). However, no pathogen has yet been isolated from such lesions. A complex of factors involving rust infection, insects, and secondary fungi may be responsible for this condition.

While deficiency symptoms in Monterey pine have not been apparent in the United States, a number of abnormal conditions, such as rosette, needle fusion, bud resinosis, and extreme retardation of growth and death of trees, have been ascribed to deficiencies in zinc, potassium, calcium, phosphorus, and other elements on other continents (*1047*). The mineral requirements of Monterey pine seedlings have been reviewed by Will (*1582*).

There is an extensive literature on the diseases of *Pinus radiata* abroad. References to this material have been appended to Offord's review of the diseases of this species in the United States (*1047*), and much of it is cited by Spaulding (*1336*).

Red pine
Pinus resinosa

An intolerant tree of the Northeast and Lake States, red pine thrives with cold winters, mild summers, low-to-medium rainfall, sandy and acid soils, and level-to-rolling topography (*1214*). The tree matures at about 100 years, and specimen trees as old as 307 years have been authenticated, with one Minnesota veteran estimated to be 400 years old. It is sensitive to fire through the sapling stage but very resistant at sawtimber sizes. Fire scars result in deep pitch-soaking of the wood behind them, and this often seals the wounds against infection (*1471*). Red pine is fairly resistant to damage from salt spray (*1005*). It has been injured by sulfur dioxide near oil refineries (*869*).

Red pine is fairly resistant to 2, 4-D and 2, 4, 5-T herbicides at concentrations used for controlling hardwoods. It suffers breakage from ice because its full foliage may accumulate a great weight of it. On soils deficient in potassium, growth may stagnate severely. The species is relatively free of serious enemies over most of its natural range. However, when grown on soils that are less acid, finer textured, and less well-drained than soils to which it is adapted, or under climatic conditions warmer than normal, it is subject to many troubles (*1214*). When injured by extreme cold, recovery has been excellent unless more than 25 percent of the foliage had been injured (*1213*). In both the Lake States and in Canada, planted red pines have occasionally suffered heavily from summer frosts (*1128*).

The salient features of the pathology of red pine are: high susceptibility to many nursery diseases, a needle droop and autumn browning, a tendency to fork, "burn blight" in the Lake States, a decline in New York and Pennsylvania probably related to soil drainage factors and analogous to loblolly pine spot dieout, and a tendency to killing by *Fomes annosus* root rot following thinning.

Seedling Diseases.—Rathbun-Gravatt (*1144*) concluded that poor germination of red pine resulting from damping-off fungi is due mainly to the destruction of radicles after emergence from the seed coat but before seedlings break through the soil. Such fungi can also decay unruptured seed. Emerging radicles were rotted by *Pythium ultimum, P. aphanidermatum, Pythiacystis citrophora, Phytophthora* spp., *Fusarium sporotrichioides, F. discolor sulphureum, F. arthrosporioides, Botrytis cinerea, Phomopsis juniperovora*, some lines of *Corticium vagum* (*Rhizoctonia solani*), and *F. moniliforme*.

Fisher (*449*) found the following fungi to decay radicles just emerging from seed coats: *Botrytis* (*cinerea?*), *Fusarium* spp., *Pythium debaryanum, P. ultimum, Rhizoctonia* sp., *Sphaeropsis ellisii* (*Diplodia pinea*), and *Verticillium* sp. Eliason (*408*) produced damping-off of red pine by inoculation with many *Pythium* isolates, mainly *P. debaryanum*.

Root exudates of red pine were shown to contain three sugars and 13 amino acids, and nutrient mixtures containing certain of these sugars and amino acids were very effective in stimulating mycelial growth and the number of germ tubes per sporangium of *Pythium ultimum* (*15*).

In the nursery red pine has many fungus enemies. *Cylindrocladium scoparium* (*296*) has been damaging in Pennsylvania and New Jersey (*294*) and more recently in Minnesota (*33*), *Dothistroma pini* in Ohio, *Fusarium avenaceum* and *F. oxysporum* in Pennsylvania, *Phytophthora cinnamomi* and *Diplodia pinea* in Delaware and Maryland (*299, 304*), *P. cactorum* in Maryland and Minnesota (*305*), *Pythium irregulare* in Wisconsin, *P. ultimum* widely, *Rhizina undulata* in Maryland, *Rhizoctonia solani* widely (*1212*), and *Thielaviopsis basicola* in Canada (*1462*). In Quebec nurseries red pine has suffered heavily from damping-off due to *Fusarium* spp. Other fungi causing damping-off in Canada were *Rhizoctonia solani* and *Pythium debaryanum*. Vaartaja (*1458*) killed seedlings by inoculation with *Phytophthora cinnamoni* in the laboratory.

The snow mold fungi (*Phacidium infestans* and related species— *1155, 1157*) have also damaged red pine seedlings, but snow molds are not as severe as on spruce and fir (*1124*). *Pestalotia funerea,* while reported as a seedling pathogen, likely plays a secondary role. Soil fumigation, so helpful against soil-borne nursery diseases where the stock grown is 1–0, as in the South, is not nearly as effective in controlling nursery pathogens where the stock must be kept in the nursery longer than 1 year.

Even when the two species were grown in the same nursery beds in the Chittenden Nursery in Michigan, red pine was undamaged by the seedling disease ascribed to *Cylindrocladium scoparium* that has been so destructive to white pine. However, in other nurseries in the Lake States, and in inoculation experiments, red pine has readily succumbed to *C. scoparium* (*32*).

Scleroderris lagerbergii (see also Stem Diseases) has been killing patches of seedlings, mostly 3–0 and 2–0, in Ontario, Canada, nurseries. Punter (*1138*) describes attack on red pine. By May infected seedlings took on a gray-green color. Apical buds failed to break, and the old needles turned brown. The bark of moribund seedlings separated readily from the wood. The following spring pycnidia of the imperfect stage (*Brunchorstia pinea*) formed on needles and stems. Inner bark and outer wood sometimes became yellow to dark green. Small lesions sometimes occurred at the level of the first branch whorl. Tissue isolations yielded the characteristic greenish, cottony mycelium from which pycnidia readily arose (see also *Pinus banksiana*). Attacks in Canadian nurseries involved red, jack, and Scots pine.

Rhizina undulata caused some damage to red pine and white spruce seedlings in an area in a Maryland nursery where slash had been burned (*336*). This fungus causes the roots to become rotted and matted.

Although 14 species of nematodes, in 11 genera, have been identified from the roots or rhizosphere of red pine trees, in no case did Ruehle (*1222*) indicate a direct association with plant injury. However, Sutherland (*1370*) found that red pine seedlings in Canada, while not hosts to *Paratylenchus projectus* and *Praty-*

lenchus penetrans, were excellent hosts to *Tylenchus emarginatus* (*1371*).

Foliage Diseases.—Three species of *Coleosporium* (*46*), particularly *C. asterum* (*887*), cause needle rusts, with infection often heavy where the alternate hosts abound, but the impact on growth is light. Nicholls et al. (*1029*) give the life cycle and host relations of *Coleosporium asterum* as it alternates between red pine and species of goldenrod (*Solidago*). This rust will not infect asters. A similar form infects native asters in the Lake States but will not infect goldenrods. The authors state that the western form of *Coleosporium asterum* has its II and III stages on *Aster* and has larger spores than their *Solidago* rust in the Lake States.

Meloderma desmazierii from New York northward and *Ploioderma lethale* mostly further south also cause browning of older needles. *Lophodermium pinastri* has been reported causing needle cast in red pine nurseries after heavy fall frosts (*1334*); however, proof of pathogenicity of this fungus to previously healthy foliage of North American pines has not yet been established. Darker's (*328*) revision of the nomenclature in the Hypodermataceae is followed here.

Young red pines in the Lake States and Northeast sometimes suffer from a "needle droop" considered by Patton and Riker to be the result of sudden and excessive transpiration at a time of limited moisture supply (*1089*). A striking droop and autumn browning of the current year's needles of red pine have also occurred in Canada, where Haddow ascribed these conditions to the combined effects of a Cecidomyid gall midge and the ubiquitous fungus *Pullularia pullulans* (*564*). Patton and Riker, dealing with similar conditions, have considered "droop" and "blight" of different origins with the droop due to unfavorable water relations, the fall blight probably due to the gall midge, and *P. pullulans* having no role in either disease but functioning occasionally as a weak parasite (*1089*).

Anderson (*30*) reported red pine to commonly show needle droop in plantations in the Lake States in 1956 and 1957. He believes that the syndrome can have any of a number of causes including: insufficient moisture, frost, a gall midge (*Thecodiplosis* sp.), a fungus (*Pullularia pullulans*), and in some cases drooping has occurred when none of these factors appeared responsible.

Stem Diseases.—Branch and stem cankers and blights of red pine are caused by *Atropellis tingens* (*877*) and *Diplodia pinea*, the latter seldom a primary invader but able to cause much injury to ornamental trees (*1513*).

Philip Rusden [48] calls attention to the fact that red pine is subject to attack by *Matsucoccus resinosae* which, unlike the injury to *Pinus pungens* by *M. gallicola*, does not leave a tiny pit at the base of a twig. He also calls attention to possible confusion between the damage done by the pine shoot moth and that caused by *Diplodia pinea*. The presence of frass, together with hollowing of the terminal shoot, clearly indicates shoot moth damage.

Although *Dasyscypha ellisiana* and *Ophionectria scolecospora*

---

[48] Personal communication from Philip L. Rusden, formerly pathologist, Bartlett Tree Expert Company, Stamford, Conn.

occur on dying and dead shoots, they are now regarded as saprophytic invaders.

Cronartium comptoniae (*25, 1341*), *C. comandrae* (*151*), and *C. quercuum* (*630*) distort and sometimes kill young trees and can be bothersome seedling diseases, but they are not serious on red pine. Peterson (*1108*) questions reports of *C. comandrae* on red pine.

A bark canker (*Tympanis confusa*) is injurious to red pine south of its natural range in the Northeast, both as a weak primary pathogen and through the decay and defects resulting from the cankers (*552, 588*). Some outbreaks in Connecticut have been related to drought.

Planted red pine has developed basal cankers of undetermined cause in Michigan (*361*) which, in respect to position at the ground line, shrunken appearance, and lack of an associated pathogen, resemble a basal cankering of white pine in New York (*1307*).

Scleroderris lagerbergii has been identified as a pathogen of *Pinus resinosa* and *P. banksiana* in plantations in western Ontario, upper Michigan, and northern Wisconsin. Its range now extends to upper New York, where French and Silverborg (*476*) described and isolated the fungus. Lower branches were attacked first, followed by invasion and girdling of the main stem. Apothecia and pycnidia form on the lesions (see also *Pinus banksiana*).

Tracheomycosis following bark beetle attack has had attention in the case of red pine. The *Ips* bark beetle attacks were followed by *Ceratocystis ips* and *Tuberculariella ips* in what was described as a mutually beneficial relationship. Other insects followed, and the red pine logs, both heartwood and sapwood, were then decayed, mostly by *Peniophora gigantea* (*842, 843*).

Root Diseases.—*Armillaria mellea* is occasionallly found invading the inner bark and cambium of the roots and root collar, but there is some evidence that on red pine this fungus is not a primary invader of a healthy root system (*426*). However, in Ontario *A. mellea*, following its usual habit of growing from a food base in hardwood stumps, has killed a large percentage of the red pines in some plantations (*736*), and it has been listed as common on red pine in the Lake States (*887*). In Michigan (*1363*) conks appeared on planted trees that died following thinning.

Fomes annosus, whose capacity to kill residual trees in thinned pine plantations is now being realized, is already a problem in some areas and may often have to be taken into account where partial cutting is done in red pine plantations (*764*). The incidence and behavior of this disease in planted red pine is much like that in white, slash, and loblolly pines. Miller (*986*) studied damage from annosus root rot in New Hampshire in 13 thinned red pine plantations covering 58 acres. He found some trees dead or dying of root rot in all plantations, with a total of 149 trees dead and 61 dying on the 58 acres. He later reported on 52 red pine plantations (*985*) and found that 68 percent of those thinned had losses from annosus root rot, while only 6 percent of the unthinned stands had root rot losses. *F. annosus* is also known to kill planted red pine in thinned stands in Michigan.

Trunk Rots.—*Polyporus schweinitzii* sometimes causes a root and butt rot of basally injured red pine, and *Fomes pini* is responsible for trunk/rot mainly in mature stands (*887*). The commonest wood-destroying fungi fruiting on red pine stumps in New Hampshire were *Peniophora gigantea, Stereum* spp., *Corticium* spp., and *Fomes annosus* (*985*).

There is little information on rot cull in red pine. In Ontario a study involving 462 trees from 141 to 160 years old showed only 1 percent rot cull. Almost half of this was caused by *Polyporus tomentosus*, with the remainder by *P. schweinitzii, Fomes pini, Corticium galactinum, Fomes cajanderi*, and *Poria subacida* (*73*).

Mycorrhizal Relations.—Trappe (*1442*) reports the fungi that form mycorrhizae with red pine as *Boletinus pictus, Boletus felleus, Cenococcum graniforme, Gomphidius superiorensis, G. vinicolor*, and *Suillus cothurnatus*.

The differential role of different mycorrhizal fungi in assimilating potash from ground feldspar has been demonstrated for red pine (*1442*). Sites unfavorable to red pine have been reported to result in weak mycorrhizal development, copious pseudomycorrhizae, and infection of roots by *Polyporus schweinitzii* (*1634*).

Polyporus tomentosus failed to form mycorrhizae with red pine or white spruce seedlings in pure culture (*1572*).

Miscellaneous Pathology.—Planted red pine often has a tendency to fork excessively. The cause has not been determined, but it seems unlikely to be due to an organism. Late season elongation of lateral buds in the terminal cluster, called prolepsis (see *Pinus banksiana*), has been given as one explanation. Forked trees that have had the extra leader pruned off showed no greater tendency to fork again than did unforked trees (*902*). *Pullularia pullulans* has been suspected by some as having a role in excessive forking (*284, 767*).

Burn blight is a disease of red and jack pine mainly affecting planted trees in the Lake States. It causes a heavily damaged stand to appear as though a fire had singed the upper parts of the trees. The disease results from attacks by the Saratoga spittle bug (*Aphrophora saratogensis*) debilitating the trees and introducing the fungus *Nectria cucurbitula* through its punctures. In the punctured, injured bark the fungus produces necrotic lesions which result in the killing of shoots (*555*). There is a good possibility that *N. cucurbitula*, for which the name *Thyronectria balsamea* was used (*1150*), is the fungus involved in a dieback of balsam fir in Canada.

Red pine on poorly drained sites in New York and Pennsylvania has often died or become stunted after many years of good growth. This condition has been studied by many, and there is a good possibility that the so-called resinosis disease and the one attributed to *Phytophthora cinnamomi* in Pennsylvania, as well as some of the dying attributed to *Fomes annosus*, are all the same malady. This trouble has been highly correlated with poor internal soil drainage coupled with high May rainfall, leading to critically low soil oxygen at a time of major root activity (*1362*). The characteristics of this disease are very similar to that of loblolly spot-dieout (*290*). In both cases the onset typically follows good early growth with trees suffering most on the lowest, usually flat, part of the affected area with conditions improving upwards on a slope. Internal drainage is very poor in the center or worst part of the affected areas, and no pathogens appear involved, although good techniques were used to sample for *P. cinnamomi, F. annosus*, and other suspects in both the New York red pine study (*1362*) and the loblolly spot-dieout study (*290*).

Although some of the Pennsylvania cases of red pine mortality on poorly drained sites have been ascribed to *Phytophthora cinnamomi* (*741*), the evidence is now under question, and there is a strong possibility that these cases, and the New York condition ascribed to low soil oxygen, have the same origin.

Basham (*66*) studied the deterioration of fire-killed jack, red, and white pines in Ontario and described three stains, designated blue stain, brown stain, and orange-ring stain. He also lists the isolation of 17 "white saprot" fungi and 10 "brown saprot" fungi, and gives the roles played by the more important ones in the course of the deterioration process.

Red pine is notably sensitive to competition from black walnut. The walnut trees have a toxic effect on red pines within their zone of root influence.

Mineral deficiencies in red pine seedlings appear as follows (*689*):

N—Foliage short, pale green, not yellow. Seedlings sometimes reddish. No necrosis. Growth stunted. Plants spindly.

P—Seedlings greatly stunted. Lower needles reddish.

K—Seedlings greatly stunted, foliage blue-green. No necrosis except at tips of basal needles. Seedlings very irregular in size.

Mg—Needles of new growth chlorotic their entire length. Affected needles necrotic at tips. Old needles normal green.

Pitch pine
Pinus rigida

Pitch pine is an undemanding, hardy species that will grow under a wide range of soils and sites (*874*) and is therefore often found on dry, burned-over gravelly slopes, on rocky cliffs at high elevations, and even in swamps. Intermediate in tolerance (*54*), it grows best intermixed with hardwoods on the better soils. It matures at about 100 years and has a longevity often exceeding 200 years. It is very resistant to fire after the sapling stage, and it also resists damage from ice, extreme changes in temperature, and animal damage (*916*). It has been considered more resistant to salt spray than many associated coastal species (*1005*), but it can be damaged by heavy deposits of salt (*874*), and it was one of the species most seriously damaged by salt spray following a New England hurricane (*1632*). While slow-growing, its capacity to sprout from dormant buds assists its survival following injury, but this tendency to "feather" plus its normal limbiness make it typically a rough tree. Its root system is capable of extensive growth below the water table in saturated soils (*916*). Its definite taproot, laterals, and sinker roots are like those of the major southern pines.

Sparrow et al. (*1331*), studying tolerance of trees to a 10-year exposure to chronic irradiation from cobalt-60, found native *Pinus rigida* particularly sensitive to damage. After 8 years, 50 percent of the trees had been killed by a cumulative exposure of 5.8 Kr (3.1 r. per day). Harmful effects were also noted in reduced cone formation and interference with seed maturity. The authors expect pitch pine to fairly well represent the pines as a whole in sensitivity to gamma radiation and that other gymnosperms are not expected to exceed the sensitivity of pitch pine by a factor of more than 2, based on chromosome volume per species.

Wounding results in considerable gum flow and pitch-soaking of the wood, and, of the North American pines, pitch pine follows only longleaf and slash pine in this capacity to produce oleoresin.

Seedling Diseases.—Pitch pine is not often raised in nurseries, so little is known of its seedling diseases. However, *Cylindrocladium scoparium* (*296*) has been known to seriously attack seedlings in New Jersey.

Many species of nematodes have been reported from roots or rhizospheres of pitch pine, but none has been associated with injury to the trees (*1222*).

Foliage Diseases.—Nine species of *Coleosporium* produce needle rusts on pitch pine, and the foliage is also spotted or blighted locally by *Meloderma desmazierii* northward and *Ploioderma lethale, P. hedgcockii,* and *Scirrhia acicola* further south. Although *Lophodermium pinastri* is common on senescent or browned foliage, its pathogenicity is under question. Hedgcock (*625*) considered the snow mold *Hemiphacidium* (*Phacidium*) *convexum* parasitic to pitch pine needles. None of the needle fungi seem to have a noticeable impact on growth.

Stem Diseases.—Twigs may be cankered or blighted by *Atropellis tingens* (*380, 877*), *Caliciopsis pinea, Diplodia pinea* (*1513*), or *Fusarium lateritium* f. sp. *pini* (*665*). *Septobasidium linderi* and *S. pinicola* can produce a brown felt on scale insects that inhabit branches in New England. *Cenangium atropurpureum* fruits on dead twigs (*238*).

Four stem rusts attack pitch pine. The most damaging is *Cronartium comptoniae,* the sweetfern rust, mainly from New York northward and westward wherever sweetfern (*Comptonia*) or sweetgale (*Myrica*) occurs (*25, 1341*). The rust stunts, distorts, and kills young trees. Peterson (*1108*) provides information on the aecial and telial hosts of *C. comptoniae* that corrects some past reports and updates the known distribution of this rust on its various hosts.

C. fusiforme has attacked pitch pine lethally, occasionally, in North Carolina (*630*). *C. comandrae,* a killing stem canker rust (*629, 966*), occurs in a few eastern localities that support its alternate host *Comandra umbellata. Cronartium quercuum,* the eastern gall rust, makes round or somewhat elongated galls with "collars," chiefly on limbs, and does little damage. A killing of shoots by a scale insect (*Matsucoccus gallicola*) resembles a twig blight, but the insect leaves a very small, dark pit at the base of a killed shoot (see *Pinus pungens*).

Root Diseases and Trunk Rots.—The root diseases include the root rot and root collar necrosis caused by *Armillaria mellea* which usually radiates out by rhizomorphs from a food base in a hardwood stump, the root rot caused by *Fomes annosus* (*92, 1202*), and the white pocket root and butt rot caused by *Polyporus tomentosus.* None of these three root rots have become serious forest problems to pitch pine, but the first two have killed many individual trees. The trunks of trees old enough to have branch stubs exposing heartwood may be rotted by *Fomes pini*. The limbiness of pitch pine makes it particularly subject to red heart, but little rot cull should ordinarily be expected up to an age of 75 years (*874*).

Mycorrhizal Relations.—Fungi recorded by Trappe (*1442*) as mycorrhizal or probably so with pitch pine include *Boletus aurantiacus, B. brevipes, B. pictus, B. rubellus, Cenococcum graniforme, Gomphidius vinicolor*, and *Russula lepida*.

Miscellaneous Pathology.—Mineral deficiencies in seedlings appear as follows (*689*):

N—Needles short, pale green, not yellow. Growth stunted. Plants spindly. No necrosis.

P—Necrosis of lower needles, preceded sometimes by purplish-red coloration.

K—Stunting. Foliage often blue-green, never yellow. Necrosis common around terminal meristems. Great irregularity in seedling size.

Mg—Moderate stunting. Best symptom is tip chlorosis of needles, with sometimes full needle involvement. Chlorotic tips later necrotic. Tip chlorosis only in Mg deficiency.

Digger pine
Pinus sabiniana

Digger pine is a very intolerant, pale-foliaged, thin-crowned, gaunt, and usually misshapen tree characteristic of California's dry interior. Past the seedling stage it demands full sunlight, occurs singly or in small scattered groups, and grows well in dry, shallow, coarse, gravelly soils. Its range is limited to foothills, low slopes, and high valleys, and although occupying elevations from 500 to 4,000 ft. it is most frequent between 1,000 and 2,500 ft. It dots dry country from the Siskiyou Mountains through parts of the Sierra Nevada southward to the San Bernardino Mountains (*279*).

Digger pine can adapt itself to sites with average annual rainfall as low as 5 in. and temperatures that range from 10° to 110° F. It sometimes mingles with *Pinus coulteri, P. attenuata*, and *P. ponderosa*, and in some areas it competes only with chaparral. It is characterized by its thin, grayish foliage; very irregular form; crooked, forking trunk; drooping branches; and very large, heavy cones. It appears to mature at about 80 years, and a probable longevity of 150 years has been postulated (*1367*). When this tree is planted in fertile, irrigated soil, the needles are stouter, the general appearance more thrifty, and the cones are smaller (*279*). The dry sites occupied by Digger pine tend to preclude successful attack by pathogens, and only dwarfmistletoe would be considered a major disease of this species. Attacks are limited to localized situations.

Seedling and Foliage Diseases.—Since Digger pine is seldom raised in nurseries, virtually nothing is known of its seedling diseases. The species has no serious foliage diseases. Dead needles and parts of needles may bear the black hysterothecia of *Soleella (Bifusella) striiformis*, but the pathogenicity of this fungus is in question (*323*). The black, sooty or cottony growth of *Lembosia acicola*, called black mildew, can occur on the surface of living needles. *Lophodermium pinastri*, like *S. striiformis*, appears commonly on dead or moribund needles. In the South, where Digger pine has occasionally been planted as an ornamental, the brown spot fungus *Scirrhia acicola* has produced lesions and fruited on needles.

Stem Diseases.—*Cenangium ferruginosum* (*C. abietis*) is considered by some to cause cankers, branch killing, and dieback of Digger and other pines when trees are in low vigor. However, this fungus, so common on many American conifers, is now widely regarded as secondary, following other impacts, and primarily saprophytic (*542*).

The most damaging disease is western dwarfmistletoe (*Arceuthobium campylopodum* f. *campylopodum*). Although heavy infection is not widespread, it is common in some localities where it adds to the thinness of the already thin crowns of Digger pine. It causes swellings, distortions, growth retardation, browning of foliage, and heavy mortality (*508*). On Digger pine the mistletoe shoots tend to be unusually slender and brownish (*505*). The endophytic system of dwarfmistletoe in Digger pine is closely associated with branch swelling, and the growth rate of this system varies directly with the vigor of the host (*1240*).

Western gall rust (*Peridermium harknessii*) makes round- or pear-shaped galls, and individual trees may have many galled branches, thus becoming badly disfigured. This rust seldom attacks main stems of Digger pine (*1102*).

Root Diseases.—Two root diseases are known to attack Digger pine. *Fomes annosus*, a killer of single trees and small groups of western pines, generally in the vicinity of one or more dead trees or stumps, killed many well-established Digger pines in an epidemic in a California arboretum (*92*). *Polyporus schweinitzii*, in its usual role of a decayer of roots and butts, is generally associated with basal or root injuries and is not a common cause of death of Digger pine.

Pond pine
Pinus serotina

Intolerant, maturing at about 100 years, seldom living over 150 years, pond pine occurs most abundantly in poorly drained southern coastal flats and boggy areas on organic soils. However, it grows best on mineral soils of heavier texture and with good internal drainage (*1553*). Although the species characteristically grows in poorly drained areas, its seedlings suffer more after several months of flooding than do those of loblolly pine. The tree is reasonably fire-resistant when small and tolerates fire well when past the sapling stage. Fire is an important element, as with sand pine, in causing the serotinous cones of these two species to open (*1553*).

Pond pine is usually a ragged-appearing tree, of poor form, and generally limby with a pronounced tendency to "feathering" along the trunk and branches. The latter condition is due to its prolific formation of dormant buds and bud clusters that can result in sprouting whenever so induced by fire, other injury, or opening of the stand. This capacity to sprout from stem or stump permits

351

pond pine to survive climatic and other impacts that other pines could not withstand.

Seedling Diseases.—Pond pine is seldom grown in nurseries and, therefore, little is known of its seedling diseases. However, in one pocosin (raised coastal peaty marsh) in North Carolina, the rate of mortality of natural seedlings was 30 percent the first year, 19 percent the second, 11 percent the third, and 3 percent the fourth. The causes were not recorded (*1553*).

Foliage Diseases.—Five species of *Coleosporium* cause needle rusts on pond pine (*46*), *Ploioderma lethale* causes a common late winter browning of foliage (*156*), and the brown spot fungus (*Scirrhia acicola*) causes a needle blight that often appears first in the fall or early winter (*156, 1304*). The cause of still another needle browning is unknown (*155*). None of these needle diseases are known to materially affect growth.

Stem Diseases.—Both *Cronartium fusiforme* and *C. quercuum* attack pond pine stems (*630*), and the fusiform rust is occasionally damaging where the prevalence of pointed-leaved oaks and high humidity results in a heavy build-up of the rust. *Atropellis tingens* causes a minor twig and stem canker (*380, 877*).

The sequence of bark beetles followed by blue stain, leading to rapid death of trees, common with all southern pines, also occurs with pond pine.

Witches' brooms occur occasionally. Some are due to one of the *Cronartium* species, but others seem not to be induced by any organism, but result from a stimulatory aberration of certain buds.

Root Diseases and Trunk Rots.—Pond pine is subject to *Polyporus schweinitzii* root and butt rot following injury and to red heart (*Fomes pini*) when old enough to have broken branch stubs that expose heartwood.

Mycorrhizal Relations.—The only fungus reported as mycorrhizal on pond pine is *Cenococcum graniforme* (*1442*).

Eastern white pine
Pinus strobus

A five-needled species long considered the finest of the eastern pines, white pine grows throughout the Northeast, the Lake States, and into Canada, and extends in fingers or patches into the Central States and down the Appalachian Mountains as far as Georgia. It is intermediate in tolerance, hardy, and thrives on deep, light, slightly acidic loams but will grow under a wide variety of soil conditions. It has a higher requirement for soil moisture and atmospheric moisture than the hard pines. Its altitudinal range is from sea level in the North to 4,000 ft. in elevation in the Appalachian Mountains. The tree matures at about 90 years—with many old stands averaging over 200 years old—and has a maximum longevity of about 350 years (*279*).

Eastern white pine withstands summer temperatures in excess of 100° F. and very low winter temperatures. In tests of 16 woody species, eastern white pine withstood lower winter temperature (—94° F.) than any other species (*1080*). Although the stems and branches are flexible and will bend and often recover from the weight of ice and snow, this species is more subject to breakage from ice accumulation than any of the several eastern conifers with which it has been compared (*310*). White pine is also intolerant to drought and flooding (*16*) and is easily injured by fire. It is highly sensitive to damage from sulfur dioxide (*865*), stack gases from large-scale consumption of coal (*103*) and from oil refining (*869*), fluorine, gas emissions from brick kilns probably involving fluorine and sulfur dioxide (*1325*), and atmospheric ozone at concentrations as low as 7 p.p.h.m. (*104, 652*) (see Miscellaneous Pathology).

White pine has been considered the conifer most sensitive to salt sea spray (*1005, 1632*) and to submergence in salt water (*687*).

According to Sparrow and Sparrow (*1332*), the sensitivity of white pine to gamma radiation from a cobalt–60 source was high among a group of 12 coniferous and hardwood species (see *Picea glauca*).

Miksche et al. (*967*) found changes in apical meristems after 20-day exposures at rates as low as 3.5 to 15 r. per 20-hour day. Accumulated doses of 600 to 800 r. in 50 to 60 days were nearly lethal to white pine.

The species often retains its dead branches past 50 years and can do so even with close spacing. This makes pruning essential if wood of high quality is to be produced (*9*), although pruning itself introduces decay hazards (*1339*) unless the branches removed are small.

While white pine can endure many impacts and still survive, it is subject to a greater array of diseases than any other North American species. Hirt (*687*) has brought together much of the literature on the pathology of eastern white pine. Its soft, blue-green foliage is responsive to many impacts, biotic and abiotic, displaying spotting, russetting, mottling, tipburn, etc. Its tender bark, when young, is easily injured by animals, insects, heat (for example, sunscald (*721*)), and mechanical forces. It is prey to some of the most aggressive killing diseases on the continent, including seedling diseases as destructive as Cylindrocladium blight and virulent forms of damping-off, the notorious white pine blister rust, shoestring root rot, and the ruinous annosus root rot, in many thinned stands. It is in a class by itself in its sensitivity to atmospheric insults.

Seedling Diseases.—The nursery diseases (*360*) fall into three general categories: (1) pre- and post-emergence damping-off, with the commonest causes *Rhizoctonia solani* (*1555, 1575*) (*Ceratobasidium filamentosum* (*1567*)), *Fusarium* spp., *Pythium debaryanum* and *P. ultimum* (*360*), and *Phytophthora cinnamomi* (*304*); (2) damping-off and root or collar rot mainly caused by any of the preceding fungi or by *Cylindrocladium scoparium* (*294, 296*), *Diplodia pinea* (*299*), or a little-known stem canker fungus *Rhabdospora mirabilissima;* and (3) blights of foliage as well as succulent stems caused by *C. scoparium, D. pinea, Phacidium infestans* and other fungi (*151, 1155, 1157*) on seedlings under prolonged snow cover, and *Rhizina undulata* (*1533*), mainly on seedlings in burned areas. *Thelephora terrestris* may surround seedlings with its sporophores but is seldom harmful to seedlings unless they are very short.

In the field seedlings have been attacked by *Armillaria mellea*

(706), *Diplodia pinea, Phacidium infestans,* and *Rhizina undulata.*
Virtually all of the foliage pathogens, as well as blister rust, can
attack seedlings and thus can be considered nursery diseases, since
white pine requires at least 2 years in the nursery. Most of the
white pine seedling pathogens also attack many other conifer species. *Cylindrocladium scoparium,* however, is particularly aggressive on white pine, causing damping-off, root rot, stem canker, and
a reddening needle blight and has been a serious limiting factor in
nurseries raising white pine in Delaware (*294*), North Carolina
(*694*), and Michigan (*32, 192*) (see also *Liriodendron*). Earlier
the Michigan (Chittenden Nursery) problem was regarded as probably resulting from attack by a complex of fungi and nematodes,
somewhat like the etiology of black root rot of southern pine seedlings. Later research (*192*) showed the main disease to be caused
by *C. scoparium,* with black spruce and red pine also very susceptible. Both the Michigan trouble and southern black root rot yielded
to methyl bromide fumigation (*39, 696*).

White pine has been severely attacked by *Scirrhia acicola* in nurseries in North Carolina, Tennessee, and Georgia.[49]

Polyporus schweinitzii has also been proved able to parasitize
white pine seedling roots, although it is not known as a nursery
disease (*1526*).

Inhibition of shoot growth and a dense arrangement of distorted
needles led to the term "cabbaging" for a disease of unknown
cause in Ontario nurseries. Many fungi were isolated from diseased trees and the soil about them, but none were considered
primary (*1463*).

White pine in nurseries often develops heat lesions, a condition
also called "white-spot," at and above the ground line, that can be
confused with damping-off (*360*). Nematodes also attack the species in nurseries (*39, 1220*). The diagnosis of many of the white
pine nursery diseases has proved difficult because of multiple-cause
complexes, and because the combined skills of the pathologist, ne-
matologist, and soil scientist have often been required to solve a
problem.

Foliage Diseases.—White pine foliage is a target for many fungi,
some attacking vigorous foliage and others attacking damaged or
dead needles. Needle age also influences needle pathology. Only
those organisms regarded as causing disease or confusable with
those that are pathogens will be considered here. The fungus diseases of needles do not become obvious until autumn of the year the
foliage is formed or later. However, the condition called emergence
tipburn (possibly ozone injury), which has been split off from the
catch-all grouping of miscellaneous troubles for many years called
"white pine needle blight," develops during or shortly after needle
emergence (*104*), and acute forms of air pollution, as from sulfur
dioxide or halogens, can burn foliage as soon as it is out of the
fascicle. Special attention has been given to the differentiation of
white pine needle blights in the appraisal of fume damage (*655*).

Bifusella linearis, which forms large, long, black stromata, can
cause a copious loss of year-old needles throughout the crown

---

[49] Personal communication from A. Alfred Foster, formerly pathologist,
Tennessee Valley Authority, Norris, Tenn.

(*323, 655*). It typically strikes individual trees. *Meloderma* (*Hypoderma*) *desmazierii* commonly turns foliage brown by fall and gray by the spring after emergence, and its attack is largely confined to low or shady parts of the crown (*1351*). *Lophodermium nitens* and *L. pinastri* may appear on spotted or senescent foliage anywhere through the crown. While both have at one time or another been considered pathogenic, they are considered by most investigators (*153, 1351*) as weak parasites at best, usually on senescent foliage, or simply as saprophytes. Banfield (*57*), however, holds that in Massachusetts there is a *Lophodermium* he calls *L. pinastri*, which is an active needle pathogen in the upper crown and is easily distinguishable from *Meloderma desmazierii*, which strikes individual needles in the lower crown.

Scirrhia acicola, the brown spot fungus, has sometimes caused a heavy shedding of all foliage on individual trees in late spring, practically denuding large trees in North Carolina and West Virginia (*158*). Although prompt refoliation after defoliation has saved most of the trees, the weakening effect of the disease was obvious. It is quite possible that the *Septoria spadicea* reported on white pine needles is a synonym for the imperfect stage (*Lecanosticta acicola*) of this fungus.

A tipburn, chlorosis, and needle blight of seedlings in Ohio was reportedly proved to be caused by a *Pestalotia*, probably *P. funerea* (*1470*). *Diplodia pinea*, usually following weather damage or other injury, can cause a blighting of foliage, infecting needles directly or growing into the needles from infected twigs (*1513*). It is regarded as weakly parasitic on many pines, including white pine, but aggressive on Austrian pine.

Capnodium pini, a muriform-spored fungus, causes a surface sooty mold growing on aphid secretions on needles, and a species of *Dimerosporium* also causes a dark smudge on needle surfaces.

Ostreola sessilis is a muriform-spored, lophiaceous fungus on white pine in Quebec (*324*).

Although Hedgcock (*625*) and others imply a connection between needle blighting and many additional fungi, there is much cause to doubt the capacity of some to cause disease, and it is quite certain that most of these other fungi can be disregarded so far as growth impact or mortality is concerned on trees other than seedlings. Some of these organisms are *Asterina pinastri*, *Hendersonia pinicola*, *Pestalotia* spp., *Cenangium ferruginosum*, *Pezizella minuta*, *Hemiphacidium planum* (*807*), and *Sclerophoma pini* (*625*). In trying to understand the nomenclature of the white pine foliage fungi, and in using Hirt's literature review (*687*) and certain older publications, one must be wary of the confusion resulting from synonymy. For example, many fungi already herein referred to on white pine are commonly cited in the older literature under such different and obsolete names as *Lophodermium brachysporum*, *Cenangium abietis*, *Phacidium planum*, and *Sphaeropsis ellisii*.

Emergence tipburn (oxidant or sulfur dioxide injury) is characterized by pinkish spots forming quite uniformly over a tree during active growth, some distance back from the tips of emerging needles, with needle necrosis developing acropetally (from the spots to the tips) (*104, 866*), and not acrogenously. Sometimes the spots do not involve the tissue deeply and do not result in further necrosis.

Thus, in a fascicle of five needles, each may have just a spot one-half inch back, or the last one-half inch of the tip may be dead, or any combination of these conditions. The line of demarcation in a needle between a necrotic tip and a green healthy base is sharp (655).

Chronic coal gas injury (103) often results in the shedding of older needles or a gradual tipburn of older needles starting at the tip and extending toward the base. It may start any time of year. There is no sharp line separating a browned needle tip from a green base, and a stippling or mottling of needles often develops.

Chlorotic dwarf is a marked stunting of shoot growth and foliage, typically from the seedling stage all through life, almost always with chlorosis, and often with tipburn and stippling of needles. It is probably related to the atmospheric environment (386).

Stem Diseases.—The most important disease of white pine is blister rust (*Cronartium ribicola*) (151), a major problem in the Northeast, the Lake States, and the Northwest. It causes damage wherever highly susceptible species of the alternate host genus *Ribes* occur, provided microclimatic conditions favor sporidial formation, dissemination, and germination (91, 1466). Quick access to the main literature on those aspects of blister rust of concern in diagnosis and in understanding the behavior of the disease is obtainable through Hirt's bibliography of the pathology of eastern white pine (687) and his own work on the growth and reproduction of the fungus in the tissues of eastern white pine (688).

The symptoms of blister rust on pine and *Ribes* are clearcut when the fungus is fruiting and on young smooth-barked pines even when not fruiting. However, on trees with rough bark, other lesions can be confused with blister rust, especially Caliciopsis canker (*C. pinea*), distinguished by the hairlike fruiting structures of the fungus (483, 1146); Atropellis canker (*A. pinicola* and *A. tingens*), distinguished by irregular, black apothecia and a blue-black staining of the wood beneath (380, 877); Monochaetia canker (*M. pinicola*) on small twigs, distinguished by deeply sunken, discrete, often girdling, lesions with fruiting rare (157); Dasyscypha canker (*D. pini*), with its yellow-orange apothecia (576); and Valsa canker (*V. kunzei* var. *superficialis*) that develops somewhat inconspicuously at nodes and is usually accompanied by resin flow (1519). In one Michigan area *D. fusco-sanguinea* appeared to be an aggressive canker pathogen on understory trees (687). *Valsa pini* has been reported to form cankers on branches of white pine.

Boyer and Isaac (165) describe and illustrate the histological characteristics of *Cronartium ribicola* growing in white pine, as revealed by light and by electron microscopy. Krebill (814) describes and illustrates the histology of the cankers, comparing it with cankers caused by several North American stem rusts of hard pines.

Serological tests (see *Pinus taeda*) indicate the specific identity of *C. ribicola* as compared with *C. fusiforme* and *C. quercuum*.

Several fungi have been described as associated with cankers and twig blights, but little is known concerning their parasitism to uninjured white pine bark. They are not considered as economically important. They include *Phomopsis conorum* in Iowa (509), *Dermea pinicola* in Vermont (551), three species of *Tympanis* (552), *Cenangium ferruginosum* (542), *Diplodia pinea* (1513), and *Pote-*

bniamyces (*Phacidiella*) *coniferarum* (*1315*), the conidial stage of which is *Phacidiopycnis* (*Phomopsis*) *pseudotsugae* (*573*). The latter is a common coniferous canker pathogen in Europe and causes sunken, sharply defined lesions on white pine in the Northeast (*572*). It also inhabits the dead tissue of blister rust cankers.

Blister rust cankers and other dead areas on white pine support many saprophytes including the spiral-spored *Ophionectria scolecospora*, *Nectria cucurbitula* (possibly same as *Thyronectria balsamea* (*1271*)) associated with insects, *Physalospora obtusa*, *Phomopsis strobi*, the resin-inhabiting *Biatorella* (*Zythia*) *resinae*, *Dasyscypha agassizii* and *D. ellisii*, and other species (*678*).

Bark may be invaded by the normally harmless fungus *Aleurodiscus amorphus*, but sometimes this fungus becomes parasitic, causing cankers (*587*). *Septobasidium pinicola* produces a brown, resupinate, effused, generally circular sporophore from 1 to 3 centimeters in diameter. It occurs on the bark of living trees mainly at nodes, living on scale insects (*1324*), and is harmless to the tree. A slime mold (*Orcadella operculata*) was reported from Iowa, and a copious, felty, non-pathogenic growth over the base of trees, consisting of the tough thallus of *Sebacina helvelloides*, has been observed in North Carolina (*908*).

A highly constricted basal canker has been associated with anthills, and the fungus *Fusicoccum abietinum* has occurred within the cankered areas (*560*). This association of basal cankers and ants was first reported in 1917, but similar association of such cankers with ant (*Formica fusca*) mounds have been observed in New York in the 1960's. Still another constricted, basal canker of pole-sized planted white pine has been described and illustrated from New York (*1307*) and in this case the condition is regarded as the result of planting on shallow, poorly drained fragipan soil.

Graves (*537*) found long, necrotic stripes on white pine branches in north Georgia on which either flat, disc-like, papillate, black pycnidia or simple, pustular pycnidia of *Coccomyces pini* were borne.

Root Diseases.—White pine is subject to some damaging root diseases. *Armillaria mellea* can destroy much of the white pine seedling and sapling reproduction for distances up to 30 ft. or more away from hardwood stumps. The fungus, radiating outward from these food bases, will girdle pines at the root collar, cause resinosis, and produce rhizomorphs on the roots and mycelial fans under the root collar bark (*848*). Another fungus, *Polyporus schweinitzii*, originally considered important mainly in overmature trees, has caused destructive root and butt rot in plantings in New York (*247*), North Carolina (*660*), the Lake States, and elsewhere. In the North Carolina case (Biltmore plantations, thinned five times) two additional fungi, *Fomes annosus* and *Polyporus tomentosus* (*660*), had entered the roots of trees cut in the fifth thinning at age 40-45 years. *P. schweinitzii* damage has been so severe in New York that for a while it was strongly suspected as being the cause of the "resinosis disease" (*1635*) that now is regarded as a soil problem.

Polyporus tomentosus (*P. circinatus*) has long been known as an important root and butt rot fungus in Canada (*687*), and while it produces a rot resembling *Fomes pini*, cultures reveal clear differences (255). Hubert contrasts these two fungi and their rots with *P. schweinitzii* and *Poria subacida* (724).

Fomes annosus, considered a native, widespread, cosmopolitan fungus, had been observed rotting white pine roots in the early part of the century; but—whereas there was published speculation that thinning at Biltmore, North Carolina, would hinder the fungus—history there (660), over the East and South (1136), and in Europe (159, 1179) proved the opposite—that thinning exposed a stand to attack and accelerated damage from existing foci of infection. This fungus destroys roots leading to windthrow and also causes a virulent cambial necrosis in the root collar region that commonly results in death before any obvious rotting of roots has taken place. Losses to residual trees in thinned white pine planted on loamy-to-light soils in the southern Appalachians have been high (1133). On heavier soils killing is not common, but attack results in "pipes" of decay running up from roots into the trunk.

Corticium galactinum is a fungus that envelops white pine roots and produces felts of buff-colored mycelium in the soil around them. It is not generally destructive but has produced a white root rot in white pine in New York, Connecticut, Pennsylvania, and Delaware (927) and made up over 10 percent of the root rot infections in two Canadian areas (1562). *Poria subacida* has also caused root rot in some stands in New England, and *Odontia bicolor*, entering roots, causes a white stringy butt rot in Canada (1039).

Of the nematodes in soils under white pine in the Southeast, the genus most commonly isolated was *Criconemoides;* next in abundance were species of *Xiphinema, Helicotylenchus, Hemicycliophora, Hoplolaimus,* and *Hemicriconemoides;* with the least abundant in the genera *Tylenchorhyncus, Paratylenchus,* and *Meloidodera* (1220).

Ruehle (1222) reports that 34 species of nematodes, in 15 genera, have been reported from the roots or root zones of eastern white pine. Few of these were related in any way to plant damage. Ruehle's account indicates those nematodes associated with injury.

Trunk Rots.—The most important heartrot is caused by *Fomes pini* and is commonly called red heart in the East. While White (1562) isolated 13 decay fungi from felled white pines in Canada, 90 percent of the volume loss was attributed to *F. pini*. Its firm, reddish, incipient stage and the white-lined pockets of its advanced stage are diagnostic but, in roots or butts, it can be confused with *P. tomentosus* (724). The fungus has been intensively studied on white pine (563, 687, 1096). While it has long been known to enter older trees readily, through large branch stubs exposing heartwood (456), it is now known also to enter through weevil-killed shoots, and thus it becomes a factor in younger trees (368). White (1562) indicates a pathological rotation age of 160–170 years for Canadian white pine; in the United States, and especially in the Appalachian region where this tree grows very rapidly, the economic felling age is well under this (9).

Since pruning is a necessity in order to raise white pine of high quality (9, 661), it should be done early enough to avoid large wounds which in the North have led to decay by *Stereum sanguinolentum* (1339).

A large number of fungi can rot the heart and sapwood of damaged white pines, but the main ones attacking roots, butts, and trunks in the United States have already been mentioned. Among the other trunk rot fungi encountered in mature or damaged trees are *Fomes officinalis, F. pinicola,* and *F. roseus.*

In Ontario, Basham and Morawski (*73*) found the rot cull in white pine to be 2.4 percent at age class 121–140, 21 percent at class 141–160, and 36 percent at 201–220. Thirteen hymenomycetes were isolated from the decayed wood, with *Fomes pini* accounting for 76 percent of the rot volume, *Corticium fuscostratum* 7 percent, and *Corticium galactinum* 4 percent.

Mycorrhizal Relations.—Forty fungi have been reported as mycorrhizal associates of eastern white pine (*1442*). Of these, 14, an unusually high number, have been proved by pure-culture techniques. Mycorrhizal fungi vary greatly in their own requirements and in their effect on the host. This is illustrated for well-nourished white pine seedlings by an inhibition of growth following inoculation with *Boletus rubellus* and a stimulation with *Amanita muscaria.* With a less available nitrogen source, both fungi were beneficial (*383*).

Trappe (*1442*) has assembled the world literature on fungus associates of ectotrophic mycorrhizae, and Slankis (*1310*) has provided a thorough review of the morphogenesis and physiology of tree mycorrhizae. Eleven papers dealing specifically with mycorrhizae on eastern white pine in the United States have been abstracted by Hirt (*687*).

Stains.—Tracheomycosis resulting from blue-stain fungus infection following bark beetle attack takes place in eastern white pine, as in the other pines. The relation between *Ips* bark beetles and the blue-stain fungus *Ceratocystis ips* (*1227*) has been established for white pine (*687*). The blue-stain fungus *C. minor* is associated with attacks by the southern pine beetle *Dendroctonus frontalis* (*1226*).

Griffin (*545*) lists the insects likely associated (bark beetle, ambrosia beetle, wood-boring vectors) with blue-staining species of *Ceratocystis* on white pine in Canada as follows:

	Insect likely associated
Ceratocystis species:	
C. allantospora.......	*Ips pini, Neocanthocinus pusillus, Rhagium inquisitor*
C. ips..............	*Ips pini, Monochamus mutator, Neocanthocinus pusillus, Orthotomicus caelatus, Tetropium cinnamopterum, T. sp.*
C. minuta...........	*Ips pini*
C. pilifera..........	*N. pusillus, R. inquisitor*

Griffin lists similar relationships for stainers and their vectors in *Abies balsamea, Picea glauca, P. mariana, Pinus banksiana, P. resinosa,* and *Tsuga canadensis.*

Wright and Cain (*1629*), as well as Griffin (*545*), have been instrumental in bringing descriptions, nomenclature, taxonomy, and other information on the species of *Ceratocystis* forward from Hunt's monographic treatment (*732*).

Fungi in many genera can stain the wood of white pine either blue, gray, brown, green, or red (*66, 687*), in some cases in the living tree and sometimes after felling. Except for the tracheomycotic stain fungi introduced by bark beetles, stain fungi are not factors in the health of trees. A pink to cinnamon-brown stain of white pine heartwood lumber is caused by the fungus *Ascocybe grovesii* (*349*).

Miscellaneous Pathology.—A serious, although localized, dying of white and red pine, called "resinosis disease," has had much attention in Pennsylvania and New York (*1635*). This decline, associated with poor internal soil drainage and high spring rainfall, leading to low soil oxygen (*1362*) and often occurring in soils of high pH, is discussed under *Pinus resinosa*.

Abnormal forking in white and red pine has been ascribed to late-season elongation of lateral buds of terminal clusters, producing "lammas shoots" (*902*). Further discussion is provided under *Pinus resinosa*.

Witches' brooms form on white pine, usually locally on a branch. Most of the pine species of the United States have had brooms described that appeared to be induced not by an organism but by localized overstimulation of buds (*612*). Grafts from a white pine broom continued to produce a broomed scion but did not transmit a brooming principle to the stock (*687*). Viruses are not regarded to cause such brooms in conifers.

Basham (*66*) studied the deterioration of fire-killed jack, red, and white pine in Ontario and described three stains, designated blue stain, brown stain, and orange-ring stain. He isolated 17 "white saprot" fungi and 10 "brown saprot" fungi, and gave the roles played by the more important ones, in wood deterioration.

Isolated cases of eastern dwarfmistletoe (*Arceuthobium pusillum*) have occurred on white pine in northern New York.

A condition in young white pines in which there is an overdevelopment of phloem in successive internodes, leading to swollen, lumpy, soft tissue and pliable shoots, has been observed widely by many investigators. It has been called dropsy or edema, although there is no evidence of excessive water in the tissues. No cause has been ascribed (*687*). This limp tissue seems to have much in common with that associated with the "twig droop" of white pine, ascribed by Hoffman, Hepting, and Roth (*701*) to a shoot aphid in the genus *Pineus*.

The heartwood of eastern white pine is characterized by distinct wet areas which surround embedded branches and extend up and down the tree (*868*). Etheridge had an explanation for this type of wetwood in balsam fir, based on moisture absorption by dead branches (*422*).

The mechanisms responsible for frost ring formation were determined by Glerum and Farrar (*512*), who subjected seedlings of several conifers to conditions conducive to frost rings. Differentiating tracheids and xylem mother cells were killed by the frost, leaving a permanent band of underlignified and crumpled tracheids inside a band of dead cell tissue. They worked with *Pinus strobus*,

360

P. resinosa, P. banksiana, Picea glauca, P. mariana, and *Larix laricina.*

The subject of eastern white pine's pathology should not be left without some warnings to the diagnostician. One concerns the needle blights. Many agencies, including several fungi, atmospheric ozone, stack gas from soft coal consumption, and herbicides (655), may spot, blight, or tipburn white pine needles. Also, any one agency may produce different symptoms on different trees of the same species in the same stand. Coal fumes in Pennsylvania thus affected different neighboring trees differently, causing either russeting, mottling, general yellowing, tipburn, dwarfing, or no effect at all. One of the commonest types of needle blight, now called emergence tipburn, to which many causes have been ascribed, is now considered to be due to an oxidant (104, 291). A condition in the Central States and elsewhere called chlorotic dwarf, also ascribed in the past to many causes, appears to be due to one or more atmospheric factors acting directly on the foliage (386).

The "emergence tipburn" (ET) of Berry and Ripperton (104) and "semimature-tissue needle blight" (SNB) of Linzon (870) have much in common: symptoms, distribution, time of onset, et al. They may prove to be one and the same disease. However, at present ET is regarded as caused by oxidant (104, 291), whereas Linzon (871) does not believe that his SNB is caused by oxidant, expressed as ozone.

Gordon and Gorham (522) reported on extensive forest changes attributed to sulfur dioxide around an iron-sintering plant at Wawa, Ontario, where white pine failed to appear on test plots leeward of the plant for a distance of 30 miles, indicating that this species was the most readily injured of the 30 woody plants recorded on the plots.

Care must also be used in ascribing pathogenicity to fungi such as *Pullularia pullulans, Lophodermium pinastri, Cenangium ferruginosum,* and *Diplodia pinea* unless proved by accepted techniques. Under some conditions, including aging of needles, trauma, or senescence, some fungi that ordinarily would be harmless may attack.

Deficiency symptoms in white pine seedlings have been described as follows (689):

Nitrogen—Foliage pale green, but not yellow. Growth stunted and spindly. Needles short and necrotic at tips.

Phosphorus—Mild chlorosis. Color variable. Slight necrosis of lower needles. Great reduction in dry weight.

Potash—Chlorosis and stunting. Necrosis at needle tips. Much irregularity of size.

Magnesium—Moderate stunting. Best symptom is tip chlorosis of needles, sometimes with necrosis that may involve whole needles.

Scots pine

Pinus sylvestris

An undemanding exotic from Europe, Scots pine grows over a wide range of soils and sites and has thus had utility where tree growth is difficult to establish, such as in sand dune stabilization

361

areas and in areas subject to great fluctuations in weather. Like most pines, it is intolerant of shade and, in this country, has a deserved reputation for bad form, mainly as a result of the lack of attention to European seed sources in the early plantings. Later importations of seed of the Riga strain are more promising for timber (*279*). The tree has shown a capacity to grow well, from western North Carolina to Canada, and west through Nebraska. Its silvical characteristics are much like those of pitch pine. It was more prone to damage from salt spray than pitch pine in one place (*1005*) and resisted salt spray and inundation with salt water much better than pitch pine in another place (*1632*) following the same storm. Scots pine has been injured by sulfur dioxide near oil refineries (*869*).

Scots pine tolerates the weight of ice very well (*310*) and also withstands drought, wind, sudden exposure, and fill around the base. It is remarkable in its resistance to cold, withstanding temperatures of −80° F. in Europe (*1080*). Peace (*1091*) considers Scots pine particularly hardy with respect to spring frosts under European conditions. When this species was injured by extreme cold, recovery was excellent unless more than 25 percent of the foliage had been injured (*1213*).

The species is prey to a large number of fungus enemies, most of which are minor. Locally, the tree has suffered from some fungus attacks, chiefly by stem rusts, the pitch canker *Fusarium*, and in the nursery from several damping-off and root-rot fungi.

Seedling Diseases.—Seedlings in nurseries (*1465*) have been attacked particularly by *Phytophthora cactorum, P. cinnamomi, Pythium debaryanum, Rhizoctonia solani,* and *Cylindrocladium scoparium* (*296*), all of which can cause damping-off and root rots. Vaartaja (*1458*) also killed seedlings with *P. cactorum* in the laboratory. *Diplodia pinea* causes a seedling collar rot and *Thelephora terrestris* (*360*) often surrounds seedlings but does little or no damage. Smith and Bega (*1323*) describe severe damage to coniferous nursery stock, including Scots pine, in California nurseries (see *Pinus lambertiana*), as a result of mid- to late-season attack of roots by *Sclerotium bataticola* (*Macrophomina phaseoli*). Certain species of *Alternaria, Cylindrocarpon, Fusarium,* and *Phoma* had some pathogenic potential for jack pine seedlings in test tubes (*1461*) and may cause some damage to Scots pine seedlings in the field (*1465*).

In Canada test tube pathogencity tests with seven isolates of *Pythium debaryanum* and *P. ultimum* put Scots pine seedlings in the "resistant" category along with jack pine. Most isolates were very damaging to other conifer species (*1464*). Other tests, using soil, showed high losses to Scots pine from *Rhizoctonia solani, Phytophthora cactorum, Pythium debaryanum,* and *Thielaviopsis basicola,* with *Pythium* the least damaging (*1462*).

Seedlings in Canadian nurseries have been killed out singly and in patches by *Scleroderris lagerbergii* (see *Pinus resinosa*).

Many nematodes have been reported from the roots or root zones of Scots pine, both in North America and elsewhere in the world. There has been little association, however, between nematodes and damage to the trees (*1222*). Although Sutherland (*1370*), in Canada, showed Scots pine seedlings to be poor hosts to *Pratylen-*

chus penetrans and non-host to *Paratylenchus projectus*, they were good hosts to *Tylenchus emarginatus (1371)*.

Foliage Diseases.—The foliage is attacked by five species of *Coleosporium (46)*, by *Scirrhia acicola (1304)*, *Naemacyclus niveus (323, 328)*, and *Cytospora pinastri*, none of which have proved serious. *Lophodermium pinastri* and *Pestalotia funerea* appear in their customary roles on senescent needles. The snow blight caused by *Phacidium infestans* and some related fungi can kill lower foliage in the North, and occasionally be lethal to seedlings *(1155, 1157)*.

Stem Diseases.—Twig blights are caused by *Atropellis tingens (380)*, *A. pinicola (877)*, and *Diplodia pinea*, the latter often damaging specimen trees *(1513)*. *Diplodia pinea* causes a serious disease of Scots pine and other hard pines planted in the Great Plains (see *Pinus nigra*).

The following are secondary fungi or saprophytes, frequently following death or major injury from other causes: *Cenangium atropurpureum (238)*, *C. ferruginosum (542)*, *Dasyscypha calycina (574)*, *D. ellisiana (575)*, and *Ophionectria scolecospora. Caliciopsis pseudotsugae* is a minor twig-inhabiting fungus on Scots pine in British Columbia *(483)*.

Scots pine has been heavily attacked by the western gall rust *(Peridermium harknessii)* in New York, following early introduction of the rust into the Adirondack area *(151)*. In slit inoculations of eight species of hard pines by Boyce, who used aeciospores from round *Peridermium* galls on *Pinus ponderosa, P. sabiniana,* and *P. radiata*, infection with gall formation was obtained only on *P. ponderosa, P. radiata,* and *P. sylvestris*. Although he got few infections, Boyce feels, considering the historical evidence, that there is a strong case for the "Woodgate rust" being *Peridermium harknessii (150)*. Trees bearing hundreds of round galls of the Woodgate rust have not been uncommon in northern New York.

W. W. Wagener [50] cites two cases involving heavy *Peridermium harknessii* attacks on Scots pine raised in nurseries where the rust was no longer a problem after nearby heavily rust-galled knobcone pines *(Pinus attenuata)* were cut down.

This pine is also susceptible to eastern gall rust *(C. quercuum) (630)*, the Comandra rust *(C. comandrae) (966)*, and the sweet-fern rust *(C. comptoniae) (25, 1341)*. In localized areas where their alternate hosts abound, these rusts have done major damage. Losses of over 25 percent in nurseries have been ascribed to eastern gall rust, and plantations have suffered heavily from this rust *(31)*. Scots pine is occasionally injured by the weak parasite *Tympanis confusa (552)* and has proved very susceptible to pitch canker *(Fusarium lateritium* f. sp. *pini)* both naturally in North Carolina and in outdoor inoculations *(667)*. The latter could prove troublesome if this fungus found its way to Europe.

Scots pine planted in northeastern Washington has been attacked by the larch dwarfmistletoe *Arceuthobium campylopodum* f. *lari-*

---

[50] Personal communication from W. Willis Wagener, deceased, formerly pathologist, USDA Forest Service, Pacific Southwest Forest and Range Experiment Station, Berkeley, Calif.

cis and the lodgepole pine species *A. americanum* (*527*). The larch form attacked so severely that it is doubtful if Scots pine should be planted where this parasite occurs.

The blue-stain fungi that can function as pathogens in the tracheomycosis following bark beetle attacks include *Ceratocystis ips* and *C. pilifera*.

Aleurodiscus penicillatus fruits on dead twigs in Canada (*858*).

Root Diseases.—Root and butt rots have been caused by *Armillaria mellea, Fomes annosus* (*764*), and *Polyporus schweinitzii* in the Northeast. *F. annosus* is known as a major butt rotter and, to a lesser extent, a killer of Scots pine in some parts of Europe, yet this pine is unaffected by the fungus in spite of similar cutting practices in other nearby parts of the continent (*1162*). Red heart (*F. pini*) commonly develops in trees old enough to have large heartwood-bearing branch stubs.

Mycorrhizal Relations.—Trappe (*1442*) lists 118 fungi reported to form mycorrhizae with Scots pine, with 28 of these proved through pure-culture techniques. Such a situation makes one speculate at the probable number of fungi that will be discovered in this symbiotic relationship as more species are given the intensity of study accorded Scots pine in Europe.

Loblolly pine
Pinus taeda

Intermediate in tolerance, maturing at about 100 years, seldom living over 220 years, loblolly pine grows well over a wide range of soils, from swamps to deep sands, from coastal Maryland through the South Atlantic and Gulf States to east Texas. It thrives in soils with a deep permeable surface layer and a firm subsoil (*1554*). On heavy Piedmont clays with little A horizon and poor internal drainage it is subject to littleleaf, but to a lesser degree than shortleaf pine. Tending to large limbs, it is subject to damage by ice, wind, and drought (*1502*), but is damaged less by ice than slash or longleaf pine (*912*). It is resistant to damage from flooding. While loblolly pine is sensitive to coastal salt spray, most hardwoods are more sensitive. Thus, loblolly will often persist and regenerate along coastal areas of Maryland and Virginia. Virginia pine suffered from inroads of brackish water following coastal storms that left loblolly not obviously affected (*875*).

Since loblolly pine is the leading commercial timber species in the southern United States and has adapted itself to so many soils and climates, the pathologist dealing with this species should familiarize himself with Wahlenberg's monograph on loblolly pine (*1502*).

The characteristics of the pathology of loblolly pine are: seedling susceptibility to black root rot and fusiform rust; sapling susceptibility to fusiform rust, brown spot, Atropellis cankers, and spot dieout in the Piedmont; root rot by *Fomes annosus* in thinned plantations; littleleaf in the Piedmont; and heartrot in old stands with *Fomes pini* in the bole and mostly *Polyporus schweinitzii* in the butts.

Seedling Diseases.—Nursery seedlings are subject to damping-off and root rot caused, alone or in combination, by *Rhizoctonia solani, Fusarium* spp., and *Sclerotium bataticola* (*Macrophomina* *phaseoli*), in soils with pH above 6.0 under moist conditions (*696*). The so-called black root rot (*Fusarium* sp. + *S. bataticola*) becomes severe only if soil temperature remains over 90° F. for long periods (*695*). The black root rot fungi also have caused decay of roots of loblolly pine in 2- to 3-year-old outplantings in the west Florida sandhills (*1313*). *Pythium* spp. as nursery pathogens are discussed under *Pinus echinata*.

Fusiform rust (*Cronartium fusiforme*) is a major nursery disease in many parts of the South, requiring rigid spray programs to keep losses low (*696*).

Thelephora terrestris commonly fruits harmlessly around seedlings in the field and sometimes in the nursery (*360*). The fast growth of most southern pine seedlings leaves this fungus behind, harmlessly encircling the lower stem, while the green shoots and foliage flourish. Damage by *T. terrestris* is confined to species that grow slowly and must remain more than 1 year in the seedbeds.

A summer chlorosis of loblolly and shortleaf pines in an Arkansas nursery was related to a high calcium content of the soil (*1584*). Loblolly pine seedlings proved susceptible to *Phytophthora cinnamomi* root rot when the seedlings were grown in liquid culture (*1646*).

Hendrix and Campbell (*634*) demonstrated that all eight species of *Pythium* used to infest soil in which seedlings of shortleaf and loblolly pine were grown brought about a reduction in the weight of roots and shoots. They believe that pythiaceous fungi restrict the growth of pine seedlings in some nurseries.

The predominant species of nematodes on the roots of outplanted seedlings, with respect to damage in North Carolina, were *Xiphinema americanum, Hoplolaimus coronatus, Helicotylenchus nannus,* and *Meloidodera floridensis* (*1225*). Large numbers of these are considered able to stunt seedlings. In addition to these species, *Belonolaimus gracilis, Meloidogyne arenaria,* and *Tylenchorhynchus claytoni* can feed and reproduce on loblolly roots in plantations (*704*). Others reported from nurseries include *Pratylenchus brachyurus, Tylenchorhynchus claytoni, Belonolaimus* spp., *Hemicycliophora* spp., *Criconemoides* sp., *Dolichodorus* sp., *Dorylaimus,* and *Longidorus* sp. (*704, 1220*). Some fungus feeders or plant parasites in the genera *Aphelenchoides, Aphelenchus, Ditylenchus, Psilenchus, Tylenchus,* and others (*1220*) have occurred in association with loblolly roots and could have a role in mycorrhizal or other soil-mycofloral relationships.

In summarizing the literature on nematode associations with trees, Ruehle (*1222*) lists 22 species of nematodes on roots or within the rhizosphere of loblolly pines. He also showed (*1221*) that loblolly, longleaf, and Virginia pine seedlings were either poor hosts or non-hosts to *Pratylenchus zeae*.

Adams et al. (*13*) found that stylet-bearing nematodes, and those of *Criconemoides* sp. in particular, were abundant in the root zones of trees with *Fomes annosus* root rot.

Foliage Diseases.—While many foliage diseases are common, few become damaging. Ten needle rusts occur on loblolly pine, and all are species of *Coleosporium*. Attack on planted stock is sometimes so heavy that one cannot walk through an infected plantation without choking on the aeciospore load in the air, yet the growth effects have usually been temporary and light.

Ploioderma (*Hypoderma*) *lethale* causes the most striking late winter and spring browning on trees of any size (*155*), and brown spot (*Scirrhia acicola*) often kills much foliage on seedlings, saplings, and larger trees (*154*), usually appearing first in the fall. Brown spot on longleaf is damaging only to small seedlings, but on loblolly young saplings can be severely browned. *Lophodermium pinastri* is common but invades only old, injured, or dead needles (*153*).

Boyce (*156*) discusses and illustrates the differences among the needle fungi on southern pines, stressing the black, elongated fruiting bodies of *Ploioderma* (*Hypoderma*) *lethale* that open by a central slit, in comparison to the black, ovate fruiting bodies of *Scirrhia acicola* that open by slits at the edges.

Parris (*1088*) describes a needle curl of loblolly pine foliage growing in an overheated greenhouse. Needles were folded, curled tightly, or otherwise distorted. He compares this malady with the "needle curls" reported here under *Pinus echinata* and that of American pines grown overseas.

Stem Diseases.—Minor twig blights and cankers are caused by *Caliciopsis pinea* (*483*), *Atropellis tingens* (*380*), and, less commonly, by *A. piniphila*. Loblolly is free of pitch cankers except in eastern North Carolina where it is attacked by a local strain of *Fusarium lateritium* f. sp. *pini*, producing the typical reactions of gum flow, twig blight, and pitch-soaking of wood (*665*). *Cenangium atropurpureum* is a twig fungus on loblolly pine, regarded as secondary in the absence of any proof of pathogenicity (*238*).

The most serious disease is the stem rust *Cronartium fusiforme* (see also *Pinus elliottii*) which kills and disfigures young trees from Virginia to Texas. The round galls of *C. quercuum* also occur on loblolly pine, and some galls have the typical bark collar of the latter at the proximal end and the spindle of the former at the distal end. Most cankered loblolly trees in the sawtimber sizes, however, are good risks. Out of 21 such trees with 10 to 50 percent of their circumferences cankered that were observed for 10 years in windy coastal South Carolina, not one was broken or lost (*805*).

Gooding and Powers (*521*) made serological comparisons among *Cronartium fusiforme* from *Pinus taeda* and *P. elliottii; C. quercuum* from *P. virginiana;* and *C. ribicola* from *P. strobus*. In interspecific tests they cross-reacted strongly, but in intraspecific tests between separate collections no antigenic differences could be detected.

Loblolly pine in the Cumberland Plateau of Tennessee has been suffering increasing damage from *Cronartium comandrae* since its apparent introduction into the area in the 1930's on *Pinus ponderosa* nursery stock. Powers et al. (*1134*) describe the extent of attack and characterize the rust on loblolly pine.

Cronartium comptoniae, the sweetfern rust, has been reported on loblolly in New Jersey but could have only a very limited occurrence (*25, 1341*) because of the paucity of the alternate hosts, *Comptonia* and *Myrica gale*, in the South.

In loblolly pine, as with many other pines, there are possibilities for confusion between insects and fungi as causes of shoot

366

blights. Thus, *Matsucoccus gallicola* is a scale insect that causes "flagging" (see *Pinus pungens*), weevils feed on and girdle twigs, and shoot moths hollow out mainly leaders and often leave their telltale frass.

Tracheomycosis (*167*) following bark beetle attack results from invasion of the sapwood by species of *Ceratocystis*, mainly *C. ips* and *C. minor*. *C. pilifera* causes blue stain in lumber.

Root Diseases.—Littleleaf (*207*) kills loblolly pine from Virginia to Alabama in the heavy soil areas of the Piedmont. Loblolly is much less susceptible than shortleaf and often escapes damage where shortleaf is being lost. However, on heavy, poorly aerated clay soils highly conducive to littleleaf (*207*), loblolly may also be hard hit. *Phytophthora cinnamomi* (*1646*), together with the adverse soil factors discussed under shortleaf, bring about littleleaf.

Sapling and older trees, especially if planted, are subject to attack by *Fomes annosus* in stands where some cutting or killing has taken place (*1136*). Where the fungus has established itself in the roots of stumps following thinning or tree killing from some other cause, many neighboring residual trees may be killed by annosus root rot. It is considered a disease problem in plantation management second only to fusiform rust (*1133*). Losses in natural stands or in the absence of some cutting are generally negligible. Miller and Kelman (*990*) reported that mycelial growth of *F. annosus* in inoculated living roots and in root segments of loblolly pine was inversely related to root reserve carbohydrates.

Planted stands of sapling loblolly pine on heavy soils often cease rapid growth abruptly, fade, and die, over areas up to about two acres. The trouble is called spot dieout, and it is a conspicuous problem in the Piedmont. It has been ascribed to localized unfavorable soil conditions with respect to aeration and permeability, expressed in terms of the oxidation-reduction potential, leading to excessive root mortality (*290*). The trouble is very similar to a common red pine malady in New York and Pennsylvania (*1362*).

The root rot caused by *Clitocybe tabescens*, general on many woody plants, attacks loblolly pine in Florida (*1168*) but is not considered an important forest disease. The cotton root rot fungus *Phymatotrichum omnivorum* has been damaging enough to loblolly to cause this tree to be classed as unusable in infested areas of Texas and Oklahoma (*1627*), although losses in test shelterbelt plantings of this species in this area were light.

Polyporus schweinitzii causes a root and butt rot, mainly following basal or root injuries, and in the Deep South it has caused more loss in some areas than *Fomes annosus*. Butt rot from fire scars on loblolly pine depends upon the size and age of the wounds. Fortunately, they are typically too small to result in much cull. However, old wounds (over 60 years old) that were 10 to 19 inches wide at the stump, resulted in over 100 board feet of cull (*494*). Most such rot is caused by *Polyporus schweinitzii*.

Poria cocos produces tuckahoes (also called Indian bread) on the roots, which seem to do little harm. They are tuberous growths of fungus tissue.

Trunk Rots.—*Fomes pini* (red heart), entering almost entirely through dead branch stubs, is rarely a factor under the age of 60 years. When branches large enough to have heartwood begin to die, red heart can get started and destroy much of a tree; however, in undamaged stands rot cull should not exceed 2 percent up to 60 years (657). One representative stand in the Atlantic coastal plain showed the increase of infection with age as follows (1016):

Age class—years:	Trees with red heart Percent
40–90	5
91–140	9
141–190	60
191–230	72

Two loblolly pine stands in coastal North Carolina, one of old-field and the other of forest origin, had mean ages of 89 and 125 years, respectively and cull percentages of 2 and 12 percent, respectively. Almost all rot was red heart (*Fomes pini*) (556).

Mycorrhizal Relations.—High light intensity and a well-developed A-horizon were associated with the best mycorrhizal development in loblolly pine on a North Carolina silt loam (1552).

The fungi reported definitely to form mycorrhizae are *Amanita muscaria; Boletinus pictus; Boletus betula, B. brevipes, B. chrom-apes, B. communis, B. eximius, B. granulatus, B. luteus, B. sub-luteus; Cantharellus cibarius; Cenococcum graniforme; Laccaria (Clitocybe) laccata; Rhizopogon parasiticus;* and *Russula lepida* (181, 182, 1554). All but *R. parasiticus* have been proved by pure-culture synthesis.

Additional species on loblolly pine reported by Trappe (1442) as mycorrhizal somewhere in the world are: *Amanita virosa; Boletus miniatoolivaceus; B. aeruginascens, B. bovinus, B. grevillei, B. scaber, B. variegatus; Gomphidius vinicolor; Rhizopogon luteolus; Scleroderma aurantium;* and *Suillus cothurnatus.*

Zak and Bryan (1645) succeeded in isolating several mycorrhizal fungi directly from the roots of southern pines, including loblolly pine.

Miscellaneous Pathology.—A study of mortality in 177 loblolly pine seed trees that died within an average of 3 years after logging, on the sandy soils of coastal Virginia, disclosed the following causes of death: lightning, 36 pecent; wind, 24 percent; logging and insects, 15 percent; unknown, 10 percent; fire, 8 percent; and no record, 6 percent (1448).

Mineral deficiencies in seedlings are as follows:

N—Short, stiff, yellow-green needles (469). Low limit for terminal foliage about 1.2 percent (oven dry weight) below which deficiency symptoms appear.

P—Early abscission of needles. Purplish shoot tips (469). Exuding resin from terminal. Low limit 0.10 percent.

K—Purpling and browning of all shoot tips but terminal. Then the terminal needles purple and spiral around the tip. Ultimately, needles short, twisted up to 10 turns, with death of terminals and much stunting (1366). Lower limit 0.16–0.26 percent.

Ca—Resin exudation from dying terminal and branch buds. Varied needle discoloration. Some bud death without resin. Older needles tough, leathery, deep green (1366). Lower limit 0.04 per-

368

cent. Needles, needle cells, and buds small. Root tips blunt and rounded (*469*).

Mg—Stunting, yellow-brown needles, dieback. Needle tips pure yellow, then brown. Weak lateral branching. Small, weak roots with necrotic areas (*1366*). Lower limit 0.05–0.08 percent.

B—Resin exudation from terminals (*1366*).

Virginia pine
Pinus virginiana

An intolerant species, often a pioneer in pure stands on abandoned fields (*1311*), Virginia pine grows well on a variety of soils, preferably the clays and loams of the Appalachian foothills and Piedmont. It is common from New Jersey to Georgia and extends westward through Kentucky and Tennessee. It will persist on shaly or very sandy soils, growing poorly, but will not tolerate poorly drained, wet sites, as will loblolly, slash, and pitch pines (*1326*). Usually straight, the tree often has poor form and is not only limby but also the dead limbs on trees 40 or more years old often persist to the ground. In spite of its limbiness, it withstands ice fairly well, except in combination with wind, and can stand drought and rigorous weather changes. It is particularly susceptible to damage by fire. It matures at about 80 years and can live to 200 years. Tests have indicated a high sensitivity of Virginia pine to sulfur dioxide. The species is also sensitive to the salt in brackish water, following inroads of such water during coastal storms (*875*).

Virginia pine is usually fairly free of disease. It often supports many branch galls of *Cronartium quercuum;* and, where the alternate host abounds, many trees are killed by *C. appalachianum.* An autoecious *Coleosporium* attacks the needles, and some twig blights are common. Pitch canker, caused by a *Fusarium,* is a common killer of trees of any size in scattered localities.

Seedling and Foliage Diseases.—Since Virginia pine has not been grown in nurseries to a great extent, little is known of its seedling diseases.

The foliage is susceptible to attack by six species of *Coleosporium,* but attacks are usually light. Of special interest is *C.* (*Gallowaya*) *pinicola,* because it is autoecious, producing only telia on the pine needles. Unlike most of the other southern pines, Virginia pine foliage is seldom blighted or browned by fungi. *Ploioderma lethale,* **P. hedgcockii,** and the brown spot fungus (*Scirrhia acicola*) can brown older needles, but their attack is rarely severe enough to command attention.

Stem Diseases.—*Atropellis tingens* (*380*), *A. apiculata* (*878*), and *Caliciopsis pinea* (*483*) often kill twigs; *A. piniphila* does so occasionally; and *Tympanis confusa* will sometimes cause branch cankers near the northern end of the range of Virginia pine. The *Atropellis* spp. turn the wood very dark under the canker. The *Caliciopsis* has hairlike projections.

The most conspicuous of the diseases of Virginia pine are the stem rusts and pitch canker. The eastern gall rust (*Cronartium quercuum*) is sometimes so abundant that hundreds of round galls will occur on the branches and trunk of a single tree, but they usually do little harm. On a small stem they can ruin tree form or

369

kill, and on a large stem they can lead to an open rotten wound (*1311*). Out of 225 specimens of the hyperparasite *Tuberculina maxima* on Peridermiums reported on by Hedgcock (*626*), only seven were on *Cronartium quercuum*, and all seven were on *Pinus virginiana* galls from the Middle Atlantic States.

Serological tests (see *Pinus taeda*) indicate the specific identity of *C. quercuum* on *Pinus virginiana*, as compared with *C. fusiforme* and *C. ribicola*.

Cronartium comptoniae can attack Virginia pine near sweetfern in the North and Middle West, stunting and deforming small trees (*25, 1341*). The most lethal rust is *C. appalachianum*, which is similar in action and as lethal to Virginia pine as blister rust is to white pine (*647*). Fortunately, its alternate host *Buckleya distichophylla* is not widely distributed, or Virginia pine would have a mortal enemy. This rust is known only in the southern Appalachian Mountains. It was this rust, rather than *C. comandrae*, that Arthur (*46*) observed on *Buckleya* from Tennessee. Krebill (*814*) illustrates and·describes the histology of *C. appalachianum* and several other North American stem rusts of hard and soft pines.

The other quite damaging stem disease is pitch canker (*Fusarium lateritium* f. sp. *pini*) (*665*). The fungus, usually entering twigs or stems through small insect wounds, will girdle, killing shoots in a few weeks and trunks in a few years. The telltale heavy pitch exudation and pitch-soaking of the wood beneath the lesion are characteristic only of this disease (*102*).

Snyder, Toole, and Hepting (*1329*) provide a complete description of the pitch-canker fungus and also illustrate variation in the morphology of this forma specialis of *Fusarium lateritium*. They also describe some other *Fusaria*, both pathogens and saprobes, on southeastern tree species.

Dasyscypha oblongospora (*574*) and *Cenangium atropurpurum* (*238*) are saprophytes on twigs.

Root Diseases and Trunk Rots.—Red heart (*Fomes pini*) causes little cull in Virginia and North Carolina in stands up to 50 years old (*1311*), but in mature stands on trees with many large branch stubs, it can cause heavy losses. An eastern Maryland stand, ranging in age from 50 to 90 years, had less than 2 percent decay cull, and 85 percent of this occurred in trees 70 to 90 years old. The indications in this area were that Virginia pine probably suffers little heartrot loss before an age of 70 years. The rot was virtually all red heart (*Fomes pini*) (*434*).

Poria subacida and *Polyporus schweinitzii* cause some root and butt rot in injured Virginia pine trees, and *Fomes annosus* is known to rot roots of this species in South Carolina.[51]

The genera of nematodes that have been isolated in large numbers from soil around Virginia pine roots include *Hemicycliophora*, *Criconemoides*, and *Helicotylenchus*. Genera of nematodes isolated in less abundance were *Xiphinema*, *Hoplolaimus*, *Meloidodera*, *Scutellonema*, *Paratylenchus*, and *Tylenchorhynchus* (*1220*).

The nematodes that have been reported in association with Virginia pine roots and the literature referring to them are listed by

---

[51] Personal communication from Elmer R. Roth, pathologist, USDA Forest Service Southeastern Area, S. & P.F., Atlanta, Ga.

Ruehle (*1222*). He also showed (*1221*) that Virginia, longleaf, and loblolly pine were poor hosts or non-hosts to *Pratylenchus zeae*.

Mycorrhizal Relations.—The fungi reported proved able to form mycorrhizae with roots of Virginia pine are *Amanita caesaria, A. citrina, A. flavorubescens, A. frostiana, A. mappa, A. muscaria, A. rubescens, A. solitaria, A. verna, Boletus betula, B. bicolor, B. cyanescens, B. edulis, B. felleus, B. frostii, B. indecisis, B. luteus, B. pallidus, B. punctipes, B. rimosellus, B. subtomentosus, B. variegatus, Cenococcum graniforme, Gomphidius vinicolor, Lepiota rhacodes, Paxillus rhodoxanthus, Rhizopogon roseolus, Russula emetica,* and *Scleroderma aurantium* (*1442, 1485*). Those reported by Vozzo and Hacskaylo (*1485*) were proved by pure-culture synthesis. There is evidence that *Lactarius piperatus* and *Tricholoma portentosum* are also mycorrhiza-formers on this species (*561*).

Vozzo and Hacskaylo (*1486*) describe and illustrate Virginia pine mycorrhizae and emphasize the differences between white-mantled types, the black-mantled *Cenococcum* type, and non-mycorrhizal long-roots with root hairs.

Hacskaylo (*562*) proved, in pure culture, that *Thelephora terrestris* forms mycorrhizae with Virginia pine.

For Virginia pine, it has been demonstrated that much larger amounts of cations (as Sodium-22) were absorbed from the external supply through roots inoculated with *Rhizopogon roseolus* than through non-mycorrhizal roots (*946*).

Miscellaneous Pathology.—As on other hard pines, occasional witches'-brooms that appear to be unassociated with an organism occur. They are considered to be of localized genetic origin (*1311*).

Mineral deficiencies in Virginia pine seedlings appear as follows: N and P—As described for loblolly pine.

K—As in loblolly except that the purpling comes earlier and is more pronounced (*1366*).

Ca—Progressive death of, and often resin exudation from, terminal and branch buds; reduced growth, and needles discolored in many patterns. The older needles are tough, leathery, and deep green (*1366*). Lower limit for terminal foliage about 0.04 percent (oven dry weight), after which deficiency symptoms appear.

London plane

Platanus acerifolia

In the last half century the London plane, according to Walter (*1506*), has become one of the most important shade trees in the United States. It has been planted by the thousands in cities and towns, along streets and highways, mainly in the East, Midwest, and South, but also along the West Coast. Metcalf (*955*) places it among the most widely used shade trees in California.

The London plane will grow where scarcely any species (other than ailanthus) will thrive because of its basic vigor and its resistance to the vicissitudes of the soil and air environment of cities (*1081*). Its tall, colorful trunk and multiple seed balls are noteworthy, and its resistance to anthracnose (see *Platanus occidentalis*) and ease of transplanting add to its usefulness as a street tree. The Oriental plane *P. orientalis* enjoys few of these qualities, and therefore its popularity has given way to the London plane.

The London plane is a cross between *Platanus occidentalis* and *P. orientalis*. There are at least four named varieties: one with yellow variegation of the foliage, one with the leaves blotched with white, one with erect branching, and one with the leaves 5-lobed and with serrated lobes (*1154*).

Unfortunately, the canker-stain disease has taken an enormous toll of London planes since about 1925, killing thousands of trees in several Eastern States (*1506*).

Foliage Diseases.—Few foliage diseases have been described for London plane. While it is much less susceptible to anthracnose (*Gnomonia platani*) than either the eastern or the California sycamore, leaf and shoot blight have occurred when conditions are especially suitable for the fungus (see *P. occidentalis*).

The only other of the many foliage diseases described for sycamore that also attack London plane is the very common *Phyllactinia guttata* (*P. corylea*). Its conidia are oidia, and the black perithecia have straight appendages with bulbous proximal ends.

Stem Diseases.—A disease called canker stain (*Ceratocystis fimbriata* f. sp. *platani*) began killing London plane trees in Philadelphia, Pennsylvania, about 1926. Spread is almost entirely by man, largely by pruning tools or through some other injuries. Combined losses for several eastern cities were by 1952, placed at over $1 million (*1507*). Some cities have lost most of their London planes, with particularly heavy losses in Philadelphia and nearby areas in Delaware and New Jersey, but some losses have occurred in cities and towns from South Carolina to New York and broadly westward to Mississippi, Tennessee, and Missouri. The staining cankers may occur on trunks or branches. Brown or black coloration, generally in a lens-shaped pattern, is the first symptom on the smooth, yellow or green bark. After a year, a canker may be only 2 in. wide but 20 to 40 in. long. Each year cankers widen, and they often coalesce, girdling the tree or branch. Older cankers shed their darkened, dead bark, exposing the wood, which dries, checks, and collects soot. A tree with an infected trunk is a doomed tree, according to Walter (*1506*), who did most of the early research on this disease.

The reddish-brown or bluish-black discoloration of the wood, in cross section behind the cankers, is the most distinctive symptom, and is coextensive with the stain fungus *C. fimbriata* f. sp. *platani* in the wood. Stain patterns are radial, generally reaching the pith. The fungus sporulates abundantly on newly-killed wood in wet weather, from May until October. It produces two kinds of endoconidia; one, long and hyaline; the other, short and brownish; and also, long-beaked perithecia (*732*).

A canker and twig blight of sycamore and London plane is caused by *Massaria platani* (see *Platanus occidentalis*) and by a species of *Dothiorella*. The latter may be the imperfect stage of *Botryosphaeria ribis* which is largely saprobic on sycamore.

A so-called "rosy canker" of London plane has been reported from several cities in the Northeast and described and illustrated by May et al. (*942*). It is attributed to soil poisoning by manufactured illuminating gas. The striking cankers have their furrowed, hypertrophied, often decorticated centers composed of rosy-to-brown proliferated tissue. This tissue pushes away the bark and forms a soft, watery, rose-colored mass of thin-walled cells. These masses then dry and become hard, brown, and furrowed. Branch and trunk cankers are of irregular shape but tend to be elongated. The above authors mention similarities between this London plane canker and gas-injury cases in *Populus* and *Salix*.

A cankering of London plane in Asheville, North Carolina, was associated with *Hypoxylon tinctor*, a fungus known to be associated with cankering of sycamore (see *Platanus occidentalis*) in Georgia (*900*) and Louisiana (*8*). Under the dark patches of carbonaceous stroma (*978*), the bark is discolored a bright, deep orange. Spread may extend several inches peripherally and a foot or more vertically in a single year. Cankers may be several feet long and tend to retain the bark.

Crandall (*300*) describes bacterial infection and decay of the inner wood of winter-injured young London plane trees. Frost cracks and poor callusing of wounds appeared in 5-year-old trees on a Maryland nursery site. The weakened trees showed watersoaking and discoloration of the three innermost annual wood rings, a condition that terminated sharply 5 in. from the ground line. A slime flux developed at many pruning wounds, and the open wounds were invaded by what appeared to be *Polyporus versicolor*. A wetwood condition (*603*) of the trunk yielded a Gram-negative rod-shaped bacterium. The trouble was attributed to very cold spring weather following a warm winter. The bases of the trees were protected by snow. The frost cracks were apparently limited to wetwood trees and occurred 2 years later during subzero weather.

American sycamore
Platanus occidentalis

The sycamore is a common streambank tree east of the Great Plains, except in Florida, Minnesota, and the northern parts of New England and New York. As Fowells (*468*) puts it, "Sycamore occurs most frequently and reaches its largest size in alluvial soils along streams and in bottom lands. The tree is tolerant of wet soil conditions, and in the northern parts of its range it grows on the edges of streams and lakes . . . . Farther south it commonly grows on the alluvial soils of flood plains adjacent to the larger rivers, on former streambanks . . . and in the moist coves, lower slopes, and ravines." It has done well on coal strip-mine soil banks in the Central States and has been used commonly as a fast-growing shade or street tree, although it is generally less suitable to urban conditions than the London plane (*Platanus acerifolia*).

Sycamores can grow remarkably large, with trees on record that reached 14 ft. in diameter and exceeded 140 ft. in height (*279*). Intermediate in tolerance to shade, it competes successfully with cottonwood and willow, mainly as a pioneer species, but it tends ultimately to give way to other wetland species along many of the major river flood plains. It grows to ages exceeding 300 years in some interior valleys (*468*).

Sycamore is readily distinguished from the London plane and the Oriental plane by the single seed ball of the former, and the pairs or double pairs of the latter species. It reproduces abundantly by stump sprouts or from seed (which is favored by light). Cuttings can be easily rooted.

In a study area in Tennessee (*583*) flooding injured sycamore more readily than 20 other mesophytic or wetland species, but in Illinois even 3 ft. of floodwater failed to affect sycamore growth over a 6-year period (*468*). In pots flooded for 38 days and then well drained, sycamore seedlings recovered but not as rapidly as did cottonwood or green ash (*711*).

Sycamore proved relatively resistant to air pollution, mainly from sulfur dioxide, in Texas (*911*).

Forest sycamores suffer little damage from disease except for the trunk rots associated with basal wounds, large branch stubs, and old age. Some diseases, however, can render individuals unsightly, defoliate them, or cause a dieback of shoots. The only ones recorded as lethal to sycamore are the canker-stain disease and Armillaria root rot.

There are two named varieties of sycamore: var. *glabrata*, with small, leathery foliage, growing mainly in west Texas, and var. *attenuata*, a form widely intermixed with the type species over the East (*468*).

Foliage Diseases.—The most important of the sycamore diseases is the anthracnose caused by *Gnomonia platani*. Earlier, the common anthracnoses of both sycamore and oak were known as *Gnomonia veneta* (*Gloeosporium nervisequum*). *G. platani* blights the foliage early, often when leaves are still very small, and has been confused with frost damage. Hepting and Fowler (*661*) show heavy early defoliation that was followed by a second crop of leaves. Carter (*231*) illustrates several effects of anthracnose. Later, this fungus and also some others may produce irregular, brown areas along the veins, midribs, and leaf tips. Shoot blight and twig cankering (*1143*) are also caused by *G. platani*. In moist weather, small, pinhead-sized, cream-colored spots form on the underside of the leaf on dead tissue along the veins. This is the *Gloeosporium*, or imperfect, stage. The *Gnomonia* stage, consisting of black perithecia with 2-celled, hyaline ascospores, forms on overwintered fallen leaves and on twig cankers. During some spring seasons, sycamores are virtually completely defoliated by this disease (*661, 1143*). Anthracnose occurs wherever sycamores grow, both in the East and the West.

Schuldt (*1265*) points out differences between the anthracnose fungus on sycamore and the one on oak (see *Quercus*, foliage diseases). Neely and Himelick (*1015*) reviewed the literature on the nomenclature of the anthracnose fungi of sycamore and oak, indicated that they should be recognized as distinct, and proposed that the name *Gnomonia platani* Kleb. be used for the sycamore fungus. In the spring as the leaves unfold, it produces spores of the imperfect *Discula* (*Gloeosporium*) *platani* stage on infected twigs, while the *Gnomonia* stage forms later on fallen leaves.

Neely and Himelick (*1014*) determined that if the mean daily temperature for the 2 weeks immediately following budbreak was below 55° F., severe shoot blight (*G. platani*) ensued. Shoot blight decreased with increasing temperature for those 2 weeks, and if the mean daily temperature was 60° F. or higher, no shoot blight occurred.

In the South and the Midwest two other leaf diseases are sometimes more prominent than the anthracnose. These are the spot diseases caused by *Mycosphaerella platanifolia* (*Cercospora platanicola*) and by *M. stigmina-platani*. Wolf (*1602*) notes that lesions caused by the first appear about mid-June in North Carolina and, by the second, late in July. *M. platanifolia* first forms very small (1 mm.), irregular, brown spots in great numbers. Eventually, many hundreds may form and fuse on one leaf.

M. stigmina-platani first forms scattered, pale green areas, and ultimately the upper surface may be largely pale green and the lower covered with an effuse, black weft or sooty film.

Wolf (*1602*) illustrates the multiseptate *Cercospora* conidia and the 2-celled *Mycosphaerella* ascospores of *M. platanifolia* and the broadly clavate or grub-shaped multiseptate *Stigmina* conidia and the 2-celled ascospores of *M. stigmina-platani*. Spermogonia of both fungi form in the fall, and the perithecia mature over the winter on fallen leaves. The two fungi often occur together. *Phyllosticta platani* is the likely spermogonial stage of *M. platanifolia*.

Also in the South and Midwest, leaf spots occur caused by *Septoria platanifolia* and by *Phloeospora multimaculans*. On sycamore, *Phloeospora multimaculans* produces discrete, irregular, dark brown to purple spots 1–3 mm. across on the upper leaf surface (*620*). They often have a brown center. The underside is brown throughout, with a darker border. Spots can become confluent and produce dirty-brown, extended necrosis and can result in defoliation. For pycnidium and spore characters, see *Juglans nigra*. This disease is known mainly in Texas.

The common powdery mildews *Microsphaera alni* (and *M. alni* var. *extensa*) (*1153*) and *Phyllactinia guttata* (*P. corylea*) attack sycamore, mainly late in the summer and on vigorous sprout foliage (see *Castanea*). New growth formed in August may be severely distorted, stunted, and covered with a white bloom of spores, yet the older foliage may be unaffected.

Stem Diseases.—The canker-stain disease (*Ceratocystis fimbriata* f. sp. *platani*) can be lethal to sycamore, but, since it is much more important as a killing disease of London plane (*Platanus acerifolia*), it is discussed under the latter species. Since this disease is spread almost entirely by man, mainly through pruning, it has been essentially a shade tree disease. Rows of the American sycamore in Magnolia, North Carolina, were killed by it, and occasional infection has appeared among forest sycamores (*1506*). Sycamores in Tennessee and Kentucky also have died of the canker-stain disease (*1001*).

Gnomonia platani causes a twig blight as well as a leaf blight. Neely (*1011*) illustrates the formation, by *G. platani*, of "pressure cushions" that form under the phellem of twigs, rupturing it. The pycnidium forms in the cortical cells beneath the cushion, and the conidia are released through the ruptured phellem.

A killing trunk canker of sycamore followed thinning of a forest stand in Georgia. McAlpine (*900*) noted that the cankers had indistinct margins, followed the grain of the wood, and that longitudinal cracks often developed. The bark in the area of the canker was light orange and often sunken. Many trees were killed or had broken over. *Hypoxylon tinctor* was consistently associated with these cankers (see also *Platanus acerifolia*).

Thompson (*1402*) also described a stem disease of sycamore

from Georgia, but his report concerned a dieback that started in the small branches and progressed back to the trunk. In one area, 40 percent of the trees were in various stages of degeneration, including wilting of foliage and brown streaking of the branch wood. *Diplodia natalensis,* the imperfect stage of *Physalospora rhodina (1484),* was isolated, and inoculations with it produced the disease.

Toole *(1421),* and later Filer *(442),* describe a sycamore canker in the Mississippi Delta that caused much top kill in the early 1950's, during drought years, but which abated with normal rainfall in the early 1960's. The cankers seldom girdled trees but were in long, narrow strips, some as long as 12 ft. First, sunken areas appear on the bark of any part of a tree. This bark is covered with the small black pycnidia of the causal fungus. Later, the bark sloughs off, and the wood beneath becomes darkly stained. Filer says that the disease occurs widely over the South and attributes it to *Botryodiplodia theobromae.* Since this is a synonym for *Diplodia natalensis,* both imperfect stage names for *Physalospora rhodina (1484),* this disease can be linked with Thompson's *(1402).*

A twig blight and branch canker have been attributed to *Massaria platani* in the South and Midwest. Sphaeriaceous perithecia with dark, multiseptate, oblong-fusoid spores, with a mucous sheath, form on the bark lesions.

Weak parasitism to twigs has also been ascribed to *Botyrosphaeria ribis* var. *chromogena* (see *Cercis*) and to species of *Physalospora, Dothiorella* (probably *B. ribis*), *Cytospora,* and *Myxosporium.*

The common superficial sooty blotch of fruits, caused by *Gloeodes pomigena (1555),* sometimes forms on shoots of sycamore. The dark, surface mycelium can usually be rubbed off with the fingers.

The eastern leafy mistletoe, *Phoradendron serotinum,* can parasitize sycamore in the South.

Root Rots.—Shoestring root rot *(Armillaria mellea)* has been reported from several states, and, in a case observed by the author, it seemed to be directly responsible for the death of several sycamores along a stream bank in North Carolina. There was a copious development of flat, black rhizomorphs, mycelial fans at the root collar, and fruiting of the fungus *(151).*

Sycamore has been used with some success in the Texas root rot *(Phymatotrichum omnivorum)* belt in Texas and Oklahoma. Although classed by Taubenhaus and Ezekiel *(1379)* as resistant in their mass seedling tests, in a 6-year period in the field 3.1 percent of 11,906 sycamores planted in test areas died of root rot. This annual loss of 0.8 percent was, however, low. Therefore, Wright and Wells *(1627)* considered this species of "intermediate susceptibility, possibly usable on sandy sites." Symptoms of this root rot are described in standard texts *(151, 1555).*

Trunk Rots.—A large number of saprobic fungi rot the wood of dead trees or injured areas of living trees. This saprobic flora, while including many common species, includes some that are not common on hardwoods in general.

Among the sycamore heartrot fungi, the most destructive are

Hydnum erinaceus, which can rot out and hollow the entire central cylinder of a tree; *Fomes applanatus*, a localized wound-rot fungus; and the still more saprobic *F. pinicola, F. scutellatus, Daedalea ambigua*, and *D. confragosa*. The fungi mentioned by Overholts (*1067*) as capable of causing either rot of the central cylinder or rot at wounds of living *Platanus* spp. include *Fomes applanatus, F. fraxinophilus, F. marmoratus, F. meliae, Polyporus cuticularis, P. fissilis*, and *P. spraguei*.

Toole (*1429*) demonstrated the pathogenicity of *Corticium galactinum* to sycamore and illustrated the thick felts investing the root systems of sycamore, green ash, and oak seedlings inoculated 2 years before.

While three species of nematodes have been reported from the root zone of sycamore trees in New Jersey, none were associated with plant damage (*1222*). Ruehle (*1223*) showed, however, that the sting nematode *Belonolaimus longicaudatus*, when introduced into pots at rates of 500 to 2500 per pot, stunted sycamore seedlings in proportion to the nematode population. A later tabulation by Ruehle (*1224*) lists 9 species of nematodes, in 7 genera, associated with sycamore roots in the Southeast.

California sycamore
Platanus racemosa

A native forest tree, mainly under 60 ft. in height, the California sycamore is confined to the borders of streams and in moist canyons in both interior valleys and coast ranges in California to an elevation of 4,000 ft. at the southern end of the state to 2,000 ft. in the north. Trunks are typically short and the branches long and crooked, making an irregular wide crown. The thick, wooly leaves are from 5 to 11 in. wide. The bark is thick and furrowed near the base but thin, smooth, and ashy white above.

The California sycamore is intolerant, sprouts readily, can stand high temperatures, and grows to ages exceeding 100 years. Metcalf (*955*) notes that while the tree is common along streams in coastal southern California and in the foothills of the Sierra Nevada, many are in a ragged condition because of repeated defoliation by the anthracnose disease. It is seldom used as an ornamental in California, because the London plane has better form, grows faster, is better adapted to city environments, and is more resistant to anthracnose.

The pathology of California sycamore is dominated by the anthracnose disease. The effects are much the same as those described under *Platanus occidentalis*. Virtually complete defoliation for several years in succession is not uncommon, and attacks will rank with the worst in the East. However, refoliation following early defoliation can keep trees alive indefinitely.

A leaf spot caused by *Stigmella platani-racemosae* in California is very similar to that reported under *P. occidentalis* to be caused by *Stigmina platani*. Wolf (*1602*) compared the two fungi and noted that they are closely related. However, he felt that they were sufficiently distinct to be regarded as separate species so long as the two form genera *Stigmina* and *Stigmella* are retained. The California leaf spot is not important.

The common powdery mildew caused by *Microsphaera alni* appears in late summer, mainly on sprout growth. It is conspicuous but harmful only because it disfigures foliage.

The twig blight caused by *Massaria platani* has been reported from this sycamore in California (see *P. occidentalis*), and so has the leafy mistletoe *Phoradendron tomentosum* var. *macrophyllum*.

Armillaria mellea has caused the death of large trees and is common enough as a pathogen to gain respect in California (see *P. occidentalis*).

Texas root rot is known to attack both *Platanus racemosa* and *P. wrightii* in Arizona.

The pin nematode *Gracilacus anceps* has been reported associated with the roots of *P. racemosa* in California (*1222*).

Morrison (*1004*) has reported *Clitocybe olearia* to be associated with a decline of coast live oak and California sycamore in the San José Hills of California (see *Quercus*, Root Rot).

Poplar
Populus spp.

There are many common species of *Populus* in North America, some native and some introduced. Since many of the diseases of poplars affect two or more species, the pathology of *Populus* will be handled as it was with *Carya;* first, by characterizing all of the tree species dealt with, and then annotating each disease only once and indicating host relationships. Also as with *Carya*, the poplars fall into natural botanical groups. The following grouping is that used in the Index of Plant Diseases in the United States (*8*); namely, the white poplars, the black poplars, and the balsam poplars. Berbee (*99*) gives an up-to-date, partly annotated listing of the diseases of *Populus* spp., worldwide. Although his annotations are brief and he gives no references, his account should be a valuable supplement to the following account because of his wide geographic coverage, his listing of saprobes as well as parasites, and his emphasis on aspects of the pathology of *Populus* different from the current account.

WHITE POPLARS, OR ASPENS

Populus alba, the white poplar or abele, is native to central and southern Europe and western Asia. It has long been cultivated in North America because of its rapid growth, its silvery foliage, its freedom from disease, and the aesthetic appeal of some of its many horticultural varieties (*1154*). It grows tall, with an irregular branching habit, has whitish-gray bark, and its grayish leaves are usually silvery-tomentose below. It is adapted to mild climates and will thrive on sites ranging from droughty hillsides to the edges of swamps. It resisted salt-spray damage in New England (*1632*). Abundant reproduction by root suckers can cause this tree to become a nuisance whether used as an ornamental or in the forest.

Populus grandidentata, the bigtooth aspen, extends from Canada to the mountains of western North Carolina and across the Lake States and the Central States. Typically a small tree of minor importance, it has a straight trunk, and the bark of older trees near the base is likely to be black, thick, and fissured. Further up, large,

378

flat, smooth, light-colored patches appear. Bigtooth aspen thrives on moist, cool sites on a wide variety of soils. It can stand intense cold (*468*).

Bigtooth aspen's thin bark, when young, makes it very sensitive to fire. Tops break easily from wind or ice, and trees are prone to windthrow because of their shallow rooting habit. The pathology of the species is dominated by rot fungi, mainly *Fomes igniarius,* which, together with Hypoxylon canker, contribute to limiting longevity to 40 to 70 years. Other cankers and rot fungi contribute to the decline of stands at an early age (*468*).

Populus tremuloides, quaking aspen, is the most widely distributed tree species in North America, being one of the few with a transcontinental range from the Atlantic Ocean to the Pacific. It occurs from Newfoundland to Alaska and southward at increasingly higher elevations in the Sierra Nevada and in the Rocky Mountains to Mexico. East of the Great Plains it extends southward to a line from about Iowa to Virginia, and it is abundant in the Lake States and the Northeast. It can stand very cold winters and hot summers but does best on cool to cold, moist sites with porous, humic soils. Some of the finest stands of large, straight, sound aspens occur at high elevations in the Rocky Mountains as far south as Arizona.

Aspen sites are typically fertile, and the tree is regarded as a soil-builder, redistributing nitrogen, calcium, and other minerals through root uptake and leaf fall. The silvical characteristics have been described by Strothman and Zasada and published by Fowells (*468*). The species has several varieties. It reproduces by seed, sprouts, and suckers. It is intolerant.

The literature on the pathology of quaking aspen is extensive. While the tree has a maximum longevity of about 200 years, cankers and decay, in particular, limit its life span to less than half this age in most areas. On the best sites in Colorado (*346*) and Ontario (*68*), the rotation need not be limited to ages under 130 years (*346*), but in Utah the cutting age is limited to 80 to 90 years (*945*), in Minnesota to 50 to 60 years (*1255*), in Iowa to 50 years (*174*), and in Wisconsin, Michigan, and New England to even lower ages in some stands, with decay the major limiting factor.

Because of a persistent periderm, aspen bark remains smooth unless injured. Fungi, lichens, and mechanical injuries can stimulate the formation of rough, fissured bark. The fungus *Diplodia* (*Macrophoma*) *tumefaciens,* which penetrates the periderm, is, according to Kaufert (*773*), the main cause of rough bark, with lichens apparently having a role in inducing this condition.

In summarizing the enemies of aspen in the Lake States, Christensen et al. (*256*) state that ". . . leaf diseases probably are of little importance, Hypoxylon canker is an important killer of trees in many areas, and decay caused by *Fomes igniarius* results in a serious reduction of wood volume in older trees." They also mention aspen's tendency to fire damage, to storm and ice breakage, and to windthrow.

In diagnosing the leaf diseases, cankers, and rots of aspen, it is particularly important to recognize the region of occurrence. The pathogens vary widely in incidence, depending upon the region.

Thus, there are cankers and leaf blights in the West that do not occur in the East; and though *Fomes igniarius* is the major rot fungus of aspen, 16 other rot fungi in living aspens occur in Colorado alone (*346*), with the little-known fungus *Cryptochaete polygonia* (*Corticium polygonium*) the most frequently isolated rot fungus there on *Populus tremuloides*.

Aspen can be injured by frost. Ouelette (*1059*), in Quebec, traced to frost injury foliar dwarfing, deformation, blight-like lesions, and canker-like lesions on young shoots.

THE BLACK POPLARS

Populus deltoides, the eastern cottonwood, is a very widely distributed species on sites providing an abundant and continuous supply of moisture throughout the growing season. Loamy sites along river bottoms and lower slopes close to streams are preferred sites. The tree abounds in the Mississippi River Flood Plain and on river bottoms of tributary streams and other rivers of the Central States and the South. Cottonwoods occur naturally east of the Great Plains from the Lake States to the Gulf of Mexico and east to the Atlantic Ocean except in northern New England, the uplands of New York and Pennsylvania, the Southern Highlands, and Florida. A variety, *occidentalis,* called the plains poplar, is confined to the Great Plains Region. The silvical characteristics of the eastern cottonwood have been described by Maisenhelder and revised by Fowells (*468*). They describe the differences in appearance of the tree depending upon its geographic location.

Cottonwood withstands temperature extremes, is intolerant, attains heights over 180 ft. and diameters over 6 ft. in the Mississippi Delta, and commonly makes height growth of 5 ft. per year for the first 5 years. It grows mostly in pure stands.

Cottonwood is very susceptible to fire injury and very resistant to flood damage (*583*). Diseases have not had important impacts on cottonwood in the past, but with the advent of intensive poplar culture in the South, some recent losses in southern outplantings have resulted from Valsa (Cytospora) canker and from the Melampsora leaf rusts.

Populus nigra var. italica is the Lombardy poplar, a native of central and southern Europe and western Asia. It has closely arranged, ascending branches that form a narrow columnar head. Its leaves are narrowly cuneate. It is used as an ornamental, a street tree, and a windbreak or screen tree and has been planted widely over the United States. It has done well in the Northeast and the Midwest and has been widely planted in California, where, according to Metcalf (*955*), it is a common sight in towns both east and west of the coastal mountains. Undemanding as to soil, it has thrived in areas of temperate climate or moderate rainfall. The Lombardy poplar has not done well in the South, where, although it is easily established, it tends to die out at a very early age, often by the tenth year, as a result of a combination of unsuitable climate, cankering by *Dothichiza populea,* and massive infection of the woody cylinder by a rod-shaped, wetwood bacterium (see Stem Diseases). In the North both cankering and wetwood infection also take place, but many rows of trees have still lived more than 100 years.

Hartley (*603*) states that Lombardy poplar represents the most striking association of wetwood with mortality in the United States. The tree is notorious for early death in the East and the South, and this development has been observed more recently in Utah and California. Hartley says that some trees in Washington, D. C., die by the fifth year and that few there live over 20 years. Since the Lombardy poplar is a clonal line, it is easy to understand how a bacterial infection of the wood would be perpetuated through vegetative reproduction. Wilting seldom appears following wetwood infection in this species until August.

A leaf spot and scab caused by *Didymosphaeria populina* attacks Lombardy poplar. Young leaves, and sometimes entire shoots, are blackened and wilted (*928*).

THE BALSAM POPLARS

Populus balsamifera, called balsam poplar, tacamahac, and balm-of-Gilead, includes *P. tacamahaca* and *P. candicans* as synonyms, along with some lesser known specific and varietal names (*872*). The buds are resinous and fragrant with the odor of balsam. This is a boreal and transcontinental species, occuring predominantly in Canada, where it extends from Newfoundland to Alaska. In the United States its variety *subcordata* occurs mainly in New England, New York, and northern Michigan. The type species may be found from the Lake States to Connecticut, and in the West from the Inland Empire to Colorado at high elevations in the Rocky Mountains (*468*).

Balsam poplar will grow on all but the wettest soils, but will not tolerate dry sites. It is undemanding as to soil texture, but needs abundant moisture and cool to cold climate. It is associated with our northernmost species and finds its preferred habitat along inundated bottoms and bordering streams and lakes.

Groups of trees up to 40 in. in diameter and over 100 years old occur in Minnesota, and trees 48 in. in diameter and over 200 years old occur in Canada. In the United States, however, it is regarded as a short-lived tree.

Like the other poplars, the balsam poplar reproduces by seed, sprouts, and root suckers. It is intolerant, hardy, flood-resistant, and less susceptible to loss from disease than the aspens. A review of the silvics of balsam poplar was prepared by Roe and presented by Fowells (*468*).

A gall midge (Cecidomyidae) causes a papillate leaf spot of balsam poplar in Alberta. Typically, the spots are necrotic, circular, dry, dark brown, and surrounded by a faint chlorotic halo, and they often have fungus spores in the area of the papilla. Their mean diameter is 5.5 mm. (*1566*).

A late-appearing leaf spot, *Mycosphaerella populorum*, Melampsora leaf rusts, and Linospora leaf blight are common, but generally are not damaging. Loss from Hypoxylon canker is negligible. *Fomes igniarius* and *Armillaria mellea*, although common, cause far less loss to balsam poplar than to the aspens. The only other noteworthy disease is a canker of young trees caused by *Neofabraea populi.*

A roughening of the normally smooth, greenish to brownish bark of balsam poplar, resulting in the bark's turning gray and becoming deeply furrowed, results from infection by *Rhytidiella moriformis,* a sphaeriaceous ascomycete. Zalasky (*1652*), describes this fungus as "Perithecia erumpent, superficial, hemispherical, very black, usually with a truncate base; apex sulcate, pored; Asci cylindric to clavate, bitunicate, paraphysate; Ascospores scoleco-sporous, hyaline to yellow-brown, septate."

Populus trichocarpa, black cottonwood, is the largest of the American poplars, and it is the largest hardwood in much of its native range of the Pacific Northwest. It extends from Kodiak Island, Alaska, along the Pacific Coast to northern California, and then it occurs spottily at high elevations to southern California. Its broadest and deepest inland penetration is through the Northwest States to the Rocky Mountains of the Inland Empire. South of the Snake River it occurs occasionally at high elevations into Utah and Nevada (*468*). It occurs mostly on bottom lands, river bars, forest meadows, and stream banks. It withstands a wide range of climatic extremes and soil types, provided the sites are generally cool and moist. Its optimum soil pH is rather high, ranging from 6 to 7. Roe and Fowells (*468*) give a good account of the silvics of black cottonwood, a species of considerable importance to the Far West. In appraising the growth and health of this species, they stress how these vary with respect to geographic races and how these adaptions must be recognized in planting programs involving this species. If planted out of its range, it is highly susceptible to disease. On good sites within its range, it makes remarkably rapid, healthy growth during its early years.

The main diseases are a canker of young trees caused by *Valsa* (*Cytospora*) *sordida* and fungus decay in old or damaged trees. The decay fungi include at least 70 species, of which six caused significant losses in British Columbia and two, *Polyporus delectans* and *Pholiota destruens,* caused 92 percent of the loss in the Fraser River region of British Columbia (*1394*). Melampsora rusts and many other fungi attack the foliage to varying degrees depending upon the region in which the tree is growing.

Black cottonwood is sensitive to fire and to soil droughtiness and is very intolerant to shade. Late frosts frequently injure or kill trees, and frost cracks are common. Since their superior height growth often places their crowns above those of other species and since the wood is weak, top breakage from wind and ice is common in black cottonwood.

Diseases of Seedlings or Cuttings.—Much of the poplar stock planted in the United States is from cuttings representing clonal lines of hybrids. As a result of concern over spreading two canker diseases (*Septoria musiva* and *Dothichiza populea*) and a leaf blotch (*Septotinia populiperda*) to new locations on cuttings, means have been developed to surface sterilize poplar cuttings. Chemical dips were effective in killing the spores of these fungi on the resinous buds, in lenticels, and elsewhere, and most of the dips did not affect growth of the cuttings (*1518*).

The foliage of cuttings of *Populus deltoides* and some hybrids grown in the South have been severely attacked by *Melampsora medusae,* even though no trees of the alternate hosts (*Larix* spp.) grow within hundreds of miles.

Cuttings grown in the Mississippi Delta and planted in this area have also often been severely cankered by *Cytospora chrysosperma* within 2 years after outplanting.

Boyce (*151*) states that damage as a result of Cytospora canker has resulted in the loss of up to 75 percent of the poplar cuttings in some propagating beds.

With respect to Cytospora canker of poplar and willow as a seedling disease, Stoeckeler and Jones (*1361*) state that wildlings on sand bars along streams in the Lake States can develop cankers following hail damage. Healed-in stock and trees planted on poor sites have developed cankers. On young, smooth-barked shoots new infections cause brownish, shrunken patches on seedlings. Stoeckeler and Jones stress the relation of this disease to low vigor. Gray et al. (*541*) have described a bark necrosis in Central States nurseries, the cause of which is, in part, due to *C. chrysosperma.* Cuttings of *P. trichocarpa* can be attacked by *C. chrysosperma* in Canada (*132*).

Bier (*112*) found a strain of *Fusarium lateritium* attacking stored cuttings and nursery stock of *Populus trichocarpa* in Vancouver. Many active cankers, centering at nodes and lenticels, occurred on single stems. This disease has not been found in well-established plantations or in field trees, and Bier considered it as probably strictly a nursery disease.

Foliage Diseases.—An "ink spot" leaf blight of *P. tremuloides* (aspen) can be caused either by *Ciborinia* (*Sclerotinia*) *bifrons* in the East and Lake States or by *C. confundens* on aspen and on *P. deltoides* from Colorado westward. Anyone wishing to treat himself to an entertaining few minutes should read Seaver's (*1269*) acrimonious attack on H. H. Whetzel for the latter's views on the identity of the eastern and the Colorado forms of these fungi on aspen. However, whether one adopts *Ciborinia* or *Sclerotinia* as the genus or *bifrons, confundens,* or *whetzelii* as the species, the effect on aspen trees is much the same. Brown spots form during the summer, and these darken and become sclerotia up to several millimeters across. Later the entire leaf may turn brown and die, while unaffected leaves remain green (see Seaver's color photo (*1269*)). During the following spring stipitate, cupulate apothecia form from the sclerotia on the ground. In the western form in particular, the sclerotia often fall free from the leaves while the foliage is still attached to the tree. There have been notable attacks on aspen in Idaho (*406*). There are no conidial stages among the Sclerotiniaceae. A fungus named *Myrioconium comitatum* occurs on leaves associated with *C. bifrons,* but there is reason to suspect that this may simply be the spermogonial stage of *C. bifrons.*

Dance (*320*), in a well-illustrated paper on *Venturia populina* (*Didymosphaeria populina*), states that the imperfect stage has been called *Pollaccia elegans, Fusicladium radiosum, F. r. balsamiferae,* and sometimes, mistakenly, *Napicladium tremulae* (*V. tremulae*). He regards *V. populina* as a pathogen only of the balsam poplars (section *Tacamahaca*), which include *Populus balsamifera* and *P. trichocarpa.* Dance (*320*) questions any reports of this fungus on poplars other than balsam poplars. The nomenclature confusion surrounding *V. populina, V. tremulae,* and their imperfect stages is so complicated that anyone attempting identification to species should consult Dance's papers (*319, 320*) and Barr's monograph (*63*).

One of the common poplar leaf-spot syndromes can be caused by either of two fungi, *Venturia populina* or *V. tremulae*. Although both have been called *Didymosphaeria populina* and, also, several imperfect-stage names in *Pollaccia* and *Fusicladium*, Peace (*1091*) points out that they are distinct and can be separated taxonomically, apart from the fact that in Europe *V. populina* attacks mainly black poplars and *V. tremulae* attacks white poplars.

Angular black spots form in early summer and enlarge until they kill the leaf. The fungus then spreads down the petiole and blackens the shoot, which then withers and appears hooked. McCallum (*904*) considered the disease (*V. tremulae*) common in eastern Canada on *P. tremuloides* and *P. grandidentata*. Shoots blackened, bent double, and bore only the imperfect stage, which he referred to as *Napicladium tremulae*. The fungus has short, subfasciculate, smooth conidiophores and solitary, oblong, acrogenous, olivaceous, mainly 1- to 2-septate conidia. Referring to *V. tremulae*, Marshall and Waterman (*928*) call the disease "scab" and say that in moist weather dark olive-green masses of spores form on blighted parts. This fungus has caused blighting of *P. alba*, *P. tremuloides*, *P. grandidentata*, and *P. nigra* var. *italica* in the United States. In some seasons it has been very aggressive on leaves and shoots of the golden aspen *P. tremuloides* var. *aurea* through northern Idaho, with the conidial stage sporulating luxuriantly on trees on the more moist sites (*406*).

The manner in which *V. tremulae* attacks, spreads, and involves the terminal shoot, causing a crook, is similar to the behavior of *V. populina*.

Barr (*63*), in a monograph of the Venturiaceae of North America, cites the following among the synonyms for or conidial states of *Venturia macularis: Didymosphaeria populifolia*, *Venturia tremulae*, *Pollaccia radiosum*, *Fusicladium tremulae*, and *Napicladium tremulae*. Among the equivalents for *Venturia populina* she lists *Didymosphaeria populina*, *Pollaccia elegans*, and *Fusicladium radiosum*.

Marks et al. (*926*) describe and illustrate a leaf disease of aspen in Wisconsin that conforms to the disease in Europe that Peace (*1091*) ascribes to *Venturia tremulae* attacking "white poplars." The disease symptoms and many features of the pathogen, acervuli, and spores fit the above account of *V. tremulae*. Marks et al., on aspen, illustrate blackish-brown leaf spots, vein necrosis, petiole infections, stem lesions bearing acervuli, and shoot blight, and present drawings of the acervulus and spores. They state that since the name *Gloeosporium* has been discarded, their pathogen becomes a *Colletotrichum* (*C. gloeosporioides*). Since this is synonymous with *G. fructigenum* f. *chromogenum*, it is in turn synonymous with *Glomerella cingulata*. Thus, once again a noteworthy pathogen was given a new name, based on its conidial stage, only to discover later that the organism was *G. cingulata* in its perfect state (see *Persea americana*).

One of the most widespread leaf spots of poplars is caused by *Marssonina populi* (perfect stage *Drepanopeziza populorum*). It produces small, discrete, circular or lens-shaped lesions that contain at their center a gelatinous mass of 2-celled, ovate or pyriform conidia in subcuticular acervuli. As a result of variability in morphology and in host preference, many isolates of the *M. populi* complex were studied by Boyer (*163*) with respect to whether or not hyphal anastomosis took place, and the results of his work indicated that, except for one form, the isolates constituted a closely related although variable group of fungi that could not be separated taxonomically. He thus agreed with Thompson (*1398*) that no sufficient criteria exist that enable *M. populi* to be broken into additional species. While *M. populi* occurs widely in North America on most poplar species, another species, *M. castagnei* (perfect stage *Drepanopeziza populi-albae*), replaces it on *Populus alba* and, possibly, on *P. grandidentata* (*8*).

The damage caused to *Populus tremuloides* by *M. populi* in the Rocky mountains is described by Mielke (*963*). Symptoms generally appear in August, with the diseased foliage appearing small. From a distance affected trees seem bronzed. The irregular leaf spots are tan at first and turn almost black. Their borders are a yellow to golden hue. Premature defoliation may follow. Individual trees and clonal lines vary greatly in susceptibility to attack.

Peace (*1091*) raised questions of speciation in *Marssonina* in Europe, even with reference to *M. populi*, *M. castagnei*, and *M. rhabdospora*, and he chose to consider them as one species. However, current research indicates that differences of specific rank do exist and that two or more species of *Marssonina*, including *M. brunnea*, will be recognized as important to poplar breeding in Europe.

Thompson (*1403*), after reviewing the nomenclature applied to *Marssonina rhabdospora*, a fungus described from New York, and also reviewing some controversy regarding similarity with some European fungi, decided to consider the American species on *P. tremuloides* and *P. grandidentata* (not on *P. alba*) as distinct and named it *Pleuroceras populi*. He also determined that the conidial form of a fungus referred to as *Septogloeum rhopaloideum* on *P. tremuloides* and *P. balsamifera*, which caused a leaf-spot disease, also had spermatial and perithecial stages, and he named the latter *Guignardia populi*.

Thompson (*1400*) described another leaf disease of *P. balsamifera* in Canada, caused by *Linospora tetraspora*, that has also been seen occasionally in the Lake States. The leaf lesions vary in size and are dark brown with irregular and diffuse margins. Complete leaf involvement and early defoliation can occur. Small, black, circular stromata (pseudoclypei) form abundantly on the upper surface and later turn ashen. Spermatia, but not conidia, have been observed. The perithecia form over winter beneath the pseudoclypei. The asci are 4-spored, and the ascospores are filiform, somewhat curved, hyaline, and 6- to 8-septate.

Thompson (*1401*) also described two species of *Mycosphaerella* that attack the leaves of the native species of poplar in North America and also many exotics. They are *M. populorum* (*Septoria musiva*) and *M. populicola* (*S. populicola*). The symptoms of the two diseases are similar, consisting of large or small, discrete, necrotic, often irregular lesions. In *M. populorum* the dark, globose pycnidia form all summer on both leaf surfaces. The conidia are hyaline, elongate, narrow, and 1- to 4-septate. Spermogonia and spermatia are formed. The perithecia develop over winter. They are black, globose, and bear 8-spored asci, and the ascospores are 1-septate, hyaline, equal-celled, and average $16–28\mu \times 4.5–6\mu$.

In *M. populicola* the dark, globose pycnidia form during the summer on both leaf surfaces. The conidia are hyaline, filiform, and 2- to 5-septate. Spermogonia are formed. The perithecia form over the winter; they are mostly hypophyllous, black, and globose, with 8-spored asci, containing ascospores that are 1-septate, hyaline, equal-celled, and average $22–33\mu \times 6–6.5\mu$, thus being larger than those of *M. populorum*.

A striking leaf blotch of hybrid poplar clones in the Northeast has been attributed to *Septotinia populiperda* by Waterman and Cash (*1522*). It appears in the spring as small, brown spots, often near the leaf margins. They enlarge, turn gray at the center, and develop an irregular, but sharply defined, margin. On the lower surface the blade, and particularly the veins, become dark brown, with white sporodochia forming on the veins. On the upper surface small, white masses of conidia appear in concentric circles. The conidia are ellipsoid, 1- to 3-septate, and constricted at the septa, and they often break into 2-celled parts. Sclerotia form along the veins. The apothecia are tough, fleshy, stipitate, shallowly cupulate, and brownish. The asci are 8-spored. The ascopores are hyaline, ovoid, unsymmetrical and swollen on one side, and average $10–13\mu \times 4–5\mu$. Spermatia are also formed in what are referred to as spermadochia.

Boyer (*164*) describes a leaf-spotting disease of hybrid and native aspens in Canada that he was able to transmit by budding and by insects. He regards it likely that it is virus-caused. Yellow lesions later become brown, sunken, and circular, with a raised, chlorotic halo. Distortion, cupping, and twisting of foliage are common symptoms. There were some macroscopic similarities to the disease caused by *Plagiostoma populi* as described by Cash and Waterman (*239*).

The Plagiostoma blight appears in September as small, scattered, reddish spots and yellowing of leaves from the tip and margin inward and between the veins on hybrids of *Populus tremuloides* and *P. grandidentata* in Massachusetts (*239*). Soon after, the entire leaf blade becomes involved, turning reddish to brown, with the veinal areas turning color last. Small, subcuticular, acervulus-like structures appear with non-germinable, subglobose, hyaline spores. Overwintered, fallen leaves produce perithecia with lateral breaks piercing the lower leaf surface. They bear asci aligned horizontally, 2- to 6-spored, mainly 4-spored, with hyaline, ellipsoid-clavate, 1-septate, unequal-celled ascospores.

Cercospora populina causes irregular leaf spots 3–7 mm. across that often coalesce. The color ranges from brown to gray. Fruiting is epiphyllous on small, dark, globular stromata. Fascicles are dense, conidiophores are non-septate, and conidia are indistinctly septate, pale olivaceous, $2–3\mu \times 15–60\mu$. It is known on *P. alba*, *P. balsamifera*, and *P. nigra italica* in Missouri, Louisiana, and Alabama (*260*).

Cercospora populicola forms circular spots 3–10 mm. across, brown to gray, and darkened by the fruiting fungus. The stromata are small, fascicles are dense, conidiophores are plainly multiseptate, and conidia are hyaline, acicular, curved, and indistinctly multiseptate, $2.5–4\mu \times 60–150\mu$. It is known in Texas on *P. delto-ides* (*260*).

There are five rusts affecting poplar foliage. All are in the genus *Melampsora*, and all have their uredo and telial stages on *Populus* spp. *M. medusae* is the most widespread, occurring from Canada to the Gulf States and west to Arizona. Its aecial stage is on *Larix* spp., but how it overwinters in the Deep South in the absence of larches is yet to be explained. The rust in the South may result from aeciospores carried south in air currents from northern larches. There is yet no evidence of overwintering uredinia in the South.

M. albertensis alternates between *Populus* spp. and *Pseudotsuga menziesii* and is confined to the northern Rocky Mountains and Canada. The II and III stages have been so aggressive in Idaho in some seasons that aspen foliage has turned yellow and dried by midsummer (*406*). Attacks can also be heavy in the southern Rocky Mountains. *M. occidentalis* also alternates between *Populus* spp. and *P. menziesii* (*1663*) and has a similar range, but it is distinguished by having much larger teliospores than *M. albertensis* has on poplar leaves. *M. abietis-canadensis* alternates between *Populus* spp. and *Tsuga canadensis* and extends from Canada to the mountains of north Georgia.

Ziller (*1668*) determined from inoculation experiments that conifers of six genera (*Abies, Larix, Picea, Pinus, Pseudotsuga,* and *Tsuga*) are susceptible to the poplar rusts of western Canada. He also suggests that *Melampsora albertensis* be reduced to synonymy with *M. medusae* because the two are indistinguishable in morphology, life history, host range, and host reaction.

The species of poplar involved in the *Melampsora* rusts do hold to a pattern as to poplar taxonomic grouping. Reference to Arthur and Cummins (*46*) is suggested for the host relationships of these poplar leaf rusts. Some of them, notably *M. medusae*, can be injurious, with some poplar hybrids contracting uniformly heavy infection of virtually all leaves by mid-July, followed by almost complete defoliation in August. Schreiner (*1262*) presents a system for rating poplars for leaf-rust infection.

The leaves of *Populus alba*, both in the East and the West, sometimes bear uredinia of the rust *Melampsora aecidioides*. Pycnia and aecia are unknown. Uredinia from primary (uredospore) infection in the spring are large and caeomoid. Later they are small, round, and aecidioid (*46*).

The powdery mildew caused by *Uncinula salicis*, which attacks many poplars (*945*) and willows, has simple, terminally hooked perithecial appendages (*1153*). Reports of it are lacking for *Populus alba* and *P. nigra* (*8*). *Erysiphe cichoracearum* is known on aspen in Utah.

A yellow-leaf blister (*Taphrina aurea* $=$ *T. populina*) has been reported repeatedly on *Populus nigra* and its var. *italica* from coast to coast in the more northerly states. *T. populi-salicis* causes similar leaf blistering of *P. trichocarpa* in Canada. Although these are the only species of *Taphrina* on *Populus* listed by Mix (*994*) for North America, he describes many others on species of *Populus* elsewhere in the world and on exotic poplars in the United States.

A leaf spot of balsam poplar, caused by a midge, could be confused with a fungus spot (see *Populus balsamifera*).

Stem Diseases.—Hypoxylon canker (*H. mammatum = H. pruinatum*) (*978*) is considered the most serious disease of aspen in the Lake States, and occurs widely from the Rocky Mountains (*345*) eastward in the United States and Canada. It is particularly damaging to *Populus tremuloides*, less so to *P. grandidentata*, and occasionally to *P. balsamifera* and *P. trichocarpa* (*100*).

Anderson (*36*) describes young cankers as first sunken, with yellowish-orange areas surrounded by irregular margins. Later the outer bark rises in blisterlike patches and sloughs off, exposing the black, crumbling cortex. Old cankers may be several feet long and are rough and blackened except for the peripheral, yellowish margin. Callus seldom has an opportunity to form. Cutting at the margins reveals the cortex as mottled black and yellow, and at the cambium white mycelial fans may be seen.

The asexual spore stage produces gray, powdery masses of one-celled, hyaline conidia on seta-like structures under the blistered bark. About 3 years later the perithecia are formed in small, crust-like stromata up to a few millimeters across. When young, they are covered with a grayish bloom. Later they turn black. The ascospores are elliptic, brown, and one-celled.

Older cankers kill by girdling. Decay that develops under cankers often leads to breakage. Trees from 15 to 40 years old are particularly susceptible regardless of crown class. The heaviest incidence of the disease is associated with poor stocking (*36*).

Gruenhagen (*553*) describes and illustrates symptoms and signs aiding in diagnosis of Hypoxylon canker, and Graham and Harrison (*528*) point out the possibility of cankers originating at injuries produced by a few specific insect species. More recent accounts of this important disease are provided by Anderson (*37*), Berbee and Rogers (*100*), and Hubbes (*719*).

Hinds and Peterson (*685*) illustrate aspen cankers in the Rocky Mountains caused by *Cenangium singulare, Ceratocystis fimbriata, Cystospora chrysosperma*, and *Hypoxylon pruinatum* (= *H. mammatum*).

Cytospora canker (*C. chrysosperma*, perfect stage *Valsa sordida*) is distinguished mainly by the black pycnidia in the dead bark of cankered stems. They exude allantoid, hyaline conidia in yellow to red, mucilaginous tendrils during moist weather. Perithecia are not often seen, except on *P. tremuloides*. They occur deeper in the bark, their ostioles typically arranged circularly around the edge of a protruding, grayish, stromatic disc. The ascospores are hyaline, allantoid, and about twice the size of the conidia. Boyce (*151*), who gives a good account of Cytospora canker, describes symptoms and signs and also mentions that *C. nivea* (*Valsa nivea*) causes a similar, but less frequently encountered, disease of poplars and willows.

Cytospora cankers may develop by the gradual killing of bark in an elliptical pattern, usually with the bark remaining attached. Girdled or partly girdled stems often put out vigorous sprouts below the canker. On larger trees with rough bark, it is not easy to recognize Cytospora cankers unless spore tendrils ooze out. Other symptoms are dead cambium with discolored, watery, smelly wood beneath. Some trees, notably of *Populus alba*, are affected more by

388

a Cytospora-caused dieback of branches than by cankers.

In general, it appears that the *Cytospora* spp. on *P. alba* cause mostly twig blight and on *P. grandidentata,* occasional twig blight. On *P. tremuloides, P. deltoides, P. balsamifera, P. nigra,* and *P. trichocarpa* they occur commonly on branches, not necessarily as primary pathogens, but sometimes able to cause cankers. Reference has already been made to the heavy cankering and killing of cottonwood (*P. deltoides*) rooted cuttings when outplanted in the Mississippi Delta.

A very good account of *Cytospora chrysosperma* its relationship to *Valsa sordida;* its symptoms, signs, description of spores and spore stages; its cultural characters and host relationships; and illustrations of cankers and fungus stages is provided by Christensen (*254*). Povah (*1131*) concluded that, while *C. chrysosperma* was a damaging pathogen to cuttings of several native poplars, it was not harmful to native *P. grandidentata* and *P. tremuloides* in New York unless it followed major injury. He found heavy killing by this fungus following fire injury. Bloomberg and Farris (*132*) have provided information on the attack of *P. trichocarpa* cuttings by *C. chrysosperma* in Canada.

One of the most widely known of the poplar cankers is caused by *Dothichiza populea.* It attacks many hybrids and all of the poplar species treated herein except for *P. balsamifera.* However, it has only attacked young planted trees and those in nurseries and has not yet been reported from the natural forest. Cankers form on twigs, trunks, and branches, mainly at wounds on young trees. The bark becomes darkened and cracked, and callus tissue forms in old cankers. Water sprouts may form below, and then die (*928*).

Dark pycnidia form in the spring in the diseased bark as numerous, hemispherical pustules about a pinhead in size, each with a hole in the top through which tiny, 1–celled, hyaline, subglobose spores $9–13\mu \times 7–9\mu$ extrude in sticky, cream- to amber-colored tendrils. Waterman (*1521*) has given an excellent account of this disease in the United States. A perfect stage has not been found in this country. Peace (*1091*) refers this latter stage in Europe to *Cryptodiaporthe populea.*

Mainly a disease of *P. nigra italica, P. deltoides, P. alba,* hybrids, and exotic poplars, *Dothichiza populea* has been reported only once from *P. tremuloides* and *P. grandidentata* (*1521*). Clones vary greatly in susceptibility. The pycnidial, conidial, and cultural characters of the causal fungi serve to distinguish the cankers caused by *Dothichiza populea, Cytospora chrysosperma,* and *Septoria musiva* (*151, 1401, 1521*).

In parts of the Rocky Mountains, two kinds of large, black cankers often occur on *P. tremuloides* (aspen). One has been referred to by Boyce (*151*) as "black canker of aspen." It is characterized by black, outrolled, flaring areas of dead bark. No fungus has been known to be associated consistently with this type of canker in the past. Recently, however, Davidson, Hinds, and Toole (*347*) report isolating a new species of *Ceratocystis, C. tremuloaurea,* from "aspen black cankers." This fungus also fruited on the cankers. A photograph of their "black canker" showing outrolled, flaring margins makes it seem highly likely that this is the black canker mentioned by Boyce (*151*) and illustrated by Meinecke (945). Davidson and his coworkers describe the new fungus.

Hinds and Davidson (683), in isolating from aspen cankers in Colorado, discovered another undescribed species of *Ceratocystis* that they named *C. populina*. Inoculations produced blue-stained lesions that, in 5 weeks, produced mature perithecia containing gelatinous masses of bean-shaped ascospores.

Another black canker has been described and well illustrated by Davidson and Cash (344) from the Central Rockies which they call sooty-bark canker and attribute to *Cenangium singulare*. It occurs mostly in stands over 60 years old, and its incidence increases with stand age and with degree of damage to aspens. Cankers may occur anywhere on the trunk, not necessarily at wounds. The bark becomes black and remains intact and firm over the canker. Vertical spread is rapid, and cankers may reach a length of 15 ft. before girdling. Some zonation may appear. Except for a few sporocarp primordia, little or no fruiting takes place until a tree dies and falls. Then, masses of small, gray apothecia form over the cankered bark. They curl into angular and hysteroid shapes, and may develop any time of year. Inoculations in Colorado have proved the pathogenicity of *C. singulare* (682). This disease has also been found in New Mexico (42).

A canker of the lower stem of young trees of *P. grandidentata*, *P. tremuloides*, and *P. balsamifera* was reported by Thompson (1399) from Ontario, Canada, as being caused by the discomycete *Neofabraea populi*. It has not been reported from the United States. Cankers may be up to 6 in. long and girdle half or more of the stem. The bark is sunken and splits vertically. Callus may or may not form. Apothecia often occupy the center of a canker, while the conidial acervuli (*Myxosporium*) occupy the marginal areas. The conidia are somewhat fusiform, with ends slightly pointed, are 1-celled, hyaline, $25–45\mu \times 4.5–5\mu$, and ooze out in pinkish masses that become whitish when dry. The apothecia are under 2 mm. in diameter, flesh colored to brown, becoming dark when dry. The ascospores are hyaline, 1- to 4-celled, and $16–22\mu \times 5–5.6\mu$.

A leaf disease of poplars was mentioned earlier as caused by *Mycosphaerella populorum* (1401), the imperfect stage of which is *Septoria musiva*. This fungus also causes cankers on some exotic species and hybrid poplars in the United States, particularly those with parentage of *Populus balsamifera, P. deltoides, P. nigra*, or *P. trichocarpa*, and it is also known in Canada and Argentina. Damage to hybrid clones in the East led to the studies, mainly by Bier (112) and Waterman (1515, 1517), on this disease, which is commonly called Septoria canker. Leaf infection precedes twig or stem infection. Pycnidia are rare on cankers; perithecia, still rarer. Secondary organisms invade rapidly; and, with the symptoms of Septoria canker not being particularly characteristic, it is not easy to distinguish this canker from those caused by *Cytospora chrysosperma* or *Nectria galligena*. However, the conidial stage of the *Cytospora* and the red perithecia of the *Nectria* are of diagnostic value, provided they are formed. The Septoria canker on highly susceptible young stems appears sunken, with smooth bark and raised margins. By the end of a growing season the spread of the mycelium produces a canker with several slightly raised, irregularly concentric rings of unbroken bark. Some cankers are flat faced, some have swollen marginal callus, and some girdle rapidly. Waterman (1515) illustrates this canker and notes that identification usually depends on finding pycnidia (see Foliage Diseases), usually in lenticels, or in isolating the *Septoria* from the cankers.

Fusarium solani causes a canker of *Populus trichocarpa* in the Lake States and Canada. Berbee (98) described the disease from a young plantation in Wisconsin. He stated that the bark first appeared watersoaked, then was followed by a soft, wet, necrosis of the bark. Later the outer bark cracked, became stringy, and dried. Some trees were girdled. He successfully inoculated *P. nigra, P. deltoides,* and some crosses, hybrids, and exotic poplars.

Dochinger (384) reported a canker of planted cottonwood and hybrid poplars in Iowa, caused by *Fusarium solani.* Symptoms included linear bark cracks, beneath which the wood was olive to pink. In many cases knot-like protuberances, 1- to 2-in. long, appeared on the stems. *F. solani* causes cankers on many hardwoods, including *Populus tremuloides,* in Canada (917), *Liriodendron,* and *Liquidambar.* See Diseases of Seedlings or Cuttings for reference to a canker by *Fusarium lateritium.*

A shoot blight, resulting in withering, blackening, and curling of new shoots, results from attack by the species of *Venturia* described under Foliage Diseases of *Populus.* It occurs either in its leaf blight or shoot blight form on all North American poplar species in the East and West, but is uncommon in the South and is rare on *P. deltoides.*

Crown gall (*Agrobacterium tumefaciens*) has been reported causing stem and branch galls of *P. alba* in several Eastern and Midwestern States and has been transmitted to *P. deltoides* and *P. trichocarpa* in Texas. The warty galls and characteristic bacteria in the tissues are of diagnostic value.

Zalasky (1648, 1649) reported that *Diplodia* (*Macrophoma*) *tumefaciens,* mentioned earlier as a cause of rough bark in aspen, also caused branch galls as well as rough bark on *P. tremuloides, P. balsamifera, P. trichocarpa, P. nigra italica,* and the Brooks hybrid. He illustrated and described the histopathology of these small stem and branch galls as they occur on *P. trichocarpa.*

The common Nectria canker (*N. galligena*), described particularly in connection with eastern species of *Acer* and *Betula,* is common in the Northeast and the Lake States on *Populus grandidentata* and *P. tremuloides,* and there are cankers on the latter in the Rocky Mountains that resemble it. The symptoms and signs as given for *Acer* and *Betula* hold in a general way for aspen, including the "target effect," bark shedding over the canker face, and the peripheral occurrence of red perithecia. Manion and French (924) illustrated Nectria cankers on aspen in Minnesota and succeeded in producing cankers by inoculating with *Nectria galligena* and also with *Ceratocystis fimbriata.* Cankers caused by the former continued to enlarge after 2 years, while those caused by the latter did not. Isolations from 92 so-called Nectria-type cankers yielded *N. galligena* only once, *C. fimbriata* 5 times, and, occasionally, other species of *Ceratocystis.* The authors have never seen perithecial fruiting by *N. galligena* on Minnesota aspen and conclude that certain diagnosis of Nectria canker in Minnesota is very difficult.

Wood and French (1612) describe the "target" canker of *P.*

tremuloides from Minnesota caused by *Ceratocystis fimbriata* that tends to retain the bark, as in the case of Strumella cankers (see *Quercus*). Also, like *Strumella*, the canker tends to be concave and, as a result, gives the stem a crook. *C. fimbriata* was cultured, and inoculations showed the isolate able to canker *P. alba* var. *pyramidalis* and to induce some reaction in several other hardwoods, including some other species of *Populus*. This disease also occurs in Pennsylvania, but it is rare there (*1611*).

Zalasky (*1650, 1651*) describes the process of infection of aspen by *Ceratocystis fimbriata* and also the morphology of the fungus as it occurs in Canada. The two types of symptoms are a leaf spot and twig dieback and a target canker of the stem. The former results from rapid infection of the young petiole, leaf trace, cortex, phloem, and cambium of the stem. The canker results from slow invasion of the older petioles and bark. The leaf spots were blackish, angular, and very irregular in shape. Zalasky (*1650*) gives the symptoms in full detail.

Dance et al. (*322*) describe a stem canker of *P. tremuloides* from Ontario, Canada, that is associated with *Pezicula ocellata*. Young trees bore single or multiple cankers on the stems. These were oval, from .25 to 2.0 in. wide, and often joined to form necrotic areas that ranged up to 4 ft. long. The canker periphery was defined by a continuous narrow ridge of yellowish-brown bark. In June and July, acervuli of the fungus appeared in concentric circles on the surface of the blackened bark within the cankers.

Filer (*441*) reports cankering of 1- to 10-year-old cottonwood trees in the Mississippi Delta by *Phomopsis macrospora*. This is the first record of this fungus in the United States. He later proved by inoculations that heavy cankering of 2- to 3-year-old planted cottonwood (*P. deltoides*) in that area was caused by each of three fungi: *Cytospora chrysosperma*, *Phomopsis macrospora*, and *Hypomyces* (*Fusarium*) *solani*. These canker fungi were most virulent in November and on trees on unfavorable sites (*443*).

Table 1 summarizes poplar canker diseases, causal organisms, hosts, and major areas of occurrence.

A good example of the problems facing the pathologist in dealing with poplar cankers is provided in a brief, illustrated account of cankering encountered in a 4,075-tree study of aspen in Colorado (*1186*). Five specific canker entities were identified; namely, Cytospora, black, sooty-bark, Hypoxylon, and "Nectria-like" cankers. Since these represent less than one-half of the kinds of poplar cankers known in North America and since many are not distinctive, the problems in diagnosis become obvious.

Bier and coworkers have published a series of papers on the relation of bark moisture, bark extracts, and bark saprophytes to the development of canker diseases of *Populus* and *Salix* spp. caused by native facultative parasites such as *Hypoxylon pruinatum* (*H. mammatum*), *Cytospora chrysosperma*, and *Septoria musiva*. This literature can be found in a number of papers (*115, 116, 117, 124*).

Table 1.—*Summary of poplar canker diseases, causal organisms, hosts, and major areas of occurrence*

Canker	Fungus	Main hosts, in decreasing order of susceptibility (approx.)	Main region
Hypoxylon canker	H. pruinatum	P. tremuloides, P. grandidentata, P. balsamifera, and P. trichocarpa	Rocky Mtns., Lake States, Canada
Cytospora canker	C. chrysosperma	P. tremuloides, P. deltoides, P. balsamifera, P. trichocarpa, P. nigra, P. grandidentata, P. alba	U.S. and Canada, general
Dothichiza canker	D. populea	P. nigra, P. deltoides, P. alba, rare on others	Widespread
Black canker	Ceratocystis tremulo-aurea	P. tremuloides mainly	Rocky Mtns.
Sooty-bark canker	Cenangium singulare	P. tremuloides mainly	Rocky Mtns.
Neofabraea canker	N. populi	P. tremuloides and P. balsamifera	Canada
Septoria canker	S. musiva	P. nigra, P. trichocarpa, P. balsamifera, P. deltoides	U.S. and Canada
Nectria canker	N. galligena	Occasional on any species	U.S. and Canada
Shoot blight	Venturia spp.	P. tremuloides and P. grandidentata mainly	Canada and Northern U.S.
Fusarium canker	F. (Hypomyces) solani	P. trichocarpa	Ontario, Canada
Fusarium canker	F. lateritium	P. trichocarpa	B.C., Canada
Ceratocystis canker	C. fimbriata	P. tremuloides	Minnesota
Pezicula canker	P. ocellata	P. tremuloides	Canada
Phomopsis canker	P. macrospora	P. deltoides	Mississippi Delta

The leafy mistletoe *Phoradendron tomentosum* subsp. *macrophyllum* (*1580*) has been reported from *Populus balsamifera* and *P. deltoides* from the Southwest. However, even though typical cottonwood prevails in the wetlands of the South, it has not proved a congenial host for the type species *Phoradendron serotinum* (*1580*).

Poplar and willows in Lake County, California, may bear mistletoe (*P. tomentosum* subsp. *macrophyllum*) that is parasitized by the imperfect fungus *Protocoronospora phoradendri* (*330*). The latter forms large, light-brown lesions, indefinite in shape, that bear erumpent, clustered acervuli with dark-brown setae, clavate conidiophores, and falcate, continuous, hyaline conidia (20–24μ $\times$ 4.5–6.5μ) that are creamy white in mass.

Vascular Diseases.—The poplars are notably susceptible to a condition known as wetwood. Hartley, Davidson, and Crandall (*603*) give a general review of wetwood as it occurs in many species of conifers and hardwoods. Among some genera, including *Ulmus, Populus,* and *Salix,* there are species in which wetwood is the rule rather than the exception. Typically, wetwood is a condition of the central cylinder in which the wood is not only high in moisture, but is darker than normal and has a pH on the alkaline side. In some species of *Salix* and *Ulmus* specific bacteria have been responsible for some wetwood conditions. Many poplar species, whether growing as ornamental or forest trees, are known to develop a wetwood condition, including *P. alba, P. balsamifera, P. deltoides, P. grandidentata, P. nigra, P. tremuloides,* and *P. trichocarpa.*

In the case of the Lombardy poplar (*P. nigra* var. *italica*), wetwood bacterial infection produces a disease characterized by a water-soaked appearance of the trunk wood and a darkening to brownish red in an irregular pattern in cross section. A fermentation odor may become noticeable. Fluxing and gas evolution may develop if xylem elements are severed. Branches die, and entire trees often die prematurely. In much of the South, Lombardy poplars cannot be grown beyond an age of 15 years before succumbing, largely as a result of wetwood. Normal sap pH ranges between 5.5 and 6.5, while the sap of wetwood areas ranges between 7.5 and 8.5. Seliskar (*1272*) has intensively studied wetwood in Lombardy poplar and has isolated and named *Corynebacterium humiferum,* a non-motile, Gram-positive rod, as the cause. In the North and West, Lombardy poplars appear to tolerate wetwood longer since, although most of the trees normally carry this infection, they can grow to large size and old age before dying of wetwood with or without the complications of several canker diseases that also beset the species. Seliskar (*1272*) infected *P. tremuloides* with his isolates of *C. humiferum* from *P. nigra.*

The high gas pressure often encountered while increment-boring cottonwoods and some other poplars is one of the manifestations of a bacterial wetwood condition. Toole (*1430*) reports that in 13 stands along the Mississippi River between Vicksburg and Memphis, 86 percent of the cottonwoods over 6 in. in diameter contained wetwood. Wetwood had a higher moisture content and higher pH than normal sapwood. Gas pressure in wetwood trees was as high as 25.5 p.s.i. A rod-shaped, Gram-negative bacterium was consistently isolated from wetwood. Toole does not say whether or not he regards this to be Seliskar's *Corynebacterium humiferum*.

The species of *Populus* contract none of the common vascular wilt diseases, such as those caused by species of *Verticillium, Fusarium, Cephalosporium,* or *Ceratocystis.*

Root Diseases and Mycorrhizae.—An oddity of the pathology of the genus *Populus* is the paucity of reports on root diseases of poplars. Except for occasional reports of *Armillaria mellea* on *P. balsamifera* on the West Coast and Schmitz and Jackson's (*1255*) mention of this fungus causing some root and butt rot of aspen in Minnesota, root rot as a field disease of poplars has not often been noted. However, many of Basham's (*65*) butt-rot fungi of *P. trichocarpa* in Canada doubtless invade roots.

In inoculation tests in Texas (*1379*), four poplar species proved moderately to highly susceptible to attack by *Phymatotrichum omnivorum*. These were *P. balsamifera, P. nigra, P. deltoides,* and *P. canadensis.* The plains poplar, *P. sargentii,* has been used to some extent as a shelterbelt tree in the Southwest. However, when almost 7,000 trees planted in the Texas root-rot belt sustained a 3.3 percent loss in 6 years from *Phymatotrichum omnivorum,* the species was classed by Wright and Wells (*1627*) as "susceptible to root rot (not usable on any soil type)."

Although there have been a few reports of nematodes on roots and within the root zone of North American trees in the genus *Populus,* mostly from New York, New Jersey, Utah, and Canada, the number is small considering the wide distribution and the large number of species of *Populus.* No noteworthy damage to American poplars is known to be due to nematodes (*1222*). However, Ruehle (*1224*) lists 7 species of nematodes, in 6 genera, that are associated with cottonwood in South Carolina.

Only a few mycorrhizal associations have been reported for named American species of *Populus* (*1442*), as follows: *Cenococcum graniforme* on *P. balsamifera, P. canadensis, P. deltoides, P. nigra, P. tremuloides,* and *P. trichocarpa; Tuber borchii* on *P. canadensis; Lepista nuda* on *P. deltoides* and *P. nigra; Leccinum aurantiacum* and *L. scabrum* on *P. tremuloides;* and *Amanita muscaria, Boletus edulis,* and *Hebeloma crustuliniforme* on *P. trichocarpa.*

Trunk Rots.—Anyone faced for the first time with the large number of leaf diseases and cankers of poplars might wonder that these trees grow as well as they do and are such valuable economic assets. Poplars, in general, can flourish because many of these diseases are localized geographically and because some strike certain poplars but not others. Thus, we find handsome stands of large aspens in the Rockies, a great acreage of large, fast-grown cottonwoods in the Mississippi Delta, and a predominance of young aspen in the Lake States that feed the pulp mills of that area.

Many of the diseases already mentioned (for example, Hypoxylon canker) are very important, but aspen's biggest enemy is the heartrot caused by *Fomes igniarius.* In the Lake States and the Northeast this fungus is the principal factor responsible for the short economic life, often only 40 to 50 years, of so many stands of *Populus tremuloides* and, to a lesser extent, *P. grandidentata.*

The importance of *Fomes igniarius* to aspen was soon recognized, and Meinecke (*945*), as early as 1929, wrote a technical bulletin,

Quaking Aspen, a Study in Applied Forest Pathology, in which *F. igniarius* accounted for most of the loss and concerning which Meinecke wrote, *"Fomes igniarius* follows aspen throughout its range, and everywhere heavy loss goes with it."

The principal decay fungi of aspen are well described in standard texts (*81, 151*). In addition to *F. igniarius,* which makes up most of the aspen cull nationwide, *F. applanatus* and *Armillaria mellea* are important. In the Lake States the latter two cause only limited butt rot originating at wounds. In a Colorado study *Collybia velutipes* caused most of the butt rot in aspen (*346*), and *Pholiota squarrosa* has also been shown capable of causing butt rot. In the Rocky Mountains, *F. applanatus* ranks as a major decay fungus of aspen.

The conks of *F. igniarius* on aspen are distinctively hoof shaped, and it is not unusual for many to appear on a single tree, forming at old branch traces. A Minnesota study (*709*) showed that a small conk on aspen indicated from 2 to 2.5 linear feet of decayed wood and a large conk 2.8 to 5.0 ft. above and below the conk. Obviously, it would take few conks to indicate total cull for a small aspen. Many cull studies have been run on aspen; depending upon the region, aspen cull, due mainly to *F. igniarius,* may limit the economic rotation age to 40, 60, 90, or 130 years (see section on *P. tremuloides*).

The conks of *Fomes igniarius* on aspen are so distinctive that many authors have used for this form the variety name *populinus* (*174, 1175*). Sometimes this fungus forms punk knots instead of conks at branch stubs, and sometimes it fails to give any evidence of fruiting, even after causing much rot. Silverborg (*1305*) reported and illustrated sterile conks of *F. igniarius* on aspen in New York. They resembled the sterile conks of *Poria obliqua* on birch.

Roll-Hansen (*1191*), in Norway, compared *Phellinus (Fomes) igniarius* with *P. tremulae,* both on European aspen (*Populus tremula*) and on other hardwoods. He concluded that the common hoof-shaped form on aspen in Europe and North America that has in the past generally been considered a variety of *F. igniarius,* is a distinct species, *Phellinus (Fomes) tremulae.* He based his conclusions on: (1) antagonism between the two fungi in culture, (2) differences in growth rate and appearance, (3) differences in fruit-bodies, (4) difference in mean size of basidiospores. Nevertheless, in view of the extensive North American literature in which *P. tremulae* is called *F. igniarius,* the latter name is used in this current account.

Riley (*1175*) studied the biology of *F. igniarius* in Canada on the two aspen species, adding information on sporulation, inoculation, symptoms, cull and net increment in relation to age and site, and other phases of attack on aspen by this fungus.

Basham (*68*) also studied aspen decay (mainly by *F. igniarius*) in Canada and determined gross, net, and decay volumes, entrance points and external indications of decay, relationships of decay to site, and other factors. His mention of a "yellow stringy trunk rot" and a "brown or yellow stringy butt rot" indicates that some fungi other than *F. igniarius* were involved in his decay cases. In an earlier study Basham (*65*) had shown that, while *F. igniarius* caused most trunk rot, a yellow, stringy trunk rot was caused by *Radulum caesarium;* and stringy butt rots yielded, in culture, mostly *Pholiota spectabilis, Armillaria mellea, Radulum caesarium, P. adiposa,* and *Collybia velutipes.* Many other hymenomycetes were isolated occasionally from aspen rots. In addition, two heartwood stains, one brown and the other mottled red, appeared; isolation yielded *Corticium polygonium* and two imperfect fungi, *Libertella* sp. and *Phialophora alba.*

In an Ontario cull survey the rot-cull percentage did not reach 26 percent until age 140 and over. Stains contributed to the total defect deduction of 42 percent at that age. Twenty-five hymenomycetes were isolated more than once from the rots, with 70 percent of the rot caused by *Radulum caesarium, Fomes igniarius* var. *populinus,* and *Corticium (Cryptochaeta) polygonium (73).*

Brown (*179*) worked out a method for estimating the cull percentage due to heartrot in Minnesota aspen and concluded that diameter alone was as useful a measure of decay-cull percentage as any other of the factors studied.

Good and Nelson (*518*) isolated many organisms from the wood of aspen trees being decayed or stained by *F. igniarius.* Most of these "other" fungi were widely distributed in the trees, with no consistent association with any stage of decay. Up to 36 different fungi were isolated from certain decay zones, and bacteria were isolated from every zone. Water extracts of the wood from different zones ranged from pH 3.8 to 9.4, the high values indicating a bacterial wetwood reaction (*603*). In this connection Shigo (*1290*) studied the fungi surrounding and in advance of rot columns of *Fomes igniarius* in living trees, including both of the aspens. He found that a high pH wetwood zone surrounded the columns, and several nonhymenomycetous fungi and certain bacteria colonized the surrounding area. The fungi were mostly species of *Phialophora, Trichocladium,* and *Acrostaphylus.*

While *F. igniarius* is the single most important heartrot fungus attacking the aspens, it is seldom mentioned as a major cause of decay among the other species of *Populus* in North America. Thomas and Podmore (*1394*), studying decay in *P. trichocarpa* in British Columbia, report that although 70 species of fungi were associated with decay, only six caused significant loss in living trees. Two of these, *Polyporus delectans* and *Pholiota destruens,* caused 92 percent of this loss. They describe the sporophores and associated decays of some of these fungi and indicate their importance.

Among six trunk-rot fungi rotting aspen in Colorado, *Cryptochaeta polygonia* caused most of the infections, but much less rot volume than *F. igniarius* (*346*).

The Index of Plant Diseases in the United States (*8*) reports some decay fungi occasionally attacking the wood of living poplars as follows: On *P. tremuloides* group—*Fomes connatus, F. fomentarius, F. pinicola,* and *Polyporus dryophilus;* on *P. deltoides* group —*F. applanatus* (common), and *Pleurotus ostreatus;* on *P. balsamifera* group—*F. annosus* (West), *F. applanatus, F. connatus,* and *F. igniarius;* on *P. trichocarpa* group—*Armillaria mellea* (West), *F. applanatus, F. igniarius, Pholiota adiposa,* and *P. destruens.*

Fungi mentioned by Overholts (*1067*) as capable of causing either rot of the central cylinder or rot at wounds of living *Populus* spp. include, in North America, *Daedalea ambigua, Fomes applanatus, F. everhartii, F. geotropus, Polyporus cuticularis, P. glomeratus, P. squamosus, P. zonalis, P. farlowii* and *P. munzii.*

Berbee (*99*) lists most of the heartrot and other wood-rot fungi known to attack species of *Populus* in the world.

Miscellaneous Pathology.—The poplars are subject to stains of the wood in living trees, caused by many hymenomycetes, ascomycetes, fungi imperfecti, and bacteria. Some of these stains are mentioned in the section on trunk rots. There is also a pink stain of cottonwood (*P. deltoides*) caused by *Graphium rubrum.* The stains of poplar wood products are discussed by Scheffer and Lindgren (*1252*).

"Rough bark" of aspen has already been described in the discussion of the silvical characteristics of *P. tremuloides,* and rough bark of balsam poplar was described under *P. balsamifera.*

The Lake States Forest Experiment Station of the Forest Service, U. S. Department of Agriculture, has put out a series of 21 reports on the properties and uses of aspen. Report No. 19, by Kaufert (*774*), deals with the preservative treatment of aspen. He discusses the rapid decay of untreated aspen, several fungi that rot aspen in service, and service records for aspen fence posts treated with different materials and by different methods, thus providing a general guide to the use of aspen where it is exposed to decay.

A deformity of the catkins of many species of poplar, including *Populus alba, P. deltoides, P. grandidentata, P. tremuloides,* and *P. trichocarpa,* is caused by *Taphrina johansonii.* This fungus causes golden-yellow enlargements of the carpels. The characteristics of the asci and the confusion between this species and *T. aurea* (which causes a leaf blister of some species of *Populus*) are discussed by Mix (*994*).

Merrill and French (*952*) demonstrated, using aspen matchsticks as a substrate, that an *Alternaria* sp. isolated from decayed fiberboard and a *Penicillium* sp. isolated from decayed paper could cause up to a 13 percent weight loss in 6 months. There were losses in holocellulose and in alpha cellulose, caused by these "soft rot" fungi.

Cherry
Prunus spp.

The genus *Prunus* consists of about 175 species of trees and shrubs worldwide and is important largely for the horticultural and ornamental species and varieties it embraces. It includes cherry, peach, plum, prune, apricot, almond, sloe, and other species, varieties, and cultivars. There are about 25 species native to the United States, and many of these reach tree size. However, only the wild black cherry, *Prunus serotina,* is important as a forest tree (*468*).

Since so many species of *Prunus* are small orchard trees of little or no importance for forest or shade use, only four representative species will be dealt with in this account. These are *Prunus avium,* a sweet cherry of Europe and Asia that is widely grown in the United States; *P. caroliniana,* the Carolina laurel-cherry, a small

Coastal Plain tree native to the Southeast; *P. pensylvanicum,* a small, commonly defective tree that is a pioneer on burned, logged, and abandoned land in much of the Northeast; and *P. serotina,* a valuable forest hardwood.

Information on the diseases of the major species of *Prunus* that are used for orchard purposes is readily available from State and Federal agricultural extension sources. In addition, Westcott (*1555*) provides a ready reference to the diseases of peach, plum, and other *Prunus* spp. For information on the many virus diseases of these stone fruits, including excellent color photographs, the handbook Virus Diseases and Other Disorders with Viruslike Symptoms of Stone Fruits in North America (*1457*) is an excellent source.

Prunus avium, called mazzard or common sweet cherry, is a native of Europe and Asia that has escaped cultivation and is now naturalized locally in southeastern Canada and the Eastern United States to Florida. It is cultivated in the East, the Lake States, and the Far West. It is the most common of the exotic cherries now found in a wild state. The mazzard can be distinguished from the sour cherry by its larger, sweeter fruit, its glabrous foliage, and the much larger size of the tree (*274*). The mazzard grows up to 75 ft. and has a pyramidal crown, compared with the low-spreading crown of the sour cherry. The oblong-obovate leaves are also wider than those of the sour cherry. On older trunks it is normal for the bark to peel off in strips, exposing the light-colored inner bark.

Prunus mahaleb, called mahaleb or St. Lucie cherry, is a small tree closely related to *P. avium.* It is sometimes used as an understock and sometimes as an ornamental. The diseases of the two species are here considered together.

Foliage Diseases.—The most common and most damaging leaf disease is the leaf spot and shot hole caused by *Coccomyces hiemalis* (see *Prunus pensylvanicum*). Also important is the bacterium *Xanthomonas pruni,* which causes a black leaf spot, a canker, and gummosis of the stem (see *P. caroliniana*).

There are several minor leaf spots as follows: *Cercospora circumscissa* (see *Prunus caroliniana*), which may be the imperfect stage of *Mycosphaerella cerasella,* a common spot fungus in the South; *Coryneum carpophilum,* a shot-hole fungus of the West; and *Phyllosticta pruni-avium* in the Northwest. Shaw (*1278*) provides references to descriptions of these western fungi. With respect to *M. cerasella,* Jenkins (*755*), who gives an illustrated acount of its morphology and life history, states that it reaches important proportions in North Carolina. She illustrates the imperfect stage, which she calls *Cercospora cerasella,* a name considered by Chupp (*260*) to be a synonym of *C. circumscissa.*

Among the fungus leaf diseases two others, not in the leaf-spot category, are common on sweet cherry; namely, the rust *Tranzschelia pruni-spinosae* and the powdery mildew *Podosphaera oxyacanthae.* See *P. pensylvanicum* for annotations to these fungi.

Sweet cherry is subject to a large number of virus diseases, almost all of which produce symptoms in foliage, but which also are largely systemic. So far as is known, they are mainly diseases of cherry trees in cultivation as an orchard crop. They include albino cherry, buckskin, crinkle-leaf, deep-suture, mosaic, mottle-leaf, rasp leaf, rusty mottle, twisted leaf, veinclearing, and western X-disease, all in the West; and prune dwarf, peach necrotic leaf spot, and tatter leaf in the East. The diagnosis of many of these diseases is very difficult and requires time and special horticultural techniques. Anyone not familiar with the stone-fruit virus diseases should make use of the excellent U.S. Department of Agriculture handbook on the subject (*1457*). Deficiencies, such as the littleleaf condition in the West caused by lack of zinc; and excesses, such as the chlorosis in the Southwest caused by alkali soil, are also discussed in this volume.

Stem Diseases.—There are several important shoot and stem diseases of sweet cherry. In both East and West the bacterium *Pseudomonas syringae* causes a canker, gummosis, and shoot blight. Some bacterial blighting and fruit rot of sweet cherry can be caused by *Erwinia amylovora,* the fire-blight organism (see *Malus pumila*). In *Pseudomonas* the characteristics of the bacteria are: Gram-negative, non-sporing, long rods, motile with polar flagella; in *Erwinia* (*Bacterium*): Gram-negative, non-sporing, short rods with blunt ends, and generally motile with peritrichous flagella. Dowson (*392*) recognizes the cherry and plum form of *Pseudomonas syringae* in Europe as forma specialis *prunicola*. Lesions appear in the spring as sunken areas with gummosis. Cracks and cankering follow, and girdling is the end result. The foliage becomes yellowed, curled, and withered. Wet spring weather can result in shoot blight and in a small, angular leaf spot of the foliage. There are simple stains for use in determining the bacteria (*194*).

Another important bacterial disease affecting sweet cherry is crown gall. Warty masses or galls may form at the root collar or anywhere on the stem. When transmitted on pruning tools, galls may appear at a large proportion of the pruning wounds. This disease is caused by *Agrobacterium tumefaciens* and is illustrated in all standard texts and manuals on plant pathology (*619, 1503, 1555*).

Black knot (*Dibotryon morbosum*) is a very conspicuous and common disease of most species of *Prunus,* including sweet cherry and pin cherry (see *P. pensylvanicum*). The notorious brown-rot fungi *Monilinia fructicola* and *M. laxa* (see *P. caroliniana*) cause mainly a fruit rot, but their blossom-blight phase can extend down the pedicel into the green shoot.

In California, collar rot and trunk cankers can result from attack by *Phytophthora cactorum* or *P. citrophthora. P. cactorum* cankers are described under *Arbutus, Cornus*, and *Acer; P. citrophthora* cankers are described under *Citrus*.

The disease known as silver leaf, caused by infection of the wood by *Stereum purpureum,* results in the development of an ashy or leaden cast to the foliage. The foliage symptoms appear quite remote from the bark and xylem infections. The disease is described under *Malus*.

A witches' brooming of sweet cherry results from infection by *Taphrina cerasi*. Members of the genus *Prunus* are preferred hosts to many species of *Taphrina* (*994*). *T. cerasi* causes a leaf curl with some thickening, and it induces brooming by having perennial mycelium in the twigs. It occurs on many *Prunus* species

400

and is common in Europe and Asia as well as North America.

Septobasidium retiforme forms brown felts over scale insects on branches of sweet cherry in the South (*292*).

Root and Trunk Rots.—*Armillaria mellea* in the West and *Xylaria mali* in Virginia have been reported to cause root rots of living sweet cherry trees. *A. mellea* is annotated under *Citrus* and *X. mali,* under *Malus.*

A species of *Pratylenchus,* one of the lesion nematodes, has been reported attacking roots in Oregon. They are vagrant nematodes that enter and leave roots both as larvae and as adults. In Europe both *P. pratensis* and *P. penetrans* attack the root cortex of *Prunus avium* (*259*).

Virtually nothing is known of mycorrhizal relations in the genus *Prunus.*

The mazzard proved highly susceptible to Texas root rot in inoculation tests (*1379*).

Carolina laurelcherry
Prunus caroliniana

This small tree, sometimes given the generic name *Laurocerasus* or *Padus* or the common name cherry-laurel, is an evergreen confined to the Atlantic Coastal Plain, mainly from Virginia to northern Florida, on light soils on banks and bluffs near streams. It also grows along the Gulf Coast from Florida to Texas. It is a beautiful tree and is used often in the eastern Coastal Plains and in California as an ornamental (*274*). It has white flowers and black fruits and can grow 30 ft. in height and a foot in diameter. It has been recommended by the California Association of Park Administrators as suitable for parkway planting in the Southwest (*947*).

In the Southeast the most common disease is the bacterial leaf and fruit spot caused by *Xanthomonas pruni* (*392*). It also results in raised and elongated lesions on the shoots. A shot-hole effect is produced on foliage, and cankers may form on branches. The terete or elliptic bacteria have one polar flagellum, and they may be seen by crushing the leaf-spot tissue and applying a suitable quick stain (*194*).

Also in the Southeast, occasional spotting has been observed with which one of the following fungi has been associated:

● *Auerswaldiella puccinioides,* a dothidiaceous ascomycete with a superficial, multiloculate, dark stroma within which 8-spored asci bear single-celled, dark spores.

● *Cercospora cladosporioides,* a fungus which attacks only *Olea europaea,* according to Chupp (*260*), but has been reported repeatedly from laurelcherry in the Deep South (*8*). Spots are lacking or indistinct, fruiting is hypophyllous, effuse, and olivaceous. The long conidia are almost hyaline, 1- to 5-septate, with ends rounded bluntly, and average 4–6μ × 25–65μ.

● *Cercospora circumscissa,* leaf spots distinct and circular, 0.5–5 mm. across, ranging from uniform, bright red-brown to a gray center with an almost black margin. Shot hole is common. Fruiting is mainly hypophyllous. Conidia are olivaceous, obclavate, tip often acute, sometimes curved, 1- to 7-septate (mostly 3), and 2.5–5μ × 30–115μ. Chupp (*260*) states that the Cercosporas on *Prunus* are difficult to classify because they are so often overrun by species of *Alternaria, Helminthosporium, Heterosporium,* and fungi of other genera. However, *C. circumscissa* can be distinguished by its non-clavate, long conidiophores and the dimensions and septation of the conidia. Jenkins (*755*) illustrates and describes this fungus from North Carolina under the names *C. cerasella* for the conidial stage and *Mycosphaerella cerasella* for the perithecial stage.

Some minor leaf spots have been attributed to *Coccomyces lutescens* in Mississippi, to *Phyllachora beaumontii* in Alabama, to *Phyllosticta laurocerasi* in California and Florida, and to *Septoria ravenelii* in South Carolina (*8*).

A shoot and twig blight, but mainly a fruit rot, is caused mainly by *Monilinia fructicola* east of the Rocky Mountains and by the very similar *M. laxa* on the Pacific Coast. An earlier perfect-stage name of *M. fructicola* is *Sclerotinia fructicola,* and this fungus is distinct from *S. fructigena* in Europe. All three fungi cause the common disease known as the brown rot of stone fruits. Westcott (*1555*) gives a particularly clear account of this disease, which affects peach, plum, cherry, apricot, almond, and occasionally apple and pear. Flowers turn brown and rot in moist weather. Discoloration may extend from calyx cup to pedicel. Leaf and twig blight, and occasionally cankering, may result. The fruit rot is the common soft rot of stone fruits that spreads rapidly through the fruit, leaving the rotted surface covered with gray to brownish sporodochia. The single-celled, hyaline conidia are borne in chains on the sporodochia. Such fruit, left on the ground over winter, may mummify and produce brown apothecia in the spring. Whetzel (*1559*) provides descriptions of the genera of the Sclerotiniaceae, in which *Monilinia* and *Sclerotinia* fall. He also illustrates many apothecial stages, and provides species synonymy and references to descriptions of species. He lists *M. laxa* as one of the many synonyms of *M. cydoniae.*

Death of laurelcherry in California has been attributed to Verticillium wilt (*V. albo-atrum*). This disease is annotated under *Acer saccharum.* It is an important cause of mortality in a wide range of ornamental trees, fruit trees, and bush fruits. It is typified by a dark ring or partial ring, involving the last annual ring and sometimes others; and by wilting, dwarfing of foliage, and premature coloration and leaf fall. This disease in fruit trees can result in additional discoloration of the wood, leading to the term "black heart."

The leafy eastern mistletoe *Phoradendron serotinum* has been reported on laurelcherry from Florida.

Rhoads (*1168*) lists the laurelcherry as commonly attacked by Clitocybe root rot (*C. tabescens*) in Florida (see *Casuarina*). It is also a host of *Phytophthora cinnamoni* (*303*).

In Texas tests the laurelcherry appeared only moderately susceptible to Texas root rot (*1379*).

Pin cherry
Prunus pensylvanica

The pin cherry, fire cherry, or wild red cherry is mainly a small tree of the Northeast and Canada. It occurs from Newfoundland to

British Columbia in Canada. In the United States it extends southward through New England and New York to Pennsylvania, and at high elevations into the southern Appalachian Mountains. It also occurs in Iowa, Michigan, Illinois, and Indiana. It is intolerant and fastgrowing, and it often completely takes over a burned-over area. It is both a pioneer and a temporary species, with a very short life. It seldom attains a diameter of 12 in., although larger specimens occur in the Great Smoky Mountains. Its many diseases are a factor in the short life of the pin cherry. A variety *saximontana* (*1154*) has coarser, broader, and more serrate leaves than the type species, and a Rocky Mountain form is common in Manitoba, the Flathead Lake Region of Montana, northern Wyoming, and into Colorado.

The most common of the leaf diseases is the cherry leaf spot caused by *Coccomyces hiemalis*. On some other species of *Prunus* its counterpart, *C. lutescens,* produces virtually the same disease. The spots are first purplish and then brown; then they usually fall out, producing the very characteristic shot-hole effect that makes this disease easy to diagnose. The shot-holing alone would not be serious, but yellowing and premature leaf fall accompany it. Small, disc-shaped apothecia form on the infected fallen leaves in the spring, and these break through a star-like opening. Primary infection is by ascospores and secondary infection, by conidia that form in whitish masses on the leaf spots in moist weather during the summer. Repeated attacks reduce the vigor of trees. The conidial stage is a *Cylindrosporium* sp. that produces elongate, 1–septate conidia. Heald (*619*) gives a good, illustrated account of this disease and the fungi that cause it; namely, *Coccomyces hiemalis* on *Prunus avium, P. cerasus, P. mahaleb,* and *P. pensylvanicum;* and *C. lutescens* on *P. mahaleb, P. serotina,* and *P. virginiana.*

Other leaf spots on pin cherry, none of which are important, are caused by *Cercospora circumscissa* (see *Prunus caroliniana*), *Coryneum carpophilum,* and three species of *Phyllosticta* (*8*).

The foliage is often whitened by the powdery mildew *Podosphaera oxyacanthae* and its var. *tridactyla.* The perithecia contain a single ascus, and the perithecial appendages are dichotomously branched. Reed (*1153*) separates the species from its variety on the basis of the species having spreading, equatorially-inserted appendages, while the variety has somewhat erect appendages arising from near the apex of the perithecium.

The rust *Tranzschelia pruni-spinosae* (II, III) occurs on the foliage. The very coarsely verrucose, otherwise *Puccinia*-like teliospores are characteristic. The Cummins supplement to Arthur (*46*) should be consulted regarding varietal separation in this fungus.

Taphrina cerasi causes a leaf curl, with slight thickening and witches' brooms on several species of *Prunus,* including pin cherry (*994*). Although *Taphrina insititiae* has been reported to cause brooming of pin cherry in several states, Mix (*994*) takes issue with this, stating that the latter fungus attacks *Prunus* species that are not closely related to pin cherry and that it causes twig malformations not resembling brooms.

Certainly one of the most widespread and commonly-observed diseases of pin cherry is black knot (*Dibotryon morbosum*). Elongated, rough, black galls up to 2 in. across appear abundantly on affected twigs and on branches. Early in the spring a swelling appears on a shoot and becomes progressively darker. By summer the excrescence takes on a pale-green tinge, followed by the formation of an olive-green, velvety pile over the surface of the gall. Soon this disappears and the knot blackens. Single-celled conidia form on the velvety pile, and perithecia develop later on the blackened stromatic overgrowth. Heald (*619*) gives a good illustrated account of black knot.

Although little has been reported on the virus diseases of pin cherry, two diseases have been transmitted to pin cherry seedlings by budding or grafting. One is sour cherry yellows (*Chlorogenus cerasae*), and the other is necrotic ring spot. The symptoms depend upon the species of *Prunus*, the point in time during the growing season, and other factors (*1457*).

In New England the common hardwood Nectria canker (*N. galligena*) occurs on pin cherry. Its bark-free "target" aspect, resulting from killed callus folds, and the peripheral fruiting by red perithecia are characteristic (see *Betula alleghaniensis*). *Nectria cinnabarina*, called coral spot, has been associated with dieback of pin cherry, but it is probably in a secondary role, being almost entirely a saprobe on native hardwood forest trees. Its large, coral-colored sporodochia are useful for identification.

Armillaria mellea has been reported attacking species of *Prunus* related to pin cherry in the Northwest, but no records of primary root rots of pin cherry have been found.

Extensive trunk rot of living pin cherry in the East has been caused by *Fomes pomaceus* (*F. fulvus*) (*1067*). The decay is of the delignifying type, the wood becoming soft, stringy, and discolored brown, with flecks and streaks.

Black cherry
Prunus serotina

Black cherry is the largest of the *Prunus* species in North America and the only one of commercial importance as a timber tree. Its range extends from Nova Scotia to central Florida and west to a line from central Minnesota to east Texas, except for the Mississippi Delta. Within this extensive range several varieties occur that are characteristic of certain areas. Thus, the Deep South has a var. *alabamensis*, the Edwards Plateau of Texas has var. *rufula*, and the Southwest has var. *salicifolia*. Rehder (*1154*) recognizes six varieties.

The silvical characteristics of black cherry were described by Hough and revised and published by Fowells (*468*). While the species and its varieties occur on soils ranging from semiarid in the Southwest to cold and wet in Maine, black cherry sites are typically cool and moist. The common associated species, namely white pine, northern red oak, white ash, hemlock, and the northern hardwoods, indicate its site preference.

The very high value put on black cherry as a furniture and panel wood has stimulated interest in promoting it in silvicultural operations, especially from southern New England to Pennsylvania and West Virginia and through the southern Appalachian Mountains. Since defect is a matter of major loss in such a valuable wood; the pathology of black cherry has taken on special significance.

Black cherry seedlings make very good early growth and tolerate shade for a few years, but later the tree must be classed as intolerant (*54*). It will not stand flooding; of 39 species studied in a Tennessee flood test, black cherry was the most sensitive to high water (*583*). It is also very sensitive to fire. Flowering later than cultivated cherries, it takes a late spring frost to harm the flowers. Black cherry of intermediate ages, tending to extend above its associated hardwoods, is prone to storm damage. Thus, Downs (*390*) found, following a severe glaze storm in Pennsylvania, that only small percentages of the hemlock, beech, birch, and maple were badly damaged, while 41 percent of the black cherry was so injured (see *Acer saccharum*). This tendency to storm damage also exposes black cherry to considerable infection by top-rot fungi.

The leaves, twigs, and bark of black cherry contain cyanic acid, and wilted foliage is poisonous to domestic livestock. Deer feed on unwilted foliage without harm (*468*).

Seedling Diseases.—Since black cherry is the only cherry that is a valuable timber tree, it is the only one of the *Prunus* species raised as forest nursery stock. There are, however, some species, such as *P. armenica* or varieties, that are used to some extent for shelterbelt planting in the Great Plains States (*1*). Davis et al. (*360*) mention that cherry leaf spot, which in the case of black cherry is caused by *Coccomyces lutescens* rather than *C. hiemalis*, can cause severe damage (see *C. hiemalis* on *P. pensylvanicum*). In Pennsylvania, *C. lutescens* is reported to assume importance in the reproduction of black cherry on the Allegheny Plateau (*1640*). They also report heavy attacks of powdery mildew (*Podosphaera oxyacanthae*, at some nurseries—see *Prunus pensylvanicum*) and refer to occasional damage to wild cherries from *Bacterium* (*Xanthomonas*) *pruni*. Since the wild black cherry is not reported as a host to this organism, their attacks must refer to other species of *Prunus*.

A seedling blight in several Eastern States is caused by *Monilinia rhododendri* (*M. seaveri*). The disease is similar to that caused by *M. fructicola* (see *P. caroliniana*), but some mycological aspects of the fungus are different (*1559*).

Black cherry forms a taproot and firm laterals, giving it a good competitive position when young and contributing to height growth up to 2.5 ft. the first year.

Foliage Diseases.—Many of the black cherry leaf diseases are annotated under other cherry species. These are as follows: *Coccomyces lutescens*, shot hole and spot, see *P. pensylvanicum; Monilinia fructicola*, brown rot and spot, see *P. caroliniana; Mycosphaerella cerasella*, spot, see *P. avium; Podosphaera oxyacanthae*, powdery mildew, see *P. pensylvanicum; Tranzschelia pruni-spinosae*, rust, see *P. pensylvanicum*.

There are a few other leaf diseases reported for black cherry. *Cercospora graphioides* is easily recognized because of its coremoid fascicles (*260*). *Phyllosticta serotina* produces typical spermatioid pycnidia and spores. *Taphrina farlowii* (*994*) causes a leaf thickening and curl and malforms shoots, but does not form witches' brooms. *Tranzschelia arthuri* is a rust described from

Iowa and Michigan that has been segregated from *T. pruni-spino-sae* and is cited by Cummins (*46*).

Stem Diseases.—Many of the stem diseases have also been annotated under other cherry species. These are as follows: *Dibotryon morbosum*, black knot, see *P. pensylvanicum; Monilinia fructicola* and *M. rhododendri*, shoot blight and brown rot, see *P. caroliniana; Nectria galligena*, canker, see *P. pensylvanicum; Phorandendron serotinum*, mistletoe, see *P. caroliniana*.

In addition, twig blight and dieback have been attributed to *Diaporthe pruni* in the North and to *Valsa leucostoma* in the South. The latter fungus is known on pome and stone fruit trees throughout Europe, Australia, and North America, but it has been generally considered hardly more than a secondary parasite on black cherry. Its attack was described as largely confined to twigs that are either senescent or have been injured by hail, cold, or other agents. The perithecia are within a strongly convex stroma, 2–3 mm. thick, and are whitish and granular within. Ascospores are biseriate, allantoid, hyaline, $9–12\mu \times 2–2.5\mu$. The conidia (*Cytospora leucostoma* = *C. rubescens*) are formed in an erumpent, reddish stroma and are allantoid and only 4μ in length (*1352*).

Gross (*548*) states that *Cytospora* (*Valsa*) *leucostoma* causes cankers responsible for widespread branch mortality of black cherry in Pennsylvania. He established proof of pathogenicity on *Prunus pensylvanicum* and *P. serotina*. Common infection courts are decaying fruit racemes and bark fissures caused by excessive gum production following passage of the larvae of *Phytobia pruni*, a cambium mining insect.

Root and Trunk Rots.—Several basidiomycetes can rot the root wood of living black cherry trees, but none have been reported capable of killing trees. All have the capacity to grow into and cause decay in the butts of the trees. These are *Armillaria mellea*, *Coniophora cerebella*, *Polyporus berkeleyi*, *P. dryophilus*, *P. spraguei*, and *P. sulphureus*. Lorenz and Christensen (*887*) considered *A. mellea* as causing a common root rot of black cherry in the Lake States. In addition to these root and butt fungi, many other fungi are able to cause heartrot of the main trunk. These include *Fomes fomentarius* and *F. pinicola*, both mostly saprobic; and *Poria inflata*, *P. laevigata*, *P. mutans*, *P. prunicola*, and *P. sericio-mollis* (*889*, *892*).

The fungi mentioned by Overholts (*1067*) as capable of causing either rot of the central cylinder or rot at wounds of living *Prunus* spp. include also *Fomes applanatus*, *F. meliae*, *F. pomaceus*, *Polyporus curtisii*, *P. dryophilus*, and *P. spraguei*.

Campbell (*204*) studied the incidence of butt rot in sprout stands of northern hardwoods and concluded, for black cherry, that sprouts from stumps up to 10 in. in diameter were reasonably safe from stump-to-sprout decay and that stumps that had become healed over by their sprouts before the latter were 35 years old were not likely to be a source of decay infection to the sprouts.

Miscellaneous Pathology.—Large burls of unknown origin sometimes form on the trunks of black cherry and black walnut, greatly enhancing the value of these already valuable woods for furniture.

The sapwood of black cherry tends to stain a reddish-yellow or rusty color (*151*). This is a normal, probably oxidative, reaction following exposure to air after felling.

Ruehle (*1224*) lists 6 species of nematodes, in 6 genera, that are associated with black cherry in the southern Appalachian Mountains.

Douglas-fir
Pseudotsuga menziesii

Douglas-fir is one of the most valuable timber species in North America. Two major varieties are generally recognized: var. *menziesii,* the dark-green coast form, which is distributed from British Columbia along the Coast Ranges and the Cascades to below San Francisco, and also southward from Oregon along the northerly slopes of the Sierra Nevada to central California (*744*) ; and var. *glauca,* the blue-green mountain form, which grows in the Inland Empire and the Rocky Mountains. The coast form occurs mainly in humid areas with a mild climate and annual precipitation from 20 to 100 in. Temperature extremes range from −25° to 110° F. The altitudinal range is from sea level to 6,000 ft., and at the higher elevations much of the precipitation is snow. The mountain form extends to an elevation of 11,000 ft. in the Rocky Mountains and also occurs in some dry situations in the interior and the Southwest, with annual precipitation as low as 15 in. Some botanists (*148*) recognize three varieties: a coast form, *viridis;* an intermountain form, *caesia;* and a mountain form, *glauca.*

Douglas-fir grows in soils with a pH mostly from 5.0 to 5.5 and with textures from gravelly loam to clay loam. It will not thrive in poorly drained soils or in soils with an impervious layer near the surface. Considered a moderately tolerant tree east of the Cascade Range and in the Southwest (*54*), it is quite intolerant compared to most of its associated species west of the Cascades (western hemlock, western redcedar, redwood, Sitka spruce, and several others). The coast form can grow to heights of 300 ft., diameters of 17 ft., and ages up to 1,000 years (*279*), running second in size to the Sequoias. The mountain form does not reach such sizes and ages. In the future, rotation ages of Douglas-fir may not often exceed 150 years (*744*).

Douglas-fir is potentially deep rooted and has a taproot, often much-branched, with branched, buttressed, descending laterals. McMinn (*914*), in his study of the roots of this species, mentions that such a much-branched system leads to greater windfirmness than the superficial lateral and sinker root patterns so typical of pines and spruces. Soil depth, however, often limits root development.

The thin bark of young trees makes them sensitive to fire. Large trees often have bark over a foot thick, and these resist fire damage. The tree is windfirm, except where long rains weaken anchorage or where root rots caused weakening. Douglas-fir is hardy and can be grown successfully as an ornamental in the East, where it has shown remarkable resistance to ice damage (*310*). The coast form has done very well in fairly well-matched climates in Europe, New Zealand, and elsewhere abroad. Peace (*1091*) considers this species very susceptible to spring frosts under European conditions.

The mountain form was rated second out of eight conifers in

Montana in susceptibility to the "red-belt" type of winter injury (*1249*), which tends to follow contours. In western Washington and Oregon, Douglas-fir is subject to "parch blight," which occurs during brief periods in the winter when dry winds from the east blow across the Cascades (*151*). Parch blight can also result from cold easterly winds blowing through west slope canyons in the northern Sierras in California.

Douglas-fir is rated second out of eight conifers in sensitivity to sulfur-dioxide damage from smelting in Montana, and fifth out of 12 conifers in sensitivity to this gas in Washington (*1249*).

Extensive summer and fall drought can be very damaging, having caused much mortality to Douglas-fir reproduction in California, with losses exceeding those suffered by ponderosa pine, sugar pine, and white fir (*151*). Neither can this species tolerate flooding (*16*).

Death of residual trees following logging, a form of post-logging decadence common with northern hardwoods and eastern hemlock in the East, has taken place on the Olympic Peninsula and is still common in southwestern Oregon.

Treatments of 1 to 4 pounds per acre of several herbicides applied to seedlings at 2-week intervals indicated that Douglas-fir might be expected to recover from applications used to kill brush in a 4-month period during spring and summer (*1028*).

McMinn (*913*) gives a good account of water relations and the growth of coast Douglas-fir in Vancouver, British Columbia; Isaac and Dimock (*744*) describe the silvical characteristics of this form; and Bates (*75*) deals with the physiological requirements of the Rocky Mountain form. He rates this tree as particularly well adapted to conserve water and as an efficient user of light, and he compares several Rocky Mountain tree species with respect to responses to heat, cold, dryness, and other factors.

The pathology of Douglas-fir is dominated by moderate susceptibility to damping-off of seedlings; moderate foliage damage by Rhabdocline needle cast and parch blight; major crown damage inland by dwarfmistletoe; severe damage in parts of the Northwest from laminated root rot and, to a lesser extent, Armillaria root rot; and important trunk-rot losses mainly from *Fomes pini* and also from many other fungi. Douglas-fir is host to hundreds of fungi (T. W. Childs compiled a list of 343 for North America), and their importance to the tree's performance depends much upon the region or locale involved. This point is brought out in considering Boyce's (*146*) statements in reference to Douglas-fir in western Washington and Oregon to the effect that *F. annosus* is not a pathogen of this tree in this region and that dwarfmistletoe, destructive to the species elsewhere, is unknown on Douglas-fir there.

Seedling Diseases.—Seedlings are moderately subject to damping-off (*602*). The following fungi are known to be pathogenic to seedlings: *Sclerotium bataticola* (*Macrophomina phaseoli*) (*1323*), *Rhizoctonia solani* (*408, 1323*), *Phytophthora cinnamomi* (*817*), *Pythium aphanidermatum* (*408*), *P. debaryanum* (*408*), *P. ultimum* (*8*), *Aphanomyces euteiches* (*408*), *Fusarium moniliforme* (*408*), *F. oxysporum* and its forma *pini*, and *F. avenaceum* (*8*). *Diplodia pinea*, largely an eastern pathogen of pine, can occasionally cause a collar rot and seedling rot (*8*). *P. debaryanum* is rated as particularly important in damping-off in Douglas-fir.

Smith and Bega (*1323*) describe severe damage to coniferous nursery stock, including Douglas-fir, in California nurseries (see *Pinus lambertiana*) as a result of mid- to late-season attack of roots by *Sclerotium bataticola* (*Macrophomina phaseoli*).

In British Columbia losses from damping-off tend to be low, except in new nurseries. Salisbury (*1234*) attributes this low incidence to sandy soils of low pH and somewhat low fertility. The fungi associated with damping-off there are: *Rhizoctonia solani* with early disease; *Fusarium* spp. (including *F. oxysporum*) with later losses; and *Pythium* spp. at any time, but less frequently than the others.

Bloomberg (*129*) found that *Fusarium oxysporum* was mainly responsible for root disease in Douglas-fir seedlings in a British Columbia nursery. He postulated that some of the favorable results of chemical treatments may have been through effecting a predominance of *Trichoderma viride,* which is antagonistic to the root rot *Fusarium.*

Bloomberg (*131*) describes a corky root disease of Douglas-fir seedlings from several nurseries in British Columbia. The taproot is swollen and there is a paucity of laterals, accompanied by stunting. The nematode *Xiphinema bakeri* and the fungus *Cylindrocarpon radicicola* appear to be involved.

Cox (*296*) reported that the mountain form of Douglas-fir was subject to damping-off, root rot, and seedling blight from *Cylindrocladium scoparium* in a Delaware nursery.

Under moist conditions the cosmopolitan *Botrytis cinerea* (*B. douglasii*) can cause its gray-mold blight of current-year's foliage of seedlings in field or nursery in the Northwest and Canada, and it sometimes develops as a snow mold. However, its damage is usually secondary to damage by late frosts. Another snow-mold seedling blight, of minor importance on Douglas-fir, is caused by *Phacidium abietis. Phytophthora cinnamomi,* in addition to causing damping-off, causes a lethal root rot of young Douglas-fir in nursery and ornamental plantings in the Pacific Northwest. It has not, however, made headway in forest areas (*1211*).

Rhizina undulata causes a root rot of young conifers up to about 5 years old, occurring in circular patches mainly where wood, slash, or sawdust had been burned. The roots may appear matted by a white mycelium.

Thelephora terrestris often forms its funnel-shaped sporophores around seedlings and can have a smothering effect, but it is generally harmless around fast-growing seedlings.

The smothering fungus *Rosellinia herpotrichioides* (*659*), which bears large, black perithecia on a felty subiculum, has destroyed lower foliage and sometimes killed 2–0 Douglas-fir seedlings in a British Columbia nursery (*1235*). Heretofore known only from North Carolina on *Tsuga canadensis,* this fungus has also recently been noted as a nursery pathogen of *Picea sitchensis* in the Northwest.[52]

[52] Personal communication from Keith R. Shea, pathologist, USDA Forest Service, Pacific Northwest Forest and Range Experiment Station, Portland, Oreg.

Bloomberg (*130*) reported on endophytic fungi in Douglas-fir seedlings and seed. Seedlings yielded mainly *Fusarium oxysporum, Mycelium radicis atrovirens, Cylindrocarpon didymum* and *C. radicicola.* Without exception, fungi grew from surface-sterilized seed placed on agar. Stained sections clearly showed hyphae and chlamydospores well within the tissue of roots, shoots, and seed coat. Bloomberg cited a case in British Columbia: ". . . at the Quinsam nursery, repeated frost heaving left only 125,000 plantable seedlings out of a total of 2,000,000." In some cases the bark at the root collar was stripped.

Many seedlings are lost in the field as a result of summer drought and heat injury, the latter resulting from high temperatures at the soil surface (*601*).

Foliage Diseases.—The most conspicuous fungus needle disease is caused by *Rhabdocline pseudotsugae*, a phacidiaceous fungus with dumbbell-shaped ascospores which causes a mottling and premature shedding of needles older than the current year's. In the United States both the coast and mountain varieties of Douglas-fir are attacked, with the mountain form considerably more susceptible. This is mainly a disease of young trees, and it reaches damaging proportions only after long rainy periods while the new needles are appearing. The mountain form is much more susceptible under a given set of conditions, but is much less often exposed to prolonged rain during the spring growth period.

Boyce (*151*) gives a good account of the differences in behavior of this fungus in North America and in Europe. Brandt (*168*) gives an up-to-date description of the disease and stresses the damage it can cause to Christmas trees grown in the Eastern United States.

Farris (*428*) has developed a stain technique that clearly differentiates the mycelium of *Rhabdocline pseudotsugae* from host tissue. Counterstaining is not required.

Two species of the "imperfect" genus *Rhabdogloeum* have been described from Douglas-fir, *R. pseudotsugae* and *R. hypophyllum.* Neither have been reported often. The account by Ellis and Gill (*411*) of *R. hypophyllum* from the Southwest leaves little doubt that this pycnidial fungus, with conidia resembling the dumbbell-shaped ascospores of *Rhabdocline pseudotsugae*, is the imperfect stage of the latter fungus.

The needles of the coast form of Douglas-fir and, to a much lesser extent, of the mountain form may show rows of tiny black perithecia of *Phaeocryptopus gäumanni* on the underside, issuing from stomata and with one stripe dotted with fruiting bodies on each side of the midrib. Boyce (*148*) gives a good account of this disease. The fungus is apparently native, endemic, and harmless in most of the West, but is reportedly a cause of damaging needle blight in parts of Europe and, to some extent, in the Southwest, New England, and Virginia. It causes a casting of older needles, sometimes leaving only the current year's needles. Barr (*63*) has clarified the taxonomy and nomenclature involving *Phaeocryptopus, Adelopus, Asterina, Meliola*, and *Dimerosporium* species on *Abies* and *Pseudotsuga.*

Another surface smudge or "flyspeck" of needles is caused by

Leptothyrium pseudotsugae, which has black, circular sporocarps and hyaline, oval or globose conidia (*366*).

A dark, sooty mold develops on the underside of foliage of Douglas-fir, particularly in coastal California. Caused by *Dimeriella pseudotsugae,* it forms a thin network of superficial mycelium that bear brown perithecia with septate, obtuse appendages. The ascospores are biseriate, hyaline, fusiform, 2–celled, and 10–15μ × 2.5–3.6μ (*991*).

Two snow blights can attack needles remaining long under snow: the brown-felt blight (*Herpotrichia nigra*) and Phacidium blight (*Phacidium abietis*), the latter mainly in the Inland Empire. These molds damage only seedlings or young trees.

Douglas-fir has two minor needle rusts, *Melampsora albertensis* and *M. occidentalis,* which produce identical hypophyllous aecia on the current year's needles from the northern Rocky Mountains into Canada (*1663*). *M. albertensis* has its II and III stages on *Populus tremuloides,* and *M. occidentalis* has its II and III stages on *P. trichocarpa. M. occidentalis* has larger aeciospores than *M. albertensis.*

Ranking high among the important foliage disturbances of Douglas-fir in the West is parch blight, a form of winter drying occurring when occasional dry winds from the east blow across the Cascade Range (*151*). This injury, most severe on the east side of trees, can kill young twigs as well as foliage.

The use of weed killers along highways has led to a type of foliage injury referred to as "guard-rail burn." Sulfur dioxide from smelters reddens and kills needles and can cause damage as far as 50 miles from the source of the gas. The older needles discolor and shed first (*1249*). Late spring frosts often kill new shoot growth.

Stem Diseases.—The most damaging stem disease of Douglas-fir is the dwarfmistletoe caused by *Arceuthobium douglasii.* It occurs through most of the tree's range, except west of the Cascades and north of the Siskiyou Mountains of Oregon. This parasite is of importance only on Douglas-fir. The effects are brooming, cankering, stunting, distortion, and death. The brooms grow to immense sizes, and some trees become virtually all broom. Graham (*526*) gives a good account and fine photographs of this disease. *A. douglasii* is parasitized by *Septogloeum gillii* in the Southwest (*409, 410*).

Young saplings are occasionally severely distorted or killed by a gall disease caused by *Bacterium pseudotsugae* (*591*). Although mainly reported from California and British Columbia, pathologists in the Southwest have reported galled young Douglas-firs to be common in parts of that region. This disease is not considered important in Oregon or Washington. The galls are globose, rough, and persistent, and they occur mostly on trees of low vigor.

Although Douglas-fir is subject to attack by many branch and twig fungi, only a few are worthy of mention in connection with damage. *Caliciopsis pseudotsugae* causes sharply delineated stem and twig cankers, and its ascocarps are slender, black columns up to 3 mm. long (*483*). This fungus can also fruit on trunks of mature trees (*485*). This disease is common on sites that are drier than average, but rare on other sites.

411

Valsa kunzei var. *kunzei* causes cankers that frequently start around the base of a twig or branch and develop slowly, sometimes with resin flow (*1519*). This is mainly a New England disease, but has also occurred in Colorado and Washington. The roughened cankers may grow to considerable size, with an indefinite outline, and may involve the trunk. Black *Cytospora* pycnidia often form on the lesions. *C. friesii*, a different species, colonizes fire scars in British Columbia (*367*), and *C. (Valsa) abietis* (*1616*) is an inhabitant of dead or senescent branches in the Northwest. *Cytospora (Valsa)* cankers are often associated with recurrent parch blight. In extreme cases the two troubles combine to cause a gradual but serious decadence that can even lead to the death of mature trees.

Many species of *Dasyscypha*, with their conspicuous orange apothecia, find Douglas-fir a congenial host, but only two, *D. pseudotsugae* and *D. ellisiana*, cause cankers. *D. pseudotsugae*, occurring in the West Coast states, causes a branch and trunk canker. Mainly a disease of unvigorous saplings, the cankers are open, commonly 2- to 3-inches long, swollen on the flanks, with hairy, orange apothecia (*151, 567*). *D. ellisiana* (*575*) causes lesions on living twigs in New England and has been observed in Washington. Saprophytic species in the West include *D. arida, D. ciliata* (*567*), and *D. calycina* (*574*); and in the East, *D. oblongospora* (*574*). Hahn and Ayers (*578*), concerned about the possibility of attack on Douglas-fir by the larch-canker fungus, *D. willkommii*, found that it and related large-spored species would not parasitize this tree.

A disease called Lokoya canker (*Phomopsis lokoyae*) developed ominously in one locality in California in 1930, but further study indicated it to be a normally benign native diseases extending to southern Oregon on sites marginal for Douglas-fir (*147*). It has also been reported from British Columbia (*1392*). The cankers look like those of the eastern fungus *Phacidiopycnis (Phomopsis) pseudotsugae* (*572*). Hahn (*566*) describes the distinct cultural characteristics of some of these species of *Phomopsis* and notes that they are also morphologically distinct in nature. *P. lokoyae* occurs only on Douglas-fir, only in the West, and only on the coast form of the tree, except for a single occurrence on *Tsuga heterophylla*. The perfect stage was later described by Funk (*491*) and named *Diaporthe lokoyae*.

In the East the discomycete fungus called *Phacidiella coniferarum* by Hahn (*572*) and *Potebniamyces coniferarum* by Smerlis (*1315*), the imperfect stage of which is *Phacidiopycnis (Phomopsis) pseudotsugae*, lives as a saprophyte or a minor, cortical parasite causing sharply defined cankers on the Rocky Mountain form of Douglas-fir and on balsam fir, white pine, and some of the larches. This is the same organism that has been called *Phomopsis strobi* and other names and is reputed to cause material damage in other parts of the world. Smerlis (*1315*) discusses the nomenclature of this and related fungi.

Dermea pseudotsugae was associated with extensive damage to young Douglas-fir following severe early frosts in British Columbia. Tests proved the fungus able to invade bark wounds and cause necrosis. Funk (*489*) describes the life history and cultural characters of this fungus. It produces very small, hard (fleshy when moist), black or yellow acervuli. The condial fruiting bodies

412

(*Micropera*) are immersed or erumpent, somewhat flattened, under 1 mm. across and yellow to black; they bear sickle-shaped, 0–3-septate, subhyaline macroconidia and hyaline, filiform, curved microconidia.

Phomopsis occulta (*570*), the imperfect stage of *Diaporthe conorum*, may appear on senescent or dead tissue of the coast form.

Funk (*483*) has described *Caliciopsis pseudotsugae* as causing cankers on small branches of Douglas-fir and later found it fruiting in peridermal cracks, without necrosis, on large trunks. It also cankers small branches of *Abies amabilis* (*485*) in British Columbia.

Superficial stem lesions on small saplings on dry sites in the Northwest and British Columbia have been ascribed to *Chondropodium pseudotsugae* of the Fungi Imperfecti (*1564*). Circular or oval areas of outer bark are killed, and these bear black pycnidia which appear as short, blunt stalks. There is no cambial necrosis. The conidia are 4-celled and sickle-shaped. Later, Funk (*482*) found apothecia of this fungus and placed it in *Durandiella* (*D. pseudotsugae*), making it the first member of this genus known on a conifer in North America. The apothecia are erumpent, gregarious, stalked, and less than a millimeter in width and height; they bear hyaline, elongate 0- to 3-septate ascospores.

Other weak bark parasites, living mainly in damaged, senescent, or dead tissue, are *Aleurodiscus amorphus* (*587*), *Cenangium ferruginosum* (*542*), *Diplodia pinea* (*1513, 1524*), and *Tympanis pseudotsugae* (*552*). In addition to *A. amorphus*, five other species of *Aleurodiscus* have been reported on Douglas-fir (*858*). However, these latter fungi (all of which have flat, irregular apothecia) are saprophytic, although sometimes appearing on the outer bark of living trees.

A stilbaceous, sooty mold, *Arthrobotryum spongiosum* (*700*), occurs in northern California (*991*) on the surface of twigs and branches. It makes a thick, dark mat over the substrate.

Root Diseases.—The two most important root diseases are laminated root rot (*Poria weirii*) and shoestring root rot (*Armillaria mellea*). *P. weirii* is widespread on conifers in the northwestern United States and in Canada and is especially damaging to Douglas-fir. The disease occurs in patches up to an acre or more. Its damage is largely as a killer, and it seldom extends far above the stump. Trees die or are blown over alive. They exhibit a brown root rot, separating at the annual rings in advanced stages. The sporophores are brown crusts and are usually inconspicuous. Childs (*249, 250*) has given good accounts of this disease in the United States. Bier, Buckland, and associates have described the disease as it occurs in Canada (*119, 190, 191*). *P. weirii* causes a root rot of less importance in many other conifers and is made up of clones which may show striking incompatibility with each other in culture (*250*).

Wallis and Reynolds (*1505*), studying the initiation and spread of *P. weirii* on Douglas-fir, found infection to take place when healthy roots came in contact with residue-infected roots of the previous stand. Mycelium grew ectotrophically, well in advance of growth in the wood, and penetrated living tissue through sound

413

as well as injured bark. Spread through soil was very limited. *P. weirii* has been shown to survive in 2 by 2 in. blocks buried in soil for 5 years.

Roff (*1189*) states that, contrary to the literature, *Poria weirii* develops mycelium freely in the wood, and it grows in the random, much-branched manner common to many Basidiomycetes. Its hyphal growth is not of the unbranched type that tends to proceed radially in wood and then constricts where it penetrates tracheid walls. The latter is common among Fungi Imperfecti.

Armillaria mellea may also kill patches of Douglas-fir, but some feel that, as a primary killer of trees in natural forest stands of the West, its importance has probably been over-emphasized (*848*). Nevertheless, there appears little doubt that in immature as well as in older trees both in the Northwest and in British Columbia, this fungus can be a major killer. Foster and Johnson (*466*) attributed 95 percent of the growth loss and mortality in some British Columbia plantations to *A. mellea*. This disease is distinguished by gum flow at the root collar, cortical necrosis and decay in that area, black rhizomorphs on the roots, and white mycelial fans under the dead bark. The advanced rot is white, soft, and stringy. Buckland (*188*) related much lethal attack by *A. mellea* in young planted trees on Vancouver Island to poor planting and planting on rocky sites.

Foster and Johnson (*465*) also consider the gains and losses resulting from root rot and frost damage in young Douglas-fir plantations in coastal British Columbia from the standpoint of optimum spacing.

Other root- and butt-rot fungi cause a limited amount of killing and cull in Douglas-fir, including *Corticium galactinum* (*466*), *Fomes annosus, F. nigrolimitatus, Polyporus berkeleyi, P. schweinitzii* (*998*), *P. tomentosus* (*724*), *Poria subacida, P. vaillantii, Sparassis radicata* (*1538*), and many others (*466, 1277*). Only a few of the root fungi can be recognized readily, but fortunately they include the most important ones. The others require cultural confirmation.

Polyporus schweinitzii (*627*), already noted as common in the West, has caused severe root and butt rot, leading to windthrow, of Douglas-fir in a North Carolina plantation. Later, *Fomes annosus* ultimately destroyed this entire planting.

Phytophthora cinnamomi has killed young Douglas-fir in many nursery and ornamental situations in the Pacific Northwest, but not in the natural forest. Although this aggressiveness to one of our most important forest trees on the part of one of the world's most damaging pathogens has caused concern, neither Roth (*1210*) nor Kuhlman (*817*) expect important forest damage in the Pacific Northwest because of the dry summers and the coolness of the wet winters (*1211*). The symptoms are extensive necrosis of the root system and the root-collar area.

Kuhlman (*818*) suggests that there are three plateaus of survival of *P. cinnamomi*, in particular reference to the Pacific Northwest. High recovery level during the first 6 months after soil invasion suggests that sporangia, mycelia, and chlamydospores from the inoculum all remain functional. During the next 12 months, only chlamydospores appeared functional, and after that only occasional chlamydospores remained viable. The fungus will not tolerate prolonged drying of the soil.

Douglas-fir proved moderately susceptible to *Phymatotrichum omnivorum* in inoculation tests in Texas (*1379*).

The root and vascular disease caused by *Verticicladiella wagenerii* and described under *Pinus jeffreyi* has been found to affect Douglas-fir in California. Cobb and Platt (*270*) reported isolating the fungus from a 39-year-old Douglas-fir, showing severe needle chlorosis, needle casting, growth reduction, and discolored xylem, and proved its pathogenicity.

Only a few nematode species in the genera *Criconemoides, Hemicycliophora, Hoplolaimus, Paratylenchus, Pratylenchus, Rotylenchus,* and *Xiphinema* have been identified from roots and rhizospheres of Douglas-firs, and none were associated with root damage (*1222*).

Trunk Rots.—The most damaging and widespread of the heart-rot fungi is *Fomes pini.* Boyce (*151*) puts the matter as follows: "Losses resulting from red ring rot far exceed those from any other decay. In Douglas-fir stands of western Oregon and Washington, where the loss from decay may be 50 percent or more of the gross board-foot volume in some areas, with an average for the region of 17 percent, red ring rot comprises about 81 percent of the loss."

Boyce, in two classic bulletins of his own (*143, 146*) and one with Wagg (*152*), gives a very comprehensive picture of decay in Douglas-fir timber of the Pacific Northwest. He describes infection courts, the principal one being knots; scars, the main ones being due to fire, lightning, and falling trees; and the fungi that cause heartrot. *Fomes pini* predominated in all studies, followed by *F. officinalis, F. roseus,* and *Polyporus schweinitzii.*

Boyce (*146*) gives age, diameter, site, and other relationships to cull caused by rot and other impacts and suggests a rotation age not over 110 years for Douglas-fir in western Washington and Oregon. He and Wagg (*152*) feature diagnostic characteristics, cull deductions for individual trees, and stand characteristics in relation to decay.

Much has been published on *Fomes pini* decay. Percival (*1096*) gives a good account of the biology of the fungus; Boyce (*151*) and Hubert (*725*) give fine general accounts; and Kimmey (*793*) gives detailed cull-percentage tables for northwest California, arranged according to site, tree-diameter class, and presence and location of conks and injuries. *F. pini* rot, in the advanced stage, is a white-lined pocket rot; and, while its development in concentric bands several rings wide that gives it one of its common names, red ring rot, is a feature of its effect on Douglas-fir, this is not a common characteristic on some other species of the West and the East.

In the West, in addition to conks, *Fomes pini* causes punk knots, swollen knots resulting from attempts to overgrow punk knots, and blind conks which are swollen, completely overgrown punk knots (*151*). Several studies confirm that coast Douglas-fir is subject also to considerable heartrot by *Fomes officinalis* (*793*), *F. cajanderi* (*F. subroseus*), and *Polyporus schweinitzii* (*744*), with *Stereum sanguinolentum* accountable for heartrot in some local-

415

ities. Also among the less common heartrot fungi are *Echinodontium tinctorium, F. roseus, Pholiota adiposa,* and *Polyporus anceps.*

Thomas and Thomas (*1395*), working in coastal British Columbia, found decay in old-growth Douglas-fir there to be low (2.6 percent of the gross volume). Twenty-five decay fungi were isolated; the most important were *Fomes pini, Polyporus schweinitzii,* and *F. pinicola.* Even dead trees, which made up a considerable proportion of some stands, were remarkably sound (7.3 percent decay loss). Sporophores and swollen knots were good indicators of *F. pini* rot. There are close to 200 wood-destroying fungi known to attack living or dead Douglas-fir wood. In parts of the Southwest, while *F. pini* is again the predominant heartrot fungus, *E. tinctorium, F. cajanderi* (*890*), and *F. pinicola* are rated as also important, along with the root- and butt-rotters *Polyporus schweinitzii* and *P. tomentosus.*[53]

Kimmey's cull tables (*793*) show the amount of defect that can be expected to follow in coast Douglas-fir as a result of dead or broken tops and fire scars, even when no conks are obvious on the trees. Trees over 2 ft. in diameter can be expected to have cull involve from 25 to 100 percent of the tree volume, depending upon site class and diameter class.

In the Pacific Northwest, wounds on residual trees caused by thinning resulted in more decay in western hemlock than in Douglas-fir (*734*). *Fomes annosus* accounted for 80 percent of the decay volume following wounding of hemlock, and *Stereum sanguinolentum* accouted for 72 percent of such decay in Douglas-fir.

Harvey (*608*), who describes and illustrates the major heartrots and the fungi causing them, lists as "by far the most common of these rots," *Fomes pini, Polyporus schweinitzii, F. officinalis,* and *F. subroseus.*

Mycorrhizal Relations.—While Trappe (*1442*) lists 51 fungi as reported to form mycorrhizae with Douglas-fir somewhere in the world, only *Cenococcum graniforme* has been confirmed by pure culture techniques.

Examination of roots of 11-month-old coast form Douglas-fir seedlings grown at an Oregon nursery from 17 seed sources disclosed significant differences in abundance of mycorrhizal development among some seed sources, but by the second year differences in mycorrhiza abundance were no longer significant (*1620*). The ectotrophic mycorrhizae were mostly digitate and gray or black in color. The black form was identified as *C. graniforme.* White forms also occurred.

Wright and Tarrant (*1626*) found more mycorrhizae on very young seedlings in unburned areas than on seedlings in burned areas. Mycorrhizae also formed nearer the soil surface on 1-year-old seedlings in unburned areas than on 1-year-old seedlings in burned areas. Mycorrhizal occurrence was not related to soil pH. Their color was white, brown, or black, and they were unbranched. The black types were considered those of *C. graniforme.*

Zak (*1644*) found an undescribed nematode species of *Meloido-*

---

[53] Personal communication from Paul D. Keener, deceased, formerly plant pathologist, University of Arizona, Tucson, Ariz.

dera infecting mycorrhizae in Oregon. Only two of at least six distinct types of Douglas-fir mycorrhizae were infected. White, pearl-like, mature females bursting through surface tissues were abundant on a pale-olive mycorrhizal type, but much rarer on a white type.

A tuberculate mycorrhiza formed by two fungi in combination commonly occurs only on *P. menziesii* vars. *menziesii* and *glauca*. One fungus is a white basidiomycete that infects a rootlet to form a compact, much-branched ectotrophic mycorrhiza. The other is a phycomycete that covers the above aggregate in a dense, dark sheath. Moth fungi spread by rhizomorphs (*1443*).

Deterioration of Killed Timber.—Much coast Douglas-fir has been killed by fire, bark beetles, other insects, and windthrow; and the rate of deterioration of large volumes of this valuable wood has claimed much attention from pathologists in the United States and Canada. Wright and Wright (*1628*) studied a beetle kill of 2 billion board feet of Douglas-fir in western Oregon and Washington. The heartwood was penetrated by the fourth year after death; by the sixth year from 25 to 50 percent of the volume was lost. The indicators of decay are described. *Polyporus volvatus* was a sap-rot fungus that fruited copiously on trees killed one year previously. On trees killed two or more years earlier, *Fomes pinicola* conks appeared, indicating destruction of sapwood and invasion of heartwood.

Kimmey and Furniss (*800*) give an excellent account of deterioration of coast Douglas-fir, following killing by fire. In general, 80 percent of the volume of the young growth was lost by the 10th year after death, 80 percent of the volume of the intermediate growth volume was lost by the 25th year, and 80 percent of the old growth volume was lost by the 35th year. *Fomes pinicola* was the main rotter of sapwood and heartwood, *Polyporus abietinus* was the main rotter of sapwood only, *F. officinalis* and *Lenzites saepiaria* rotted some sapwood and heartwood, and *P. volvatus* and *Stereum* spp. were additional sapwood rotters.

Boyce (*144*) studied the deterioration following the blowdown of 1921 on the Olympic Peninsula that caused a windfall of several billion board feet of timber, including much Douglas-fir. Six years later the volume lost, on a board-foot basis, was, for western hemlock, 92 percent; Pacific silver fir, 74 percent; Sitka spruce, 46 percent; Douglas-fir, 35 percent; and western redcedar, 27 percent. In Douglas-fir the main decay fungi were *Fomes applanatus, F. pinicola, F. annosus*, and *Polyporus abietinus*.

Poria carbonica is known to rot the heartwood of Douglas-fir poles, and a species of the Fungi Imperfecti, *Scytalidium* sp., has been demonstrated to inhabit the heartwood and to be antagonistic to *P. carbonica* in culture (*1169*).

Stains.—Four species of *Ceratocystis* (*732*) have been identified in connection with sapstains of Douglas-fir. *C. minor* (*C. pseudotsugae* (*1227*) is carried into living trees by the bark beetle *Dendroctonus pseudotsugae*, staining the wood gray and causing a lethal tracheomycosis. Both *C. pilifera*, a common blue stain fungus of coniferous lumber in many parts of the world; and *C. piceae*, another widespread sapstainer, mainly of spruce and fir lumber, occur on Douglas-fir. The latter, although common, produces only a light-brown discoloration or none at all (732). *C. coerulescens,* another widespread lumber-stain fungus that is very common on hardwoods as well as conifers, also occurs on Douglas-fir sapwood.

A pink to cinnamon-brown stain of Douglas-fir heartwood lumber is caused by the fungus *Ascocybe grovesii* (349).

Two ambrosia-beetle symbiont fungi in Douglas-fir are *Monilia ferruginea,* associated with *Trypodendron lineatum;* and *Tuberculariella ambrosiae,* associated with *Platypus wilsoni* (429, 487).

Trichoderma viride, a common green mold, will increase the permeability of Douglas-fir and southern pine wood to liquids without diminishing strength (864).

Miscellaneous Pathology.—In the introductory account of some of the silvical responses of Douglas-fir, mention was made of such physiogenic impacts as spring frosts, parch blight, smelter-fume injury, and "guard rail burn." Another source of damage associated with highways has occurred where soil sterilant chemicals have been applied to rights-of-way and later washed down into and through sloughs, resulting in killing of trees of considerable size many years later.

Large, dense witches' brooms not due to dwarfmistletoe or any other demonstrable pathogen occur occasionally. This same type of brooming, considered due to highly localized genetic aberrancies, has been noted occasionally on most species of pines and on other conifers (612).

Another localized disorder that has been observed on Douglas-fir is a fasciation of the current shoots. This is a flattening and twisting that, in the case of ornamental hardwoods, has often followed over-fertilization.

Burls attaining great size may occur on the trunk, apparently without association with mistletoe or any other organism. They often develop interesting grain, but if any cortical necrosis develops, decay usually follows (152).

The use of the increment borer causes localized staining and other effects a few inches above and below the holes, and the minor damage caused has not been alleviated by plugging the holes (956),

Douglas-fir suffers heavily from winter drought in Quebec.

In the Interior Wet Belt of British Columbia a decline of Douglas-fir has been taking place, leading to mortality prior to the established rotation age of 160 years. No single factor appeared to be responsible, but contributions to the loss were attributed to *Poria weirii, Armillaria mellea, Polyporus schweinitzii, Rhabdocline pseudotsugae,* bark beetles, and undetermined physiogenic factors (998).

Green cones of Douglas-fir stored in burlap bags not only became moldy and lost viability in the Pacific Northwest, but have become attacked by *Schizophyllum commune,* which is suspected by Shea and Rediske (1282) to deteriorate the seeds.

Pear

Pyrus communis

The pear, a native of Europe and Asia, has long been cultivated in North America for its fruit. It has escaped cultivation and become naturalized in parts of the United States. Since it is not a forest tree, nor is it used to any great extent as an ornamental, it does not merit much attention in this compendium. However, mention of some of the more notable of the diseases of the pear appears justified.

The pear is a slow-growing tree with an erect or ascending branching habit comprising a pyramidal crown, in contrast to the round crown of the apple. The numerous varieties of *Pyrus communis* preclude any reference to the many deviations from the type, but an excellent detailed account of the history of the pear, its varieties, and its culture is provided by Bailey (*51*). Abundant literature is available on pear growing from those states where pear-orchard culture has been particularly successful, mainly in the Northeast, the Lake States, and the Northwest. The pear does best where temperatures are cool and do not vary greatly. For this reason, northern to northeastern slopes are preferred. Soil requirements are modest, so long as the soil is deep and has good internal drainage. The pear is not well adapted to the climate of the South, although the tree is grown to some extent in all of the Southern States.

Seedling propagation is used only for the production of stocks or in searches for new varieties. Most propagation is by budding.

Of the 37 species examined by Croxton (*310*) after a severe ice storm, pear trees were among the species least damaged. Pear trees also proved resistant to salt-spray damage in a New England hurricane (*1632*).

Foliage Diseases.—Pear scab (*Venturia pyrina*) is similar to apple scab (see *Malus*) with respect to the spotting of foliage and fruit and the lesions formed on twigs. The perithecia mature on the fallen, overwintered foliage later than perithecia of apple scab.

Brown to black leaf and shoot lesions result from infection by *Erwinia amylovora,* the fire-blight bacterium. The blackening and blighting of blossoms, leaves, shoots, and fruit and the cankering and girdling of stems and branches are so severe on pears, the most susceptible host, that pear culture is made impossible in many localities. Pear is so susceptible that one of the most common names of the disease is "pear blight." The symptoms, as described under *Malus,* are also characteristic of this disease on pear.

The fungus *Fabraea maculata* causes a leaf and fruit spot of pomaceous plants known as pear-leaf blight. Small, purplish spots on leaves later extend to become brown, circular lesions $\frac{1}{4}$ in. or less in diameter, each with a raised, black dot in the center. The latter is the conidial fruiting body (*Entomosporium*) that bears distinctive cruciate, 4-celled conidia (*1555*).

Monilinia fructicola in the East and, occasionally, in the West and *M. laxa,* widespread in the West, cause not only the common brown rot of fruit, but also a leaf and shoot blight (see *Prunus* spp.).

A spot anthracnose and shot hole of pear foliage in the Pacific Northwest is caused by *Elsinoë piri*. The scabby spots on leaves and fruit are numerous, small, circular, and red to purple with light centers, giving rise to the conidial (*Sphaceloma*) fructifications. Jenkins et al. (*753*) describe and illustrate this spot.

Mycosphaerella sentina (*Septoria piricola*) causes spots on foliage and fruit of pear, quince, and, occasionally, apple in the East and Southeast. Pear varieties vary greatly in susceptibility. The

419

ashy-hued spots are small, up to ¼ in. across, are gray in the center with a definite dark-brown margin, and are dotted with black fruit bodies bearing the long, narrow *Septoria* spores (*1555*).

There are a few other minor leaf spots of pear that are regional in distribution.

Taphrina bullata causes small, slightly thickened, knob-like or bubble-like, irregular brown spots on pear leaves in the Pacific Northwest (*994*).

There are two powdery mildew species on pear, *Podosphaera leucotricha* from Colorado to the Northwest and *P. oxyacanthae* in the East. The former has basal appendages on the perithecia in addition to apical, typically unbranched appendages. The latter has no basal appendages (*1153*).

There are eight species of the rust genus *Gymnosporangium* that have their O and I stages on pear. *G. clavariiforme* is southern, occurs on leaves and fruit, and goes to *Juniperus communis*. *G. clavipes* is southern, attacks mainly fruit, and goes to *J. virginiana*. *G. globosum* is eastwide, on leaves and fruit, and goes to *J. virginiana*. *G. hyalinum* is confined to Florida. The species is based on aecia, and telia are unknown. *G. kernianum* occurs in the Southwest on leaves, and goes to *J. pachyphlaea* (*776*). *G. libocedri* occurs on the Pacific Coast, on leaves and fruit, and goes to *Libocedrus;* and *G. nelsonii* occurs in the Southwest, on leaves and fruit, and goes to *Juniperus* spp. Some of these rusts can be identified only on their telial hosts (*46*).

Ziller (*1667*) gives an account of *G. fuscum*, which is very locally established in British Columbia, and which is described as "the most common and serious pear disease in Europe due to a species of *Gymnosporangium*." Its III stage is on *Juniperus*.

Stem Diseases.—Definitely the most important pear disease is fire blight, which, among its depredations (see Foliage Diseases of pear, and see also *Malus*), causes cankers and shoot blight. Occasionally another bacterium, *Pseudomonas syringae*, will cause a blossom blight, twig blight, and stem canker (see *Prunus avium*), but the bacteria can be readily distinguished from *Erwinia* (*392*).

A southeastern disease that Tims (*1407*) calls limb blight, and that is characterized by pink fungus mats of *Corticium salmonicolor* surrounding the stems, is annotated under *Ficus*.

Cankers with which species of *Cytospora* are associated (see *Populus*) occur in the Northwest.

A superficial bark disease that occurs in the East and West is caused by *Myxosporium* (*Cryptosporiopsis*) *corticola*, the perfect stage of which is *Pezicula corticola*. The conidia, borne in dark acervuli on the bark, are 1-celled, hyaline, $18–36\mu \times 6–9\mu$, and ooze out in white cirri (*1352*).

Several species of *Septobasidium* (*292*) form brown felts on scale insects infesting the bark of stems and branches.

Nectria galligena (see *Betula alleghaniensis*) causes a "target" canker of the stem that is free of bark, exposing successively killed callus folds.

Nectria cinnabarina, coral spot, while usually a saprobe on hardwoods, has often been indicated as a cause of dieback and bark killing in pear and apple (see *Malus*). Its large, coral-colored sporodochia are distinctive.

Occasionally twig blights and cankering have been attributed to either *Fusarium acuminatum, F. avenaceum, F. lateritium,* or *F. sambucinum (1610)*. Speciation in *Fusarium* today would not recognize the name *F. acuminatum*. Fusarium cankers tend to be annual types rather than the bark-free, perennial "target" cankers typified by *Nectria galligena*.

In the Northwest, the discomycete *Neofabraea (Pezicula) malicorticis* attacks apple, pear, and quince, and can cause twig blight and cankering to a serious degree in areas of heavy rainfall. The cankers are oval, sunken, 3 to 4 in. wide and 10 to 12 in. long *(1555)*. The imperfect stage *(Gloeosporium)* appears as cream-colored cushions in bark slits, turning black with age. The apothecia generally form on infected fruit on the ground.

Many additional fungi have been considered to cause twig blights and bark disease of pear *(8)*, but these others are either doubtful as primary parasites or cause damage only locally or only when a tree is under stress.

Root Diseases.—Both *Phytophthora cactorum* and *P. cinnamomi* can kill the roots of seedling pears *(200)* and attack by them has been considered as a possible explanation for a serious "pear decline" in the Pacific Northwest. These fungi are discussed, herein, in connection with root and basal-stem rots of many species including *Acer, Arbutus, Castanea, Citrus, Cornus,* and *Persea. P. cactorum* causes a collar rot as well as a root rot.

Pear trees are subject to damage from *Armillaria mellea* mainly on the West Coast *(848)*, and to a similar root rot by a similar fungus, *Clitocybe tabescens,* in Florida (see *Casuarina* and *Aleurites*).

The nematode *Pratylenchus pratensis* has been associated with a littleleaf condition which often is attributed wrongly to zinc or boron deficiency.

Pear roots are extremely susceptible to Texas root rot *(Phymatotrichum omnivorum)*, and damage is severe in the root-rot belt of Texas, Oklahoma, and west to Arizona. Westcott *(1555)* provides a good description of the damage caused by this important disease.

Species of the genus *Xylaria* have been occasionally considered primary root rots of pear in various parts of the country. They are not known to be distinct from the forms of *Xylaria* that occur on apple roots (see *Malus*).

Miscellaneous Pathology.—A glance at the diseases listed last under *Pyrus communis* in the Index of Plant Diseases in the United States indicates many conditions of the leaf, stem, bark, and fruit for which the cause is either a virus, is uncertain, or is related to soil characteristics.

A condition known as pear decline occurs widely in the Northwest and is a cause of great concern. This highly destructive disease of pear was described first from Italy in the 1940's. A few years later reports of a similar nature came from British Columbia; then in the early 1950's from Washington, and since then it has destroyed or greatly weakened over a million orchard trees on the West Coast from Canada through California.

Two types of decline are recognized—slow and quick. In slow decline terminal growth is short, leaves are small, and the trees have a thin or open appearance. Decline is progressive but slow, and the trees never regain normal vigor. In quick decline trees wilt suddenly and die, usually in hot weather, in as short a time as one or two weeks.

Other symptoms include a reddening of foliage late in the growing season, paucity of feeder roots, and a necrosis of the phloem below the graft union that is sometimes visible to the naked eye. It has many symptom similarities to tristeza of citrus. It is also similar to tristeza (see *Citrus* spp.) in that the type of rootstock influences disease severity. Tristeza is particularly severe in sweet orange trees on sour orange rootstocks, while pear decline is particularly severe when the rootstocks are of *Pyrus ussuriensis* or *P. serotina,* which were introduced from the Orient to provide stocks resistant to fire blight.

Quick decline has been determined to be a virus disease, transmissible, although with difficulty, by grafting. It is introduced into the pear scion by the pear psylla. Although virus multiplication in the scion may cause little damage, once the virus moves down into the susceptible stocks a girdling necrosis takes place. This account of "pear decline" is a digest of a personal communication from Dr. T. A. Shalla, and is based on the research of many, particularly the authors of the papers cited in the California bulletin by Nichols et al. (*1030*).

A gnarling, pitting, and general deformity of pear, occurring on the West Coast mainly in Oregon and Washington, and in New York, is caused by a graft-transmissible virus of which there are many strains. While its importance is as a fruit disease, striking stem and shoot symptoms also occur from some virus strains. Bark cracks develop in concentric and other patterns, a condition referred to by Kienholz (*789*) as "measled bark." Leaf symptoms are generally lacking, although the leaves of trees with stony pit fruit may exhibit a mild mottling along the veins. A wood pitting occurred on Bosc trees inoculated with the rough bark virus strain. In Oregon the Bosc variety was affected in most orchards, the Anjou, in several, and the Comice and Bartlett, only occasionally (*969*).

Fungi capable of causing either rot of the central cylinder or rot at wounds of living *Pyrus* spp. include *Fomes applanatus, F. igniarius, F. meliae, Polyporus fissilis,* and *P. obtusus* (*1067*).

Oak

Quercus spp.

There are more American species in the genus *Quercus* than in any other hardwood genus. The oaks comprise our most abundant hardwoods, not only with respect to number of species but also in timber volume, in breadth of distribution throughout the country, and in economic importance. In briefly describing the main species of this prolific genus, the oaks are grouped in somewhat the same manner as they are in the Index of Plant Diseases in the United States (*8*). Fowells' (*468*) silvical compendium summarizes the characteristics of most of the species included here.

The pathogens of oak tend to attack many species of *Quercus* within a given region, in contrast to the more species-specific pathogens that attack the species of *Populus*. Differences in pathogen flora among the oaks is likely to be more a matter of degree of attack, which often is determined by microclimatic influences, than a matter of clear host specificity. Nevertheless, there are many diseases that are confined largely to certain oak species.

In addition to the many native oaks, specimen trees of the English oak (*Q. robur*) have succeeded in the cooler parts of the country, both West and East. Many cork oaks (*Q. suber*) have also been planted in the South and in California, and there are some fine street and highway plantings in Pasadena and elsewhere in California (*955*).

Kuntz (*822*), in bringing together a listing of oak diseases of the United States, goes further than the Index of Plant Diseases in the United States (*8*) in that he annotates some of them and gives some indications of their importance. This present account, however, gives fuller annotation from the point of view of diagnosis and pathological significance and also provides the documentation lacking in the aforementioned accounts.

Along with the following annotations of many individual species of oak, information is given on their pathology with respect to diseases significantly related to these oak species or confined to one or more of them. Then, following these accounts of major oak species, the diseases of oaks in general are presented in the format used throughout this book.

WHITE AND CHESTNUT OAKS OF EASTERN AND CENTRAL UNITED STATES

Quercus alba—This species, the white oak, is the outstanding member of its genus in size, form, longevity, and the useful properties of its wood. Trees have been known to attain heights of over 150 ft. and ages over 800 yrs. (*279*). The wood is light in color fairly hard and durable, and attractive in grain. Its quick rate of tylose formation makes it suitable for liquid-holding (tight) cooperage.

White oak occurs throughout the United States east of the Great Plains except for most of Florida, the immediate Gulf Coast strip from Florida to Texas, and the Mississippi Delta, where its role as a white oak is taken over largely by overcup oak (*Q. lyrata*). It thrives over a wide range of climate and soils and is a component of 27 forest types (*468*). It is intermediate in tolerance, being much more tolerant than yellow-poplar, and reproduces either from seed, or as seedling sprouts, or sprouts from stumps of trees under 80 years old.

White oak is moderately resistant to ice breakage (*310*), sensitive to flooding, resistant to salt spray and to brief salt-water submergence (*1632*). It is sensitive to fire injury but less so than scarlet oak (*1020*). Mericle et al. (*949*) describe injury to white oaks after 10 years exposure to gamma radiation from a nearby cobalt-60 source. The damage was much less than that sustained by *Pinus rigida* in the same stand, but it can be cumulative.

In spite of the reputation of the oaks for withstanding the vicissitudes of nature, there have been many instances of major declines —mostly involving the red oak group. However, many episodes of white oak dying over considerable areas have been observed from Pennsylvania and Maryland through the southern Appalachian and

Piedmont Regions. Severe dieback has taken place following droughts, and dieback and mortality have followed insect defoliation.

Sulfur dioxide produces an irregular, angular blotch of white oak foliage, in comparison to the symmetrical, intervenal browning caused in maples, ash, and beech by this gas.

White oak is less susceptible to oak wilt than the red oak species and may lose only a limb at a time or sustain infection by the pathogen without ever showing symptoms.

Strumella and Nectria cankers cause much damage to white oak wherever ice and snow accumulation (*530*) is common, as in western Maryland and parts of the Lake States and Central States. Roth and Hepting (*1207*) describe the very severe cankering of oak by the pathogens of these two diseases in Maryland and the lack of effectiveness of large-scale canker eradication in attempts at control.

Anthracnose can be very damaging to individual white oaks, whereas leaf blister is more severe on the red oaks. *Physalospora glandicola*, usually called by the imperfect-stage names *Dothiorella quercina* or *Diplodia longispora*, causes a twig blight grossly resembling cicada-killing, and while most severe on chestnut oak, it also can be very damaging to white oak, particularly in the Central States (Carter *231*).

Hepting et al. (*664*) describe the tendency of white oaks to develop cracks in the trunk base and exposed roots following sudden severe cold, with the cracks uniformly developing a yeast-induced slime flux. Hundreds of such cases were seen following the severe winter of 1950-51.

White oaks cut 10 years after increment boring (Hepting et al. *669*) disclosed that they healed the borer wounds rapidly, and only an average of 3 vertical inches of stain and virtually no decay developed as a result of the borings.

Corticium galactinum is a fungus that has occasionally gained prominence as a root-rot pathogen of large trees (see *Malus pumila*) but has seldom acted aggressively. Toole (*1419*) reports several cases of severe pathogenicity to white oak by this fungus in Arkansas, and he successfully inoculated seedlings (*1429*). In diagnosis care should be taken not to confuse the light, basal, poreless sporophores of *C. galactinum* with those of *Sebacina helvelloides*, a harmless fungus that also produces similar felts around the bases of many species of living trees but does not affect the inner bark or cambium (*908*).

White oak has a reputation for soundness that is not fully justified. Its average cull percentage in sawlog stands is comparable to other commercial oaks (*663*) and often exceeds many of them. It commonly is subject to damage from flagworms (Columbian timber beetle), and its rate of decay following fire wounding (Hepting *640*) suggests a relatively high decay rate, generally, compared to other oaks.

The volume deduction due to rot in sawtimber stands in eastern North Carolina was computed for several hardwood species (*557*), with the cull percentage due to rot in yellow-poplar and white oak, 4 percent; in sweetgum, 5 percent; and in red maple, 38 percent.

The heartwood of white oak in laboratory tests was not more

resistant to decay than chestnut oak but was more resistant than species in the red oak group (*1247*).

Hart (*598*) has demonstrated that sapwood of white oak discolored as a result of wounding is similar morphologically to normal heartwood but differs chemically in having a higher pH, higher ash content, and a higher moisture content.

Huppuch (*737*) illustrates large trunk swellings that are commonly observed on white oak in the southern Appalachian Region. This curious "bumpiness" may extend 25 ft. up a trunk. It occurs mostly on trees on poor sites. The bark appears normal, and the wood within these swellings is sound, but embedded knots or dormant buds were disclosed at the center of these persistent swellings.

An exfoliation of layers of outer bark of white oak and post oak, usually called smooth patch or white patch, is described and illustrated by Lair (*825*), who determined the cause to be a new *Corticium* species which he named *C. maculare*. Lair considers his bark disease to be the same as that described by Tehon and Jacks (*1389*) in the Midwest and attributed by them to *Aleurodiscus oakesii*. He considers the latter fungus to be secondary and believes *C. maculare* to cause smooth patch widely over the ranges of the two affected oak species.

Wilson (*1585*), in studying the common Appalachian and Ozark insect defect known as "flag worm" or "splotch worm" injury, found that the galleries of the causal insect, the Columbian timber beetle, yielded two fungi, *Ceratocystis piceae* and *Pichia* sp., and that the vertical, stained areas also yielded a *Fusarium* sp. He suspects a mutualistic relationship between *C. piceae* and the timber beetle.

The later section dealing with the diseases of oaks in general should be consulted for the many other pathogens attacking white oak as well as other oaks.

Quercus bicolor—This species, called swamp white oak, is a lowland tree extending mainly from southern New England westward through the Central States and southern part of the Lake States to the Great Plains (*468*). There is little extension of its range south of the Ohio River or north of the 45th parallel. It occurs in wet areas having a hardpan, in flooded areas, in wet muck, and other poorly drained soils.

Swamp white oak can grow rapidly and to ages over 300 years. It is typically short boled, and has a shallow root system. It is intermediate in tolerance, reproduces by seeds, seedling sprouts, and stump sprouts, and generally occurs as single trees in one of the three middlewest swamp forest cover types (*468*).

Little attention has been given specifically to the diseases of swamp white oak. However, they are little different from those of white oak. Carter (*231*) has described some twig-blight fungi, and he and Wysong reported oak wilt specifically from swamp white oak (*468*). Anthracnose also blights the leaves of this species.

Quercus garryana—Called Oregon white oak, this is the only western white oak included in this compendium. It is also the only oak of the Pacific Northwest. It is well described by Collingwood and Brush (*279*) as "a tree of dark green foliage and rugged appearance, which sometimes attains massive proportions." It

425

extends from British Columbia south to the Santa Cruz Mountains of California, reaching its best development from the Willamette Valley of Oregon to Puget Sound.

Oregon white oak grows on soils that range from deep and moist to shallow and dry. It frequently occupies gravelly sites that merge from forest to grassland, or southwest slopes that are hot and dry in summer. Not only is it the Northwest's only oak, but it is a desirable tree, the wood being hard, tough, durable, and not highly defective. It normally grows slowly but can attain heights up to 90 ft., diameters over 4 ft., and ages over 300 years on its best sites.

A number of leaf-spot, mildew, and anthracnose fungi attack the foliage, but none are economic parasites. *Armillaria mellea* and *Polyporus dryophilus* root and butt rots are probably the principal diseases, with mistletoe and several wound-rot fungi causing some damage.

Quercus lyrata—Known as overcup oak because of the encasement of the acorn by the cup (*279*), this southern species has a range virtually the opposite of that of scarlet oak. While the latter is largely an Appalachian and Piedmont tree, overcup oak is a Coastal Plain, lowland, backwater species occurring throughout the wetter sites of the South and extending up the Mississippi Delta to Illinois. It is most common on the alluvial, heavy soils of the southern river flood plains, on first bottoms, and on terraces.

Overcup oak is moderately tolerant; very resistant to flooding, ranking third in resistance out of 37 species in a Tennessee flooding study; makes very rapid early diameter growth in rich soil, but grows slowly otherwise; and can reach an age of 400 years in the Mississippi Delta (*279*). It tends to be defective, to a large degree because of large wood-boring insects and insects that cause bark pockets and stained areas (*468*).

Hepting (*637*) states that overcup oak is notoriously defective in the Mississippi Delta south of Arkansas, and that the heartwood not only decays rapidly following fire scarring but is commonly riddled with insect galleries, and the wood is "shaky." He pointed out, however, that overcup oak healed over its scars at a rate greatly exceeding that of any of the other seven Delta species he studied. Toole (*1417*) also found overcup oak, along with sugarberry, to decay rapidly when wounded. No major foliar or branch pathogens have been reported as common in overcup oak.

Combining Hepting's (*637*) study and Toole's (*1417*), fourteen identified fungi were isolated from decaying heartwood above fire scars in overcup oak.

Quercus macrocarpa—Bur oak, *Q. macrocarpa*, occupies a triangular range—delimited by lines drawn from western New York to North Dakota to central Texas and back to New York—that excludes the entire Southeast. It is slow growing, moderately tolerant, cold resistant, drought resistant, fire resistant when large, and does well on calcareous ridges and gravelly, moist flats. It is one of the prairie border trees occupying lands just east of the Great Plains. It is used as a shelterbelt tree in the Northern Plains area. Its very long taproot enhances its resistance to drought and wind. Longevit yis generally 200 to 300 years and, exceptionally, to 400 years.

Bur oak is commonest on deep, rich prairie soils. It is the most fire resistant of all Midwest trees. It has well-insulated bark, reaching a thickness of 4 in.

Sprouting is prolific, but a repetition of killing by fire and resprouting in certain areas has led to a type of reproduction called stool sprouts, that make very poor trees. Natural root grafts are common on the lighter soils.

Among the diseases of bur oak, oak wilt has had the most attention, although bur oak is less susceptible than members of the red oak group. Local spread of the disease in bur oak has, in many cases, been through root grafts (*823*), and entire groves of this species have been killed out by the gradual spread from foci of infection.

Strumella and Nectria cankers (*661*) destroy many bur oaks, and Fergus (*435*) reports a plantation of this species in Pennsylvania in which half of the trees had Strumella cankers at age 20 years, and one-fourth of these had died by then. A canker of bur oak and post oak in Kansas caused by *Fusicoccum ellisianum* is described by Rogerson (*1190*). Bur oak was rated only moderately susceptible to Texas root rot, but the tree is used for shelterbelts mainly north of the root-rot belt in Texas and Oklahoma (*1379*).

Quercus michauxii—This tree has two common names, swamp chestnut oak and cow oak. Its botanical nomenclature was confused, and for many years cow oak in the Mississippi Delta was referred to as *Q. prinus*, the name now applied to chestnut oak (*872*). Swamp chestnut oak sites are the better, loamy, first-bottom ridges and terraces of major streams of the South from New Jersey to Texas. Its climate is characterized by hot summers, short, mild winters, and no distinct dry season (*468*). Abundant moisture is required, but the tree is only moderately resistant to flooding (*583*).

Swamp chestnut oak is rather intolerant, neither drought resistant nor cold resistant, and reproduces by seeds and sprouts. It matures between 150 and 180 years and can live to be 350 years old (*279*). Unlike overcup oak the wood of living trees is not highly defective, and there is little hidden defect. It is used along with white oak even for tight cooperage and fine furniture.

Except for minor leaf diseases and the usual decay that follows fire wounds, logging injuries, or the breakage of major limbs, swamp chestnut oak suffers little from fungus attack.

Quercus prinus—This species, chestnut oak, for many years was erroneously called *Q. montana* (*872*). It is typically a tree of the Appalachian Mountains from New England to Georgia, growing to an elevation of 4,500 ft., and on the drier upland sites from southern New England westward to southern Indiana. Reproducing by seeds and sprouts, it holds the soil in much of the steep, rough, watershed protection land and occupies rocky, inhospitable sites that few other species would tolerate. It is a prolific sprouter and this has led to a multiple-stem characteristic not conducive to best growth or form. These sprouts are often rotted as a result of decay that originated in the parent stump (*1209*).

Chestnut oak makes a desirable tree on the better soils, but other species usually preempt these sites. It is intolerant, drought resistant, and cold resistant. Its habit of occupying dry ridges and steep slopes has resulted in litter accumulations on the upper side which, during forest fires, have badly burned the upper sides of the tree.

427

It is likely because of this that Hepting and Hedgcock (*663*) found chestnut oak to lead all six Appalachian oak species studied, on commercial logging operations, in percentage of rot cull. Once cut into lumber, chestnut oak was the most resistant of the several oaks tested by Scheffer et al. (*1247*) to decay of the heartwood.

Along the Appalachian ridges chestnut oaks can in some years be identified in the distance by the large number of dead "flags." These are killed branch terminals. Such damage is generally caused either by *Diplodia longispora* (*Dothiorella quercina*), the perfect stage of which is *Physalospora glandicola,* or the 17-year cicada (see Stem Diseases).

Another branch canker and dieback of chestnut oak is caused by a species of *Botryodiplodia.* Schmidt and Fergus (*1253*) found that this twig blight occurs widely in Pennsylvania and they produced lesions by inoculation. The common association of this fungus with the scale insect *Asterolecanium variolosum* made them suspect the insect to be a vector of the fungus. They provide a description of the fungus pycnidia and their brown, 1-septate conidia.

Chestnut oak is susceptible to oak wilt, but like white oak it is much less so than the species of the red oak group. It is also subject to Nectria and Strumella cankers from Virginia northward (*661, 1207*).

Many leaf-spot fungi can damage occasional chestnut oak trees, but there are no economic leaf parasites of this species.

Quercus stellata—This species, post oak, occupies mainly dry sites from Long Island, New York, westward to the Great Plains, and throughout the South except for the tropical part of Florida, the Mississippi Delta, the Texas Gulf Coast, and the coves, other better sites, and high elevations of the Appalachian Mountains. Typically associated with other poor site species it tends to be a short-boled tree of low quality (*279*). Post oak is intolerant, drought resistant (*468*), often insect riddled, and knotty as well as cankered. It seldom reaches diameters in excess of 2 ft.

A variety, *mississippiensis,* that occurs in the higher terraces of the Mississippi Valley, grows to much greater size than the species and is much less defective.

Post oak has sustained much defect as well as mortality from the chestnut blight fungus *Endothia parasitica.* Clapper et al. (*262*) reported cankering over wide areas of the tree's range with up to 30 percent of the trees cankered in a Connecticut area; and Bryan (*180*) reported 14 percent of the post oaks cankered by *E. parasitica* on a large number of plots in the Southern Piedmont. A canker of bur and post oaks in Kansas caused by *Fusicoccum ellisianum* is described by Rogerson (*1190*).

Post oak is also subject to oak wilt north of the 35th parallel but not to the same degree as are the red oaks.

An exfoliation of outer bark reported on post oak and white oak, called smooth patch, is annotated under *Quercus alba.*

RED, BLACK, AND PIN OAK GROUP

Quercus coccinea—Scarlet oak has a range very similar to that of chestnut oak, geographically, but is less likely to occur on the thin-soiled, steep, upper slopes of the southern Appalachian Moun-

428

tains. Within its range it is abundant, occurring in 16 forest-cover types and often making up much of the stand. It is the fastest growing of the northern oaks and along with *Q. falcata* has the shortest life of the timber oaks, with a longevity seldom exceeding 100 years. It is a shallow-rooted upland species, growing on average to poor sites, is intolerant, drought resistant, and cold resistant. The wood is much like the other red oaks but tends to be harder.

Scarlet oak is a very limby tree, bearing many persistent dead branches and loose knots. Pruning this fast-growing tree could well pay. While the wood of scarlet oak is not particularly susceptible to decay compared with other red oaks (*1247*), scarlet oak tends to have a high cull percentage in the field, because fires make larger scars on scarlet oak than on other oaks (*1020*) since its bark is thin and hard, and because the species so often inhabits dry sites. It also tends to have localized rot pockets at dead-branch traces (*661*).

Scarlet oak is very susceptible to oak-leaf blister, to two of the pine-oak rusts, and to Actinopelte leaf spot. From Virginia northward and westward it is subject to Strumella canker and oak decline (*1348*), and from North Carolina northward and westward it is subject to oak wilt. Nevertheless, on average or better sites, if protected from fire and pruned early, scarlet oak can by its rapid growth provide a good return.

Following increment boring scarlet oak (*669*) developed a narrow, sapwood stain band with mean vertical length of 20 in. Virtually no decay resulted, even 10 years after boring.

Quercus falcata var. *falcata*—Known as southern red oak or Spanish oak, this is one of the commonest upland species of the South. The southern red oak grows throughout the South and as far north as the Ohio River west of the Appalachian Mountains, and north to Long Island east of them. It does not occur in the higher elevations of the Appalachian range, the first bottoms of the Mississippi Delta, and the tropical part of Florida. It is intermediate in tolerance, heat resistant, fast growing, and reaches maximum age at about 150 years or less. It is sensitive to fire. It generally occurs scattered among other species, on hot and dry sites, and on either sandy or clay soils. Yet a report from Arkansas indicated that southern red oak is considerably more susceptible to drought injury than the other upland southern oaks. It is commonly grown as a shade tree in southern towns and cities.

Because it is so readily fire scarred or otherwise injured, heart rots and root rots are major problems with this species. Although many fungi rot its heartwood, those most often seen fruiting are *Fomes everhartii*, *Hydnum erinaceus*, *Polyporus hispidus*, *P. obtusus*, and *P. sulphureus*.

While *Q. falcata* is highly susceptible to oak wilt, this disease is virtually unknown south of the 35th parallel (southern Tennessee border), except for one Texas report. Either leaf blister or *Actinopelte dryina* (see Foliage Diseases) can severely mar the foliage, and two of the pine-oak rusts commonly colonize the foliage.

A spot anthracnose (*Elsinoë quercus-falcatae*) can speckle the leaves of southern red oak, producing tiny spots (*977*) mostly smaller than those caused by *Actinopelte dryina*. In the case of the *Elsinoë* the spots appear only on the upper surface, are blackish brown, becoming lighter toward the center, and scarcely reach over a millimeter in diameter. *A. dryina* (*863*) makes spots 2–5 mm. across, and it is amphigenous.

Thick, white- to smoky-hued felts of the non-parasitic thelephoraceous fungus *Sebacina helvelloides* can develop copiously on the bark around the bases of the oaks, notably *Q. alba* and *Q. falcata.*

Quercus nuttallii—Nuttall oak, while not well known outside the Mississippi Delta and adjoining areas, is very important economically in this productive region. Strictly a lowland tree of the South, it occupies the alluvial bottoms of the Delta and flood plains of tributary rivers, extending from Alabama through Louisiana and from the Gulf of Mexico to the southeast tip of Missouri (*468*). However, it does not grow in permanent swamps or river lakes as do cypress, tupelo, willow, and cottonwood.

Nuttall oak grows very fast with annual-ring widths commonly exceeding ¼ in. The bole is typically tall and clear. The tree is intolerant, very susceptible to fire damage and to decay that starts from these wounds. Nuttall oaks made up a large proportion of the red oaks studied by Hepting (*637*) and Toole (*1417*) in their studies on rate of decay from fire wounds in Delta hardwoods. Of 22 Delta species or species groups studied by Toole (*1422*) in connection with the incidence and rate of rot entering dead branches, Nuttall oaks made up the largest single species sample.

Toole [54] found Nuttall oak very susceptible to seedling cankers following inoculation with *Fusarium solani* from natural red oak cankers.

Toole (*1415*) reports that 3 percent of the Nuttall oaks and 13 percent of the willow oaks on the Delta Experimental Forest near Stoneville, Mississippi, bore the cankers and decay of *Polyporus hispidus*.

Toole also has successfully inoculated Nuttall oaks with *Corticium galactinum* (*1429*), *Pleurotus ostreatus* (*1425*), *Polyporus fissilis, P. hispidus,* and *Poria ambigua* (*1427*).

Increment borings in Nuttall oak healed rapidly. When made in the spring, they developed an average of 11 vertical inches of sapwood stain but very little rot (*1433*).

Quercus palustris—This species, known commonly as pin oak, is typically a wet-site tree of the Midwest, extending from Long Island, New York, westward across the Central States to the Great Plains and southward through the western half of Tennessee and the northern half of Iowa (*468*). It occurs naturally also in eastern Pennsylvania, Maryland, and Virginia, and has been planted commonly as a street tree in the Carolinas and further south. Metcalf (*955*) states that pin oak is finding favor in California because of its pyramidal form and other desirable growth habits, and fine plantings can be found near Napa and Lodi.

Like *Q. coccinea*, pin oak is short-lived, seldom reaching ages over 100 years and diameters over 3 ft. While often planted as a street or shade tree, it has little value for lumber because of an excessive number of small knots (*279*).

Pin oak has often failed when planted in the southern Piedmont,

---

[54] Unpublished report of E. Richard Toole, formerly pathologist, USDA Forest Service, now at Mississippi State University, State College, Mississippi.

where heat, dryness of soil, and mineral deficiencies combine to produce conditions unfavorable for this species.

A chlorosis of pin oak, correctable by adding iron chelate, occurs from New Jersey to Michigan and Texas. This difficulty, apparently due to iron deficiency, would scarcely account for the widespread decline of pin oaks in the South, described above, especially since the southern Piedmont soils are typically acid. Pirone's (1116) successful treatments in Newark, New Jersey, using ferric phosphate indicate the iron-deficiency nature of the common pin oak chlorosis.

While pin oak will grow under a variety of soil and climatic conditions, it has not performed as expected when planted in much of the South. It does well on wet soil, including poorly drained sites, and pin-oak flats are common in the southern parts of Ohio, Indiana, and Illinois. The tolerance of pin oak to fresh-water flooding up to a few weeks is well known (468), and in Tennessee a flooding experiment showed pin oak fifth in order of tolerance to flooding among the 39 species ranked. However, potted pin-oak seedlings flooded for 38 days lost most of their roots and made weak recovery (711). Pin oak in the field will not withstand permanent flooding.

Pin oak is intolerant of shade and highly susceptible to fire injury. It is subject to oak wilt, and pin oaks have been among the trees commonly killed by this disease in many parts of the Central States. It is subject to many of the diseases discussed here, subsequently, under the pathology of oaks in general and is notably susceptible to attack by the leaf-blister fungus *Taphrina caerulescens* and the shoot-blight and twig-canker fungus *Dothiorella quercina.*

Viggars and Tarjan (1479.) describe a pin-oak disease in Delaware that they believe may be due to root attack by nematodes, mainly *Hoplolaimus coronatus* (1377). Symptoms are hypersensitivity to drought; chlorosis of foliage on certain limbs; marginal leaf necrosis, spreading inward, then premature abscission; a fluted root collar; and the formation of "water sprouts." In the fall leaves are dull and tan instead of a "lively" reddish brown.

Quercus rubra—This species, the northern red oak, is one of the most widely distributed of the oaks, occurring in all parts of the East to the Great Plains, except for the Gulf States and the hotter parts of the South Atlantic States (468). *Q. velutina,* a common associate, has much the same range but extends somewhat further south and southeast into hotter and drier sites than will support northern red oak. The latter thrives on moist, loamy soils of northerly or easterly aspect. Although its distribution is wide, it makes a fast-growing timber tree only on these cooler, moist soils of fairly fine texture. Intermediate in tolerance, it responds well to release and can produce high-grade timber, with trees growing to ages over 200 years and diameters over 3 ft. The bole is relatively clean. The common variety name, *maxima,* used along with the discarded species name, *borealis,* denoted a particularly large taxonomic unit now called *Q. rubra.* For many years *Q. rubra* was used to denote the southern red oak, herein called *Q. falcata* (872).

Red oak is highly susceptible to oak wilt, and large numbers of trees have been killed from Pennsylvania to Wisconsin and Iowa. It is also highly subject to Strumella and Nectria cankers and to the leaf anthracnose, mildews, rusts, blister, and spots common to other oaks.

Hepting and Hedgcock (663) found that red oaks cut on Appalachian logging operations tended to have less rot per diameter class than most other oaks, including white oak.

Staley's intensive study of a decline of oaks in Pennsylvania, Virginia, and West Virginia pertained specifically to death of red and scarlet oak (1348). He points out the role of leaf-roller insects, *Agrilus* attack, late spring frost, root rot, and unfavorable soil. He concluded that diminished carbohydrate synthesis resulted, and that this brought about the decline, but that ultimate mortality "reflected" extreme moisture stress. Decline of the type that Staley describes has taken place in many areas of the Northeast. Dance and Lynn (321) reported excessive red oak mortality following ice-storm damage in Canada, but this syndrome is not Staley's oak decline.

Crandall et al. (304) report the susceptibility of red oak seedlings to attack by *Phytophthora cinnamomi* in a Maryland nursery.

According to Sparrow and Sparrow (1332) northern red oak was less sensitive to gamma radiation from a Cobalt-60 source than most species of a group of 12 hardwoods and conifers which were tested.

A disease of red and pin oaks in Delaware suspected to be of nematode origin is described under *Quercus palustris.*

Quercus velutina—Known as black oak, this species is, next to white oak, the most widely distributed oak in the United States, occupying the entire East except for the coldest areas of the Northeast and Lake States bordering Canada, the hot coastal strip of the Gulf and South Atlantic Coasts, all of Florida, and the Mississippi Delta proper (468). It is typically an upland hardwood that withstands a wide range of temperature and soil types, and thus it is found on many sites too hot or too dry to support northern red oak. It is intermediate to intolerant of shade, grows about as fast as scarlet oak, with which it commonly occurs, and while it will make a clean-boled tree on good soil, it is likely to be as defective and limby as scarlet oak on the many poor and dry sites on which it occurs (180). Black oaks have a maximum longevity of about 250 years and can grow to over 4 ft. in diameter.

Decay cull is largely a matter of amount of fire scarring (640) and overage (662).

Gruschow and Trousdell (557) show the red oak group including many black oaks in the coastal area of North Carolina to have about twice the rot-cull percentage of white oak in that area.

In some areas (for example the Missouri Ozarks, where 33 percent of the black oaks are worthless, (468) a combination of fire injury, trunk rot, stubs, and insects, together with rot in sprout trees contracted from the parent stumps, make black and scarlet oaks worth little, except for crossties or pulpwood.

Black oaks are very susceptible to oak wilt and to Strumella and Nectria canker, mainly in the Northeast and the Lake States where ice damage is common. The foliage diseases are the same as those typical of the red oak group in general.

With the exception of blackjack oak (*Quercus marilandica*), a small, limby, short-lived, defective tree of the poorer and drier sites of much of the East, the other species of this group have so much in common with respect to their pathology that they are treated together here. All are entire-leafed oaks, or, in the case of water oak, partly so. The shingle oak (*Q. imbricaria*) is mainly a tree of the Central States, while laurel oak (*Q. laurifolia*), water oak (*Q. nigra*), and willow oak (*Q. phellos*) are southern species. All four of these species occur mainly in river valleys and other moist situations, but they also are components of low elevation, upland forest types. While they occur naturally on alluvial and well-drained lowland sites, they cannot withstand flooding for long periods (*583*).

These species, again excepting blackjack oak, grow to large size, have full crowns, and generally have tight bark, smoother than most oaks. They are popularly used for shade and ornament throughout the South, and it is a rare southern town that does not have water oaks, willow oaks, or laurel oaks. They all produce high grade lumber, grow rapidly, and may attain ages close to 200 years. Good silvical accounts are given by Fowells (*468*) and by Putnam and Bull (*1140*).

All of the species of this group are highly susceptible to oak wilt; but since their ranges, except for shingle and blackjack oaks, are largely southern, and the wilt extends but little below the 35th parallel (latitude of southern Tennessee), losses from the wilt have been slight.

Aside from wound decays the most noticeable diseases of these species are leaf blister, the uredo and telial stages of the southern pine rusts, Actinopelte spot, and powdery mildew, the latter mostly on sprout foliage late in the growing season. Nectria and Strumella cankers are not problems with the oak species that occur far enough south to suffer little from bending by ice and snow. The relation between axillary cracks due to the weight of ice and snow, and cankering by *Nectria* spp., as described by Grant and Spaulding (*530*), seems to explain, at least in part, why these cankers rarely occur in the South.

Laurel oaks growing near citrus in Florida have been found to have a branch condition similar to leprosis of citrus. The scabrous, irregular, depressed lesions are illustrated by Fawcett and Rhoads (*433*). While the cause of leprosis is unknown, mites in the genus *Brevipalpus* are suspected.

The decay problem in water and willow oaks, as related to fire wounds, is dealt with by Hepting (*637*) and by Toole (*1417*). Rot entrance through dead branches and the tree factors influencing the incidence of such rot are explained in detail by Toole (*1422*) for water and willow oak. In the cited work on decay following fire and decay entering branch stubs, the fungi involved, their linear, annual rate of spread, and the influence of size and type of wound on ultimate decay cull were determined.

Canker-rot is a term coined to denote those types of heartrot in living trees where the causal organism commonly rots the heartwood and also kills the bark, resulting in large, irregular cankers. Toole (*1416*) describes the incidence, severity of decay, and other characteristics of the canker-rots of southern hardwoods, and notes particularly the frequent attack of water, willow, Nuttall, and other southern red oaks, by *Irpex mollis, Polyporus hispidus, Poria laevigata,* and *Poria spiculosa,* all of which cause canker-rots.

A survey of the Delta Experimental Forest in Mississippi disclosed that 13 percent of the willow oaks and 3 percent of the Nuttall oaks exhibited the cankers and rot of *Polyporus hispidus* (*1415*).

Edgerton (*403*) reported *Ganoderma curtisii* to cause a root rot of water oak, *Albizia, Cercis,* and *Citrus,* in Louisiana.

THE LIVE OAKS

The live oaks are evergreen, grow to large diameters, and their use is largely restricted to shade and ornamental purposes and the production of acorns for game. They are not regarded as timber trees.

Quercus agrifolia, the California live oak, or so-called coast live oak of the Far West, grows along the Pacific Coast ranges from northern to southern California and into Mexico. It is a very tolerant tree (*1367*) that occurs on hillsides and in canyons, particularly within a few miles of the ocean. In dry situations the form is shrublike (*955*). In moist, fertile ravines it attains large size, and Metcalf reported one in Pasadena over 8 ft. in diameter, 108 ft. high, and 129 ft. in crown spread (*7*). Stunted trees occur along the exposed seashore. A striking brooming disease is caused by *Sphaerotheca lanestris,* and black mildews grow on the foliage (see Foliage Diseases).

In the interior valleys of central and northern California, the acorns of *Quercus agrifolia* and *Q. wislizenii* develop a disease described by Hildebrand and Schroth (*679*) as drippy-nut. Cynipid wasp punctures are followed by copious oozing and sometimes rot of the acorn. The ooze is plant sap, and it may come from the acorn or from the acorn cup if the nut is detached. The pathogen causing the ooze is described as *Erwinia quercina* n. sp., a Gram-negative, peritrichous rod that ferments glucose anaerobically.

Decay in *Q. agrifolia* is discussed under Root Diseases.

Quercus chrysolepis, the canyon live oak, has the densest and heaviest wood of any oak, and according to Metcalf (*955*) trees of this oak have grown to a larger size than any other oak in America. This, however, likely refers to diameter or crown spread, rather than to height, since the largest canyon live oak reported (*7*) is 12 ft. in diameter with a crown spread of 130 ft. but a height of only 70 ft. However, heights over 100 ft. have been reported (*279*). The leaves are glossy above and typically holly-like (*1367*).

The canyon live oak extends from southwestern Oregon along the Coast Range and the western slopes of the Sierra Nevada Mountains of California into Mexico. It is common in narrow canyon bottoms, coves, sheltered depressions, and along steep canyon sides. It is short boled and spreading with large, horizontal limbs much like those of the live oak *Q. virginiana* in the South. The species is tolerant, growth is slow and uniform, and a maximum longevity of 250 to 300 years has been estimated (*1367*).

Quercus virginiana, the live oak, has a very restricted range, extending in a narrow coastal strip from North Carolina to Georgia where the range widens to embrace the southern third of Georgia and all of Florida. It again becomes a coastal strip tree from western Florida to Texas, where its range widens, extending about 300 miles inland (*468*). The gnarled, spreading, moss-draped live oak, although having a limited natural range, has been planted throughout the South. Little success has attended the planting of live oaks outside the South Atlantic Coastal Plain, the southern half of Georgia, Alabama, and Mississippi, all of Louisiana, and east Texas. A dwarf variety, *gemmata*, and what appear to be intermediate forms, occupy much of Florida. Variety *fusiformis* occurs in the western extremity of the range.

Live oak will grow on a variety of soils from dune sand to clay, but it must have abundant soil moisture, a humid atmosphere, and warm, temperate to tropical temperatures. It is remarkably resistant to salt. Wells (*1550*) points out that live oak is the most important component of what he calls a salt-spray climax on the North Carolina Coast.

Declines of live oak have had much attention from Virginia (*554*) to Texas (*397*). Much of this gradual dying out a limb at a time and stagheading from Virginia to Louisiana appears to have been caused by the chestnut-blight fungus *Endothia parasitica* in some cases following cold damage to the trees. Live oaks are subject to frost cracks, and occasional winters have brought temperatures below 15 degrees F., even to the coast of the Gulf of Mexico. *E. parasitica*, known to invade wounded live oak, has been identified on cankers on live oak following these cold periods. The effect of this fungus on live oak is much as has already been described for it on *Q. lyrata*, the post oak, to which it is clearly pathogenic. Cankering is less obvious on live oak.

The decline in Texas is a different syndrome. It has occurred, sporadically at least, since 1933, and consists of a yellowing or mottling of foliage, dying of branches, and death of whole trees. The onset may be very rapid and an apparently healthy tree may decline and succumb in a few weeks. Dunlap and Harrison (*397*), after carefully examining diseased trees and culturing from them, could come to no conclusion as to the cause. The Texas condition is thus distinct from the live oak decline further east that involved *Endothia parasitica* attack of bark tissues following abiotic injury.

Another unusual aspect of the pathology of live oak is that in January and February the foliage supports the uredo and telial stages of the southern cone rust *Cronartium strobilinum*. Since only an evergreen oak could provide inoculum to infect the pine strobili at this time of year, there is a very close correlation (Matthews and Maloy *937*) between the range of live oak and the distribution and intensity of cone rust on longleaf and slash pine.

A feature of the picturesqueness of live oak is its almost universal drapery of Spanish moss *Tillandsia usneoides*. While this epiphyte does not parasitize trees, it can become so abundant that it chokes out inner foliage, resulting in poorly foliated branches of very low vigor.

Seedling Diseases.—Most acorn rot by fungi is associated with weevil injury. Davis et al. (*360*) state that even when weevil tunnels involve only a very small portion of the cotylendons, ensuing fungus decay can destroy the acorns. They mention a decay of the radicle of germinating white oak acorns caused by *Rosellinia quercina*.

Although *Phoma glandicola* has been identified frequently on acorns of white oak and bur oak (*8*), and a dry rot has been attributed to it (*822*), proof of pathogenicity is lacking.

In Pennsylvania seedlings in patches 2 ft. across have died of a collar rot caused by a fungus with conspicuous mycelium, that grows over the soil and attacks the stems at the ground line (*360*).

Phytophthora cinnamomi has been reported killing white oak seedlings in an eastern nursery, and Crandall and Gravatt (*303*) list many other native oak species as susceptible. Others, notably *Quercus agrifolia* and *Q. stellata*, are listed as resistant.

Powdery mildews have become abundant enough to stunt and deform seedlings in nurseries.

Thelephora terrestris, widely cited as a smothering fungus, can be a pathogen when its sporocarp surrounds and engulfs a slow-growing seedling. In the case of pine seedlings it has been shown to be mycorrhizal.

Hart (*599*) reported a root rot of seedlings of northern pin oak (*Q. ellipsoidalis*) caused by *Cylindrocarpon radicicola*, a fungus known to cause root rot in seedlings of conifers and hardwoods in Europe. Roots were gradually girdled over a 2-year period following sowing of acorns, and many had necrotic zones 2 to 4 in. below the ground line. Hart illustrates the very conspicuous sporodochia which formed on the dead areas, and also the typically 1- to 2-septate conidia. He found that black oak (*Q. velutina*) and scarlet oak (*Q. coccinea*) were also susceptible to infection. Some races and some individuals were able to overcome small areas of infection.

Dodder (*Cuscuta*) (*856*) can be a nursery pest, feeding upon seedlings by means of its slender, leafless, curling, yellow-orange, twining stems.

Nematodes (see *Q. palustris*) are strongly suspected of having a role in the decline and death of some oak seedlings. Notes on nematodes are provided under Root Diseases of *Quercus* spp.

Foliage Diseases.—Many fungi produce spots, blotches, and blights of oak foliage, but rarely do any of these leaf diseases result in damage exceeding unsightliness. The principal diseases are anthracnose, mainly on white oaks; leaf blister, mainly on red oaks; Actinopelte spot, on all oaks; Monochaetia blotch, all on oaks; the pine-oak rusts; and some powdery mildews.

For many years anthracnose of both sycamore and the oaks was all attributed to *Gnomonia veneta*. Comparison of anthracnose isolates from sycamore, oaks, walnut, and elm, together with pathogenicity and culture studies, led Schuldt (*1265*) to erect two categories: Type I (*Gnomonia veneta*), obtained from sycamore, white oak, and bur oak, which produced conidia measuring about $6-8\mu \times 3-6\mu$, and a beaked, ascus stage on overwintered foliage; and Type II (*Gloeosporium quercinum*), obtained from white oak, red oak, elm, and walnut, which produced conidia measuring $10-19\mu \times 4-13\mu$, and no perithecia. Schuldt cites still other differences.

There has been a tendency to regard *Gloeosporium quercinum* as the conidial stage of *Gnomonia quercina* and to attribute all anthracnose on oaks to it (*8, 822*). However, Schuldt (*1265*) never obtained a perfect stage for his *Gloeosporium* that attacks oaks, elm, and walnut, and he does not mention *Gnomonia quercina* in his paper. He does attribute infections on white and bur oaks both to the *Gloeosporium* and to *Gnomonia veneta*. He concedes that these two fungi (his Type I and Type II) may simply be different biotypes of one fungus, *G. veneta*. Neely and Himelick (*1015*) suggest that the anthracnose fungi on sycamore and on oaks be considered as distinct species and prefer the name *Gnomonia platani* for the sycamore fungus (see *Platanus occidentalis*). This would presumably correspond to Schuldt's Type I, but this latter typé attacks not only sycamore but also white and bur oak (*1265*).

Anthracnose is more common on white oaks, chiefly *Quercus alba*, than on any of the other oaks. In early summer irregular, brown areas develop, which often adjoin veins and the midrib and may involve most of the leaf area. Irregularity of shape of spots and blotches, often with some leaf distortion and papery texture, are diagnostic characteristics. Late in the growing season the dark-brown acervuli of the *Gloeosporium* sp. can be seen as raised pustules, mainly on the veins and midrib.

Another oak leaf disease that is particularly severe in the South on all oaks but those in the white oak group is the leaf blister (*Taphrina caerulescens*). Leaf blister is rated one of the major shade tree diseases of the South on all of the "red" oaks, although not otherwise economically important. Hepting and Fowler (*661*) illustrate, together, examples of leaf blister on scarlet oak foliage and anthracnose on white oak foliage that serve to distinguish these diseases. Whereas the blister causes discrete, roundish bulges in the leaf tissues, with some cupping and twisting, anthracnose causes a formless, ragged blighting.

Ovoid ascospores of *T. caerulescens*, like those of the closely related peach-leaf-curl fungus, are formed in a palisade of asci that form between the cuticle and the upper epidermis (*619*). The asci and expelled spores form a whitish bloom over the blisters—usually by midsummer. The ascospores may bud in the asci or form germ tubes. They overwinter on bud scales, where they are easily destroyed by dormant sprays (*520, 644*).

A small leaf spot that often reaches epidemic proportions on members of the red oak group in the South, and occasionally appears on species of the white oak group and on *Acer saccharum, Cercis canadensis, Liquidambar styraciflua*, and *Carya* spp. is caused by *Actinopelte dryina*. It forms small, roundish, red-brown, discrete spots 2-5 mm. across. Fruiting bodies are epiphyllous and superficial, $60-110\mu \times 20-40\mu$, with a membranous scutellum, and the surface is ribbed with radiating, yellow to brownish strands. The scutellum is borne on a columella with the conidia pushed out from under the scutellum. The conidia are elliptic, hyaline, and about $12\mu \times 18\mu$ (Limber and Cash, *863*).

By August Actinopelte spots can be so numerous and confluent as to cause major blighting. While itself a primary pathogen, *A. dryina* often fruits on lesions caused by other fungi or by abiotic agents, and, in spite of the oddness of its manner of fruiting, it is often misidentified.

A spot anthracnose (*Elsinoë*) of *Quercus falcata* is described under this oak species.

The so-called oak pine rusts are those whose aecial stages either cause cankers or abort cones on the hard pines of the South, and whose uredial and telial stages are formed typically on the lower surfaces of oak foliage. The white oaks are seldom affected, but in severe-rust years heavy infection takes place—particularly on leaves of the red oaks, water oaks, willow oaks, and runner oaks. *Cronartium fusiforme,* the fusiform rust (see *Pinus elliottii*) ; *C. quercuum,* the eastern gall rust (see *Pinus* spp.) ; and *C. strobilinum,* the southern cone rust (see *Pinus elliottii*), all form uredo and telial stages on southern oaks, but these rusts cannot yet be distinguished from each other on their oak hosts. In its oak stages *C. conigenum,* a southwestern gall rust which alternates between the cones of *Pinus leiophylla* and the leaves of *Quercus emoryi* and *Q. hypoleuca,* also appears to be like the others.

While the above rusts look virtually identical on oak leaves, there are differences in oak-host preference and in time of fruiting. Thus, since *C. strobilinum* infects pines in midwinter, the telia must form their sporidia on evergreen oaks. This explains the close relationship between cone rust and the range of the evergreen live oak (see *Q. virginiana*). Other oaks in Florida and south Georgia sometimes behave as evergreens (e.g. *Q. nigra* and *Q. phellos*), and these may harbor the cone-rust fungus in their leaves from spring until the time of pine infection the following January or February.

However, *Cronartium fusiforme* and *C. quercuum* must produce their telia and sporidia in the spring, at which time the new growth of the southern pines is infected. Thus, for example, April telia on new oak leaves indicate *C. fusiforme* or *C. quercuum* (which may ultimately prove to be one species), while late-January telia on evergreen foliage of the preceding summer indicate *C. strobilinum.* These three formae are not distinguishable morphologically on most telial hosts, but *C. fusiforme* and *C. strobilinum* can be differentiated from *C. quercuum* on black oak (*Quercus velutina*) on the basis of infection types, as described by Dwinell (*399*).

The time span from oak-leaf infection to sporidial exhaustion in *C. fusiforme* in the South is usually a matter of only 3 or 4 weeks in early spring, according to Powers and Roncadori (*1135*) ; in *C. quercuum* further north on jack pine it may be 2 months; while in *C. strobilinum* it may be 9 months (from April to January). Thus, identification of these rusts has often been based upon the dates when viable telia were observed and on which oak they appeared. The mycological characteristics are given by Arthur (*46*), who lumps all four of the American *Cronartium* spp. alternating between oak and pine under *C. quercuum,* although the Cummins supplement separates *C. quercuum* from *C. fusiforme.*

A brown-bordered "eye-spot" is caused by *Marssonina martini* (probable synonyms are *M. quercina* and *M. quercus*) on the eastern oaks, excluding live oak. Hyaline, 1-septate, fusoid conidia are formed in epiphyllous acervuli on discrete spots. Although often abundant, these eye-spots form too late to constitute a problem.

Virtually all of the eastern oaks that reach into the South are subject to the black mildew of the foliage caused by *Morenoella quercina,* especially trees in moist, warm situations. It can cause a twig blight of white oak (*1555*). Leaf spots are dark purple, appearing subcircular, ranging from tiny to ½ in. across on the upper surface, and irregular and brown below. Although the mycelium is superficial early, it develops subcuticular hyphae in late summer, with a black shield covering a cushion of fertile cells. In the spring the shield ruptures with maturing of the asci.

A large, brown, zonate leaf spot commonly develops late in the growing season, mainly in the southern Appalachian Region on *Castanea* spp. and on several oaks, mainly *Q. alba, Q. stellata, Q. prinus,* and most members of the red, willow, and water oaks as well as live oak, red maple, winged elm, and most of the hickories (*624*). Graves (*536*) illustrates and describes the disease (see *Castanea dentata*), and refers the cause to *Monochaetia desmazierii*. Guba's monograph (*558*) places this species under *M. monochaeta*.

The foliage of *Quercus gambelii, Q. garryana, Q. imbricaria,* and *Q. lyrata* sometimes bears the "black yeast" *Microstroma album.* Cooke (*284*) describes it as having "acervuli white, hypophyllous, scattered to gregarious, plane; conidiophores club-shaped, rarely weakly branched, hyaline, 20–25μ long; conidia ovate-oblong, unequal, 1–2 guttulate, hyaline, 5–7μ."

Among the most common leaf diseases are the powdery mildews, and they have also been singled out as of importance in nurseries (*360*). They are of virtually no importance on the well-aerated foliage of large trees in the field, but foliage on oak sprouts 1 to 5 years old is very likely to be whitened and disfigured by powdery mildew with the approach of fall weather.

The most common mildew species on the oaks is *Microsphaera alni,* which has been reported from oaks in all of the groupings, whether red, white, or live oak, and it occurs countrywide. It can be easily identified by the much-branched distal ends of the perithecial appendages (*151*) and the fact that the perithecia have several asci. Another common species is *Phyllactinia guttata* (*P. corylea*), the perithecia of which also have several asci, but the appendages are unbranched and have bulbous proximal ends. It has been reported on most of the oak species, regardless of whether red or white, except for the chestnut oak group.

A third powdery mildew fungus known as brown mildew occurs on leaves and shoots and is confined to the oaks. It has not been reported from the willow, water, and live oaks of the South but is known on *Q. alba, Q. macrocarpa, Q. michauxii,* and *Q. stellata,* and in California it can cause witches' brooms on the coast live oak *Q. agrifolia* (*988*). It is caused by *Sphaerotheca lanestris,* the perithecium of which has one ascus and simple, sinuate appendages (*1555*). On the West Coast live oak the most conspicuous symptom is a powdery, white, stunted growth, developing from certain buds that produce swollen, fleshy shoots, with bract-like foliage.

Hawksworth and Mielke (*617*) record the fungi known to cause brooming diseases of western oaks. These include, in addition to *Sphaerotheca lanestris* brooming *Quercus agrifolia,* a *Cronartium* brooming *Q. chrysolepis,* a species of *Exoascus* probably responsible for brooming *Q. lobata,* and *Articularia quercina* var. *minor* brooming *Q. gambelii* in the central to southern Rocky Mountains.

The leaves of *Quercus agrifolia* sometimes are covered, mostly on the upper surface, with so-called "black mildew." The symptoms and cause, *Vertixore atronitidum,* are described under *Umbellularia.* Another black mildew, caused by *Chaetophomella setigera* (*991*), is much less common on this oak. A dark, sooty mold on the upper surface of the foliage of *Q. chrysolepis* is caused by *Acantharia echinata* (*991*).

In California the foliage of *Quercus kelloggii* and some other oaks is occasionally very severely attacked by *Septoria quercicola.* It produces small, angular, dead spots visible on both sides of a leaf. Branches may be bare of leaves by the end of August.

Late in the growing season oak foliage may be spotted by many fungi. Thus, discrete spots have been attributed to several species of *Phyllosticta,* and dead leaves on the ground in the spring often bear perithecia of *Mycosphaerella* spp., notably *M. maculiformis* but others also. It is likely that some of the *Phyllosticta* spp. are spermatial stages of the *Mycosphaerella* spp.

Tehon (*1383*) stated that the species of *Septoria* that he examined appeared to fall into five species: *S. quercus, S. querciti, S. dryina, S. quercina,* and *S. quercicola.* He provided a small and simple key to the separation of these species. He also named *Leptostroma querci* as a leaf-spot fungus on *Quercus imbricaria,* characterized by amphigenous, tan, membranous to carbonaceous pycnidia that open by a slit, releasing 1-celled, hyaline, long-oval spores, $7–10\mu \times 2–3\mu$.

Tehon (*1382*), in examining species of *Phyllosticta* on leaves of *Quercus* spp., recognized 15 species and provided a key to their separation based on morphologic characteristics of the affected host tissues and of the fungi themselves.

Stem Diseases.—The oaks are subject to many canker diseases. Some of these have already been mentioned in the accounts of specific oaks because they have noteworthy host preferences. Thus, while the chestnut-blight fungus *Endothia parasitica* may be found harmlessly fruiting as a saprophyte on virtually any oak, it probably causes the most important killing and disfiguring disease of post oak (*262*) and can be a major wound parasite of live oak. In an oak-defect study in the southern Piedmont, Bryan (*180*) found 14 percent of the post oaks he examined had cankers caused by *E. parasitica.* This fungus, following cold injury to live oak, appears to have been a major cause of a decline of this tree from Virginia to Alabama (see *Quercus virginiana*).

Another *Endothia, E. gyrosa,* that produces conspicuous, dark-red, perithecial stromata on dead bark around stem injuries and exposed and damaged roots, is almost entirely saprophytic but may have the capacity to aggravate injury from other causes. It is distinct from *E. parasitica* in culture (*1283*). Weir (*1542*) inoculated the exposed roots of trees of *Quercus velutina* and *Fagus grandifolia,* and extended lesions were formed, spread being fastest in the oak roots. He considered the fungus able to act as a wound pathogen on oak roots.

Strumella canker (*S. coryneoidea*) is a major oak disease in the Lake States, Central States, and parts of the Northeast. Although it is now well established that this *Strumella* is the imperfect stage of the discomycete *Urnula craterium* (*338, 715*), the disease will likely continue to be known as Strumella canker because only the black, sooty cushions of *Strumella* spores appear in association

440

with the highly distinctive cankers, while the *Urnula* stage, with its blackish, fingerlike, dentate-rimmed ascocarps (*338*), fruits mainly on fallen, decaying branches, old stumps, and other oak debris.

Strumella cankers are concentrically fluted, retain the bark, typically cause the tree to bulge on the side opposite the canker, and the canker fungus causes rot behind the canker. Illustrations are provided by Bidwell and Bramble (*110*) and by Boyce (*151*). Hepting and Fowler (*661*) show photographs of Strumella cankers together with comparative photographs of some other hardwood cankers. Efforts to control this disease by eradication in a forest in which it was abundant were unsuccessful. Two areas in western Maryland where experiments in the efficacy of eradication were carried out by Roth and Hepting (*1207*) had, respectively, 50 and 132 Nectria-cankered oaks per acre and 25 and 74 Strumella-cankered oaks per acre.

Another canker that often occurs along with Strumella throughout the Northern States, especially in western Maryland and Virginia, is caused by *Nectria galligena* (see *Betula alleghaniensis*). Also a target canker, its face is typically free of bark, the wood behind it is usually sound, and red perithecia may appear around the canker margins. The concomitance of Nectria and Strumella cankers in certain areas of high rime-ice accumulation, and their virtual absence in most of the South below Virginia, might be accounted for by Grant and Spaulding's explanation of axillary infection of *Nectria galligena* resultings from cracks caused by the weight of ice and snow (*530*).

While Nectria and Strumella cankers are common in many parts of the North, the so-called canker-rots are particularly common in the South. The latter are caused by heartrot fungi which grow outward from their rot columns, penetrating the sapwood, and then killing areas of cambium. This results in the formation of large, irregular, partially callused stem lesions on which the causal fungi generally can be found fruiting. Toole (*1416*) describes and illustrates the canker-rots caused by *Irpex mollis, Polyporus hispidus,* and *Poria spiculosa. P. spiculosa* tends to be circular with a depressed center, and instead of a conk on the living tree it usually produces brown punk tissue in the canker (see *Carya* spp.) (*180, 215*).

Davidson et al. (*342*) describe and illustrate depressed cankers on several hardwoods, including oaks, behind which the rotted wood of the central cylinder was white to light brown and had a sweetish odor. These cankers and rot were caused by *Stereum murrayi*, the thin sporophores of which occurred occasionally on cankers on living trees but more often after death.

Roth (*1200*) gives a good illustrated account of cankers and decay by *Irpex mollis* which he found to be common in the Southeast on white oak, chestnut oak, southern red oak, and black oak. A branch stub almost always occurred at the center of the canker. The sporophores are small, whitish, and leathery, and the pore surface is made up of short teeth. The decayed wood projects outward in lobes, in transverse section, from the rotted center of the woody cylinder. The rotted wood is white and has a spongy but tough texture.

441

Polyporus hispidus cankers are usually several feet long with irregular, partly callused margins and bear the dark, soft-velvety, applanate sporophore (*661*) of the fungus often at the top of the lesion. These conks deliquesce at the end of the growing season, drop from the tree in late fall, and for months thereafter can usually be found as remnants on the ground beneath.

Living oaks, beech, and hickory in northern Georgia have been observed to die back from a bark disease caused by *Hypoxylon atropunctatum*. Following killing of cambium and invasion of sapwood, the rough bark sloughs off, exposing effuse, thin stromata bearing brownish, dusty masses of 1-celled, spherical conidia, 3–4μ across. Thompson (*1404*) suspected that lack of vigor predisposed oaks to this disease. *H. atropunctatum*, after conidial production, forms perithecia in pores that appear as black dots peppered over the flat stromata covering the inner bark. Thompson describes and illustrates this disease. Many other species of *Hypoxylon* occur on oaks, both as simple saprophytes and as sapwood invaders that immediately follow infection by the oak wilt fungus.

Branches of southern oaks infested with scale insects are very likely to bear the brown felts of *Septobasidium* spp. Couch (*292*) lists 14 species of *Septobasidium* on species of *Quercus*, and many of these occur on the branches of several species of oak. Occasionally lesions are caused by the thalli of these fungi, although they always live on scale insects. Species of *Septobasidium* are virtually confined to the South.

One of the commonest oak-twig blights is caused by *Physalospora glandicola*, long known by one of the following imperfect-stage names: *Diplodia longispora, Dothiorella quercina,* or *Sphaeropsis quercina*. It has already been annotated under *Quercus prinus*, a prime host in the Appalachian Mountains. It has not been reported from the West. Severe attack leaves trees looking as if they had been subjected to cicada injury. By midsummer dead shoots with attached brown leaves appear scattered over the trees. Infection takes place in twig wounds, ultimately killing twigs and branches, and sometimes causing brown, sunken branch cankers. The black, multiloculate stromata develop on killed parts, producing single-celled, ovate, hyaline conidia. Overwintered stromata can produce typical clustered perithecia, the asci of which each produce eight hyaline ascospores. Usually only the conidial stage, with its innate, covered pycnidia, is seen by casual observation of blighted shoots. This fungus has been observed on oak galls and on acorns, as well as on shoots and leaves.

There are four species of *Physalospora* on oaks, but only one, *P. glandicola*, is a pathogen. The others (*P. abdita, P. obtusa,* and *P. rhodina*) are saprobes on oak. The perfect and imperfect stages of these fungi have had a complex nomenclatural history with much synonymy (*1484*).

Warty excrescences occur on stems or branches of most oak species which, for many years, were regarded as manifestations of the crown-gall disease. These tumors, which occur on both oaks and hickories over most of their ranges, were proved by Brown (*177*) to be caused by a species of *Phomopsis*. Her illustrations of oak tumors, including large ones of burl size, from which she isolated her *Phomopsis* indicate that the Phomopsis galls and the rough burls so common on oaks throughout the East represent the same disease.

A non-gall condition of large, localized stem swellings common on white oak is described under *Q. alba*.

The eastern leafy mistletoe, *Phoradendron serotinum,* is common on oaks in the South. Live oaks are often heavily infected, but the mistletoe may be masked by the normal evergreen foliage of the tree. Davis (*356*) reports an interesting case of the "gluing fungus," *Hymenochaete agglutinans,* spreading from *Quercus nigra* twigs to *P. serotinum* shoots, producing necrotic, girdling lesions on the mistletoe stems.

The hairy, leafy mistletoe of the West, *Phoradendron villosum* subsp. *villosum* (*1445*), causes witches' brooms of *Q. agrifolia, Q. chrysolepis,* and some minor western oaks. It is known mainly in California and Oregon (*1580*).

Vascular Diseases.—The most important vascular disease of *Quercus* spp. is oak wilt (*Ceratocystis fagacearum*). Although species of the red oak groups succumb most readily to this disease, all oaks tested and some relatives and near relatives in *Castanea, Castanopsis, Lithocarpus,* et al. are also susceptible (*171*). Members of the white oak group die slowly, often a limb at a time, and sometimes harbor the pathogen in their vascular system without showing any symptoms. The range of the wilt embraces 18 states and occurs within an area delimited by a line from central Pennsylvania south along the Appalachian Mountains almost to Georgia westward through Tennessee and northern Arkansas to the eastern edge of the Great Plains, then northward into Minnesota, and eastward through Wisconsin and southern Michigan to central Pennsylvania. It has also been reported from Texas (*707*), well outside its main range.

External symptoms in the red oaks may show as early as May, with a bronzing and apparent water-soaking of irregular leaf areas followed by copious abscission of leaves, often while still green. The last annual ring may or may not be darkened by gums, as in other vascular wilts; but when chips for isolating are cut so as to include the last ring, in defoliating trees, they generally yield the fungus in culture, whether or not this ring is discolored. The literature on oak wilt surpasses in volume that on any American tree disease, with the possible exception of the white pine blister rust. For purposes of diagnosing the disease and identifying the causal organism, reference to a few inclusive publications such as the following would suffice: True (*1452*), Kuntz and Riker (*823*), Fowler (*473*), and Hepting (*646*). Many aspects of the etiology of *C. fagacearum* as it affects bur oak are discussed in a series of notes by Nair, Kuntz, and Beckman (*1009*).

In addition to knowing the range of oak wilt and the gross symptoms as described above for red and white oaks, anyone attempting diagnosis should be familiar with the sporulating mats and pressure cushions (*671, 1452*); the use of a proper culture medium for isolating the fungus and its appearance in culture (Barnett, (*61*); and the sex and compatibility makeup of the fungus which, as Hepting et al. (*671*) showed, determines the production of perithecia. The endoconidia, the angular growth habit in culture, and the beaked perithecia are also very useful characteristics in diagnosis (*732*).

Merrill (*951*) provides an analysis of oak-wilt incidence over a period of many years in Pennsylvania and West Virginia.

The only other noteworthy vascular disease in oak is wetwood. While not as common in oak as it is in *Ulmus, Populus, Salix,* and some other genera, infection of wounds by bacteria and yeasts often takes place, resulting in fluxing, sour odor, and discoloration localized in sapwood near the wound (*603*). In some trees of the red oak group, bacterial infection of the entire bole may result in unusually dark heartwood and a foul odor following cutting while the wood is still moist.

Periodically, following very cold weather roots and butts of white oak can develop a cracking and fluxing on an epidemic scale (see *Quercus alba*).

Root Diseases.—The root-rot fungi of oak fall into three categories: (1) those few that are not Hymenomycetes; (2) those Hymenomycetes which play a secondary role in the death of trees and cause little butt rot; (3) those which play a secondary role in tree death, but can rot not only the woody tissue of roots but also can cause extensive butt rot. It is doubtful that any of the root-rot fungi could be termed a primary pathogen on oak.

In the first group are *Phytophthora cinnamomi,* known to rot occasional oak nursery seedlings in the Southeast; and *Phymatotrichum omnivorum,* to which several oak species tested by inoculation in Texas proved moderately susceptible. Oaks, however, are not grown extensively in the Texas root-rot belt.

Ustulina vulgaris (*U. deusta*) (*211*) is an ascomycete that rots hardwood stumps and only occasionally invades the roots and butts of living trees. It produces black, crustose stromata on exposed rotted areas and on stumps.

In the second group are *Armillaria mellea* and its Deep South analogue, *Clitocybe tabescens.* For characteristics separating these two fungi see *Aleurites.* Rhoads (*1168*) indicates killing of *Q. falcata, Q. laurifolia, Q. suber,* and *Q. virginiana,* by *C. tabescens* in Florida. Klotz (*806*) gives illustrations in color of the rots and mushrooms of both fungi. The two organisms behave very much alike with respect to pathogenicity.

On oak and most other hardwoods *A. mellea* is secondary, or at most, weakly pathogenic. Staley (*1348*), in determining the role of this fungus in his oak-decline complex, came to this conclusion, and Boyce (*151*) also assigns this secondary role to *A. mellea* on hardwoods. For declining oaks Staley describes and illustrates necrosis of the cortical tissue toward the root ends and whitish, subcortical felts beneath the bark. He found the fungus difficult to isolate unless tissue from the advancing margin of a massive mycelial mass was used. As a tree declines from some other cause *A. mellea* follows up the cortical region of the root to and beyond the root collar. Mycelial fans and felts appear, and black, copiously branching rhizomorphs form. The latter are flat when under bark and round when growing free in soil (*151*).

Wood rot follows subcortical invasion and may extend, at the most, only a very few feet into the trunk. The decayed wood is white, becomes very soft and wet, and often displays fine, black lines through the rotted wood. The cultural characteristics of *A.*

mellea are distinguished by scantness or lack of aerial hyphae and the formation of branched, brown rhizomorphs that penetrate the agar deeply, as described by Davidson et al. (*343*) .The formation of rhizomorphs in culture depends upon the media used and varies among isolates.

It is common for the stumps of oaks that were healthy when felled to produce large numbers of the honey-colored, annulus-bearing mushrooms of *A. mellea* several years after felling, indicating that this fungus can live on or near roots or perhaps in the wood of minor dead roots without causing visible injury to forest oaks.

Oak stumps are also known to provide the food base for *A. mellea,* enabling it to ramify through the soil (*883*) and kill young white pines for a radius of at least 30 ft. around large stumps.

Aggressiveness by *A. mellea,* of the type shown and described by Klotz (*806*) for California citrus and as cited under *Aleurites fordii* and *Pinus strobus,* does not apply to the oaks except on the West Coast, where this fungus is especially damaging. In California *A. mellea* is known to attack many woody plants, and Raabe (*1141*) reports it there as a pathogen to *Quercus virginiana* and other tree genera. Although *A. mellea* is frequently suspected when forest oaks decline for unknown reasons, because it usually appears somewhere on the roots of the declining trees often in rhizomorph form, it is rarely if ever a primary parasite on hardwoods under forest conditions in most of the country.

This last-stated point of view seems in conflict with Long's conclusion (*883*) in 1914 that *A. mellea,* although it was what he termed a hemiparasite, was directly responsible for the death of oaks and chestnut in a New York area. As omnipresent as this fungus is in the oak forests of the East, if it could kill otherwise vigorous oaks, acting as a primary parasite, we would expect the oaks to be virtually exterminated rather than thriving as our most abundant hardwood group.

Polyporus dryadeus is another example of a fungus that, in oak, confines its activity to the roots. In white fir, however, it can also cause butt rot (*885*). Fergus (*438*) provides excellent illustrations of extensive root rot of a large, overmature scarlet oak by *Polyporus dryadeus*. He also reviewed the literature on this fungus as a root-rot pathogen and questioned whether it can be considered more than a "low grade" pathogen, able to rot root wood but with little capacity to kill trees.

Morrison (*1004*) has reported *Clitocybe olearia* associated with declining *Quercus agrifolia* and *Platanus racemosa* in the San José Hills of California. The sporophores of *C. illudens*, a similar species, fluoresce, but those of *C. olearia* do not. Other decay fungi isolated or observed on declining oaks in that area included *Armillaria mellea, Fomes applanatus, Hypholoma sublateritium, Pleurotus ostreatus,* a *Daldinia* sp., and a *Polyporus* sp. Morrison postulates that the California oak decline has been in progress for many years and that *Clitocybe olearia* may occur late in a succession of implicated fungi, and thus has become obvious only in recent years.

As mentioned under the discussion of white oak, Toole (*1419*) describes cases of pathogenicity to pole-size white oaks ascribed to *Corticium galactinum,* a fungus occasionally considered an active root parasite on other deciduous trees, particularly apple (see *Malus*).

Root fungus group three, which is comprised of root and butt fungi with a normally minor role in causing death but a major role in causing butt rot, includes mainly *Polyporus berkeleyi, P. curtisii, P. dryadeus, P. lucidus, P. spraguei,* and *P. sulphureus.*

The fungi in group three are what are sometimes called wound-rot fungi, in that they infect through dead roots and scarred roots and butts. Old street trees and old lawn trees, trees on grazed wood-lots, and forest trees with scars from fires or logging are particularly subject to the root and butt rots of this group.

It is appropriate here to call special attention to the publication by Davidson, Campbell, and Vaughn (*343*) on the cultural identification of 50 fungi that cause decay in living oaks in the United States. Methods as outlined in this bulletin and in the work by Nobles (*1038*) in Canada now form the basis for the determination of most wood-rot fungi in the absence of sporophores. Although one may feel that he can identify certain wood-rot fungi without sporophores (e.g. *Polyporus berkeleyi* by the honey-like odor, or *A. mellea* by the soft, wet, white texture of the decayed wood), experience has shown that for all but a few fungi identification requires culturing the organism or having an unquestioned relationship between a sporophore and the main body of rotted wood. Therefore, the diagnostician is referred to the above publications with reference to cultures and to the works of Overholts (*1067*), Boyce (*151*), and Lowe and Gilbertson (*892*), in particular, for identification of the conks (sporophores) of wood-destroying fungi.

Two phanerogamic plants parasitize oak roots in the East. They are not noticeably harmful, but more study is needed to determine their effects on tree vigor. *Conopholis americana* forms large, rounded woody knobs on the roots. The plant, called squaw root, has several thick, subcylindric, brown to yellow stems resembling open white pine cones arising from the roots. *Pyrularia pubera,* called oilnut or buffalo nut, is a small parasitic shrub with obovate-oblong, pointed leaves that are distinctly veiny. The fruit is very characteristic, as it is finger-sized, long-pyriform, and has a flat top and a tapering base. Plant and fruit yield an acrid, poisonous oil.

The nematodes of American oaks, except as reported under *Quercus palustris,* the pin oak, have received very little attention. Root-knot nematodes (*Meloidogyne* spp.) have been reported on oak seedlings from California nurseries, and meadow nematodes (*Pratylenchus*), from Maryland nurseries.

While many nematode species have been isolated from the roots or rhizosphere of species of oak in the United States (*1222*), few of the reports indicate root damage associated with the nematodes. Injury was indicated in the cases of *Hoplolaimus galeatus* on *Quercus palustris* and *Q. rubra* in Delaware; *Meloidogyne* sp. on *Q. agrifolia* in California; *Pratylenchus* sp. on *Q. palustris* in Delaware; *Trichodorus* sp. on *Quercus* sp. in Alabama; *Xiphinema* sp. on *Q. stellata* in Texas; and *X. americanum* on *Q. laurifolia* and *Quercus* sp. in Florida. A later tabulation by Ruehle (*1224*) lists 12 species of nematodes in 10 genera, associated with oaks in the Southeast.

Trunk Rots.—Some of the most comprehensive forest pathology studies made in the South have been devoted to the decay problems of the oaks. Hepting and Hedgcock (*663*), working with Appalachian oaks on commercial logging operations, found that 94 percent of the butt rot and 70 percent of the total rot was ascribable to fire damage. They also related cull to tree age, tree diameter, and other variables. Later Hepting (*640*), in a separate study of Appalachian oaks of saw-log size, more clearly defined the relation of cull to age and size of basal wound and provided a statistical mechanism for estimating and predicting cull losses in oaks, based on incidence and size of basal wounds. Earlier he had determined the rate of decay associated with fire in young Mississippi Delta hardwoods to be rising from 2 to 4 linear inches per year upward from a scar, the rate depending in part upon the causal fungus. In addition, he related decay to oak species, scar size, repeated scarring, fungi responsible, and also listed the principal insects that attacked the wood behind fire scars.

Toole (*1417*), working in the Mississippi Delta 25 years later, extended Hepting's Delta study to trees of saw-log size and included a larger number of non-oak species. Toole's study also provided methodology for estimating decay, using new knowledge on hollows, butt bulges, and additional observable tree features. Toole found that decay in his oaks spread upward from scars 2 ft. per decade for overcup oaks and 1.3 ft. for red oaks. These rates, which were in general agreement with Hepting's, although somewhat slower, also depended to a major degree on the fungus causing the rot.

Hepting's (*640*) Appalachian oak study on predicting rot in fire-damaged oak was followed by a study of trunk rots in oaks of that region of saw-log size (*662*). Oaks were placed in four risk classes, based upon the number of rotten stubs, holes, wounds, and blind knots visible on a tree. Class A trees were those with clean boles and they averaged less than 5 bd. ft. of rot cull per tree; class B trees had one or two large, rotten knots and averaged 25 bd. ft. of cull; class C trees had three or four large, rotten stubs and averaged 100 bd. ft. of cull; and class D trees, with four or more rotten stubs and wounds or eight or more blind knots, had 220 bd. ft. of rot cull. Up to age 150 years the average amount of trunk rot was negligible, even among trees in the high-risk class, indicating 150 years to be a safe rotation age for Appalachian oaks insofar as rot is concerned.

The extensive studies of cull determined from Appalachian commercial logging operations, as reported by Hepting and Hedgcock (*663*), showed the oaks to vary in rot-cull percentage from 7 percent in post oak to 16 percent in chestnut oak, on a board-foot basis. In the North Carolina Coastal Plain, Gruschow and Trousdell (*557*) found saw-log size trees of white oak to have a rot cull of 4 percent, and other oaks, 7 percent.

Toole (*1422*) followed his fire-decay work with a study of rot-fungus entrance through dead branches in southern hardwoods, a large percentage of which were oaks. Although 25 fungi were identified with these rots, four species caused 52 percent of the identified causes of rot. These were *Stereum gausapatum* (29 percent) (*343*), *Poria andersonii* (9 percent) (*210*), *Stereum subpileatum* (7 percent) (*884*), and *Pleurotus corticatus* (7 percent) (*772*).

Over 80 percent of the dead branches sampled were 3 in. or less in diameter. Few such branches had much rot behind them at the time, but a high percentage were infected with fungi that would eventually cause much decay.

In addition to the root rots caused by fungi such as *Armillaria mellea* and *Corticium galactinum,* the root and butt rots caused by fungi such as *Polyporus berkeleyi* and *P. sulphureus,* and the trunk rots caused by fungi such as *Stereum frustulatum* and *Polyporus hispidus,* there is still another type of decay that has come to be called "sprout rot," and in the oaks by far the predominant organism involved is *Stereum gausapatum.*

Sprout rot, which is very common in the oaks and basswood of stump-sprout origin and less common in the northern hardwoods, is a decay of a parent stump that progresses into sprouts arising from this stump, ultimately developing into butt rot of the attached sprouts by the time they are old enough to have formed heartwood.

Roth and Sleeth (*1209*), reporting on studies of 3,200 trees in seven oak species all of stump-sprout origin, in seven states, found sprout rot in from 11 percent of the chestnut oaks to 39 percent of the black oaks. The average linear extent of rot was slightly over 3 ft. above ground. Sprouts arising at or below ground level showed extremely little sprout rot, while those arising 2 or more inches above ground level had a high percentage of such rot. Cultures from the decayed wood yielded *Stereum gausapatum* in 62 percent of the cases, with *Fistulina hepatica* and *Armillaria mellea* the next two most frequently isolated fungi. *F. hepatica* causes a firm, brown rot that involves mostly the parent stump and extends little into the living sprout.

Roth and Hepting (*1205*) worked out the factors that affect the likelihood of oak sprouts to decay and discovered that the slight apical dominance afforded the sprout arising highest on a stump, even by just an inch or two, tends to result in the sprout of highest origin becoming ultimately the dominant residual sprout of a clump. Being of highest origin, it is the one most likely to develop stump rot. They also found (*1206*) that some rot develops when a companion sprout, especially if over 3 in. in diameter, is cut or girdled. Such rot is less common than that which develops from the parent stump through the stump-to-sprout heartwood bridge.

Roth (*1198*) also studied healing and defects following oak pruning and found that when wounds over 1.5 in. across were created in pruning, 15 percent of the wounds resulted in decay with a linear-decay extent exceeding 2 ft. in 10 years. Scarlet and black oaks "feathered" little after pruning, chestnut oak feathered to some extent, white oak feathered prolifically, and the sprouts persisted.

Hepting and Fowler (*661*) have diagrammed the procedures recommended in thinning sprout stands so as to keep decay to a minimum. Basically this involves (1) favoring low-origin sprouts; (2) favoring those that are separated from a companion sprout by a low U-shaped crotch; and (3) making a flush, slanted, saw cut when removing a companion sprout.

Roth (*1197*) found that crossties and posts cut from sprout trees that had been incipiently butt-rotted, but including no obviously decayed wood, rotted faster in service than ties cut from entirely sound trees. The principal fungi that decayed the wood in use were, in order, *Hypholma sublateritium, S. gausapatum, a Poria* sp., and *Polyporus versicolor;* thus, except for *S. gausapatum,* they were not the fungi that caused the main sprout rot in the living trees.

Although more than 50 fungi can cause heart rot in living oaks, a few deserve special mention. Their rots and sporophores are described in the standard reference works alluded to earlier (*151, 892, 1067*), and in leaflets by Roth (*1203*) and by Toole (*1416*).

The incidence of the different rot fungi cannot be judged by sporophores, and for this reason the earlier publications on several oak-rot fungi gave false impressions of their importance. Thus, important oak heartrotters such as *Poria cocos* and *P. andersonii* (*640*) were not even mentioned in the earlier cull publications because they do not fruit on living trees, and early observers based their decay reports on the fungi they saw fruiting on the trees, not on fungi isolated in pure culture from the decaying wood. Other fungi which do fruit readily on living, heart-rotted trees, such as *Fomes everhartii* and *Fomes robustus*, have made up a very small proportion of the fungi isolated in the many later oak-decay studies in which cultures were made routinely to determine the fungi mostly responsible for the decays. Yet, as Riley (*1174*) reports for *Polyporus obtusus,* some commonly fruiting fungi may be locally important. In this connection it is worth mention that in most of the reports of *F. igniarius* on oaks, this name has been mistakenly applied to *F. robustus*. Most authorities now question whether *F. igniarius* is more than a rarity on oaks.

Several oak decay studies in recent years have involved extensive culturing from the decaying wood, and lists of the fungi isolated, frequency of isolation, and some measure of extent or linear rate-of-decay per year have been provided (*637, 640, 663, 1417, 1422*). The following list of the more important oak-decay fungi is in approximate order of importance, based on incidence and decay rate.

Fungus:	Main region: North, East South, West	Relative decay rate	Mainly confined to root and butt (B) or generally through the trunk (T)
Hydnum erinaceus	N,E,S,W	Fast	T
Stereum frustulatum	N,E,S	Fast	T
Pleurotus ostreatus	N,E,S,W	Moderate	T
Stereum gausapatum	N,E,S,W	Fast	B
Polyporus hispidus	N,E,S,W	Fast	T
Polyporus berkeleyi	N,E,S,W	Fast	B
Polyporus spraguei	N,E,S,W	Fast	B
Armillaria mellea	N,E,S,W	Slow	B
Polyporus lucidus	E,S,W	Fast	B
Polyporus curtisii	E,S	Moderate	B
Polyporus dryophilus	E,S,W	Moderate	T
Poria spiculosa	E,S	Moderate	T
Lentinus tigrinus	S	Moderate	T
Polyporus sulphureus	N,E,S,W	Slow	B
Polyporus obtusus	N,E,S,W	Moderate	T
Fomes everhartii	N,E,S,W	Moderate	T
Poria andersonii	N,E,S,W	Moderate	T
Fomes geotropus	S	Slow	B
Polyporus zonalis	S	Moderate	B
Polyporus fissilis	S	Moderate	B
Poria nigra	E,S	Moderate	B
Stereum subpileatum	S,W	Moderate	T
Polyporus frondosus	E,S	Moderate	B

More complete tabulations of sprout-rot, butt-rot, and trunk-rot fungi isolated from oaks, as determined from the studies of many investigators, are provided by Davidson et al. (*343*). Many of the fungi in these latter lists are saprobes and, as in the case of *Fistulina hepatica* and *Ustulina vulgaris*, have a very limited capacity to decay the wood in a living tree. Thus, a complete listing of fungi found in association with rot of any kind in an old or damaged oak tree (*8, 822*) has little meaning in terms of heartrot capacity.

Bryan (*180*), working on defect as apart from cull in southern Piedmont hardwoods, dealt primarily with species of oak. The main characteristics of the wood that limited "clear-cuttings" for lumber were knots, epicormic branching, insect holes, trunk scars, and decay. The decay in most cases was caused by *Poria spiculosa* and *Polyporus hispidus*, both of which he illustrated. He also encountered some cases of *Fomes everhartii* rot and many post oaks with *Endothia parasitica* cankers.

Hepting and Roth (*666*) determined how long several heartrot fungi would continue to fruit on felled trees, if the common sanitation recommendation of felling "conky" trees and knocking the conks off were followed. Several oaks were felled that, when standing, bore conks of either *Fomes everhartii*, *F. robustus*, *Polyporus hispidus*, *P. sulphureus*, *P. obtusus*, or *P. dryophilus*. After felling, the conks were knocked off. Both *Fomes* species continued to produce annual hymenial layers for over 10 years after cutting, but none of the species of *Polyporus*, except *P. sulphureus*, produced fresh conks after 5 years.

The question of relative decay resistance of the wood of seven species of native oaks was studied by Scheffer et al. (*1247*) Laboratory tests showed that wood of trees of the white oak group was substantially more resistant than wood of trees of the red oak group. *Q. prinus* was most resistant, then *Q. garryana*, then *Q. alba*, and then *Q. bicolor*. Among red oaks, although *Q. coccinea* has often been regarded as particularly decay-susceptible, there was no significant difference in its decay rate as compared with that of *Q. rubra* and *Q. velutina*. Resistance was variable among individual trees of a species but not notably variable between regions. Decay resistance increased from pith to the outer heartwood and from lower trunk to upper trunk.

Zabel (*1639*) conducted studies on decay resistance within individual white oak trees using as test organisms *Stereum frustulatum*, which caused the greatest weight loss; *Daedalea quercina*, which caused less; and *Lenzites trabea*, which caused the least decay. Decay resistance was highest in the outer heartwood. White oak had hot-water extractives that were highly toxic to *L. trabea*, that Zabel considered as belonging to the tannin complex, since removal of tannins from the extract eliminated its toxicity.

Stains and Discolorations.—Changes in color of wood in living oaks can occur as a result of wetwood (see Vascular Diseases) and, to a local extent, around wounds. Studies on effects of increment boring (*669, 1433*) showed the oaks to heal the borer holes within a very few years with a minimum of discoloration and decay. Staining seldom extended more than a few inches above and below the holes, and a negligible amount of decay and no cankers resulted from boring oaks. Species with diffuse-porous wood, however, developed extensive sapwood staining.

Oak sapwood is subject to several kinds of abiotic discoloration after being cut into lumber (*1252*). Much of this darkening has been called oxidation stain and is attributable to the formation of brown, gummy, phenolic substances in the rays, parenchyma, and other living cells. Abiotic stains in oak have developed as a result of air drying, kiln drying, improper placement as flooring, and in certain other situations.

In most cases the abiotic stains are characterized by the gum deposits inside what had been living sapwood cells at time of felling, while the biotic stains are characterized by colored mycelium in these cells. Iron fastenings, or dip solutions high in iron, will generally produce an inky-black stain in moist oak wood as a result of the iron reacting with tannin of the wood to produce iron tannate.

The biotic stains, which are grouped under the term sap stain or blue stain are not always bluish or gray. In oak the bluish stains are most likely to be caused by *Graphium rigidum*, *Ceratocystis coerulescens*, or other related fungi, while a purple to pink stain can result from the pigments of *Penicillium roseum* or *P. aureum*, a yellow stain from *P. divaricatum*, and a crimson to orange stain from the soluble pigment of a species of *Geotrichum*. The subject of sap stain cannot be covered with justice here. Pursuit of it can well begin with the Scheffer and Lindgren bulletin (*1252*) and the published work of Rumbold, Verrall, Davidson, and others as listed in Moore's bibliography (*1003*).

Verrall (*1476*) reports on specific fungi associated with some ambrosia beetles, and Wilson (*1585*), on fungi associated with the Columbian timber beetle, the insect that produces what is known as flag-worm injury to white oaks.

Funk (*487*) has described an ambrosia beetle symbiont fungus on Oregon white oak as *Monilia brunnea*, associated with *Monarthrum scutellare*.

Miscellaneous Pathology.—The "sturdy oak," in certain decades and certain areas, has revealed a marked tendency to decline and die in situations and on a scale that has caused much bafflement and concern. Drought is known to cause stagheading and dieback over extensive areas, as shown by reports of scouts surveying oak forests for wilt. McIntyre and Schnur (*909*) determined that the drought of 1930 in Pennsylvania had little effect on the growth of white, chestnut, and red oaks, but resulted in a loss of 3-percent basal area in black oak and 37-percent basal area in scarlet oak.

During the early 1960's the extent of oak dieback and mortality by unknown cause in the entire Southeast became so alarming that the USDA Forest Service ordered an inquiry into what seemed the dubious future of large areas of southern hardwoods, mostly oak. Undoubtedly some of this decline was a result of the dry years of the middle 1950's. Some resulted from attacks of the elm span worm and canker worms. A midsummer defoliation can have a drastic effect on an oak, and in some cases one defoliation can kill a tree.

Staley (*1348*) investigated one of the types of decline, reported by many, that occurred mainly from Pennsylvania to North Carolina and affected *Quercus coccinea*, scarlet oak, and *Q. rubra*, northern red oak. Initial symptoms were reduced increment, chlorotic and aborted foliage, crown thinning, "feathering," dieback, "lammas shoot" formation, diminished carbohydrate reserves, and rootlet mortality. Later symptoms included browning and wilting of foliage, *Agrilus* attack, absence of starch in root phloem, heavy rootlet mortality, and death. He concluded that his "oak decline" resulted from a sequence of events starting with leaf-roller defoliation and then aggravated by *Agrilus* attack, *Armillaria* root rot, late spring frost, drought, and unfavorable soil, all causing diminished food production and leading to decline and death.

The heavy mortality of red oak in Canada that followed ice-storm damage (*321*) is another example of the unfavorable response of many oaks to injury.

It is likely that other declines of oaks, in areas and with species not studied by Staley (*1348*), also have had their genesis in defoliation by insects or hail, followed by the many omnipresent insects and root fungi that do not ordinarily attack healthy oaks but are quick to invade weakened oaks. When any climatic impact, particularly drought, is added to defoliation, a major recession of oak is likely to occur. The defoliating insect phase of oak "declines," which can trigger the decline process has often been missed by investigators, since this phase may precede obvious decline on a major scale by several years. Staley's careful inquiries into the history of the cases he discovered bore testimony to this important point. His cited literature is valuable material to anyone faced with diagnosing enigmatic declines of oak. Nichols (*1031*) has assessed the different kinds of mass oak mortality that took place in Pennsylvania over a 10-year period, with special attention to oak declines, oak wilt, insect activity, and weather effects.

The cause of a serious dieback and death of many live oaks in Texas has not been determined (see *Q. virginiana*). This malady is a different entity from the dieback of this species further east, with which *Endothia parasitica* is associated.

Iron-deficiency chlorosis has been a common problem with pin oaks (see *Q. palustris*) in some of the less acid soils of the Central States. In these cases the nature of the trouble has been evident because of the success obtained in curing it with chelated iron compounds.

Several species of *Quercus* (*Q. alba*, *Q. nigra*, *Q. palustris*, *Q. stellata*, and *Q. virginiana*) reacted to air pollution in the Houston, Texas, area, presumably mainly from sulfur dioxide, by the loss of isolated trees with or without burning of foliage (*911*).

Little is known of mycorrhizal relationships in the genus *Quercus*. Trappe's worldwide review (*1442*) lists a very large number of fungi reported as being mycorrhizal with oaks, but out of over 100 such ectotrophic fungal associations there was support by experimental proof in the case of only two fungi, *Hebeloma crustuliniforme* on *Quercus* sp., and *Tuber magnatum* on *Q. robur*, the English oak. Very few mycorrhizal associations were reported for American oaks, and most of these involved *Cenococcum graniforme*. In the case of native oaks no mycorrhizal associations have been proved by pure-culture synthesis.

A bacterial disease of the acorns of two western live oaks is described under *Quercus agrifolia*.

Ciborinia candolleana is a fungus that produces dark, glabrous apothecia on plant parts on the ground in the spring. It attacks leaves, bud scales, and the bark of small twigs of *Quercus rubra* in North America and other oaks in Europe (*76*).

According to Sparrow and Sparrow (*1332*) the sensitivity of red oak to gamma radiation from a cobalt–60 source was close to average for hardwoods but less than the sensitivity of softwoods (see *Picea glauca*).

Black locust
Robinia pseudoacacia

The range of black locust is uniquely split in two parts, with one embracing essentially the Appalachian, Allegheny, and Cumberland Mountains from Pennsylvania to Alabama, and the other reaching from central Missouri south to south-central Arkansas and west to the Great Plains. Natural, scattered pockets and much planted acreage have widened this basic range (*468*).

Black locust thrives in humid situations, typically on moist slopes below 3,400 ft., in coves, and on most eastern mountain sites that are neither poorly drained nor hot and dry. Soil type is otherwise not critical. The tree does best on limestone soils and on those with a friable texture. While it has done well on many acid spoil banks, it has failed consistently when planted on badly eroded, compacted, clayey soils of the southern Appalachian Region. Black locust is intolerant, average in sensitivity to ice damage (*310*), and a high-ranking soil-builder both because of its legume root nodules and because of the high calcium content of its foliage (*244*). It resisted damage from salt spray in New England (*1632*).

Black locust regenerates commonly from root suckers, and hardwood cuttings root readily. Grafting succeeds well and has been used to propagate the so-called shipmast locust (*R. pseudoacacia* var. *rectissima*), a variety which, along the North Atlantic seaboard, produces trees of superior form and durability. Other cultivars are available in the nursery trade.

Growth is fast for the first 20 to 30 years, but trees seldom live over 100 years. The root system is shallow. The wood is hard and very durable. Black locust, especially on poor or dry sites, is often ruined by the locust borer. When stands are attacked by the locust leaf miner, another insect, they look as brown as though dead, but late summer defoliation is not very harmful. The pathology of the species is dominated by the almost ubiquitous attacks of the heart-rot fungus *Fomes rimosus* and by the striking virus witches' broom.

With respect to black locust plantations in Alabama, Goggans and May (*516*) considered as most injurious the borer, leaf beetles, fire, cattle, and undergrowth. Fire and grazing were particularly harmful. Because it is very intolerant, the species cannot withstand competition from undergrowth and vines.

Seedling Diseases.—Susceptibility to damping-off in nursery beds is considered by some to be high (*468*). However, Davis et al. (*360*), while conceding that losses have been high in some nurseries, consider black locust ordinarily free of nursery diseases. Seeds may fail to germinate properly if not suitably treated to make the seed coats permeable to water. Too drastic treatment, however, with sulfuric acid, hot water, or scarification, can lead to molding in the soil.

Davis et al. (*360*), who give a comprehensive account of the nursery diseases affecting black locust, stress the difference in the disease situation from nursery to nursery. Thus, *Phytophthora parasitica* caused a shrivelling of the tender tops of young seedlings in some nurseries, *P. cinnamomi* caused a taproot rot in another, *P. citrophthora* has been known to cause root rot, and *Rhizoctonia solani* sometimes caused damping-off or "sore shin," and has been known, in dense stands, to cause a leaf blight characterized by the coarse, mycelial strands binding the foliage together. Heat lesions sometimes were common.

Lambert and Crandall (*828*) give a complete description and illustrations of the seedling wilt caused by *P. parasitica* as it occurred in nurseries in Virginia and North Carolina. The most severe damage was to plants 1 to 3 weeks old; often, all of the plants in a patch would die, and the patches varied in size. Cotyledons drooped at first, then the entire remaining parts collapsed and shrivelled without any clearcut lesions at the ground line. Older seedlings sometimes developed necrotic lesions on stem, petiole, or leaf, and continued to function. The roots remain uninjured in this disease.

Sclerotium bataticola (*Macrophomina phaseoli*) can cause damping-off and root rot of seedlings of any age. In woody seedlings the stems just above the ground line may be filled with the small, black sclerotia of this common pathogen.

As in the case of most tree species commonly raised in quantity in forest nurseries, losses have also at times been attributed to species of *Pythium* (*360, 957*), particularly *P. ultimum;* to species of *Fusarium;* and to nematodes in the genera *Meloidogyne* (root knot) and *Pratylenchus.* Buchanan (*185*) lists additional fungi associated with black locust seedling diseases in other parts of the world.

Attack of foliage by *Fusicladium robiniae* is common but not serious, unless the onset takes place when the seedlings are in the cotyledonary stage. The spots are small, with light centers and dark margins. Late in the season the spots produce a stroma under the cuticle, with dark, 2–celled conidia produced successively as they are pushed out from the ends of new growing tips. Davis and Davidson (*359*) describe this disease and also a Macrosporium blight in forest nurseries.

Iron-deficiency chlorosis is not uncommon on calcareous nursery soils. In the Texas root-rot belt high susceptibility to the rot precludes raising black locust (*1379*).

The yellow, leafless, twining stems of dodder have been known to attack seedlings (*856*). *Cuscuta arvensis* has been specifically identified as a black locust pathogen in several eastern nurseries.

Seedling wilt has been ascribed to *Verticillium albo-atrum* in Illinois, but this fungus is not known to cause a vascular wilt of black locust trees that are well beyond the seedling stage, as it does with maple, catalpa, and elm.

Foliage Diseases.—The leaf diseases of black locust are only of academic interest, except in nurseries where proximity of large

454

numbers of plants of uniform size plus the usual watering practices can create a situation where leaf diseases become important. *Phytophthora parasitica* and *Fusicladium robiniae* have already been mentioned in this connection.

Three species of powdery mildew attack the foliage, particularly the leaves of rank-growing sprouts and seedlings in nurseries. They are the very common *Erysiphe polygoni* in the far West, *Microsphaera diffusa* in the East, and *Phyllactinia guttata* (*P. corylea*) in the Southwest (*151, 1555*).

Whenever a widespread and severe browning of foliage takes place, the locust leaf miner (*Chalepus dorsalis*) should be suspected (*297*).

Stem Diseases.—Aside from the heartrots and the brooming disease, which are described later, no stem diseases of black locust are either economically important or notably disfiguring. On reasonably good sites the tree is generally clean boled and is not successfully attacked by canker fungi or shoot-blight pathogens. On poor sites, however, perhaps mainly due to attack by the locust borer (*Megacyllene robiniae*), dead areas on the stem are common, and infection by secondary fungi together with *Fomes rimosus* or *Polyporus robiniophilus* results in highly defective boles.

The canker and dieback fungi listed by Buchanan (*185*) and in the Index of Plant Diseases in the United States (*8*) as "on twigs" or "on branches" are all either saprobes or secondary invaders. Only three organisms have been reported to actively parasitize the stems of trees out of the seedling category. *Nectria galligena*, sometimes in part *N. coccinea* as a synonym, has produced occasional stem cankers. It is not easily recognized on black locust in the absence of its red perithecia, because attack is usually irregular, conforming to borer-injury patterns, and any tendency to "target" cankering is likely to be obscured by the thick, uneven bark.

The eastern leafy mistletoe, *Phoradendron serotinum*, is known to attack branches mainly on wetland sites of the Southern Coastal Plains.

The fungus *Aglaospora anomia* (*A. profusa*) can cause twig blighting and some minor cankering. The fungus is characteristic in its fruiting on stems, in that walled perithecia are themselves enclosed in an innate stroma. The conidia are formed on the stroma. The ascospores are dark and multiseptate (*267*).

Among the common saprobes on black locust twigs are *Botryosphaeria ribis* (see *Cercis*), *Fusarium lateritium* (see *Morus*), *Nectria cinnabarina* (see *Acer*), and *Physalospora obtusa* (see *Malus*).

Root Diseases.—There are no important or noteworthy root diseases of black locust in the United States other than within the Texas root-rot belt, where this tree is classified as extremely susceptible to *Phymatotrichum omnivorum* (*1379*). For this reason black locust is not among the trees planted there (*1627*), although farther north it has a place as a shelterbelt tree in reasonably moist situations.

Armillaria mellea is in its usual role on hardwoods a secondary parasite, aiding in the coup-de-grâce to trees already considerably weakened from other causes.

Although *Thielavia basicola* has been reported from black locust

455

roots, it is likely not parasitic. *Thielaviopsis basicola* causes a black root rot of vegetable crops including legumes, and is described by Westcott (*1555*). On black locust it may precede *Thielavia* in the roots (*8*).

It is worthy of note that in Japan their *Helicobasidium mompa*, which causes a violet root rot much like *H. purpureum* (*Rhizoctonia crocorum*) in the United States, is very destructive to *Robinia pseudoacacia* plantings. Purplish rhizomorphs and purplish mycelium growing on the roots and stem base, and resupinate, velvety sporophores at the base of the trunk are characteristic. Fine roots and the cambium of larger roots are killed by this fungus (*185*).

Trunk Rots.—By far the predominant trunk rot is *Fomes rimosus*. Its conks are applanate, hard, woody, and become black and cracked above and soft, dark brown below. The rotted wood is soft, yellow, and spongy. Most black locust trees of large size in the southern Appalachian Region bear conks of this fungus. A conk 3 to 4 in. across may have rot behind it that extends only a foot or two up and down the trunk (*661*). Large conks, however, often mean that a 6- to 10-ft. section of the trunk is rotten. Many conks may develop on a single living tree, and the dead bark areas associated with them indicate that many infections start at locust-borer holes.

Polyporus robiniophilus is a fungus that is rare over much of the tree's range, occasional in the southern Appalachian Region, and common in the Ohio River Valley. It forms small, corky, white conks, often in imbricate clusters. Even a few linear feet of rotted heartwood may produce a conk. The rotted wood is soft, white, and spongy.

Occasionally other fungi will cause heart rot in living locust trees. These include *Fomes applanatus* (California), *F. igniarius*, *F. ohiensis*, *Polyporus lucidus*, *P. obtusus*, and *P. sulphureus* (*1067*). The other wood-destroying fungi listed as occurring on locust in the United States (*8, 185*) are almost entirely saprobic.

Scheffer and Hopp (*1250*), in laboratory tests using *Fomes rimosus* and *Poria incrassata*, found the Flowerfield strain of black locust to decay the slowest, shipmast locust next, and common locust somewhat faster. As in oak, resistance to decay was greatest in the outer heartwood, and within this zone, in the lower part of the tree. Also as in oak (*1639*), resistance was positively correlated with concentration of hot-water extractives. Such extractives were highly toxic to the fungi.

Miscellaneous Pathology.—One of the most unusual forest-tree diseases is the brooming disease of black locust, which occurs over most of the tree's natural range and is caused by a graft-transmissible virus (*Chlorogenus robiniae* H., *Polycladus robiniae* McK.) (*531*). Symptoms are vein clearing, greatly reduced leaflet size and tapered bases, proliferation of buds and branches, and a brooming habit that varies from a single broom to many, intermixed with normal branches. In extreme cases an entire small locust tree is itself a broom, with such proliferation of fine shoots and such reduction in foliage size that the small broom-tree resembles a redcedar tree. Hartley and Haasis (*604*) reported on the transmissibility of the virus, and Grant et al. (*529*) reported on the history and symptoms of the disease. Similar symptoms are produced by this virus in honeylocust (*Gleditsia triacanthos*).

There are viruses infecting species of *Robinia, Ulmus*, and many other tree genera, that are referred to as NEPO viruses. This term refers to those polyhedral viruses that are transmitted by nematodes (*199*). In the case of trees, *Xiphinema* spp. are the main carriers of NEPO viruses. NEPO viruses can also be transmitted by species of *Longidorus*. The symptoms expressed by a single NEPO virus may be very different on different species and even on different varieties within a species.

In California a littleleaf condition has resulted from zinc deficiency in the soil.

Trappe (*1442*), in his worldwide review, reports only one fungus to have made mycorrhizal association with black locust, namely *Clathrus cancellatus*.

Willow
Salix spp.

Alluding to the willows by species presents no problem when dealing with such species as *Salix alba, S. babylonica*, or *S. discolor*. However, for a large segment of this genus nomenclature has approached the confused situation found in *Crataegus*, and often for the same reason, namely hybridization or sport formation. Compare the statements of Illick (*743*) and of Ball (*56*) on the subject. Illick says, "It is, however, difficult to distinguish the different willows from each other. . . . Very often one leaves a willow in despair because of the fact that it was impossible to identify it." Ball says, "Willows have been called a difficult group of plants by so many writers that many people believe it to be true. . . . The willows really are not a difficult group." Since willows are dioecious, care must be used in basing identification on sexual characteristics.

Illick puts the number of native species of *Salix* in North America at about 175. Little (*872*) includes 36 in his check list of native American willows. In dealing herein with the diseases of willows, the pathology of four native species and two introduced species is described. This is deemed sufficient to bring out the main diseases of important willows in the United States.

While the willows are rated very intolerant by Baker (*54*), they exhibit tenacious vitality within the 50 to about 100 years that they live, by sprouting and suckering. The wood is weak, and the trees tend to become hollow with age.

Salix alba, white willow. Introduced from Europe, this species has escaped widely over the United States, except in the hotter parts of the South, appearing mainly along streams, in low wet areas, near cities, and around farmsteads (*56*). It reproduces copiously and can grow to fairly large size, but it is short-lived. The color effect of the tree is whitish because the serrulate leaves are glaucous below. The branchlets are yellowish and brittle.

The pathology of this species is not distinctive among willows. Of the diseases, only willow scab (*Fusicladium saliciperdum*) has at times been notable. The leaf rusts *Melampsora paradoxa* (=*M. bigelowii*) and *M. epitea* (=*M. abieti-capraearum*) are sometimes conspicuous in the Northeast and the Lake States. The former alternates with *Larix* spp., and the latter, with *Abies* spp.

Salix babylonica. Known as the weeping willow because of its long, pendulous branches, this tree has become a familiar species on the American landscape, especially around lakes and bordering other wet sites. A native of China (*872*), it is widely cultivated in the United States but seldom escapes cultivation. On moist, warm sites, it grows very fast and with single or multiple stems can grow to large size, occupying much ground. It is likely to be short-lived and to develop excessive stem rot resulting in hollowing. Its prolific branching makes it very susceptible to ice damage (*310*).

Typical weeping willow is fairly resistant to scab and to black canker, but the weeping form, known as *Salix blanda,* has been considered susceptible to "willow blight," which is comprised of these two diseases—scab and canker. Freedom from blight may often be mostly the result of the good air drainage around isolated weeping willows, as compared with the poorer air drainage around native forest-grown black willow (*S. nigra*) trees bordering streams. Weeping willow is susceptible to Cytospora canker (see *Populus*) and to crown gall, but the latter is mostly a disease of nursery trees, and infected stock can be culled out before shipment. The leaf rusts (*Melampsora* spp.) rarely cause serious injury to weeping willow foliage. *Trametes suaveolens* is a major cause of heartrot and wound decay.

Salix discolor. This tree, the pussy willow, has highly pubescent catkins and glaucous undersides of the leaves. It is a shrub or small tree of the North, extending across the continent (*872*), and occurring in the South only in the Appalachian Mountains. It occurs mostly along streams and on moist hillsides, but when planted it will grow in fairly dry situations (*743*). As a street tree, it is resistant to ice damage (*310*). Its only importance is as an ornamental, because of its decorative wooly catkins in the spring.

There are no major diseases of pussy willow. It is subject to scab, black canker, the leaf rusts, and tar spot, but these have rarely done material damage. In the South *Botryosphaeria ribis* (see *Cercis*) has occasionally caused a twig blight, and in the North *Cryptodiaporthe salicina* has sometimes become an aggressive twig-blight pathogen.

Salix eriocephala (*S. cordata* Muehl., *S. missouriensis*). Known as the Missouri River willow, this species has also been called heart-leaf willow and diamond willow. Its heart-shaped (cordate) leaf base is distinctive. It is a tree of the eastern edge of the Great Plains and extends from Manitoba, Canada, southward and eastward into the Ozark Mountains through Missouri, Kentucky, and into the hilly or mountain parts of the Southern States. Ball (*56*) describes it as usually several-stemmed, 5 to 20 ft. high, growing mainly along streams and ditches, around springs, and in wet· ground.

Willow scab is common, but black canker has not been reported from this species. Tar spot, two of the leaf rusts (*Melampsora paradoxa* and *M. epitea*), and two powdery mildews (*Phyllactinia guttata* and *Uncinula salicis*) are the only other common diseases, and they are not notably damaging.

Salix lasiandra. Known as Pacific willow, this tree grows along streams, waterholes, and lakes in damp, gravelly or sandy soil (*1367*), from Canada to southern California west of the Sierra Nevada Mountains (*872*). It is common in western Oregon and Washington, reaching heights over 30 ft. and diameters over 14 in. In identification it helps to know that the bark is cut by cross-seams into flat plates. It is one of the most tolerant of the willows. Its longevity is probably not much over 50 years (*1367*).

Since it is a western willow, many of its diseases are quite different from those of the other willows discussed here. Thus, while Shaw (*1277*) does not report scab or black canker on this species in the Northwest, he shows is host to several western fungi, including *Melampsora epitea, Septogloeum salicis-fendlerianae* (a leaf-spot fungus), and *Sphaceloma murrayi* (a spot anthracnose). Most of the other common pathogens are those found on willows in all parts of the country, including *Rhytisma salicinum* (tar spot), *Uncinula salicis* (powdery mildew), and *Cytospora chrysosperma* (see *Populus* spp.).

Additional fungi peculiar to western species of *Salix* include a leaf spot (*Marssonina apicalis*), a yellow leaf blister (*Taphrina populi-salicis*), and a bark-patch fungus (*Aleurodiscus helveolus*).

Salix nigra. The black willow is, by far, the most widely known, the most abundant, and the largest of the native willows. It occupies moist to wet sites throughout the East and from New England and the Lake States to the Gulf Coast, except for the southern peninsula of Florida. Westward it grows from Minnesota to western and southern Texas, extending into the Great Plains along watercourses (*468*). Its shallow roots require abundant moisture and it will grow in areas almost continually flooded. In tolerance to new flooding it rated highest among the 39 species studied in Tennessee (*583*). Common from the borders of mountain streams to the swamps of Louisiana, it thrives along the entire length of the Mississippi River, reaching its largest size and best quality in the almost continuously flooded batture lands of the Delta. The batture is alluvial riverbank land unprotected by levees.

Black willow is intolerant (*54*), very susceptible to damage by fire and drought, and short-lived, with trees rarely surviving to an age of 80 yrs. The wood is weak, breaking readily under ice or wind stress. In wet flatlands willow tends to grow in pure stands, and since it is ineffective about asserting dominance, such stands often stagnate.

Black willow was listed among the species most resistant to air pollution damage, presumably mainly from sulfur dioxide, in the Houston, Texas area (*911*).

Top and branch rots account for more than 80 percent of the rot in black willow (*468*), and many trees are hollow. The low incidence of butt rot reflects the habit of black willow of growing near water, in water, or in otherwise moist situations, and thus escaping fire.

Particularly in the North and extending into the mountains of North Carolina and Tennessee, willow blight (scab and black canker) has in some years been very destructive, and often at least conspicuous. Boyce (*151*) shows a striking photograph of large black willows killed by this blight.

Melampsora spp. rust the foliage of black willow, and powdery

459

mildew is common but not serious. Both *Botryosphaeria ribis* (see *Cercis*) and *Cytospora chrysosperma* (see *Populus*) occasionally cause some twig blight.

Seedling Diseases.—Little is known of the seedling diseases of the willows. Seed is planted immediately after collection, since no dormancy is required. They germinate in a day or two (*1*). High boards placed around the nursery beds tend to conserve the soil and air moisture so important to early growth of the willows. Root and stem cuttings are sometimes used in field planting.

It is occasionally advisable to spray, in situations where the *Melampsora* rusts or powdery mildews attack heavily. These diseases are described below. Willow blight and crown gall are also known as nursery diseases in the North (*360*).

Cytospora canker (see *Populus,* Seedling Diseases) can be an important disease of poplars and willows whenever seedling vigor is impaired by other influences.

It is noteworthy that none of the common damping-off and seedling root-rot pathogens belonging to the genera *Fusarium, Phytophthora, Pythium, Rhizoctonia,* or *Sclerotium* have been reported from willow.

Dodder (*Cuscuta* spp.) has frequently been reported to parasitize willow seedlings, particularly in the West. Its yellowish, twining, leafless stems are easily recognized.

Violet root-rot (*Helicobasidium purpureum*) damage is discussed under Root Diseases.

Foliage Diseases.—The most important disease of willow in North America is called willow blight and results from the combined effects of two pathogens, one referred to as the scab fungus *Fusicladium* (*Pollaccia*) *saliciperdum* (*Venturia saliciperda*) (*63*) and the other, the black-canker fungus *Physalospora miyabeana.* Although both fungi have ascigerous stages, only the conidial stages have been observed in connection with the disease in the United States. Boyce (*151*) gives a good account of this disease and sums up the controversial joint role of these two fungi by stating, "Apparently *P. miyabeana* follows *F. saliciperdum* and increases the damage." Both fungi appear to have been introduced from Europe about the same time. The imperfect-stage name is used for the latter fungus because the *Venturia* stage is so seldom seen.

While *Salix eriocephala* and *S. nigra* are very susceptible to blight, and *S. alba* and *S. discolor* are susceptible (*268*), *S. babylonica* seems resistant. Both of the parasites have the same effect on the host. In the early spring the scab fungus attacks the unfolding leaves, killing and blackening them as it grows into the petioles and new shoots, which also become blackened and, if old enough, develop cankers. Later in the season the black-canker fungus attacks and behaves much like the scab fungus, often attacking foliage missed by the latter or adventitious foliage that formed following the killing of earlier shoots by the scab fungus.

In some moist growing seasons defoliation can be virtually complete, and, if this happens in successive years, large trees can be killed, as shown in Boyce's illustration (*151*) and in Clinton's several striking illustrations (*268*) of severe blight in the Northeast.

Conners et al. (*281*), reporting on willow blight in British Columbia, state, "The constant association of two organisms in willow blight is a remarkable fact." Rupert and Leach (*1229*), as a result of inoculation experiments in West Virginia, observed that the black-canker fungus was much more virulent than the scab fungus and thus tended to assign the major role in the disease to *P. miyabeana.*

F. saliciperdum fruits mainly on dead leaves, particularly on the midrib of the lower leaf surface, during moist weather. Dense, velvety, olive-brown pustules appear, consisting of conidiophores and spores borne singly on them. The spores are ellipsoid, rounded above, narrowed below, and consist of two cells of unequal size. The conidial stage of *P. miyabeana* is a *Gloeosporium.* The acervuli appear mainly in early summer as pink masses. The conidia are one-celled, hyaline or greenish, ellipsoid, and slightly curved.

Blighted willow foliage, bearing the typical olivaceous masses of 1–septate spores of *F. saliciperdum,* has been observed on a few trees in Michigan and abundantly in western North Carolina in addition to the main "blight" areas of the Northeast and British Columbia (*597*).

The commonest foliage pathogens of willows are rusts in the genus *Melampsora.* They produce their uredial (II) and telial stages (III) on *Salix* spp. and their pycnial (0) and aecial stages (I) on either *Abies* spp. or *Tsuga* spp. The uredia are hypophyllous, round, very small, pulverulent, and orange in color, with globoid spores. The telia are hypophyllous, roundish, red brown, and subepidermal, and the teliospores are oblong-prismatic with light-brown walls.

Melampsora epitea is widespread from the Atlantic to the Pacific Coasts in Canada and southward to West Virginia, Iowa, and New Mexico. Its 0 and I stages are on *A. balsamea* in the East and on several *Abies* spp. and two *Tsuga* spp. in the West (*46*). Synonyms are the names *M. abieti-caprearum, M. americana,* and *M. humoldtiana.* Ziller (*1666*) has erected *M. epitea* f. sp. *tsugae* to accommodate the form that attacks western hemlocks and some of the Pacific Northwest willows, leaving under *M. epitea* the forms that attack other conifer hosts and all of the species of *Salix* herein described.

Savile (*1238*) says, "At present it seems advisable to . . . call the whole complex (willow rusts in *Melampsora*) *Melampsora epitea* regardless of aecial host. As our knowledge increases, it will probably be possible to set up several varieties on the basis of host relationship and small morphological distinctions. The only alternative seems to be to make species of the forms on almost every other willow." Later Ziller (*1666*) set up *M. epitea* f. sp. *tsugae* as a step toward defining the elements of this complex. He also recognizes *M. paradoxa, M. ribesii-purpureae,* and *M. arctica* as distinct from the *M. epitea* complex.

Another very common rust of willows is *M. paradoxa,* a species widely known for many years as *M. bigelowii* (*1666*). Of the willows described here all have been reported as hosts to this rust except *S. babylonica.* Its 0 and I stages are on species of *Larix.* On willow Arthur (*46*) separates *M. paradoxa* from *M. epitea* by describing the uredospores of the former as large ($17–24\mu$ long) and the latter as small ($12–20\mu$ long).

M. ribesii-purpureae is a western rust with its 0 and I stages on species of *Ribes* and its II and III stages on many species of *Salix,* including *S. eriocephala* and *S. lasiandra*. It can be distinguished from *M. paradoxa* by its shorter uredospores, as in *M. epitea*, and from *M. epitea* by the very thick $(2–3.5\mu)$ uredospore walls.

M. arctica is an Alaskan, Greenlandic, and Canadian rust that alternates between species in the Saxifragaceae (O and I) and some arctic willows (II and III) not included herein.

A leaf spot of *S. babylonica*, *S. alba*, and *S. nigra*, mainly in the South, is caused by *Cercospora salicina* (*260*). Spots are numerous, irregular, dark red brown, 0.5–5 mm. across, often surrounded with a purplish zone. Fruiting is amphigenous. The long conidia $(2–3\mu \times 15–60\mu)$ have indistinct septa. Chupp (*260*) describes another species, *C. salicis*, on *S. alba*, known only from its type area in Wisconsin.

Two powdery mildews are common on most of the willows, namely *Phyllactinia guttata* (*P. corylea*), which has proximally bulbous perithecial appendages, and *Uncinula salicis*, which has parallel-sided, terminally curved appendages. The powdery mildews can become particularly copious and conspicuous late in the season and on the leaves of vigorous sprouts.

Another widespread willow leaf spot on *S. eriocephala*, *S. discolor*, *S. lasiandra*, and *S. nigra* is the tar spot (*Rhytisma salicinum*). Like the well-known tar spot of maple the spots are very thick, jet black, discrete, and about ¼ in. across. The black spot is a stroma within which the asci form in overwintered foliage on the ground. The ascospores are filiform.

The leaves of *Salix eriocephala* may bear spots caused by *Microstroma boreale*. The spots are brown, reaching 1–2 cm. across, hypophyllous, with acervuli 60–140μ across, and clavate conidia producing one to many acrogenous, fusoid, 1–celled, hyaline conidia 8–14μ × 2–3μ in size (Cooke *284*).

The foliage of some of the western willows, including *Salix lasiandra*, develops numerous "arid," brown, angular to subcircular spots 2–4 mm. across, bounded by an unbordered, distinct line (*363*) caused by *Septogloeum salicis-fendlerianae*. Acervuli are mostly epiphyllous, becoming circular, yellowish depressions. Sporules are hyaline, curved, mostly 1–septate $(3.5\mu \times 15–50\mu)$.

Occurring also on *S. lasiandra* and other western willows, the spot-anthracnose fungus *Sphaceloma murrayae* causes a disease commonly known as gray scab. Leaf spots are round, irregular and somewhat raised, of grayish hue, with narrow, dark-brown margins. The spots are often confluent and may form long, narrow patches along the veins (*1555*).

Yellow leaf blister is a disease of the foliage of *Populus fremontii*, *P. trichocarpa*, *Salix laevigata*, *S. lasiandra*, and possibly some poplars and willows of the Pacific Coast States, caused by *Taphrina populi-salicis* (*994*). Golden-yellow, convex to concave spots form within which palisades of asci are produced on the lower leaf surface.

Several other fungi cause willow leaf spots of minor importance in scattered areas, and many of these have been reported on only one willow species, as indicated in the U.S. Index of Plant Diseases (*8*).

Tehon (*1382*), in examining the leaf diseases of willow caused by species of *Marssonina*, concluded that he had observed 10 disstinct species and that they could be distinguished with "reasonable sharpness." He provides a key to their separation. *Marssonina* is characterized by an open acervulus, bearing hyaline, 2–celled spores.

Stem Diseases.—Willow blight involves some cankering of new shoots as well as leaf and shoot blighting. In its total effects it represents the most important disease of willows in North America (see Foliage Diseases).

A canker recorded from several willows, including *Salix alba*, *S. babylonica*, *S. discolor*, and *S. nigra*, mainly in the South, is caused by *Botryosphaeria ribis* (see *Cercis*). A complete description of this disease on willow is provided by Wolf and Wolf (*1609*). Long, depressed, girdling lesions form on branches and trunks. A single stroma on willow may simultaneously bear conidia, microconidia, and ascospores. The *Dothiorella* stage (*D. gregaria*) was formed in culture. Both pycnidia and perithecia appear as numerous, raised locules in the black stroma. The conidia are 1–celled, fusoid, hyaline, and mainly $5–6\mu \times 18–20\mu$. The ascospores (8 per ascus) are hyaline, ellipsoid, and measure mostly $6–9\mu \times 18–24\mu$.

A canker of willows that occurs also in Europe has been reported from the East, the South, and the Pacific Northwest. Caused by *Cryptodiaporthe salicina*, it is known on *Salix alba*, *S. scouleriana*, *S. nigra*, and some unnamed species of *Salix* in the United States, and on young stems of *S. hookeriana* and *S. scouleriana* in Vancouver. Bier (*111*) stated that in the Vancouver outbreaks during the winter many active cankers could be found on a single stem, originating at nodes, lenticels, and insect wounds. Lesions retain the bark, have a raised or cracked margin when arrested, and under moist conditions will extrude conidial tendrils of the imperfect stage, *Discella carbonacea*. The pycnidia are discoid and imperfectly formed. The conidia are hyaline, 2–celled, and fusoid. The *Cryptodiaporthe* stage forms a beaked perithecium with 8–spored asci and hyaline, 2–celled ascospores. It forms on those parts of the cankers that have been dead the longest.

Cytospora chrysosperma, causing a canker of hardwoods, mainly species of *Salix* and *Populus*, has been described herein under *Populus*. The perfect stage is *Valsa sordida*, but, as in the case of so many pathogens in which the perfect stage is obscure in comparison to the imperfect, the cause of this canker usually is referred to by its imperfect-stage name. Cankers form on trunks and branches, mostly on small trees and trees in poor vigor. The cankers are subcircular, red brown, and if old will expose the wood and reveal killed callus folds. The pycnidia are in a valsoid stroma with irregular cavities. The conidia, which are often extruded in long, fine tendrils during wet weather are hyaline, 1–celled, and allantoid in shape. It occurs countrywide, but it is basically a weak pathogen. *Cytospora salicis* (*Valsa salicina*) has also often been reported as a twig-blight pathogen of several willow species. However, since some of the species of *Cytospora* and their perfect stages in *Valsa* are poorly defined (five species of *Valsa* have been reported on *Salix* in the United States), the accuracy of specific identity may be suspect in the case of some records.

Crown gall (*Agrobacterium tumefaciens*) has been reported from many willow species. However, it is mainly a nursery disease of *Salix babylonica,* since this tree is usually propagated vegetatively, and the disease is spread in the handling and propagation of the plant material. Roundish, warty galls form on any woody parts of the trees, and sectioning or macerating followed by an appropriate stain (*194*), will disclose the bacteria (*392*).

The eastern leafy mistletoe *Phoradendron serotinum* will parasitize willows, but even in the Deep South the willows are not favored hosts to mistletoe. In Lake County, California, willow mistletoe caused by *P. tomentosum* subsp. *macrophyllum* (*1580*) is sometimes parasitized by a species of *Protocoronaria* (see *Populus*).

Occasionally the common hardwood canker caused by *Nectria galligena* occurs on willow (see *Betula alleghaniensis*). In addition, the saprobes *N. cinnabarina* and *N. coryli* grow on the bark or dead wood. The former develops conspicuous, coral-colored stromata that support both red pycnidia and red perithecia. The latter fruits on twig bark and is distinguished by conidia accompanying ascospores in the ascus (*879*).

Root Diseases.—All of the willow species tested for resistance to Texas root rot (*Phymatotrichum omnivorum*) proved either highly susceptible or extremely susceptible (*890*), and therefore no species of *Salix* is among the trees recommended for planting in the root-rot belt (*1627*).

The violet root-rot fungus *Helicobasidium purpureum* (*Rhizoctonia crocorum*) has attacked roots of willow seedlings in the Southwest. The pale-violet mycelium aggregates into strands easily visible to the naked eye. Deep violet-brown sclerotia form on the larger strands, either on the host root or in the soil. Small, stromatoid aggregates of mycelium form on the host surface (*1503*).

Except on the Pacific Coast, *Armillaria mellea* is not known as a root-rot pathogen of willow. Reports of this disease from California and Washington on unnamed species of willow are consistent with the notable aggressiveness of *A. mellea* on citrus, avocado, and other tree species in that region.

Many species of nematodes have been reported from the rhizosphere of species of *Salix,* but the only instance of plant damage concerned root-knot nematodes (*Meloidogyne* sp.) on *S. babylonica,* the weeping willow, in Arizona (*1222*).

Trunk Rots.—Since willows have a short life, and since the wood is very subject to decay, it is not surprising that the Hymenomycete flora of *Salix* is very rich (*8*). However, with a few exceptions these fungi (22 species of *Polyporus* alone) are saprobes, and, if appearing on a living tree, they would be attacking dead branches, dead areas on the bole, or otherwise inhabiting wounds.

Marshall and Waterman (*928*), as well as others, have singled out *Trametes suaveolens* as the most important trunk rot of willow in the North, and this is the only willow-rot fungus that they describe and illustrate in their shade tree disease bulletin. It causes a dry, corky, white rot. The conk is bracket-shaped, about 4 in. across, corky, white to gray, with the upper surface velvety to the touch and the lower having the feel of chamois skin, and with an anise-like odor. Breakage and poor pruning can lead to severe rot by *T. suaveolens.*

Toole (*1427*) determined the amount, cause, and infection courts of decay in black willow in the Mississippi Delta. Cull volume rose from 0 at 7 yrs. to 41 cu. ft. per acre at 34 yrs., but even then it represented less than 1 percent of the gross volume. Most of the rot originated at branch stubs with lesser amounts originating at butt wounds, top breaks, and insect holes. Isolation from decayed wood yielded 19 rot fungi. Those identified were *Daedalea confragosa, Lentinus tigrinus* (see *Quercus*), *Pleurotus corticatus* (see *Quercus*), *P. ostreatus* (see *Quercus*), *Polyporus supinus, P. versicolor,* and *Schizophyllum commune.* All except those indicated "see *Quercus*" are saprobes.

Fungi capable of causing either rot of the central cylinder or rot at wounds of living *Salix* spp. include *Daedalea ambigua, Fomes applanatus, F. connatus, F. fraxinophilus, F. igniarius, F. robustus, Pleurotus ulmarius, Polyporus cuticularis, P. glomeratus, P. hispidus, P. lucidus, P. munzii* (in the Southwest), *P. squamosus, P. sulphureus, P. texanus,* and *Trametes suaveolens* (if the tree is declining) (*1067*).

Willows often develop hollows, and this characteristic, taken together with the weakness of its normal wood and the brief life span of willows, makes it necessary to use judgment in planting weeping willows near homes and play areas, and to check frequently on their condition as they approach large size.

Miscellaneous Pathology.—Bacterial wetwood is discussed in detail under *Populus* and *Ulmus.* With respect to *Salix*, Hartley et al. (*603*) state that in both erect and weeping varieties of *Salix babylonica* and *S. cinerea* and in unidentified, native, streambank willows in Virginia and Nebraska, wetwood was found in nearly all of the trees examined. The willows, along with poplars and elms, are considered particularly subject to bacterial wetwood. When the wetwood of elms and poplars dries, the darkened wood is generally considered heartwood, but when the wetwood cylinder of a willow dies, it takes on the same color as uninfected sapwood and thus is not easily distinguished from it.

The watermark disease of *Salix alba* and *S. caerulea* in Europe is also caused by bacterial infection of the woody cylinder.

The bark of willows, if dead and sometimes if living, supports the growth of species of *Aleurodiscus*, which appear as flat, thin, smooth fruiting bodies often with revolute edges, constituting shallow cupulate structures. Lemke (*858*) describes many amyloid species of *Aleurodiscus. Corticium bombycinum* also may appear on the bark of living willows. Some species of *Aleurodiscus* have been confused with species of *Corticium.*

Approximately 70 fungi have been reported to form mycorrhizae with the roots of trees of *Salix* spp. Most of the reports are from Europe (*1442*), and none of the fungi reported were proved to make such association through pure-culture technique. Most abundant among the fungi reported were *Cenococcum graniforme* and species of *Cortinarius, Hebeloma, Inocybe,* and *Lactarius.*

Toole (*1427*) mentions heavy mortality of *Salix nigra* at a very early age in the Mississippi Delta, and, since he found little rot involved, he concluded that factors unknown to him were responsible for the early stand breakup.

Sassafras
Sassafras albidum

There are only three species of sassafras; one in China, one on Taiwan, and one in the eastern United States, which is described here. The latter's range is bounded roughly by a line from southern New England to Michigan and then southwestward through central Illinois to east Texas and eastward across the Gulf Coast to the Atlantic Ocean, missing the southern half of Florida. The tree occurs throughout the area delimited by the Atlantic Coast and the line indicated above.

Sassafras is a pioneer on abandoned fields and is frequent in open woods. It may be found on any moist, well-drained site, regardless of soil type, but thrives on river-bottom terraces and along the deep-soiled, loessial bluffs along the Mississippi River. It is generally a temporary species, very intolerant, readily giving way to others in the competition of the mixed forest (*468*). Reproduction is sparse and erratic, except for ready sprouting from either stumps or roots. Trees can grow to over 100 ft. in height and up to 6 ft. in diameter, but typically sassafras dies well before reaching 20 in. in diameter. Its short life is seldom due to disease but rather to competition. It is also very sensitive to fire and to salt spray (*1632*), and its lack of hardiness is implicit in its absence from northern New England, northern New York and Michigan, and all of Wisconsin and Minnesota.

Its bark contains spicy, aromatic extractives.

Foliage Diseases.—Sassafras is one of the hosts of the interesting small-spot fungus *Actinopelte dryina* (*863*). This is largely a southern fungus, severely blighting mainly members of the red oak group, sweetgum, black gum, and sassafras (see *Quercus*, Foliage Diseases). This fungus is probably synonymous with the *Actinothyrium gloeosporioides* of Tehon (*1381*).

Glomerella cingulata causes a large, brown spot, and has been described in connection with leaf spotting of species of *Aesculus*, *Cinnamomum, Diospyros, Ficus, Magnolia, Mangifera*, and *Persea*.

The fungus *Stigmatophragmia sassafrasicola* (*1391*) produces circular to somewhat angular spots, 3–5 mm. across, tan to brown above, sharply limited by a distinct, very fine, unraised, purplish margin. Below, it is obscured by leaf bloom. Thyrothecia are few, scattered, hypophyllous only, 200–225μ across, opening with a carbonaceous ostiole. The spores arc hyaline, 3–septate, terete, with tapered end-cells, 14–17μ × 3–4μ. This fungus often occurs on leaves that also bear spots with acervuli of the common *Gloeosporium affinis*.

Tehon and Stout (*1391*), on the same tree as they described the *Stigmatophragmia*, also described *Pseudodictya sassafrasicola*. It produces spots 3.5–6.5μ across, light brown, with a dark-brown to black margin. Pycnidia are abundant, epiphyllous, scattered, becoming carbonized with age, 135–180μ across. Conidia are brown, spherical, 2-septate, 8.5μ × 8.5–11μ. The spores, under the microscope, often appear globose with muriform septation, but when rotated the cells appear as they are, end to end with the center cell largest.

Tehon and Stout (*1391*) also described *Diplopeltis sassafrasi-cola*. The spots are irregularly circular, 3–10 mm. across, dark brown above, with a distinct, conspicuous, purplish marginal line turning to tan. Pycnidia are epiphyllous, few per spot, black, distinctly carbonized, 120–170µ across. Conidia are brown, 1–septate, oblong with rounded ends, 18.5–22µ × 7.5–11µ.

A fourth sassafras leaf-spot fungus described by the same authors (*1391*) is *Metasphaeria sassafrasicola*. The spots are subcircular, with a narrow, dark-brown border, 3–7 mm. across. Perithecia are scattered, membranous, 75–100µ across, with ostiole erumpent epiphyllously. Asci are few, with a short, blunt foot, 44–45µ × 12–13µ. Ascospores are 3–septate, hyaline, 16–18µ × 2.2–2.4µ, and the preapical cell is round.

One of the most widely occurring leaf spots of sassafras is caused by *Mycosphaerella sassafras*, the spermatial stage of which is probably *Leptothyrium kellermannii*. Other sassafras leaf fungi include *Gnomonia sassafras*, *Phyllosticta illinoensis*, *P. sassafras*, and a species of *Septoria*.

Phyllosticta illinoensis (*1387*) causes diaphyllous spots, subcircular, becoming dehiscent, 3–4 mm. across. Pycnidia are membranous, 70–120µ across, with a carbonous ostiole. Spores are bacillar, oblong, straight; ends are hyaline to smoky, 1-celled, issuing out in fuliginous cirrhi. Its spores average 2µ × 3.5µ, while those of *P. sassafras* average 1.5µ × 7µ.

Phyllactinia guttata (*P. corylea*), one of the commonest of the powdery mildews (see *Quercus*), can often be found on the foliage in the autumn.

According to the Index of Plant Diseases in the United States (*8*) both a leaf mosaic (in New York) and a yellows (in Texas) have been observed, and both are regarded as possibly of virus origin.

Stem Diseases.—While a large number of fungi have been reported from twigs and branches of sassafras, none of them are primary parasites. The cankers and diebacks attributed to them, mainly species of *Cytospora*, *Diplodia*, and *Sphaeropsis*, invade tissue weakened from other causes, mostly drought, winter-injury, and age. The *Sphaeropsis* spp. are probably imperfect stages of the common species of *Physalospora* (*P. fusca, P. glandicola, P. obtusa*, and *P. rhodina* (*1484*)), and some of the *Cytospora* spp. are likely imperfect stages of species of *Valsa*.

A nectria stem canker is fairly common in the southern Appalachian Region. Target cankers typical of *N. galligena* appear along the trunks, but isolations and inoculations by the author have failed to confirm the species as *N. galligena*. The perithecia that develop peripherally around the lesions are unusually small and unusually dark red, and cultures had many points of difference from *N. galligena* (*879*). However, this latter fungus also may canker sassafras (*1340*).

The so-called gluing fungus *Hymenochaete agglutinans* grows as a brown felt on branches and, in addition to fastening them together, can kill bark and rot the wood beneath (*151*).

Rots.—Remarkably few reports of wood-rot fungi on sassafras have appeared in the literature. Almost all of those listed in the Index of Plant Diseases in the United States (*8*) are saprobes, except for *Armillaria mellea*. The latter can cause a secondary root rot of living trees. The true heartrot fungi noted are *Fomes igniarius* and *F. ribis,* the latter producing a very small (1–3 cm. × 1–4 cm. × .2–.5 cm.), yellow-brown conk that becomes grayish to black with age. When conks of *F. ribis* are confluent the total dimensions are larger.

Fomes torulosus (1067), which appears to be a large and perennial form of *Polyporus gilvus,* fruits on wounded or dying sassafras trees.

Miscellaneous Pathology.—The only fungus reported to form mycorrhizae with sassafras is *Xerocomus subtomentosus (1442).*

Two root-inhabiting nematodes have been identified from the root zones of this host, namely *Helicotylenchus erythrinae* and a species of *Hemicycliophora,* both from New Jersey *(1222).*

Giant sequoia
Sequoia gigantea

The giant sequoia, in terms of wood volume, is the world's largest tree *(1302).* It grows in isolated groves along a 260-mile belt on the west slopes of the Sierra Nevada in central California *(1264).* Its habitat has a colder and drier climate than the redwood belt along the coast. Annual precipitation ranges from 18 to over 60 in. (mostly 45 to 60 in.), much of it as snow, with snow depths over 10 ft. common. The extreme temperature range is from −12° to 100° F. *(1367).*

The giant sequoia can grow on a wide variety of soils, including moderately dry and shallow types, but its best development is on slightly acid, moist, well-drained soils. Most groves are at elevations of 4,500 to 7,500 ft. and tend to occur in canyons and other moist situations. Many trees are over 2,000 years old, some have exceeded 3,000 years, and estimates of longevity run as high as 5,000 years *(1367).* Intermediate in tolerance, the giant sequoia has few enemies. Fire is destructive through the sapling stage, but old trees, the bark of which may be from 12 to 18 in. thick, are very fire resistant. Lightning can be damaging, and long periods of freezing weather can kill young trees *(1264).*

The wood is bright purplish to rose red when cut, darkening with age. It is very light, brittle, high in phlobatannin *(1264),* and remarkably durable *(1367).* The sap may exude in rosy-purple drops. The tree has been raised in nurseries and grown extensively in California, in the Eastern United States, and in other parts of the world *(279).* Sprout reproduction from roots and stumps, as in redwood, does not occur.

Seedling Diseases.—Heat canker, a ground-line lesion of seedlings, can be damaging, but light shade will greatly reduce its incidence *(1264).* Litter is effective in conserving moisture and keeping the soil temperature around seedlings low enough to discourage fungus attack. High winter light intensities will often turn seedling foliage brownish purple. *Sclerotium bataticola,* a heat-loving, soil-borne fungus *(695),* can kill giant sequoia seedlings where the exposure or aspect leads to high soil temperatures *(1264).* It causes what is called charcoal root rot, and its perfect-stage name is *Macrophomina phaseoli (1323).*

Botrytis cinerea and *B. douglasii (932)* (possibly both one species, *B. cinerea*) cause a gray-mold blight that can kill many seedlings, under mild moist conditions. *Pestalotia funerea* is reported to have caused a seedling needle blight in Texas, but this fungus usually has a weak capacity for pathogenicity.

Foliage Diseases.—A needle blight of giant sequoia in the Eastern States has been attributed to *Cercospora sequoiae* (*693*). The conidia are 3- to 5-septate and echinulate, and while it has some of the characteristics of a *Heterosporium* (*260*), Hodges keeps it in *Cercospora* and discusses its taxonomy (*693*). A tawny mold that grows over the needle surface, caused by *Acanthostigma sequoiae*, can occur in very moist situations. *Wallrothiella consociata* is a harmless needle fungus.

Stem Diseases.—Giant sequoia has proved subject to crown gall (*Agrobacterium tumefaciens*) by inoculation (*1319*). Occasionally a minor branch dieback caused by *Botryosphaeria* sp. has been observed. The harmless saprophyte *Phomopsis occulta* sometimes fruits on dead twigs (*570*).

Root and Trunk Rots.—*Fomes annosus* has been observed as an occasional root- and butt-rotter. The only disease of importance to giant sequoia, however, is a brown, cubical heartrot that has the pocket or pecky characteristics of *Poria sequoiae* rot of redwood. However, the identity of the cause of this principal heartrot of giant sequoia has not been established with certainty.

Sequoia gigantea var. *pendulata* proved moderately susceptible to Phymatotrichum root rot, in inoculations in Texas (*1379*).

Mycorrhizal Relations.—No ectotrophic mycorrhizal fungi have been reported (*1442*).

Miscellaneous Pathology.—Rennerfelt (*1163*), in his study of heartwood constituents affecting resistance to decay, lists the heartwood density of 22 species, most of which had notably durable characteristics. Giant sequoia and incense-cedar had the lowest densities (0.29 and 0.27, respectively) and yet both are very resistant to decay.

Mature trees along roads or openings have been known to topple over on a calm day, and although the cause has not been established, it has been attributed to an imbalance in crown weight, perhaps because of increased growth leading to increased branch weight on the side receiving the most light (*1264*).

Burls, or large trunk and branch galls, occur on some trees, but their cause is not known.

Redwood
Sequoia sempervirens

The redwood attains a greater height than any other American tree and reaches ages exceeded only by its sister species, *Sequoia gigantea*. The largest redwoods tower over 300 ft. tall and grow to ages over 2,000 years. Even many of those which are cut commercially exceed 500 years in age and 200 ft. in height (*279*). The species occurs from the southwestern tip of Oregon along the California coast to Monterey County, south of San Francisco. It grows from sea level to 3,000 ft. in elevation along slopes facing the sea and on flats and ravines where heavy fogs are common.

The redwood has a straight trunk with little taper, much butt swell and buttressing, and very thick bark (sometimes 12 in. thick) when old. These older trees are highly resistant to fire, but young trees can be badly scarred. The tree thrives in a mild, cool climate with ample soil moisture and high atmospheric humidity. Its stands usually receive from 30 to 60 in. of rain annually (279), and temperatures range from 15° to 100° F., with an average of 50° to 60° F. (1367) S. gigantea will grow under colder and drier conditions than redwood (1264). Redwood is tolerant of shade (54) but cannot withstand drought. It is very windfirm (1482). Success in growing it out of its natural range, such as in the Eastern United States and in New Zealand, has been highly variable and generally not successful. The heartwood is fairly light in weight, light to dark red brown in color, and resistant to decay in contact with the ground.

Redwood can be reproduced by stump sprouts, root sprouts, seedling sprouts, or seeds. All of these means can produce trees of good form. The tree has few disease enemies, the most damaging of which is a heartrot. Bega (93) gives an account of the pathology of the sequoias, both the redwood and the giant sequoia, and provides an annotated list of their diseases worldwide.

Seedling Diseases.—Redwood seed germinates best on mineral soil. Only about 20 percent of the viable seed sown produce 1–0 seedlings. Much of the poor germination is due to empty seed rather than lack of dormancy. One–one stock is preferred for field planting (1). The only pathogens reported to damage redwood seedlings in the field are species of *Botrytis* (*B. cinerea* and *B. douglasii*, 932) which may, in fact, be one species, *B. cinerea* (8). The high humidity and moderate temperatures of redwood sites provide optimum conditions for Botrytis blight.

Vaartaja and Salisbury (1464) inoculated seedlings of many plants in test tubes with isolates of *Pythium debaryanum* and *P. ultimum*. *Sequoia sempervirens* was rated as moderately susceptible, with mortality resulting from both pathogens.

Foliage Diseases.—Redwood has had fewer foliage pathogens reported on it than any major tree species in the United States. *Mycosphaerella sequoiae* causes occasional blighting of needles and *Chloroscypha chloromela* can be found on senescent or dead needles and is of questionable parasitism.

The sooty mold *Chaetasbolisia falcata* produces a dark mycelium, that is epiphyllous on foliage and also occurs on twigs (991). While occurring on living tissue such molds generally live on insect "honey dew" and are not harmful. Two other epiphyllous sooty molds, *Chaetophomella setigera* and *Phaeosaccardinula dematia*, occur on redwood in moist situations, and Miller and Bonar (991) deal with all three species in their account of the sooty molds of California.

Stem Diseases.—A few fungi have been described that fruited on twigs and branches of redwood, but available information does not indicate that any of them are primary pathogens. They include *Clithris sequoiae*, *Cytospora pinastri*, *Leptostroma sequoiae* (1482), *Phomopsis occulta* (570), and, in the East, a species of *Macrophoma*. Von Schrenk (1482) described the redwood fungi other than *Poria sequoiae* as "rare and insignificant."

Considerable damage has been caused to plantations of redwood in Mendocino County, California, by a species of *Coryneum* that causes twig and stem cankers on otherwise thrifty trees (*93*).

Dermatea livida, a fungus with cup-shaped *Cenangium*-like ascocarps, is sometimes associated with lesions on branches and small stems.

Leucostoma (*Cytospora*) *sequoiae*, is an ascomycete occurring on dead twigs (*135*), and a species of *Cistella* with small, light-colored apothecia grows on the wood of *Sequoia* (*237*).

The crown gall organism, *Agrobacterium tumefaciens* (from peach), was inoculated by Smith (*1316*) into small redwoods in the open, and he obtained evidence of some gall formation. Later Smith (*1319*) repeated his inoculations and readily produced the warty galls typical of this disease.

Burls, or large trunk galls, occur on redwood, but their cause has not been determined.

Root Diseases.—Both *Armillaria mellea* and *Fomes annosus* can cause root and butt rot of redwood, but killing has not been ascribed to them, and their rots have rarely been encountered in the field.

Phymatotrichum omnivorum has been shown, experimentally, to cause root rot of redwood (var. *glauca*) in Texas (*1379*).

Trunk Rots.—Two heartrots make up almost all of the trunk decay in living redwoods. One is a very distinctive brown, cubical rot, often developing in "pipes" several inches to several feet long. It is caused by *Poria sequoiae* and occurs throughout the redwood range. The other, caused by *P. albipellucida*, is a soft, cinnamon-brown rot, that early involves separation along annual rings and later results in an orange-brown, soft, fibrous mass of finely-pitted wood laminae, as well as other distinctive features. Kimmey and Lightle (*802*) describe and illustrate these decays and point out that *P. albipellucida* rot increases in incidence from Sonoma County, California, northward, becoming responsible for most of the rot cull in the northern part of the redwood range. They mention that incidence of this rot is correlated with the proportion of western redcedar in the stands, and point out Buckland's (*187*) findings that this fungus caused more than 40 percent of the decay infections in western redcedar on the coast of British Columbia.

As early as 1903, von Schrenk (*1482*) described the redwood brown rot, but he attached little importance to it. The fungus causing it was later named *Poria sequoiae* by Fritz and Bonar (*479*). They stressed the great amount of loss this fungus caused and stated that entrance was mostly through fire scars. They also mention that the rot resembles both pecky cypress and *Polyporus amarus* rot of incense-cedar. The sporophores of the redwood brown rot are seldom seen, occurring in cool, damp, dark hollows or in the kerf area between logs. They are often covered with a mat of *Penicillium* spp. Fritz and Bonar (*479*) also mention a brown rot of bark that resembles the brown rot of the wood, but the cause was not determined.

Kimmey and Lightle (*802*) found a very small amount of redwood rot loss to be caused by *Poria versipora*, *Trametes carbonaria* (usually rotting fire-charred wood *1067*), and *Fomes annosus*, with *Polyporus abietinus* causing some decay of dead sapwood. Several other fungi can rot dead sapwood and heartwood of redwood (*8*).

Kimmey and Hornibrook (*801*) give extensive data on redwood cull and cull indicators. Redwood, studied in four counties, had the following amounts of cull on a board-foot, gross-volume basis: rot, 34 percent; shake, 1.8 percent; fire, 1.3 percent; and an additional small loss from broken tops. Close to two-thirds of the advanced decay resulted from *Poria sequoiae* and one-third from *P. albipellucida*. The only reliable cull indicators were bole wounds, goosepens (deep fire wounds extending to or beyond the center of the tree), and broken tops. Cull ranged from as low as 12 percent in trees 3 ft. in diameter, to 78 percent in trees 14 ft. in diameter.

Mycorrhizal Relations.—No ectotrophic mycorrhizal fungi have been reported for redwood (*1442*).

Miscellaneous Pathology.—The species of *Sequoia* are unique conifers in having no diseases caused by rusts, needle-cast fungi, or dwarfmistletoe.

Rennerfelt and Nacht (*1164*) point out that in the family Taxodiaceae there are several species with resistant heartwood, such as those species in the genera *Cryptomeria, Sequoia,* and *Taxodium,* and yet little is known of the heartwood chemistry of the family. Later Rennerfelt (*1163*) reported the heartwood of redwood to contain tannins, pinitol, and sequoyin, none of which are toxic to fungi.

Meinecke (*944*) studied the effects of excessive tourist travel on redwood parks and concluded that compaction reduces root development, roads cut through dense forest can lead to windthrow, and abuse can result in the loss of very large trees.

Redwood lumber sometimes develops a black, abiotic stain during drying (*151*).

American mountain-ash
Sorbus americana

The American mountain-ash is a small tree, seldom exceeding a height of 25 ft. or a trunk diameter of more than 1 ft. Its range extends mainly from eastern Canada to Manitoba and southward into the Northern States and along the Appalachian Mountains to North Carolina. Distinctly.a northern species, it grows mainly bordering cold swamps or on cold, rocky, wet, mountain ridges (*546*). In few localities it is a common tree. It grows slowly and is short-lived. While the wood is seldom used, the tree makes a lovely ornamental with its interesting, small, compound leaves and the large, flat-topped clusters of white flowers that appear in May or June, followed by brilliant, orange-red fruit clusters in the fall. The fruit is inedible for humans, being very acid, but is eaten by birds.

The European mountain-ash, or rowan (*Sorbus aucuparia*), is similar in many respects to the American species and has many of the same diseases as the American tree. While Rehder (*1154*) recognizes no named varieties of the American species, he recognizes nine varieties of the European.

Fire blight is by far the most important and the only noteworthy disease of mountain-ash.

Foliage Diseases.—Fire blight causes, among other symptoms, a blackening and shrivelling of the leaves. It is discussed under Stem Diseases.

Two leaf rusts produce their epiphyllous pycnial stages and hypophyllous aecial stages on *Sorbus americana* in the Northern States. On *Sorbus, Gymnosporangium aurantiacum* is widespread, but only occasional on its native telial host, *Juniperus communis* var. *depressa. G. globosum,* in its pycnial and aecial stages, is a very common rust on *Crataegus* and *Malus* but is much less common on *Pyrus* and *Sorbus.* Its telia are formed on the twigs of *Juniperus virginiana,* and the rust is also common on this host. Although Arthur (*46*) separates these species in his key according to telial characters they can also be separated on the basis of minor morphologic differences in aecia and aeciospores.

Known as the cause of pear leaf blight (*1555*), *Fabraea maculata* (*Entomosporium maculatum*) is generally distributed on pear and quince (see *Pyrus*) and some other rosaceous hosts. Small, purple spots form early, extending later to brownish, circular lesions ¼ in. or less across with the raised dot of a conidial fruiting body in the center of each. When infection is severe, defoliation follows. The disease also develops into twig cankers (see Stem Diseases).

Another common leaf spot is caused by *Phyllosticta sorbi.* Small, round spots bear scattered, black pycnidia that produce hyaline, 1-celled, ovate to ellipsoid conidia. This fungus is likely the spermatial stage of *Mycosphaerella aucupariae,* which forms its 2-celled ascospores in perithecia on fallen leaves in the spring.

An epidermal proliferation of enlarged and varicolored cells, that superficially resembles a fungus, is caused by mites and is referred to as erineum (see *Acer rubrum*).

The apple scab fungus *Venturia inaequalis* and a variety, *cinerascens,* produces lesions on the foliage and fruit, similar to those produced on apple (see *Malus*).

Stem Diseases.—Fire blight (*Erwinia amylovora*), the only serious disease of mountain-ash, can blight and blacken leaves, shoots, and blossoms, and form hold-over cankers as it does on pear (see *Pyrus*). Leaves and blossoms of mountain-ash affected by fire blight wilt suddenly, turning brown and then black. Extensive cankers that are bounded by cracks between the dead and living bark (*231*) form. Bacterial ooze from these cankers provides primary inoculum in the spring.

In the case of the so-called "pear leaf blight" (*Fabraea maculata*) mentioned above, twig lesions may appear on the current season's growth by midsummer. They are indefinite, purple to black areas that merge to form cankers. Primary spring infection comes more often from the cruciate, 4-celled, appendaged conidia formed in these twig cankers than from the 2-celled, hyaline ascospores formed in apothecia on fallen leaves.

Crown gall (*Agrobacterium tumefaciens*) causes warty excrescences near the ground line or along the stem and branches and particularly at pruning wounds.

A glance at a list of the fungi inhabiting stems of mountain-ash (*8*) discloses many species that are pathogenic, or weakly so, to *Malus* and *Pyrus.* Those of occasional concern on mountain-ash have been mentioned. Others include *Cytospora,* spp., *Dermatea ariae, Gloeodes pomigena, Glomerella cingulata, Nectria cinnabarina, Nummularia discreta* (see *Amelanchier*), *Physalospora obtusa,* and *Valsa* spp.

Schoenweiss (*1257*) reports and illustrates a canker of the European species *Sorbus aucuparia* caused by a species of *Fusicoccum*. Trees under stress developed severe cankering when inoculated. Symptoms are wilting, dieback, and cankering. The bark remains attached over the lesions and becomes covered with dark, spherical, erumpent pycnidia, one to several per stroma. Conidiophores are short and simple, and the conidia are hyaline, 1-celled, and fusoid. The canker is reported to be potentially highly destructive in Illinois nurseries.

Miscellaneous Pathology.—Mountain-ash appeared to be only moderately susceptible to Texas root rot in seedling tests (*1379*). This tree is totally unsuited, anyway, to the soil and climatic conditions of the root-rot belt.

Nothing is known of the mycorrhizal or nematode relations of *Sorbus americana*, but *Cenococcum graniforme* has been identified with mycorrhizae of *S. aucuparia* (*1442*), and species of nematodes in several genera have been associated with the roots or root zones of the latter species in the United States and Europe (*1222*).

Baldcypress
Taxodium distichum

Baldcypress is a deciduous conifer, intermediate in tolerance, that is largely restricted to very wet sites consisting of mucks, clays, or fine sands, on flat or nearly flat land at elevations less than 100 ft. above sea level (*829*). It is distributed mainly in coastal areas from Maryland to Florida and west to Texas but also occurs along the coastal plain streams of the South and extends up the Mississippi and tributary valleys to southern Illinois. Although it is widely associated with wet lands, the tree is properly reputed to be adaptable to land or water (*279*). It thrives on deep, moist, well-drained soils and can be grown successfully not only in southern wetlands but also from the mountains of North Carolina almost to Canada. On the "better" forest sites it is outgrown by its competitors, including the more tolerant hardwoods, and on poor dry sites it will not grow at all.

The distribution of cypress with respect to water is not entirely a matter of its growing faster than other species on very wet land, but rather that the exacting requirements for moisture seem to furnish the key to the question of distribution (*829*). First, the seeds are large and are water-borne to a much greater extent than wind-borne. Then, they must have free surface water over the soil to germinate, and in addition the seedling must grow high enough (often 8 or 10 in.) the first year to stay above any recurring high water. While seedlings can survive a considerable depth of water, they die if kept completely submerged for prolonged periods (*829*).

Cypress knees help anchor the trees growing on a soft and watery substrate and also supply air to submerged roots. The extensive and complex root system makes trees windfirm, and the durable heartwood helps keep cypress sound in a climate, and under site conditions, especially conducive to decay. Anyone concerned with the pathology of cypress should become familiar with the silvical characteristics of this unusual tree (*829*). Cypress matures at about 200 years, with longevity of 1,000 years not uncommon and ages up to 1,300 years recorded. Cypress heartwood becomes durable with age, but an age of several hundred years must be reached before cypress heartwood develops the characteristic strong resistance to decay for which it is famous (*203*).

Seedling Diseases.—In the nursery cypress needs abundant soil moisture, but when delivered from above, in frequent irrigation, it has sometimes led to blighting of the tops. Heat lesions at the soil line have also taken a toll in nurseries where the moisture balance has not been properly maintained between too little, to that essential for growth, and finally to that which gives damping-off and root-rot fungi optimum conditions for attack. Baldcypress is regarded as among the species least susceptible to damping-off (*602*).

Foliage and Stem Diseases.—A few needle and twig fungi have been reported on cypress (*8*), including *Mycosphaerella taxodii* (*625*) and the questionable pathogen, *Pestalotia funerea* (*625*), but none are known to be serious. Twigs and larger stems are sometimes covered with thalli of the brown-felt fungi of the genus *Septobasidium*, particularly *S. pseudopedicellatum* and *S. taxodii*, which live on scale insects and do little or no harm. *Phomopsis occulta* is a secondary invader of tissue killed by other causes (*570*).

Root Diseases and Trunk Rots.—*Fomes taxodii* is common on dead cypress, *F. geotropus* has been mistakenly reported as the cause of peck (*354*), and a few other fungi, among them *Polyporus meliae* (*910*), can attack the sapwood and heartwood. However, by far the most important wood-destroying heartrot fungus is *Stereum* (*Echinodontium*) *taxodii*, the true cause of peck or pecky-cypress (*348*). This brown pocket rot extends down from rotted branch stubs in old trees and produces a deep, pitted or chambered effect in the wood that many users find decorative. It also can hollow out the trunk. The wood between the pockets is normally firm. The decay process stops once the trees are cut, even when pecky wood is used outdoors for posts or poles.

Shortly after the cause of peck was described as *Stereum taxodii*, Gross (*547*), who monographed the genus *Echinodontium*, placed this fungus as *E. taxodii*, with a range extending from the United States to Taiwan and Japan. It occurs on *Cryptomeria, Chamaecyparis,* and *Torreya* in the Orient as well as on *Taxodium* in the United States.

Cypress is susceptible to cotton root rot (*Phymatotrichum omnivorum*) in Texas (*1379*), but the tree is not suited to the cotton root-rot area anyway.

Neither nematodes nor mycorrhizal fungi have been reported for cypress.

A pink stain in the sapwood and heartwood of southern cypress is caused by a species of *Geotrichum* (*246*).

English yew
Taxus baccata

A small tree with dark-green, glossy needles, growing up to 60 ft. in height, with reddish, flaky bark, English yew is widely known as an ornamental. Rehder (*1154*) lists 34 cultivated varieties, and they differ widely in color of foliage, shape, hardiness, and in other characteristics. In the United States the species is hardy as far north as New England and northern New York, and it is very tolerant of shade. It grows best in moist, sandy loam but can tolerate a wide range in soil texture, fertility, and moisture.

Taxus sp. was resistant to injury from hydrofluoric acid gas but moderately sensitive to sulfur dioxide, following experimental fumigation (*1669*). The species of *Taxus* are very resistant to damage from salt spray (*1005, 1632*).

Miksche et al. (*967*) found changes in apical meristems of *Taxus media* and *Pinus strobus* after 20-day exposures of gamma radiation at rates as low as 3.5 to 15 r. per 20-hour-day. Accumulated doses of 600 to 800 r. in 50 to 60 days was nearly lethal to these species.

Most ornamental propagation is by rooting cuttings. Seeds usually germinate the second year after planting, and germination is aided by the seeds' passage through the digestive system of birds (*1*). Seedlings have been killed by damping-off caused by *Rhizoctonia solani* in Connecticut and by *Phytophthora cinnamomi* in the East, Southeast, and Pacific Northwest.

English yew and its varieties, as well as Japanese yew (*Taxus cuspidata*), as ornamental nursery stock are highly susceptible to *Phytophthora cinnamomi* (*304*). Heavy losses have occurred, especially in heavy soils or wet and poorly drained soils, in North Carolina and in the Pacific Northwest. The entire fibrous root mass becomes rotted and dark brown with necrosis extending up into the stem a few inches beyond the root collar.

Manning and Crossan (*925*) inoculated rooted cuttings of six *Taxus* cultivars (varieties of *T. cuspidata* and *T. media*) with one or more of 13 isolates of *P. cinnamomi* obtained from several hosts and geographic localities. Much variation in pathogenicity appeared, and this was attributed either to pathogenic variation in opposite mating types of fungus or to the existence of biotypes of *P. cinnamomi* within the species, based on differential pathogenic responses to the same host plant.

Yew leaf scorch, ascribed to *Sphaerulina taxi*, occurs in the West. The upper leaf surface, after turning brown, becomes studded with thin, warty pustules corresponding to the embedded pycnidia (*932*). Yew leaf blight (*Macrophoma taxi*) (*932*) occurs in New Jersey and in the Pacific Northwest. It can involve twigs and entire branches, causing conspicuous damage. Small, black, sunken perithecia occur on the underside of the leaf, often arranged along the midrib, and sometimes a few appear on the upper side. *Phyllosticta taxi* has been reported on needles in Virginia.

Botryosphaeria ribis can cause twig cankers, and *Pestalotia funerea* has been reported to cause a twig blight in Massachusetts, but the parasitism of the latter fungus to yew is open to question. The harmless saprophyte *Phomopsis occulta* (*570*) is common on dead twigs of English yew in the Northeast.

Typical galls were produced on English yew after inoculation with the crown gall bacterium *Agrobacterium tumefaciens* (*1319*), but this disease has seldom been a problem in the field.

Yews (*Taxus* sp.) in eastern Maryland displaying poor growth for many years were found growing in soil with a population of nematodes in 5 genera. Yews in a Washington, D. C. nursery were growing in soils with 4 genera of nematodes, one of which (*Tylenchus*) occurred in the Maryland area (*1377*).

Phytophthora cinnamomi is known to cause a root rot of *Taxus baccata* and *T. cuspidata* in British Columbia (*48*). Bart (*64*) isolated an unidentified species of *Pythium* from the rotted roots of stunted, nursery-grown *Taxus* plants in Ohio. The symptoms were much like those of *P. cinnamomi* root rot. Inoculations of *T. capitata* and *T. brownii* plants with the *Pythium* sp. resulted in severe root rot in 60 days.

Neither stem rots, nor mycorrhizal fungi have been reported for English yew in the United States.

Rennerfelt (*1163*) tested the heartwood of 22 coniferous species for resistance to decay by 3 wood-destroying fungi. English yew was in the group with the least resistance to decay. Only one heartwood constituent, isotaxiresinol, was extracted, and it was an inactive (non-fungicidal) substance.

Pacific yew
Taxus brevifolia

Pacific yew is a small tree, seldom exceeding 70 ft. in height, with a somewhat rounded but unsymmetrical crown (*279*). The trunk is straight, with decided fluting, making it irregular in cross section. The foliage typically is dark green, and the bark, thin and purplish. The species extends along the West Coast from Alaska to northern California and in California also occurs through the Sierra Nevada to the southern part of the state. It is found also in the Inland Empire area of the Rocky Mountains (*279*). Its climatic requirements are much like those of coast Douglas-fir, occupying sites near margins of low mountain streams, moist flats and benches, deep ravines and coves, and other fairly rich soils (*1367*). The species is very tolerant (*54*) and grows slowly. Trees 12 to 20 in. in diameter range from 140 to 245 years old, with a maximum longevity believed to be about 375 years (*1367*). The tree is sensitive to damage from fire.

Pacific yew resists damage from sulfur dioxide, and, in the case of the study of damage from the Trail, British Columbia, smelter (*1249*), Pacific yew was the least sensitive of 12 species of western conifers.

The fresh heartwood is rose red in color, becoming duller on exposure to light. It is very decay-resistant, strong, fine grained, and heavy.

Seedling Diseases.—Yew seeds are slow to germinate, with natural germination usually not taking place until the second year (*1*). As in the case of many related genera, successful germination usually follows the passage of seeds through the digestive system of birds. The disease enemies of Pacific yew seedlings have not been studied, but *Rhizoctonia solani*, *Phytophthora cinnamomi*, and *Pythium* sp. have caused damping-off or seedling root rot of other yews in the East, and the snow blights named below cause minor damage in the West.

Foliage Diseases.—No serious leaf diseases have been reported. Both of the brown-felt snow blights, the pine type (*Neopeckia coulteri*), and the non-pine type (*Herpotrichia nigra*) have caused localized damage to foliage that remained long under snow. Four other fungi are reported to cause needle blights: *Phoma hystrella* (*625*), *Macrophoma taxi* (*625*), *Mycosphaerella taxi* (*625*), and *Sphaerulina taxi* (*8, 1277*).

Macrophoma taxi (*Sphaeropsis* sp.) causes "yew leaf blight" in the Pacific Northwest. It can involve twigs and entire branches. Small, black perithecia occur on the underside of the leaf, often arranged along the midrib, and sometimes a few occur on the upper side (*932*).

Sphaerulina taxi causes yew leaf scorch. The upper surface, after turning brown, becomes studded with tiny, warty pustules, corresponding to the imbedded pycnidia (*932*).

A snow blight is caused by *Phacidium taxicolum*. (*1157*).

Stem Diseases.—As in the case of the needle diseases, a few fungi have been reported parasitic on stems, but little is known about them. A stem canker is ascribed to *Diplodia taxi*, and twig blights to *Phoma hystrella* and *Physalopsora gregaria* (*1277, 1278*).

Pacific yew produced galls after inoculation with the crown-gall bacterium *Agrobacterium tumefaciens* (*1319*), but the disease has not been a problem in the field.

Root Diseases.—*Armillaria mellea* and *Polyporus schweinitzii* have both been reported on Pacific yew from Idaho, but the paucity of reports suggests that this tree suffers little from root and butt rots.

Trunk Rots.—The heartrot fungi include *Fomes nigrolimitatus, F. pini, F. robustus* (*F. hartigii*), and *F. roseus* (*8, 1277*). Only a few sapwood-decay fungi have been collected from dead trees or dead parts of trees of this species.

Mycorrhizal Relations.—No ectotrophic mycorrhizal fungi have been reported for a species of *Taxus* (*1442*).

Northern white-cedar
Thuja occidentalis

Northern white-cedar, commonly known as arborvitae, occurs mainly in patches, in cool swamps, or around streams or lakes from Canada through the Appalachian Mountains to Georgia. It is essentially a tree of the North, and in the southern mountains it occurs only at high elevations, and there it is reduced in size to a shrub. It is tolerant, slow-growing, and matures early, but can reach ages of 250 to 300 years (*279*). Having thin, oily bark, it is easily injured or killed by fire, and being shallow rooted, it is not particularly windfirm (*1021*). The tree is widely used as an ornamental, and nurserymen recognize about 50 horticultural varieties (*514*).

While it is generally found on cool, wet sites and neutral or alkaline soil, and thrives even in rocky pastures, suitable clones of northern white-cedar will grow well in a variety of soils and sites, as demonstrated by the wide use of this tree as an ornamental virtually all over the country.

Northern white-cedar can withstand heavy loads of ice (*310*), moderate drought, and a wide range in temperature; but sudden cold not preceded by a suitable hardening-off period will turn

478

foliage brown. Hedges in Quebec are often damaged by winter drought. Another type of foliage browning resulting from winter injury occurs when warm, dry winds blow while the ground is still cold or frozen. Arborvitae was badly injured by wind-blown salt water in Connecticut (*1005*). The species has few enemies as a forest tree, but in cultivation, it is subject to many foliage disorders. It has been damaged by sulfur dioxide near oil refineries (*869*).

In addition to reproduction from seed, in swamps regeneration is achieved commonly by layering, a type of rooting from branches or fallen stems in contact with soil. Root rot is regarded as one of the causes of mortality associated with layering (*1021*).

According to Sparrow and Sparrow (*1332*) northern white-cedar was more sensitive to gamma radiation from a cobalt-60 source than most species of a group of 12 hardwood and conifers tested (see *Picea glauca*).

Seedling Diseases.—The fungi reported to cause seedling diseases are the root organisms *Rhizoctonia solani* and *Fusarium solani*, the foliage-blight fungi *Phomopsis juniperovora* (*569*) and *Didymascella thujina* (*661*), and the snow-blight fungus *Phacidium infestans* (*151*). Since reproduction for ornamentals is by cuttings, seedling diseases are not a problem in such culture. Test tube pathogenicity tests in Canada, using mainly isolates of *Pythium debaryanum* and *P. ultimum*, resulted in a rating of "resistant" for northern white-cedar, while many other conifer seedlings were attacked more severely (*1464*). However, both of these species of *Pythium*, and also *P. acanthicum*, caused mortality to 5-week-old seedlings in test tubes. Species of *Thuja* and close relatives seldom sustain important losses from damping-off (*360*).

Two nematodes, *Pratylenchus penetrans* and *Tylenchus emarginatus*, proved excellent hosts to northern white-cedar seedlings in Canada, and *Paratylenchus projectus* was a good host (*1370*).

While most varieties of arborvitae tested have been resistant to attack by *Phytophthora cinnamomi*, var. *compacta* is listed as susceptible in California (*303*).

Bugbee (*192*) found that of 12 species of conifers exposed to infection by *Cylindrocladium scoparium* in Minnesota only seedlings of northern white-cedar were resistant to this root and foliage pathogen.

Mortality of seedlings in the field, excluding that caused by browsing, is often largely a matter of dessication. In many cases the seeds germinate on moss, stumps, or logs during the spring wet season, only to dry out in summer. Other causes of loss are late spring frost, root rot, mechanical inteference, poorly developed roots, and grass competition. Where flooding or a high water table develops in the spring, frost heaving causes much loss (*514*).

Foliage and Stem Diseases.—Beyond the seedling stage, *Didymascella* (*Keithia*) *thujina* causes some unsightliness but seldom damages older trees. Under humid conditions, however, it can kill a large percentage of seedlings less than 4 years old (*1143*). *Lophodermium sawadae* (= *L. thuyae*), a taxonomically inter-

479

esting fungus (*323, 328*) is of no other importance. Pomerleau [55] states that a snow-blight fungus (*Phacidium* sp.) is responsible for important damage to arborvitae in nurseries and hedges in Quebec.

Phomopsis occulta and *Pestalotia funerea* are widespread on the twigs of arborvitae but are secondary invaders of tissue injured from other causes (*569*). The former's similarities with *P. juniperovora*, a true parasite, can cause confusion (*568, 570*). *P. juniperovora* blights foliage and shoots in the East and Central States under humid conditions but is chiefly a pathogen of seedlings.

The bark of this species may develop smooth patches caused by the harmless fungus *Aleurodiscus nivosus*. Other saprophytic species of *Aleurodiscus* are *A. canadensis* and *A. tsugae*, in Canada, and *A. lividocoeruleus* and *A. botryosus*, widely in North America (*858*).

Species of *Ceratocystis* and *Hormodendron* have been isolated from stained wood of this speices. The heartwood of living northern white-cedar is often blue-stained by what was early considered to be a non-sporulating fungus (*258*). The stain usually appears above and below branch stubs, but may be extensive. Later work established that the causal fungus is *Kirschsteiniella thujina*, the same organism that causes the stain reported in dead branches and heartwood of balsam fir (see *Abies balsamea*).

Root Diseases and Trunk Rots.—The root- and butt-rot fungi mainly attack old or damaged trees and have not yet proved to be economically important. They include (*887*) *Armillaria mellea*, *Fomes annosus*, *F. pini*, *F. pinicola*, *Polyporus balsameus*, *P. schweinitzii*, and *Poria subacida*. There is some question as to the validity of claims that *Poria weirii*, an important western root- and butt-rot fungus, attacks eastern arborvitae (*184*). Hubert (*723*) found *Polyporus balsameus* causing extensive decay of roots of some suppressed northern white-cedars in one locality in Wisconsin.

Isolations of root-rot fungi from the roots and root zones of this species by Hendrix and Campbell (*633*) in the Southeast yielded *Rhizoctonia* spp., *Pythium vexans*, and at least two other species of *Pythium*.

The roots have been demonstrated to be susceptible to attack by *Clitocybe tabescens* in Florida (*1168*) and to *Phymatotrichum omnivorum* in Texas (*8*) and Arizona. An ornamental form is listed as susceptible to *Phytophthora cinnamomi* (*1659*) (see also Seedling Diseases).

Mycorrhizal Relations.—This species is the only northeastern conifer for which no mycorrhizal fungi have been reported (*1021*).

Western redcedar
Thuja plicata

One of the most important commercial species of the Pacific Northwest, western redcedar occurs from southern Alaska south-

[55] René Pomerleau, pathologist, Canada Department of Forestry, Forest Entomology and Pathology Branch, Sillery, Quebec, retired.

ward to Mendocino County, California, along the Coast Ranges. An inland part of its range extends through the northern Rocky Mountains, from eastern British Columbia through parts of the Inland Empire to north-central Idaho. The species is almost confined to areas of high precipitation and high humidity, reaching its optimum where, in addition to ample rainfall, summers are cool and winters, mild (*162*). There are many differences between the climätic adaptations of western redcedar as it grows, a majestic tree, in the rainy, mild Puget Sound area, and as it grows, often hardly more than a windswept bush, in the snowy, cold mountains of the Inland Empire (*279*), where temperatures drop as low as −35° F. (*1367*). Under European conditions, Peace (*1091*) considers this species very susceptible to spring frosts.

As with many western conifers, ample soil moisture is more critical than soil depth, texture, or fertility. Thus western redcedar is generally found along stream bottoms, moist flats, lower slopes, and in ravines (*162*). Its altitudinal range extends from sea level on the coast to as high as 7,000 ft. in the Rocky Mountains. The species is very tolerant to shade (*54*), ranking among the most tolerant of any western species.

Very large trees 200 to 500 years old are common in the coastal part of the range, and the largest trees have been estimated to reach an age of 800 to 1,000 years (*279*). Western redcedar's main enemy is fire because of its thin bark and shallow roots. The roots extend deepest on dry sites, and there the tree is fairly windfirm. Snow damages this species less than many associated species in the Inland Empire because of its drooping branches. Young western redcedar can suffer conspicuous winter injury, particulary when severe cold periods follow mild autumn weather (*162*). The species is very sensitive to sulfur dioxide from ore smelting; and in the case of the Trail, British Columbia damage investigation (*1249*), of 12 species of western conifers, western redcedar was exceeded in susceptibility to damage only by two highly sensitive firs, *Abies grandis* and *A. lasiocarpa*. Western redcedar is not ordinarily subject to heavy damage from insects or disease, despite the impression that might be gained from Shaw's (*1277*) list of 172 fungi reported to occur on this host. The most curious aspect of the mycology of this species is that its dead wood is subject to decay by at least 44 species of the Thelephoraceae, in five genera.

Seedling Diseases.—None of the strictly seedling pathogens are known to be damaging, since species of *Thuja* and closely related species seldom sustain important losses from damping-off (*360*). Vaartaja (*1458*) found western redcedar the most resistant of 11 conifers tested for susceptibilty to seedling destruction by *Phytopthora cactorum. Thelephora terrestris* often grows harmlessly around seedlings but sometimes too copiously (*195, 1540*), and the brown-felt snow mold *Herpotrichia nigra* kills some seedlings that remained long under snow in the Rocky Mountains. Other leaf diseases, particularly cedar leaf blight, will attack seedlings.

The seeds have a high viability, with the germinative capacity the highest (73 percent) of the species in the western white pine type (*581*). However, only a small percentage of these new seedlings develop into established reproduction. First-year mortality, before the seedlings have hardened off, is high, and has been attributed to fungi, birds, and insects (*581*), with the fallen leaves of deciduous shrubs accounting for some losses. Poor seedling root penetration results in succulent seedlings that often succumb to the high heat and dryness of surface soil when exposed to full sunlight (*162*).

Foliage Diseases.—Cedar leaf blight, caused by *Didymascella (Keithia) thujina* (*406*), is primarily a disease of field seedlings and saplings and occurs throughout the range of western redcedar. Boyce (*151*) and Hubert (*725*) present good accounts of this disease. Lower branches may appear as though scorched by fire, especially in humid situations; and if the killed foliage is not shed by autumn, it becomes ash gray, and many pits appear where the small, blackened fructifications drop out.

Coryneum thujinum causes a less common leaf blight (*625*), sometimes appearing as very small, black pustules on the underside of the same leaves as were attacked by *Didymascella thujina* (*364*).

Herpotrichia nigra can produce its brown-felt mold on foliage long under snow, and *Limacinia alaskensis* causes a minor surface sooty mold in the colder parts of the range (*1278*).

A large number of saprophytes, occasional parasites, and fungi inhabitating senescent foliage occur on western redcedar (*1277*), including *Sphaerella canadensis* (*625*), *Mycosphaerella thujae* (*625*), *Microthyrium thujae* (*625*), and *Chloroscypha seaveri* (*406*).

The older foliage of western redcedar is cast by dropping entire branchlets rather than individual leaf scales. Although this is considered normal leaf shedding, it is sometimes called "cedar flagging" and is most pronounced in late summer and following dry seasons. Species of the subtropical genus *Cunninghamia* also have this normal habit of casting branchlets, and, like the western redcedar flagging, this leads many casual observers to suspect pathology where none exists.

No hypodermataceous fungi, rusts, or dwarfmistletoes have been reported from western redcedar.

Stem Diseases.—There are no major stem diseases, but many fungi occur on moribund or damaged branches and stems. *Aleurodiscus amorphus* (*587*) will make lesions on the bark of suppressed trees, and five other species, *A. amylaceus* (*Corticium amylaceum*), *A. cerussatus*, *A. lividocoeruleus*, *A. tsugae*, and *A. weirii*, occur on dead wood (*858*).

Hedgcock (*625*) reports *Valsa weiriana* as likely parasitic on western redcedar and as probably the perfect stage of *Cytospora weiriana*, a fungus also occurring on this host. *Valsa kunzei*, the cause of the so-called Cytospora canker of many conifers, has been reported on this host (*1519*), but it is of little importance.

The commonest of the fungi found on weakened, dying, or dead stem tissue are *Chloroscypha seaveri* (*406*), *Coryneum thujinum* (*625*), *Cucurbidothis conjuncta*, *Hendersonia thyoides*, *Pestalotia funerea* (*625*), and *Valsa abietis*.

Smith (*1318*) produced crown gall in western redcedars by inoculation. Species of *Thuja* were among the most susceptible of the Cupressaceae, and the galls were rough, almost from the first. Crown gall is not, however, an economic disease of western red-cedar.

Root Diseases.—The principal root- and butt-rot fungus is *Poria weirii*, which causes a yellow-ring rot that not only results in much cull but also in windthrow and wind breakage (*725*). This fungus, so important as a root rot of Douglas-fir, was first collected on western redcedar. While Buckland et al. (*190*) mention that "annual"-sporophored *P. weirii* attacks trees of many genera, the "perennial"-sporophored form attacks only western redcedar.

Armillaria mellea is a common root-rot fungus on this host, but it does not damage western redcedar to the extent it does most other species in the western white pine type. Other root- and butt-rot fungi that have been reported to attack this species are *Corticium galactinum, Fomes annosus, Odontia bicolor, Polyporus schweinitzii, P. tomentosus, Poria subacida,* and *P. vaillantii.*

Hubert (*729*) gives special attention to the identification of the root rots of species in the western white pine type, including western redcedar, and gives a table of characteristics (see *Abies grandis*) separating *Armillaria mellea, Poria subacida, Fomes annosus,* and *P. weirii.*

Trunk Rots.—Buckland's study of decay in western redcedar in British Columbia (*187*) indicated that decrement from decay did not exceed growth increment up to 450 years, but nevertheless considerable decay could occur in young age classes. For his coastal areas he listed the following fungi as causes of trunk rot, in decreasing order of importance: *Poria asiatica* (*P. sericeomollis*), *P. albipellucida* (which is rare inland), *Fomes pini, Merulius* sp. (*M. fugax* and *M. lacrymans* occur in British Columbia), and *P. subacida.*

Kimmey (*795*) conducted an extensive study of cull in Sitka spruce, western hemlock, and western redcedar in southeast Alaska (see *Picea sitchensis*). On the basis of tree age or diameter, western redcedar was by far the most defective species. The fungi responsible for cull in this species, expressed in terms of the total cubic-foot rot-cull volume, were as follows: *Poria albipellucida,* 45 percent; *Poria weirii,* 41 percent; *Poria ferrugineofusca,* 3 percent; and others, 11 percent.

Many fungi other than those already mentioned have been found to cause butt and trunk rots of western redcedar, including the well-known species *Echinodontium tinctorium, Fomes pinicola,* and *F. roseus.* One of the interesting aspects of the Basidiomycete flora of this species, whether living or dead, is the large number of species of the Thelephoraceae that colonize it, including at least 17 species of *Corticium,* 13 of *Peniophora,* 6 of *Stereum,* 5 of *Hymenochaete,* and 3 of *Coniophora* (*8, 1277*).

Mycorrhizal Relations.—No fungi have been reported as forming ectotrophic mycorrhizae with western redcedar (*1442*).

Miscellaneous Pathology.—The wood of western redcedar is soft, brittle, reddish to dark brown, aromatic, and durable. While most durable woods are heavy (*Tectona, Robinia, Taxus,* and *Lophira*), western redcedar is remarkably light and also decay-resistant

(*1164*). Rennerfelt (*1161*) reported the isolation of isomers of a substance from the heartwood of western redcedar that he named thujaplicin. Thujaplicin has a strong fungicidal effect on blueing and decay fungi on malt-extract agar, and it is about as fungicidally active as sodium pentachlorophenol.

Sapwood rots of redcedar poles include mainly "golden-glow," which is a brown, cubical rot caused by *Ptychogaster rubescens* (*Polyporus guttulatus*); other typical brown, cubical saprots caused by *Coniophora puteana* and *C. arida;* and rots "associated with" golden-glow rot itself, caused by *C. olivacea* and *C. olivascens* (*1330*). *Paxillus panuoides,* a brown-rot fungus, and *Poria vaillantii,* which causes only a slight darkening in the early stages of decay, made up some of the sapwood loss to redcedar poles.

Scheffer (*1245*) intensively studied decay resistance in western redcedar heartwood, and found that, in general, resistance increased from the inner to the outer heartwood and from the upper to the lower trunk. The level of resistance to decay by *Lenzites trabea, Fomes subroseus,* and *Lentinus lepideus* was uniformly high, but to *Poria incrassata* and *P. monticola* was variable. Site and growth rate had little relation to decay resistance.

Boyce (*144*) studied deterioration following the great Olympic Peninsula blowdown of 1921. Six years later the volume loss, on a board-foot basis was, for western hemlock, 92 percent; Pacific silver fir, 74 percent; Sitka spruce, 46 percent; Douglas-fir, 35 percent; and western redcedar, 27 percent. Only 3 fungi were identified in connection with western redcedar: *Polyporus cuneatus,* which was confined to this host; *P. versicolor;* and *Fomes applanatus.*

In their presentation of the anatomy of boron-deficient *Thuja plicata,* Blaser et al. (*127*) include good photomicrographs of root and stem tissue of normal and boron-deficient plants.

American basswood
Tilia americana

The species of *Tilia* are known to forestry as basswoods and to horticulture as lindens. The American basswood is the predominant species of *Tilia* in North America. Next in abundance is white basswood (*T. heterophylla*), a commercially important tree of the southern Appalachian region and adjoining Piedmont and Cumberland regions (*468*). There are two lesser known southern species, *T. caroliniana* and *T. floridana.* In addition, the handsome European linden *T. cordata,* with its smaller and darkly lustrous green foliage, has been widely and successfully planted in the East. Since the pathology of the two important American species is much the same, this subject is treated here under *T. americana* unless otherwise indicated.

Although many additional species and varieties have been described, based largely on leaf and twig characteristics, Coker and Totten (*274*) put the matter of identification well when they stated that "The person who has only an average interest in trees will be satisfied when he has traced this group of plants down to the genus and knows that he has found a linden or basswood."

American basswood's range extends from Alaska and the Great

Plains of Canada southward roughly to a line drawn from south-western North Carolina to northwestern Arkansas. While basswood occurs on a variety of sites, good or poor, wet or dry, it makes a satisfactory commercial tree only under rather exacting conditions (*468*).

Basswood is one of our more demanding species with respect to site requirements and seldom thrives unless the site is moist and the soil loamy, deep, with a slit-plus-clay fraction of at least 35 percent, a minimum of 3-percent organic matter, and a pH between 5.5 and 7.3.

It makes up an important component of the better, cooler, more moist hardwood sites of the Lake States, Central States, and the Northeast. Its Appalachian counterpart, white basswood, is an important cove hardwood, occupying the deep, rich, moist cove sites and lower slopes, along with yellow-poplar, ash, walnut, and the more desirable oaks.

Preferring slightly acid or neutral soils, basswood is considered a soil-builder, based on the high calcium content of its foliage. Of 27 species analyzed by Chandler (*244*), only yellow-poplar and redcedar had higher foliar calcium. It is also high in magnesium, nitrogen, phosphorus, and potassium (*468*). Basswood's sensitivity to highly localized conditions is obvious from striking changes in its occurrence with small changes in topography and soil moisture.

Basswood is drought-resistant, fire-sensitive, early-frost-sensitive, tolerant, hardy, and can withstand temporary exposure to sea spray and salt water (*1632*). It grows fast, the wood is soft and brittle, and it lacks durability in contact with soil. Longevity is seldom much over 100 years (*663*). While not easily regenerated by seed, basswood sprouts from stumps more copiously than any other American tree of commercial size. The clumps of many large sprouts often serve to identify basswood at a distance. This sprouting characteristic is partly responsible for the very high cull percentage in basswoods of sawlog size in many areas. Trunks of sprout origin are often hollowed to a height of 20 to 30 ft. (*663*).

Except for its tendency to hollowing and its high rot cull, the species of *Tilia* suffer little from disease.

Basswood seed tends to be difficult to germinate because of an impermeable seed coat, a dormant embryo, and in some species a tough pericarp (*1*). Much research has gone into finding suitable methods to obtain a reasonable seedling stand in nurseries. Although pathology is not involved in this problem, it might be suspected, and the matter is important enough to emphasize here. Johnson (*758*) hastened germination by presoaking of the fruit, sulphuric-acid digestion of the pericarp, sulfuric-acid scarification of the testa, and stratification of the seed.

A local nurseryman raising *Tilia* (either *americana* or *heterophylla*) seedlings for the Great Smoky Mountain National Park had remarkable success by picking the fruits green in early fall and planting them immediately without removing the seed.

Foliage Diseases.—A number of fungi cause minor leaf-spot diseases late in the season. The most widespread is the spot caused by *Gnomonia tiliae*, the linden anthracnose. On both the American and European species it results in a blotch or scorch when many small, subcircular, brown spots with dark margins develop along veins, petioles, and greenwood shoots. Rose-colored pustules of the conidial stage *Gloeosporium tiliae* appear on the spots. These are the acervuli, and and they bear 1-celled, hyaline, ovoid spores. The perithecia of the *Gnomonia* stage form in the spring on fallen, over-wintered leaves. They are innate, beaked, and produce 2-celled, hyaline ascospores. In wet seasons this fungus has been known to defoliate small trees. It could easily present a problem in nurseries, because it can strike early enough in the summer to be damaging.

In wet weather it is not unusual to find a heavy, black, moldy growth over the leaves of basswood and other hardwoods. It has often been attributed to *Fumago vagans*, considered to be a fungus that thrives on the sweet, honeydew secretions from aphids and other insects. It has been described as having dark conidiophores, bearing terminal and lateral, dark, variable, muriform conidia. *Fumago* has long been regarded as the imperfect stage of a *Capnodium*. Friend (*477, 478*), however, rejects *Fumago vagans* as a valid name and considers the type material as made up of two fungi, *Aureobasidium pullulans* and *Cladosporium herbarum*. His work in England indicates that the sooty mold on *Tilia* sp. is made up of the latter two fungi and other species, none of which is a *Capnodium*.

Three powdery mildews occur on *Tilia*. They find the rank-grow-ing sprout foliage in the fall a particularly suitable substrate. Their whitish, surface mycclium and oidia look much alike, but their black perithecia are distinctive. *Microsphaera alni* perithecia have several asci and multibranched appendages. *Phyllactinia guttata* (*P. corylea*) has several asci and straight perithecial appendages with bulbous proximal ends. *Uncinula clintonii* has several asci and simple but terminally curved perithecial appendages. Reed (*1153*) describes *U. clintonii* as "appendages thick-walled, refractive or rough at base, perithecia 64–146μ in diameter."

A leaf- and shoot-spot fungus *Cercospora microsora* (*260*), occurs widely in North America and Europe on many species of *Tilia*. On twigs, dark, oval spots appear, occasionally with a brown-line border and a gray center. The appearance of the leaf spots varies with the species of *Tilia*. Some have large, brown, circular spots with a dark-line margin, while others have small, white specks with a wide, dark margin. Fruiting is amphigenous. Conidiophores become dark toward the base, and the conidia are pale olivaceous, subcylindric, slightly curved, 1- to 5-septate, and $2.5–4\mu \times 20–60\mu$. It is likely that this fungus represents the imperfect stage of *Mycosphaerella microsora*, a fungus that produces its perithecia in the spring on fallen leaves.

A few other fungi occur on leaf spots of *Tilia* spp., including two *Phyllosticta* spp., *Phlyctaena tiliae*, and *Asteroma tiliae*.

Stem Diseases.—*Nectria galligena* (see *Betula alleghaniensis* and *Juglans nigra*), can cause very abundant cankering of Ameri-can basswood. Welch (*1546*), in New York, followed for 10 years the development of 431 basswoods, 151 of which had one or more Nectria cankers on them. The stand as a whole was not thrifty. At the end of 10 years the cankered trees had grown faster than the uncankered. Excessive mortality in two of his 10 plots was attributed to shading, not to cankering.

Strumella coryneoidea (*Urnula craterium*), while mainly a pathogen of oaks (see *Quercus*), sometimes produces cankers on basswood, and the symptoms are very similar to those on oak.

Verticillium wilt (*V. albo-atrum*) kills occasional ornamental or street basswoods (*412*). The symptoms are as reported for *Acer saccharum* except that the streaks in the wood (usually forming a ring in cross section) are brown, as in *Cercis*, rather than green, as in *Acer*.

Botryosphaeria ribis has been repeatedly observed on dead branches of basswood, but it has seemed in most cases to have only a saprobic role on species of *Tilia* rather than a primary parasitic role, as in *Cercis*. However, Wester et al. (*1556*) found much cankering of trees of several species of *Tilia* in Washington, D. C., with many of the cankers large. While they classified several canker types, only one type occurred on *T. americana* and *T. heterophylla*. *B. ribis* was consistently isolated from these cankers, and in one case *Physalospora rhodina* (see *Aleurites*) appeared. *B. ribis*, from any given species of *Tilia* or from *Cercis*, readily produced cankers on the species from which it was isolated, but cross-infection was mostly negative. The *B. ribis* type canker was described as "bark area first raised, later sunken; dead bark exfoliating, exposing target-like rings on the wood beneath." *Physalospora rhodina* (*Diplodia theobromae*), in inoculations, parasitized *Tilia neglecta* and *T. cordata*.

Nectria cinnabarina, although generally a secondary pathogen or saprobe, has been considered by Dodge and Rickett (*388*) as causing cankering of *Tilia* spp. Called the coral fungus, it is easily identified by its large, pinkish stromata, sporodochia, and roughened red perithecia (*879*).

Occasionally in the South, the eastern leafy mistletoe *Phoradendron serotinum*, occurs on white basswood or on one of the two southern basswood species.

Wood Rots.—In a comprehensive study of decay in trees cut on Appalachian logging operations Hepting and Hedgcock (*663*) found decay in the oaks to range, on a board-foot basis, from 7 to 16 percent, depending upon the species; in yellow-poplar, 14 percent; and in basswood, 30 percent. There was a direct relation between tree diameter and rot-cull percentage in basswood (mainly *Tilia heterophylla*), from 15-percent cull, among 12-in. trees, to almost 40 percent, among 26-in. trees. They state, "Basswood shows a much higher butt cull in sprouts and a somewhat higher cull in seedlings than any other species. The amount of butt cull in trees of seedling origins that had not been wounded at the base was low." Basswood trees of sprout origin that had no butt wounds (e.g. from fire or skidding) had 16-percent cull, while unscarred chestnut oak of sprout origin had 0.2-percent cull. Butt-wounded basswoods had 39-percent cull compared with less than half this amount in the butt-wounded trees of other hardwood species.

Basswood should be subjected to the type of "stump-rot" study that Roth and Sleeth (*1209*) reported for the oaks, Campbell (*204*) reported for northern hardwoods, and Toole reported for sweetgum (*1420*). A proper early selection of which basswood sprouts to favor and which sprouts to cut, in reducing sprout clumps to single stems, could lead to much lower cull than is now encountered.

The tendency of basswoods to develop hollows makes virtual shells or "stovepipes" out of entire trunks. Some of these trees have a wide enough band of sound sapwood outside the hollow to provide considerable usable volume.

It is not yet possible to properly appraise the relative importance of the many rot fungi reported from basswood. In oaks, poplars, conifers, and some other groups, enough culture work has been done in conjunction with rot studies to provide a basis for appraising the importance of certain fungi. In the case of basswood the appearance of conks has been almost the sole method of determining the rot fungi. This has proved an unreliable measure of either incidence or importance of a given fungus in other tree species. The following are the fungi known to either rot the central cylinder of basswood or rot wood exposed by wounding, other than those known to be entirely saprobic (*8, 1067*): *Fomes applanatus, F. connatus, F. geotropus, F. squamosus, Hydnum septentrionale, Pholiota adiposa, Pleurotus ostreatus, Polyporus cuticularis, P. resinosus, Irpex mollis,* and *Stereum murrayi.*

No true root rots have been reported for basswood. The *Tilia* spp. were highly susceptible to Texas root rot under test conditions (*1379*), but they do not grow in the root-rot belt. *Ustulina vulgaris* has a low capacity to rot roots of *Tilia* and other hardwoods (*211*).

Miscellaneous Pathology.—Very few fungi have been reported to form mycorrhizae with species of *Tilia,* even in Europe. *T. americana* is reported to form mycorrhizae with *Cenococcum graniforme, Scleroderma aurantium,* and *Russula* sp. (*1442*).

A brown to gray-black stain, often in the form of streaks in the sapwood and heartwood of many hardwoods, including basswood, is caused by *Torula ligniperda.* Chains of dark spores form in the cells invaded by this fungus.

Eastern hemlock
Tsuga canadensis

A very tolerant tree, distributed widely, particularly in the Northeast, the Appalachian Mountains, and the Lake States, eastern hemlock is characteristic of sites that are predominantly cool and moist at all seasons. Its site temperatures range from January averages of 10° F. in the North, to 42° F. in the South, with July averages from 60° F. in Maine, to 78° F. in the southern Appalachians (*713*). The tree has withstood temperatures as low as −76° F. making it one of our most cold-resistant species (*1080*). It puts out shoot growth so late in the spring that it is almost immune to spring frost injury. It is also very resistant to fall frosts (*1333*). Annual precipitation on hemlock sites ranges from 28 in. to over 56 in. per year.

The species is very adaptable with respect to soils, growing on a wide range from the rocky, glacial soils of the Northeast, to neutral loams and moist benches in the Lake States, and to the deep fertile loams of coves, and also shallow rocky soils in the southern Appalachians. It grows over a wide altitudinal range in the North, mostly from 1,000 to 3,000 ft. on the Allegheny Plateau, and from 2,000 to 5,000 ft. in the southern mountains. Eastern hemlock matures at from 250 to 300 years, often growing to an age of

600 years (*279*), and with a record age of **988** years. The tree is shallow rooted, making it prone to injury from drought, sudden exposure after stand opening, and windthrow (*481, 713*). Exposed to salt spray in a New England hurricane, it was one of the species most severely damaged at two localities (*1005, 1632*). It is hit by lightning about as frequently as any tree in the woods, apparently a result of its tall spire-like form and, therefore, often has characteristic, long lightning scars. Eastern hemlock has a high bark-tannin content (7 to 12 percent).

Spaulding as early as 1914 gave a good account of the pathogenic and physiogenic disorders of eastern hemlock, as known at that time, much of which, except for nomenclature changes, is still valid (*1333*). Eastern hemlock is subject to several leaf, shoot, and cone rusts; and many other fungi can attack foliage and twigs. The species is seldom damaged by fungi after the seedling stage, but it can decline rapidly when suddenly exposed following cutting or clearing, and the wood tends to be "shaky."

Young hemlock is very sensitive to fire injury. The tree's ultimate emergence as a major component in many stands is due less to resistance to impacts than to its great tolerance to shade, its capacity to thrive on a wide range of soils, and its resistance to ice damage. Hemlock's limber branches droop with loads of ice or snow, and recover well later (*310, 390*).

Hemlocks of sawlog size are notoriously subject to wind-shake (*481*), to radial stress cracks, and, following sudden exposure, to sunscald of the bark, and to death. These reactions may be the result of many adverse effects associated with a changed regime of solar heat and soil moisture and culminate in a decline often referred to as post-logging decadence. When hemlocks are left as residual trees following partial cutting, and when they are exposed, through road or other construction or clearing, they often die, even when their root area is covered with understory brush (*661*). Eastern hemlock is also considered to be one of the species most sensitive to sulfur fumes from smelters (*1333*). An interesting type of hemlock ring-shake follows sapsucker injury (*1292*).

Seedling Diseases.—Seed germination is commonly as low as 20 to 30 percent but can be raised by stratification (*713*). In one study area more trees originated from seed falling on rotten wood and on mineral soil on dry sites than on well-watered sites (*712*). The slow-growing seedlings are often subject to being smothered under hardwood leaf-mold during their first 3 to 5 years.

In seedbeds, eastern hemlock is subject to damping-off and root rots. *Pythium debaryanum, Rhizoctonia solani,* and *Cylindrocladium scoparium* (*296*) have caused nursery losses. *Rhizina undulata* has caused occasional damage in spots where slash or trash has been burned, and *Botrytis cinerea* can mold seedlings. In commercial nurseries raising ornamental hemlocks in the southern Appalachians, hemlocks a few years old are often rendered unsalable by the autoecious leaf and twig rust *Melampsora farlowii*, that produces telia on areas of the shoots that turn orange when wet, in summer. The rust curls and kills the new shoots, making the trees appear to be singed (*670*). The other three hemlock leaf rusts, which bear aecia on the needles, can also cause yellowing and shedding of needles of nursery plants.

Foliage Diseases.—Needle rusts are caused by *Melampsora abie-tis-canadensis*, with its II and III stages on *Populus* spp.; *M. far-lowii*, which is autoecious, having its III stage on *Tsuga* spp.; *Pucciniastrum hydrangae*, with its II and III stages on *Hydrangea* spp.; and *P. vaccinii*, with its II and III stages on several plants in the Ericaceae (*46*). *M. farlowii* also causes a shoot blight and shoot curl, *M. abietis-canadensis* and *M. farlowii* also rust cones (*670*), and the other two only rust needles.

Fabrella (*Didymascella, Keithia*) *tsugae* (*807*) causes a needle blight that commonly singles out individual needles, attacks the underside, and causes rapid browning and death but prevents shedding (*658, 1333*). Another striking needle disease is caused by *Rosellinia herpotrichioides*, which involves mostly the lower foliage in shady, ultra-moist situations. The needles and twigs become matted with a gray to tawny felt on which very large perithecia are formed (*659*).

Dimerosporium tsugae causes a black, sooty growth on the surfaces of needles; *Phacidium tsugae* (*238*), recently renamed *Korfia tsugae* (*1158*), is associated with yellowing needles in North Carolina, with proof of pathogenicity lacking; and the harmless *Adelopus nudus* appears as tiny perithecia on the underside of green foliage, issuing, in rows, from the stomata.

Stem Diseases.—Eastern hemlock has no important fungus-canker diseases. The appearance of fruiting bodies of *Caliciopsis orientalis* (*483*), *Phomopsis occulta* (*570*), *Micropera abietina* (*55, 387*), *Valsa abietis*, or *V. kunzei* (*1519*) may give the impression of aggressive pathogenicity, but these fungi are ordinarily weakly or nonpathogenic to eastern hemlock. *C. orientalis* caused many cankers in a hemlock stand in Ontario, Canada (*483*). *Dermatea balsamea* is a canker and twig-blight fungus that produces discrete lesions, centering usually at a twig axil, and bearing patches of whitish mycelium beneath which fruiting bodies erupt. It is not common. *Tympanis tsugae*, a saprophyte, produces, small, black apothecia on dead bark (*552*).

A bleeding canker of hemlock in Pennsylvania was associated, by Gross and Weidensaul (*549*), with *Phacidiopycnis pseudo-tsugae* (see *Pseudotsuga*). The cankers were on large, mature, dying trees, on the lower bole, butt, or exposed roots. They are narrow, elongate, usually annual, and form during the host's dormant season.

A hemlock canker is regarded as of physiogenic origin and has killed hemlock in large numbers, in many nurseries and home plantings, in West Virginia. It is characterized by localized bark splitting and a clear, resinous exudate oozing from necrotic areas in the lower trunk region. Trees become off-color, yellow, and with dead and dying branches (*55*).

The gluing fungus, *Hymenochaete agglutinans*, can sometimes cause girdling bark lesions beneath its brown felt.

The hemlock dwarfmistletoe (*505*) *Arceuthobium campylopodum* f. *tsugensis* and the western heartrot fungus *Echinodontium tinctorium* can attack eastern hemlock, but they do not occur on this tree in the East.

Aleurodiscus farlowii and *A. penicillatus* fruit on dead twigs (*858*).

Root Diseases.—The root-rot fungi *Armillaria mellea, Fomes annosus,* and *Polyporus schweinitzii* (*887*) can be pathogenic to eastern hemlock but seldom kill trees. Even those who collected assiduously in the past seldom if ever collected the conks of, or reported damage from, these species (*1333*). Later experience has not disclosed any important root-rot diseases of eastern hemlock. Hubert (*723*) indicates that *P. balsameus,* under the name *P. crispellus,* is a root- and butt rotter of this species, and Lorenz and Christensen (*887*) give eastern hemlock as a host of *P. balsameus.*

Trunk Rots.—Any discussion of the pathology of this species of trees should mention the common, large, conspicuous, red-varnished-topped fungus *Ganoderma* (*Polyporus*) *tsugae,* which rots the stumps and wood of fallen trees. It is not, however, a heartrotter of living hemlocks. There are few true heartrot fungi of eastern hemlock that warrant attention within the age span of managed stands, although old trees are commonly butt-rotted (*481*). *Polyporus sulphureus, Poria subacida,* and *Fomes pini* (*887*) are of some consequence, but it is notable that in Percival's (*1096*) many herbarium searches for hosts of *F. pini,* he only reported one collection of this ubiquitous conifer fungus that was taken from an eastern hemlock. *Fomes robustus* causes some decay of living hemlock in New England.

Polyporus borealis, which causes a cuboidal, delignifying rot with white flecks in the wood, occurs occasionally as a heartrotter of living hemlock in the Northeast (*1143*), and *Pholiota adiposa* has been reported causing heartrot in the Lake States (*887*).

In Ontario the cull percentage due to rot never got above 13 percent, even up to ages exceeding 260 years. Many fungi were involved, but by far the predominant one was *Stereum sanguinolentum* (*73*).

Mycorrhizal Relations.—The only mycorrhizal fungi reported associated with eastern hemlock are *Cenococcum graniforme* and *Boletus granulatus,* and neither of these associations were established by pure-culture technique (*1442*).

Miscellaneous Pathology.—Newly-formed cones of eastern hemlock are often aborted by *Melampsora abietis-canadensis* or *M. farlowii.* The loss to the cone crop can be material from these rusts (*670*). *Ascochyta conicola* and *Mycosphaerella tsugae* occur on cone scales but do not damage the seed.

The common coniferous "bark-patch" fungi *Aleurodiscus amorphus* (*587*), *A. farlowii,* and *A. penicillatus* are inhabiters of dead bark and are not injurious (*858*).

Ruehle (*1224*) lists 10 species of nematodes in 9 genera associated with hemlock in the Southeast.

Carolina hemlock
Tsuga caroliniana

Carolina hemlock is a very tolerant tree occurring in the southern Appalachian Mountains at elevations from 2,500 to 4,000 ft., from southwest Virginia to north Georgia. It grows singly or in small groups, usually along streams or other moist situations

(*279*), attaining/much smaller size than eastern hemlock. Its stiffer shoots and the habit of its needles extending outward in several planes make it a distinctive and desirable ornamental. However, it does not withstand dry soil conditions or hot summer temperatures well, and although it is grown in several commercial ornamental nurseries in North Carolina, its use should be restricted to cool, moist situations. It is sensitive to damage by fire and is commonly shallow rooted, making it subject to windthrow. Its soil and environmental requirements are like those of eastern hemlock except for a lower tolerance to heat and low soil moisture than its sister species *Tsuga canadensis*. It is seldom damaged by cold, snow, or ice, and it leafs out too late to be often injured by late spring frosts.

In the nursery, seedlings do best with partial shade for the first year or two. While little trouble has been experienced with damping-off, all of the North Carolina nurseries raising Carolina hemlock have had damage from the hemlock twig rust (*Melampsora farlowii*). This rust, which requires no alternate host, builds up where large numbers of hemlocks are grown together, as in nurseries or hedges, and it diminishes when trees are outplanted individually. In the early summer it produces on the new shoot growth telial areas that are orange colored when moist. The shoots then become limp at the infected area and droop, curl, and die, giving trees a singed appearance (*670*).

Beyond the seedling stage Carolina hemlocks continue to be injured slightly by rusts, but these diseases then become important only from an aesthetic point of view. Hemlock hedges in the southern Appalachians, whether eastern or Carolina hemlock, often are trimmed and sprayed because of recurrent rust attacks (*496*). In addition to *Melampsora farlowii*, an autoecious rust attacking leaves, twigs, and cones, Carolina hemlock is also attacked by *M. abietis-canadensis*, which yellows and causes a casting of scattered, current year's needles, as well as rusting cones; and also by *Pucciniastrum hydrangae* and *P. vaccinii*, both of which rust, yellow, and cast individual needles, but do not infect shoots or cones. All of the latter rusts produce aecia on needles and have alternate stages, respectively, in *Populus, Hydrangea*, and members of the Ericaceae (*46*). *Fabrella* (*Didymascella, Keithia*) *tsugae* browns scattered needles on Carolina hemlock (*807*), and *Dimerosporium tsugae* causes a black, sooty growth on the surface of the needles (*151*).

It is likely that further study of this little-known tree would reveal other fungi that inhabit living tissue, but Carolina hemlock is, nevertheless, a tree with few disease enemies, although demanding in its site requirements.

Western hemlock
Tsuga heterophylla

A very tolerant tree of northwest California, the western third of Oregon and Washington, north Idaho, and northwest Montana, western hemlock thrives best in the humid and mild climate of the Pacific slopes. Average annual precipitation in the Coast hemlock region varies from 38 to 100 in. and in the Rocky Mountain hemlock area from 25 to 53 in. Minimum temperatures below –20° F. and maximum temperatures up to 108° F. occur in the inland type. The species withstands cold well in this country, but Peace (1091) considers it very susceptible to spring frosts under European conditions. Along the Pacific coast, it grows from sea level to 2,000 ft. and in the northern Rocky Mountains to an elevation of 6,000 ft. (101).

Like its eastern counterpart as to preference for moist sites, it is, nevertheless, very adaptable with respect to soil texture. It occurs on soils derived from sandstones, shales, or igneous rocks and does very well on most well-drained soils, so long as they are abundantly moist most of the year. The species reproduces well from seed, responds well to release, and is a good competitor. It tends to be shallow rooted, making it subject to windthrow, and thin-barked, making it easily injured by fire. The bark has a very high tannin content (12 to 22 percent) (101). The tree matures at about 200 years, and many trees reach ages in excess of 500 years (279). In the Queen Charlotte Islands of British Columbia, ages over 700 years were recorded (460).

Western hemlock has proved to be one of the species most sensitive to damage by sulfur dioxide from ore smelting. At one major polluted area, it led all associated pines, spruces, and Douglas-fir in the extent of damage sustained (1249).

The pathology of western hemlock is dominated by its defectiveness due to heartrot, mostly caused by *Echinodontium tinctorium* and *Fomes pini,* and its susceptibilty to a form of western dwarfmistletoe.

Seedling Diseases.—In the field, drought is the worst enemy to seedling establishment, since seeds often fall and germinate on partly decomposed forest debris that easily dries out. In the nursery the species is subject to damping-off in neutral or alkaline soils (1). Botrytis blight (*B. cinerea*), *Rhizina undulata, Thelephora caryophyllea,* and *T. terrestris* have all been reported attacking seedlings in Idaho but have not been major factors in nursery production. It is questionable if the Thelephoras are harmful at all unless their growth is very copious (1540) or seedling growth very slow.

Western hemlock is listed as a host to *Phytophthora cinnamomi* in Oregon (303).

Foliage Diseases.—The leaf diseases of western hemlock include two rusts, *Caeoma dubium* and *Uraecium holwayi,* occurring in the northern part of the United States range of the tree and into Canada. Until recently, only pycnial and aecial stages were known (46). *C. dubium,* however, has recently been shown to produce *Melampsora* stages on *Salix* spp. in Canada (1666) and has been named *M. epitea* f. sp. *tsugae.* It is considered indistinguishable from *M. abieti-capraearum* on *Abies.*

The snow mold *Herpotrichia nigra,* the black sooty surface growth caused by *Dimerosporium tsugae* (151), and a browning of individual needles by *Fabrella* (*Didymascella, Keithia*) *tsugae* (807) occasionally occur on western hemlock. The latter fungus is suspected to infect living needles and retard normal shedding by preventing the formation of the abscission layer.

Stem Diseases.—This species is generally free of damaging canker diseases, although *Caliciopsis pseudotsugae* causes twig cankers (*483*), and an annual, irregularly elliptical stem canker caused by *Cephalosporium* sp. develops on suppressed trees (*373*). Both diseases have been reported only from British Columbia.

The main disease enemy is the hemlock dwarfmistletoe (*Arceuthobium campylopodum* f. *tsugensis*) (*505*). Horizontally flattened brooms are characteristic of attack on western hemlock, and, in addition to the usual retardation of growth and ultimate killing, trunk infections are particularly damaging to this species in Canada (*1551*). While western hemlock is severely parasitized in Alaska and parts of Canada, it is only occasionally infected and damaged only slightly in western Oregon and Washington, where it reaches its optimum development (*151*). However, in some stands sampled by Englerth (*415*) in this area, 31 percent of the trunk decay was traceable to dwarfmistletoe cankers and swellings.

Baranyay (*59*) found nine ascomycetes and two Fungi Imperfecti associated with cankers on branch swellings of western hemlock caused by *A. campylopodum* f. *tsugensis* in British Columbia. He considers this colonization to be due largely to the low bark moisture of the cankered bark, excessive resin flow, and the occurrence of dead bark.

Botryosphaeria tsugae, described and illustrated by Funk (*484*), is a fungus with a *Macrophoma* conidial stage that causes branch and leader cankers and dieback of western hemlock in British Columbia. The ascocarp is a black, subglobose, uniloculate stroma with a short beak. The pycnidia are very similar. Both ascospores and conidia are 1-celled and hyaline; the former averaging about $44\mu \times 15\mu$, and the latter, about $38\mu \times 20\mu$.

A discomycete, *Discella parksii*, with small, yellow to orange apothecia, grows on bark and decorticated wood of Sitka spruce and western hemlock in California (*237*).

Funk (*488*) describes a new species of *Ascoconidium*, a phialophorous Hyphomycete associated with a bark disease of western hemlock in British Columbia. It occurs on dying branches, producing phialides erumpent through the outer periderm, from a dark-brown stromatic mat. The conidia are terete, 4- to 8-celled, and sometimes muriformly septate. Funk named the fungus *A. tsugae*.

Discocainia (*Atropellis*) *treleasei* causes swollen, fusiform cankers on branches of western hemlock and Sitka spruce (see *Picea sitchensis, 1160*).

Coccomyces heterophyllae is a saprobe and weak parasite associated with bark diseases of western hemlock in Washington and British Columbia. It produces black apothecia in the periderm and has hyaline, non-septate, filiform ascospores that are broadest at their upper end (*490*).

Aleurodiscus lividocoeruleus and *A. penicillatus* occur on dead twigs (*858*).

Root Diseases.—There are few root rots of western hemlock. *Armillaria mellea* occurs widely, and its rhizomorphs are familiar to those who work with roots, but it seldom kills and is not a major source of cull. *Fomes annosus* and *Polyporus schweinitzii*, both important root pathogens on pines, are mainly butt rotters in western hemlock. *Poria weirii* causes a distinctive laminated root and butt rot of Douglas-fir and western redcedar in particular, occasionally killing and causing heartrot of other conifers, including western hemlock (*184, 1189*). The latter is usually listed as a host for *P. weirii*, but beyond that little has been reported on the extent of its damage to this species (*190*). *Polyporus tomentosus* occasionally rots the roots and butts of western hemlock (*724*). A yellow stringy rot, largely of the roots and sometimes butts, caused by *Flammula alnicola*, occurs widely in Canada (*374*). Buckland et al. (*189*), working in British Columbia, rated the following as the major root and butt rot fungi: *Poria subacida, Fomes annosus, Armillaria mellea, Polyporus sulphureus*, and *P. tomentosus*.

Driver and Wood (*393*) found a high incidence of stump infection by *Fomes annosus* in western hemlock 2 to 8 months after thinning. Effects on the residual stands were not reported.

Trunk Rots.—Western hemlock is host to many fungi that live in exposed, damaged, and dead wood (*1277*). The principal heartrotters that are associated with wounding and breakage injuries are caused by *Fomes annosus* (predominantly), *Stereum* spp., *S. sanguinolentum*, and *Poria weirii*. The main heartrot fungi in typical older stands of this species in its optimum range in the United States were found by Englerth (*415*) to be *F. annosus, F. pini, F. applanatus, F. robustus, Polyporus oregonensis, F. pinicola, Echinodontium tinctorium*, and eight other fungi, listed in order of prevalence.

It is interesting that, whereas *E. tinctorium* has been generally considered ubiquitous on western hemlock (*1544*), it accounted for none of the decay in a study by Wright and Isaac (*1623*) and only 5 percent of the total cull from fungi in a study by Englerth (*415*). Nevertheless, *E. tinctorium* (Indian paint fungus) often develops early in the life of the tree, with Hubert finding as high as 46 percent of the trees in a 41–80 year group already infected (*101*). Much higher incidences of decay occurred in British Columbia (*459*). Susceptibility to this heartrot has been considered largely responsible for the frequent classification of this tree as an inferior species in the western white pine type. Kimmey (*798*) gives a detailed, illustrated account of the rot and the fungus causing it.

Later, Kimmey (*797*), writing on the "heartrots of western hemlock" placed the nine major white rot fungi, in order of importance, on this tree as: *Fomes annosus, Poria subacida, F. pini, F. robustus, Armillaria mellea, F. applanatus, Stereum sanguinolentum, Pholiota adiposa*, and *Echinodontium tinctorium*. He lists the four most important brown rot fungi as *F. pinicola, Polyporus sulphureus, Stereum abietinum*, and *P. schweinitzii*. Kimmey discusses the occurrence, appearance, location in tree, entry points, and indicators of these fungi on western hemlock.

Kimmey (*795*) conducted an extensive study of cull in Sitka spruce, western hemlock, and western redcedar in southeast Alaska (see *Picea sitchensis*). In western hemlock the fungi responsible for cull, expressed in terms of the total cubic-foot rot-cull volume, were as follows: *Armillaria mellea*, 26 percent; *Fomes pinicola*, 22 percent; *F. annosus*, 21 percent; *Pholiota adiposa*, 9 percent; *Polyporus sulphureus*, 6 percent; *P. schweinitzii*, 5 percent; *F. robustus,* 5 percent; *Hydnum* sp., 3 percent; *F. pini,* 1 percent; *F. applanatus,* 1 percent; other, 1 percent.

The defectiveness of western hemlock led Weir and Hubert (*1544*) to suggest an 80-year rotation.

On residual trees in the Pacific Northwest, wounds caused by thinning resulted in more decay in western hemlock than in Douglas-fir (*734*). *Fomes annosus* accounted for 80 percent of the decay volume under wounds on the hemlock, and *Stereum sanguinolentum* accounted for 72 percent of such decay in Douglas-fir.

Foster, Browne, and Foster (*458*), reporting on intensive studies of decay in western hemlock and silver fir in the Kitimat region of British Columbia, ranked the fungi responsible for the decay. Earlier, Foster, Craig, and Wallis (*459*) similarly ranked the western hemlock fungi responsible for decay in the Upper Columbia River region. The following listing compares the two findings.

Fungus:	Kitimat	Upper Columbia
	Total decay (cubic-volume basis)	
	Percent	*Percent*
Brown cubical rots—		
Stereum abietinum	5.8	1.9
Fomes pinicola	4.6	4.8
Polyporus sulphureus	0.3	—
Omphalia campanella	0.1	—
Other fungi	0.3	2.3
White rots—		
Fomes pini	47.9	25.2
Echinodontium tinctorium	19.8	62.4
Stereum sanguinolentum	6.6	0.2
Armillaria mellea	2.6	—
Poria tsugina	2.6	—
Fomes annosus	1.1	0.2
Other fungi	1.4	3.0
Mixed and unknown	6.9	—

The principal fungi decaying western hemlock vary greatly by region. Thus, while in Englerth's study (*415*) *Fomes annosus* led the heartrot fungi in prevalence and volume loss, in the Kitimat study (*458*) it accounted for only 1 percent of the decay loss and occurred in only 2 percent of the infected trees. Similarly, while *Echinodontium tinctorium* caused most of the heartrot in the inland Upper Columbia region of British Columbia (*459*), it caused none in the Queen Charlotte Islands and apparently does not occur in the region. (*460*).

The importance of regional differences in the ranking of fungi is again apparent in the paper by Buckland et al. (*189*), working in the Franklin River area of British Columbia, where *Poria subacida* and *Fomes annosus* led the butt rotters, accounting for 18 percent of the total decay but caused little or no damage in the Kitimat and Upper Columbia areas. *Fomes pinicola* led, by far, all trunk rotters in loss (41 percent), with *F. pini* second, whereas *F. pinicola* was a minor fungus in the other two study areas. *Hydnum abietis* was listed among the Franklin River fungi, but *Echinodontium tinctorium* was not. Buckland et al.

(*189*) found that maximum periodic increment was reached at ages between 225 and 275 years. Roots and scars led, in importance, the other avenues of infection.

The decay fungi invading living western hemlock are very numerous. Foster, Craig, and Wallis (*459*) name 18 of secondary importance in addition to those listed under "Upper Columbia" in the accompanying table, and in the Queen Charlotte Islands 27 were identified as causing decay in living western hemlock trees (*460*).

There is a large literature on many aspects of decay in western hemlock, including relations to tree age, diameter, and stand factors, and also entrance courts, external indications, and other features of the decays caused by many fungi. In addition to the references already cited on heartrot in western hemlock, further information can be obtained on this subject from the series of three articles by Foster and Foster (*461, 462, 463*) on estimating decay in this species and in another Canadian paper on a decadence classification for mature stands (*467*).

Mycorrhizal Relations.—Twenty-one fungi have been reported to form mycorrhizae with western hemlock, although none of the relationships has been established by pure-culture technique (*1442*).

Miscellaneous Pathology.—The significance of many discolorations in western hemlock and noble fir wood destined for manufacture into aircraft structures are described and illustrated by Englerth and Hansbrough (*417*).

Black streaks, often several feet long, appear in western hemlock wood. They are caused by maggots of a small fly and have little influence on strength of the wood (*899*).

Much attention has been given to decay in windthrown timber in the Pacific Northwest, and western hemlock has been one of the species involved. The many fungi causing decay in this dead and fallen timber are listed by Buchanan (*183*), and the characteristics of the losses they cause are described. Eight years after one major blowdown, 80 percent of the volume of decayed wood was ascribed to *Fomes applanatus* and *F. pinicola*.

The deterioration of western hemlock timber on Vancouver Island killed by the hemlock looper was studied first by Foster and Hurn (*464*) and later by Engelhardt (*431*). By the eighth year following the kill, 86 percent of the rot was traceable to *Fomes pinicola*, with the remainder caused by eight other identified fungi.

Boyce (*144*) studied deterioration following the great Olympic Peninsula blowdown of 1921. Six years after the blowdown the volume loss, on a board-foot basis, was, for western hemlock, 92 percent; Pacific silver fir, 74 percent; Sitka spruce, 46 percent; Douglas-fir, 35 percent; and western redcedar, 27 percent. The main fungi identified in connection with decay in western hemlock were *Fomes pinicola, F. applanatus, Polyporus abietinus, Lenzites saepiaria,* and *F. annosus*.

American elm
Ulmus americana

This account deals mainly with the American elm, and unless otherwise stated, the information given pertains to this species. Other elms, such as the winged elm of the South (*Ulmus alata*), slippery elm (*U. rubra*), rock elm (*U. thomasii*), cedar elm (*U. crassifolia*), and Siberian elm (*U. pumila*), are mentioned in connection with certain diseases. While these other elms have many of the same diseases as the American elm, fewer diseases have been reported for them. Some diseases of these other elm species have not been reported for American elm.

No American tree has a wider natural range than *Ulmus americana*. This range embraces the entire area east of the Great Plains, except for the southernmost third of Florida. This species has also been grown successfully in many parts of the West. It is not demanding as to soil type, growing well in sands, loams, and clays, nor is soil moisture critical, except on droughty sites or those with a very high summer water table.

In the South, American elm is common on clay and silty clay-loams on first bottoms of rivers and on terraces where growth is fair on the wetter sites and good on the well-drained flats (*468*). It is intermediate in tolerance, responds well to release, and is reasonably drought-resistant. It is sensitive to prolonged spring floods but average in general sensitivity to flooding (*583*). Of our common shade trees, it ranks among those most readily damaged by ice because of its many fine branches and its forked stems (*310*). The roots are shallow and widespread in moist soils, but a long taproot forms in dry soils. Some trees live approximately 200 years in age and grow to over 10 ft. in diameter.

The American elm has a notorious pathology. The Dutch elm disease has already killed a large percentage of our American elm population in the Northeast and Middle West. In the latter area the phloem necrosis virus is just as damaging as the Dutch elm disease in many cities. Before these diseases struck, this elm was already known to be subject to Verticillium wilt, *Dothiorella* wilt, the killing wetwood disease and attendant slime flux problems, black leaf spot, and also many minor diseases. In addition, a recession of elm (*645*), coincident with and as severe as sweetgum blight, was uncovered during surveys for the latter disease in the South in 1954.

A few horticultural forms and at least one variety, *floridana*, of the American elm are known (*1154*). A great many crosses have been made between *Ulmus americana* and elm species resistant to Dutch elm disease (mostly *U. pumila*, and *U. pedunculata*). A few of such crosses have succeeded, and at least one of the hybrids with *U. pumila* has remained healthy after repeated inoculation with *Ceratocystis ulmi*.

Seedling Diseases.—Because of the Dutch elm disease, there has been a major decline in the nursery culture of the American species of elm. Earlier, *Ulmus americana* in particular was widely grown for ornamental, shade, and shelterbelt use. Now, in the region of shelterbelts north of the Texas root rot belt of Texas and Oklahoma, *U. pumila* and *U. parvifolia* are the elm species commonly used for protection against wind.

Rhizoctonia solani has occasionally caused damping-off of elm in nurseries of the Great Plains States (*360*). This pathogen strikes early in the season and can cause pre-emergence damping-off. The fungus is characteristic in culture, with constricted mycelium at the points of branching, as illustrated by Westcott (*1555*).

498

American elm seedlings studied in Nebraska were highly susceptible to damping-off from *Pythium ultimum,* under high soil moisture conditions, but much less susceptible to attack by *Rhizoctonia solani.* With soil at 50 percent of moisture-holding capacity, both of these fungi, and also species of *Fusarium,* attacked the seedlings to a moderate degree (*1617*).

The violet root rot caused by *Helicobasidium purpureum* (*Rhizoctonia crocorum*) is known to attack elm and willow seedlings in the Southwest (see *Salix*). Also in the Southwest, root knot nematodes (*Meloidogyne* spp.) deform elm roots, but they do not constitute a major seedling problem.

A serious root rot problem with Siberian elm (*U. pumila*) and Chinese elm (*U. parvifolia*) has developed on nursery stock grown throughout the Great Plains region (Lamb et al. *827*). Caused by *Chalaropsis thielavioides,* a pathogen of lupine and of walnut grafts, infections take place in the seed beds and can spread rapidly in transit. A grayish-white, mold-like growth appears at injuries on the roots. Outer root tissues turn brown to black and break down to a slimy mass. The terete, endogenously-formed microconidia and the ovoid macroconidia form on seedlings and in culture. They appear similar to the conidia of *Ceratocystis fimbriata* (*732*).

The powdery mildews discussed under Foliage Diseases are more likely to constitute nursery than field diseases, partly because of late-season watering practices in nurseries.

Foliage Diseases.—Although the elms are subject to some noteworthy leaf diseases, these are dwarfed in importance by the many lethal vascular wilts. The most conspicuous leaf disease is the black spot that is widespread on American, English, and Chinese elms. The spots, when fully developed, are small, black, shiny, and somewhat raised (*1143*). Caused by *Gnomonia ulmea,* this disease can defoliate an elm tree in the spring, and when this happens a heavy twig mortality ensues. The imperfect stage, *Gloeosporium ulmeum,* can form during the summer while the foliage is attached. Tiny acervuli exude a creamy slime of elliptic, single-celled, hyaline conidia. The dead leaf tissue is grayish and visible only on the upper leaf surface. The shiny, black pustules are scattered on the gray areas. After leaf fall, the *Gnomonia* perithecia form within these black areas. Pomerleau (*1123*) gives a complete and well-illustrated account of this disease.

Another common leaf spot of American and English elm is caused by *Gloeosporium inconspicuum.* The spots are roughly circular, brown, with still darker brown margins and with centers visible from both surfaces of the leaf. This fungus can also cause a blighting of greenwood shoots.

Still another elm leaf spot is caused by *Gloeosporium ulmicola.* The spots are elongated on midribs, veins, and leaf margins and are visible from both leaf surfaces.

With at least three species of *Gloeosporium,* in addition to many other late summer leaf pathogens fruiting on elm foliage toward fall, the separation of these organisms becomes a mycological problem of the first order. The relation of some of the imperfect fungi to some of the known perfect stages on elm foliage is yet to be established (*8*).

Occasionally, the leaf blister caused by *Taphrina ulmi* becomes conspicuous early in the growing season on many American species of elm. As compared with the blisters of *T. caerulescens* on oak, those of *T. ulmi* on elm are very small, causing yellowish to brown, unthickened or slightly puffed spots (*994*). The mycelium is subcuticular and bears palisades of asci, as illustrated by Pomerleau (*1122*).

Three species of powdery mildew fungi attack the elms, and as new shoots and foliage emerge late in the growing season, for example mid-August, they may be cupped, stunted, and covered with the oidial bloom of either *Microsphaera alni*, *Phyllactinia guttata*, or *Uncinula macrospora*. These genera are annotated under *Alnus, Salix*, and other hardwoods, and the species are described by Reed (*1153*).

An infectious chlorosis of elm, called elm mosaic, produces a yellow and green mottling accompanied by roughening of the leaf texture. Some leaves are normal, others are abnormally large or small, stiff, and distorted. A moderate amount of brooming sometimes develops (*1374*).

Wester and Jylkka (*1557*) have described a systemic virus disease, called elm scorch, in which the older foliage becomes brown between the veins and along the leaf margins, producing the same definite pattern illustrated by Carter (*232*) for elm bacterial wetwood. There have been suggestions that these diseases may be one and the same. They are described here under the Vascular Diseases. Elm scorch has been identified by Wester generally over the East and South. Most of his cases resembled what had heretofore commonly been referred to as drought effects or other physiogenic disorders.

The winged elm *Ulmus alata* is subject to the common oak leaf spot caused by *Actinopelte dryina* (see *Quercus*). Large numbers of these small, often confluent spots can be very disfiguring by August.

Stem Diseases.—This section does not include the vascular diseases, which are treated separately. Except for those causing vascular diseases, none of the remaining stem pathogens of elm is a major economic parasite. The more common of them are annotated below.

Target cankers caused by *Nectria galligena* (see *Betula alleghaniensis*) occur occasionally on forest and shade elms in the North. It is likely that most of the canker-forming *Nectria* spp. on eastern hardwoods belong to *N. galligena* rather than to *N. coccinea* or some other *Nectria* species (*879*). The coral-colored sporodochia and red perithecia of *N. cinnabarina* often appear on twigs and branches killed or severely weakened by other causes, but it is not a primary parasite of elm (*928*).

Botryosphaeria ribis (see *Cercis*) is also a weak parasite of elm and has been known to canker seedlings in Georgia. Luttrell (*894*) proved the pathogenicity to elm seedlings and provides good descriptions of the cankers and the fungus.

In Illinois, American elms attacked by *Cytosporina ludibunda* developed wilting and dieback, followed by cankering, when infection reached the larger and older parts of branches. Carter (*227*) succeeded in obtaining infection with this fungus. Its pycnidia are in a stroma, and they exude elongated to filiform, 1-celled, hyaline conidia.

Hubert (725) provides a detailed illustrated description of a widespread canker, mainly of American elm, caused by *Sphaeropsis ulmicola* (also known under several synonyms, 8). Branch dieback results in stagheading. Infected areas of shoots are sharply delimited. These areas are reddish and mottled with black blotches. Later, they are covered with small, black pycnidia with small necks that barely protrude from the bark. The spores are dark, 0- to 1-septate, ovoid, and variable in size. This disease can be separated with certainty from the many other twig diebacks of elm only by identification of the causal organism.

A zonate canker of American elm has been described and illustrated by Swingle and Bretz (1373). Bark-covered, strongly zonate lesions formed where patches from virus-infected elms were grafted into healthy stems. The disease is considered to be virus caused and transmissible by grafting and other means. It has been found from New Jersey to Ohio and Missouri, both alone and in combination with the elm mosaic virus (1374).

Another disease of *Ulmus americana* and *U. fulva*, called pit canker, has long been known in the Northeast and was demonstrated by Caroselli and Tucker (225) to be caused by *Phytophthora inflata*. Deeply sunken lesions are usually bark-free and show their age by narrow, tightly-packed, healing callus folds. Many cankers may develop on a single tree. Isolations revealed this new species of *Phytophthora*. It can be readily identified in culture by its large, inflated, and variously lobed or distorted antheridia.

The leaf spot fungus *Gloeosporium inconspicuum* can cause a late-season spotting and blighting of greenwood shoots, with symptoms as described for it under Foliage Diseases.

Endothia gyrosa behaves as described under *Quercus*. In its fruiting on trees, it resembles the chestnut blight fungus, but the perithecia are larger and more brightly reddish (1283). It is essentially a saprobe living in exposed and injured buttress root bark or trunk bark.

Septobasidium pseudopedicellatum forms brown felts over scale insects on branches and can have a partly pathogenic role (292).

The eastern leafy mistletoe (*Phoradendron serotinum*) can parasitize elms, mainly in the Central and Southern States.

It is interesting to note that the spring crimp nematode *Aphelenchoides fragariae*, which is mainly a bud parasite of strawberries, has been identified from a cankered elm twig in New Jersey (1222).

The bleeding canker disease caused by *Phytophthora cactorum* (see *Acer saccharum*) is reputed to affect elms in New England. This fungus attacks so many divergent hosts (*Acer, Arbutus, Cornus, Fagus, Quercus*, et al.) that attack of an occasional elm would hardly be surprising. Caroselli (223), who illustrates and describes this disease, states that the cankers are typically indefinite in size and are more often distributed vertically than laterally. In these cankers, fissures develop from which a reddish-brown, watery fluid oozes, which, upon drying, resembles dried blood.

A canker and dieback of Siberian elm, *Ulmus pumila*, reported

501

from Illinois, develops on trunks and branches in early spring, and black sporodochia of a *Tubercularia* sp. form in the disease bark. Small cankers heal over their first year, but larger ones take up to 2 years. They are essentially annual lesions. Conidiophores cover the sporodochium and produce hyaline, 1–celled, ovoid to oblong conidia. Fruiting is general on the bark-covered lesions and is of great diagnostic value. Carter (*229*) described the disease and named the fungus *T. ulmea*. Trees or branches weakened from other causes are most likely to develop this canker.

Carter (*226*) also described a trunk canker of *U. pumila* in Illinois that generally appears at the soil line, retains the bark, and is caused by *Thyrostroma compactum*. Tubercles, which later become erumpent, appear as dark brown to black, circular, convex cushions. The conidia are produced singly over the face of the tubercle and are oblong to clavate, 1- to many-septate, partly muriform, and deep tan, averaging $14.5\mu \times 10–20\mu$.

Paul Keener [56] mentioned a bacterial canker of *U. pumila* in the Southwest that he described as a "bleeding disease associated with bacteria and other factors." It is quite possible that this disease is one of the manifestations of bacterial wetwood (see Vascular Diseases).

Vascular Diseases.—The Dutch elm disease now has spread over most of the East-to-West range of American elm and extends from Canada south to North Carolina, Tennessee, Arkansas, and Texas. First symptoms are wilting, curling, and yellowing of leaves on one or more branches, followed by leaf fall and death of affected branches. A tree may die within a few weeks of the onset of symptoms or die a limb at a time over a year or more. The springwood of the last annual ring of an affected tree shows in cross section as a dark brown ring or a series of dark dots and dashes. Similar streaks and rings are formed by *Verticillium albo-atrum, Dothiorella (Cephalosporium) ulmi,* and sometimes even by bacterial wetwood, and crown symptoms of the latter three diseases, as well as those of phloem necrosis, can be confused with those of Dutch elm disease. Proof of the latter depends upon obtaining the causal organism *Ceratocystis ulmi* in culture. The appearance of the fungus in culture, where it produces a *Cephalosporium*-like stage and a coremium stage, is described by May (*940*). In case of possible confusion with *Dothiorella ulmi*, it is best to refer cultures to authorities until one's own ability to identify the Dutch elm disease fungus is assured.

Swingle et al. (*1375*) give field techniques for the identification of Dutch elm disease and phloem necrosis. Their criteria are presented in this account. However, since the three fungus vascular wilts and bacterial wetwood can all be confused with each other in the field, cultural identification is paramount, once phloem necrosis, is ruled out, in confirming the fungus involved. A technique developed by Pomerleau and Pelletier (*1127*) for determining the presence of *Ceratocystis ulmi* in fresh elm leaves, shoots, and wood involves placing the unsterilized pieces in question on 1.5 percent

---

[56] Personal communication from Paul D. Keener, deceased, formerly plant pathologist, University of Arizona, Tucson, Ariz.

502

water agar in Petri dishes. If the fungus is present, typical coremia form at the invaded tissue, and they can be readily identified or cultured from.

Dutch elm disease affects all of our native elm species, with *Ulmus americana* being particularly susceptible. Some elms succeed in recovering from infection by "burying" an annual ring harboring the fungus beneath successive rings of uninvaded xylem tissue, since there is very little radial spread through the xylem. The main carriers of this disease in the United States are the elm bark beetles *Scolytus multistriatus* and *Hylurgopinus rufipes*.

Banfield (*58*), in the publication Dutch Elm Disease Recurrence and Recovery, traces pathogenesis from twig infection, through dissemination of the pathogen through the vascular system, to saprogenesis in killed tissue. He discusses the mechanisms of recovery following infection and gives a full, illustrated account of the pathological histology in this disease. His photographs and drawings of spores and mycelium in the different xylem elements effectively support his account of rapid, extensive vascular involvement following infection in early June.

Wilson (*1590*), in evaluating his findings of sparse blocking of xylem water-conducting elements by gums, spores, or hyphae, at the time of early crown symptom development, concludes that such blockage can hardly explain these symptoms.

A large literature has accumulated on the Dutch elm disease (*151*), some of which is summarized in a bulletin by Whitten and Swingle (*1574*), and most of which is available through the INTREDIS Register for literature retrieval in forest pathology (*653*).

Ouellett and Pomerleau (*1058*) confirmed the lack of resistance to Dutch elm disease on the part of natural populations of American elm. However, exposure to thermal neutrons or X-rays induced some degree of resistance in 4 out of 150,000 seedlings, and one withstood 9 inoculations, remaining uninfected. This slow-growing tree appears to be immune.

Elm phloem necrosis, caused by a systemically distributed virus, has killed large numbers of trees from the Great Plains eastward to West Virginia and south to Mississippi. The virus is highly infectious, spreading through root grafts and by leafhoppers. In some Central States cities, more trees have been killed by phloem necrosis than by Dutch elm disease. Affected trees show a drooping and curling of leaves, which then become yellow, then brown, and then fall off. The inner phloem develops a butterscotch color (*231, 1375*). When inner bark of an infected tree is stripped and promptly put in a capped bottle for a few minutes, a wintergreen odor can be detected. Most trees noticeably affected in June die the same summer. Good accounts of phloem necrosis are provided by Swingle (*1372*) and by others (*231, 928*).

Leaf mosaic and elm scorch are caused by viruses different from the phloem necrosis virus.

Mention has already been made, under Foliage Diseases, of a virus disease of elm named and described by Wester and Jylkka (*1557*) as elm scorch, because the main symptoms appear on the older foliage. Little has been published on this systemic virus disease, but enough has been said about it to warrant a closer look at the similarities and differences between scorch and the bacterial wetwood disease of elm, on the part of research pathologists working with elms, to determine if there is any likelihood that they are one disease.

An elm virus that causes rosette in peach may be the prune dwarf virus. Although this elm virus produces symptoms on hosts other than elms, the virus has been recovered only from species of *Ulmus*.

Elms are also subject to Verticillium wilt (*V. albo-atrum* or *V. dahliae*) from East Coast to West Coast, but while a common disease, it has not approached the destructiveness of either Dutch elm disease or phloem necrosis. Symptoms include sudden wilting and browning of foliage while trees are in full leaf, leaves emerging dwarfed, often gradual decline over several years, a limb at a time, and a brown ring or broken ring in the latest springwood, in cross section, as in Dutch elm disease. May and Gravatt (*941*) reported that 4 percent of the elm samples sent to the U. S. Department of Agriculture's Dutch Elm Disease Laboratory over many months proved to be cases of Verticillium wilt. This disease has been annotated and literature cited under *Acer saccharum* and *A. platanoides*. Again, cultural identification is essential. In view of the questions on speciation among Verticillium wilt pathogen isolates, expert advice (*1581*) is suggested in making determinations. The fungus is soil-borne and infects through the roots.

Another vascular wilt, easy to confuse with Dutch elm disease, is caused by *Dothiorella* (*Cephalosporium*) *ulmi*. It is sometimes called elm dieback (*941*) and has been widely reported since 1929 in planted trees and natural stands of *Ulmus americana, U. crassifolia,* and *U. rubra* from New England to Mississippi. In a 5-year period 42 percent of the samples sent to the Federal Dutch Elm Disease Laboratory for "confirmation" proved to be cases of Dothiorella wilt. Many of the symptoms of the latter are like those of Dutch elm disease and Verticillium wilt, including wilting and yellowing of foliage, top dieback, and brown discoloration in the tracheae of the last one or more annual rings. It often takes the Dothiorella wilt and Verticillium wilt organisms several years to kill a tree, while Dutch elm disease and phloem necrosis are more likely to result in death in a single year.

In Dothiorella wilt, flat cankers with dead bark adhering may appear on small branches, and small, black pycnidia of the causal fungus develop on them. Elongate, hyaline, 1-celled, parallel-sided conidia are exuded from the pycnidia. In culture, hyaline, ovate conidia pull up into false heads. This fungus is well-illustrated and described by Verrall and May (*1478*). Goss and Frink (*524*) also provide a well-illustrated bulletin on this disease, which at that early date, 1934, was known as Cephalosporium wilt. The conidial heads and spores they illustrate are of the fruiting type formed in culture or in water, and not of the type that occurs in natural pycnidia. Dothiorella cankers sometimes harbor other fungi also.

504

Still another very important disease of elm is called wetwood. Wetwood is a term in wide use and refers to generalized bacterial infection of the woody cylinder (603), resulting in a strong alkaline reaction of the wood, a high moisture content, and slime-fluxing. In some tree species wetwood is lethal, while in others little harm results. Carter (228) made a thorough study of wetwood in elm caused by *Erwinia nimipressuralis* and determined that it occurred in *Ulmus americana* and its cultivars Moline and Littleford, in *U. fulva, U. procera,* and *U. pumila,* and in species of *Acer, Morus, Quercus, Populus,* and *Salix.*

Wetwood is conspicuous in heartwood and sapwood as brown bands or streaks, with the wood appearing watersoaked. Sap oozes out and gas is emitted following severance of xylem tissue. Carter (231) states that the grayish-brown streaks in the wood of wilting branches resemble xylem symptoms of Verticillium wilt, Dothiorella wilt, and Dutch elm disease. Gas pressure, generated by fermentation, leads to and accompanies fluxing and tends to keep wounds from callusing over. Cracks in the bark form in winter, and some never heal. Intervenal and marginal leaf browning develops, with marginal curling, wilting, and defoliation, depending upon the extent of infection.

The wetwood bacterium can be isolated from discolored heartwood or sapwood. It is described by Carter (228) as a short rod, with rounded ends, motile, with six peritrichiate flagella, anaerobic, Gram-negative, and not acid-fast.

Tehon and Harris (1388) describe a chytrid fungus in the xylem of a young Moline elm (a cultivar of *U. americana*). They suspect it to be the cause of a vascular disease. It produced an amoeboid thallus, variable in shape and highly vacuolated. Attenuate thalli are very fine, with bead-like enlargements. Oospores with companion cells are formed. The fungus inhabits parenchyma, fiber, and ray cells in the xylem.

Root Diseases.—Considering the large number of leaf, stem, and vascular diseases of elm, it is noteworthy that few root diseases have been reported, aside from the transmission of vascular pathogens through root grafts.

Tehon and Jacobs (1390) gave a fully illustrated account of what they called, in 1934, Verticillium root disease of elm and which they ascribed to a new species they called *Verticillium rhizophagum.* The external symptoms agree with those of phloem necrosis, and even though the authors show positive inoculation results with the *Verticillium,* others have attributed this so-called Dayton (Ohio) elm disease, as it occurs in the field, to phloem necrosis followed by secondary invasion by a Verticillium and the other fungi reported by Tehon and Jacobs.

In contrast to the wilt caused by *Verticillium albo-atrum,* in the Dayton disease there is no vascular discoloration, and the fungi isolated were obtained only from roots and not from above-ground xylem tissue. In the Dayton disease, root ends were dead, the cortex of larger roots could be sloughed off, or at least showed an "off color." With small roots the cortex could be slid off the stele like "a tube being pulled off a pencil."

U.S. Department of Agriculture elm disease research workers

obtained *Verticillium rhizophagum* only occasionally in routine isolating from diseased elms. They also obtained it from dead and dying pine seedlings at Marietta, Ohio. They were not able to demonstrate pathogenicity for this fungus on 3- to 5-year-old American elm seedlings.[57]

Armillaria mellea, in its attack on elm roots, is in its familiar role on hardwoods, of being a wound pathogen of doubtful potentiality for active, aggressive, lethal behavior. As a root inhabitant, it is almost always associated with severe wounding or other debilitating influences such as drought or grade changes (*257*). Three species of *Xylaria* are also secondary root rotters of elm (*8*).

The American species of elm are all highly susceptible to Texas root rot (*Phymatotrichum omnivorum*), except for *Ulmus crassifolia*, which is fairly resistant (*1379*). Losses to *U. americana* and *U. pumila*, over a 6–year period, when planted as shelterbelt trees in the root rot area of Oklahoma and Texas, accounted for 3 percent of the 15,000 elm trees planted. This rate of killing was considered too high for these species to be useable in the Texas root rot belt (*1627*).

The seedling root rots of elm have been discussed under Seedling Diseases.

There are no reports of fungi involved in mycorrhizal relationships with American elm species (*1442*).

Root damage to American elm was reported in association with the root knot nematode *Meloidogyne ovalis* in Wisconsin (*1171*) and *Meloidogyne* sp. in Oklahoma (*1222*).

Trunk Rots.—The elms are attacked by many heartrot fungi, and most of them attack the woody cylinder of many species of hardwoods. Among these heart rotters are *Fomes applanatus* (mostly saprobic), *F. connatus* (which typically causes little rot before fruiting), *F. igniarius, Pleurotus ostreatus, Polyporus dryadeus, P. sulphureus,* and *Stereum subpileatum* (see also *Acer saccharum* and *Quercus* spp.).

Other fungi capable of causing either limited rot of the central cylinder or rot at wounds of living *Ulmus* spp. include *Daedalea ambigua, Fomes densus, F. everhartii, F. marmoratus, F. ohiensis, Polyporus cuticularis, P. lucidus, P. resinosis, P. spraguei, P. squamosus,* and *P. zonalis* (*1067*). *Fomes annosus* colonized stump wood in Canada.

Among the somewhat more host-specific fungi that rot the wood of living elms are *Fomes fraxineus, F. fraxinophilus, F. geotropus,* and *Pleurotus ulmarius.*

Most of the elm decay fungi are described by Overholts (*1067*), Lowe and associates (*890, 892*), and Boyce (*151*). The cultural characters of most of these organisms have been determined by Davidson et al. (*343*) and by Nobles (*1038*).

Bryan (*180*) studied the causes of defect in second-growth Southern Piedmont hardwoods. Among the many species studied were elms, mainly *Ulmus alata.* He obtained a higher percentage of clear, 2–foot cuttings (7.2 percent of the elm cuttings were clear) from elms than from any of the other nine species groups studied.

---

[57] Personal communication from Roger V. Swingle, deceased, formerly pathologist, USDA Agricultural Research Service, Delaware, Ohio.

This indicates that although elms, partly because of the intensive scrutiny given the American elm and its many diseases, have earned a bad pathological reputation, the forest elms of the South can yield unusually clear lumber.

Miscellaneous Pathology.—Irregular, large or small, smooth, gray areas on the bark have been attributed to *Aleurodiscus oakesii* (see *Quercus*) and to *A. griseo-canus*, a species not described in Lemke's (*858*) monograph of the amyloid-spored species of *Aleurodiscus*. The basidiocarps of *A. oakesii* are discoid, small, gregarious, with margins sometimes inrolled on drying, and occur on the smooth surfaces of exfoliated bark areas (*1389*).

The American elm is notorious for developing slime-fluxes. To some degree this subject has been covered in the discussion of wetwood, under Vascular Diseases. Slime fluxes occur in hardwood trees that have been injured, and then infected by bacteria or yeasts that multiply in the sap. They may be localized or general throughout the woody cylinder. Fluxes are seepage of sap either already infected or about to be. The viscid, beery-smelling, fermenting, insect-attracting slime is toxic to bark tissues, and for this reason many fluxes never heal. Some, however, close but result in a wetwood condition of the tree. Since elms tend to have stem crotches at acute angles that may be sprung open by the action of wind or the weight of ice, snow, or simply the normal bending of the tree, elms are especially prone to slime fluxes.

A failure of American elm to leaf out properly in the spring of 1950 in Saskatchewan, Canada, was attributed to low temperature injury to the roots, following recordings as low as minus 32.3° F. at Saskatoon (*705*). Trees showed many abnormalities, including heavy spring blossom production, failure of many buds to open, small and chlorotic foliage, and others. Some trees 40 or more years old and healthy until 1950 died as a result of the intense cold of January 1950.

A dieback of southern elms, mostly *Ulmus alata*, ranking in geographic extent and degree of damage with accompanying sweetgums affected by "blight," was uncovered when data were analyzed on the condition of sweetgum and many other accompanying hardwoods on a southwide survey for sweetgum blight (*645*). Other species were virtually unaffected. The cause of the dieback is likely physiogenic, as explained for sweetgum blight (see *Liquidambar*).

California-laurel
Umbellularia californica

California-laurel, also known as Oregon myrtle or pepperwood (*955*), is an evergreen that is easily distinguished by a strong, pungent, camphor-like odor emitted from its foliage when crushed (*1367*). The odor is that of a light, volatile oil produced in green bark and leaves, and if inhaled through the nose, it can cause violent sneezing (hence the name pepperwood) and severe pain. Leaves are retained from 2 to 6 years. The tree grows near the higher foothill streams and lower mountain slopes and canyons, from southwestern Oregon along the Pacific Coast to southern California. It also grows along the west side of the Sierra Nevada Mountains. It forms clumps and patches, along with madrone, canyon live oak, red alder, and other Pacific hardwoods. Its range is similar to that of *Lithocarpus densiflora.*

This species is very tolerant, thrives under the conditions described for *Alnus rubra,* and can grow to very large size and to over 200 years old. Its soils may be gravelly, rocky, or rich in humus. Constant, abundant soil moisture is essential. The silvical characteristics are summarized by Fowells (*468*).

The wood is heavy, hard, fine-grained, yellow-brown, often beautifully mottled, and the sapwood is wide (*1367*). Not only is the wood useful for attractive small products, but the tree has high esthetic value in many of its native situations and is widely used in home and park landscaping.

In native stands, wind and snow have caused appreciable damage. Blowdown is common during severe north or southeast winds and rain storms (*468*). The lack of a taproot and restrictedness of root spread cause this species to be more subject to windthrow than any tree in California. It is also readily injured by fire.

Like all broad-leafed evergreens, the foliage is host to many fungi (*1277*), but these seldom claim more than academic interest. However, during the winter of 1957–58 in the central coastal area of California, an extensive blighting of foliage occurred. Parmeter et al. (*1083*) determined that this leaf blight was the result of attack by the bacterium *Pseudomonas lauracearum* and the fungi *Kabatiella phoradendri* f. sp. *umbellulariae* and *Colletotrichum gloeosporioides* (see *Persea*). Subsequent branch dieback was associated with a *Botryosphaeria* sp., and this latter fungus has been blamed for much damage to this tree.

Pseudomonas lauracearum produces small, angular, black lesions that yield the bacteria upon suitable staining (*194*). The pathogenicity of the organism has been established by Harvey (*610*). The *Kabatiella,* together with the *Colletotrichum* (= *Glomerella cingulata*), produce very irregular, large, brown spots or blotches. The *Kabatiella's* pathogenicity has been established by Harvey (*609*). Illustrations of the three elements of this leaf blight complex are provided by Parmeter et al. (*1083*), and the *Kabatiella,* under the synonym *Microstroma umbellulariae,* is described by Cooke (*284*).

A so-called "black mildew" develops on the foliage, mostly on the upper surface, and may be caused by any of several fungi. One, *Vertixore atronitidum,* produces a dark, crustose mycelium. The perithecia are globose, sessile, black, lustrous, 70–125μ in diameter, the upper half bearing dark, septate, acute appendages. The ascospores are clavate, hyaline, 5- to 8-celled, and 17–30μ × 3–7μ.

Phaeosaccardinula anomala produces a light, dusty-brown subiculum that appears granular. The perithecia, which collapse early, are brown and are 112–184μ in diameter. The ascospores are hyaline, muriform, fusoid, 3– to 5–septate, and measure 10–18μ × 3–6μ. Miller and Bonar (*991*) describe these sooty-mold fungi and point out that the type material with *Asterina anomala,* bore two different fungi, and therefore that name fell into the synonymy of the two fungi described above as new species by these authors.

Miller and Bonar (*991*) describe another "black mildew" fungus on several California trees, including California-laurel, as *Phaeosaccardinula dermatia*. Its thallus, on leaves and twigs, appears as loose, thick, black masses of rigid, much-branched mycelium. Its perithecia are dark, somewhat tuberculate, without appendages, and 27–150μ in diameter. The ascospores are biseriate, brown, fusoid, 5- to 6-celled, muriform, constricted at the septa, and 26–33μ × 7–13μ in size.

Other sooty molds occurring on this species and also described by Miller and Bonar (*991*) are *Capnodium tuba* (only the conidial stage is known) and *Chaetasbolisia falcata*, which has small, hyaline, rod-shaped conidia, 1.3–5μ × 1–2.5μ, formed in brown pycnidia.

A leaf disease that can severely defoliate madrone and can badly spot the foliage of California-laurel is caused by *Mycosphaerella arbuticola* (see *Arbutus*).

The only stem pathogen known to occasionally cause notable damage to this species is *Nectria galligena*. Mainly in California, this fungus has appeared fruiting around the edges of bark-free "target" cankers on stems and branches (see *Acer rubrum*, *Betula alleghaniensis*, and *Juglans nigra*). These cankers tend to become prevalent in regions or localities where the weight of ice or snow or the pressure of wind causes cracks in branch axils, leading to infection at these points (*530*).

Although *Nectria cinnabarina* and *N. coccinea* have been reported on this species, the former is typically secondary and the latter, when associated with cankers, has often proved to be *N. galligena* (*879*).

None of the rot fungi reported are heartrot fungi, in the sense that they can extensively decay the central woody cylinder of living trees. Limited decay, mostly associated with wounds, can be caused by *Fomes applanatus*, *F. fomentarius*, *Odontia fimbriata*, *O. subochracea*, *Phlebiella candidissima*, *Polyporus lucidus*, *P. squamosus*, *P. versicolor*, *Poria ambigua*, *P. ferrea*, *P. ferruginosa*, and *Stereum albobadium* (*1277*). These organisms are all essentially saprobes, thus leaving California-laurel without a single aggressive heartrot fungus reported to attack it. However, *F. applanatus* fruits so readily on scarred trees of this species that it may be more of a true heart rotter in California-laurel than is the case with most eastern hardwoods.

Dead wood can also be decayed by *Fomes annularis* and *F. brownii* (*1067*).

Because of the amount of injury from ice, snow, and wind, this species tends to be defective. Even in young stands, dead knots, stem malformations, and even root collars are often decayed. Total cull in one northern California study averaged 7 and 10 percent of the gross cubic volume in trees of sawlog or cordwood size and quality, respectively (*793*).

The nematode *Bakernema variabile* has been reported from *Umbellularia californica* (*1222*).

This publication reports research involving pesticides. It does not contain recommendations for their use, nor does it imply that the uses discussed here have been registered. All uses of pesticides must be registered by appropriate State and/or Federal agencies before they can be recommended.

CAUTION: Pesticides can be injurious to humans, domestic animals, desirable plants, and fish or other wildlife—if they are not handled or applied properly. Use all pesticides selectively and carefully. Follow recommended practices for the disposal of surplus pesticides and pesticide containers.

LITERATURE CITED

(1) Anonymous.
    1948. Woody-plant seed manual. U.S. Dep. Agr. Misc. Publ. 654, 416 p.

(2) Anonymous.
    1953. Distribution, symptoms, and control of some of the more important plant diseases. U.S. Dep. Agr. Plant Dis. Rep. Suppl. 221: 130–137.

(3) Anonymous.
    1953. Red hickory as strong as white hickory. USDA Forest Serv. Forest Prod. Lab. Tech. Note 171, 2 p.

(4) Anonymous.
    1955. These are the champs. Amer. Forests 61(9): 31–40.

(5) Anonymous.
    1955. White pine root rot control studies give promising results. In Annu. Rep. 1955, USDA Forest Serv. Lake States Forest Exp. Sta., p. 25–26.

(6) Anonymous.
    1955. Wood handbook. U.S. Dep. Agr. Handb. 72, 528 p.

(7) Anonymous.
    1956. These are the champs, Part II. Amer. Forests 62(4): 33–40.

(8) Anonymous.
    1960. Index of plant diseases in the United States. U.S. Dep. Agr. Handb. 165, 531 p.

(9) Anonymous.
    1960. What's known about managing eastern white pine. USDA Forest Serv. Prod. Res. Rep. 38, 69 p.

(10) Anonymous.
    1963. Important forest diseases of mutual concern to member countries of the North American Forestry Commission. Compiled by Working Group on Forest Insects and Diseases, North American Forestry Comm., FAO. 74 p.

(11) Adams, Donald F., Shaw, C. Gardner, Gnagy, Richard M., and others.
    1956. Relationship of atmospheric flouride levels and injury indexes on gladiolus and ponderosa pine, Agr. and Food Chem. 4(1): 64–66.

(12) Adams, J. F.
    1918. *Keithia* on *Chamaecyparis thyoides*. Torreya 18: 157–160.

(13) Adams, James T., Jr., Witcher, Wesley, and Lane, C. L.
    1964. Microorganisms in soil from *Fomes annosus* infected pine stands. U.S. Dep. Agr. Plant Dis. Rep. 48: 114–118.

(14) Adams, Peter B.; Sproston, Thomas; Tietz, Hans; and Major, Randolph
    1962. T. Studies on the disease resistance of *Gingko biloba*. Phytopathology 52: 233–236.

(15) Agnihotri, V. P., and Vaartaja, O.
    1967. Root exudates from red pine seedlings and their effects on *Pythium ultimum*. Can. J. Bot. 45: 1031–1040.

511

(16) Ahlgren, Clifford E., and Hansen, Henry L.
1957. Some effects of temporary flooding on coniferous trees. J. Forest. 55: 647–650.

(17) Ainsworth, G. C.
1961. Ainsworth and Bisby's dictionary of the fungi. Ed. 5, 547 p. Kew: Commonwealth Mycological Institute.

(18) Alcorn, Stanley M.
1961. Some hosts of *Erwinia carnegieana*. U.S. Dep. Agr. Plant Dis. Rep. 45: 587–590.

(19) Alexander, R. R.
1958. Silvical characteristics of Engelmann spruce. USDA Forest Serv. Rocky Mountain Forest and Range Exp. Sta. Pap. 31, 20 p.
(20) ———.
1958. Silvical characteristics of subalpine fir. USDA Forest Serv. Rocky Mountain Forest and Range Exp. Sta. Pap. 32, 15 p.

(21) Alfieri, S. A., Jr.
1968. Limb blight disease caused by *Corticium salmonicolor* B. & Br. Fla. Dep. Agr. Div. Plant Ind., Plant Pathol. Circ. 71, 2 p.

(22) Andersen, Harold E.
1959. Silvical characteristics of Alaska-cedar (*Chamaecyparis nootkatensis*). USDA Forest Serv. Alaska Forest Res. Center Sta. Pap. 11, 10 p.

(23) Anderson, A. B., Scheffer, T. C., and Duncan, Catherine C.
1962. On the chemistry of heartwood decay on ageing in incense cedar (*Libocedrus decurrens* Torrey). Chem. and Ind. (Rev.) 28: 1289–1290.

(24) Anderson, A. P.
1902. *Dasyscypha resinaria* causing canker growth on *Abies balsamea* in Minnesota. Torrey Bot. Club Bull. 29: 23–34.

(25) Anderson, Gerald W.
1963. Sweetfern rust on hard pines. USDA Forest Serv. Forest Pest Leafl. 79, 7 p.

(26) ———.
1968. The occurrence of eastern and western gall rust on a single jack pine tree. U.S. Dep. Agr. Plant Dis. Rep. 52: 328–329.

(27) ———, and French, David W.
1965. Western gall rust in the Lake States. Forest Sci. 11: 139–141.

(28) ———, and French, David W.
1965. Differentiation of *Cronartium quercuum* and *Cronartium coleosporioides* on the basis of aeciospore germ tubes. Phytopathology 55: 171–173.

(29) Anderson, I. V.
1934. Breakage losses and cull percent of timber in the Inland Empire. USDA Forest Serv. North. Rocky Mountain Forest and Range Exp. Sta. Appl. Forestry Note 63, 3 p.

(30) Anderson, Neil A.
1959. Needle droop of red pine. USDA Forest Serv. Lake States Forest Exp. Sta. Tech. Note 549: 1–2.

(31) ———.
1963. Eastern gall rust. USDA Forest Serv. Forest Pest Leafl. 80, 4 p.

(32) ———, and Anderson, Gerald W.
1963. White pine root rot at the Chittenden Nursery. USDA Forest Serv. Res. Note LS–26, 3 p.

(33) ———, and Bugbee, W. M.
1962. *Cylindrocladium* root rot of conifer seedlings in Minnesota. (Abstr.) Phytopathology 52: 721.

512

(34) ———, and French, D. W.
    1962. Stalactiform rust on jack pine. (Abstr.) Phytopathology 52: 721–722.

(35) ———, and French, D. W.
    1964. Sweetfern rust on jack pine. J. Forest. 62: 467–471.

(36) Anderson, Ralph L.
    1956. *Hypoxylon* canker of aspen. USDA Forest Serv. Forest Pest Leafl. 6, 3 p.

(37) ———.
    1964. *Hypoxylon* canker impact on aspen. Phytopathology 54: 253–257.

(38) ———, and Kaufert, F. H.
    1959. Brooming response of black spruce to dwarfmistletoe infection. Forest Sci. 5: 356–364.

(39) Anderson, R. L., Skilling, D. D., and Clifford, E. D.
    1956. Nursery root disease control by soil fumigation. USDA Forest Serv. Lake States Forest Exp. Sta. Tech. Notes 449, 1 p.

(40) Andrews, Stuart R.
    1955. Red rot of ponderosa pine. USDA Forest Serv. Rocky Mountain Forest and Range Exp. Sta. Agr. Monogr. 23, 34 p.

(41) ———.
    1957. Dwarfmistletoe of ponderosa pine in the Southwest. USDA Forest Serv. Forest Pest Leafl. 19, 4 p.

(42) ———, and Eslyn, Wallace E.
    1960. Sooty-bark canker of aspen in New Mexico. U.S. Dep. Agr. Plant Dis. Rep. 44: 373.

(43) Ark, P. A.
    1939. Bacterial leaf spot of maple. Phytopathology 29: 968–970.

(44) ———.
    1944. Pollen as a source of walnut bacterial blight infection. Phytopathology 34: 330–334.

(45) Arnold, Ruth Horner.
    1967. A canker and foliage disease of yellow birch. I. Description of the causal fungus, *Diaporthe alleghaniensis* sp. nov., and the symptoms on the host. Can. J. Bot. 45: 783–801.

(46) Arthur, Joseph Charles.
    1962. Manual of the rusts in United States and Canada—with illustrations and a new supplement by George B. Cummins. 438 p., plus 24 p. in supplement. New York: Hafner Publ. Co.

(47) Ashcroft, J. M.
    1934. European canker of black walnut and other trees. W. Va. Agr. Exp. Sta. Bull. 261, 52 p.

(48) Atkinson, R. G.
    1965. *Phytophthora* species inciting root rot of *Chamaecyparis lawsoniana* and other ornamentals in coastal British Columbia. Can. J. Bot. 43: 1471–1475.

(49) Atwell, E. A.
    1948. Red-stain and pocket-rot in jack pine: their effect on strength and serviceability of the wood. Dominion (Can.) Forest Serv. Circ. 63, 23 p. Ottawa.

(50) Bachelder, Stephen, and Orton, E. R.
    1962. *Botrytis* inflorescence blight on American holly in New Jersey. U.S. Dep. Agr. Plant Dis. Rep. 46: 320.

(51) Bailey, L. H.
    1914–1917. The standard cyclopedia of horticulture. 3639 p. New York: The Macmillan Co.

513

(52) ———.
1923. The cultivated evergreens. 434 p. New York, London: The Macmillan Co.

(53) ———.
1924. Manual of cultivated plants. 851 p. New York: The Macmillan Co.

(54) Baker, Frederick S.
1949. A revised tolerance table. J. Forest. 47: 179–181.

(55) Baldwin, Robert E., and Elliott, Edward S.
1962. Hemlock canker. Phytopathology 52: 292–294.

(56) Ball, Carleton R.
1938. The willows of the Southern States. Castanea 3: 1–9.

(57) Banfield, Walter M.
1963. Comparative development of the *Hypoderma* and *Lophodermium* needle casts of eastern white pine. (Abstr.) Phytopathology 53: 870.

(58) ———.
1968. Dutch elm disease recurrence and recovery. Mass. Agr. Exp. Sta. Bull. 568: 21–60 [Reprinted from Phytopathol. Zeitschrift 62: 21–60. 1968]

(59) Baranyay, J. A.
1966. Fungi from dwarfmistletoe infections in western hemlock. Can. J. Bot. 44: 597–604.

(60) ———, and Stevenson, G. R.
1964. Mortality caused by *Armillaria* root rot, *Peridermium* rusts, and other destructive agents in lodgepole pine regeneration. Forestry Chron. 40: 350–361.

(61) Barnett, H. L.
1953. Isolation and identification of the oak wilt fungus. W. Va. Agr. Exp. Sta. Bull. 359T, 15 p.

(62) ———.
1955. Illustrated genera of imperfect fungi. 218 p. Minneapolis: Burgess Publishing Co.

(63) Barr, Margaret E.
1968. The Venturiaceae in North America. Can. J. Bot. 46: 799–864.

(64) Bart, G. J.
1964. *Pythium* root rot of *Taxus*. (Abstr.) Phytopathology 54: 887.

(65) Basham, J. T.
1958. Decay of trembling aspen. Can. J. Bot. 36: 491–505.

(66) ———.
1958. Studies in forest pathology. XVII. The pathological deterioration of fire-killed pine in the Mississagi region of Ontario. Can. Dep. Agr. Publ. 1022, 38 p.

(67) ———.
1959. Studies in forest pathology. XX. Investigations of the pathological deterioration in killed balsam fir. Can. J. Bot. 37: 291–326.

(68) ———.
1960. Studies in forest pathology. XXI. The effects of decay on the production of trembling aspen pulpwood in the Upper Pic Region of Ontario. Can. Dep. Agr. Publ. 1060, 25 p.

(69) ———.
1966. Heart rot of jack pine in Ontario. II. Laboratory studies on the pathogenicity and interrelationships of the principal heartwood-inhabiting fungi. Can. J. Bot. 44: 849–860.

(70) ———.
1967. Heart rot of jack pine in Ontario. III. Decay relationships and their effects on management. Forest. Chron. 43: 222–238.

514

(71) ———, and Belyea, R. M.
　　1960. Death and deterioration of balsam fir weakened by spruce budworm defoliation in Ontario. Part III. The deterioration of dead trees. Forest Sci. 6: 78–96.

(72) ———, Mook, P. V., and Davidson, A. G.
　　1953. New information concerning balsam fir decays in eastern North America. Can. J. Bot. 31: 334–360.

(73) ———, and Morawski, Z. J. R.
　　1964. Cull studies, the defects and associated basidiomycete fungi in the heartwood of living trees in the forests of Ontario. Can. Dep. Forestry Publ. 1072, 69 p.

(74) ———, and Taylor, L. David.
　　1965. The occurrence of fungi and bacteria in normal and discolored heartwood in second-growth sugar maple in Ontario. U.S. Dep. Agr. Plant Dis. Rep. 49: 771–774.

(75) Bates, Carlos G.
　　1923. Physiological requirements of Rocky Mountain trees. J. Agr. Res. 24: 97–164.

(76) Batra, Lekh R.
　　1960. The species of *Ciborinia* pathogenic to *Salix*, *Magnolia*, and *Quercus*. Amer. J. Bot. 47: 819–827.

(77) ———, and Lichtwardt, Robert W.
　　1962. Red stain of *Acer negundo*. Mycologia 54: 91–97.

(78) Baxter, D. V.
　　1931. Deterioration of chestnut in the southern Appalachians. U.S. Dep. Agr. Tech. Bull. 257, 22 p.

(79) ———.
　　1931. The fungi and the decay of the American chestnut: Part I. Papers Mich. Acad. of Sci., Arts, and Letters 14: 259–290.

(80) ———.
　　1941. Some resupinate polypores from the region of the Great Lakes. XII. Papers Mich. Acad. of Sci., Arts, and Letters 26: 107–121.

(81) ———.
　　1943. Pathology in forest practice. 618 p. New York: John Wiley and Sons, Inc.

(82) ———.
　　1947. Occurrence of fungi in the major forest types of Alaska. Papers Mich. Acad. of Sci., Arts, and Letters 31: 93–115.

(83) ———.
　　1952. Some resupinate polypores from the region of the Great Lakes. XXIII. Papers Mich. Acad. of Sci., Arts, and Letters 37: 93–110.

(84) Baxter, John W.
　　1955. Proof of the connection between buckeye rust, *Aecidium aesculi*, and *Puccinia andropogonis*. U.S. Dep. Agr. Plant Dis. Rep. 39: 658.

(85) Beattie, R. K., and Diller, J. D.
　　1954. Fifty years of chestnut blight in America. J. Forestry 52: 323–329.

(86) Becking, J. H.
　　1965. In vitro cultivation of alder root-nodule tissue containing the endophyte. Nature 207(4999): 885–887.

(87) Bedwell, J. L.
　　1938. The present status of chestnut blight in the Pacific northwest. U.S. Dep. Agr. Plant Dis. Rep. 22: 66–68.

(88) ———, and Childs, T. W.
　　1938. Verticillium wilt of maple and elm in the Pacific northwest. U.S. Dep. Agr. Plant Dis. Rep. 22: 22–23.

(89) ——, and Childs, Thomas W.
    1943. Susceptibility of whitebark pine to blister rust in the Pacific North-
        west. J. Forestry 41: 904–912.

(90) ——, and Fowler, Marvin E.
    1938. Fungi found on chestnut and chinquapin in Oregon, Washington,
        and British Columbia. U.S. Dep. Agr. Plant Dis. Rep. 22: 208–210.

(91) Bega, Robert V.
    1960. The effect of environment on germination of sporidia in *Cronartium
        ribicola*. Phytopathology 50: 61–69.

(92) ——.
    1962. Tree killing by *Fomes annosus* in a genetics arboretum. U.S. Dep.
        Agr. Plant Dis. Rep. 46: 107–110.

(93) ——.
    1964. Diseases of *Sequoia*. *In* Diseases of widely planted forest trees.
        FAO/IUFRO Symp. on Int. Dangerous Forest Dis. and Insects,
        Working Group on Int. Coop. in Forest Dis. Res., p. 131–139.

(94) ——, and Smith, Richard S., Jr.
    1966. Distribution of *Fomes annosus* in natural forests of California.
        U.S. Dep. Agr. Plant Dis. Rep. 50: 832–836.

(95) Bennett, Frank A.
    1961. Silvical characteristics of southern magnolia. USDA Forest Serv.
        Southeast. Forest Exp. Sta. Pap. 139, 9 p.

(96) Benton, Vincent L., and Ehrlich, John.
    1941. Variation in culture of several isolates of *Armillaria mellea* from
        western white pine. Phytopathology 31: 803–811.

(97) Berbee, J. G.
    1959. Birch dieback: present status and future needs. (Abstr.) Ninth Int.
        Bot. Congr. Proc. 2: 28–29.

(98) ——.
    1962. Development of *Fusarium* canker of black poplars. (Abstr.) Phy-
        topathology 52: 724.

(99) ——.
    1964. Diseases of *Populus*. *In* Diseases of widely planted forest trees.
        Contrib. of FAO/IUFRO Work. Group on Int. Coop. in Forest
        Dis. Res. FAO/FORPEST 64: 168–183. [Processed.]

(100) ——, and Rogers, J. D.
    1964. Life cycle and host range of *Hypoxylon pruinatum* and its patho-
        genesis on poplars. Phytopathology 54: 257–261.

(101) Berntsen, Carl M.
    1958. Silvical characteristics of western hemlock. USDA Forest Serv.
        Pacific Northwest Forest and Range Exp. Silvical Ser. 3, 16 p.

(102) Berry, Charles R., and Hepting, George H.
    1959. Pitch canker of southern pines. USDA Forest Serv. Forest Pest
        Leafl. 35, 3 p.

(103) ——, and Hepting, George H.
    1964. Injury to eastern white pine by unidentified atmospheric constitu-
        ents. Forest Sci. 10: 2–13.

(104) ——, and Ripperton, L. A.
    1963. Ozone, a possible cause of white pine emergence tipburn. Phyto-
        pathology 53: 552–557.

(105) ——, and Thompson, George E.
    1961. Extension of range and a new host for *Cristulariella pyramidalis*.
        U.S. Dep. Agr. Plant Dis. Rep. 45: 152.

(106) Berry, Frederick H.
    1955. Investigations of possible causes of sweetgum blight. U.S. Dep.
        Agr. Plant Dis. Rep. 39: 270–272.

516

(107) ——.
1960. Etiology and control of walnut anthracnose. Univ. Maryland Agr. Exp. Sta. Bull. A–113, 22 p.

(108) ——.
1964. Walnut anthracnose. USDA Forest Serv. Forest Pest Leafl. 85, 4 p.

(109) Bethune, James E., and Hepting, George H.
1963. Pitch canker damage to south Florida slash pine. J. Forest. 61: 517–519, 522.

(110) Bidwell, C. B., and Bramble, W. C.
1934. The *Strumella* disease in southern Connecticut. J. Forest. 32: 15–23.

(111) Bier, J. E.
1939. *Hypoxylon* canker of maple. Forest. Chron. 15, 3 p.

(112) ——.
1939. *Septoria* canker of introduced and native hybrid poplars. Can. J. Res., Sect. C, 17: 195–240.

(113) ——.
1946. The relation of research in forest pathology to the utilization of overmature timber. The significance of brown pocket rot in Sitka spruce on the Queen Charlotte Islands. Brit. Columbia Lumberman 30(6): 54-55, 74.

(114) ——.
1959. The relation of bark moisture to the development of canker diseases caused by native, facultative parasites. 1. *Cryptodiaporthe* canker on willow. Can. J. Bot. 37: 229–238.

(115) ——.
1959. The relation of bark moisture to the development of canker diseases caused by native, facultative parasites. 2. *Fusarium* canker on black cottonwood. Can. J. Bot. 37: 781–788.

(116) ——.
1961. The relation of bark moisture to the development of canker diseases caused by native, facultative parasites. V. Rooting behavior and disease vulnerability in cuttings of *Populus trichocarpa* Torrey and Gray, and *P. 'robusta.'* Can. J. Bot. 39: 145–154.

(117) ——.
1962. Acti-dione and natural bark extracts in the control of *Hypoxylon* canker of poplar. Forest. Chron. 38: 347–348, 363–365.

(118) ——.
1966. Some effects of microfloras in decay-free heartwood of *Abies lasiocarpa* (Hook) Nutt. on the growth of *Stereum sanguinolentum* Alb. and Schw. ex Fries. Can. J. Bot. 44: 139–147.

(119) ——, and Buckland, D. C.
1947. Relation of research in forest pathology to the management of second growth forests. I. *Poria weirii* root rot, an important disease affecting immature stands of douglas-fir Brit. Columbia Lumberman 31(2): 49–51, 64, 66.

(120) ——, and Foster, R. E.
1946. The relation of research in forest pathology to the preparation of forest inventories. 1. Suggested aids for cruising overmature stands of Sitka spruce on the Queen Charlotte Islands. Brit. Columbia Lumberman 30(4): 38–40, 64.

(121) ——, and Foster, R. E.
1946. The relation of research in forest pathology to the utilization of overmature timber. Significance of conk rot in Sitka spruce on Queen Charlotte Islands. Brit. Columbia Lumberman 30(5): 51–52, 65.

(122) ——, and Foster, R. E.
 1946. The relation of research in forest pathology to the preparation of forest inventories. 2. The possibility of obtaining net volumes by grade when cruising overmature stands of Sitka spruce on the Queen Charlotte Islands. Brit. Columbia Lumberman 30(7) : 52–53, 66, 68.

(123) ——, Foster, R. E., and Salisbury, P. J.
 1946. Studies in forest pathology. IV. Decay of Sitka spruce on the Queen Charlotte Islands. Domin. Can. Dep. Agr. Tech. Bull. 56, 35 p.

(124) ——, and Rowat, Marian H.
 1962. The relation of bark moisture to the development of canker diseases caused by native, facultative parasites. VIII. Ascospore infection of *Hypoxylon pruinatum* (Klotzsch) Cke. Can. J. Bot. 40: 897–901.

(125) ——, Salisbury, P. J., and Waldie, R. A.
 1948. Studies in forest pathology. V. Decay in fir, *Abies lasiocarpa* and *A. amabilis*, in the upper Fraser region of British Columbia. Can. Dep. Agr. Tech. Bull. 66, 28 p.

(126) Bingham, Richard T., and Ehrlich, John.
 1943. A *Dasyscypha* following *Cronartium ribicola* on *Pinus monticola*. II. Mycologia 35: 294–311.

(127) Blaser, H. Weston, Marr, Currie, and Takahashi, David.
 1967. Anatomy of boron-deficient *Thuja plicata*. Amer. J. Bot. 54: 1107–1113.

(128) Bloomberg, W. J.
 1963. Use of organic residues in forest nurseries. Can. Dep. Forest., Forest Ent. and Path. Branch, Bimo. Prog. Rep. 19(6) : 4.

(129) ——.
 1965. The effect of chemical sterilization on the fungus population of soil in relation to root disease of Douglas-fir seedlings. Forest. Chron. 41: 182–187.

(130)——.
 1966. The occurrence of endophytic fungi in Douglas-fir seedlings and seed. Can. J. Bot. 44: 413–420.

(131) ——.
 1968. Corky root disease of Douglas-fir seedlings. Can. Dep. Forest. and Rural Devel. Bi-mo. Res. Notes 24: 8.

(132) ——, and Farris, S. H.
 1963. *Cytospora* canker of poplars: bark wounding in relation to canker development. Can. J. Bot. 41: 303–310.

(133) Boe, Kenneth N.
 1958. Silvics of western larch. USDA Forest Serv. Intermount. Forest and Range Exp. Sta. Misc. Publ. 16, 17 p.

(134) Bonar, Lee.
 1922. The life history of *Rosellinia caryae* sp. nov. causing a hickory canker and disease. Phytopathology 12: 381–385.

(135) ——.
 1928. Studies on some California fungi. Mycologia 20: 292–300.

(136) ——.
 1962. *Stegopezizella balsameae* and *Gloeosporium balsameae*. Mycologia 54: 395–399.

(137) ——.
 1964. *Polyporus oleae* on olive in California. U.S. Dep. Agr. Plant Dis. Rep. 48: 70.

(138) ——.
 1965. Studies of some California fungi. IV. Mycologia 57: 379–396.

(139) Bonga, J. M.
    1964. An unusual witches' broom on black spruce caused by eastern dwarfmistletoe. Forest Sci. 10: 77–78.

(140) Booth, C.
    1959. Studies of Pyrenomycetes: IV. Nectria (Part I). Commonwealth Mycol. Inst., Mycol. Pap. 73, 115 p.

(141) Bourchier, R. J.
    1961. Laboratory studies on microfungi isolated from the stems of living lodgepole pine, *Pinus contorta* Dougl. Can. J. Bot. 39: 1373–1385.

(142) Boyce, John S.
    1920. The dry-rot of incense cedar. U.S. Dep. Agr. Bull. 871, 58 p.

(143) ———.
    1923. A study of decay in Douglas-fir in the Pacific Northwest. U.S. Dep. Agr. Bull. 1163, 20 p.

(144) ———.
    1929. Deterioration of windthrown timber on the Olympic Peninsula in Washington. U.S. Dep. Agr. Tech. Bull. 104, 28 p.

(145) ———.
    1930. Decay in Pacific Northwest conifers. Yale Univ. Osborn Bot. Lab. Bull. 1, 51 p.

(146) ———.
    1932. Decay and other losses in Douglas-fir in western Oregon and Washington. U.S. Dep. Agr. Tech. Bull. 286, 60 p.

(147) ———.
    1933. A canker of Douglas-fir associated with *Phomopsis lokoyae*. J. Forest. 31: 664–672.

(148) ———.
    1940. A needle-cast of Douglas-fir associated with *Adelopus gäumanni*. Phytopathology 30: 649–659.

(149) ———.
    1943. Host relationships and distribution of conifer rusts in the United States and Canada. Conn. Acad. Arts and Sci. Trans. 35: 329–482.

(150) ———.
    1957. The fungus causing western gall rust and Woodgate rust of pines. Forest Sci. 3: 225–234.

(151) ———.
    1961. Forest pathology. Ed. 3, 572 p. New York, Toronto, and London: McGraw-Hill Book Company, Inc.

(152) ———, and Wagg, J. W. Bruce.
    1953. Conk rot of old-growth Douglas-fir in western Oregon. Oreg. Forest Prod. Lab. and Oreg. State Forest. Dep. Bull. 4, 96 p.

(153) Boyce, John S., Jr.
    1951. *Lophodermium pinastri* and needle browning of southern pines. J. Forest. 49: 20–24.

(154) ———.
    1952. A needle blight of loblolly pine caused by the brown-spot fungus. J. Forest. 50: 686–687.

(155) ———.
    1954. *Hypoderma* needle blight of southern pines. J. Forest. 52: 496–498.

(156) ———.
    1958. Needle cast of southern pines. USDA Forest Serv. Forest Pest Leafl. 28, 4 p.

(157) ———.
    1958. Twig blight of eastern white pine caused by *Monochaetia pinicola*. Phytopathology 48: 516–517.

(158) ———.
    1959. Brown spot needle blight on eastern white pine. U.S. Dep. Agr. Plant Dis. Rep. 43: 420.

(159) ———.
    1960. An appraisal of *Fomes annosus* in Scotland. Forest Farmer 20(3): 10, 17.

(160) ———.
    1965. *Polyporus tomentosus* in pine plantations at Athens, Georgia. U.S. Dep. Agr. Plant Dis. Rep. 49: 322.

(161) ———, and Graves, Alfred A., Jr.
    1966. *Monochaetia* canker on Arizona cypress in Georgia and South Carolina. U.S. Dep. Agr. Plant Dis. Rep. 50: 482–483.

(162) Boyd, Raymond J., Jr.
    1959. Silvics of western redcedar. USDA Forest Serv. Intermount. Forest and Range Exp. Sta. Misc. Publ. 20, 14 p.

(163) Boyer, M. G.
    1961. Variability and hyphal anastomoses in host-specific forms of *Marssonina populi* (Lib.) Magn. Can. J. Bot. 39: 1409–1427.

(164) ———.
    1962. A leaf-spotting disease of hybrid and native aspen. Can. J. Bot. 40: 1237–1242.

(165) ———, and Isaac, P. K.
    1964. Some observations on white pine blister rust as compared by light and electron microscopy. Can. J. Bot. 42: 1305–1309.

(166) Boyle, Alice M.
    1949. Further studies of the bacterial necrosis of the giant cactus. Phytopathology 39: 1029–1052.

(167) Bramble, William C., and Holst, Eugene C.
    1940. Fungi associated with *Dendroctonus frontalis* in killing shortleaf pines and their effect on conduction. Phytopathology 30: 881–899.

(168) Brandt, Robert W.
    1960. The *Rhabdocline* needle cast of Douglas-fir. N.Y. State Univ. Coll. Forest. (Syracuse) Univ. Tech. Publ. 84, 66 p.

(169) ———.
    1963. Ash dieback in New England and New York. 39th Int. Shade Tree Conf. Proc. 1963: 38–43.

(170) ———.
    1964. Nectria canker of hardwoods. U.S. Dep. Agr. Forest Serv. Forest Pest Leafl. 84, 7 p.

(171) Bretz, T. W.
    1955. Some additional native and exotic species of Fagaceae susceptible to oak wilt. U.S. Dep. Agr. Plant Dis. Rep. 39: 495–497.

(172) ———.
    1964. Needle blight of eastern redcedar in Missouri. U.S. Dep. Agr. Plant Dis. Rep. 48: 418.

(173) Brinkman, Kenneth A.
    1957. Silvical characteristics of black walnut. USDA Forest Serv. Central States Forest Exp. Sta. Misc. Release 22, 15 p.

(174) ———, and Krajicek, J. E.
    1952. Natural mortality and cull in bigtooth aspen stands in northeast Iowa. USDA Forest Serv. Central States Forest Exp. Sta. Notes 69, 2 p.

(175) Brooks, M. G.
    1951. Effect of black walnut trees and their products on other vegetation. W. Va. Agr. Exp. Sta. Bull. 347, 31 p.

(176) Brown, Nellie A.
 1932. Canker of ash trees produced by a variety of the olive-tubercle organism *Bacterium savastanoi*. J. Agr. Res. 44: 701–722.

(177) ——.
 1938. The tumor disease of oak and hickory trees. Phytopathology 28: 401–411.

(178) ——.
 1941. Tumors on elm and maple trees. Phytopathology 31: 541–548.

(179) Brown, R. M.
 1934. Statistical analyses for finding a simple method for estimating the percentage heart rot in Minnesota aspen. J. Agr. Res. 49: 929–942.

(180) Bryan, W. C.
 1960. Losses from defect in Piedmont hardwoods. USDA Forest Serv. Southeast. Forest Exp. Sta. Pap. 109, 31 p.

(181) ——, and Zak, B.
 1961. Synthetic culture of mycorrhizae of southern pines. Forest Sci. 7: 123–129.

(182) ——, and Zak, B.
 1962. Additional syntheses of mycorrhizae on shortleaf and loblolly pines. Forest Sci. 8: 384.

(183) Buchanan, T. S.
 1940. Fungi causing decay in wind-thrown northwest conifers. J. Forest. 38: 276–281.

(184) ——.
 1948. *Poria weirii*: its occurrence and behavior on species other than cedars. Northwest Sci. 22(1): 7–12.

(185) ——.
 1964. Diseases of *Robinia*. *In* Diseases of widely planted forest trees. FAO/IUFRO Symp. on Int. Dangerous Forest Dis. and Insects, Working Group on Int. Coop. in Forest Dis. Res., p. 214–226.

(186) ——.
 1967. *Diplodia* twig blight of pine. *In* Important forest insects and diseases of mutual concern to Canada, the United States, and Mexico. Dep. Forest. and Rural Develop., Canada, Publ. 1180: 189–191.

(187) Buckland, D. C.
 1946. Investigations of decay in western red cedar. Can. J. Res. C, 24: 158–181.

(188) ——.
 1953. Observations on *Armillaria mellea* in immature Douglas fir. Forest. Chron. 29: 344–347.

(189) ——, Foster, R. E., and Nordin, V. J.
 1949. Studies in forest pathology. VII. Decay in western hemlock and fir in the Franklin River area, British Columbia. Can. J. Res. C, 27: 312–331.

(190) ——, Molnar, A. C., and Wallis, G. W.
 1954. Yellow laminated root rot of Douglas-fir. Can. J. Bot. 32: 69–81.

(191) ——, and Wallis, G. W.
 1956. The control of yellow laminated root rot of Douglas-fir. Forest. Chron. 32: 14–19.

(192) Bugbee, W. M.
 1962. Host range and bioassay of field soil for *Cylindrocladium scoparium*. (Abstr.) Phytopathology 52: 726.

(193) ——, and Anderson, N. A.
 1963. Infection of spruce seedlings by *Cylindrocladium scoparium*. Phytopathology 53: 1267–1271.

521

(194) Burkholder, W. H.
    1937. A bacterial leaf spot of geranium. Phytopathology 27: 554–560.

(195) Burt, Edward Angus.
    1914. The Thelephoraceae of North America. I. Ann. Missouri Bot.
        Gard. 1: 185–228.

(196) Buttrick, P. L.
    1925. Chestnut in North Carolina. *In* Chestnut and the chestnut blight in
        North Carolina. North Carolina Geol. and Econ. Surv., Econ. Pap.
        56: 7–10.

(197) Buxton, E. W., Sinha, Indu, and Ward, Valerie.
    1962. Soil-borne diseases of Sitka spruce seedlings in a forest nursery.
        Brit. Mycol. Soc. Trans. 45: 433–448.

(198) Byler, J. W., and True, R. P.
    1966. Root and butt rot in young yellow-poplar stump sprouts. Phyto-
        pathology 56: 1091–1097.

(199) Cadman, C. H.
    1963. Biology of soil-borne viruses. Annu. Rev. Phytopathol. 1: 143–172.

(200) Cameron, H. R.
    1962. Susceptibility of pear roots to *Phytophthora*. Phytopathology 52:
        1295–1297.

(201) Camp, A. F.
    1938. Citrus propagation. Univ. Florida Agr. Ext. Serv. Bull. 96, 58 p.

(202) Campana, Richard, and Rosinski, Martin.
    1960. Association of *Cladosporium* with needle cast of larch and spruce
        in the United States. U.S. Dep. Agr. Plant Dis. Rep. 46: 265–266.

(203) Campbell, R. N., and Clark, J. W.
    1960. Decay resistance of baldcypress heartwood. Forest Prod. J. 10:
        250–253.

(204) Campbell, W. A.
    1938. Preliminary report on decay in sprout northern hardwoods in rela-
        tion to timber stand improvement. USDA Forest Serv. North-
        east. Forest Exp. Sta. Occas. Pap. 7, 8 p.

(205) ———.
    1939. *Daedalea unicolor* decay and associated cankers of maples and
        other hardwdoods. J. Forest. 37: 974–977.

(206) ———.
    1951. Fungi associated with the roots of littleleaf-diseased and healthy
        shortleaf pine. Phytopathology 41: 439–446.

(207) ———, and Copeland, Otis L.
    1954. Littleleaf disease of shortleaf and loblolly pines. U.S. Dep. Agr.
        Circ. 940, 41 p.

(208) ———, and Davidson, Ross W.
    1938. A *Poria* as the fruiting stage of the fungus causing the sterile
        conks on birch. Mycologia 30: 553–560.

(209) ———, and Davidson, Ross W.
    1939. Sterile conks of *Polyporus glomeratus* and associated cankers.
        (Abstr.) Phytopathology 29: 3, 4.

(210) ———, and Davidson, Ross W.
    1939. *Poria andersonii* and *Polyporus glomeratus*, two distinct heart-
        rotting fungi. Mycologia 31: 161–168.

(211) ———, and Davidson, Ross W.
    1940. *Ustulina vulgaris* decay in sugar maple and other hardwoods. J.
        Forest. 38: 474–477.

(212) ———, and Davidson, Ross W.
    1940. Top rot in glaze-damaged black cherry and sugar maple on the
        Allegheny Plateau. J. Forest. 38: 963–965.

(213) ——, and Davidson, Ross W.
　　1941. Redheart of paper birch. J. Forest. 39: 63–65.

(214) ——, and Davidson, Ross W.
　　1941. Cankers and decay of yellow birch associated with *Fomes igniarius* var. *laevigatus*. J. Forest. 39: 559–560.

(215) ——, and Davidson, Ross W.
　　1942. A species of *Poria* causing rot and cankers of hickory and oak. Mycologia 34: 17–26.

(216) ——, and Gallegly, M. E.
　　1965. *Phytophthora heveae* from eastern Tennessee and western North Carolina. U.S. Dep. Agr. Plant Dis. Rep. 49: 233–234.

(217) ——, and Hendrix, Floyd F., Jr.
　　1967. *Pythium* and *Phytophthora* populations in southern forest tree nurseries. (Abstr.) Phytopathology 57: 457.

(218) ——, and Hendrix, Floyd F., Jr.
　　1967. *Pythium* and *Phytophthora* species in forest soils in the Southeastern United States. U.S. Dep. Agr. Plant Dis. Rep. 51: 929–932.

(219) ——, and Sleeth, Bailey.
　　1945. A root rot of guayule caused by *Pythium ultimum*. Phytopathology 35: 636-639.

(220) ——, and Verrall, A. F.
　　1956. Fungus enemies of hickory. USDA Forest Serv. Southeast. Forest Exp. Sta. Hickory Task Force Rep. 3, 8 p.

(221) ——, and Verrall, A. F.
　　1963. *Phytophthora cinnamomi* associated with Lawson cypress mortality in Louisiana. U.S. Dep. Agr. Plant Dis. Rep. 47: 808.

(222) Carmean, Willard H.
　　1958. Silvical characteristics of yellow buckeye. USDA Forest Serv. Central States Forest Exp. Sta. Misc. Release 29, 16 p.

(223) Caroselli, Nestor E.
　　1953. Bleeding canker disease of hardwoods. Sci. Tree Topics 2(1): 1–6.

(224) ——.
　　1957. Verticillium wilt of maples. Univ. Rhode Island Agr. Exp. Sta. Bull. 335, 84 p.

(225) ——, and Tucker, C. M.
　　1949. Pit canker of elm. Phytopathology 39: 481–488.

(226) Carter, J. C.
　　1936. *Thyrostroma compactum* on *Ulmus pumila*. Phytopathology 26: 801–804.

(227) ——.
　　1936. *Cytosporina ludibunda* on American elm. Phytopathology 26: 805–806.

(228) ——.
　　1945. Wetwood of elms. Ill. Natur. Hist. Surv. Bull. 23, Article 4: 407–448.

(229) ——.
　　1947. *Tubercularia* canker and dieback of Siberian elm (*Ulmus pumila* L.). Phytopathology 37: 243–246.

(230) ——.
　　1953. *Phytophthora* canker of Russianolive. (Abstr.) Phytopathology 43: 468.

(231) ——.
　　1955. Illinois trees: their diseases. Ill. Natur. Hist. Surv. Circ. 46, 99 p.

(232) ——.
　　1964. The wetwood disease of elm. Ill. Natur. Hist. Surv. Circ. 50, 19 p.

(233) ———.
1967. Twelve unusual tree diseases. Arborist's News 32: 9–15.

(234) Carvell, K. L., Tryon, E. H., and True, R. P.
1957. Effects of glaze on the development of Appalachian hardwoods. J. Forest. 55: 130–132.

(235) Cash, Edith K.
1941. An abnormality of *Abies balsamea*. U.S. Dep. Agr. Plant Dis. Rep. 25: 548.

(236) ———.
1945. Some new species of fungi on *Libocedrus*. Mycologia 37: 311–317.

(237) ———.
1958. Some new Discomycetes from California. Mycologia 50: 642–656.

(238) ———, and Davidson, Ross W.
1940. Some new species of Ascomycetes on coniferous hosts. *Mycologia* 32: 728–735.

(239) ———, and Waterman, Alma M.
1957. A new species of *Plagiostoma* associated wtih a leaf disease of hybrid aspens. Mycologia 49: 756–760.

(240) Catani, S. C., and Peterson, J. L.
1967. Antagonistic relationships between *Verticillium dahliae* and fungi isolated from the rhizosphere of *Acer platanoides*. Phytopathology 57: 363–366.

(241) Cave, M. S.
1944. Modification of procedure for differentiating the telia of *Cronartium ribicola* and *C. occidentale*. Stain Technol. 19: 141–142.

(242) Cayford, J. H., and Waldron, R. M.
1965. Multiple jack pine seedlings. Can. J. Bot. 43: 481–482.

(243) Cech, M., Kralik, O., and Blattny, C.
1961. Rod-shaped particles associated with virosis of spruce. Phytopathology 51: 183–185.

(244) Chandler, Robert F., Jr.
1939. The calcium content of the foliage of forest trees. Cornell Univ. Agr. Exp. Sta. Mem. 228, 15 p.

(245) Cheyney, Edward G.
1942. American silvics and silviculture. 472 p. Minneapolis: Univ. Minn. Press.

(246) Chidester, Mae Spradling.
1940. A pink stain of wood caused by a species of *Geotrichum*. Phytopathology 30: 530–533.

(247) Childs, Thomas W.
1937. Variability of *Polyporus schweinitzii* in culture. Phytopathology 27: 29–50.

(248) ———.
1959. *Elytroderma* needle blight of ponderosa pine. USDA Forest Serv. Forest Pest Leafl. 42, 4 p.

(249) ———.
1960. Laminated root rot of Douglas-fir. USDA Forest Serv. Forest Pest Leafl. 48, 6 p.

(250) ———.
1963. *Poria weirii* root rot. Phytopathology 53: 1124–1127.

(251) ———, and Bedwell, J. L.
1948. Susceptibility of some white pine species to *Cronartium ribicola* in the Pacific Northwest. J. Forest. 46: 595–599.

(252) ——, and Edgren, J. W.
1967. Dwarfmistletoe effects on ponderosa pine growth and trunk form. Forest Sci. 13: 167–174.

(253) Christensen, Clyde M.
1937. *Cephalosporium* canker of balsam fir. Phytopathology 27: 788–791.

(254) ——.
1940. Studies on the biology of *Valsa sordida* and *Cytospora chrysosperma*. Phytopathology 30: 459–475.

(255) ——.
1940. Observations on *Polyporus circinatus*. Phytopathology 30: 957–963.

(256) ——, Anderson, Ralph L., Hodson, A. C., and Rudolf, Paul O.
1951. Enemies of aspen. USDA Forest Serv. Lake States Forest Exp. Sta. Aspen Rep. 22, 16 p.

(257) ——, and Hodson, A. C.
1954. Artificially induced senescence of forest trees. J. Forest. 52: 126–129.

(258) ——, and Kaufert, F. H.
1942. A blue-staining fungus inhabiting the heartwood of certain species of conifers. Phytopathology 32: 735–737.

(259) Christie, Jesse R.
1959. Plant nematodes; their bionomics and control. 256 p. Gainesville, Fla.: [Univ. Fla. Agr. Exp. Sta.]

(260) Chupp, Charles.
1953. A monograph of the fungus genus *Cercospora*. 667 p. Ithaca, N.Y. [Cornell Univ.]

(261) Clapper, Russell B.
1954. Stimulation of pine oleoresin flow by fungus inoculation. Econ. Bot. 8: 269–284.

(262) ——, Gravatt, G. F., and Stout, Donald C.
1946. *Endothia* canker on post oak. U.S. Dep. Agr. Plant Dis. Rep. 30: 381.

(263) Clark, F. Bryan.
1958. Silvical characteristics of butternut. USDA Forest Serv. Central States Forest Exp. Sta. Misc. Release 28, 9 p.

(264) ——.
1963. Endotrophic mycorrhizae influence yellow-poplar seedling growth. Science 140(3572): 1220–1221.

(265) ——.
1966. Increment borers cause serious degrade in black walnut. J. Forest. 64: 814.

(266) Clark, J., and Barter, G. W.
1958. Growth and climate in relation to dieback of yellow birch. Forest. Sci. 4: 343–364.

(267) Clements, Frederic E., and Shear, Cornelius L.
1931. The genera of fungi. 496 p. New York: H. W. Wilson Co.

(268) Clinton, G. P., and McCormick, Florence A.
1929. The willow scab fungus *Fusicladium saliciperdum*. Conn. Agr. Exp. Sta. Bull. 302: 443–469.

(269) Cobb, Fields W.
1957. Pitch streak—a disease of turpentined slash pine. Naval Stores Rev. 67(9): 4, 5.

(270) ——, and Platt, William D.
1967. Pathogenicity of *Verticicladiella wagenerii* to Douglas-fir. Phytopathology 57: 998–999.

525

(271) Coe, Donald M., and Wagener, Willis W.
   1949. Ash anthracnose appears in California. U.S. Dep. Agr. Plant Dis. Rep. 33: 232.

(272) Cohen, L. I.
   1957. *Hypodermella laricis*, its relation to spur shoot mortality of *Larix occidentalis*. Mont. Acad. Sci. Proc. 17: 47–48.

(273) ———.
   1967. The pathology of *Hypodermella laricis* on larch, *Larix occidentalis*. Amer. J. Bot. 54: 118–124.

(274) Coker, William Chambers, and Totten, Henry Roland.
   1937. Trees of the Southeastern States. Ed. 2, 417 p. Chapel Hill, N.C.: Univ. N.C. Press.

(275) Cole, J. R.
   1933. Liver spot disease of pecan foliage caused by *Gnomonia caryae pecanae*, nov. var. J. Agr. Res. 47: 869–881.

(276) ———.
   1935. *Gnomonia nerviseda*, the perfect stage of the fungus that causes the vein spot disease of pecan foliage. J. Agr. Res. 50: 91–96.

(277) ———.
   1953. Problems in growing pecans. U.S. Dep. Agr. Yearb. 1953: 796-800.

(278) ———, and Hunter, J. H.
   1965. Abnormal flowering of pecans following freeze damage in 1955. U.S. Dep. Agr. Plant Dis. Rep. 49: 146–147.

(279) Collingwood, G. H., and Brush, Warren D.
   1947. Knowing your trees. Ed. 9, 312 p. Washington: Amer. Forest. Assoc.

(280) Condit, Ira J.
   1947. The fig. V. 9, 222 p. Waltham, Mass.: Chronica Botanica Co.

(281) Conners, I. L., McCallum, A. W., and Bier, J. E.
   1941. Willow blight in British Columbia. Phytopathology 31: 1056–1058.

(282) Cook, David B.
   1939. European larch reproduces in eastern New York. J. Forest. 37: 891–893.

(283) Cooke, Wm. Bridge.
   1952. Western fungi-II. Mycologia 44: 245–261.

(284) ———.
   1962. A taxonomic study in the "black yeasts." Mycopathol. et Mycol. Applicata 17: 1–43.

(285) Cooley, J. S., and Davidson, Ross W.
   1940. A white root rot of apple trees caused by *Corticium galactinum*. Phytopathology 30: 139–148.

(286) Cooper, Robert W.
   1957. Silvical characteristics of slash pine (*Pinus elliottii* Engelm. var. *elliottii*). USDA Forest Serv. Southeast. Forest Exp. Sta. Pap. 81, 13 p.

(287) ———.
   1957. Silvical characteristics of sand pine. USDA Forest Serv. Southeast. Forest Exp. Sta. Pap. 82, 8 p.

(288) Copeland, Otis L., Jr.
   1955. The effects of an artificially induced drought on shortleaf pine. J. Forest. 53: 262–264.

(289) ———, and McAlpine, Robert G.
   1955. The interrelations of littleleaf, site index, soil, and ground cover in Piedmont shortleaf pine stands. Ecology 36: 635–641.

(290) ———, and McAlpine, Robert G.
1962. Soil characteristics associated with spot die-out in loblolly pine plantations. Forest Sci. 8: 12–15.

(291) Costonis, A. C., and Sinclair, W. A.
1967. Seasonal development of symptoms of ozone injury on eastern white pine. (Abstr.) Phytopathology 57: 339.

(292) Couch, John N.
1938. The genus *Septobasidium*. 480 p. Chapel Hill: University of North Carolina Press.

(293) Cowling, Ellis B.
1961. Comparative biochemistry of the decay of sweetgum sapwood by white-rot and brown-rot fungi. U.S. Dep. Agr. Tech. Bull. 1258, 79 p.

(294) Cox, R. S.
1953. Etiology and control of a serious complex of diseases of conifer seedlings. (Abstr.) Phytopathology 43: 469.

(295) ———.
1954. Some common diseases of flowering dogwood in Delaware. Univ. Del. Agr. Exp. Sta. Circ. 27, 8 p.

(296) ———.
1954. *Cylindrocladium scoparium* on conifer seedlings. Univ. Del. Agr. Evp. Sta. Bull. 301 (Tech.) 40 p.

(297) Craighead, F. C.
1950. Insect enemies of eastern forests. USDA Misc. Publ. 657, 679 p.

(298) Cram, W. H., and Vaartaja, O.
1955. Toxicity of eight pesticides to spruce and caragana seed. Forest. Chron. 31: 247–249.

(299) Crandall, Bowen S.
1938. A root and collar disease of pine seedlings caused by *Sphaeropsis ellisii*. Phytopathology 28: 227–229.

(300) ———.
1943. Bacterial infection and decay of the inner wood of winter injured young London plane trees. Phytopathology 33: 963–964.

(301) ———.
1945. A new species of *Cephalosporium* causing persimmon wilt. Mycologia 37: 495–498.

(302) ———, and Baker, W. L.
1950. The wilt disease of American persimmon, caused by *Cephalosporium diospyri*. Phytopathology 40: 307–325.

(303) ———, and Gravatt, G. Flippo.
1967. The distribution of *Phytophthora cinnamomi*. Ceiba (Hond.) 13: 43–53.

(304) ———, Gravatt, G. Flippo, and Ryan, Margaret Milburn.
1945. Root disease of *Castanea* species and some coniferous and broadleaf nursery stocks, caused by *Phytophthora cinnamomi*. Phytopathology 35: 162–180.

(305) ———, and Hartley, Carl.
1938. *Phytophthora cactorum* associated with seedling diseases in forest nurseries. Phytopathology 28: 358–360.

(306) Creager, D. B.
1937. *Phytophthora* crown rot of dogwood. J. Arnold Arbor. 18: 344–348.

(307) Critchfield, W. B.
1957. Geographic variation in *Pinus contorta*. Maria Moors Cabot Found. Publ. 3, 118 p.

(308) Crowell, Ivan H.
    1936. Index to the relative susceptibility of orchard apples to cedar-apple rust. Phytopathology 26: 459–461.

(309) Croxton, Ralph J.
    1966. Detection and classification of ash dieback on large-scale color aerial photographs. USDA Forest Serv. Res. Pap. PSW–35, 13 p.

(310) Croxton, W. C.
    1939. A study of the tolerance of trees to breakage by ice accumulation. Ecology 20: 71–73.

(311) Cruikshank, James W., Hepting, George H., Toole, E. Richard, and Roth, Elmer R.
    1951. Chestnut extract production and the timber supply, 1951. USDA Forest Serv. and Bur. Plant Ind. Soils and Agr. Eng. Spec. Rep. 26 p.

(312) Crum, P.
    1954. Chelating agents for the control of lime-induced chlorosis in southern magnolia. Nat. Shade Tree Conf. Proc. 30: 267–270.

(313) Cummins, George B.
    1938. A new microcyclic *Coleosporium* on limber and piñon pine. Phytopathology 28: 522–523.

(314) ———, and Stevenson, John A.
    1956. A checklist of North American rust fungi (Uredinales). U.S. Dep. Agr. Plant Dis. Rep. Suppl. 240: 109–193.

(315) Cunningham, H. S.
    1928. A study of the histologic changes induced in leaves by certain leaf-spotting fungi. Phytopathology 18: 717–751.

(316) Curtis, James D., and Lynch, Donald W.
    1957. Silvics of ponderosa pine. USDA Forest Serv. Intermount. Forest and Range Exp. Sta. Misc. Publ. 12, 37 p.

(317) Dale, Jim, McComb, A. L., and Loomis, W. E.
    1955. Chlorosis, mycorrhizae, and the growth of pines on a high-lime soil. Forest Sci. 1: 148–157.

(318) Dana, B. F.
    1921. Two new species of *Sclerotinia*. (Abstr.) Phytopathology 11: 106.

(319) Dance, B. W.
    1959: A cultural connection between *Venturia tremulae* Aderh. and its imperfect stage in Ontario. Can. J. Bot. 37: 1139–1140.

(320) ———.
    1961. Leaf and shoot blight of poplars (section *Tacamahaca* Spach) caused by *Venturia populina* (Vuill.) Fabric. Can. J. Bot. 39: 875–890.

(321) ———, and Lynn, D. F.
    1963. Excessive red oak mortality following ice storm damage. Can. Dep. Forest. Bimo. Progr. Rep. 19(6): 3.

(322) ———, Lynn, D. F., and Jansons, V.
    1964. Observations on the effects of stem cankers associated with *Pezicula ocellata* (Pers.) Seaver in young trembling aspen. Can. Dep. Forest. Bimo. Progr. Rep. 20(3): 2–3.

(323) Darker, G. D.
    1932. The Hypodermataceae of conifers. Arnold Arboretum Contrib. 1, 131 p.

(324) ———.
    1963. A new genus of the Lophiaceae. Can. J. Bot. 41: 1383–1388.

(325) ———.
    1963. A new genus of Phacidiaceae on *Picea mariana*. Can. J. Bot. 41: 1389–1393.

(326) ———.
 1964. A new *Leptosphaeria* species, an agent in the biological control of certain Hypodermataceae. Can. J. Bot. 42: 1005–1009.

(327) ———.
 1965. The occurrence of *Rhizothyrium* on *Abies* and *Tsuga*. Can. J. Bot. 43: 11–14.

(328) ———.
 1967. A revision of the genera of the Hypodermataceae. Can. J. Bot. 45: 1399–1444.

(329) ———.
 1967. A new *Davisomycella* species on *Pinus banksiana*. Can. J. Bot. 45: 1445–1449.

(330) Darling, Louise.
 1940. *Protocoronospora* on *Phoradendron flavescens* in California. Madroño 5: 241–246.

(331) Davidson, A. G.
 1952. Decay of white spruce in New Brunswick. Can. Dep. Agr. Sci. Serv., Div. Forest Biol. Bimo. Progr. Rep. 8(1): 1.

(332) ———.
 1957. Studies in forest pathology. XVI. Decay of balsam fir, *Abies balsamea* (L.) Mill., in the Atlantic Provinces. Can. J. Bot. 35: 857–874.

(333) ———, and Etheridge, D. E.
 1963. Infection of balsam fir, *Abies balsamea* (L.) Mill., by *Stereum sanguinolentum* (Alb. and Schw. ex Fr.) Fr. Can. J. Bot. 41: 759–765.

(334) ———, and Newell, W. R.
 1953. Pathological deterioration in wind-thrown balsam firm in Newfoundland. Forest. Chron. 29: 100–107.

(335) ———, and Redmond, D. R.
 1957. Decay of spruce in the Maritime Provinces. Forest. Chron. 33: 373–380.

(336) Davidson, Ross W.
 1935. Forest pathology notes 3. *Rhizina inflata* on red pine and white spruce seedlings. U.S. Dep. Agr. Plant Dis. Rep. 19: 96.

(337) ———.
 1935. Fungi causing stain in logs and lumber in the southern States, including five new species. J. Agr. Res. 50: 789–807.

(338) ———.
 1950. *Urnula craterium* is possibly the perfect stage of *Strumella coryneoidea*. Mycologia 42: 735–742.

(339) ———.
 1955. Wood-staining fungi associated with bark beetles in Engelmann spruce in Colorado. Mycologia 47: 58–67.

(340) ———.
 1966. New species of *Ceratocystis* from conifers. Mycopathol. et Mycol. Applicata 28: 273–286.

(341) ———, and Campbell, W. A.
 1944. Observations on a gall of sugar maple. Phytopathology 34: 132–135.

(342) ———, Campbell, W. A., and Lorenz, Rolland C.
 1941. Association of *Stereum murrayi* with heart rot and cankers of living hardwoods. Phytopathology 31: 82–87.

(343) ———, Campbell, W. A., and Vaughn, Dorothy Blaisdell.
 1942. Fungi causing decay of living oaks in the Eastern United States and their cultural identification. U.S. Dep. Agr. Tech. Bull. 785, 65 p.

(344) ———, and Cash, Edith K.
1956. A *Cenangium* associated with sooty-bark canker of aspen. Phytopathology 46: 34–36.

(345) ———, and Hinds, Thomas E.
1956. *Hypoxylon* canker of aspen in Colorado. U.S. Dep. Agr. Plant Dis. Rep. 40: 157–158.

(346) ———, Hinds, Thomas E., and Hawksworth, Frank G.
1959. Decay of aspen in Colorado. USDA Forest Serv. Rocky Mount. Forest and Range Exp. Sta. Pap. 45, 14 p.

(347) ———, Hinds, T. E., and Toole, E. R.
1964. Two new species of *Ceratocystis* from hardwoods. Mycologia 56: 793–798.

(348) ———, Lentz, Paul L., and McKay, Hazel H.
1960. The fungus causing pecky cypress. Mycologia 52: 260–279.

(349) ———, and Lombard, Frances.
1954. Brick red stain of Sitka spruce and other wood substrata. Phytopathology 44: 606–607.

(350) ———, Lombard, Frances, and Campbell, W. A.
1959. A white heart rot of *Fraxinus* caused by *Fomes johnsonianus* (Murr.) Lowe. U.S. Dep. Agr. Plant Dis. Rep. 43: 1148–1149.

(351) ———, and Lorenz, Rolland C.
1938. Species of *Eutypella* and *Schizoxylon* associated with cankers of maple. Phytopathology 28: 733–745.

(352) ———, and Mielke, James L.
1947. *Fomes robustus*, a heart rot fungus on cacti and other desert plants. Mycologia 39: 210–217.

(353) ———, and Patton, Robert F.
1961. *Paxillus atrotomentosus* causes brown root rot in dead jack pine in plantations in Wisconsin. U.S. Dep. Agr. Plant Dis. Rep. 45: 836–838.

(354) ———, Toole, E. R., and Campbell, W. A.
1959. A preliminary note on the cause of "pecky" cypress. U.S. Dep. Agr. Plant Dis. Rep. 43: 806–808.

(355) Davis, Everett F.
1928. The toxic principle of *Juglans nigra* as identified with synthetic juglone, and its toxic effects on tomato and alfalfa plants. Amer. J. Bot. 15: 620.

(356) Davis, Terry C.
1968. *Hymenochaete agglutinans* on *Phoradendron flavescens*. U.S. Dep. Agr. Plant Dis. Rep. 52: 496.

(357) Davis, W. B., and Church, C. G.
1931. The effect of ethylene on the chemical composition and the respiration of the ripening Japanese persimmon. J. Agr. Res. 42: 165–182.

(358) Davis, William C.
1941. Damping-off of longleaf pine. Phytopathology 31: 1011–1016.

(359) ———, and Davidson, Ross W.
1939. *Fusicladium robiniae* and *Macrosporium* sp. in forest tree nurseries. U.S. Dep. Agr. Plant Dis. Rep. 23: 63–65.

(360) ———, Wright, Ernest, and Hartley, Carl.
1942. Diseases of forest-tree nursery stock. Civil. Conserv. Corps Forest. Publ. 9, 79 p.

(361) Day, Maurice W., and Strong, Forrest C.
1944. A basal stem canker of red pine. Mich. Agr. Exp. Sta. Quart. Bull. 26:1-3.

(362) Dearness, John.
1916. New or noteworthy species of fungi. Mycologia 8: 98–107.

(363) ———.
1917. New or noteworthy North American fungi. Mycologia 9: 345–364.

(364) ———.
1924. New and noteworthy fungi. III. Mycologia 16: 143–176.

(365) ———.
1926. New and noteworthy fungi. IV. Mycologia 18: 236–255.

(366) ———
1928. New and noteworthy fungi. V. Mycologia 20: 235–246.

(367) ———, and Hansbrough, J. R.
1934. *Cytospora* infection following fire injury in western British Columbia. Can. J. Res. 10: 125–128.

(368) De Groot, Rodney C.
1966. Phenolic extractives in lateral branches and injured leaders of *Pinus strobus* L. Can. J. Bot. 44: 57–61.

(369) ———.
1967. Additional fungi associated with American beech in New York. Mycopath. et Mycol. Applicata 32: 356–359.

(370) Demaree, J. B., and Cole, J. R.
1930. Pecan leaf blotch. J. Agr. Res. 40: 777–789.

(371) ———, and Cole, J. R.
1936. A disporous *Gnomonia* on pecan. Phytopathology 26: 1025–1029.

(372) Denton, Robert E., and Leaphart, Charles D.
1959. Symptoms of abnormal crown deterioration in western white pine stands. USDA Forest Serv. Intermount. Forest and Range Exp. Sta. Res. Note 69, 4 p.

(373) Denyer, W. B. G.
1953. *Cephalosporium* canker of western hemlock. Can. J. Bot. 31: 361–366.

(374) ———.
1960. Cultural studies of *Flammula alnicola* (Fr.) Kummer and *Flammula conissans* (Fr.) Gillet. Can. J. Bot. 38: 909–920.

(375) ———, and Riley, C. G.
1953. Decay in white spruce at the Kananaskis Forest Experiment Station. Forest. Chron. 29: 233–247.

(376) ———, and Riley, C. G.
1964. Drought effects on young spruce stands in poor sites. Forest. Chron. 40: 206–209.

(377) ———, and Riley, C. G.
1964. Dieback and mortality of tamarack caused by high water. Forest. Chron. 40: 334–338.

(378) Dickey, R. D., and Drosdoff, Matthew.
1943. Control of manganese deficiency in a commercial tung orchard. Amer. Soc. Hort. Sci. 42: 74–78.

(379) ———, Drosdoff, Matthew, and Hamilton, Joseph.
1948. Copper deficiency of tung in Florida. Univ. Fla. Agr. Exp. Sta. Bull. 447, 32 p.

(380) Diller, Jesse D.
1943. A canker of eastern pines associated with *Atropellis tingens*. J. Forest. 41: 41–52.

(381) ———, and Clapper, Russell B.
1965. A progress report on attempts to bring back the chestnut tree in the Eastern United States, 1954–1964. J. Forest. 63: 186–188.

(382) Dimock, Edward J., II.
1958. Silvical characteristics of Pacific silver fir. USDA Forest Serv. Pacific Northwest Forest and Range Exp. Sta. Silvical Ser. 4, 12 p.

(383) Doak, K. D.
1936. Mycorrhizae of trees and shrubs. Univ. P. Morris Arboretum Bull. 1(4): 45–49.

(384) Dochinger, Leon S.
1967. Occurrence of poplar cankers caused by *Fusarium solani* in Iowa. U.S. Dep. Agr. Plant Dis. Rep. 51: 900–903.

(385) ——, and Seliskar, Carl E.
1962. *Fusarium* canker found on yellow-poplar. J. Forest. 60: 331–333.

(386) ——, and Seliskar, Carl E.
1963. Susceptibility of eastern white pine to chlorotic dwarf. (Abstr.) Phytopathology 53: 874.

(387) Dodge, B. O.
1932. Notes on three hemlock fungi. Mycologia 24: 421–430.

(388) ——, and Rickett, H. W.
1943. Diseases and pests of ornamental plants. 638 p. Lancaster, P.: Cattell Press.

(389) Dowding, Eleanor S.
1931. *Wallrothiella arceuthobii*, a parasite of the jack pine mistletoe. Can. J. Res. 5: 219–230.

(390) Downs, Albert A.
1938. Glaze damage in the birch-beech-maple-hemlock type of Pennsylvania and New York. J. Forest. 36: 63–70.

(391) ——.
1946. Response to release of sugar maple, white oak, and yellow-poplar. J. Forest. 44: 22–27.

(392) Dowson, W. J.
1949. Manual of bacterial plant diseases. 183 p. London: Adam and Charles Black.

(393) Driver, Chas. H., and Wood, R. E.
1968. Occurrence of *Fomes annosus* in intensively managed young-growth western hemlock stands. U.S. Dep. Agr. Plant Dis. Rep. 52: 370–372.

(394) Drosdoff, Matthew.
1944. Leaf composition in relation to the mineral nutrition of tung trees. Soil Sci. 57: 281–291.

(395) Duncan, Donald P.
1954. A study of some of the factors affecting the natural regeneration of tamarack (*Larix laricina*) in Minnesota. Ecology 35: 498–521.

(396) Dunegan, John C.
1954. Blight of pears, apples, and quinces. U.S. Dep. Agr. Leafl. 187, 2 p.

(397) Dunlap, A. A., and Harrison, A. L.
1949. Dying of live oaks in Texas. Phytopathology 39: 715–717.

(398) Dunning, Duncan.
1928. A tree classification for the selection forests of the Sierra Nevada. J. Agr. Res. 36: 755–771.

(399) Dwinell, L. D.
1969. Reaction of black oak (*Quercus velutina*) to infection by *Cronartium fusiforme* and *C. quercuum*. Abstr. Phytopathology 59: 113.

(400) Dwyer, Walter W., Jr.
1951. *Fomes annosus* on eastern redcedar in two Piedmont forests. J. Forest. 49: 259–262.

(401) Eades, H. W.
1932. British Columbia softwoods, their decays, and natural defects. Can. Dep. Interior Forest Serv. Bull. 80, 126 p.

(402) Edgerton, C. W.
1911. Diseases of the fig tree and fruit. Louisiana Agr. Exp. Sta. Bull. 126, 20 p.

(403) ———.
1954. A *Ganoderma* and its association with root rot of trees in Louisiana. (Abstr.) J. Tenn. Acad. Sci. 29: 178.

(404) Ehrlich, John.
1934. The beech bark disease, a *Nectria* disease of *Fagus*, following *Cryptococcus fagi* (Baer.). Can. J. Res. 10: 593–692.

(405) ———.
1939. A preliminary study of root diseases in western white pine. USDA Forest Serv. North. Rocky Mount. Forest and Range Exp. Sta. Pap. 1, 10 p.

(406) ———.
1942. Recently active leaf diseases of woody plants in Idaho. U.S. Dep. Agr. Plant Dis. Rep. 26: 391–393.

(407) Eide, Carl J., and Christensen, C. M.
1940. Wood decay in apple trees in Minnesota. Phytopathology 30: 936–944.

(408) Eliason, E. J.
1928. Comparative virulence of certain strains of *Pythium* in direct inoculation of conifers. Phytopathology 18: 361–367.

(409) Ellis, Don E.
1939. A fungus disease of *Arceuthobium*. Phytopathology 29: 995–996.

(410) ———.
1946. Anthracnose of dwarfmistletoe caused by a new species of *Septogloeum*. J. Elisha Mitchell Sci. Soc. 62: 25–50.

(411) ———, and Gill, Lake S.
1945. A new *Rhabdogloeum* associated with *Rhabdocline pseudotsugae* in the Southwest. Mycologia 37: 326–332.

(412) Engelhard, Arthur W., and Carter, J. C.
1956. Isolations of *Verticillium albo-atrum* from woody hosts in Illinois, 1945–1955. U.S. Dep. Agr. Plant Dis. Rep. 40: 459–462.

(413) Engelhardt, N. T.
1957. Pathological deterioration of looper-killed western hemlock on southern Vancouver Island. Forest Sci. 3: 125–126.

(414) ———, Foster, R. E., and Craig, H. M.
1961. Studies in forest pathology. XXIII. Pathological deterioration of wind-damaged white spruce and alpine fir in the Crescent Spur area of British Columbia. Can. Dep. Forest., Forest Ent. and Path. Lab., Victoria, B.C., 20 p.

(415) Englerth, G. H.
1942. Decay of western hemlock in western Oregon and Washington. Yale Univ. Sch. Forest. Bull. 50, 53 p.

(416) ———.
1947. Decay of Sitka spruce in southeastern Alaska. J. Forest. 45: 894–900.

(417) ———, and Hansbrough, J. R.
1945. The significance of the discolorations in aircraft lumber: noble fir and western hemlock. USDA Forest Path. Spec. Release 24, 10 p.

(418) Etheridge, D. E.
1956. Decay in subalpine spruce on the Rocky Mountain Forest Reserve in Alberta. Can. J. Bot. 34: 805–816.

(419) ———.
  1957. Comparative studies of *Coryne sarcoides* (Jacq.) Tul. and two species of wood-destroying fungi. Can. J. Bot. 35: 595–603.

(420) ———.
  1958. Decay losses in subalpine spruce on the Rocky Mountain Forest Reserve in Alberta. Forest. Chron. 34: 116–131.

(421) ———.
  1963. Infection of balsam fir, *Abies balsamea* (L.) Mill., by *Stereum sanguinolentum* (Alb. and Schw. ex Fr.) Fr. Roy. Soc. Can. Trans. 1(4): 357–360.

(422) ———, and Morin, L. A.
  1962. Wetwood formation in balsam fir. Can. J. Bot. 40: 1335–1345.

(423) ———, and Morin, L. A.
  1963. Colonization by decay fungi of living and dead stems of balsam-fir following artificial injury. Can. J. Bot. 41: 1532–1534.

(424) ———, and Morin, L. A.
  1967. The microbiological condition of wood of living balsam fir and black spruce in Quebec. Can. J. Bot. 45: 1003–1010.

(425) Eugenio, Cesaria P., and Anderson, Neil A.
  1968. The genetics and cultivation of *Pleurotus ostreatus*. Mycologia 60: 627–634.

(426) Eyre, F. H., and Zehngraff, Paul.
  1948. Red pine management in Minnesota. U.S. Dep. Agr. Circ. 778, 70 p.

(427) Ezekiel, Walter N., and Nelson, Chris, Jr.
  1941. Sclerotial seedling blight of black walnut. U.S. Dep. Agr. Plant Dis. Rep. 25: 336–337.

(428) Farris, S. H.
  1966. A staining method for mycelium of *Rhabdocline* in Douglas-fir needles. Can. J. Bot. 44: 1106–1107.

(429) ———, and Funk, A.
  1965. Repositories of symbiotic fungus in the ambrosia beetle *Platypus wilsoni* Swaine (Coleoptera: Platypodidae). Can. Entomol. 97: 527–532.

(430) Faull, J. H.
  1932. Taxonomy and geographical distribution of the genus *Milesia*. Arnold Arboretum Contrib. 2: 1–138.

(431) ———.
  1938. Taxonomy and geographical distribution of the genus *Uredinopsis*. Arnold Arboretum Contrib. 11: 5–120.

(432) ———.
  1938. The biology of the rusts of the genus *Uredinopsis*. J. Arnold Arboretum 19: 402–436.

(433) Fawcett, H. S., and Rhoads, A. S.
  1939. Lesions on *Quercus laurifolia* similiar to those of leprosis on citrus in Florida. Phytopathology 29: 907–908.

(434) Fenton, R. H., and Berry, F. H.
  1958. Red ring rot in Virginia pine in Maryland. J. Forest. 56: 280–284.

(435) Fergus, Charles L.
  1951. Strumella canker on bur oak in Pennsylvania. Phytopathology 41: 101–103.

(436) ———.
  1954. An epiphytotic of *Phyllosticta* leaf spot of maple. U.S. Dep. Agr. Plant Dis. Rep. 38: 678–679.

534

(437) ———.
1956. An unusual cone fasciculation of Table Mountain pine. U.S. Dep.
Agr. Plant Dis. Rep. 40: 752–754.

(438) ———.
1956. Some observations about *Polyporus dryadeus* on oak. U.S. Dep.
Agr. Plant Dis. Rep. 40: 827–829.

(439) Ferguson, Edwin R.
1959. Wood treated with penta can damage pine nursery seedlings. USDA
Forest Serv. Tree Planters' Notes 38: 21–22.

(440) Ferris, J. M., and Leiser, A. T.
1965. Control of nematodes associated with blue spruce. U.S. Dep. Agr.
Plant Dis. Rep. 49: 69–71.

(441) Filer, T. H., Jr.
1964. Outbreak of cankers on plantation-grown cottonwoods in Mississippi. U.S. Dep. Agr. Plant Dis. Rep. 48: 588.

(442) ———.
1965. Sycamore canker—pesky but not disastrous. South. Lumberman
211 (2632): 169–170.

(443) ———.
1967. Pathogenicity of *Cytospora*, *Phomopsis*, and *Hypomyces* on *Populus
deltoides*. Phytopathology 57: 978–980.

(444) ———.
1967. Damping-off of sweetgum by *Pythium sylvaticum*. Phytopathology
57: 1284.

(445) ———, and Toole, E. Richard.
1965. Isolations from mycorrhizal roots of sweetgum. U.S. Dep. Agr.
Plant Dis. Rep. 49: 869–870.

(446) ———, and Toole, E. Richard.
1968. Effect of methyl bromide on mycorrhizae and growth of sweetgum
seedlings. U.S. Dep. Agr. Plant Dis. Rep. 52: 483–485.

(447) Fisher, D. F., and Reeves, E. L.
1931. A *Cytospora* canker of apple trees. J. Agr. Res. 43: 431–438.

(448) Fischer, Fran E.
1961. Greasy spot and tar spot of citrus in Florida. Phytopathology 51:
297–303.

(449) Fisher, P. L.
1941. Germination reduction and radicle decay of conifers caused by certain fungi. J. Agr. Res. 62: 87–95.

(450) Fitzpatrick, Harry Morton.
1942. Revisionary studies in the *Coryneliaceae*. II. The genus *Caliciopsis*. Mycologia 34: 489–514.

(451) Fletcher, E. F.
1935. The native persimmon. U.S. Dep. Agr. Farmers' Bull. 685, 21 p.

(452) Foiles, Marvin W.
1959. Silvics of grand fir. USDA Forest Serv. Intermount. Forest and
Range Exp. Sta. Misc. Publ. 21, 12 p.

(453) Ford, Donald H., and Rawlins, T. E.
1956. Improved cytochemical methods for differentiating *Cronartium
ribicola* from *Cronartium occidentale* on *Ribes*. Phytopathology
46: 667–668.

(454) Fosberg, F. R.
1941. Notes on Mexican plants. Lloydia 4: 274–290.

(455) Foster, A. A., and Harrison, Robert P.
1957. Seedling losses in Arizona cypress. USDA Forest Serv. Tree Planters' Notes 29: 20–21.

535

(456) Foster, C. H.
1953. The importance of timber quality as a goal in silviculture. J. Forest. 51: 487–490.

(457) Foster, R. E.
1957. Pole blight of western white pine. Timber of Canada 18(9): 60, 62–63, 65–66, 100.

(458) ———, Browne, J. E., and Foster, A. T.
1958. Studies in forest pathology. XIX. Decay of western hemlock and amabilis fir in the Kitimat Region of British Columbia. Can. Dep. Agr. Publ. 1029, 37 p.

(459) ———, Craig, H. M., and Wallis, G. W.
1954. Studies in forest pathology. XII. Decay of western hemlock in the upper Columbia region, British Columbia. Can. J. Bot. 32: 145–171.

(460) ———, and Foster, A. T.
1951. Studies in forest pathology. VIII. Decay of western hemlock on the Queen Charlotte Islands, British Columbia. Can. J. Bot. 29: 479–521.

(461) ———, and Foster, A. T.
1952. Estimating decay in western hemlock. Suggested aids to the inventory in the Queen Charlotte Islands. Brit. Columbia Lumberman 36(11): 42–43, 93, 96, 100, 118.

(462) ———, and Foster, A. T.
1953. Estimating decay in western hemlock. II. Suggested aids to utilization in the Queen Charlotte Islands. Brit. Columbia Lumberman 37(4): 40–41, 56, 58, 102.

(463) ———, and Foster, A. T.
1953. Estimating decay in western hemlock. III. Suggested aids to the management of mature hemlock-spruce forests on the Queen Charlotte Islands. Brit. Columbia Lumberman 37(10): 42–47.

(464) ———, and Hurn, D. R.
1949. A preliminary report on dèterioration in the western hemlock–Douglas-fir type on lower Vancouver Island following attack by the western hemlock looper (*Lambdina* f. *lugubrosa*). Forest Chron. 25: 202–214.

(465) ———, and Johnson, A. L. S.
1963. The significance of root rot and frost damage in some Douglas-fir plantations. Forest Chron. 39: 266–272.

(466) ———, and Johnson, A. L. S.
1963. Studies in forest pathology. XXV. Assessments of pattern, frequency distribution, and sampling of forest disease in Douglas-fir plantations. Can. Dep. Forest. Publ. 1011, 52 p.

(467) ———, Thomas, G. P., and Browne, J. E.
1953. A tree decadence classification for mature coniferous stands. Forest Chron. 29: 359–366.

(468) Fowells, H. A.
1965. Silvics of forest trees of the United States. U.S. Dep. Agr. Handb. 271, 762 p.

(469) ———, and Krauss, Robert W.
1959. The inorganic nutrition of loblolly pine and Virginia pine with special reference to nitrogen and phosphorus. Forest Sci. 5: 95–112.

(470) ———, and Schubert, G. H.
1956. Silvical characteristics of sugar pine. USDA Forest Serv. Calif. Forest and Range Exp. Sta. Tech. Pap. 14, 19 p.

(471) Fowler, Marvin E.
1938. Twig cankers of Asiatic chestnuts in the Eastern United States. Phytopathology 28: 693–704.

536

(472) ———.
1949. Leaf spot of magnolia. Amer. Forests 55(7): 26.

(473) ———.
1958. Oak wilt. USDA Forest Serv. Forest Pest Leafl. 29, 7 p.

(474) ———, and Aldrich, K. F.
1953. Re-survey for European larch canker in the United States. U.S. Dep. Agr. Plant Dis. Rep. 37: 160–161.

(475) ———, and Stevenson, John A.
1944. A canker and some decay fungi on mimosa. Phytopathology 34: 985–987.

(476) French, William J., and Silverborg, S. B.
1967. Scleroderris canker of red pine in New York State plantations. U.S. Dep. Agr. Plant Dis. Rep. 51: 108–109.

(477) Friend, R. J.
1965. A study of sooty mould on lime trees (Tilia X vulgaris). Brit. Mycol. Soc. Trans. 48: 367–370.

(478) ———.
1965. What is Fumago vagans? Brit. Mycol. Soc. Trans. 48: 371–375.

(479) Fritz, Emmanuel, and Bonar, Lee.
1931. The brown heart-rot of California redwood. J. Forest. 29: 368–380.

(480) Froelich, R. C., and Snow, G. A.
1965. Pine trees near power substations damaged by urea herbicides. U.S. Dep. Agr. Plant Dis. Rep. 49: 970–971.

(481) Frothingham, E. H.
1915. The eastern hemlock. U.S. Dep. Agr. Bull. 152, 43 p.

(482) Funk, A.
1962. Durandiella pseudotsugae n. sp.: taxonomy, cultural characteristics, life history, and host response. Can. J. Bot. 40: 331–335.

(483) ———.
1963. Studies in the genus Caliciopsis. Can. J. Bot. 41: 503–543.

(484) ———.
1964. Botryosphaeria tsugae n. sp., causing dieback of western hemlock in British Columbia. Can. J. Bot. 42: 769–775.

(485) ———.
1964. Extensions of the host ranges and distribution of Caliciopsis species on western conifers. U.S. Dep. Agr. Plant Dis. Rep. 48: 677.

(486) ———.
1965. A new parasite of spruce from British Columbia. Can. J. Bot. 43: 45–48.

(487) ———.
1965. The symbiotic fungi of certain ambrosia beetles in British Columbia. Can. J. Bot. 43: 929–932.

(488) ———.
1966. Ascoconidium tsugae n. sp. associated with bark diseases of western hemlock in British Columbia. Can. J. Bot. 44: 219–222.

(489) ———.
1967. Dermea pseudotsugae n. sp., A causal agent of phloem necrosis in Douglas-fir. Can. J. Bot. 45: 1803–1809.

(490) ———.
1967. Coccomyces heterophyllae n. sp., A hypodermataceous fungus from the periderm of western hemlock. Can. J. Bot. 45: 2263–2266.

(491) ———.
1968. Diaporthe lokoyae n. sp., the perfect state of Phomopsis lokoyae. Can. J. Bot. 46: 601–603.

(492) ———, and Parker, A. K.
1966. *Scirrhia pini* n. sp., the perfect state of *Dothistroma pini* Hulbary. Can. J. Bot. 44: 1171–1176.

(493) Funk, David T.
1957. Silvical characteristics of honeylocust. USDA Forest Serv. Central States Forest Exp. Sta. Misc. Release 23, 14 p.

(494) Garren, Kenneth H.
1941. Fire wounds on loblolly pine and their relation to decay and other cull. J. Forest. 39: 16–22.

(495) ———.
1949. Leader dieback—a "new" disease of sweetgum. U.S. Dep. Agr. Plant Dis. Rep. 33: 351–353.

(496) Garriss, Howard R.
1959. Hemlock twig rust in North Carolina. N.C. Agr. Ext. Serv. Ext. Folder 172, 8 p.

(497) Gerdemann, J. W.
1965. Vesicular-arbuscular mycorrhizae formed on maize and tuliptree by *Endogone fasciculata*. Mycologia 57: 562–575.

(498) Gerry, Eloise.
1921. American storax production: results of different methods of tapping red gum trees. J. Forest. 19: 15–24.

(499) ———.
1942. Radial streak (red) and giant resin ducts in spruce. USDA Forest Serv. Forest Prod. Lab. Rep. 1391, 2 p.

(500) Gilbert, Adrian M.
1960. Silvical characteristics of yellow birch. USDA Forest Serv. Northeast Forest Exp. Sta. Pap. 134, 18 p.

(501) Gilbertson, R. L., Lombard, Frances F., and Hinds, T. E.
1968. *Veluticeps berkeleyi* and its decay of pine in North America. Mycologia 60: 29–41.

(502) Gill, D. L.
1958. Effect of root-knot nematodes on *Fusarium* wilt of mimosa. U.S. Dep. Agr. Plant Dis. Rep. 42: 587–590.

(503) ———.
1963. Mimosa wilt. Arborist's News 28: 31–32.

(504) ———.
1964. Wilt of mimosa wilt-resistant cultivars. U.S. Dep. Agr. Plant Dis. Rep. 48: 648.

(505) Gill, Lake S.
1935. *Arceuthobium* in the United States. Conn. Acad. Arts Sci. Trans. 32: 111–245.

(506) ———.
1953. Broomrapes, dodders, and mistletoes. U.S. Dep. Agr. Yearb. 1953: 73–77.

(507) ———.
1957. Dwarfmistletoe of lodgepole pine. USDA Forest Serv. Forest Pest Leafl. 18, 7 p.

(508) ———, and Hawksworth, Frank G.
1961. The mistletoes. A literature review. U.S. Dep. Agr. Tech. Bull. 1242, 87 p.

(509) Gilman, J. C., and McNew, G. L.
1940. Fungi associated with tree cankers in Iowa. II. *Diaporthe, Apioporthe, Cryptodiaporthe, Pseudovalsa*, and their related conidial forms. Iowa State Coll. J. Sci. 14: 129–144.

(510) Gilmour, J. W.
    1966. The pathology of forest trees in New Zealand. New Zealand Forest
        Serv. Tech. Pap. 48, 82 p.

(511) Ginns, J. H., and True, R. P.
    1967. Butt rot in yellow-poplar seedling-sprout stands. Forest Sci. 13:
        440–447.

(512) Glerum, C., and Farrar, J. L.
    1966. Frost ring formation in the stems of some coniferous species.
        Can. J. Bot. 44: 879–886.

(513) Godman, R. M.
    1957. Silvical characteristics of sugar maple. USDA Forest Serv. Lake
        States Forest Exp. Sta. Pap. 50, 24 p.

(514) ——.
    1958. Silvical characteristics of northern white-cedar. USDA Forest Serv.
        Lake States Forest Exp. Sta. Pap. 67, 17 p.

(515) ——.
    1959. Winter sunscald of yellow birch. J. Forest. 57: 368–369.

(516) Goggans, J. F., and May, J. T.
    1950. Black locust plantations in the Piedmont Region of Alabama. Ala.
        Polytech. Inst. Agr. Exp. Sta. Circ. 98, 7 p.

(517) Good, H. M., Basham, J. T., and Kadzielawa, S. D.
    1968. Respiratory activity of fungal associations in zones of heart rot
        and stain in sugar maple. Can. J. Bot. 46: 27–36.

(518) ——, and Nelson, Jane I.
    1962. Fungi associated with *Fomes igniarius* var. *populinus* in living
        poplar trees and their probable significance in decay. Can. J. Bot.
        40: 615–624.

(519) Goodding, L. N.
    1931. *Didymosphaeria oregonensis*, a new canker organism on alder.
        Phytopathology 21: 913–918.

(520) Goode, Monroe J.
    1953. Control of oak leaf-blister in Mississippi. (Abstr.) Phytopathology
        43: 472.

(521) Gooding, G. V., Jr., and Powers, H. R., Jr.
    1965. Serological comparison of *Cronartium fusiforme, C. quercuum*,
        and *C. ribicola* by immunodiffusion tests. Phytopathology 55:
        670–674.

(522) Gordon, Alan G., and Gorham, Eville.
    1963. Ecological aspects of air pollution from an iron-sintering plant at
        Wawa, Ontario. Can. J. Bot. 41: 1063–1078.

(523) Goss, R. W.
    1960. Mycorrhizae of ponderosa pine in Nebraska grassland soils. Nebr.
        Agr. Exp. Sta. Res. Bull. 192, 17 p.

(524) ——, and Frink, Paul Raymond.
    1934. *Cephalosporium* wilt and dieback of the white elm. Univ. Nebr. Agr.
        Exp. Sta. Res. Bull. 70, 24 p.

(525) Gosselin, Roger.
    1944. Studies on *Polystictus circinatus* and its relation to butt-rot of
        spruce. Farlowia 1: 525–568.

(526) Graham, Donald P.
    1961. Dwarfmistletoe of Douglas-fir. USDA Forest Serv. Forest Pest
        Leafl. 54, 4 p.

(527) ——, and Leaphart, C. D.
    1961. Larch and lodgepole pine dwarfmistletoes attack Scotch pine. J.
        Forest. 59: 375–376.

(528) Graham, Samuel A., and Harrison, Robert P.
　　1954. Insect attacks and *Hypoxylon* infections in aspen. J. Forest. 52: 741–743.

(529) Grant, Theodore J., and Hartley, Carl.
　　1938. A witches'-broom on black locust and a similar disease on honey locust. U.S. Dep. Agr. Plant Dis. Rep. 22: 28–31.

(530) ———, and Spaulding, Perley.
　　1939. Avenues of entrance for canker-forming Nectrias of New England hardwoods. Phytopathology 29: 351–358.

(531) ———, Stout, Donald C., and Readey, J. C.
　　1942. Systemic brooming, a virus disease of black locust. J. Forest. 40: 253–260.

(532) Gravatt, G. F.
　　1926. Maple wilt. U.S. Dep. Agr. Circ. 382, 13 p.

(533) ———, and Crandall, Bowen S.
　　1945. The *Phytophthora* root disease of chestnut and chinkapin. 35th Annu. Rep. North. Nut Growers Assn., 83–87.

(534) ———, and Gill, L. S.
　　1930. Chestnut blight. U.S. Dep. Agr. Farmers' Bull. 1641, 18 p.

(535) ———, and Marshall, R. P.
　　1926. Chestnut blight in the southern Appalachians. U.S. Dep. Agr. Circ. 370, 11 p.

(536) Graves, Arthur H.
　　1912. The large leaf spot of chestnut and oak. Mycologia 4: 170–174.

(537) ———.
　　1913. Notes on diseases of trees in the southern Appalachians. I. Phytopathology 3: 129–139.

(538) ———.
　　1914. Notes on diseases of trees in the southern Appalachians. Phytopathology 4: 63–72.

(539) ———.
　　1923. The *Melanconis* disease of the butternut. Phytopathology 13: 411–435.

(540) ———.
　　1926. The cause of the persistent development of basal shoots from blighted chestnut trees. Phytopathology 16: 615–621.

(541) Gray, L. E., Jokela, J. J., and Wycoff, H. B.
　　1965. Blackstem of cottonwood. U.S. Dep. Agr. Plant Dis. Rep. 49: 867–868.

(542) Gremmen, J.
　　1958. Bemerkungen ueber einige *Cenangium ferruginosum* aehnliche pilze. Phytopathol. Zeitschrift 33: 371–374.

(543) Griffin, G. D., and Epstein, A. H.
　　1964. Association of dagger nematode, *Xiphinema americanum*, with stunting and winterkill of ornamental spruce. Phytopathology 54: 177–180.

(544) Griffin, H. D.
　　1965. Maple dieback in Ontario. Forest. Chron. 41: 295–300.

(545) ———.
　　1968. The genus *Ceratocystis* in Ontario. Can. J. Bot. 46: 689–718.

(546) Grimm, William Carey.
　　1962. The book of trees. Ed. 2, 487 p. Harrisburg, Penn.: The Stackpole Company.

(547) Gross, Henry L.
　　1964. The Echinodontiaceae. Mycopathol. et Mycol. Applicata 24: 1–26.

(548) ——.
1967. *Cytospora* canker of black cherry. U.S. Dep. Agr. Plant Dis. Rep. 51: 941–944.

(549) ——, and Weidensaul, T. C.
1967. *Phacidiopycnis pseudotsugae* associated with bleeding cankers on eastern hemlock. (Abstr.) Phytopathology 57: 340.

(550) Grossenbacher, J. G., and Duggar, B. M.
1911. A contribution to the life history, parasitism, and biology of *Botrysphaeria ribis*. New York (Geneva) Agr. Exp. Sta. Tech. Bull. 18: 127–202.

(551) Groves, J. Walton.
1946. North American species of *Dermea*. Mycologia 38: 351–431.

(552) ——.
1952. The genus *Tympanis*. Can. J. Bot. 30: 571–651.

(553) Gruenhagen, R. H.
1945. *Hypoxylon pruinatum* and its pathogenesis on poplar. Phytopathology 35: 72–89.

(554) ——.
1965. Live oak decline in Virginia. U.S. Dep. Agr. Plant Dis. Rep. 49: 269.

(555) ——, Riker, A. J., and Richards, C. Audrey.
1947. Burn blight of jack and red pine following spittle insect attack. Phytopathology 37: 757–772.

(556) Gruschow, George F., and Trousdell, Kenneth B.
1958. Incidence of heart rot in mature loblolly pine in coastal North Carolina. J. Forest. 56: 220–221.

(557) ——, and Trousdell, Kenneth B.
1959. Incidence of rot in hardwood sawtimber in coastal North Carolina. J. Forest. 57: 370–371.

(558) Guba, Emil Frederick.
1961. Monograph of *Monochaetia* and *Pestalotia*. 342 p. Cambridge: Harvard University Press.

(559) Guilkey, Paul C., Rudolph, Victor J., and Sheppard, George.
1958. Effects of sweetfern rust on the growth of young jack pine in northern lower Michigan. J. Forest. 56: 900–903.

(560) Haasis, F. W.
1917. Dying of young pines in circles about anthills. J. Forest. 15: 763–771.

(561) Hacskaylo, Edward.
1951. A study of the roots of *Pinus virginiana* in relation to certain Hymenomycetes suspected of being mycorrhizal. J. Wash. Acad. Sci. 41: 399–400.

(562) ——.
1965. *Thelephora terrestris* and mycorrhizae of Virginia pine. Forest Sci. 11:401–404.

(563) Haddow, W. R.
1938. The disease caused by *Trametes pini* (Thore) Fries in white pine (*Pinus strobus* L.). Roy. Can. Inst. Trans. 47, 22(1): 21–81.

(564) ——.
1941. Needle blight and late fall browning of red pine (*Pinus resinosa* Ait.) caused by a gall midge (Cecidomyiidae) and the fungus *Pullularia pullulans* (de Bary) Berkhout. Roy. Can. Inst. Trans. 23: 161–189.

(565) Hahn, Glenn Gardner.
1930. Life history studies of the species of *Phomopsis* occurring on conifers. Part I. Brit. Mycol. Soc. Trans. 15: 32–92.

541

(566) ———.
1933. An undescribed *Phomopsis* from Douglas-fir on the Pacific coast. Mycologia 25: 369–375.

(567) ———.
1940. Dasyscyphae on conifers in North America. IV. Two new species on Douglas-fir from the Pacific coast. Mycologia 32: 137–147.

(568) ———.
1940. Distribution and hosts of cedar blight in the United States. U.S. Dep. Agr. Plant Dis. Rep. 24: 52–57.

(569) ———.
1941. Reports of cedar blight in 1940 and notes on its previous occurrence in nurseries. U.S. Dep. Agr. Plant Dis. Rep. 25: 186–190.

(570) ———.
1943. Taxonomy, distribution, and pathology of *Phomopsis occulta* and *P. juniperovora*. Mycologia 35: 112–129.

(571) ———.
1947. Analysis of Peck's types of *Meliola balsamicola* and *Asterina nuda*. Mycologia 39: 479–490.

(572) ———.
1957. A new species of *Phacidiella* causing the so-called *Phomopsis* disease of conifers. Mycologia 49: 226–239.

(573) ———.
1957. *Phacidiopycnis* (*Phomopsis*) canker and dieback of conifers. U.S. Dep. Agr. Plant Dis. Rep. 41: 623–633.

(574) ———, and Ayers, Theodore T.
1934. Dasyscyphae on conifers in North America. I. The large-spored, white-excipled species. Mycologia 26: 73–101.

(575) ———, and Ayers, Theodore T.
1934. Dasyscyphae on conifers in North America. II. *D. ellisiana*. Mycologia 26: 167–180.

(576) ———, and Ayers, Theodore T.
1934. Dasyscyphae on conifers in North America. III. *Dasyscypha pini*. Mycologia 26: 479–501.

(577) ———, and Ayers, Theodore T.
1936. The European larch canker and its relation to certain other cankers of conifers in the United States. J. Forest. 34: 898–908.

(578) ———, and Ayers, Theodore T.
1938. Failure of *Dasyscypha willkommii* and related large-spore species to parasitize Douglas-fir. Phytopathology 28: 50–57.

(579) ———, and Ayers, Theodore T.
1943. Role of *Dasyscypha willkommii* and related fungi in the production of canker and dieback of larches. J. Forest. 41: 483–495.

(580) ———, Hartley, Carl, and Pierce, Roy G.
1917. A nursery blight of cedars. J. Agr. Res. 10: 533–540.

(581) Haig, Irvine T., Davis, Kenneth P., and Weidman, Robert H.
1941. Natural regeneration in the western white pine type. U.S. Dep. Agr. Tech. Bull. 767, 99 p.

(582) Hall, R. C.
1933. Post-logging decadence in northern hardwoods. Univ. Mich. School Forest. and Conserv. Bull. 3, 66 p.

(583) Hall, T. F., and Smith, G. E.
1955. Effects of flooding on woody plants, West Sandy dewatering project, Kentucky Reservoir. J. Forest. 53: 281–285.

(584) Hall, William L.
    1902. The hardy catalpa. I. The hardy catalpa in commercial planta-
        tions. U.S. Dep. Agr. Bur. Forest. Bull. 37: 7–48.

(585) Hallin, William E.
    1957. Silvical characteristics of California red fir and Shasta red fir.
        USDA Forest Serv. Calif. Forest and Range Exp. Sta. Tech.
        Pap. 16, 8 p.

(586) ———.
    1957. Silvical characteristics of Jeffrey pine. USDA Forest Serv. Calif.
        Forest and Range Exp. Sta. Tech. Pap. 17, 11 p.

(587) Hansbrough, J. R.
    1934. Occurrence and parasitism of *Aleurodiscus amorphus* in North
        America. J. Forest. 32: 452–458.

(588) ———.
    1936. The *Tympanis* canker of red pine. Yale Univ. Forest. Sch. Bull.
        43, 58 p.

(589) ———.
    1945. The significance of black line stain in yellow birch propeller lumber.
        U.S. Dep. Agr. Div. Forest Pathol. Spec. Release 23: 1–4.

(590) ———, and Englerth, G. H.
    1944. The significance of the discolorations in aircraft lumber: Sitka
        spruce. USDA Div. Forest Pathol. Spec. Release 21, 13 p.

(591) Hansen, H. N., and Smith, R. E.
    1937. A bacterial gall disease of Douglas-fir, *Pseudotsuga taxifolia*. Hil-
        gardia 10: 569–577.

(592) Hanzlik, Edward J.
    1925. A preliminary study of the growth of noble fir. J. Agr. Res. 31:
        929–934.

(593) Harlow, William M., and Harrar, Ellwood S.
    1941. Textbook of dendrology. Ed. 2, 542 p. New York & London:
        McGraw-Hill Book Co., Inc.

(594) Harrar, Ellwood S.
    1940. The Kimball maple. J. Forest. 38: 726–728.

(595) Hart, Arthur C.
    1959. Silvical characteristics of balsam fir (*Abies balsamea*). USDA
        Forest Serv. Northeast. Forest Exp. Sta. Pap. 122, 22 p.

(596) ———.
    1959. Silvical characteristics of red spruce (*Picea rubens*). USDA Forest
        Serv. Northeast. Forest Exp. Sta. Pap. 124, 19 p.

(597) Hart, John H.
    1965. Willow blight in Michigan. U.S. Dep. Agr. Plant Dis. Rep. 49: 1016.

(598) ———.
    1965. Formation of discolored sapwood in three species of hardwoods.
        Mich. Agr. Exp. Sta. Quart. Bull. 48: 101–116.

(599) ———.
    1965. Root rot of oak associated with *Cylindrocarpon radicicola*. Phyto-
        pathology 55: 1154–1155.

(600) ———.
    1968. Morphological and chemical differences between sapwood, discolored
        sapwood, and heartwood in black locust and osage orange. Forest
        Sci. 14: 334–338.

(601) Hartley, Carl.
    1918. Stem lesions caused by excessive heat. J. Agr. Res. 14: 595–604.

(602) ———.
    1921. Damping-off in forest nurseries. U.S. Dep. Agr. Bull. 934, 100 p.

(603) ——, Davidson, Ross W., and Crandall, Bowen S.
  1961. Wetwood, bacteria, and increased pH in trees. U.S. Dep. Agr.
    Forest Serv. Forest Prod. Lab. Rep. 2215, 34 p.

(604) ——, and Haasis, Ferdinand W.
  1929. Brooming disease of black locust (*Robinia pseudoacacia*). Phyto-
    pathology 19: 163–166.

(605) ——, Merrill, T. C., and Rhoads, Arthur S.
  1918. Seedling diseases of conifers. J. Agr. Res. 15: 521–558.

(606) Hartley, D. E., and Ticknor, R. L.
  1964. Magnesium deficiency in juniper resembles juniper blight. U.S.
    Dep. Agr. Plant Dis. Rep. 48: 581–584.

(607) Harvey A. E.
  1967. Effect of phytoactin treatment on mycorrhizae root consociations
    in western white pine. U.S. Dep. Agr. Plant Dis. Rep. 51: 1012–
    1013.

(608) Harvey, George M.
  1962. Heart rots of Douglas-fir. USDA Forest Serv. Forest Pest Leafl.
    73, 8 p.

(609) Harvey, John M.
  1951. An anthracnose disease of *Umbellularia californica*. Madroño 11:
    162–171.

(610) ——.
  1952. Bacterial leaf spot of *Umbellularia californica*. Madroño 11: 195–
    198.

(611) Hawksworth, Frank G.
  1953. *Phoradendron juniperinum*, a new host for *Uredo phoradendri*.
    U.S. Dep. Agr. Plant Dis. Rep. 37: 258.

(612) ——.
  1961. Dwarfmistletoe brooms and other brooms in lodgepole pine. USDA
    Forest Serv. Rocky Mount. Forest and Range Exp. Sta. Res.
    Notes 59, 3 p.

(613) ——.
  1961. Dwarfmistletoe of ponderosa pine in the Southwest. U.S. Dep.
    Agr. Tech. Bull. 1246, 112 p.

(614) ——, and Graham, D. P.
  1963. Dwarfmistletoes on spruce in the Western United States. North-
    west Sci. 37: 31–38.

(615) ——, and Hinds, Thomas E.
  1960. *Cytospora* canker of· Englemann spruce in Colorado. U.S. Dep.
    Agr. Plant Dis. Rep. 44: 72.

(616) ——, and Hinds, Thomas E.
  1964. Effects of dwarfmistletoe on immature lodgepole pine stands in
    Colorado. J. Forest. 62: 27–32.

(617) ——, and Mielke, James L.
  1962. Witches'-broom of Gambel oak associated with *Articularia quercina*
    var. minor. Phytopathology 52: 451–454.

(618) Hayes, G. L.
  1958. Silvical characteristics of Port-Orford-cedar. USDA Forest Serv.
    Pacific Northwest Forest and Range Exp. Sta. Silvical Ser. 7, 11 p.

(619) Heald, Frederick Deforest.
  1926. Manual of plant diseases. 891 p. New York: McGraw-Hill Book
    Co., Inc.

(620) ——, and Wolf, F. A.
  1911. New species of Texas fungi. Mycologia 3: 5–22.

(621) Heald, Weldon F.
  1964. California's Methuselah trees. Amer. Forests 70(3): 34–35.

544

(622) Hedgcock, George Grant.
1912. Notes on some diseases of trees in our National Forests. II. Phytopathology 2: 73–80.

(623) ———.
1914. Notes on some diseases of trees in our National Forests. IV. Phytopathology 4: 181–188.

(624) ———.
1929. The large leaf spot of chestnut and oak associated with *Monochaetia desmazierii*. Mycologia 21: 324–325.

(625) ———.
1932. Notes on the distribution of some fungi associated with diseases of conifers. U.S. Dep. Agr. Plant Dis. Rep. 16: 28–42.

(626) ———.
1935. Notes on the occurrence of *Tuberculina maxima* on the aecia of *Cronartium cerebrum*. Phytopathology 25: 1117–1118.

(627) ———, Gravatt, G. F., and Marshall, R. P.
1925. *Polyporus schweinitzii* Fr. on Douglas-fir in the Eastern United States. Phytopathology 15: 568–569.

(628) ———, and Long, W. H.
1912. Preliminary notes on three rots of juniper. Mycologia 4: 109–114.

(629) ———, and Long, W. H.
1915. Two new hosts for *Peridermium pyriforme*. J. Agr. Res. 5: 289–290.

(630) ———, and Siggers, Paul V.
1949. A comparison of the pine-oak rusts. U.S. Dep. Agr. Tech. Bull. 978, 30 p.

(631) Heiberg, Svend O., and White, Donald P.
1951. Potassium deficiency of reforested pine and spruce stands in northern New York. Soil Sci. Soc. of Amer. Proc. 15: 369–376.

(632) Heinselman, M. L.
1957. Silvical characteristics of black spruce (*Picea mariana*). USDA Forest Serv. Lake States Forest Exp. Sta. Pap. 45, 30 p.

(633) Hendrix, Floyd F., Jr., and Campbell, W. A.
1966. Root rot organisms isolated from ornamental plants in Georgia. U.S. Dep. Agr. Plant Dis. Rep. 50: 393–395.

(634) ———, and Campbell, W. A.
1968. Pythiaceous fungi isolated from southern forest nursery soils and their pathogenicity to pine seedlings. Forest Sci. 14: 292–297.

(635) ———, and Powell, W. M.
1968. Nematode and *Pythium* species associated with feeder root necrosis of pecan trees in Georgia. U.S. Dep. Agr. Plant Dis. Rep. 52: 334–335.

(636) Hendrix, J. Walter.
1956. Variation in sensitivity to atmospheric fluorides among ponderosa pine seedlings. (Abstr.) Phytopathology 46: 637.

(637) Hepting, George H.
1935. Decay following fire in young Mississippi delta hardwoods. U.S. Dep. Agr. Tech. Bull. 494, 32 p.

(638) ———.
1939. A vascular wilt of the mimosa tree (*Albizzia julibrissin*). U.S. Dep. Agr. Circ. 535, 11 p.

(639) ———.
1941. Eastern forest tree diseases in relation to stand improvement. Civil. Conserv. Corps Forest. Publ. 2, 26 p.

(640) ———.
1941. Prediction of cull following fire in Appalachian oaks. J. Agr. Res. 62: 109–120.

(641) ———.
1944. Sapstreak, a new killing disease of sugar maple. Phytopathology 34: 1069–1076.

(642) ———.
1945. Reserve food storage in shortleaf pine in relation to littleleaf disease. Phytopathology 35: 106–119.

(643) ———.
1950. Leaf diseases of dogwood severe this year in Appalachians. U.S. Dep. Agr. Plant Dis. Rep. 34: 227.

(644) ———.
1951. Leaf blister of oak controlled by spraying. Arborist's News 16: 53–55.

(645) ———.
1955. A southwide survey for sweetgum blight. U.S. Dep. Agr. Plant Dis. Rep. 39: 261–265.

(646) ———.
1955. The current status of oak wilt in the United States. Forest Sci. 1: 95–103.

(647) ———.
1957. A rust on Virginia pine and *Buckleya*. Mycologia 49: 896–899.

(648) ———.
1958. Southern cone rust. USDA Forest Serv. Forest Pest Leafl. 27, 4 p.

(649) ———.
1960. Spot anthracnose and other diseases of dogwood. Arborist's News 25: 25–28.

(650) ———.
1961. *Pinus radiata* susceptible to pitch canker. U.S. Dep. Agr. Plant Dis. Rep. 45: 889–890.

(651) ———.
1963. Climate and forest diseases. Annu. Rev. Phytopathol. 1: 31–50.

(652) ———.
1964. Damage to forests from air pollution. J. Forest. 62: 630–634.

(653) ———.
1967. International tree disease register. Agr. Sci. Rev. 5(1): 33–34.

(654) ———.
1968. Diseases of forest and tree crops caused by air pollutants. Phytopathology 58: 14–17.

(655) ———, and Berry, Charles R.
1961. Differentiating needle blights of white pine in the interpretation of fume damage. Int. J. Air and Water Pollution 4: 101–105.

(656) ———, and Blaisdell, Dorothy J.
1936. A protective zone in red gum fire scars. Phytopathology 26: 62–67.

(657) ———, and Chapman, A. D.
1938. Losses from heart rot in two shortleaf and loblolly pine stands. J. Forest. 36: 1193–1201.

(658) ———, and Davidson, Ross W.
1935. Some leaf and twig diseases of hemlock in North Carolina. U.S. Dep. Agr. Plant Dis. Rep. 19: 308–309.

(659) ———, and Davidson, Ross W.
1937. A leaf and twig disease of hemlock caused by a new species of *Rosellinia*. Phytopathology 27: 305–310.

(660) ———, and Downs, Albert A.
1944. Root and butt rot in planted white pine at Biltmore, North Carolina. J. Forest. 42: 119–123.

(661) ———, and Fowler, Marvin E.
1962. Tree diseases of eastern forests and farm woodlands. U.S. Dep. Agr. Inform. Bull. 254, 48 p.

(662) ———, Garren, Kenneth H., and Warlick, Paul W.
1940. External features correlated with top rot in Appalachian oaks. J. Forest. 38: 873–876.

(663) ———, and Hadgcock, George G.
1937. Decay in merchantable oak, yellow poplar, and basswood in the Appalachian region. U.S. Dep. Agr. Tech. Bull. 570, 30 p.

(664) ———, Miller, J. H., and Campbell, W. A.
1951. Winter of 1950–51 damaging to southeastern wood vegetation. U.S. Dep. Agr. Plant Dis. Rep. 35: 502–503.

(665) ———, and Roth, Elmer R.
1946. Pitch canker, a new disease of some southern pines. J. Forest. 44: 742–744.

(666) ———, and Roth, Elmer R.
1950. The fruiting of heart-rot fungi on felled trees. J. Forest. 48: 332–333.

(667) ———, and Roth, Elmer R.
1953. Host relations and spread of the pine pitch canker disease. (Abstr.) Phytopathology 43: 475.

(668) ———, Roth, Elmer R., and Luxford, R. F.
1942. The significance of the discolorations in aircraft veneers: yellow-poplar. U.S. Dep. Agr. Mimeo. 1375, 8 p.

(669) ———, Roth, Elmer R., and Sleeth, Bailey.
1949. Discolorations and decay from increment borings. J. Forest. 47: 366–370.

(670) ———, and Toole, E. Richard.
1939. The hemlock rust caused by *Melampsora farlowii*. Phytopathology 29: 463–473.

(671) ———, Toole, E. Richard, and Boyce, John S., Jr.
1952. Sexuality in the oak wilt fungus. Phytopathology 42: 438–442.

(672) Herman, F. R.
1958. Silvical characteristics of Rocky Mountain juniper. USDA Forest Serv. Rocky Mount. Forest and Range Exp. Sta. Pap. 29, 20 p.

(673) Hesterberg, Gene A.
1957. Deterioration of sugar maple following logging damage. USDA Forest Serv. Lake States Forest Exp. Sta. Pap. 51, 58 p.

(674) Hibben, Craig R.
1962. Status of sugar maple decline in New York woodlands. (Abstr.) Phytopathology 52: 736.

(675) ———.
1964. Identity and significance of certain organisms associated with sugar maple decline in New York woodlands. Phytopathology 54: 1389–1392.

(676) ———.
1965. A ringspot-like virus in leaves of white ash: symptoms and transmission. (Abstr.) Phytopathology 55: 128.

(677) ———.
1966. Transmission of a ringspot-like virus from leaves of white ash. Phytopathology 56: 323–325.

(678) Hilborn, M. T., and Markin, F. L.
1938. List of causes of fungus and bacterial plant diseases in Maine to 1936 inclusive. U.S. Dep. Agr. Plant Dis. Rep. Suppl. 105: 1–60.

(679) Hildebrand, D. C., and Schroth, M. N.
    1967. A new species of *Erwinia* causing the drippy nut disease of live
        oaks. Phytopathology 57: 250–253.

(680) Himelick, E. B., and Neely, Dan.
    1960. Juniper hosts of cedar-apple and cedar-hawthorn rust. U.S. Dep.
        Agr. Plant Dis. Rep. 44: 109–112.

(681) ———, and Neely, Dan.
    1963. Select junipers for resistance to cedar-apple, cedar-hawthorn rusts.
        Ill. State Nurserymen's Assn. Newsletter 58: 2, 3.

(682) Hinds, Thomas, E.
    1962. Inoculations with the sooty-bark canker fungus on aspen. U.S.
        Dep. Agr. Plant Dis. Rep. 46: 57–58.

(683) ———, and Davidson, Ross W.
    1967. A new species of *Ceratocystis* on aspen. Mycologia 59: 1102–1106.

(684) ———, Hawksworth, Frank G., and Davidson, Ross W.
    1960. Decay of subalpine fir in Colorado. USDA Forest Serv. Rocky
        Mount. Forest and Range Exp. Sta. Pap. 51, 13 p.

(685) ———, and Peterson, Roger S.
    1966. Antibiotic tests on western gall rust and aspen cankers. U.S. Dep.
        Agr. Plant Dis. Rep. 50: 741–744.

(686) Hiratsuka, Y., Morf, W., and Powell, J. M.
    1966. Cytology of the aeciospores and aeciospore germ tubes of *Peri-
        dermium harknessii* and *P. stalactiforme* of the *Cronartium
        coleosporioides* complex. Can. J. Bot. 44: 1639–1643.

(687) Hirt, Ray R.
    1959. *Pinus strobus* L. A literature review and discussion of its fungous
        diseases in North America. N.Y. State Univ. Coll. Forest. (Syra-
        cuse) Tech. Publ. Co. 82, 90 p.

(688) ———.
    1964. *Cronartium ribicola*. Its growth and reproduction in the tissues of
        eastern white pine. N.Y. State Univ. Coll. Forest. (Syracuse)
        Tech. Publ. 86, 30 p.

(689) Hobbs, C. H.
    1944. Studies in mineral deficiency in pine. Plant Physiol. 19: 590–602.

(690) Hocking, D.
    1966. *Cuscuta* parasitic on hardwood seedlings. U.S. Dep. Agr. Plant
        Dis. Rep. 50: 593–594.

(691) Hodges, Charles S.
    1961. Freezing lowers survival of three species of southern pines. USDA
        Forest Serv. Tree Planters' Notes 47: 23–24.

(692) ———.
    1961. New hosts for *Cercospora thujina* Plakidas. U.S. Dep. Agr. Plant
        Dis. Rep. 45: 745.

(693) ———.
    1962. Comparison of four similar fungi from *Juniperus* and related
        conifers. Mycologia 54: 62–69.

(694) ———.
    1962. Fungi isolated from southern forest tree nursery soils. Mycologia
        54: 221–229.

(695) ———.
    1962. Black root rot of pine seedlings. Phytopathology 52: 210–219.

(696) ———.
    1962. Diseases in southeastern forest nurseries and their control. USDA
        Forest Serv. Southeast. Forest Exp. Sta. Pap. 142, 16 p.

(697) ——, and Green, H. J.
1961. Survival in the plantation of eastern redcedar seedlings infected with *Phomopsis* blight in the nursery. U.S. Dep. Agr. Plant Dis. Rep. 45: 134–136.

(698) ——, and Haasis, Frank A.
1962. Etiology of *Cercospora* leaf spot of magnolia. Mycologia 54: 448–454.

(699) ——, and Haasis, Frank A.
1964. The perfect stage of *Cercospora magnoliae*. Mycologia 56: 53–57.

(700) Hoerl, Ruth A.
1939. A new species of *Arthrobotryum*. Madroño 5: 75–77.

(701) Hoffmann, C. H., Hepting, G. H., and Roth, E. R.
1947. A twig droop of white pine caused by *Pineus*. J. Econ. Entomol. 40: 229–231.

(702) Holmes, Francis W.
1961. Salt injury to trees. Phytopathology 51: 712–718.

(703) Hopkins, J. C.
1963. *Atropellis* canker of lodgepole pine: etiology, symptoms, and canker development rates. Can. J. Bot. 41: 1535–1545.

(704) Hopper, B. E.
1958. Plant-parasitic nematodes in the soils of southern forest nurseries. U.S. Dep. Agr. Plant Dis. Rep. 42: 308–314.

(705) Hord, H. H. V., Groenewoud, H. Van, and Riley, C. G.
1957. Low temperature injury to roots of white elm. Forest. Chron. 33: 156–163.

(706) ——, and Quirke, D. A.
1955. Province of Quebec, Annu. Rep., Forest Insect and Disease Surv. Can. Dep. Agr., Forest Biol. Div., Sci. Serv. p. 56–69.

(707) Horne, C. Wendell, and Halliwell, Robert S.
1964. Oak wilt in Texas. U.S. Dep. Agr. Plant Dis. Rep. 48: 419.

(708) Hornibrook, E. M.
1950. Estimating defect in mature and overmature stands of three Rocky Mountain conifers. J. Forest. 48: 408–417.

(709) Horton, Gerald S., and Hendee, Clare.
1934. A study of rot in aspen on the Chippewa National Forest. J. Forest. 32: 493–494.

(710) Hosley, N. W.
1936. Norway spruce in the Northeastern United States. A study of existing plantations. Harvard Forest Bull. 19, 80 p.

(711) Hosner, John F.
1959. Survival, root and shoot growth of six bottom land tree species following flooding. J. Forest. 57: 927–928.

(712) Hough, A. F.
1941. The forests of the Allegheny Plateau; their ecology and silviculture. USDA Forest Serv. Northeast. Forest Exp. Sta. 383 p. [Unpublished.]

(713) ——.
1960. Silvical characteristics of eastern hemlock (*Tsuga canadensis*). USDA Forest Serv. Northeast. Forest Exp. Sta. Pap. 132, 23 p.

(714) Houston, David R.
[n.d.] Maple decline in the northeast. USDA Forest Serv. Northeast. Forest Exp. Sta. Office Rep. 4600–FS–NE–2302, 9 p.

(715) ——.
1963. Inoculation of oaks with *Urnula craterium* (Schw.) Fr. produces cankers identical to *Strumella* cankers. U.S. Dep. Agr. Plant Dis. Rep. 47: 867–869.

(716) ——, and Fisher, Kenneth D.
  1964. Sapstreak disease of sugar maple found in the northeast. U.S.
    Dep. Agr. Plant Dis. Rep. 48: 788.

(717) Howard, F. L.
  1941. The bleeding canker disease of hardwoods and possibilities of con-
    trol. Western Shade Tree Conf. Proc. 8: 46–55.

(718) Howell, J. T.
  1966. *Viscum album* in California. Leaflets of Western Bot. 10: 244.

(719) Hubbes, Martin.
  1964. New facts on host-parasite relationships in the *Hypoxylon* canker
    of aspen. Can. J. Bot. 42: 1489–1494.

(720) ——, and Etheridge, D. E.
  1965. A chemical basis for selection of heartwood fungi in balsam fir. Can.
    J. Bot. 43: 181–183.

(721) Huberman, M. A.
  1943. Sunscald of eastern white pine, *Pinus strobus* L. Ecology 24: 456–
    471.

(722) Hubert, Ernest E.
  1929. Sap stains of wood and their prevention. U.S. Dep. Comm. Nat.
    Comm. Wood Util., 77 p.

(723) ——.
  1929. A butt-rot of balsam fir caused by *Polyporus balsameus* Pk. Phyto-
    pathology 19: 725–732.

(724) ——.
  1929. A root and butt rot of conifers caused by *Polyporus circinatus* Fr.
    Phytopathology 19: 745–747.

(725) ——.
  1931. An outline of forest pathology. 543 p. New York: John Wiley and
    Sons, Inc.

(726) ——.
  1935. A disease of conifers caused by *Stereum sanguinolentum.* J. Forest.
    33: 485–489.

(727) ——.
  1935. Some agencies attacking blister rust on white pine. J. Forest. 33:
    603–606.

(728) ——.
  1935. Observations on *Tuberculina maxima,* a parasite of *Cronartium
    ribicola.* Phytopathology 25: 253–261.

(729) ——.
  1950. Root rots of the western white pine type. Northwest Sci. 24: 5–17.

(730) ——.
  1954. Needle cast diseases of western larch. Idaho Agr. Ext. Serv. Bull.
    215, 2 p.

(731) ——.
  1955. Decay—a problem in the future management of grand fir. J. Forest.
    53: 409–411.

(732) Hunt, John.
  1956. Taxonomy of the genus *Ceratocystis.* Lloydia 19: 1–58.

(733) ——.
  1959. *Phytophthora lateralis* on Port-Orford-cedar. USDA Forest Serv.
    Pacific Northwest Forest and Range Exp. Sta. Res. Note 172, 6 p.

(734) ——, and Krueger, Kenneth W.
  1962. Decay associated with thinning wounds in young-growth western
    hemlock and Douglas-fir. J. Forest. 60: 336–340.

550

(735) Hunt, Stuart S.
 1932. European larch in the Northeastern United States. Harvard Forest
  Bull. 16, 45 p.

(736) Huntly, J. H., Cafley, J. D., and Jorgensen, E.
 1961. *Armillaria* root rot in Ontario. Forest. Chron. 37: 228–236.

(737) Huppuch, Charles D.
 1960. Observations on white oak stem swellings. U.S. Dep. Agr. Plant
  Dis. Rep. 44: 238–239.

(738) Hutchinson, Jay G., and Bramlett, David L.
 1964. Frost damage to shortleaf pine flowers. J. Forest. 62: 343.

(739) Hutnik, Russell J., and Cunningham, Frank E.
 1961. Silvical characteristics of paper birch. USDA Forest Serv. Northeast. Forest Exp. Sta. Pap. 141, 24 p.

(740) ———, and Yawney, Harry W.
 1961. Silvical characteristics of red maple. USDA Forest Serv. Northeast. Forest Exp. Sta. Pap. 142, 18 p.

(741) Ibberson, Joseph E.
 1949. A preliminary report on the diseased condition of red pine in
  southeastern Pennsylvania. Forests and Waters a Bull. 1: 124–
  125, 141.

(742) Ike, Albert F.
 1968. Symptoms of nutrient deficiency in yellow-poplar seedlings. USDA
  Forest Serv. Res. Note SE–94, 4 p.

(743) Illick, Joseph S.
 1928. Pennsylvania trees. Ed. 5, Pa. Dep. Forests and Waters Bull. 11,
  237 p.

(744) Isaac, Leo A., and Dimock, Edward J., II.
 1958. Silvical characteristics of Douglas-fir var. *menziesii*. USDA Forest
  Serv. Pacific Northwest Forest and Range Exp. Sta. Silvical Ser.
  9, 18 p.

(745) Ito, Kazuo, and Hayashi, Hiroko.
 1962. Studies on some anthracnoses of woody plants—VI. Anthracnose
  fungus of *Cinnamomum camphora* Nees et Eberm. Govt. Forest
  Exp. Sta., Tokyo, Japan, Bull. 135, 13 p.

(746) ———, and Kobayashi, Takao.
 1962. Studies on some anthracnoses of woody plants—VII. Anthracnose
  fungus of yellow poplar. Govt. Forest Exp. Sta., Tokyo, Japan,
  Bull. 146, 11 p.

(747) Jackson, L. W. R.
 1945. Root defects and fungi associated with the little-leaf disease of
  southern pines. Phytopathology 35: 91–105.

(748) ———.
 1948. "Needle curl" of shortleaf pine seedlings. Phytopathology 38: 1028–
  1029.

(749) ———, and Hepting, G. H.
 1964. Rough bark formation and food reserves in pine roots. Forest Sci.
  10: 174–179.

(750) Jenkins, Anna E.
 1938. Emendations to the descriptions of *Taphrina lethifera* and *T. aceris*
  on maple (*Acer*). J. Wash. Acad. Sci. 28: 350–352.

(751) ———.
 1938. A new species of *Taphrina* on sugar maple and black maple. J.
  Wash. Acad. Sci. 28: 353–358.

(752) ———, Bitancourt, A. A., and Pollack, Flora G.
 1946. Spot anthracnoses in Pacific Coast States. J. Wash. Acad. Sci. 36:
  416–421.

(753) ——, Forsell, M. J., and Boyle, L. W.
    1946. Identity and known distribution of *Elsinoë piri* in Washington and
        Oregon. Phytopathology 36: 458–461.

(754) ——, Miller, Julian H., and Hepting, George H.
    1953. Spot anthracnose and other leaf and petal spots of flowering dog-
        wood. Nat. Hort. Mag. 32: 57–69.

(755) Jenkins, W. A.
    1930. The cherry leaf-spot fungus, *Mycosphaerella cerasella* Aderh., its
        morphology and life history. Phytopathology 20: 329-337.

(756) Jewell, F. F., and Walker, Nely M.
    1967. Histology of *Cronartium quercuum* galls on shortleaf pine. Phyto-
        pathology 57: 545–550.

(757) Johnson, H. W., and Edgerton, C. W.
    1936. A heart rot of magnolia caused by *Fomes geotropus*. Mycologia
        28: 292–295.

(758) Johnson, L. P. V.
    1946. A practical method of overcoming seed dormancy in *Tilia ameri-
        cana*. Forest. Chron. 22: 182–190.

(759) Johnson, T. W., Jr., Goforth, M. H., Powell, R. W., Jr., and Haar, N. D.
    1957. Observations on yellow-poplar dieback. Forest Sci. 3: 84–89.

(760) Johnston, H. W., and Sproston, Thomas, Jr.
    1965. The inhibition of fungus infection pegs in *Gingko biloba*. Phyto-
        pathology 55: 225–227.

(761) Jones, LeRoy, Barber, John C., and Mabry, J. E., Jr.
    1964. Effect of methyl bromide fumigation on germination of longleaf,
        slash and loblolly pine seed. J. Forest. 62: 737–739.

(762) Jones, Thomas W.
    1961. First report of pine mortality caused by *Fomes annosus* root rot in
        Ohio. U.S. Dep. Agr. Plant Dis. Rep. 45: 980.

(763) ——, and Bretz, T. W.
    1958. First report of tree mortality from *Fomes annosus* root rot in
        Missouri. U.S. Dep. Agr. Plant Dis. Rep. 42: 988.

(764) Jorgensen, Erik.
    1956. *Fomes annosus* (Fr.) Cke. on red pine in Ontario. Forest. Chron.
        32: 86–88.

(765) ——, and Cafley, J. D.
    1961. Branch and stem cankers of white and Norway spruce in Ontario.
        Forest. Chron. 37: 394–400.

(766) Jorgensen, J. R., and Shoulders, Eugene.
    1967. Mycorrhizal root development vital to survival of slash pine nur-
        sery stock. USDA Forest Serv. Tree Planters' Notes 18(2): 7–11.

(767) Jump, John Austin.
    1938. A study of forking in red pine. Phytopathology 28: 798–811.

(768) Kabir, A. K.
    1965. The Columbian timber beetle and its associated micro-organisms
        in soft maple. (Abstr.) Rev. Appl. Mycol. 44: 161–162.

(769) Kanouse, Bessie B.
    1941. New and unusual species of Discomycetes. Mycologia 33: 461–467.

(770) ——, and Smith, Alexander H.
    1940. Two new genera of Discomycetes from the Olympic National Forest.
        Mycologia 32: 756–759.

(771) Kaufert, Frank.
    1935. Heart rot of balsam fir in the Lake States, with special reference
        to forest management. Univ. Minn. Agr. Exp. Sta. Tech. Bull.
        110, 27 p.

(772) ——.
   1936. The biology of *Pleurotus corticatus* Fries. Univ. Minn. Agr. Exp.
      Sta. Tech. Bull. 114, 35 p.

(773) ——.
   1937. Factors influencing the formation of periderm in aspen. Amer. J.
      Bot. 24: 24–30.

(774)` ——.
   1948. The preservative treatment of aspen. USDA Forest Serv. Lake
      States Forest Exp. Sta. Aspen Rep. 19, 19 p.

(775) Keener, Paul D.
   1951. An ascigerous stage of *Darluca filum* (Biv.) Castagne. U.S. Dep.
      Agr. Plant Dis. Rep. 35: 86–87.

(776) ——.
   1953. A species of *Gymnosporangium* on quince, pear, and hawthorn in
      Arizona. U.S. Dep. Agr. Plant Dis. Rep. 37: 235.

(777) ——.
   1956. Two fungi associated with a microcyclic rust, *Coleosporium cro-
      wellii* Cummins, on needles of *Pinus edulis* Engelm. in Arizona.
      Madroño 13: 189–195.

(778) Kelman, Arthur.
   1962. Needle blight taking toll of Christmas trees. Research and Farming
      20(3–4), p. 6.

(779) ——, and Gooding, Guy V., Jr.
   1965. A root and stem rot of yellow-poplar caused by *Cylindrocladium
      scoparium*. U.S. Dep. Agr. Plant Dis. Rep. 49: 797–801.

(780) ——, Hodges, C. S., and Garriss, H. R.
   1960. Needle blight of redcedar, *Juniperus virginiana* L. U.S. Dep. Agr.
      Plant Dis. Rep. 44: 527–531.

(781) Kendrick, W. Bryce.
   1962. The *Leptographium* complex, *Verticicladiella* Hughes. Can. J. Bot.
      40: 771–797.

(782) ——, and Molnar, A. C.
   1965. A new *Ceratocystis* and its *Verticicladiella* imperfect state asso-
      ciated with the bark beetle *Dryocoetes confusus* on *Abies lasio-
      carpa*. Can. J. Bot. 43: 39–43.

(783) Kennedy, Lorene L., and Stewart, Archibald W.
   1967. Development and taxonomy of *Apiosporina collinsii*. Can. J. Bot.
      45: 1597–1604.

(784) Kern, F. D.
   1964. Lists and keys of the cedar rusts of the world. N.Y. Bot. Gard.
      Mem. 10: 305–326.

(785) Kessler, K. J., Jr.
   1962. The endotrophic mycorrhiza of *Acer saccharum* Marsh. (Abstr.)
      Phytopathology 52: 738.

(786) ——.
   1963. Dieback of sugar maple, upper Michigan—1962. USDA Forest
      Serv. Res. Note LS–13, 2 p.

(787) ——, and Anderson, R. L.
   1960. *Ceratocystis coerulescens* on sugar maple in the Lake States. U.S.
      Dep. Agr. Plant Dis. Rep. 44: 348–350.

(788) ——, and Ohman, John H.
   1965. *Cryptostroma corticale*—allergen, plant pathogen, saprophyte. Phy-
      topathology 55: 811–812.

(789) Kienholz, J. R.
   1939. Stony pit, a transmissible disease of pears. Phytopathology 29:
      260–267.

(790) Kimbrough, James W.
  1963. The development of *Pleochaeta polychaeta* (Erysiphaceae). Mycologia 55: 608–618.

(791) ――――, and Korf, Richard P.
  1963. Nomenclatural notes. V. *Uncinula polychaeta* and the genera *Pleochaeta* and *Uncinulopsis*. Mycologia 55: 619–626.

(792) Kimmey, James W.
  1946. Notes on visual differentiation of white pine blister rust from pinyon rust in the telial stage. U.S. Dep. Agr. Plant Dis. Rep. 30: 59–61.

(793) ――――.
  1950. Cull factors for forest-tree species in northwestern California. USDA Forest Serv. Calif. Forest and Range Exp. Sta. Forest Surv. Release 7, 30 p.

(794) ――――.
  1954. Cull and breakage factors for pines and incense-cedar in the Sierra Nevada. USDA Forest Serv. Calif. Forest and Range Exp. Sta. Forest Res. Notes 90, 4 p.

(795) ――――.
  1956. Cull factors for Sitka spruce, western hemlock, and western redcedar in southeast Alaska. USDA Forest Serv. Alaska Forest Res. Cent. Sta. Pap. 6: 1–31.

(796) ――――.
  1957. Application of indicator cull factors to white and red fir stands in the Sierra Nevada. USDA Forest Serv. Calif. Forest and Range Exp. Sta. Forest Res. Notes 127, 5 p.

(797) ――――.
  1964. Heart rots of western hemlock. USDA Forest Serv. Forest Pest Leafl. 90, 7 p.

(798) ――――.
  1965. Rust-red stringy rot. USDA Forest Serv. Forest Pest Leafl. 93, 8 p.

(799) ――――, and Bynum, H. H., Jr.
  1961. Heart rots of red and white firs. USDA Forest Serv. Forest Pest Leafl. 52, 4 p.

(800) ――――, and Furniss, R. L.
  1943. Deterioration of fire-killed Douglas-fir. U.S. Dep. Agr. Tech. Bull. 851, 61 p.

(801) ――――, and Hornibrook, E. M.
  1952. Cull and breakage factors and other tree measurement tables for redwood. USDA Forest Serv. Calif. Forest and Range Exp. Sta. Forest Surv. Release 13, 28 p.

(802) ――――, and Lightle, Paul C.
  1955. Fungi associated with cull in redwood. Forest Sci. 1: 104–110.

(803) ――――, and Mielke, James L.
  1959. Western dwarfmistletoe on ponderosa pine. USDA Forest Serv. Forest Pest Leafl. 40, 7 p.

(804) ――――, and Wagener, Willis W.
  1961. Spread of white pine blister rust from *Ribes* to sugar pine in California and Oregon. U.S. Dep. Agr. Tech. Bull. 1251, 71 p.

(805) Klawitter, Ralph A.
  1957. Most cankered trees are good risks in loblolly pine sawtimber stands. USDA Forest Serv. Southeast. Forest Exp. Sta. Res. Notes 107, 2 p.

(806) Klotz, Leo J.
  1961. Color handbook of citrus diseases. Ed. 3, 75 p. Riverside, Calif.: Univ. of Calif.

554

(807) Korf, Richard P.
1962. A synopsis of the Hemiphacidiaceae, a family of the Helotiales (Discomycetes) causing needle blights of conifers. Mycologia 54: 12–33.

(808) Korstian, C. F., and Brush, W. D.
1931. Southern white cedar. U.S. Dep. Agr. Tech. Bull. 251, 76 p.

(809) Kotheimer, J. B., Rich, A. E., and Shortle, W. C., Jr.
1967. The role of ions in the etiology of maple decline. (Abstr.) Phytopathology 57: 342.

(810) Kozlowski, Theodore T., and Scholtes, Wayne H.
1948. Growth of roots and root hairs of pine and hardwood seedlings in the Piedmont. J. Forest. 46: 750–754.

(811) Krajicek, John E.
1958. Silvical characteristics of hackberry. USDA Forest Serv. Central States Forest Exp. Sta. Misc. Release 31, 11 p.

(812) Krebill, R. G.
1965. Comandra rust outbreaks in lodgepole pine. J. Forest. 63: 519–522.

(813) ———.
1967. Gymnosporangium clavariiforme in witches'-brooms of Juniperus communis. U.S. Dep. Agr. Plant Dis. Rep. 51: 143–147.

(814) ———.
1968. Histology of canker rusts in pines. Phytopathology 58: 155–164.

(815) ———, and Patton, R. F.
1962. Wounds in jack pine roots as entry points for a succession of fungi. (Abstr.) Phytopathology 52: 739.

(816) Kriebel, Howard B.
1957. Patterns of genetic variation in sugar maple. Ohio Agr. Exp. Sta. Res. Bull. 791, 56 p.

(817) Kuhlman, E. George.
1961. Survival and pathogenicity of Phytophthora cinnamomi Rands in forest soils. 95 p. (Thesis, Ph.D., Oregon State Univ.)

(818) ———.
1964. Survival and pathogenicity of Phytophthora cinnamomi in several western Oregon soils. Forest Sci. 10: 151–158.

(819) ———, and Hendrix, Floyd F., Jr.
1963. Phytophthora root rot of Fraser fir. U.S. Dep. Agr. Plant Dis. Rep. 47: 552–553.

(820) ———, Hendrix, Floyd F., Jr., and Hodges, C. S.
1962. Inoculation and colonization of stumps of Pinus echinata by Fomes annosus. (Abstr.) Phytopathology 52: 739.

(821) Kuijt, Job.
1955. Dwarfmistletoes. Bot. Rev. 21: 569–627.

(822) Kuntz, James E.
1964. Diseases of Quercus in the United States. In Diseases of widely planted forest trees, FAO/IUFRO Symp. on Int. Dangerous Forest Dis. and Insects, Working Group on Int. Coop. in Forest Dis. Res., p. 184–213.

(823) ———, and Riker, A. J.
1956. Oak wilt. Univ. Wis. Agr. Exp. Sta. Bull. 519, 12 p.

(824) Lacasse, Norman L., and Rich, Avery E.
1964. Maple decline in New Hampshire. Phytopathology 54: 1071–1075.

(825) Lair, Eugenie D.
1946. Smooth patch, a bark disease of oak. J. Elisha Mitchell Sci. Soc. 62: 212–220.

(826) Lake States Forest Exp. Sta.
 1964. The causes of maple blight in the Lake States. USDA Forest Serv. Res. Pap. LS–10, 15 p.

(827) Lamb, Howard, Wright, Ernest, and Davidson, Ross W.
 1935. A root rot of Chinese elms. Phytopathology 25: 652–654.

(828) Lambert, Edmund B., and Crandall, Bowen S.
 1936. A seedling wilt of black locust caused by *Phytophthora parasitica*. J. Agr. Res. 53: 467–476.

(829) Langdon, O. G.
 1958. Silvical characteristics of baldcypress. USDA Forest Serv. Southeast. Forest Exp. Sta. Pap. 94, 7 p.

(830) Lanier, L.
 1964. A disease of cypress due to a *Coryneum* sp. (Abstr.) Rev. Appl. Mycol. 43: 217.

(831) Large, John R.
 1948. Canker of tung trees caused by *Physalospora rhodina*. Phytopathology 38: 359–363.

(832) ———.
 1949. Rough bark of tung, a virus disease. Phytopathology 39: 718–720.

(833) Larsen, J. A.
 1930. Forest types of the northern Rocky Mountains and their climatic controls. Ecology 11: 631–672.

(834) Latham, A. J.
 1969. Zonate leafspot of pecan caused by *Cristulariella pyramidalis*. Phytopathology 59: 103–107.

(835) Latham, Dennis H.
 1936. *Rhizoctonia* tip killing of red spruce. U.S. Dep. Agr. Plant Dis. Rep. Suppl. 96: 248–249.

(836) Laurent, T. H.
 1966. Dwarfmistletoe on Sitka spruce—a new host record. U.S. Dep. Agr. Plant Dis. Rep. 50: 921.

(837) Laut, John G., Sutton, B. C., and Lawrence, J. J.
 1966. Brown spot needle blight in Canada. U.S. Dep. Agr. Plant Dis. Rep. 50: 208.

(838) Lavallée, André.
 1964. A larch canker caused by *Leucostoma kunzei* (Fr.) Munk ex Kern. Can. J. Bot. 42: 1495–1502.

(839) ———.
 1965. Modes d'entrée des caries du tronc de l'epinette noire. Phytoprotection 46: 163–168.

(840) ———, and Lortie, Marcel.
 1968. Relationships between external features and trunk rot in living yellow birch. Forest. Chron. 44(2): 5–10.

(841) Leach, J. G.
 1940. Insect transmission of plant diseases. 615 p. New York: McGraw-Hill Book Co., Inc.

(842) ———, Orr, L. W., and Christensen, Clyde.
 1934. The interrelationships of bark beetles and blue-staining fungi in felled Norway pine timber. J. Agr. Res. 49: 315–342.

(843) ———, Orr, L. W., and Christensen, Clyde.
 1937. Further studies on the interrelationship of insects and fungi in the deterioration of felled Norway pine logs. J. Agr. Res. 55: 129–140.

(844) Leak, William B.
 1958. Silvical characteristics of sweet birch. USDA Forest Serv. Northeast. Forest Exp. Sta. Pap. 113, 14 p.

(845) Leaphart, Charles D.
  1958. Pole blight—how it may influence western white pine management in light of current knowledge. J. Forest. 56: 746–751.

(846) ———.
  1958. Root characteristics of western white pine and associated tree species in a stand affected with pole blight of white pine. USDA Forest Serv. Intermount. Forest and Range Exp. Sta. Res. Pap. 52, 10 p.

(847) ———.
  1960. A root stain disease of eastern white pine. U.S. Dep. Agr. Plant Dis. Rep. 44: 704–706.

(848) ———.
  1963. Armillaria root rot. USDA Forest Serv. Forest Pest Leafl. 78, 8 p.

(849) ———, Copeland, Otis L., Jr., and Graham, Donald P.
  1957. Pole blight of western white pine. USDA Forest Serv. Forest Pest Leafl. 16, 4 p.

(850) ———, and Denton, Robert E.
  1961. Needle discolorations of western larch. USDA Forest Serv. Forest Pest Leafl. 61, 7 p.

(851) ———, and Gill, Lake S.
  1959. Effects of inoculations with Leptographium spp. on western white pine. Phytopathology 49: 350–353.

(852) ———, and Wicker, Ed. F.
  1966. Explanation of pole blight from responses of seedlings grown in modified environments. Can. J. Bot. 44: 121–137.

(853) LeBarron, Russell K.
  1944. Influence of controllable environmental conditions on regeneration of jack pine and black spruce. J. Agr. Res. 68: 97–119.

(854) ———.
  1948. Silvicultural management of black spruce in Minnesota. U.S. Dep. Agr. Circ. 791, 60 p.

(855) LeBlanc, Joseph Henri.
  1955. A mode of vegetative propagation in black spruce. Pulp and Paper Mag. of Can. 56: 146–153.

(856) Lee, W. O., and Timmons, F. L.
  1958. Dodder and its control. U.S. Dep. Agr. Farmers' Bull. 2117, 20 p.

(857) Leiser, A. T., and Ferris, J. M.
  1965. Tolerances of Picea spp. to a nematocide and fertilizer salts. U.S. Dep. Agr. Plant Dis. Rep. 49: 72–73.

(858) Lemke, Paul Arenz.
  1964. The genus Aleurodiscus (sensu stricto) in North America. Can. J. Bot. 42: 213–282.

(859) Lewis, G. D.
  1956. Botryosphaeria canker and fruit rot of apple in New York. U.S. Dep. Agr. Plant Dis. Rep. 40: 228.

(860) Li, C. Y., Lu, K. C., Trappe, J. M., and Bollen, W. B.
  1967. Selective nitrogen assimilation by Poria weirii. Nature 213(5078): 814.

(861) Lightle, Paul C.
  1954. The pathology of Elytroderma deformans on ponderosa pine. Phytopathology 44: 557–569.

(862) ———, Standring, Elizabeth T., and Brown, J. G.
  1942. A bacterial necrosis of the giant cactus. Phytopathology 32: 303–313.

(863) Limber, Donald P., and Cash, Edith K.
  1945. Actinopelte dryina. Mycologia 37: 129–137.

(864) Lindgren, R. M., and Wright, E.
    1954. Increased absorptiveness of molded Douglas-fir posts. J. Forest.
    Prod. Res. Soc. 4: 162–164.

(865) Linzon, S. N.
    1958. The influence of smelter fumes on the growth of white pine in the
    Sudbury region. Ontario Dep. Lands and Forests and Ontario
    Dep. Mines, Toronto, Ont. 45 p.

(866) ———.
    1960. The development of foliar symptoms and the possible cause of origin
    of white pine needle blight. Can. J. Bot. 38: 153–161.

(867) ———.
    1961. Locomotive smoke damage to jack pine. Forest. Chron. 37: 102–106.

(868) ———.
    1962. Artificial inoculation of wet and dry heartwood of living eastern
    white pine trees. Forest Sci. 8: 163–167.

(869) ———.
    1965. Sulphur dioxide injury to trees in the vicinity of petroleum re-
    fineries. Forest. Chron. 41: 245–247, 250.

(870) ———.
    1967. Histological studies of symptoms in semimature-tissue needle blight
    of eastern white pine. Can. J. Bot. 45: 133–143.

(871) ———.
    1967. Ozone damage and semimature-tissue needle blight of eastern white
    pine. Can. J. Bot. 45: 2047–2061.

(872) Little, Elbert L., Jr.
    1953. Check list of native and naturalized trees of the United States
    (including Alaska). U.S. Dep. Agr. Handb. 41, 472 p.

(873) Little, S.
    1959. Silvical characteristics of Atlantic white-cedar. USDA Forest Serv.
    Northeast. Forest Exp. Sta. Pap. 118, 16 p.

(874) ———.
    1959. Silvical characteristics of pitch pine (*Pinus rigida*). USDA Forest
    Serv. Northeast. Forest Exp. Sta. Pap. 119, 22 p.

(875) ———, Mohr, J. J., and Spicer, L. L.
    1958. Salt-water storm damage to loblolly pine forests. J. Forest. 56:
    27–28.

(876) Lockard, C. R., Putnam, J. A., and Carpenter, R. D.
    1963. Grade defects in hardwood timber and logs. U.S. Dep. Agr. Handb.
    244, 39 p.

(877) Lohman, M. L., and Cash, Edith K.
    1940. *Atropellis* species from pine cankers in the United States. J. Wash.
    Acad. Sci. 30: 255–262.

(878) ———,Cash, Edith K., and Davidson, Ross W.
    1942. An undescribed *Atropellis* on cankered *Pinus virginiana*. J. Wash.
    Acad. Sci. 32: 296–298.

(879) ———, and Watson, Alice J.
    1943. Identity and host relations of *Nectria* species associated with dis-
    eases of hardwoods in the Eastern States. Lloydia 6: 77–108.

(880) Loman, A. A.
    1965. The lethal effects of periodic high temperatures on certain lodge-
    pole pine slash decaying Basidiomycetes. Can. J. Bot. 43: 334–338.

(881) ———, and Paul, G. D.
    1963. Decay of lodgepole pine in two foothills sections of the boreal forest
    in Alberta. Forest. Chron. 39: 422–435.

(882) Lombard, Frances F., and Davidson, Ross W.
1946. An undescribed *Coryneum* on diseased Italian cypress. Phytopathology 36: 775–777.

(883) Long, W. H.
1914. The death of chestnuts and oaks due to *Armillaria mellea*. U.S.
Dep. Agr. Bull. 89, 9 p.

(884) ———.
1915. A honeycomb heart-rot of oaks caused by *Stereum subpileatum*.
J. Agr. Res. 5: 421–428.

(885) ———.
1930. *Polyporus dryadeus*, a root parasite on white fir. Phytopathology
20: 758–759.

(886) ———, and Goodding, L. N.
1940. Notes on *Gymnosporangium cypressi*. Mycologia 32: 489–492.

(887) Lorenz, Rolland C., and Christensen, Clyde M.
1937. A survey of forest tree diseases and their relation to stand improvement in the Lake and Central States. USDA Bur. Plant Indus.,
52 p. [Processed.]

(888) Lortie, Marcel.
1964. Production of perithecia of *Nectria galligena* Bres. in pure culture.
Can. J. Bot. 42: 123–124.

(889) Lowe, Josiah L.
1946. The Polyporaceae of New York State (The genus *Poria*). N.Y.
State Coll. Forest. (Syracuse) Tech. Publ. 65, 91 p.

(890) ———.
1957. Polyporaceae of North America. The genus *Fomes*. N.Y. State Coll.
Forest. (Syracuse) Tech. Publ. 80, 97 p.

(891) ———.
1963. A synopsis of *Poria* and similar fungi from the tropical regions
of the world. Mycologia 55: 453–486.

(892) ———, and Gilbertson, Robert L.
1961. Synopsis of the Polyporaceae of the Southeastern United States.
J. Elisha Mitchell Sci. Soc. 77: 43–61.

(893) ———, and Gilbertson, Robert L.
1961. Synopsis of the Polyporaceae of the Western United States and
Canada. Mycologia 53: 474–511.

(894) Luttrell, E. S.
1950. *Botryosphaeria* stem canker of elm. U.S. Dep. Agr. Plant Dis. Rep.
34: 138–139.

(895) ———, Davis, T. S., and Murray, B. R.
1962. *Botryosphaeria* twig blight of Arizona cypress. U.S. Dep. Agr.
Plant Dis. Rep. 46: 261–264.

(896) Lutz, H. J.
1952. Occurrence of clefts in the wood of living white spruce in Alaska.
J. Forest. 50: 99–102.

(897) Lutz, John F.
1955. Hickory for veneer and plywood. USDA Forest Serv. Southeast.
Forest Exp. Sta. Hickory Task Force Rep. 1, 12 p.

(898) Luxford, R. F., and Krone, R. H.
1943. Chemical stain in noble fir as related to strength. USDA Forest
Serv. Forest Prod. Lab. Mimeo. 1329, 6 p.

(899) ———, Wood, L. W., and Gerry, Eloise.
1943. "Black streak" in western hemlock: Its characteristics and influence
on strength. USDA Forest Serv. Forest Prod. Lab. Mimeo. 1500,
16 p.

(900) McAlpine, Robert G.
   1961. *Hypoxylon tinctor* associated with a canker on American sycamore trees in Georgia. U.S. Dep. Agr. Plant Dis. Rep. 45: 196–198.

(901) ———.
   1961. Yellow-poplar seedlings intolerant to flooding. J. Forest. 59: 566–568.

(902) McCabe, Robert A., and Labisky, Ronald L.
   1959. Leader forking of red and white pines in plantations. J. Forest. 57: 94–97.

(903) McCain, Arthur H.
   1963. New or unusual hosts of *Verticillium albo-atrum*. U.S. Dep. Agr. Plant Dis. Rep. 47: 233.

(904) McCallum, A. W.
   1920. *Napicladium tremulae*. A new disease of the poplar. (Abstr.) Phytopathology 10: 318.

(905) McCarthy, E. F.
   1933. Yellow-poplar characteristics, growth, and management. U.S. Dep. Agr. Tech. Bull. 356, 58 p.

(906) McDaniel, A. T., and Wilson, C. L.
   1962. A study of symptoms and control of *Phomopsis juniperovora* on Arizona cypress. U.S. Dep. Agr. Plant Dis. Rep. 46: 364–365.

(907) McDermott, R. E.
   1954. Effect of saturated soil on seedling growth of some bottom land hardwood species. Ecology 35: 36–41.

(908) McGuire, J. M.
   1941. The species of *Sebacina* (Tremellales) of temperate North America. Lloydia 4: 1–43.

(909) McIntyre, A. C., and Schnur, G. Luther.
   1936. Effects of drought on oak forests. Penn. State Coll. School Agr. and Exp. Sta. Bull. 325, 43 p.

(910) McKay, Hazel H.
   1967. Cultural studies of *Polyporus meliae* and two similar species. Mycologia 59: 1050–1058.

(911) McKee, Herbert C.
   1964. Air pollution and its effect on trees. 40th Int. Shade Tree Conf. Proc. 1964: 149–163.

(912) McKellar, A. D.
   1942. Ice damage to slash pine, longleaf pine, and loblolly pine plantations in the Piedmont section of Georgia. J. Forest. 40: 794–797.

(913) McMinn, R. G.
   1960. Water relations and forest distribution in the Douglas-fir region on Vancouver Island. Can. Dep. Agr. Publ. 1091, 71 p.

(914) ———.
   1963. Characteristics of Douglas-fir root systems. Can. J. Bot. 41: 105–122.

(915) ———.
   1965. Further observations on pole blight of white pine. Can. Dep. Forest. Bimo. Progr. Rep. 21(6): 3.

(916) McQuilkin, William Everett.
   1935. Root development of pitch pine, with some comparative observations on shortleaf pine. J. Agr. Res. 51: 983–1016.

(917) Maini, J. S., and Dance, B. W.
   1965. Temperature relationships of a blight attributed to *Fusarium solani* (Mart.) Sacc. on trembling aspen suckers. Can. Dep. Forest. Bimo. Progr. Rep. 21(2): 2–3.

(918) Major, Randolph T.
   1967. The gingko, the most ancient living tree. Science 157(3794): 1270–1273.

560

(919) ———, Marchini, P., and Sproston, T.
1960. Isolation from *Gingko biloba* L. of an inhibitor of fungus growth. J. Biol. Chem. 235: 3298–3299.

(920) Maloy, Otis C., Jr.
1961. Advance of rot caused by *Fomes pini* in mature western white pine. Northwest Sci. 35: 83–90.

(921) ———.
1963. Sporulation and sporophore survival of *Echinodontium tinctorium*. U.S. Dep. Agr. Plant Dis. Rep. 47: 627–631.

(922) ———.
1968. Decay fungi in young grand fir. U.S. Dep. Agr. Plant Dis. Rep. 52: 489–492.

(923) ———, and Gross, Henry L.
1963. Decay in young grand fir. J. Forest. 61: 850–853.

(924) Manion, Paul D., and French, D. W.
1967. *Nectria galligena* and *Ceratocystis fimbriata* cankers of aspen in Minnesota. Forest Sci. 13: 23–28.

(925) Manning, W. J., and Crossan, D. F.
1966. Variation in degree of pathogenicity of isolates of *Phytophthora cinnamomi* to cultivars of *Taxus*. U.S. Dep. Agr. Plant Dis. Rep. 50: 84–87.

(926) Marks, G. C., Berbee, J. G., and Riker, A. J.
1965. *Colletotrichum* shoot blight of poplars. Forest Sci. 11: 204–215.

(927) Marshall, Rush P.
1948. A white root rot which merits study as a possible cause of white pine blight. Sci. Tree Topics 1: 66–68. (Published by Bartlett Tree Res. Lab., Stamford, Conn.)

(928) ———, and Waterman, Alma M.
1948. Common diseases of important shade trees. U.S. Dep. Agr. Farmers' Bull. 1987, 53 p.

(929) Martindale, Donald L.
1958. Silvical characteristics of sweetgum. USDA Forest Serv. Southeast. Forest Exp. Sta. Pap. 90, 14 p.

(930) Martinez, A. P.
1961. *Sphaerophragmium* rust discovered in Florida on *Albizzia lebbeck* (L.) Benth. U.S. Dep. Agr. Plant Dis. Rep. 45: 560–561.

(931) Marx, D. H., and Davey, C. B.
1967. Ectotrophic mycorrhizae as deterrents to pathogenic root infections. Nature 213(5081): 1139.

(932) Massee, George.
1910. Diseases of cultivated plants and trees. 602 p. New York: The Macmillan Co.

(933) Mathre, D. E.
1965. Survey of *Ceratocystis* spp. associated with bark beetles in California. Pathogenicity of *Ceratocystis ips* and *Ceratocystis minor* to *Pinus ponderosa*. (Abstr.) Rev. Appl. Mycol. 44: 167.

(934) Matthews, F. R.
1962. Pitch canker-tip moth damage association on slash pine seedlings. J. Forest. 60: 825–826.

(935) ———.
1964. Some aspects of the biology and the control of southern cone rust. J. Forest. 62: 881–884.

(936) ———, and McLintock, Thomas F.
1958. Effects of fungicides on pollen germination of slash and longleaf pine. USDA Forest Serv. Southeast. Forest Exp. Sta. Res. Notes 122, 2 p.

(937) ———, and Maloy, Otis C.
1960. What to do about cone rust. Forest Farmer 19(4): 8, 14–15.

(938) Maul, David C.
1958. Silvical characteristics of white fir. USDA Forest Serv. Calif. Forest and Range Exp. Sta. Tech. Pap. 25, 22 p.

(939) May, Curtis.
1961. Diseases of shade and ornamental maples. U.S. Dep. Agr. Handb. 211, 22 p.

(940) ———, and Gravatt, G. F.
1931. The Dutch elm disease. U.S. Dep. Agr. Circ. 170, 10 p.

(941) ———, and Gravatt, G. F.
1937. Two native vascular diseases of eastern hardwoods. USDA Div. Forest Pathol. Tree Pest Leafl. 19, 4 p.

(942) ———, Walter, J. M., and Mook, P. V.
1941. Rosy canker of London plane associated with illuminating-gas injury. Phytopathology 31: 349–351.

(943) Meinecke, E. P.
1916. Forest pathology in forest regulation. U.S. Dep. Agr. Bull. 275, 63 p.

(944) ———.
1928. A report upon the effect of excessive tourist travel on the California redwood parks. Calif. Dep. Natur. Resources, Div. of Parks, 20 p.

(945) ———.
1929. Quaking aspen. A study in applied forest pathology. U.S. Dep. Agr. Tech. Bull. 155, 34 p.

(946) Melin, Elias, Nillson, Harald, and Hacskaylo, Edward.
1958. Translocation of cations to seedlings of *Pinus virginiana* through mycorrhizal mycelium. Bot. Gaz. 119: 243–246.

(947) Menninger, Edwin A.
1949. Evergreen trees for street planting in warm regions. *From* Florida State Hort. Soc. Proc. 1949, 8 p.

(948) ———.
1964. December 1962 cold damage in Florida. The Amer. Hort. Mag. 43(1): 620.

(949) Mericle, L. W., Mericle, R. P., and Sparrow, A. H.
1962. Cumulative radiation damage in oak trees. Radiat. Bot. 2: 265–271.

(950) Merkel, E. P.
1958. *Dioryctria* cone moth attack as related to cone rust of slash pine in north Florida. J. Forest. 56: 651.

(951) Merrill, W.
1967. The oak wilt epidemics in Pennsylvania and West Virginia: an analysis. Phytopathology 57: 1206–1210.

(952) ———, and French, D. W.
1964. Decay of wood by *Alternaria* and *Penicillium*. Phytopathology 54: 867–868.

(953) Merz, Robert W.
1957. Silvical characteristics of Ohio buckeye. USDA Forest Serv. Central States Forest Exp. Sta. Misc. Release 16, 12 p.

(954) ———.
1957. Silvical characteristics of shellbark hickory. USDA Forest Serv. Central States Forest Exp. Sta. Misc. Release 18, 14 p.

(955) Metcalf, Woodbridge.
(n. d.) Interesting trees in California. Univ. Calif. Agr. Ext. Serv. Unnumbered release, 32 p.

(956) Meyer, Walter H., and Hayward, Stanton B.
1936. Effect of increment boring on Douglas-fir. J. Forest. 34: 867–869.

(957) Middleton, John T.
1943. The taxonomy, host range, and geographic distribution of the genus *Pythium*. Mem. Torrey Bot. Club 20: 1–171.

(958) Mielke, J. L.
1935. Rodents as a factor in reducing aecial sporulation of *Cronartium ribicola*. J. Forest. 33: 994–1003.

(959) ———.
1943. White pine blister rust in western North America. Yale Univ. Forest. Sch. Bull. 52, 155 p.

(960) ———.
1950. Rate of deterioration of beetle-killed Engelmann spruce. J. Forest. 48: 882–888.

(961) ———.
1952. The rust fungus *Cronartium filamentosum* in Rocky Mountain pondersoa pine. J. Forest. 50: 365–373.

(962) ———.
1956. The rust fungus (*Cronartium stalactiforme*) in lodgepole pine. J. Forest. 54: 518–521.

(963) ———.
1957. Aspen leaf blight in the Intermountain region. USDA Forest Serv. Intermount. Forest and Range Exp. Sta. Res. Note 42, 5 p.

(964) ———.
1957. The yellow witches' broom of subalpine fir in the Intermountain region. USDA Forest Serv. Intermount. Forest and Range Exp. Sta. Res. Note 47, 5 p.

(965) ———.
1959. Infection experiments with *Septogloeum gillii*, a fungus parasitic on dwarfmistletoe. J. Forest. 57: 925–926.

(966) ———.
1961. Comandra blister rust. USDA Forest Serv. Forest Pest Leafl. 62, 7 p.

(967) Miksche, J. P., Sparrow, A. H., and Rogers, A. P.
1961. Effects of chronic gamma irradiation on the apical meristems of *Pinus strobus* and *Taxus media*. (Abstr.) Amer. J. Bot. 48: 529.

(968) Milbrath, J. A.
1940. *Coryneum* blight of Oriental arborvitae caused by *Coryneum berckmanii*, n. sp. Phytopathology 30: 592–602.

(969) ———.
1966. Stony pit of pear in Oregon. Oregon State Univ. Agr. Exp. Sta. Tech. Bull. 93, 23 p.

(970) Miller, Douglas R.
1968. *Bifusella linearis* found on both limber and whitebark pine in California. U.S. Dep. Agr. Plant Dis. Rep. 52: 305.

(971) ———, Kimmey, James W., and Fowler, Marvin E.
1959. White pine blister rust. USDA Forest Serv. Forest Pest Leafl. 36. 8 p.

(972) Miller, Frank J.
1938. The influence of mycorrhizae on the growth of shortleaf pine seedlings. J. Forest. 36: 526–527.

(973) Miller, Harold W.
1946. A new disease of Russianolive in the Pacific Northwest. J. Forest. 44: 118–120.

(974) Miller, Julian H.
1941. The Ascomycetes of Georgia. U.S. Dep. Agr. Plant Dis. Rep. Suppl. 131: 31–93.

(975) ———.
1941. Georgia Pyrenomycetes. II. Mycologia 33: 74–81.

(976) ———.
1950. A historical sketch of diseases of forest trees in Georgia. U.S. Dep. Agr. Plant Dis. Rep. Suppl. 191: 98–101.

(977) ———.
1957. *Elsinoë* on southern red oak. Mycologia 49: 277–279.

(978) ———.
1961. A monograph of the world species of *Hypoxylon*. 158 p. Athens: Univ. of Georgia Press.

(979) ———, and Jenkins, Anna E.
1955. A new species of *Elsinoë* on southern magnolia. Mycologia 47: 104–108.

(980) ———, and Thompson, G. E.
1940. Georgia Pyrenomycetes. I. Mycologia 32: 1–15.

(981) ———, and Wolf, Frederick A.
1936. A leaf-spot disease of honey locust caused by a new species of *Linospora*. Mycologia 28: 171–180.

(982) Miller, J. Kyle.
1935. A new species of *Keithia* on red cedar. J. Elisha Mitchell Sci. Soc. 51: 167–171.

(983) ———.
1943. *Fomes annosus* and red cedar. J. Forest. 41: 37–40.

(984) Miller, L. W.
1935. The Hydnaceae of Iowa. IV. The genera *Steccherinum, Auriscalpium, Hericium, Dentinum* and *Calodon*. Mycologia 27: 357–373.

(985) Miller, Orson K., Jr.
1960. The distribution of *Fomes annosus* (Fries) Karst. in New Hampshire red pine plantations and some observations on its biology. N.H. Forest. and Recreation Comm. Bull. 12, 25 p.

(986) ———.
1960. Red pine mortality from root rot. Fox Forest (New Hampshire) Notes 75, 1 p.

(987) Miller, P. A.
1941. Bleeding canker disease of California trees. Western Shade Tree Conf. Proc. 8: 39–45.

(988) ———.
1942. Powdery mildew of the coast live oak. Nat. Shade Tree Conf. Proc. 18: 358–366.

(989) Miller, Paul R., and Gravatt, G. Flippo.
1952. The sweetgum blight. U.S. Dep. Agr. Plant Dis. Rep. 36: 247–252.

(990) Miller, Thomas, and Kelman, Arthur.
1966. Growth of *Fomes annosus* in roots of suppressed and dominant loblolly pines. Forest Sci. 12: 225–233.

(991) Miller, Vera Mentzer, and Bonar, Lee.
1941. A study of the Perisporiaceae, Capnodiaceae, and some other sooty molds from California. Univ. Calif. Publs. in Bot. 19 (12): 405–427.

(992) Mircetich, S. M., and Zentmyer, George A.
1964. *Rhizoctonia* seed and root rot of avocado. Phytopathology 54: 211–213.

(993) Mix, A. J.
1938. New species of *Taphrina* and new records from western North America. Amer. J. Bot. 26: 44–48.

(994) ———.
1949. A monograph of the genus *Taphrina*. Univ. Kansas Sci. Bull. 33, Pt. I(1) : 3–167.

(995) Molnar, A. C.
1961. An outbreak of *Cronartium comptoniae* on Monterey and Bishop pines on Vancouver Island, British Columbia. U.S. Dep. Agr. Plant Dis. Rep. 45: 854–855.

(996) ———.
1965. Pathogenic fungi associated with a bark beetle on alpine fir. Can. J. Bot. 43: 563–570.

(997) ———, and McMinn, R. G.
1960. The origin of basal scars in the British Columbia interior white pine type. Forest Chron. 36: 50–60.

(998) ———, McMinn, R. G., and Foster, A. T.
1963. Decline and mortality of Douglas-fir in the Interior Wet Belt. Can. Dep. Forest. Forest Entomol. and Pathol. Br. Bimo. Progr. Rep. 19(5) : 3.

(999) ———, and Silver, G. T.
1959. Build-up of *Pullularia pullulans* (deBary) Berkhout within a severe spruce budworm infestation at Babine Lake, British Columbia. Forest. Chron. 35: 227–231.

(1000) ———, and Sivak, B.
1964. *Melampsora* infection of pine in British Columbia. Can. J. Bot. 42: 145–158.

(1001) Mook, Paul V.
1940. Three new locations for the sycamore (planetree) disease. U.S. Dep. Agr. Plant Dis. Rep. 24: 205–206.

(1002) ———, and Eno, Harold G.
1956. Relation of heart rots to mortality of red spruce in the Green Mountain National Forest. USDA Forest Serv. Northeast. Forest Exp. Sta. Forest Res. Notes 59, 2 p.

(1003) Moore, Agnes Ellis. Editor.
1957. Bibliography of forest disease research in the Department of Agriculture. U.S. Dep. Agr. Misc. Publ. 725, 186 p.

(1004) Morrison, Richard H.
1965. A species of *Clitocybe* associated with declining oak and sycamore in California. U.S. Dep. Agr. Plant Rep. 49: 870–871.

(1005) Moss, A. E.
1940. Effect on trees of wind-driven salt water. J. Forest. 38: 421–425.

(1006) Muir, John A.
1967. Occurrence of *Colletotrichum gloeosporioides* on dwarfmistletoe (*Arceuthobium americanum*) in western Canada. U.S. Dep. Agr. Plant Dis. Rep. 51: 798–799.

(1007) Murphy, Louis S.
1917. The red spruce—its growth and management. U.S. Dep. Agr. Bull. 544, 100 p.

(1008) Myren, Donald T.
1964. Insects and fungi associated with *Cronartium fusiforme*-infected tissue and comparisons of the strength of infected and healthy wood. (Abstr.) Phytopathology 54: 902.

(1009) (a) Nair, V. M. G., and Kuntz, J. E.
1963. Wound susceptibility of bur oaks to artificial inoculation by *Ceratocystis fagacearum*. Univ. Wisc. Forest Res. Notes 93, 5 p.
    (b) ———, and Kuntz, J. E.
1963. Wound susceptibility in bur oaks to natural infection by *Ceratocystis fagacearum*. Univ. Wisc. Forest Res. Notes 94, 3 p.

    (c) ———, and Kuntz, J. E.
    1963. Mat formation in bur oaks infected with *Ceratocystis fagacearum*.
        Univ. Wisc. Forest Res. Notes 95, 3 p.
    (d) ———, and Beckman, C. H.
    1963. Inoculum load versus incubation periods and incidence of oak wilt.
        Univ. Wisc. Forest Res. Notes 96, 6 p.
    (e) ———, and Kuntz, J. E.
    1963. Seasonal susceptibility of bur oaks to artificial inoculation with the
        oak wilt fungus, *Ceratocystis fagacearum*. Univ. Wisc. Forest
        Res. Notes 97, 4 p.

(1010) Nattrass, R. M., Booth, C., and Sutton, B. C.
    1963. *Rhynchosphaeria cupressi* sp. nov., the causal organism of *Cupressus* canker in Kenya. Brit. Mycol. Soc. Trans. 46: 102–106.

(1011) Neely, Dan.
    1968. The somatic pressure cushion of *Gnomonia platani*. Mycologia 60: 84–89.

(1012) ———, and Himelick, E. B.
    1961. Additional juniper hosts of cedar-apple and cedar-hawthorn rusts. U.S. Dep. Agr. Plant Dis. Rep. 45: 351.

(1013) ———, and Himelick, E. B.
    1963. *Aesculus* species susceptible to leaf blotch. U.S. Dep. Agr. Plant Dis. Rep. 47: 170.

(1014) ———, and Himelick, E. B.
    1963. Temperature and sycamore anthracnose severity. U.S. Dep. Agr. Plant Dis. Rep. 47: 171–175.

(1015) ———, and Himelick, E. B.
    1965. Nomenclature of the sycamore anthracnose fungus. Mycologia 57: 834–837.

(1016) Nelson, Ralph M.
    1931. Decay in loblolly pine on the Atlantic Coastal Plain. *In* Selective logging in the loblolly pine-hardwood forests of the Middle Atlantic Coastal Plain with special reference to Virginia. Virginia Forest Serv. Publ. 43: 58–59.

(1017) ———.
    1934. Effect of bluestain fungi on southern pines attacked by bark beetles. Phytopathol. Zeitschrift 7: 327–353.

(1018) ———.
    1940. Vigorous young yellow-poplar trees can recover from injury by *Nectria* cankers. J. Forest. 38: 587–588.

(1019) ———.
    1952. Observations on heat tolerance of southern pine needles. USDA Forest Serv. Southeast. Forest Exp. Sta. Pap. 14, 6 p.

(1020) ———, Sims, Ivan H., and Abell, Margaret S.
    1933. Basal fire wounds on some Southern Appalachian hardwoods. J. Forest. 31: 829–837.

(1021) Nelson, Thomas C.
    1951. A reproduction study of northern white-cedar. Mich. Dep. Conserv., 100 p.

(1022) ———.
    1959. Silvical characteristics of mockernut hickory. USDA Forest Serv. Southeast. Forest Exp. Sta. Pap. 105, 10 p.

(1023) ———.
    1960. Silvical characteristics of bitternut hickory. USDA Forest Serv. Southeast. Forest Exp. Sta. Pap. 111, 9 p.

(1024) ———.
    1961. Silvical characteristics of shagbark hickory. USDA Forest Serv. Southeast. Forest Exp. Sta. Pap. 135, 11 p.

566

(1025) ———.
1961. Silvical characteristics of pignut hickory. USDA Forest Serv. Southeast. Forest Exp. Sta. Pap. 137, 10 p.

(1026) ———.
1965. Silvical characteristics of the commercial hickories. USDA Forest Serv. Southeast. Forest Exp. Sta. Hickory Task Force Rep. 10, 16 p.

(1027) Newhook, F. J.
1962. Cypress canker and root rot: two serious fungous diseases of conifers. New Zeal. J. Agr. 104: 151–153.

(1028) Newton, Michael.
1963. Some herbicide effects on potted Douglas-fir and ponderosa pine seedlings. J. Forest. 61: 674–676.

(1029) Nicholls, T. H., Van Arsdel, E. P., and Patton, R. F.
1965. Red pine needle rust disease in the Lake States. U.S. Dep. Agr. Forest Serv. Res. Note LS–58, 4 p.

(1030) Nichols, Carl W., Blanc, F. L., Millecan, A. A., and Barbe, G. Douglas.
1965. A new explanation of the spread of pear psylla and pear decline virus in California. Calif. Dep. Agr. Bull. 54: 133–144.

(1031) Nichols, James O.
1968. Oak mortality in Pennsylvania: A ten-year study. J. Forest. 66: 681–694.

(1032) Nichols, Lester P.
1964. Maple canker in Pennsylvania. Arborist's News 29: 93–94.

(1033) Nickle, W. R.
1960. Nematodes associated with the rootlets of western white pine in northern Idaho. U.S. Dep. Agr. Plant Dis. Rep. 44: 470–471.

(1034) Nienstaedt, Hans.
1957. Silvical characteristics of white spruce (Picea glauca). USDA Forest Serv. Lake States Forest Exp. Sta. Pap. 55, 23 p.

(1035) Niering, W. A., Whittaker, R. H., and Lowe, C. H.
1963. The saguaro: a population in relation to environment. Science 142(3588): 15–23.

(1036) Nighswander, J. E.
1962. High water table damage to jack pine in northeastern Alberta. Can. Dep. Forest. Forest Entomol. and Pathol. Br. Bimo. Progr. Rep. 18(2): 3–4.

(1037) ———, and Patton, Robert F.
1965. The epidemiology of the jack pine—oak gall rust (Cronartium quercuum) in Wisconsin. Can. J. Bot. 43: 1561–1581.

(1038) Nobles, Mildred K.
1948. Studies in forest pathology. VI. Identification of cultures of wood-rotting fungi. Can. J. Res. C, 26: 281–431.

(1039) ———.
1953. Studies in wood-inhabiting Hymenomycetes. I. Odontia bicolor. Can. J. Bot. 31: 745–749.

(1040) Nordin, Vidar J.
1954. Forest pathology in relation to the management of lodgepole pine in Alberta. Forest. Chron. 30: 299–306.

(1041) ———.
1954. Studies in forest pathology. XIII. Decay in sugar maple in the Ottawa-Huron and Algoma Extension Forest region of Ontario. Can. J. Bot. 32: 221–258.

(1042) ———.
1956. Heart rots in relation to the management of spruce in Alberta. Forest. Chron. 32: 79–84.

567

(1043) ————.
1957. Diseases of lodgepole pine in Alberta. Can. Dep. Agr. Forest Biol. Div., Calgary, Alberta. [Unpublished.]

(1044) ————.
1958. Basal fire scars and the occurrence of decay in lodgepole pine. Forest. Chron. 34: 257–265.

(1045) ————.
1962. Forest diseases of lodgepole pine in Alberta. *In* Entomology and pathology of lodgepole pine in Alberta. Can. Dep. Forest. Bull. 127: 87–97.

(1046) ————, and Cafley, J. D.
1950. The effect of decay on recoverable volume in hard maple in Ontario. Forest. Chron. 26: 1–7.

(1047) Offord, H. R.
1963. Diseases of Monterey pine in native stands of California and in plantations of western North America. USDA Forest Serv. Pacific Southwest Forest and Range Exp. Sta. [unpublished].

(1048) Ohman, John H.
1966. *Scleroderris lagerbergii* Gremmen: the cause of dieback and mortality of red and jack pines in upper Michigan plantations. U.S. Dep. Agr. Plant Dis. Rep. 50: 402–405.

(1049) ————, and Kessler, K. J., Jr.
1963. Current status of the sapstreak disease of sugar maple in the Lake States. U.S. Dep. Agr. Forest Serv. Res. Note LS–10, 4 p.

(1050) ————, and Kessler, K. J., Jr.
1964. White trunk rot of hardwoods. USDA Forest Serv. Forest Pest Leafl. 88, 7 p.

(1051) ————, and Kessler, K. J., Jr.
1964. Black bark as an indicator of bird peck defect in sugar maple. USDA Forest Serv. Res. Pap. LS–14, 8 p.

(1052) ————, and Spike, A. Bruce.
1966. Effect of staining caused by sapstreak disease on sugar maple log and lumber values. USDA Forest Serv. Res. Note NC–12, 4 p.

(1053) Olson, A. J.
1941. A root disease of Jeffrey and ponderosa pine reproduction. Phytopathology 31: 1063–1077.

(1054) Olson, D. S.
1952. Underground damage from logging in the western white pine type. J. Forest. 50:. 460–462.

(1055) Oosting, H. J., and Billings, W. D.
1943. The red fir forest of the Sierra Nevada: *Abietum magnificae*. Ecol. Monog. 13: 260–274.

(1056) Osburn, M. R., Phillips, A. M., Pierce, William C., and Cole, John R.
1954. Insects and diseases of the pecan and their control. U.S. Dep. Agr. Farmers' Bull. 1829, 56 p.

(1057) ————, Pierce, William C., and others.
1963. Controlling insects and diseases of the pecan. U.S. Dep. Agr. Handb. 240, 52 p.

(1058) Ouellett, Charles-Eugène, and Pomerleau, René.
1965. Recherches sur la résistance de l'Orme d'Amérique au *Ceratocystis ulmi*. Can. J. Bot. 43: 85–96.

(1059) Ouelette, G. B.
1963. Frost injuries on branches of aspen. Can. Dep. Forest. Forest Entomol. and Pathol. Br. Bimo. Progr. Rep. 19(5): 1.

(1060) ———.
1965. *Cronartium stalactiforme* on *Pinus banksiana* (jack pine) in Quebec. U.S. Dep. Agr. Plant Dis. Rep. 49: 909.

(1061) ———.
1966. On *Thyriopsis halepensis* and its conidial stage. Mycologia 58: 322–325.

(1062).
1966. *Coleosporium viburni* on jack pine and its relationship with *C. asterum*. Can. J. Bot. 44: 1117–1120.

(1063) ———, and Bard, G.
1962. Observations on a canker and resinosis of white and Norway spruce. Can. Dep. Forest. Forest Entomol. and Pathol. Br. Bimo. Progr. Rep. 18(2): 2.

(1064) ———, and Bard, G.
1963. Factors predisposing sugar maple to premature leaf coloration and leaf fall. Can. Dep. Forest. Forest Entomol. and Pathol. Br. Bimo. Progr. Rep. 19(6): 1.

(1065) ———, and Bard, G.
1966. A perennial canker of balsam fir on Anticosti Island. U.S. Dep. Agr. Plant Dis. Rep. 50: 722–724.

(1066) ———, and Magasi, L. P.
1966. *Lophomerum*, a new genus of Hypodermataceae. Mycologia 58: 275–280.

(1067) Overholts, Lee Oras.
1953. The Polyporaceae of the United States, Alaska, and Canada. 466 p. Ann Arbor: Univ. Mich. Press.

(1068) Paclt, J.
1951. Fungus and related diseases of the genus *Catalpa* (Bignoniaceae). Sydowia 5: 160–168.

(1069) Pady, S. M.
1942. Distribution patterns in *Melampsorella* in the National Forests and Parks of the Western States. Mycologia 34: 606–627.

(1070) Paine, Lee A.
1960. Studies in forest pathology. XXII. Nutrient deficiencies and climatic factors causing low volume production and active deterioration in white spruce. Can. Dep. Agr. Publ. 1067, 29 p.

(1071) Pandila, Madan, Mohan.
1967. Cultural studies of *Fomes fraxinophilus* (Peck) Cooke and *Fomes ellisianus* Anderson. Diss. Abstr. 27(9): B: 2957.

(1072) Pantidou, Maria E., and Darker, G. D.
1963. The species of *Didymascella* on *Juniperus*. Mycologia 55: 415–420.

(1073) ———, and Korf, R. P.
1954. A revision of the genus *Keithia*. Mycologia 46: 386–388.

(1074) Parker, A. K.
1957. The nature of the association of *Europhium trinacriforme* with pole blight lesions. Can. J. Bot. 35: 845–856.

(1075) ———.
1959. An unexplained decline in vigor of lodgepole pine. Forest. Chron. 35: 298–303.

(1076) ———, and Collis, D. G.
1966. *Dothistroma* needle blight of pines in British Columbia. Forest. Chron. 42: 160–161.

(1077) ———, and Johnson, A. L. S.
1960. Decay associated with logging injury to spruce and balsam in the Prince George region of British Columbia. Forest. Chron. 36: 30–45.

(1078) Parker, Johnson.
1950. The effects of flooding on the transpiration and survival of some southeastern forest tree species. Plant Physiol. 25: 453–460.

(1079) ———.
1955. Annual trends and cold hardiness of pondersoa pine and grand fir. Ecology 36: 377–380.

(1080) ———.
1963. Cold resistance in woody plants. Bot. Rev. 29: 124–201.

(1081) ———.
1965. Physiological diseases of trees and shrubs. Advancing Frontiers of Plant Sci. 12: 97–248.

(1082) Parmelee, J. A.
1965. The genus *Gymnosporangium* in eastern Canada. Can. J. Bot. 43: 239–267.

(1083) Parmeter, J. R., Jr., Bega, R. V., and Hood, J. R.
1960. Epidemic leaf-blighting of California-laurel. U.S. Dep. Agr. Plant Dis. Rep. 44: 669–671.

(1084) ———, Bega, R. V., and Neff, T.
1962. A chlorotic decline of ponderosa pine in southern California. U.S. Dep. Agr. Plant Dis. Rep. 46: 269–273.

(1085) ———, Hood, J. R., and Scharpf, R. F.
1959. *Colletotrichum* blight of dwarfmistletoe. Phytopathology 49: 812–815.

(1086) ———, and Scharpf, R. F.
1963. Dwarfmistletoe on red fir and white fir in California. J. Forest. 61: 371–374.

(1087) Parris, G. K.
1966. Death of honeylocust in Mississippi associated with *Polyporus lucidus* Fr. U.S. Dep. Agr. Plant Dis. Rep. 50: 243–244.

(1088) ———.
1967. "Needle curl" of loblolly pine. U.S. Dep. Agr. Plant Dis. Rep. 51: 805–806.

(1089) Patton, R. F., and Riker, A. J.
1954. Needle droop and needle blight of red pine. J. Forest. 52: 412–418.

(1090) ———, and Riker, A. J.
1959. Artificial inoculations of pine and spruce trees with *Armillaria mellea*. Phytopathology 49: 615–622.

(1091) Peace, T. R.
1962. Pathology of trees and shrubs. 753 p. Oxford: Oxford University Press.

(1092) Pearson, G. A.
1936. Some observations on the reaction of pine seedlings to shade. Ecology 17: 270–276.

(1093) Pease, Roger W.
1953. Growing flowering dogwood from softwood cuttings. The Nat. Hort. Mag. 32: 71–73.

(1094) Penfold, A. R., and Willis, J. L.
1961. The Eucalypts. 551 p. New York: Interscience Publishers, Inc.

(1095) Perala, Donald A., and Sucoff, Edward.
1965. Diagnosing potassium deficiency in American elm, silver maple, Russianolive, hackberry, and box elder. Forest Sci. 11: 347–352.

(1096) Percival, W. Clement.
1933. A contribution to the biology of *Fomes pini* (Thore) Lloyd (*Trametes pini* [Thore] Fries). N.Y. State Coll. Forest. (Syracuse) Tech. Publ. 40, 72 p.

(1097) Peterson, Glenn W.
1962. Root lesion nematode infestation and control in a plains forest tree nursery. USDA Forest Serv. Rocky Mount. Forest and Range Exp. Sta. Res. Note 75, 2 p.

(1098) ———.
1965. Field survival and growth of *Phomopsis*-blighted and non-blighted eastern redcedar planting stock. U.S. Dep. Agr. Plant Dis. Rep. 49: 121–123.

(1099) ———.
1965. *Dothistroma* needle blight of Austrian pine: Infection and control. U.S. Dep. Agr. Plant Dis. Rep. 49: 124–126.

(1100) ———, and Wysong, David S.
1968. *Diplodia* tip blight of pines in the central Great Plains: Damage and control. U.S. Dep. Agr. Plant Dis. Rep. 52: 359–360.

(1101) ———, and Wysong, David S.
1968. *Cercospora* blight of junipers: Damage and control. U.S. Dep. Agr. Plant Dis. Rep. 52: 361–362.

(1102) Peterson, Roger S.
1960. Western gall rust on hard pines. USDA Forest Serv. Forest Pest Leafl. 50, 8 p.

(1103) ———.
1961. Host alternation of spruce broom rust. Science 134(3477) : 468–469.

(1104) ———.
1962. Comandra blister rust in the central Rocky Mountains. USDA Forest Serv. Rocky Mount. Forest and Range Exp. Sta. Res. Notes 79, 6 p.

(1105) ———.
1963. Effects of broom rusts on spruce and fir. USDA Forest Serv. Res. Pap. INT–7, 10 p.

(1106) ———.
1964. Fir broom rust. USDA Forest Serv. Forest Pest Leafl. 87, 7 p.

(1107) ———.
1966. Limb rust damage to pine. USDA Forest Serv. Res. Pap. INT–31, 10 p.

(1108) ———.
1966. On sweetfern blister rust. U.S. Dep. Agr. Plant Dis. Rep. 50: 744–746

(1109) ———.
1967. Studies of juniper rusts in the West. Madroño 19: 79–91.

(1110) ———.
1967. The *Peridermium* species on pine stems. Torrey Bot. Club Bull. 94: 511–542.

(1111) ———.
1968. Limb rust of pine: The causal fungi. Phytopathology 58: 309–315.

(1112) ———, and Shurtleff, R. G., Jr.
1965. Mycelium of limb rust fungi. Amer. J. Bot. 52: 519–525.

(1113) Phillips, Arthur M., Large, John R., and Cole, John R.
1964. Insects and diseases of the pecan in Florida. Fla. Agr. Exp. Sta. Bull. 619A, 87 p.

(1114) Phipps, Howard M.
1964. Leaf blight of boxelder attributed to 2, 4–D spray drift. USDA Forest Serv. Res. Note LS–49, 2 p.

(1115) Pierce, Roy G., and Hartley, Carl.
1916. Horse-chestnut anthracnose. Phytopathology 6: 93.

(1116) Pirone, P. P.
    1941. Treating chlorotic pin oaks by trunk injections and soil treatments.
        (Abstr.) Phytopathology 31: 18.

(1117) ———.
    1942: A new disease of sweet gum. Amer. Forests 48: 130–131.

(1118) ———.
    1957. *Ganoderma lucidum*, a parasite of shade trees. Torrey Bot. Club.
        Bull. 84: 424–428.

(1119) ———.
    1959. Tree maintenance. Ed. 3, 436 p. New York: Oxford University
        Press.

(1120) ———, and Carter, J. C.
    1966. *Phomopsis acerina* on Norway maple. Mycologia 58: 325–328.

(1121) Plakidas, A. G.
    1942. *Venturia acerina*, the perfect stage of *Cladosporium humile*. My-
        cologia 34: 27–37.

(1122) Pomerleau, René.
    1934. Notes sur le *Taphrina ulmi*. Naturaliste Canadien, December 1934:
        305–308.

(1123) ———.
    1938. Recherches sur le *Gnomonia ulmea* (Schw.) Thüm. (Biologie—Ecol-
        ogie—Cytologie). Contrib. Inst. Bot. Univ. Montreal 31, 139 p.

(1124) ———.
    1941. [Two diseases of conifers in the nursery.] La Forêt Quebeçoise
        3(9): 13–22.

(1125) ———.
    1962. Severe winter browning of red spruce in southeastern Quebec. Can.
        Dep. Forest. Bimo. Progr. Rep. 18(6): 3.

(1126) ———, and Etheridge, D. E.
    1961. A bluestain in balsam-fir. Mycologia 53: 155–170.

(1127) ———, and Pelletier, Rachel.
    1967. A new technique to determine the presence of *Ceratocystis ulmi*
        (Buis.) C. Moreau in fresh elm leaves, shoots and woods. Le
        Naturaliste Canadien 94: 59–62.

(1128) ———, and Ray, R. G.
    1957. Occurrence and effects of summer frost in a conifer plantation. Can.
        Dep. North. Aff. and Natur. Resources, Forest. Br., Forest Res.
        Div. Tech. Note 51, 15 p.

(1129) Porter, C. L.
    1944. A leaf spot of *Gingko biloba*. Indiana Acad. Sci. Proc. 53(1943):
        78–80.

(1130) Potter, George F., and Crane, Harley L.
    1957. Tung production. U.S. Dep. Agr. Farmers' Bull. 2031, 35 p.

(1131) Povah, Alfred H. W.
    1921. An attack of poplar canker following fire injury. Phytopathology
        11: 157–165.

(1132) Powell, J. M., and Morf, W.
    1965. The occurrence of *Tuberculina maxima* Rost. on *Cronartium* rust
        infected trees in Alberta. Can. Dep. Forest. Forest Entomol. and
        Pathol. Br. Bimo. Progr. Rep. 21(1): 3.

(1133) Powers, Harry, R. Jr., and Boyce, John S. Jr.
    1963. Annosus root rot in eastern pine. USDA Forest Serv. Forest Pest
        Leafl. 76, 7 p.

(1134) ———, Hepting, G. H., and Stegall, W. A., Jr.
    1967. Comandra rust on loblolly pine in eastern Tennessee. U.S. Dep.
        Agr. Plant Dis. Rep. 51: 4–8.

572

(1135) ——, and Roncadori, R. W.
1966. Teliospore germination and sporidial production by *Cronartium fusiforme*. U.S. Dep. Agr. Plant Dis. Rep. 50: 432–434.

(1136) ——, and Verrall, Arthur F.
1962. A closer look at *Fomes annosus*. Forest Farmer 21(13): 8–9, 16–17.

(1137) Preston, Richard J., Jr.
1940. Rocky Mountain trees. 285 p. Ames, Iowa: Iowa State Coll. Press.

(1138) Punter, David.
1967. *Scleroderris lagerbergii* Gremmen, a new threat to nurseries in northern Ontario. Forest. Chron. 43: 161–164.

(1139) ——, and Cafley, J. D.
1968. Two new hardwood hosts of *Fomes annosus*. U.S. Dep. Agr. Plant Dis. Rep. 52: 692.

(1140) Putnam, J. A., and Bull, Henry.
1932. The trees of the bottom lands of the Mississippi River Delta region. USDA Forest Serv. Southeast. Forest Exp. Sta. Mimeo. Release, 207 p.

(1141) Raabe, Robert D.
1965. Some previously unreported hosts of *Armillaria mellea* in California. U.S. Dep. Agr. Plant Dis. Rep. 49: 812.

(1142) ——.
1967. Plants resistant or susceptible to *Armillaria* root rot. Calif. Agr. Ext. Serv. AXT–6, 6 p.

(1143) Rankin, W. Howard.
1923. Manual of tree diseases. 398 p. New York: The Macmillan Co.

(1144) Rathbun-Gravatt, Annie.
1931. Germination loss of coniferous seeds due to parasites. J. Agr. Res. 42: 71–92.

(1145) Rau, G. J.
1958. A new species of sting nematode. Helminthol. Soc. Wash. Proc. 28: 95–98.

(1146) Ray, W. W.
1936. Pathogenicity and cultural experiments with *Caliciopsis pinea*. Mycologia 28: 201–218.

(1147) Raymond, F. L., and Reid, J.
1961. Dieback of balsam fir in Ontario. Can. J. Bot. 39: 233–251.

(1148) Redmond, D. R.
1954. Variations in development of yellow birch roots in two soil types. Forest. Chron. 30: 401–406.

(1149) ——.
1955. Studies in forest pathology. XV. Rootlets, mycorrhiza, and soil temperature in relation to birch dieback. Can. J. Bot. 33: 595–627.

(1150) ——.
1957. Infection of courts of butt-rotting fungi in balsam-fir. Forest Sci. 3: 15–21.

(1151) ——.
1959. Mortality of rootlets in balsam fir defoliated by the spruce budworm. Forest Sci. 5: 64–69.

(1152) ——, and Robinson, Robena C.
1954. Viability and germination in yellow birch. Forest. Chron. 30: 79–87.

(1153) Reed, George M.
1913. The powdery mildews-Erysiphaceae. Amer. Microscop. Soc. Trans. 32: 219–258.

(1154) Rehder, Alfred.
    1940. Manual of cultivated trees and shrubs hardy in North America. Ed. 2, 996 p. New York: The Macmillan Co.

(1155) Reid, James, and Cain, R. F.
    1962. Studies on the organisms associated with "snow-blight" of conifers in North America. I. A new genus of the Helotiales. Mycologia 54: 194–200.

(1156) ———, and Cain, R. F.
    1962. *Valsa myinda* Cooke and Ellis and *Cryptodiaporthe myinda* sensu Wehmeyer, two distinct species on *Acer*. Can. J. Bot. 40: 837–841.

(1157) ———, and Cain, R. F.
    1962. Studies on the organisms associated with "snow-blight" of conifers in North America. II. Some species of the genera *Phacidium, Lophophacidium, Sarcotrichila,* and *Hemiphacidium.* Mycologia 54: 481–497.

(1158) ———, and Cain, R. F.
    1963. A new genus of the Hemiphacidiaceae. Mycologia 55: 781–785.

(1159) ———, Dance, B. W., and Weir, H. J.
    1963. A microcyclic pine needle rust, new to Ontario. U.S. Dep. Agr. Plant Dis. Rep. 47: 216–217.

(1160) ———, and Funk, A.
    1966. The genus *Atropellis*, and a new genus of the Helotiales associated with branch cankers of western hemlock. Mycologia 58: 417–439.

(1161) Rennerfelt, Erik.
    1948: Investigations of thujaplicin, a fungicidal substance in the heartwood of *Thuja plicata* D. Don. Physiologia Plant. 1: 245–254.

(1162) ———.
    1952. [On root rot attack on Scots pine.] Meddelanden Statens Skogsforskningsinstitut 41(9): 1–40.

(1163) ———.
    1956. The natural resistance to decay of certain conifers. Saertryk ab Friesia 5(3–5): 361–365.

(1164) ———, and Nacht, Gertrud.
    1955. The fungicidal activity of some constituents from heartwood of conifers. Svensk Botanisk Tidskrift 49: 419–432.

(1165) Renshaw, James F., and Doolittle, Warren T.
    1958. Silvical characteristics of yellow-poplar. USDA Forest Serv. Southeast. Forest Exp. Sta. Pap. 89, 18 p.

(1166) Reynolds, J. E., and Milbrath, J. A.
    1962. Comparison of flowering crab apple varieties for fast detection of a common latent virus in apples. U.S. Dep. Agr. Plant Dis. Rep. 46: 243–245.

(1167) Rhoads, Arthur S.
    1945. A comparative study of two closely related root rot fungi, *Clitocybe tabescens* and *Armillaria mellea.* Mycologia 37: 741–766.

(1168) ———.
    1956. The occurrence and destructiveness of *Clitocybe* root rot of woody plants in Florida. Lloydia 19: 193–240.

(1169) Ricard, Jacques L., and Bollen, Walter B.
    1968. Inhibition of *Poria carbonica* by *Scytalidium* sp., an imperfect fungus isolated from Douglas-fir poles. Can. J. Bot. 46: 643–647.

(1170) Riffle, Jerry W.
    1962. Nematodes associated with maple dieback and maple blight. (Abstr.) Phytopathology 52: 749.

(1171) ———.
    1963. *Meloidogyne ovalis* (Nematoda: Heteroderidae), a new species of root knot nematode. Helminthol. Soc. Wash. Proc. 30: 287–292.

(1172) ———.
1968. Plant-parasitic nematodes in marginal *Pinus ponderosa* stands in central New Mexico. U.S. Dep. Agr. Plant Dis. Rep. 52: 52–55.

(1173) ———, and Kuntz, James E.
1966. Nematodes in maple blight and maple dieback areas in Wisconsin. U.S. Dep. Agr. Plant Dis. Rep. 50: 677–681.

(1174) Riley, C. G.
1947. Heart rot of oaks caused by *Polyporus obtusus*. Can. J. Res. C, 25: 181–184.

(1175) ———.
1952. Studies in forest pathology. IX. *Fomes igniarius* decay of poplar. Can. J. Bot. 30: 710–734.

(1176) ———.
1953. Hail damage in forest stands. Forest. Chron. 29: 139–143.

(1177) ———
1953. *Stereum pini* incorrectly reported as cause of decay in lodgepole pine. Forest. Chron. 29: 343.

(1178) ———, and Skolko, A. J.
1942. Rate of deterioration in spruce killed by the European spruce sawfly. Pulp and Paper Mag. June, 4 p.

(1179) Rishbeth, J.
1950. Observations on the biology of *Fomes annosus*, with particular reference to East Anglian pine plantations. Ann. Bot. (London) 14: 365–383.

(1180) Risley, John H., and Silverborg, Savel B.
1958. *Stereum sanguinolentum* on living Norway spruce following pruning. Phytopathology 48: 337–338.

(1181) Rizzi, A. D., Gripp, Russell H., and Ross, Norman W.
1960. Care of a walnut orchard. Univ. Calif. Agr. Ext. Serv. Publ., 12 p.

(1182) Robinson, Gordon P., and Stanford, Leon W.
1945. Defects in California red fir. J. Forest. 43: 439–440.

(1183) Robinson, Lytle W.
1966. Decline of the saguaro. Amer. Forests 72(5): 46, 69.

(1184) Robinson, Robena C.
1962. Blue stain fungi in lodgepole pine (*Pinus contorta* Dougl. var. *latifolia* Engelm.) infested by the mountain pine beetle (*Dendroctonus monticolae* Hopk.) Can. J. Bot. 40: 609–614.

(1185) Robinson-Jeffrey, Robena C., and Loman, A. A.
1963. Fungi isolated in culture from red heartwood stain and advanced decay of lodgepole pine in Alberta. Can. J. Bot. 41: 1371–1375.

(1186) Rocky Mountain Forest and Range Exp. Sta.
1962. Aspen cankers are widespread but not abundant. USDA Forest Serv. Rocky Mount. Forest and Range Exp. Sta. Annu. Rep. 1961: 23–26.

(1187) Roe, E. I.
1949. Sphagnum moss retards black spruce regeneration. USDA Forest Serv. Lake States Forest Exp. Sta. Tech. Note 321, 1 p.

(1188) ———.
1957. Silvical characteristics of tamarack (*Larix laricina*). USDA Forest Serv. Lake States Forest Exp. Sta. Pap. 52, 22 p.

(1189) Roff, J. W.
1964. Hyphal characteristics of certain fungi in wood. Mycologia 56: 799–804.

(1190) Rogerson, Clark T.
1953. Kansas mycological notes: 1951. Kansas Acad. Sci. Trans. 56: 53–57.

(1191) Roll-Hansen, F.
    1967. *Phellinus tremulae* (Bond.) Bond. & Boriss, and *Phellinus igniarius* (L. ex Fr.) Quél. on *Populus tremula L.* Meddeleiser fra Det Norske Skogforsoksvesen 23: 243–263.

(1192) Roncadori, Ronald W.
    1965. A nutritional comparison of some species of *Phytophthora.* Phytopathology 55: 595–599.

(1193) Ross, Eldon W.
    1964. Etiological and developmental studies on a dieback disease of *Fraxinus americana* L. 249 p. (Thesis, Ph.D. Syracuse Univ.)

(1194) ———.
    1964. Cankers associated with ash dieback. Phytopathology 54: 272–275.

(1195) ———.
    1966. Ash dieback, etiological and developmental studies. Syracuse Univ. Coll. Forest. Tech. Publ. 88, 80 p.

(1196) Roth, Elmer R.
    1941. Top rot in snow-damaged yellow poplar and basswood. J. Forest. 39: 60–62.

(1197) ———.
    1943. Effect of invisible decay on deterioration of untreated oak ties and posts. J. Forest. 41: 117–121.

(1198) ———.
    1948. Healing and defects following oak pruning. J. Forest. 46: 500–504.

(1199) ———.
    1950. Discolorations in living yellow-poplar trees. J. Forest. 48: 184–185.

(1200) ———.
    1950. Cankers and decay of oak associated with *Irpex mollis.* U.S. Dep. Agr. Plant Dis. Rep. 34: 347–348.

(1201) ———.
    1951. The viability of spores and mycelium of *Endoconidiophora virescens* on sugar maple lumber. U.S. Dep. Agr. Plant Dis. Rep. 35: 379–381.

(1202) ———.
    1952. Roots of living *Pinus rigida* decayed by *Fomes annosus.* U.S. Dep. Agr. Plant Dis. Rep. 36: 330.

(1203) ———.
    1959. Heart rots of Appalachian hardwoods. USDA Forest Serv. Forest Pest Leafl. 38, 4 p.

(1204) ———, and Copeland, Otis L.
    1957. Uptake of nitrogen and calcium by fertilized shortleaf pine. J. Forest. 55: 281–284.

(1205) ———, and Hepting, George H.
    1943. Origin and development of oak stump sprouts as affecting their likelihood to decay. J. Forest. 41: 27–36.

(1206) ———, and Hepting, George H.
    1943. Wounds and decay caused by removing large companion sprouts of oak. J. Forest. 41: 190–195.

(1207) ———, and Hepting, George H.
    1954. Eradication and thinning tests for *Nectria* and *Strumella* canker control in Maryland. J. Forest. 52: 253–256.

(1208) ———, Hepting, George H., and Toole, E. Richard.
    1959. Sapstreak disease of sugar maple and yellow-poplar in North Carolina. USDA Forest Serv. Southeast. Forest Exp. Sta. Res. Notes 134, 2 p.

(1209) ——, and Sleeth, Bailey.
1939. Butt rot in unburned sprout oak stands. U.S. Dep. Agr. Tech. Bull. 684, 43 p.

(1210) Roth, Lewis F.
1963. *Phytophthora cinnamomi* root rot of Douglas-fir. Phytopathology 53: 1128–1131.

(1211) ——, and Kuhlman, E. George.
1963. Field tests of the capacity of *Phytophthora* root rot to damage Douglas-fir. J. Forest. 61: 199–205.

(1212) ——, and Riker, A. J.
1942. The influence of temperature, moisture, and soil reaction on damping-off of red pine by *Pythium* and *Rhizoctonia*. (Abstr.) Phytopathology 32: 15–16.

(1213) Rudolf, Paul O.
1949. Recovery of winter injured pines. USDA Forest Serv. Lake States Forest Exp. Sta. Tech. Notes 323, 1 p.

(1214) ——.
1957. Silvical characteristics of red pine (*Pinus resinosa*). USDA Forest Serv. Lake States Forest Exp. Sta. Pap. 44, 32 p.

(1215) ——.
1958. Silvical characteristics of jack pine (*Pinus banksiana*). USDA Forest Serv. Lake States Forest Exp. Sta. Pap. 61, 31 p.

(1216) Rudolph, B. A.
1931. *Verticillium* hadromycosis. Hilgardia 5: 197–353.

(1217) Rudolph, Thomas D.
1964. Lammas growth and prolepsis in jack pine in the Lake States. Forest Sci. Monogr. 6, 70 p.

(1218) Ruehle, George D., and Ledin, R. Bruce.
1960. Mango growing in Florida. Univ. Florida Agr. Ext. Serv. Bull. 174, 88 p.

(1219) Ruehle, John L.
1962. Plant-parasitic nematodes associated with shortleaf pine showing symptoms of littleleaf. U.S. Dep. Agr. Plant Dis. Rep. 46: 710–711.

(1220) ——.
1964. Plant-parasitic nematodes associated with pine species in southern forests. U.S. Dep. Agr. Plant Dis. Rep. 48: 60–61.

(1221) ——.
1965. Host range studies of several plant-parasitic nematodes found in southern pine forests. (Abstr.) Nematologica 11: 45.

(1222) ——.
1967. Distribution of plant-parasitic nematodes associated with forest trees of the world. USDA Forest Serv. Southeast. Forest Exp. Sta. Unnumbered release, 156 p.

(1223) ——.
1968. Pathogenicity of sting nematode on sycamore. U.S. Dep. Agr. Plant Dis. Rep. 52: 523–525.

(1224) ——.
1968. Plant-parasitic nematodes associated with southern hardwood and coniferous forest trees. U.S. Dep. Agr. Plant Dis. Rep. 52: 837–839.

(1225) ——, and Sasser, J. N.
1962. The role of plant-parasitic nematodes in stunting of pines in southern plantations. Phytopathology 52: 56–58.

(1226) Rumbold, Caroline T.
1931. Two bluestaining fungi associated with bark-beetle infestation of pines. J. Agr. Res. 45: 847–873.

(1227) ———.
1936. Three bluestaining fungi, including two new species, associated with bark beetles. J. Agr. Res. 52: 419–437.

(1228) ———.
1941. A bluestain fungus, *Ceratostomella montium* n. sp., and some yeasts associated with two species of *Dendroctonus*. J. Agr. Res. 62: 589–601.

(1229) Rupert, Joseph A., and Leach, J. G.
1942. Willow blight in West Virginia. Phytopathology 32: 1095–1096.

(1230) Rusden, P. L.
1962. Edema of *Gingko biloba*. Sci. Tree Topics 2(9): 11–12.

(1231) Rushmore, Francis M.
1961. Silvical characteristics of beech. USDA Forest Serv. Northeast. Forest Exp. Sta. Pap. 161, 26 p.

(1232) Ruth, Robert H.
1958. Silvical characteristics of Sitka spruce. USDA Forest Serv. Pacific Northwest Forest and Range Exp. Sta. Silvical Ser. 8, 19 p.

(1233) ———, and Muerle, Gerhard F.
1958. Silvical characteristics of bigleaf maple. USDA Forest Serv. Pacific Northwest Forest and Range Exp. Sta. Silvical Ser. 13, 10 p.

(1234) Salisbury, P. J.
1954. A review of damping-off of Douglas-fir seedlings in British Columbia. Forest. Chron. 30: 407–410.

(1235) ———.
1955. *Rosellinia herpotrichioides* Hepting and Davidson on Douglas-fir seedlings in British Columbia. Can. Dep. Agr., Forest Biol. Div., Victoria. [Unpublished.]

(1236) Sasser, J. N., Haasis, F. A., and Cannon, T. F.
1966. Pathogenicity of *Meloidogyne* species on *Ilex*. U.S. Dep. Agr. Plant Dis. Rep. 50: 664–668.

(1237) Savile, D. B. O.
1950. North American species of *Chrysomyxa*. Can. J. Res., C, 28: 318–330.

(1238) ———.
1953. Short-season adaptations in the rust fungi. Mycologia 45: 75–87.

(1239) ———.
1955. *Chrysomyxa* in North America—additions and corrections. Can. J. Bot. 33: 487–496.

(1240) Scharpf, Robert F.
1962. Growth rate of the endophytic system of the dwarfmistletoe on Digger pine. USDA Forest Serv. Pacific Southwest Forest and Range Exp. Sta. Res. Note 193, 5 p.

(1241) ———.
1964. Dwarfmistletoe on true firs in California. USDA Forest Serv. Forest Pest Leafl. 89, 7 p.

(1242) ———, and Parmeter, J. R.
1962. Penetration of red fir by the dwarfmistletoe *Arceuthobium campylopdum*. (Abstr.) Phytopathology 52: 750.

(1243) Scheffer, Theodore C.
1936. Progressive effects of *Polyporus versicolor* on the physical and chemical properties of red gum sapwood. U.S. Dep. Agr. Tech. Bull. 527, 46 p.

(1244) ———.
1939. Mineral stain in hard maples and other hardwoods. J. Forest. 37: 578–579.

(1245) ————.
1957. Decay resistance of western redcedar. J. Forest. 55: 434–442.

(1246) ————, and Chapman, A. D.
1934. Prevention of interior brown stain in persimmon sapwood during seasoning. Hardwood Record, Nov., p. 17.

(1247) ————, Englerth, George H., and Duncan, Catherine G.
1949. Decay resistance of seven native oaks. J. Agr. Res. 78: 129–152.

(1248) ————, and Hansbrough, John R.
1942. The significance of the discolorations in aircraft veneers: sweetgum. USDA Forest Serv. Forest Prod. Lab. Mimeo. 1376, 8 p.

(1249) ————, and Hedgcock, George G.
1955. Injury to northwestern forest trees by sulfur dioxide from smelters. U.S. Dep. Agr. Tech. Bull. 1117, 49 p.

(1250) ————, and Hopp, Henry.
1949. Decay resistance of black locust heartwood. U.S. Dep. Agr. Tech. Bull. 984, 37 p.

(1251) ————, and Lindgren, R. M.
1936. The effect of steaming on the durability of unseasoned sap-gum lumber. J. Forest. 34: 147–153.

(1252) ————, and Lindgren, R. M.
1940. Stains of sapwood and sapwood products and their control. U.S. Dep. Agr. Tech. Bull. 714, 124 p.

(1253) Schmidt, R. A., and Fergus, C. L.
1962. Branch canker and die-back of *Quercus prinus* caused by a species of *Botryodiplodia*. (Abstr.) Phytopathology 52: 26–27.

(1254) Schmitz, Henry.
1923. Leaf cast of *Larix occidentalis* by *Hypodermella laricis* Tubeuf in north Idaho. Phytopathology 13: 505–506.

(1255) ————, and Jackson, Lyle W. R.
1927. Heartrot of aspen. With special reference to forest management in Minnesota. Univ. Minn. Agr. Exp. Sta. Tech. Bull. 50, 43 p.

(1256) Schneider, Roswitha, and Paetzholdt, M.
1964. *Ascochyta piniperda* as agent of a shoot dieback of Colorado spruce in nurseries. (Abstr.) Rev. Appl. Mycol. 43: 605–606.

(1257) Schoeneweiss, Donald F.
1965. *Fusicoccum* canker of mountain ash in Illnois. U.S. Dep. Agr. Plant Dis. Rep. 49: 251–252.

(1258) ————.
1966. *Cytospora* canker on thornless honey locust trees. U.S. Dep. Agr. Plant Rep. 50: 13–14.

(1259) Schopmeyer, C. S., and Maloy, Otis C.
1960. Dry face of naval stores pines. USDA Forest Serv. Forest Pest Leafl. 51, 7 p.

(1260) Schread, John C.
1968. Leaf miners and their control. Conn. Agr. Exp. Sta. Bull. 693: 1–15.

(1261) Schreiner, E. J.
1949. Can black walnut poison pines? Penn. Univ. Morris Arboretum Bull. 4: 94–96.

(1262) ————.
1959. Rating poplars for *Melampsora* leaf rust infection. USDA Forest Serv. Northeast. Forest Exp. Sta. Res. Note 90, 3 p.

(1263) Schubert, Gilbert H.
1957. Silvical characteristics of incense-cedar. USDA Forest Serv. Calif. Forest and Range Exp. Sta. Tech. Pap. 18, 14 p.

(1264) ——, Revised by Beetham, N. M.
1962. Silvical characteristics of giant sequoia. USDA Forest Serv. Pacific Southwest Forest and Range Exp. Sta. Tech. Pap. 20 (rev.), 16 p.

(1265) Schuldt, Paul H.
1955. Comparison of anthracnose fungi on oak, sycamore, and other trees. Contrib. Boyce Thompson·Inst. 18(2): 85–107.

(1266) Seaver, Fred J.
1909. The Hypocreales of North America—II. Mycologia 1: 177–207.

(1267) ——.
1915. Observations on *Herpotrichia nigra* and associated species. Mycologia 7: 210–211.

(1268) ——.
1942. The North American cup-fungi. Sup. ed. Published by author. 377 p. New York.

(1269) ——.
1945. *Sclerotinia bifrons*. Mycologia 37: 641–647.

(1270) Seeler, Edgar V., Jr.
1940. Two diseases of *Gleditsia* caused by a species of *Thyronectria*. J. Arnold Arboretum 21: 405–427.

(1271) ——.
1940. A monographic study of the genus *Thyronectria*. J. Arnold Arboretum 21: 429–460.

(1272) Seliskar, Carl E.
1952. Wetwood organism in aspen, poplar, is isolated. Colo. Farm and Home Res. 2(6): 8 p.

(1273) ——.
1964. Virus and viruslike disorders of forest trees. *In* FAO/IUFRO symposium on internationally dangerous forest diseases and insects. 1964, 44 p.

(1274) Serr, E. F., and Rizzi, A. D.
1965. Walnut rootstocks. Univ. Calif. Agr. Ext. Serv. Publ. AXT–120, 8 p.

(1275) Sewell, G. W. F., and Wilson, J. F.
1964. Death of maiden apple trees caused by *Phytophthora syringae* Kleb. and a comparison of the pathogen with *P. cactorum* (L. & C.) Schroet. Ann. Appl. Biol. 53: 275–280.

(1276) Seymour, Arthur Bliss.
1929. Host index of the fungi of North America. 732 p. Cambridge, Mass.: Harvard Univ. Press.

(1277) Shaw, Charles Gardner.
1958. Host fungus index for the Pacific Northwest. I. Hosts. Wash. Agr. Exp. Sta. Circ. 335, 127 p.

(1278) ——.
1958. Host fungus index for the Pacific Northwest. II. Fungi. Wash. Agr. Exp. Sta. Circ. 336, 237 p.

(1279) ——, Fischer, George W., Adams, Donald F., and Adams, Mark F.
1951. Fluorine injury to ponderosa pine. (Abstr.) Phytopathology 41: 943.

(1280) ——, and Leaphart, Charles D.
1960. Two serious foliage diseases of western white pine in the Inland Empire. U.S. Dep. Agr. Plant Dis. Rep. 44: 655–659.

(1281) Shea, Keith R.
1964. *Rosellinia herpotrichioides* on Sitka spruce seedlings in Washington. U.S. Dep. Agr. Plant Dis. Rep. 48: 512–513.

(1282) ——, and Rediske, J. H.
1964. *Schizophyllum commune* Fr. isolated from stored Douglas-fir cones. U.S. Dep. Agr. Plant Dis. Rep. 48: 234.

(1283) Shear, C. L., Stevens, Neil E., and Tiller, Ruby J.
　1917. *Endothia parasitica* and related species. U.S. Dep. Agr. Bull. 380, 82 p.

(1284) Shearer, Raymond C., and Mielke, James L.
　1958. An annotated list of the diseases of western larch. USDA Forest Serv. Intermount. Forest and Range Exp. Sta. Res. Note 53, 6 p.

(1285) Shields, J. K., and Atwell, E. A.
　1963. Effect of a mold, *Trichoderma viride*, on decay of birch by four storage-rot fungi. Forest Prod. J. 13: 262–265.

(1286) Shigo, Alex L.
　1962. Observations on the succession of fungi on hardwood pulpwood bolts. U.S. Dep. Agr. Plant Dis. Rep. 46: 379–380.

(1287) ———.
　1962. Another scale insect on beech. USDA Forest Serv. Northeast. Forest Exp. Sta. Pap. 168, 13 p.

(1288) ———. –
　1962. Logging wounds on northern hardwoods. Forest Notes (Soc. for the Protection of New Hampshire Forests) 75: 12–13.

(1289) ———.
　1963. Beech bark disease. USDA Forest Serv. Forest Pest Leafl. 75, 8 p.

(1290) ———.
　1963. Fungi associated with the discolorations around rot columns caused by *Fomes igniarius*. U.S. Dep. Agr. Plant Dis. Rep. 47: 820–823.

(1291) ———.
　1963. Relation of branch stubs to forest disease. Forest Notes 79: 4–7, 25.

(1292) ———.
　1963. Ring shake associated with sapsucker injury. USDA Forest Serv. Res. Pap. NE–8, 10 p.

(1293) ———.
　1964. A canker on maple caused by fungi infecting wounds made by the red squirrel. U.S. Dep. Agr. Plant Dis. Rep. 48: 794–796.

(1294) ———.
　1964. Collar crack of birch. USDA Forest Serv. Res. Note NE–22, 4 p.

(1295) ———.
　1964. Sapsucker injury to forest trees. Forest Notes (Soc. for the Protection of New Hampshire Forests) 82: 3–6.

(1296) ———.
　1964. Organism interactions in the beech bark disease. Phytopathology 54: 263–269.

(1297) ———.
　1965. Decay and discoloration in sprout red maple. Phytopathology 55: 957–962.

(1298) ———.
　1965. Organism interactions in decay and discoloration in beech, birch, and maple. USDA Forest Serv. Res. Pap. NE–43, 23 p.

(1299) ———, and Yelenosky, George.
　1963. Fungus and insect injury to yellow birch seeds and seedlings. USDA Forest Serv. Res. Pap. NE–11, 11 p.

(1300) Shipman, Robert D.
　1955. Quantitative distribution, forest soil microorganisms in a yellow poplar plantation. Amer. Midland Natural. 54: 433–442.

(1301) ———.
　1957. Microbial population in the rhizosphere of yellow poplar seedlings. Amer. Midland Natural. 58: 413–421.

(1302) Shirley, James C.
1947. The redwoods of coast and Sierra. Ed. 4, 84 p. Berkeley and Los Angeles.

(1303) Siegle, H.
1967. Microbiological and biochemical aspects of heartwood stain in *Betula papyrifera* Marsh. Can. J. Bot. 45: 147–154.

(1304) Siggers, Paul V.
1944. The brown spot needle blight of pine seedlings. U.S. Dep. Agr. Tech. Bull. 870, 36 p.

(1305) Silverborg, S. B.
1953. Sterile conks of *Fomes igniarius* on aspen. Phytopathology 43: 699–700.

(1306) ———.
1954. Northern hardwoods cull manual. State Univ. N.Y. Coll. Forest. (Syracuse) Bull. 31: 1–45.

(1307) ———, Risley, J. H., and Leaf, A. L.
1962. A basal canker disease of eastern white pine. U.S. Dep. Agr. Plant Dis. Rep. 46: 285–286.

(1308) ———, Risley, J. H., and Ross, E. W.
1963. Ash dieback spreads. The Conservationist 17(4): 28–29, 38.

(1309) Sites, J. W., Hammond, L. C., Leighty, R. G., and others.
1964. Information to consider in the use of flatwoods and marshes for citrus. Fla. Agr. Exp. Sta. Circ. S–135–A, 35 p.

(1310) Slankis, V.
1958. Mycorrhiza of forest trees. Forest Soils Conf. 1958: 130–137.

(1311) Slocum, G. K., and Miller, W. D.
1953. Virginia pine. Reproduction, growth, and management on the Hill Demonstration Forest, Durham County, N.C. N.C. Agr. Exp. Sta. Tech. Bull. 100, 52 p.

(1312) Small, John Kunkel.
1933. Manual of the southeastern flora. Published by author. 1554 p. New York.

(1313) Smalley, Glendon W., and Scheer, Robert L.
1963. Black root rot in Florida sandhills. U.S. Dep. Agr. Plant Dis. Rep. 47: 669–671.

(1314) Smerlis, E.
1961. Pathological condition of immature balsam fir stands of *Hylocomium-Oxalis* type in the Laurentide Park, Quebec. Forest. Chron. 37: 109–115.

(1315) ———.
1962. Taxonomy and morphology of *Potebniamyces balsamicola* sp. nov. associated with a twig and branch blight of balsam fir in Quebec. Can. J. Bot. 40: 351–359.

(1316) Smith, Clayton O.
1935. Crown gall on the sequoia. Phytopathology 25: 439–440.

(1317) ———.
1937. Crown gall on incense cedar, *Libocedrus decurrens*. Phytopathology 27: 844–849.

(1318) ———.
1939. Susceptibility of species of Cupressaceae to crown gall as determined by artificial inoculations. J. Agr. Res. 59: 919–925.

(1319) ———.
1942. Crown gall on species of Taxaceae, Taxodiaceae, and Pinaceae, as determined by artificial inoculations. Phytopathology 32: 1005–1009.

(1320) Smith, R. M.
1942. Some effects of black locusts and black walnuts on southeastern Ohio pastures. Soil Sci. 53: 385–398.

(1321) Smith, Richard S., Jr.
1967. *Verticicladiella* root disease of pines. Phytopathology 57: 935–938.

(1322) ———.
1967. Decline of *Fusarium oxysporum* in the roots of *Pinus lambertiana* seedlings transplanted into forest soils. Phytopathology 57: 1265.

(1323) ———, and Bega, Robert V.
1964. *Macrophomina phaseoli* in the forest tree nurseries of California. U.S. Dep. Agr. Plant Dis. Rep. 48: 206.

(1324) Snell, Walter H.
1922. A new *Septobasidium* on *Pinus strobus*. Mycologia 14: 55–60.

(1325) ———, and Howard, Nathaniel O.
1922. Notes on chemical injuries to the eastern white pine (*Pinus strobus* L.). Phytopathology 12: 362–368.

(1326) Snow, Albert G., Jr.
1960. Silvical characteristics of Virginia pine (*Pinus virginiana*). USDA Forest Serv. Northeast. Forest Exp. Sta. Pap. 131, 22 p.

(1327) Snow, G. A., and Allen, R. M.
1961. Damage to pine seedlings by Santomerse SX. USDA Forest Serv. Tree Planters' Notes 45: 25–26.

(1328) Snyder, William C., and Hansen, H. N.
1945. The species concept in *Fusarium* with reference to discolor and other sections. Amer. J. Bot. 32: 657–666.

(1329) ———, Toole, E. Richard, and Hepting, George H.
1949. Fusaria associated with mimosa wilt, sumac wilt, and pine pitch canker. J. Agr. Res. 78: 365–382.

(1330) Southam, Chester M., and Ehrlich, John.
1950. Etiology of some sap rots of western red cedar poles. Phytopathology 40: 439–444.

(1331) Sparrow, A. H., Schairer, L. A., and Woodwell, G. M.
1965. Tolerance of *Pinus rigida* trees to a ten-year exposure to chronic gamma irradiation from Cobalt-60. Radiat. Bot. 5: 7–22.

(1332) Sparrow, Rhoda C., and Sparrow, A. H.
1965. Relative radiosensitivities of woody and herbaceous spermatophytes. Science 147(3664): 1449–1451.

(1333) Spaulding, Perley.
1914. Diseases of the eastern hemlock. Soc. Amer. Foresters Proc. 9: 245–256.

(1334) ———.
1935. *Lophodermium pinastri* causing leafcast of Norway pine in nurseries. USDA Forest Serv. Northeast. Forest Exp. Sta. Tech. Note 18, 2 p.

(1335) ———.
1938. A suggested method of converting some heavily *Nectria*-cankered hardwood stands of northern New England to softwoods. J. Forest. 36: 72.

(1336) ———.
1956. Diseases of North American forest trees planted abroad. An annotated list. U.S. Dep. Agr. Handb. 100, 144 p.

(1337) ———.
1958. Diseases of foreign forest trees growing in the United States. An annotated list. U.S. Dep. Agr. Handb. 139, 118 p.

(1338) ———.
1961. Foreign diseases of forest trees of the world. An annotated list. U.S. Dep. Agr. Handb. 197, 361 p.

(1339) ———, Baldwin, H. J., and Boyce, J. S.
1935. Forest disease control in New England. J. Forest. 33: 469–473.

(1340) ———, Grant, T. J., and Ayers, T. T.
1936. Investigations of *Nectria* diseases in hardwoods of New England. J. Forest. 34: 169–179.

(1341) ———, and Hansbrough, J. R.
1932. *Cronartium comptoniae*, the sweetfern blister rust of pitch pines. U.S. Dep. Agr. Circ. 217, 22 p.

(1342) ———, and Hansbrough, J. R.
1944. Decay in balsam fir in New England and New York. U.S. Dep. Agr. Tech. Bull. 872, 30 p.

(1343) ———, Hepting, G. H., and Westveld, M.
1934. Revised suggestions for estimating cull in northern hardwoods. USDA Forest Serv. Northeast. Forest Exp. Sta. Tech. Note 14, 3 p.

(1344) Sproston, Thomas, Jr., and Scott, W. W.
1954. *Valsa leucostomoides*, the cause of decay and discoloration in tapped sugar maples. Phytopathology 44: 12–13.

(1345) Staebler, George R.
1958. Silvical characteristics of noble fir. USDA Forest Serv. Pacific Northwest Forest and Range Exp. Sta. Silvical Ser. 5, 12 p.

(1346) Staley, John M.
1964. A new *Lophodermium* on ponderosa pine. Mycologia 56: 757–762.

(1347) ———.
1964. A survey of coniferous foliage diseases (other than rusts) in Colorado. U.S. Dep. Agr. Plant Dis. Rep. 48: 562–563.

(1348) ———.
1965. Decline and mortality of red and scarlet oaks. Forest Sci. 11: 2–17.

(1349) ———.
1965. *Scleroderris* canker of subalpine fir in Colorado. U.S. Dep. Agr. Plant Dis. Rep. 49: 882.

(1350) ———, and Hawksworth, Frank G.
1967. *Bifusella crepidiformis* on Engelmann spruce. U.S. Dep. Agr. Plant Dis. Rep. 51: 791–792.

(1351) Stambaugh, William J.
1952. A study of needle cast diseases of conifers in Pennsylvania. J. Forest. 50: 944.

(1352) Stevens, F. L.
1913. The fungi which cause plant disease. 754 p. New York: The Macmillan Co.

(1353) Stewart, V. B.
1916. The leaf blotch of horse-chestnut. Cornell Univ. Agr. Exp. Sta. Bull. 371: 411–419.

(1354) Stewart, W. D. P.
1967. Nitrogen-fixing plants. Science 158(3807): 1426–1432.

(1355) Stillinger, C. R.
1944. Notes on *Cronartium occidentale*. Northwest Sci. 18: 11–16.

(1356) Stillwell, M. A.
1956. Pathological aspects of severe spruce budworm attack. Forest Sci. 2: 174–180.

(1357) ———.
1960. Decay associated with woodwasps in balsam fir weakened by insect attack. Forest Sci. 6: 225–231.

(1358) ———.
1964. The fungus associated with woodwasps occurring in beech in New Brunswick. Can. J. Bot. 42: 495–496.

(1359) ———, and Kelly, D. J.
1964. Fungous deterioration of balsam fir killed by spruce budworm in northwestern New Brunswick. Forest. Chron. 40: 482–487.

(1360) Stoeckeler, Joseph H.
1946. Alkali tolerance of drought-hardy trees and shrubs in the seed and seedling stage. Minn. Acad. Sci. Proc. 14: 79–83.

(1361) ———, and Jones, G. W.
1957. Forest nursery practice in the Lake States. U.S. Dep. Agr. Handb. 110, 124 p.

(1362) Stone, E. L., Morrow, R. R., and Welch, D. S.
1954. A malady of red pine on poorly drained sites. J. Forest. 52: 104–114.

(1363) Strong, Forrest C., and Lemmien, Walter A.
1964. *Fomes annosus* in southwestern Michigan. U.S. Dep. Agr. Plant Dis. Rep. 48: 110.

(1364) Stuntz, D. E., and Seliskar, C. E.
1943. A stem canker of dogwood and madrona. Mycologia 35: 207–221.

(1365) Sturgis, W. C.
1913. *Herpotrichia* and *Neopeckia* on conifers. Phytopathology 3: 152–158.

(1366) Sucoff, Edward I.
1961. Potassium, magnesium, and calcium deficiency symptoms of loblolly and Virginia pine seedlings. USDA Forest Serv. Northeast. Forest Exp. Sta. Pap. 164, 18 p.

(1367) Sudworth, George B.
1908. Forest trees of the Pacific slope. U.S. Dep. Agr., Forest Serv., 441 p.

(1368) ———.
1916. The spruce and balsam fir trees of the Rocky Mountain region. U.S. Dep. Agr. Bull. 327, 43 p.

(1369) Sutherland, C. F., Newhook, F. J., and Levy, J.
1959. The association of *Phytophthora* spp. with mortality of *Pinus radiata* and other conifers. II. Influence of soil drainage on disease. New Zeal. J. Agr. Res. 2: 844–858.

(1370) Sutherland, Jack R.
1967. Host range and reproduction of the nematodes *Paratylenchus projectus, Pratylenchus penetrans,* and *Tylenchus emarginatus* on some forest nursery seedlings. U.S. Dep. Agr. Plant Dis. Rep. 51: 91–93.

(1371) ———.
1967. Parasitism of *Tylenchus emarginatus* on conifer seedling roots and some observations on the biology of the nematode. Nematologica 13: 191–196.

(1372) Swingle, Roger U.
1942. Phloem necrosis, a virus disease of the American elm. U.S. Dep. Agr. Circ. 640, 8 p.

(1373) ———, and Bretz, T. W.
1950. Zonate canker, a virus disease of American elm. Phytopathology 40: 1018–1022.

(1374) ———, Tilford, P. E., and Irish, Charles F.
1941. A transmissible mosaic of American elm. (Abstr.) Phytopathology 31: 22.

585

(1375) ———, Whitten, R. R., and Young, H. C.
1949. The identification and control of elm phloem necrosis and Dutch elm disease. Ohio Agr. Exp. Sta. Special Circ. 80, 11 p.

(1376) Tackle, David.
1959. Silvics of lodgepole pine. USDA Forest Serv. Intermount. Forest and Range Exp. Sta. Misc. Pub. 19, 24 p.

(1377) Tarjan, A. C.
1951. Observations on nematodes associated with decline of ornamental plantings. U.S. Dep. Agr. Plant Dis. Rep. 35: 217–218.

(1378) Tarrant, Robert F.
1958. Silvical characteristics of Pacific madrone. USDA Forest Serv. Pacific Northwest Forest and Range Exp. Sta. Silvical Ser. 6, 10 p.

(1379) Taubenhaus, J. J., and Ezekiel, Walter N.
1936. A rating of plants with reference to their relative resistance or susceptibility to *Phymatotrichum* root rot. Texas Agr. Exp. Sta. Bull. 527, 52 p.

(1380) Tegethoff, Alfred C.
1965. Resurvey for European larch canker in Essex County, Massachusetts, 1965. U.S. Dep. Agr. Plant Dis. Rep. 49: 834–835.

(1381) Tehon, Leo R.
1924. Notes on the parasitic fungi of Illinois. Mycologia 16: 135–142.

(1382) ———.
1933. Notes on the parasitic fungi of Illinois. Mycologia 25: 237–257.

(1383) ———.
1937. Notes on the parasitic fungi of Illinois—VI. Mycologia 29: 434–446.

(1384) ———.
1939. New species and taxonomic changes in the Hypodermataceae. Mycologia 31: 674–692.

(1385) ———.
1948. Notes on parasitic fungi of Illinois. Mycologia 40: 314–327.

(1386) ———, and Daniels, E. Y.
1925. Notes on the parasitic fungi of Illinois—II. Mycologia 17: 240–249.

(1387) ———, and Daniels, E. Y.
1927. Notes on the parasitic fungi of Illinois—III. Mycologia 19: 110–129.

(1388) ———, and Harris, H. A.
1941. A chytrid inhabiting xylem in the Moline elm. Mycologia 33: 118–129.

(1389) ———, and Jacks, W. R.
1933. Smooth patch, a bark lesion of white oak. J. Forest. 31: 430–433.

(1390) ———, and Jacobs, Homer L.
1936. A *Verticillium* root disease of American elm. Davey Tree Expert Co., Res. Dep. Bull. 6, 32 p.

(1391) ———, and Stout, G. L.
1929. Notes on the parasitic fungi of Illinois—IV. Mycologia 21: 180–196.

(1392) Thomas, G. P.
1950. Two new outbreaks of *Phomopsis lokoyae* in British Columbia. Can. J. Res., C, 28: 477–481.

(1393) ———.
1958. Studies in forest pathology. XVIII. The occurrence of the Indian paint fungus, *Echinodontium tinctorium* E. & E., in British Columbia. Can. Dep. Agr. Publ. 1041, 30 p.

(1394) ———, and Podmore, D. G.
    1953. Studies in forest pathology. XI. Decay in black cottonwood in the Middle Fraser Region, British Columbia. Can. J. Bot. 31: 675–692.

(1395) ———, and Thomas, R. W.
    1954. Studies in forest pathology. XIV. Decay of Douglas-fir in the coastal region of British Columbia. Can. J. Bot. 32: 630–653.

(1396) Thomas, H. E., and Burrell, A. B.
    1929. A twig canker of apple caused by *Nectria cinnabarina*. Phytopathology 19: 1125–1128.

(1397) Thomas, J. E., and Lindberg, G. D.
    1954. A needle disease of pines caused by *Dothistroma pini*. (Abstr.) Phytopathology 44: 333.

(1398) Thompson, G. E.
    1937. Contributions to the life history and pathology of some *Septoria* and *Marssonina* leaf fungi of poplars. Thesis, Ph.D. Cornell Univ., Ithaca, N.Y.

(1399) ———.
    1939. A canker disease of poplars caused [by] a new species of *Neofabraea*. Mycologia 31: 455–465.

(1400) ———.
    1939. A leaf blight of *Populus tacamahaca* Mill. caused by an undescribed species of *Linospora*. Can. J. Res., C, 17: 232–238.

(1401) ———.
    1941. Leaf-spot diseases of poplars caused by *Septoria musiva* and *S. populicola*. Phytopathology 31: 241–254.

(1402) ———.
    1951. Die-back of sycamore. U.S. Dep. Agr. Plant Dis. Rep. 35: 29–30.

(1403) ———.
    1954. The perfect stages of *Marssonina rhabdospora* and *Septogloeum rhopaloideum*. Mycologia 46: 652–659.

(1404) ———.
    1963. Decay of oaks caused by *Hypoxylon atropunctatum*. U.S. Dep. Agr. Plant Dis. Rep. 47: 202–205.

(1405) Thomson, Walter G.
    1941. The influence of defect upon management of southwestern ponderosa pine stands. J. Forest. 39: 849–853.

(1406) Thyr, B. D., and Shaw, C. Gardner.
    1964. Identity of the fungus causing red band disease on pines. Mycologia 56: 103–109.

(1407) Tims, Eugene C.
    1963. *Corticium salmonicolor* in the United States. U.S. Dep. Agr. Plant Dis. Rep. 47: 1055–1059.

(1408) ———, Mills, P. J., and Exner, Beatrice.
    1954. Thread-blight (*Pellicularia koleroga*) in Louisiana. U.S. Dep. Agr. Plant Dis. Rep. 38: 634–637.

(1409) Toole, E. Richard.
    1941. *Fusarium* wilt of the mimosa tree (*Albizzia julibrissin*). Phytopathology 31: 599–616.

(1410) ———.
    1948. Rootability of cuttings. Amer. Nurseryman 88: 72.

(1411) ———.
    1950. Disease resistant mimosa trees. Amer. Forests 56(9): 28, 40.

(1412) ———.
    1951. Bleeding canker of maple in North Carolina and Tennessee. U.S. Dep. Agr. Plant Dis. Rep. 35: 119.

(1413) ———.
 1952. Two races of *Fusarium oxysporum* f. *perniciosum* causing wilt of *Albizzia* spp. Phytopathology 42: 694.

(1414) ———.
 1955. Red stain of boxelder. U.S. Dep. Agr. Plant Dis. Rep. 39: 66–67.

(1415) ———.
 1955. *Polyporus hispidus* on southern bottom land oaks. Phytopathology 45: 177–180.

(1416) ———.
 1959. Canker-rots in southern hardwoods. USDA Forest Serv. Forest Pest Leafl. 33, 4 p.

(1417) ———.
 1959. Decay after fire injury to southern bottom land hardwoods. U.S. Dep. Agr. Tech. Bull. 1189, 25 p.

(1418) ———.
 1959. Sweetgum blight. USDA Forest Serv. Forest Pest Leafl. 37, 4 p.

(1419) ———.
 1960. Root rot of white oak in Arkansas. U.S. Dep. Agr. Plant Dis. Rep. 44: 783.

(1420) ———.
 1960. Decay 5 years after thinning of sweetgum sprout clumps. U.S. Dep. Agr. Plant Dis. Rep. 44: 784–788.

(1421) ———.
 1961. New sycamore canker. U.S. Dep. Agr. Plant Dis. Rep. 45:78.

(1422) ———.
 1961. Rot entrance through dead branches of southern hardwoods. Forest Sci. 7: 218–226.

(1423) ———.
 1962. Tupelo lesion caused by *Fusarium solani*. U.S. Dep. Agr. Plant Dis. Rep. 46: 732–733.

(1424) ———.
 1963. Sweetgum lesion caused by *Botryosphaeria ribis*. U.S. Dep. Agr. Plant Dis. Rep. 47: 229–231.

(1425) ———.
 1964. Progress of oak heart rot varies with height in tree. U.S. Dep. Agr. Plant Dis. Rep. 48: 585.

(1426) ———.
 1964. Rot cull in black willow. USDA Forest Serv. Res. Note SO–14, 2 p.

(1427) ———.
 1965. Inoculation of bottom land red oaks with *Poria ambigua, Polyporus fissilis,* and *Polyporus hispidus*. U.S. Dep. Agr. Plant Dis. Rep. 49: 81–83.

(1428) ———.
 1965. Decay 10 years after thinning of sweetgum sprout clumps. U.S. Dep. Agr. Plant Dis. Rep. 49: 986.

(1429) ———.
 1967. Root rot of southern hardwood trees caused by *Corticium galactinum*. U.S. Dep. Agr. Plant Dis. Rep. 51: 500–501.

(1430) ———.
 1968. Wetwood in cottonwood. U.S. Dep. Agr. Plant Dis. Rep. 52: 822–823.

(1431) ———, and Boyce, John S., Jr.
 1952. *Fomes annosus* on Atlantic white cedar. U.S. Dep. Agr. Plant Dis. Rep. 36: 330.

(1432) ———, and Broadfoot, W. M.
  1959. Sweetgum blight as related to alluvial soils of the Mississippi River floodplain. Forest Sci. 5: 2–9.

(1433) ———, and Gammage, John L.
  1959. Damage from increment borings in bottom land hardwoods. J. Forest. 57: 909–911.

(1434) ———, and Hepting, George H.
  1949. Selection and propagation of *Albizzia* for resistance to *Fusarium* wilt. Phytopathology 39: 63–70.

(1435) ———, and Huckenpahler, B. J.
  1954. Yellow-poplar dieback. U.S. Dep. Agr. Plant Dis. Rep. 38: 786–788.

(1436) ———, and Lightle, P. C.
  1960. Status of persimmon wilt, 1959. U.S. Dep. Agr. Plant Dis. Rep. 44: 45.

(1437) ———, and Morris, R. C.
  1959. Trunk lesion of sweetgum. U.S. Dep. Agr. Plant Dis. Rep. 43: 942–945.

(1438) Torgeson, D. C.
  1954. Root rot of Lawson cypress and other ornamentals caused by *Phytophthora cinnamomi*. Boyce Thompson Inst. Contrib. 17: 359–373.

(1439) ———, Young, Roy A., and Milbrath, J. A.
  1954. *Phytophthora* root rot diseases of Lawson cypress and other ornamentals. Oregon Agr. Exp. Sta. Bull. 527, 18 p.

(1440) Toumey, J. W.
  1926. Initial root habit in American trees and its bearing on regeneration. Int. Congr. Plant Sci. 1: 713–728.

(1441) Trappe, James M.
  1960. Some probable mycorrhizal associations in the Pacific Northwest. II. Northwest Sci. 34: 113–117.

(1442) ———.
  1962. Fungus associates of ectotrophic mycorrhizae. Bot. Rev. 28: 538–606.

(1443) ———.
  1965. Tuberculate mycorrhizae of Douglas-fir. Forest Sci. 11: 27–32.

(1444) ———, Franklin, J. F., Tarrant, R. F., and Hansen, G. M. (editors).
  1968. Biology of alder. Northwest Sci. Assn. Fortieth Annu. Meeting Symp. Proc. (1967), 292 p. Portland, Oreg.: Pacific Northwest Forest and Range Exp. Sta.

(1445) Trelease, William.
  1916. The genus *Phoradendron*. A monographic revision. 224 p. Urbana, Ill.: Univ. of Illinois Press.

(1446) Trione, Edward J.
  1959. The pathology of *Phytophthora lateralis* on native *Chamaecyparis lawsoniana*. Phytopathology 49: 306–309.

(1447) ———, and Roth, L. F.
  1957. Aerial infection of *Chamaecyparis* by *Phytophthora lateralis*. U.S. Dep. Agr. Plant Dis. Rep. 41: 211–215.

(1448) Trousdell, Kenneth B.
  1955. Loblolly pine seed tree mortality. USDA Forest Serv. Southeast. Forest Exp. Sta. Pap. 61, 11 p.

(1449) True, R. P.
  1949. Dry face of turpentine pines. Forest Farmer 8: 6, 11.

(1450) ———.
1953. Studies on sprout reproduction of yellow-poplar as related to decay. W. Va. Univ. Agr. Exp. Sta. Current Rep. 3, 4 p.

(1451) ———.
1962. Decay in thinned sprout clumps of yellow-poplar. (Abstr.) Phytopathology 52: 468.

(1452) ———, Barnett, H. L., Dorsey, C. K., and Leach, J. G.
1960. Oak wilt in West Virginia. W. Va. Univ. Agr. Exp. Sta. Bull. 448T, 119 p.

(1453) ———, Tryon, E. H., and King, J. F.
1955. Cankers and decays of birch associated with two *Poria* species. J. Forest. 53: 412–415.

(1454) Tryon, E. H., and True, R. P.
1952. Blister-shake of yellow-poplar. W. Va. Univ. Agr. Exp. Sta. Bull. 350T, 15 p.

(1455) Tsoumis, George.
1965. Structural deformities in an epidemic tumor of white spruce, *Picea glauca*. Can. J. Bot. 43: 176–181.

(1456) Tweedy, B. G., and Powell, D.
1963. The taxonomy of *Alternaria* and species of this genus reported on apples. Bot. Rev. 29: 405–412.

(1457) U.S. Department of Agriculture.
1951. Virus diseases and other disorders with viruslike symptoms of stone fruits in North America. Agr. Handb. 10, 276 p.

(1458) Vaartaja, O.
1957. The susceptibility of seedlings of various tree species to *Phytophthora cactorum*. Can. Dep. Agr. Forest Biol. Div. Bimo. Progr. 13: 2.

(1459) ———.
1960. Effect of photoperiod on drought resistance of white spruce seedlings. Can. J. Bot. 38: 597–599.

(1460) ———.
1967. Occurrence of falcate antheridia in *Pythium* species, particularly in *P. irregulare* and its synonym *P. polymorphon*. Mycologia 59: 870–877.

(1461) ———, and Cram, W. H.
1956. Damping-off pathogens of conifers and of *Caragana* in Saskatchewan. Phytopathology 46: 391–397.

(1462) ———, Cram, W. H., and Morgan, G. A.
1961. Damping-off etiology especially in forest nurseries. Phytopathology 51: 35–42.

(1463) ———, Dance, B. W., and Lynn, D. F.
1964. Cabbaging of white pine seedlings. Can. Dep. Forest., Forest Entomol. and Pathol. Br., Progr. Rep. 20(5): 3.

(1464) ———, and Salisbury, P. J.
1961. Potential pathogenicity of *Pythium* isolates from forest nurseries. Phytopathology 51: 505–507.

(1465) ———, and Wilner, J.
1956. Field tests with fungicides to control damping-off of Scots pine. Can. J. Agr. Sci. 36: 14–18.

(1466) Van Arsdel, E. P., Riker, A. J., and Patton, R. F.
1956. The effects of temperature and moisture on the spread of white pine blister rust. Phytopathology 46: 307–318.

(1467) Van Der Zwet, T.
1962. A new leaf spot on seedlings of *Aleurites fordii*. (Abstr.) Phytopathology 52: 31.

590

(1468) Van Groenewoud, H.
　　1956. A root disease complex in Saskatchewan white spruce. Forest. Chron. 32: 11–13.

(1469) Van Hook, J. M., and Busteed, R. C.
　　1935. Anthracnose of *Betula nigra*. Indiana Acad. Sci. Proc. 44: 81.

(1470) Vermillion, M. T.
　　1950. A needle blight of pine. Lloydia 13: 196–197.

(1471) Verrall, A. F.
　　1938. The probable mechanism of the protective action of resin in fire wounds on red pine. J. Forest. 36: 1231–1233.

(1472) ———.
　　1939. Relative importance and seasonal prevalence of wood-staining fungi in the southern States. Phytopathology 29: 1031–1051.

(1473) ———.
　　1941. Dissemination of fungi that stain logs and lumber. J. Agr. Res. 63: 549–558.

(1474) ———.
　　1941. Fungi associated with stain in chemically treated green lumber. Phytopathology 31: 270–274.

(1475) ———.
　　1942. A comparison of *Diplodia natalensis* from stained wood and other sources. Phytopathology 32: 879–884.

(1476) ———.
　　1943. Fungi associated with certain ambrosia beetles. J. Agr. Res. 66: 135–144.

(1477) ———.
　　1958. Fusiform rust of southern pines. USDA Forest Serv. Forest Pest Leafl. 26, 4 p.

(1478) ———, and May, Curtis.
　　1937. A new species of *Dothiorella* causing die-back of elm. Mycologia 29: 321–324.

(1479) Viggars, R. M., and Tarjan, A. C.
　　1949. A new root disease of pin oaks possibly caused by the nematode, *Hoplolaimus coronatus* Cobb. U.S. Dep. Agr. Plant Dis. Rep. 33: 132–133.

(1480) Vimmerstedt, John P.
　　1957. Silvical characteristics of flowering dogwood. USDA Forest Serv. Southeast. Forest Exp. Sta. Pap. 87, 11 p.

(1481) Von Schrenk, Hermann.
　　1902. The hardy catalpa. II. The diseases of the hardy catalpa. U.S. Dep. Agr. Bur. Forest. Bull. 37: 49–58.

(1482) ———.
　　1903. The brown rot disease of the redwood. *In* The Redwood. U.S. Dep. Agr. Bur. Forest. Bull. 38: 29–31.

(1483) ———, and Spaulding, P.
　　1903. The bitter rot of apples. U.S. Dep. Agr. Bur. Plant Ind. Bull. 44: 54 p.

(1484) Voorhees, R. K.
　　1942. Life history and taxonomy of the fungus *Physalospora rhodina*. Univ. Fla. Agr. Exp. Sta. Tech. Bull. 371, 91 p.

(1485) Vozzo, J. A., and Hacskaylo, E.
　　1961. Mycorrhizal fungi on *Pinus virginiana*. Mycologia 53: 538–539.

(1486) ———, and Hacskaylo, E.
　　1964. Anatomy of mycorrhizae of selected eastern forest trees. Torrey Bot. Club Bull. 91: 378–387.

591

(1487) Wagener, Willis W.
    1925. Mistletoe in the lower bole of incense cedar. Phytopathology 15: 614–616.

(1488) ———.
    1939. The canker of *Cupressus* induced by *Coryneum cardinale* n. sp. J. Agr. Res. 58: 1–46.

(1489) ———.
    1949. Diseases of American cypresses. El Aliso 1: 257–321.

(1490) ———.
    1949. Top dying of conifers from sudden cold. J. Forest. 47: 49–53.

(1491) ———.
    1957. The limitation of two leafy mistletoes of the genus *Phoradendron* by low temperatures. Ecology 38: 142–145.

(1492) ———.
    1958. Infection tests with two rusts of Jeffrey pine. U.S. Dep. Agr. Plant Dis. Rep. 42: 888–892.

(1493) ———.
    1959. The effect of a western needle fungus (*Hypodermella medusa* Dearn.) on pines and its significance in forest management. J. Forest. 57: 561–564.

(1494) ———.
    1960. Sporadic diseases in young stands in California and Nevada. 8th Western Forest Disease Work Conf. Proc. 1960: 14–22.

(1495) ———.
    1961. Guidelines for estimating the survival of fire-damaged trees in California. USDA Forest Serv. Pacific Southwest Forest and Range Exp. Sta. Misc. Pap. 60, 11 p.

(1496) ———, and Bega, Robert V.
    1958. Heart rots of incense cedar. USDA Forest Serv. Forest Pest Leafl. 30, 7 p.

(1497) ———, and Cave, Marion S.
    1944. *Phytophthora* canker of madrone in California. U.S. Dep. Agr. Plant Dis. Rep. 28: 328.

(1498) ———, and Cave, Marion S.
    1946. Pine killing by the root fungus, *Fomes annosus,* in California. J. Forest. 44: 47–54.

(1499) ———, and Mielke, James L.
    1961. A staining-fungus root disease of ponderosa, Jeffrey, and pinyon pines. U.S. Dep. Agr. Plant Dis. Rep. 45: 831–835.

(1500) Wagg, J. W. Bruce.
    1967. Origin and development of white spruce root-forms. Can. Dep. Forest. and Rural Develop. Forest. Br. Dep. Pub. 1192: 1–45.

(1501) Wahlenberg, W. G.
    1946. Longleaf pine. 429 p. Washington, D.C.: Charles Lathrop Pack Forestry Foundation.

(1502) ———.
    1960. Loblolly pine. Duke Univ. School Forestry, Durham, N.C. 603 p.

(1503) Walker, John Charles.
    1957. Plant pathology. Ed. II, 707 p. New York: McGraw-Hill Book Co., Inc.

(1504) Walker, Laurence C.
    1955. Influence of white birch in restoring potassium to deficient soils. J. Forest. 43: 451–452.

(1505) Wallis, G. W., and Reynolds, G.
    1965. The initiation and spread of *Poria weirii* root rot of Douglas-fir. Can. J. Bot. 43: 1–9.

(1506) Walter, James M.
    1950. Canker stain of planetrees. U.S. Dep. Agr. Circ. 742, 12 p.

(1507) ——, Rex, Edgar G., and Schreiber, Ray.
    1952. The rate of progress and destructiveness of canker stain of plane-
    trees. Phytopathology 42: 236–239.

(1508) Ward, James C., and Marden, Richard M.
    1964. Sugar maple veneer logs should be graded for pitch flecks. USDA
    Forest Serv. Res. Note LS–41, 4 p.

(1509) Ward, W. W., Berglund, J. V., and Borden, F. Y.
    1966. Soil-site characteristics and occurrence of sugar maple canker in
    Pennsylvania. Ecology 47: 541–548.

(1510) Waterhouse, Grace M.
    1956. The genus *Phytophthora*. The Commonwealth Mycol. Inst., Misc.
    Publ. 12, 120 p.

(1511) ——.
    1963. Key to the species of *Phytophthora* de Bary. Commonwealth Mycol.
    Inst., Mycol. Pap. 92, 22 p.

(1512) Waterman, Alma M.
    1941. Diseases of shade and ornamental trees: Annotated list of speci-
    mens received in 1940 at the New Haven office, Division of
    Forest Pathology. U.S. Dep. Agr. Plant Dis. Rep. 25: 181–186.

(1513) ——.
    1943. *Diplodia pinea*, the cause of a disease of hard pines. Phytopa-
    thology 33: 1018–1031.

(1514) ——.
    1945. Tip blight of species of *Abies* caused by a new species of *Rehmiel-
    lopsis*. J. Agr. Res. 70: 315–337.

(1515) ——.
    1946. Canker of hybrid poplar clones in the United States, caused by
    Septoria musiva. Phytopathology 36: 148–156.

(1516) ——.
    1947. *Rhizosphaera kalkhoffi* associated with a needle cast of *Picea
    pungens*. Phytopathology 37: 507–511.

(1517) ——.
    1954. *Septoria* canker of poplars in the United States. U.S. Dep. Agr.
    Circ. 947, 24 p.

(1518) ——.
    1954. Surface sterilization of hybrid poplar cuttings. USDA Forest Serv.
    Northeast. Forest Exp. Sta. Res. Notes 32, 3 p.

(1519) ——.
    1955. The relation of *Valsa kunzei* to cankers on conifers. Phytopa-
    thology 45: 686–692.

(1520) ——.
    1956. *Verticillium* wilt of yellow-poplar. U.S. Dep. Agr. Plant Dis. Rep.
    40: 349–350.

(1521) ——.
    1957. Canker and dieback of poplars caused by *Dothichiza populea*.
    Forest Sci. 3: 175–183.

(1522) ——, and Cash, Edith K.
    1950. Leaf blotch of poplar caused by a new species of *Septotinia*.
    Mycologia 42: 374–384.

(1523) ——, and Marshall, Rush P.
    1947. A new species of *Cristulariella* associated with a leaf spot of
    maple. Mycologia 39: 690–698.

(1524) ——, and Miller, J. Armstrong.
    1936. A dieback of Douglas-fir. Phytopathology 26: 804–805.

(1525) Watson, Alice J.
    1941. Studies of *Botryosphaeria ribis* on *Cercis* and *Benzoin*. U.S. Dep.
        Agr. Plant Dis. Rep. 25: 29–31.

(1526) Wean, Robert E.
    1937. The parasitism of *Polyporus schweinitzii* on seedling *Pinus strobus*.
        Phytopathology 27: 1124–1142.

(1527) Weber, George F.
    1940. Thread blight of woody plants. Univ. Fla. Agr. Exp. Sta. Press
        Bull. 551, 2 p.

(1528) Weddell, D. J.
    1942. Damage to catalpa due to recreational use. J. Forest. 40: 807.

(1529) Weir, James R.
    1912. A *Botrytis* on conifers in the Northwest. Phytopathology 2: 215.

(1530) ――――.
    1913. Some observations on *Polyporus berkeleyi*. Phytopathology 3: 101–
        103.

(1531) ――――.
    1913. An epidemic of needle diseases in Idaho and western Montana.
        Phytopathology 3: 252–253.

(1532) ――――.
    1914. Two new wood-destroying fungi. J. Agr. Res. 2: 163–165.

(1533) ――――.
    1915. Observations on *Rhizina inflata*. J. Agr. Res. 4: 93–96.

(1534) ――――.
    1915. A new leaf and twig disease of *Picea engelmanni*. J. Agr. Res.
        4: 251–254.

(1535) ――――.
    1915. Observations on the pathology of the jack pine. U.S. Dep. Agr.
        Bull. 212, 10 p.

(1536) ――――.
    1916. Larch mistletoe: some economic considerations of its injurious
        effects. U.S. Dep. Agr. Bull. 317, 25 p.

(1537) ――――.
    1916. Mistletoe injury to conifers in the Northwest. U.S. Dep. Agr. Bull.
        360, 39 p.

(1538) ――――.
    1917. *Sparassis radicata*, an undescribed fungus on the roots of conifers.
        Phytopathology 7: 166–177.

(1539) ――――.
    1921. *Polyporus dryadeus* (Pers.) Fr. on conifers in the Northwest.
        Phytopathology 11: 99.

(1540) ――――.
    1921. *Thelephora terrestris*, *T. fimbriata*, and *T. caryophyllea* on forest
        tree seedlings. Phytopathology 11: 141–144.

(1541) ――――
    1921. Note on *Cenangium abietis* (Pers.) Rehm on *Pinus ponderosa*
        Laws. Phytopathology 11: 166–170.

(1542) ――――.
    1925. Notes on the parasitism of *Endothia gyrosa* (Schw.) Fr. Phyto-
        pathology 15: 489–491.

(1543) ――――.
    1927. Butt rot in *Diospyros virginiana* caused by *Polyporus spraguei*.
        Phytopathology 17: 339–340.

(1544) ——, and Hubert, Ernest E.
　　1918. A study of heart-rot in western hemlock. U.S. Dep. Agr. Bull.
　　　　722, 39 p.

(1545) ——, and Hubert, Ernest E.
　　1919. A study of the rots of western white pine. U.S. Dep. Agr. Bull.
　　　　799, 24 p.

(1546) Welch, D. S.
　　1939. *Nectria* canker in relation to growth and mortality in basswood
　　　　(*Tilia americana*). (Abstr.) Phytopathology 29: 23–24.

(1547) ——.
　　1963. Maple decline in the northeast. 39th Int. Shade Tree Conf. Proc.
　　　　1963: 43–48.

(1548) Wellman, Frederick L., and Grant, Theodore J.
　　1951. An apparent virus disease of *Casuarina* in the American tropics.
　　　　U.S. Dep. Agr. Plant Dis. Rep. 35: 498–499.

(1549) Wellner, Charles A.
　　1962. Silvics of western white pine. USDA Forest Serv. Intermount.
　　　　Forest and Range Exp. Sta. Misc. Publ. 26, 24 p.

(1550) Wells, B. W.
　　1939. A new forest climax: the salt spray climax of Smith Island, N.C.
　　　　Torrey Bot. Club Bull. 66: 629–634.

(1551) Wellwood, R. W.
　　1956. Some effects of dwarfmistletoe on western hemlock. Forest. Chron.
　　　　32: 282–296.

(1552) Wenger, Karl F.
　　1955. Light and mycorrhiza development. Ecology 36: 518–520.

(1553) ——.
　　1958. Silvical characteristics of pond pine. USDA Forest Serv. South-
　　　　east. Forest Exp. Sta. Pap. 91, 13 p.

(1554) ——.
　　1958. Silvical characteristics of loblolly pine. USDA Forest Serv. South-
　　　　east. Forest Exp. Sta. Pap. 98, 32 p.

(1555) Westcott, Cynthia.
　　1960. Plant disease handbook. Ed. 2, 825 p. Princeton, N.J.; New York,
　　　　N.Y. (etc.): D. Van Nostrand Co., Inc.

(1556) Wester, Horace V., Davidson, Ross W., and Fowler, Marvin E.
　　1950. Cankers of linden and redbud. U.S. Dep. Agr. Plant Dis. Rep. 34:
　　　　219–223.

(1557) ——, and Jylkka, Edward W.
　　1959. Elm scorch, graft transmissible virus of American elm. U.S. Dep.
　　　　Agr. Plant Dis. Rep. 43: 519.

(1558) Westveld, Marinus.
　　1953. Ecology and silviculture of the spruce-fir forests of eastern North
　　　　America. J. Forest. 51: 422–430.

(1559) Whetzel, H. H.
　　1945. A synopsis of the genera and species of the Sclerotiniaceae, a
　　　　family of stromatic inoperculate discomycetes. Mycologia 37:
　　　　648–714.

(1560) ——, and Wolf, Frederick A.
　　1945. The cup fungus, *Ciboria carunculoides*, pathogenic on mulberry
　　　　fruits. Mycologia 37: 476–491.

(1561) White, L. T.
　　1951. Studies of Canadian *Thelephoraceae*. VIII. *Corticium galacti-
　　　　num* (Fr.) Burt. Can. J. Bot. 29: 279–296.

(1562) ———.
1953. Studies in forest pathology. X. Decay of white pine in the Timagami Lake and Ottawa Valley areas. Can. J. Bot. 31: 175–200.

(1563) White, P. R., and Millington, W. F.
1954. The structure and development of a woody tumor affecting *Picea glauca*. Amer. J. Bot. 41: 353–361.

(1564) White, W. Lawrence.
1936. A new species of *Chondropodium* on *Pseudotsuga taxifolia*. Mycologia 28: 433–438.

(1565) ———.
1941. A monograph of the genus *Rutstroemia* (Discomycetes). Lloydia 4: 153–240.

(1566) Whitney, H. S., and Baranyay, J. A.
1968. An undescribed gall midge leaf spot of balsam poplar. Phytopathology 58: 262–263.

(1567) ———, and Parmeter, J. R., Jr.
1963. Synthesis of heterokaryons in *Rhizoctonia solani* Kuhn. Can. J. Bot. 41: 879–886.

(1568) Whitney, R. D.
1961. Root wounds and associated root rots of white spruce. Forest. Chron. 37: 401–411.

(1569) ———.
1962. Studies in forest pathology. XXIV. *Polyporus tomentosus* Fr. as a major factor in stand-opening disease of white spruce. Can. J. Bot. 40: 1631–1658.

(1570) ———.
1963. Artificial infection of small spruce roots with *Polyporus tomentosus*. Phytopathology 53: 441–443.

(1571) ———.
1963. Mycorrhizae of white spruce in relation to stand openings. *In* Annu. Rep. Forest Entomol. and Pathol. Br., Can. Dep. Forest., p. 103.

(1572) ———.
1965. Mycorrhiza-infection trials with *Polyporus tomentosus* on spruce and pine. Forest Sci. 11: 265–270.

(1573) Whittaker, Elizabeth I.
1962. The interaction of *Coryne sarcoides* and fungi associated with red heart in lodgepole pine. Can. J. Bot. 40: 255–256.

(1574) Whitten, Russell R., and Swingle, Roger U.
1964. The Dutch elm disease and its control. U.S. Dep. Agr. Inform. Bull. 193, 12 p.

(1575) Wiant, J. S.
1929. The *Rhizoctonia* damping-off of conifers, and its control by chemical treatment of the soil. Cornell Univ. Agr. Exp. Sta. Mem. 124.

(1576) Wicker, Ed F.
1965. A *Phomopsis* canker on western larch. U.S. Dep. Agr. Plant Dis. Rep. 49: 102–105.

(1577) ———.
1967. Appraisal of biological control of *Arceuthobium campylopodum* f. *campylopodum* by *Colletotrichum gloeosporioides*. U.S. Dep. Agr. Plant Dis. Rep. 51: 311–313.

(1578) ———, and Shaw, Charles Gardner.
1962. Fungi which provide some local biological control of *Arceuthobium* spp. in the Pacific Northwest. (Abstr.) Phytopathology 52: 757.

596

(1579) Wiehe, P. O.
1952. Life cycle of *Botryosphaeria ribis* on *Aleurites montana*. Phytopathology 42: 521–526.

(1580) Wiens, Delbert.
1964. Revision of the acataphyllous species of *Phoradendron*. Brittonia 16: 11–54.

(1581) Wilhelm, Stephen, and Taylor, J. Bruce.
1965. Control of *Verticillium* wilt of olive through natural recovery and resistance. Phytopathology 55: 310–316.

(1582) Will, G. M.
1961. The mineral requirements of radiata pine seedlings. New Zeal. J. Agr. Res. 4(3, 4): 309–327.

(1583) Williamson, M. J.
1957. Silvical characteristics of eastern redcedar. USDA Forest Serv. Central States Forest Exp. Sta. Misc. Release 15, 14 p.

(1584) Wilson, Charles L.
1959. Chlorosis of loblolly and shortleaf pine seedlings related to calcium content of nursery soil. U.S. Dep. Agr. Plant Dis. Rep. 43: 964–965.

(1585) ———.
1959. The Columbian timber beetle and associated fungi in white oak. Forest Sci. 5: 114–127.

(1586) ———.
1961. An undescribed blight disease of Arizona cypress. U.S. Dep. Agr. Plant Dis. Rep. 45: 96–98.

(1587) ———.
1962. Brooming and galling of shagbark hickory in Arkansas. U.S. Dep. Agr. Plant Dis. Rep. 46: 448–450.

(1588) ———.
1963. *Fomes annosus* root rot of shortleaf, loblolly, and slash pine in Arkansas. U.S. Dep. Agr. Plant Dis. Rep. 47: 328.

(1589) ———.
1963. Wilting of persimmon caused by *Cephalosporium diospyri*. Phytopathology 53: 1402–1406.

(1590) ———.
1965. *Ceratocystis ulmi* in elm wood. Phytopathology 55: 477.

(1591) ———.
1965. Consideration of the use of persimmon wilt as a silvicide for weed persimmons. U.S. Dep. Agr. Plant Dis. Rep. 49: 789–791.

(1592) Wilson, E. E., and Magie, Allan R.
1963. Physiological, serological, and pathological evidence that *Pseudomonas tonelliana* is identical with *Pseudomonas savastanoi*. Phytopathology 53: 653–659.

(1593) ———, O'Reilly, H. J., and Rizzi, A. D.
1962. Branch wilt disease of English walnut trees. Univ. Calif. Agr. Ext. Serv. Publ. AXT–18, 10 p.

(1594) ———, Starr, Mortimer P., and Berger, Joyce A.
1957. Bark canker, a bacterial disease of the Persian walnut tree. Phytopathology 47: 669–673.

(1595) Wisconsin, Univ. of
1964. Studies of maple blight. Univ. of Wisc. Res. Bull. 250, 128 p.

(1596) Wolf, Frederick A.
1912. A new *Gnomonia* on hickory leaves. Annales Mycologici 10: 488–491.

(1597) ———.
1922. The fruiting stage of the tuckahoe, *Pachyma cocos*. J. Elisha Mitchell Sci. Soc. 38: 127–137.

(1598) ———.
1927. The morphology and systematic position of the fungus, *Microstroma juglandis* (Bereng.) Sacc. J. Elisha Mitchell Sci. Soc. 43: 97–100.

(1599) ———.
1930. A parasitic alga, *Cephaleuros irescens* Kunze, on citrus and certain other plants. J. Elisha Mitchell Sci. Soc. 45: 187–205.

(1600) ———.
1935. The perfect stage of a leaf spot fungus on red mulberry. J. Elisha Mitchell Sci. Soc. 51: 163–166.

(1601) ———.
1936. False mildew of red mulberry. Mycologia 28: 268–277.

(1602) ———.
1938. Life histories of two leaf-inhabiting fungi on sycamore. Mycologia 30: 54–63.

(1603) ———.
1939. Leafspot of ash and *Phyllosticta viridis*. Mycologia 31: 258–266.

(1604) ———.
1940. *Cercospora* leafspot of redbud. Mycologia 32: 129–136.

(1605) ———.
1940. A leafspot fungus on *Nyssa*. Mycologia 32: 331–335.

(1606) ———, and Davidson, Ross W.
1941. Life cycle of *Piggotia fraxini*, causing leaf disease of ash. Mycologia 33: 526–539.

(1607) ———, and Stanford, E. E.
1918. A *Macrophoma* disease of figs. Phytopathology 8: 24–27.

(1608) ———, and Wolf, Fred T.
1947. The fungi. V. 1, 438 p. New York: John Wiley & Sons, Inc.

(1609) Wolf, Fred T., and Wolf, Frederick A.
1939. A study of *Botryosphaeria ribis* on willow. Mycologia 31: 217–227.

(1610) Wollenweber, H. W., and Reinking, O. A.
1935. Die Fusarien. 355 p. Berlin: Paul Parey.

(1611) Wood, Francis A.
1964. *Ceratocystis* canker of aspen in Pennsylvania. U.S. Dep. Agr. Plant Dis. Rep. 48: 441.

(1612) ———, and French, D. W.
1963. *Ceratocystis fimbriata*, the cause of a stem canker of quaking aspen. Forest Sci. 9: 232–235.

(1613) ———, and Skelly, John M.
1964. The etiology of an annual canker on maple. Phytopathology 54: 269–272.

(1614) Worthington, Norman P.
1957. Silvical characteristics of red alder. USDA Forest Serv. Pacific Northwest Forest Exp. Sta. Silvical Ser. 1, 15 p.

(1615) Wright, Ernest.
1938. Further investigations of brown-staining fungi associated with engraver beetles (*Scolytus*) in white fir. J. Agr. Res. 57: 759–773.

(1616) ———.
1942. *Cytospora abietis*, the cause of a canker of true firs in California and Nevada. J. Agr. Res. 65: 143–153.

598

(1617) ———.
　　1957. Influence of temperature and moisture on damping-off of American and Siberian elm, black locust, and desertwillow. Phytopathology 47: 658–662.

(1618) ———.
　　1957. Importance of mycorrhizae to ponderosa pine seedlings. Forest Sci. 3: 275–280.

(1619) ———.
　　1963. Ectotrophic mycorrhizae on pine seedlings in Oregon. Ecology 44: 173–175.

(1620) ———, and Ching, Kim K.
　　1962. Effect of seed source on mycorrhizal formation on Douglas-fir seedlings. Northwest Sci. 36: 1–6.

(1621) ———, Coulter, W. K., and Gruenfeld, J. J.
　　1956. Deterioration of beetle-killed Pacific silver fir. J. Forest. 54: 322–325.

(1622) ———, Harvey, George M., and Bigelow, Charles A.
　　1963. Tests to control *Fusarium* root rot of ponderosa pine in the Pacific Northwest. USDA Forest Serv. Tree Planters' Notes 59: 15–20.

(1623) ———, and Isaac, Leo A.
　　1956. Decay following logging injury to western hemlock, Sitka spruce, and true firs. U.S. Dep. Agr. Tech. Bull. 1148, 34 p.

(1624) ———, Rhoads, Arthur S., and Isaac, Leo A.
　　1947. Decay losses following logging injury in partially cut stands of western hemlock and Sitka spruce. The Timberman 48: 3 p.

(1625) ———, and Slagg, C. M.
　　1942. Some tentative conclusions resulting from plot analyses of *Phomopsis*-blighted juniper seedlings in Great Plains nurseries during 1941. (Abstr.) Phytopathology 32: 19.

(1626) ———, and Tarrant, Robert F.
　　1958. Occurrence of mycorrhizae after logging and slash burning in the Douglas-fir forest type. USDA Forest Serv. Pacific Northwest Forest and Range Exp. Sta. Res. Note 160, 7 p.

(1627) ———, and Wells, H. R.
　　1948. Tests on the adaptability of trees and shrubs to shelterbelt planting on certain *Phymatotrichum* root rot infested soils of Oklahoma and Texas. J. Forest. 46: 256–262.

(1628) ———, and Wright, K. H.
　　1954. Deterioration of beetle-killed Douglas-fir in Oregon and Washington. A summary of findings to date. USDA Forest Serv. Pacific Northwest Forest and Range Exp. Sta. Res. Pap. 10, 12 p.

(1629) Wright, E. F., and Cain, R. F.
　　1961. New species of the genus *Ceratocystis*. Can. J. Bot. 39: 1215–1230.

(1630) Wright, Jonathan W.
　　1959. Silvical characteristics of white ash. USDA Forest Serv. Northeast. Forest Exp. Sta. Pap. 123, 19 p.

(1631) ———.
　　1959. Silvical characteristics of green ash. USDA Forest Serv. Northeast. Forest Exp. Sta. Pap. 126, 18 p.

(1632) Wyman, Donald.
　　1939. Salt water injury of woody plants resulting from the hurricane of September 21, 1938. Arnold Arboretum Bull. Popular Inform., Ser. 4, 7(10): 45–52.

(1633) Yelenosky, George.
　　1963. Soil aeration and tree growth. 39th Int. Shade Tree Conf. Proc. 1963: 16–25.

(1634) York, Harlan H.
1939. Mycorrhizae of red pine (*Pinus resinosa*) in relation to their environment and the well-being of the trees. (Abstr.) Phytopathology 29: 24.

(1635) ———, Wean, R. E., and Childs, T. W.
1936. Some results of investigations of *Polyporus schweinitzii* Fr. Science 84: 160–161.

(1636) Young, George Y.
1956. Progress of sweetgum blight in Maryland plots—1955. U.S. Dep. Agr. Plant Dis. Rep. 40: 249–251.

(1637) Young, P. A.
1961. Dwarf fascicle abnormality of *Pinus echinata* Mill. (Abstr.) Phytopathol. 51: 646.

(1638) ———.
1963. Dwarf fascicle abnormality of shortleaf pine. U.S. Dep. Agr. Plant Dis. Rep. 47: 1022–1023.

(1639) Zabel, Robert A.
1948. Variations in the decay resistance of white oak. N.Y. State Coll. Forest. (Syracuse) Tech. Publ. 68, 53 p.

(1640) ———, Silverborg, Savel B., and Fowler, Marvin E.
1958. A survey of forest tree diseases in the northeast—1957. USDA Forest Serv. Northeast. Forest Exp. Sta. Pap. 110, 30 p.

(1641) Zak, Bratislav.
1961. Aeration and other soil factors affecting southern pines as related to littleleaf disease. U.S. Dep. Agr. Tech. Bull. 1248, 30 p.

(1642) ———.
1961. Littleleaf disease of shortleaf pine (*Pinus echinata* Mill.). Recent advances in botany, p. 1525–1528. Univ. Toronto Press.

(1643) ———.
1964. Role of mycorrhizae in root disease. Annu. Rev. Phytopathol. 2: 377–392.

(1644) ———.
1967. A nematode (*Meloidodera* sp.) on Douglas-fir mycorrhizae. U.S. Dep. Agr. Plant Dis. Rep. 51: 264.

(1645) ———, and Bryan, W. C.
1963. Isolation of fungal symbionts from pine mycorrhizae. Forest Sci. 9: 270–278.

(1646) ———, and Campbell, William A.
1958. Susceptibility of southern pines and other species to the littleleaf pathogen in liquid culture. Forest Sci. 4: 156–161.

(1647) ———, and Marx, Donald H.
1964. Isolation of mycorrhizal fungi from roots of individual slash pines. Forest Sci. 10: 214–222.

(1648) Zalasky, H.
1964. The histopathology of *Macrophoma tumefaciens* infections in black poplar. Can. J. Bot. 42: 385–391.

(1649) ———.
1965. Additional hosts of *Diplodia tumefaciens* (Shear) Zalasky (=*Macrophoma tumefaciens* Shear). U.S. Dep. Agr. Plant Dis. Rep. 49: 50.

(1650) ———.
1965. Morphology of *Ceratocystis fimbriata* in aspen. Can. J. Bot. 43: 625-626.

(1651) ———.
1965. Process of *Ceratocystis fimbriata* infection in aspen. Can. J. Bot. 43: 1157–1162.

(1652) ———.
1968. *Rhytidiella moriformis* n. gen., n. sp. causing rough-bark of *Populus balsamifera*. Can. J. Bot. 46: 1383–1387.

(1653) ———, and Riley, C. G.
1963. Infection tests with two caulicolous rusts of jack pine in Saskatchewan. Can. J. Bot. 41: 459–465.

(1654) Zeller, S. M.
1934. Some new or noteworthy fungi on ericaceous hosts in the Pacific Northwest. Mycologia 26: 291–304.

(1655) ———, and Deremiah, J. W.
1931. Anthracnose of *Ledum* caused by a species of *Elsinoë*. Phytopathology 21: 965–972.

(1656) ———, and Goodding, L. N.
1930. Some species of *Atropellis* and *Scleroderris* on conifers in the Pacific Northwest. Phytopathology 20: 555–567.

(1657) Zentmyer, George A.
1941. *Cytospora* canker of Italian cypress. Phytopathology 31: 896–906.

(1658) ———, and Munnecke, Donald E.
1952. *Phytophthora* root rot of nursery stock. U.S. Dep. Agr. Plant Dis. Rep. 36: 211–212.

(1659) ———, and Paulus, Albert O.
1957. *Phytophthora* avocado root rot. Calif. Agr. Exp. Sta. Ext. Serv. Circ. 465, 15 p.

(1660) ———, Paulus, Albert O., and Burns, Robert M.
1962. Avocado root rot. Univ. Calif. Agr. Exp. Sta. Circ. 511, 18 p.

(1661) ———, Paulus, Albert O., Gustafson, C. D., and others.
1965. Avocado diseases. Univ. Calif. Agr. Exp. Sta. Circ. 534, 11 p.

(1662) Ziller, W. G.
1954. Studies of western tree rusts. I. A new cone rust on Sitka spruce. Can. J. Bot. 32: 432–439.

(1663) ———.
1955. Studies of western tree rusts. II. *Melampsora occidentalis* and *M. albertensis*, two needle rusts of Douglas-fir. Can. J. Bot. 33: 177–188.

(1664) ———.
1957. Studies of western tree rusts. III. *Milesia laeviuscula*, a needle rust of grand fir. Can. J. Bot. 35: 885–894.

(1665) ———.
1959. Studies of western tree rusts. IV. *Uredinopsis hashiokai* and *U. pteridis* causing perennial needle rust of fir. Can. J. Bot. 37: 93–107.

(1666) ———.
1959. Studies of western tree rusts. V. The rusts of hemlock and fir caused by *Melampsora epitea*. Can. J. Bot. 37: 109–119.

(1667) ———.
1961. Pear rust (*Gymnosporangium fuscum*) in North America. U.S. Dep. Agr. Plant Dis. Rep. 45: 90–94.

(1668) ———.
1965. Studies of western tree rusts. VI. The aecial host ranges of *Melampsora albertensis*, *M. medusae*, and *M. occidentalis*. Can. J. Bot. 43: 217–230.

(1669) Zimmerman, P. W., and Hitchcock, A. E.
1956. Susceptibility of plants to hydrofluoric acid and sulfur dioxide gases. Boyce Thompson Inst. Contrib. 18: 263–279.

INDEX

602

605

607

609

610

611

613

617

620

flagworms, *see also*
Columbian timber
beetle, 424.
flamboyant-tree, *see*
Delonix regia
Flammula
alnicola Fr., 10, 25, 82,
83, 262, 268, 269, 273,
295, 301, 302, 495.
conissans (Fr.) Gill.,
263, 269.
flies, maple, 58.
fluoride (fluorine), 211,
332, 353.
Fomes, 110, 166, 213.
annosus (Fr.) Cke., 4,
5, 15, 17, 20, 21, 24,
28, 33, 110, 129, 132,
133, 176, 197, 203,
208, 213, 258, 262,
279, 283, 285, 287,
289, 295, 297, 301,
304, 306, 312–316,
318–320, 325, 326,
328, 331, 336, 339,
341–343, 346–349,
351, 357, 358, 364,
365, 367, 370, 408,
414, 416, 417, 469,
471, 480, 483, 490,
491, 494–497, 506.
annularis (Fr.) Lloyd,
509.
applanatus (*Pers. ex*
S. F. Gray) Gill, 5,
33, 46, 60, 61, 64, 82,
90, 93, 95, 105, 113,
147, 162, 166, 167,
176, 184, 186, 225,
232, 246, 284, 286,
377, 396–398, 406,
417, 422, 445, 456,
484, 488, 495–497,
506, 509.
australis (Fr.) Cke, *see*
also F. applanatus,
186.
brownii (Murr.) Sacc.
& Trott., 509.
cajanderi Karst. *see*
also F. subroseus
(Weir) Overh., 78,
133, 203, 263, 269,
274, 280, 302, 347,
415, 416.
connatus (Weinm. ex
Fr.) Gill, 33, 43, 46,
54, 60, 83, 93, 105,
176, 181, 219, 225,
249, 252, 397, 488,
506.
densus Lloyd, 60, 105.
176, 506.
earlii Murr., *see also F.*
juniperinus
(Schrenk) Sacc. &
Syd., 197.

Fomes—Cont.
everhartii (Ell. &
Gell.) Schr. &
Spauld., 105, 110,
192, 225, 398, 429,
449, 450, 506.
fasciatus, see also
Polyporus fasciatus,
232.
fomentarius (L. ex
Fr.) Kickx., 82, 93,
232, 397, 406, 509.
fraxineus (Bull ex Fr.)
Cke., 36, 249, 506.
fraxinophilus (Peck)
Sacc. 36, 175, 177–
179, 377, 506.
fulvus (Scop. ex Fr.)
Gill., *see also F.*
pomaceus, 404.
geotropus Cke., 36, 105,
119, 158, 175, 219,
232, 398, 449, 475,
488, 506.
hartigii (Allesch.)
Sacc. & Trav., *see*
also F. robustus
Karst., 478.
igniarius (L. ex Fr.)
Kickx., 43, 46, 54, 55,
71–73, 78, 81–83, 86,
90, 93, 95, 105, 112,
145, 166, 167, 175,
176, 178, 188, 192,
252, 379–381, 395–
397, 422, 449, 456,
468, 506.
var. *laevigatus* (Fr.)
Overh., 81–83, 86, 90,
165, 166, 406.
var. *populinus* (Neu.)
Campb., 396, 397.
johnsonianus (Murr.)
Lowe, 175.
juniperinus (Schrenk)
Sac. & Syd., 197, 200,
204.
laricis, see F.
officinalis
lignosus (Klotzsch.)
Bres., 241.
mangiferae (Lev.)
Cke., *see Ganoderma*
mangiferae
marmoratus (B. & C.)
Cke., 105, 113, 120,
158, 184, 219, 232,
377, 506.
meliae (Underw.)
Murr., 178, 184, 242,
243, 377, 406, 422.
nigricans, see Poria
obliqua
nigrolimitatus (Rom.)
Egeland, 214, 262–
264, 284, 285, 414,
478.

Fomes—Cont.
nobilissimus (Cke.)
Lowe, 30.
occidentalis Overh.,
147.
officinalis (Vill. ex. Fr.)
Faull, 210, 214, 263,
269, 284, 320, 336,
359, 415–417.
ohiensis (Berk.) Murr.,
110, 147, 252, 456,
506.
pini (Thore) Lloyd, 4,
15, 21, 25, 29, 30, 117,
129, 131, 204, 208,
210, 213, 214, 216,
262–264, 269, 274,
277, 280, 283–285,
287–290, 293, 295,
297, 302, 307, 309,
312, 314, 315, 318–
320, 322, 326, 331,
336, 338, 342, 346,
347, 350, 352, 357–
359, 364, 367, 368,
370, 415, 416, 478,
480, 483, 491, 493,
495, 496.
pinicola (Swartz ex Fr.)
Cke., 4, 5, 15, 24–26,
28, 30, 33, 82, 93, 105,
131, 214, 216, 261,
262, 264, 268–270,
274, 280, 283–286,
295, 302, 309, 314,
320, 322, 336, 359,
377, 397, 406, 416,
417, 480, 483, 495–
497.
pomaceus (Pers.)
Lloyd, 147, 404, 406.
praerimosus (Murr.)
Sacc. & D. Sacc., 192.
putearius Weir, 214.
ribis (Schum. ex Fr.)
Gill., 229, 468.
rimosus (Berk) Cke.,
455, 456.
robiniophilus, see
Polyporus
robiniophilus
robustus Karst., 25, 30,
43, 83, 86, 88, 127,
162, 192, 449, 478,
491, 495, 496.
roseus (Alb. & Schw. ex
Fr.) Cke., 200, 214,
280, 302, 309, 336,
359, 415, 416, 478,
483.
sclerodermeus (Lev.)
Cke., *see also*
Polyporus fasciatus,
232.
scutellatus (Schw.)
Cke., 36, 43, 76, 143,
147, 219, 377.
squamosus see

621

625

628

638

641

647

649

650

656

☆ U. S. GOVERNMENT PRINTING OFFICE: 1971 O—389-726